## PARAGRAPH PUBLISHING

Paragraph Publishing, St Faiths House, Mountergate, Norwich, Norfolk, NR1 1PY.
Tel: 01603 633 808  Fax: 01603 632 808
Email: info@gardenersatlas.co.uk
Web site: www.gardenersatlas.co.uk

Gardeners' Atlas

Copyright © Paragraph Publishing 2002. Maps copyright © The Automobile Association.

Scale 1: 175,000

First Paragraph Publishing edition: March 2002

The cartographic data used in this book were supplied by the Cartographic Department of The Automobile Association by means of datasets extracted from their database. The AA makes no guarantee or warranty with regards to the accuracy of data supplied and accepts no liability for loss or damage incurred as a result of any reliance on the data.

British Library Cataloguing-in-Publication Data. A catalogue record for this book is available from the British Library.

ISBN 0-9540481-0-5

Reprographics by Anglia Colour, Norwich, Norfolk. Printed and bound by Heron Print, UK. Distributed by MDL, Houndmills, Basingstoke, Hampshire RG21 6XS.
9 8 7 6 5 4 3 2 1

The contents of this book are believed to be correct at the time of printing. Nevertheless, the publisher can accept no responsibility for errors or omissions.

| | |
|---|---|
| EDITOR & PUBLISHER | Damian Riley-Smith |
| PRODUCT MANAGER | Michelle Smith |
| DESIGN | Stephen Bird |
| | Ron Keenes |
| | Lorna Crosbie-Smith |
| RESEARCH & SALES | Colin Willsher |
| | Ben Weaver |
| | Joanne Morley |
| PRODUCTION MANAGER | Rubyna Sheikh |
| SOFTWARE | Kingswood |
| FINANCE | Trudi Foster |

Photographs on map pages © PhotoEssentials http://www.photoessentials.canon.com.au/ and © Corbis Corp. http://www.corbisimages.com

With thanks to The National Trust, Barnsley House Garden, Lindsay McEwen at the British Red Cross, David Ashmore, Richard Todd, Anglesey Abbey and Hamish Riley-Smith

visit www.gardenersatlas.co.uk

# GARDENERS' ATLAS
## 2002-2003

## FIND YOUR WAY TO BRITAIN'S
- **Gardens** • **Nurseries**
- **Garden centres** • **Water garden specialists**

# THE MAPS

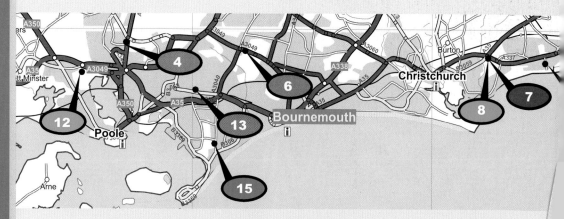

# MAP NUMBERS & KEY

**MOTORING INFORMATION**

| | |
|---|---|
| M27 | Motorway with name |
| 8 | Motorway junction |
| | Motorway under construction |
| A14 | Primary road |
| Portsmouth | Major town or city |
| A14 | A-road |
| A14 | B-road |
| A14 | Unclassified road |
| | Roundabout |
| | Road under construction |
| | Railway line and station |
| | Urban area |
| ▲ 410 | Spot height in metres |
| | River, canal, lake |
| | Island |
| 25 | Next page number |

**TOURIST INFORMATION**

| | |
|---|---|
| ⊗ | Picnic area |
| | Beach |
| ☼ | Viewpoint |
| | National Park & Area of Outstanding Beauty |
| | Forest |
| ✈ | Airport |
| i | Tourist Information |

**GARDENERS' ATLAS KEY**

- Garden
- Garden centre
- Garden & nursery
- Nursery
- Nursery & garden centre
- Water garden specialist

MAP SCALE: 1:175,000

ISLAND SCALE: 1:875,000

LONDON SCALE: 1:87,500

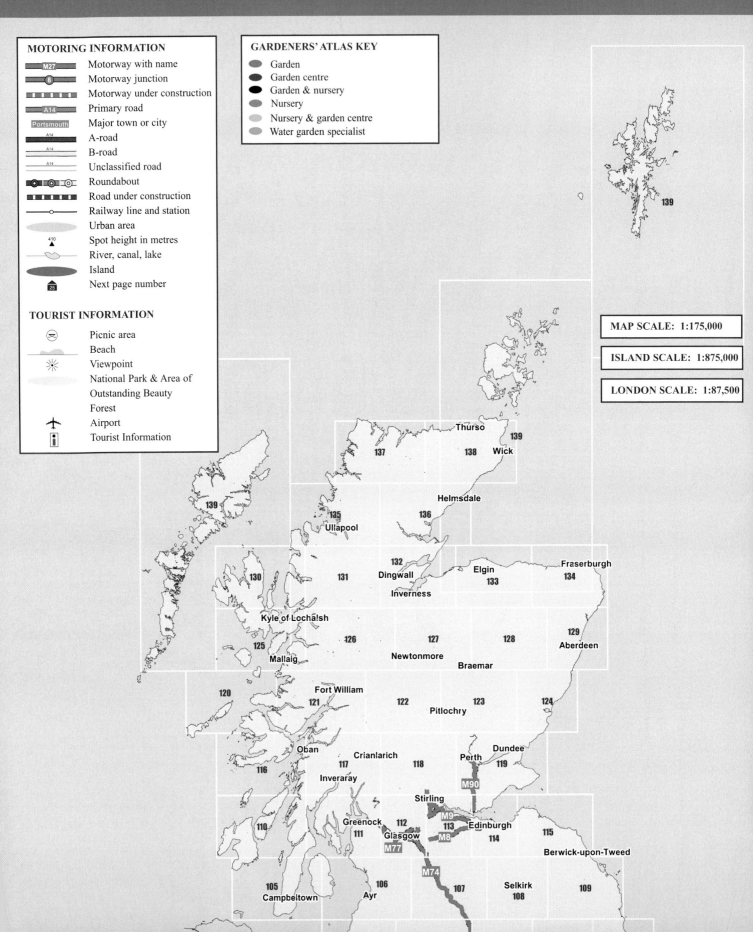

139

137  Thurso  139
138  Wick

Helmsdale

135  136
Ullapool

139

132  Elgin  Fraserburgh
130  131  Dingwall  133  134
Inverness

Kyle of Lochalsh

126  127  128  129
125  Aberdeen
Mallaig  Newtonmore  Braemar

Fort William
120  121  122  123  124
Pitlochry

Oban
116  117  Crianlarich  118  Perth  Dundee
Inveraray  119
M90

Stirling

110  Greenock  112  M9  Edinburgh
111  113  114  115
Glasgow  M8
M77  Berwick-upon-Tweed

M74

105  106  107  Selkirk  109
Campbeltown  Ayr  108

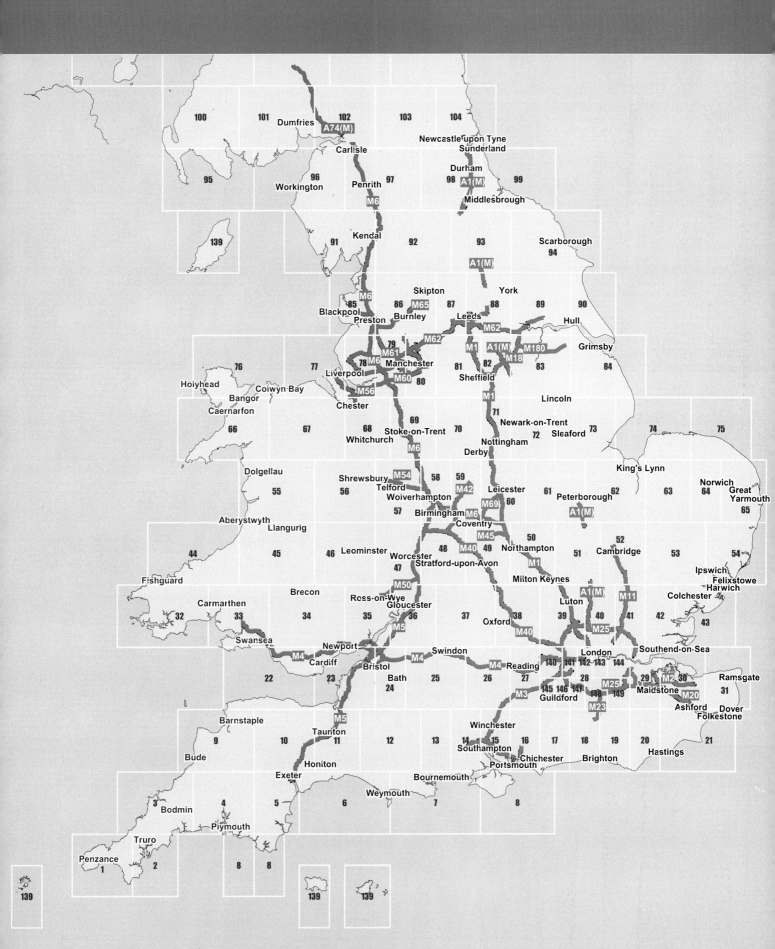

# INTRODUCTION

**WELCOME** to the 2002 edition of the *Gardener s Atlas*. I would like to thank all our readers who wrote, emailed and called us to share their comments and suggestions on how to improve the next edition of the *Gardeners Atlas*.

After looking at all the feedback it became apparent the Facilities guide in the enhanced entries proved hard to read. We have changed these into words rather than symbols.

One of our biggest challenges since last year has been our *Gardeners Atlas* website, ***www.gardenersatlas.co.uk***. You can search for outlets on the online version of the *Gardeners Atlas*. This also has a gardening Links section, the Gardeners Store offering a wide range of gardening gifts, the Calendar section and gardening Products and Services that lists companies who provide different types of gardening equipment we all need for our garden.

I would like to remind you to mention the *Gardeners Atlas* if you visit a garden or gardening outlet that has been featured in the *Gardeners Atlas*. We hope they will show you that little bit of extra attention. Indeed, those entries that show the *GA Offer* symbol will have a special something for you if you show them the *Gardeners Atlas* when you visit.

I hope the *Gardeners Atlas* helps make your visits to gardening places that little bit easier and encourages you to explore and discover even more of what the gardening world has to offer.

Damian Riley-Smith

# How the GARDENE

The *Gardeners' Atlas* shows the way to thousands of places in England, Scotland and Wales that are of interest to gardeners and garden-lovers.

When planning visits to a particular part of the country our aim is to help you find all the locations of gardening interest through easy to use maps and information. The *Gardeners' Atlas* is small enough to fit in the glove box of your car and when you find yourself travelling through a particular part of the country you can use the *Gardeners' Atlas* to find out all the gardening splendours in that particular area of the country.

We have tried to include every garden centre, nursery and water garden specialist that welcomes visitors as well as all gardens that are open to the public for at least five months of the year.

There are six different types of outlet and they all have different colour lozenges. The different outlets are as follows; Garden, Garden & Nursery, Nursery, Garden Centre, Nursery & Garden Centre and Water Garden Specialist. You will find a guide to each lozenge throughout the Atlas pages. Each outlet is identified by its own unique number. This number is shown on the map, in the listing box and in the index at the back.

For areas of the country where the density of gardens and gardening retailers is great we have used a different map scale.

As in previous editions we have asked owners with enhanced entries to supply their own descriptions. We do not include our own opinions or preferences, as we would like the *Gardeners' Atlas* to provide a comprehensive range of all the relevant outlets and hope you would come to your own conclusions after visiting the outlets.

Every entry lists the name, address and telephone number along with which category it has been placed. Before travelling long distances we suggest that you call, as some gardens and nurseries have restricted opening times.

We hope you will mention the *Gardeners' Atlas* if you visit an outlet that has been featured. We hope this will ensure you get that little extra special service.

## SURREY · WEST SUSSEX

● GARDEN    ● NURSERY
● GARDEN CENTRE    ● NURSERY & GARDEN CENTRE
● GARDEN & NURSERY    ● WATER GARDEN SPECIALIST

**1 WINKWORTH ARBORETUM, NATIONAL TRUST**
Hascombe Road, Godalming   TEL: 01483 208 477

**2 HYDON NURSERIES**
Clock Barn Lane, Hydon Heath, Godalming   TEL: 01483 860 252

**3 WHEELER STREET NURSERY**
Wheeler Lane, Witley, Godalming TEL: 01428 682 638

**4 NOTCUTTS GARDEN CENTRE**
Guildford Road, Cranleigh   TEL: 01483 274 222

**5 MILLAIS NURSERIES**
Crosswater Farm, Churt, Farnham   TEL: 01252 792 698

**6 SWEETWATER NURSERY**
Sweetwater Farm, Culmer Lane, Witley
  TEL: 01428 682 211

**7 GARDENING WORLD**
Haslemere Road, Godalming   TEL: 01293 883 237

**8 GREEN STOP GARDEN CENTRE**
Haslemere Road, Brook, Godalming
  TEL: 01428 682 913

**9 WYEVALE GARDEN CENTRE**
Horsham Rd, Alfold, Cranleigh   TEL: 01403 752 359

**10 RAMSTER GARDENS**
Ramster, Chiddingfold   TEL: 01428 654 167

**11 STRIKERS NURSERIES**
2 New Building, Shillinglee, Godalming
  TEL: 01428 708 167

**12 LOXWOOD CONIFER NURSERIES**
Guildford Road, Loxwood   TEL: 01403 753 389

**13 MRS JANE SADLER**
Ingrams Cottage, Wiseborough Green, Billingshurst
  TEL: 01403 700 234

**14 ROTHERHILL NURSERIES & GARDEN CENTRE**
Stedham, Midhurst   TEL: 01370 813 687

**15 PETWORTH HOUSE AND PARK**
Petworth   TEL: 01798 342 207

**16 MURRELLS NURSERY**
Broomers Hill Lane, Pulborough, West Sussex, RH20 2DU
TEL: 01798 875 508

*Extensive range (including unusual varieties) of shrubs, herbaceous, bedding and basket plants, trees and fruit trees. House and conservatory plants.*
**OPEN:** Open 7 days a week. Summer: Mon-Sat 9-5.30, Sun 10-4. Winter: Mon-Sat 9-5. Closed Easter Sun, Christmas, Boxing & New Years Day.
**SPECIALITIES:** Climbers, Shrubs, Bonsai, Geraniums, Herbs.
**FACILITIES:** Credit cards, HTA gift tokens, Sell plants

**17 THE CITRUS CENTRE**
West Mare Lane, Marehill, Pulborough   TEL: 01798 872 786

**18 WYEVALE GARDEN CENTRE**
Stopham Road, Pulborough   TEL: 01798 872 981

**19 P VERHEUL**
Sylvan Nurseries, West Chillington Road, Pulborough   TEL: 01798 813 567

**20 PARHAM ELIZABETHAN HOUSE AND GARDENS**
Parham Park, Pulborough   TEL: 01903 744 888

**21 HILLSIDE NURSERIES**
A29, Bury, Pulborough   TEL: 01798 831 325

**22 WEALD & DOWNLAND OPEN AIR MUSEUM**
Singleton, Chichester   TEL: 01243 811 363

**23 WEST DEAN GARDENS**
West Dean, Chichester, West Sussex, PO18 0QZ.
TEL: 01243 818 210
EMAIL: gardens@westdean.org.uk
WEB: www.westdean.org.uk
*Highly acclaimed restored Victorian walled Kitchen Garden. Sixteen Victorian Glasshouses and cold-frames. Herbaceous borders, specimen trees and 300' Harold Peto designed pergola hosting climbers.*
**OPEN:** May-Sep: 11-5. Mar-Apr & Oct: 10.30-5.
**ENTRY COSTS:** £4.50, Child: £2, OAPs: £4, Family: £11.
**SPECIALITIES:** Climbers, Fruit & fruit trees, Greenhouses & sheds, Hardy plants, Shrubs.
**FACILITIES:** Coffee shop, Credit cards, Gift shop, Restaurant, Toilets, Wheelchair access.

**24 PUMPKIN COTTAGE**
4 Top Road, Slindon, Arundel   TEL: 01243 814 219

**25 ALDINGBOURNE COUNTRY CENTRE**
Blackmill Lane, Norton, Chichester
  TEL: 01243 542 075

**26 ARUNDEL ARBORETUM**
Scotland Barn, Chichester Road, Arundel, West Sussex, BN18 0AD.
TEL: 01903 883 251
EMAIL: arundel-arboretum@hinge.mistral.co.uk
*Extensive range of specialist trees 4ft-20ft. Shrubs and conifers. Deliveries and planting undertaken. Advice given.*
**OPEN:** Mon-Fri 8-5, Sat-Sun 10-4. Closed Christmas and New Year.
**SPECIALITIES:** Hardy plants, Shrubs, Trees, Topiary.
**FACILITIES:** Credit cards, Dogs allowed, Sell plants.

**27 DENMANS GARDEN**
Denmans, Fontwell, Arundel   TEL: 01243 542 808

**28 MAUDLIN NURSERY**
Westhampnett, Chichester   TEL: 01243 773 024

**29 SHOPWHYKE NURSERIES & SUPPLIES**
Shopwhyke Road, Chichester   TEL: 01243 783 123

**30 HIGHFIELD & SUNNYSIDE NURSERIES**
Yapton Rd, Barnham, Bognor Regis   TEL: 01243 553 062

**31 TORRI NURSEY**
Old Mead Road, Littlehampton   TEL: 01903 717 140

**32 P PERELLA**
Glen Villa Chalet, Old Mead Road, Littlehampton
  TEL: 01903 713 305

**33 MANOR NURSERY**
Yapton Road, Barnham   TEL: 01243 552 028

**34 LILLIES NURSERY & CARAVAN PARK**
Yapton Road, Barnham, Bognor Regis
  TEL: 01243 552 081

**35 CROFTWAY NURSERY**
Yapton Road, Barnham, Bognor Regis
  TEL: 01243 552 121

**36 ARCHITECTURAL PLANTS**
Lidsey Road Nursery, Woodgate, Chichester
  TEL: 01243 545 008

**37 BRICK KILN NURSERY & GARDEN CENTRE**
Bognor Road, Chichester   TEL: 01243 531 700

**38 FAIRHAVEN PLANTS**
Toddington Lane, Lyminster, Littlehampton
  TEL: 01903 725 642

**39 WESTHOLME NURSERIES**
Toddington Lane, Littlehampton   TEL: 01903 714 845

**40 MANOR NURSERY**
High Street, Angmering   TEL: 01903 785 123

**41 WYEVALE GARDEN CENTRE**
Bognor Road, Merston, Chichester
  TEL: 01243 789 276

**42 HASKINS ROUNDSTONE GARDEN CENTRE**
Roundstone Bypass, Angmering, West Sussex, BN16 4BD.
TEL: 01903 776 481
WEB: www.roundstonegardencentre.co.uk

*Gardeners have enjoyed the fruits of Haskins labour since 1882. Gardens can bring so much pleasure - our aim is to make sure that pleasure lasts.*
**OPEN:** Mon-Sat 9-6, Sun 10-5. Closed Easter Sun, Christmas & Boxing Day.
**SPECIALITIES:** Bedding plants, Furniture, Gifts, Hardy plants, Pet centre.
**FACILITIES:** Bookshop, Coffee shop, Credit cards, Dogs allowed, Gift shop, HTA gift tokens, Own gift tokens, Plant guarantee, Pushchair friendly, Restaurant, Sell plants, Toilets, Wheelchair access.

**43 LOWERTREES NURSERY**
Roundstone By-pass, Angmering
  TEL: 01903 770 457

**44 CINDERS LANE NURSERY**
Bilsham Road, Yapton   TEL: 01243 552 555

## Opening Times

Where provided, the company concerned has supplied opening times. Please note that nurseries and gardens can be flexible with their dates and hours of opening and the climate may alter the availability of some stock.

## Entry Costs

Gardens and Gardens & Nurseries with enhanced listings have the entry costs included. The first cost is for an adult and any concessions are listed afterwards. If in doubt please call before visiting, particularly if you are part of a group as discounts may apply.

## Facilities

Those outlets with enhanced entries list what facilities they have available. It is advised to call before travelling to check about particular facilities if you are unsure.

## Entry Groups

We have six different types of outlet and below we explain the criteria each place must fulfil to be included within the Atlas.

## ● GARDEN

We include over 600 gardens. They have to be open to the public and accessible during the key garden visiting months. Opening times may vary so we suggest you contact them first before travelling.

## ● GARDEN CENTRE

We list three types of garden centres. Small garden centres often carry a large range of popular plants and garden equipment. Medium-sized garden centres carry a much wider range of products. Large garden centres are often like department stores with restaurants and stock products that are less directly associated with gardening.

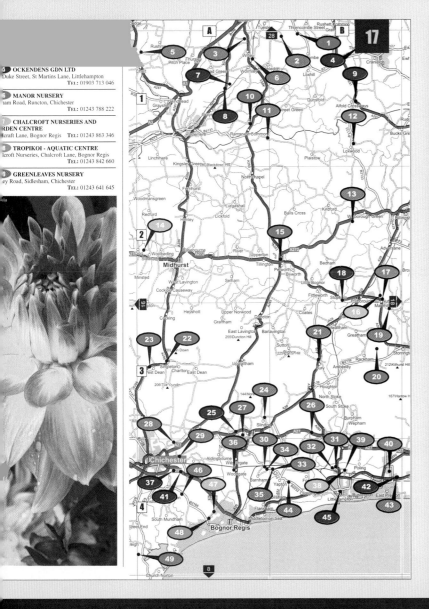

The **Gardeners' Atlas** also has it's very own website, **www.gardenersatlas.co.uk**. Here you can find an online version of the **Gardeners' Atlas** with a Gardening Links page offering you links to other sites of gardening interest, the Calendar of plant fairs and shows and Gardening Products and Services.

The website also offers you the chance to have your photograph published in the 'Photograph of the Week' section. If you have any pictures you would like to send us please use the address at the front of the publication.

www.gardenersatlas.co.uk

**www.gardenersatlas.co.uk**

## GARDEN & NURSERY

Many gardens have a specialist nursery attached to it or located nearby. We suggest you call first to confirm opening times and stock variations.

## NURSERY

All nurseries that welcome visitors, or are generally open during the summer months, have been included. It is always advised to call first to confirm opening times. All nurseries offer expert advice and many have an area of particular speciality.

## NURSERY & GARDEN CENTRE

Most nurseries grow their own plants from seeds and cuttings or buy stock to grow-on, whereas most garden centres buy plants in that are ready grown. It is not unusual to find that some garden centres have their own nursery attached or for a nursery to have its own garden centre.

## WATER GARDEN SPECIALIST

These are often on the same site as a garden centres but are a separate business. They generally sell anything to do with water gardens or aquatics. As their specialist name suggests they are staffed by experts who are able to offer advice to both a beginner and an expert and help you get the best from your water garden

## Feedback

We have done our best to ensure that all the information within the **Gardeners' Atlas** is correct at the time it was printed; however errors can occur. Please let us know if you notice any. We would also like to know if we have missed any outlets out so we can include them within the next edition if they meet our criteria. The **Gardeners' Atlas** website is growing daily and we are always open to new suggestions and ideas. You can call us on 01603 633 808, enter the details on our feedback page by visiting **www.gardenersatlas.co.uk** or enter your comments by entering our competition at the back of the Atlas. We look forward to hearing

This years gardening calendar is packed with Garden Shows, Festivals, Plant Fairs, Exhibitions and Seasonal Events around England, Scotland and Wales.

The location of the event can be found by looking for its map page or location number in the listing opposite.

For up-to-date information and tickets for each event please use the details listed to contact the venue direct. If you contact a venue listed on these pages, please remember to say you found out about them from the *Gardeners' Atlas*.

| DATE | EVENT | VENUE | CONTACT | WEB ADDRESS (Where supplied) | MAP | REF |
|---|---|---|---|---|---|---|
| 1 March | Exhibition | Longframlington Centre for Plants | 01665 570 382 | www.longframlingtongardens.co.uk | 104 | 2 |
| 2 March | Exhibition | Myerscough College | 01995 642 279 | | | |
| 9-10 March | Plant Fair | Hampton Court Palace & Gardens | 020 8781 9500 | www.hrp.org.uk | | |
| 10-31 May | Regional Festival | Cornwall | 01872 322 900 | www.cornwalltouristboard.co.uk | | |
| 10 March | Plant Fair | Capel Manor | 020 8366 4442 | www.capelmanorcollege.co.uk | 40 | 38 |
| 11-17 March | Seasonal Event | Hever Castle & Gardens | 01732 865 224 | www.hevercastle.co.uk | | |
| 12-13 March | Garden Show | R H S Horticultural Halls | 0870 906 3721 | www.rhs.org.uk | | |
| 15-17 March | Exhibition | R H S Horticultural Halls | 0870 906 3721 | www.rhs.org.uk | | |
| 16-17 Mar | Exhibition | Ambleside | 01539 432 252 | www.ambleside-show.org.uk | | |
| 30 March | Seasonal Event | Princess Pavilion | 01326 311 277 | | | |
| 31 March-1 April | Exhibition | Springfields Show Gardens | 01775 724 843 | www.springfields.mistral.co.uk | 62 | 7 |
| 5-7 April | Garden Show | Capel Manor | 0208 366 4442 | www.capel.ac.uk | 40 | 38 |
| 7 April | Plant Fair | Arley Hall Nursery | 01565 777 353 | www.nationaltrust.org.uk | 79 | 44 |
| 8-9 April | Exhibition | Central Nursery | 0191 433 3000 | www.gateshead.gov.uk | | |
| 12-15 April | Plant Fair | Norwich City Football Club | 01508 498 263 | | | |
| 13-14 April | Exhibition | Camperdown Country Park | 01382 433 815 | | | |
| 13 April | Garden Show | Plas Newydd, National Trust | 01248 714 795 | www.nationaltrust.org.uk | 66 | 4 |
| 13-14 April | Exhibition | Central Nursery | 0191 433 3000 | www.gateshead.gov.uk | | |
| 16-21 April | Regional Festival | Leeds Castle | 01622 765 400 | www.leeds-castle.com | 30 | 34 |
| 19-21 April | Garden Show | Suffolk Show Ground | 01702 549 623 | www.aztecevents.co.uk | | |
| 21 April | Plant Fair | Capel Manor | 020 8366 4442 | www.capelmanorcollege.co.uk | 40 | 38 |
| 21 April | Plant Fair | Gawsworth Hall | 01260 223 456 | www.gawsworth.co.uk | 69 | 4 |
| 23-24 April | Garden Show | R H S Horticultural Halls | 0870 906 3721 | www.rhs.org.uk | | |
| 25-28 April | Garden Show | North of England Horticultural Society | 0870 758 3333 | www.flowershow.org.uk | | |
| 26-28 April | Seasonal Event | Loseley Park | 01483 797 332 | www.loseley-park.com | | |
| 26-28 April | Plant Fair | Ipswich Showground | 01508 498 263 | | | |
| 1 May | Garden Show | Cornwall | 01752 894731 | www.cornwalltouristboard.co.uk | | |
| 2-6 May | Regional Festival | Pashley Manor Gardens | 01580 200 692 | www.pashleymanorgardens.com | 20 | 14 |
| 3 May | Plant Fair | Norwich City Football Club | 01508 498 263 | | | |
| 4-6 May | Garden Show | Leonardslee Gardens | 01403 891 212 | www.leonardslee.com | 18 | 19 |
| 4-6 May | Exhibition | Springfields Show Gardens | 01775 724 843 | www.springfields.mistral.co.uk | 62 | 7 |
| 4-6 May | Garden Show | Audley End House, English Heritage | 01799 522 842 | www.english-heritage.org.uk | 52 | 28 |
| 4-6 May | Seasonal Event | Bath Botanic Gardens / Royal Victoria Park | 01225 482 624 | | 24 | 25 |
| 4-6 May | Garden Show | Capel Manor | 020 8366 4442 | www.capelmanorcollege.co.uk | 40 | 38 |
| 4-6 May | Garden Show | Garsons Park | N/A | www.aztecevents.co.uk | | |
| 5-7 May | Garden Show | Tonbridge Sports Ground | 01732 770 929 | | | |
| 10-12 May | Garden Show | Three Counties Showground | 01684 584 924 | www.rhs.org.uk | | |
| 10-12 May | Exhibition | Orchid Paradise | 01626 352 233 | www.orchids.uk.com | 5 | 16 |
| 10-12 May | Garden Show | East of England Showground | 01702 549 623 | www.aztecevents.co.uk | | |
| 10-12 May | Plant Fair | Ipswich Showground | 01508 498 263 | | | |
| 11-12 May | Seasonal Event | Arley Hall Nursery | 01565 777 353 | | 79 | 44 |
| 11-31 May | Seasonal Event | Borde Hill Garden | 01444 450 326 | www.bordehill.co.uk | 19 | 28 |
| 12 May | Plant Fair | Colby Woodland Garden, National Trust | 01834 811 885 | | 32 | 7 |
| 13 May | Plant Fair | Petworth House & Park, National Trust | 01798 344 972 | www.nationaltrust.org.uk | | |
| 14 May | Seasonal Event | Loseley Park | 01483 797 332 | www.loseley-park.com | | |
| 17-19 May | Seasonal Event | Gardens of the Rose | 01727 850 461 | www.roses.co.uk | 39 | 33 |
| 17-19 May | Garden Show | Norfolk Showground | 01702 549 623 | www.aztecevents.co.uk | | |
| 17-19 May | Plant Fair | Ipswich Showground | 01508 498 263 | | | |
| 18-19 May | Seasonal Event | Arley Hall Nursery | 01565 777 353 | | 79 | 44 |
| 19 May | Seasonal Event | Powis Castle Gardens, National Trust | 01938 551 920 | www.nationaltrust.org.uk | 56 | 15 |
| 19 May | Plant Fair | South of England Rare Breeds Centre | 01223 861 493 | www.castanet.co.uk/rye/rarebree.htm | | |
| 19 May | Exhibition | Loseley Park | 01483 797 332 | | | |
| 20-24 May | Garden Show | Chelsea Flower Show | 0870 906 3781 | www.rhs.org.uk | | |
| 26-30 May | Garden Show | Athelhampton House and Gardens | 01305 854 363 | | 7 | 6 |
| 29-30 May | Garden Show | Woburn Abbey | 01525 290 666 | | | |
| 29-30 May | Exhibition | Cathedral of our Lady & St Philip Howard | 01903 882 297 | | | |
| 29-30 May | Garden Show | Wood Green Animal Shelter | 01702 549 623 | www.aztecevents.co.uk | | |
| 31 May-2 June | Garden Show | Holker Hall | 01539 558 328 | | 91 | 26 |
| 31 May-2 June | Garden Show | Royal Highland Showground | 0131 333 09649 | www.gardeningscotland.com | | |
| 31 May-2 June | Regional Festival | Holker Hall | 01539 558 836 | | 91 | 26 |
| 31 May-3 June | Plant Fair | Norwich City Football Club | 01508 498 263 | | | |
| 1-6 June | Exhibition | Crediton Parish Church | 01363 772 865 | | | |
| 1-4 June | Regional Festival | Bryan's Ground Gardens | 01544 260 001 | www.hortus.co.uk | 46 | 6 |
| 1-4 June | Exhibition | Royal Hospital, Ranelagh Gardens | 01626 352 233 | www.orchids.uk.com | | |
| 2-4 June | Garden Show | Kent | 01795 474 660 | www.gardenshows.com | | |
| 3 June | Seasonal Event | High Beeches Woodland & Water Gardens | 01444 400 589 | | 18 | 11 |

# WS & PLANT FAIRS

| DATE | EVENT | VENUE | CONTACT | WEB ADDRESS (Where supplied) | MAP | REF |
|------|-------|-------|---------|------------------------------|-----|-----|
| 7-9 June | Garden Show | Stanstead | 023 9241 2265 | | | |
| 7-9 June | Garden Show | Hatfield House | 01707 262 823 | | 40 | 18 |
| 8-9 June | Garden Show | Ascot Racecourse | 01702 549 623 | www.aztecevents.co.uk | | |
| 9 June | Garden Show | Capel Manor | 020 8366 4442 | www.capelmanorcollege.co.uk | 40 | 38 |
| 13-6 June | Garden Show | Borde Hill Garden | 01444 450 326 | www.bordehill.co.uk | 19 | 28 |
| 13-16 June | Garden Show | Blenheim Palace | 01993 811 091 | www.blenheimpalace.com | 37 | 12 |
| 14-17 June | Garden Show | Stapehill Abbey Crafts & Gardens | 01202 861 686 | | 13 | 24 |
| 14-17 June | Plant Fair | Norwich City Football Club | 01508 498 263 | | | |
| 15-16 June | Exhibition | Colby Woodland Garden, National Trust | 01834 811 885 | www.nationaltrust.org.uk | 32 | 7 |
| 15-16 June | Garden Show | Capel Manor | 020 8366 4442 | www.capelmanorcollege.co.uk | 40 | 38 |
| 15-16 June | Garden Show | Barleylands | 01702 549 623 | www.aztecevents.co.uk | | |
| 16 June | Seasonal Event | Powis Castle Gardens, National Trust | 01938 551 920 | www.nationaltrust.org.uk | 56 | 15 |
| 16 June | Exhibition | Colby Woodland Garden, National Trust | 01834 811 885 | | 32 | 7 |
| 18 June | Seasonal Event | Loseley Park | 01483 797 332 | www.loseley-park.com | | |
| 18 June | Exhibition | Loseley Park | 01483 797 332 | www.loseley-park.com | | |
| 19-23 June | Garden Show | BBC Gardeners' World, NEC, Birmingham | Members: 0121 767 4505 Non-members: 0121 767 4111 | | | |
| 20-23 June | Regional Festival | Royal Highland Showground | 0131 335 6216 | | | |
| 22-23 June | Garden Show | West Dean Gardens | 01243 818 210 | www.westdean.org.uk | 17 | 23 |
| 22-23 June | Garden Show | Rosemoor Garden, Royal Horticultural Society | 01805 624 067 | | 9 | 14 |
| 28-30 June | Plant Fair | Bourn Airfield | 01359 268 614 | | | |
| 29-30 June | Seasonal Event | Benington Lordship | 01438 869 668 | www.beningtonlordship.co.uk | | |
| 29-30 June | Garden Show | Arley Hall Nursery | 01565 777 353 | enquiries@arleyestate.24unet.co.uk | 79 | 44 |
| 30 June-7 July | Regional Festival | Isle of Man | 01624 686 801 | | | |
| 1-7 July | Garden Show | Hampton Court Palace & Gardens | 0870 906 3791 | www.hrp.org.uk | | |
| 1-7 July | Seasonal Event | Benington Lordship | 01438 869 668 | www.beningtonlordship.co.uk | | |
| 6-7 July | Plant Fair | Southampton Common | 023 8083 2525 | | | |
| 6-7 July | Regional Festival | Bryan's Ground Gardens | 01544 260 001 | www.hortus.co.uk | 46 | 6 |
| 6-7 July | Garden Show | Capel Manor | 020 8366 4442 | www.capelmanorcollege.co.uk | 40 | 38 |
| 6-7 July | Garden Show | Brentwood Centre | 01702 549 623 | www.aztecevents.co.uk | | |
| 7-13 July | Regional Festival | Jersey | 01534 500 723 | www.jersey.com | | |
| 13-14 July | Garden Show | Parham Elizabethan House and Gardens | N/A | www.parhaminsussex.co.uk | 17 | 20 |
| 19-21 July | Garden Show | Loseley Park | 01483 797 332 | www.loseley-park.com | | |
| 26-28 July | Garden Show | Central Nursery | 0191 433 3000 | | | |
| 27-28 July | Garden Show | Capel Manor | 020 8366 4442 | www.capelmanorcollege.co.uk | 40 | 38 |
| 3 August | Exhibition | Arundel | 01580 880 467 | | | |
| 9-11 August | Garden Show | Ayr | 01292 618 395 | | | |
| 16-17 August | Garden Show | Shrewsbury | 01743 234 050 | | | |
| 17-18 August | Garden Show | Capel Manor | 020 8366 4442 | www.capelmanorcollege.co.uk | 40 | 38 |
| 18 August | Seasonal Event | High Beeches Woodland & Water Gardens | 01444 400 589 | www.highbeeches.com | 18 | 11 |
| 22-24 August | Plant Fair | Southport | 01704 547 147 | | | |
| 24-26 August | Garden Show | Audley End House, English Heritage | 01799 522 842 | www.english-heritage.org.uk | 52 | 28 |
| 24-26 August | Garden Show | Kempton Park Racecourse | 01702 549 623 | www.aztecevents.co.uk | | |
| 26 August | Garden Show | Bude | 01288 352 114 | | | |
| 30 August -1 Sept | Garden Show | Suffolk Show Ground | 01702 549 623 | www.aztecevents.co.uk | | |
| 5 September | Plant Fair | Arley Hall Nursery | 01565 777 353 | | 79 | 44 |
| 6-8 September | Flower Show | Camperdown Country Park | 01382 434 940 | www.dundeecity.gov.uk | | |
| 7-8 September | Garden Show | Borde Hill Garden | 01444 450 326 | www.bordehill.co.uk | 19 | 28 |
| 7-8 September | Seasonal Event | Parham Elizabethan House and Gardens | N/A | www.parhaminsussex.co.uk | 17 | 20 |
| 7-8 September | Garden Show | Capel Manor | 020 8366 4442 | www.capelmanorcollege.co.uk | 40 | 38 |
| 13-15 September | Garden Show | North of England Horticultural Society | 0870 758 3333 | www.flowershow.org.uk | | |
| 14-15 September | Garden Show | Capel Manor | 020 8366 4442 | www.capelmanorcollege.co.uk | 40 | 38 |
| 15 September | Seasonal Event | Borde Hill Garden | 01444 450 326 | www.bordehill.co.uk | 19 | 28 |
| 15 September | Plant Fair | Gawsworth Hall | 01260 223 456 | www.gawsworth.co.uk | 69 | 4 |
| 15 September | Exhibition | Loseley Park | 01483 797 332 | www.loseley-park.com | | |
| 17 September | Garden Show | R H S Horticultural Halls | 0870 906 3721 | www.rhs.org.uk | | |
| 21 September | Regional Festival | Capel Manor | 020 8366 4442 | www.capelmanorcollege.co.uk | 40 | 38 |
| 28-29 September | Plant Fair | Three Counties Showground | 01684 584 924 | www.rhs.org.uk | | |
| 28-29 September | Regional Festival | Capel Manor | 020 8366 4442 | www.capelmanorcollege.co.uk | 40 | 38 |
| 29 September | Seasonal Event | Belsay Hall, English Heritage | 01661 881 636 | www.english-heritage.org.uk | 104 | 6 |
| 1 October | Exhibition | Loseley Park | 01483 797 332 | www.loseley-park.com | | |
| 9-13 October | Seasonal Event | Leeds Castle | 01622 765 400 | www.leeds-castle.com | 30 | 34 |
| 12-13 October | Garden Show | Capel Manor | 020 8366 4442 | www.capelmanorcollege.co.uk | 40 | 38 |
| 26-7 October | Garden Show | Capel Manor | 020 8366 4442 | www.capelmanorcollege.co.uk | 40 | 38 |
| 26-27 October | Garden Show | Capel Manor | 020 8366 4442 | www.capelmanorcollege.co.uk | 40 | 38 |
| 2-3 November | Seasonal Event | Benington Lordship | 01438 869 668 | www.beningtonlordship.co.uk | | |

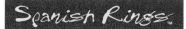

# MAPS

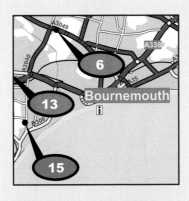

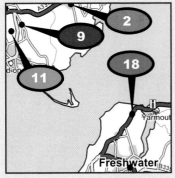

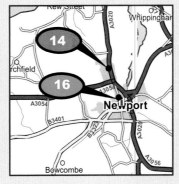

- GARDEN
- GARDEN CENTRE
- GARDEN & NURSERY
- NURSERY
- NURSERY & GARDEN CENTRE
- WATER GARDEN SPECIALIST

# CORNWALL

- GARDEN
- GARDEN CENTRE
- GARDEN & NURSERY
- NURSERY
- NURSERY & GARDEN CENTRE
- WATER GARDEN SPECIALIST

**1  GREEN LANE NURSERIES**
Redruth
**TEL:** 01209 313 245

**2  ROSEWARNE COLLECTIONS**
Duchy College, Rosewarne, Camborne
**TEL:** 01209 710 077

**3  BARBARA HEPWORTH MUSEUM & SCULPTURE GARDEN**
Barnoon Hill, St Ives
**TEL:** 01736 796 226

**4  CAMBORNE GARDEN CENTRE**
North Roskear Terrace, Camborne
**TEL:** 01209 613 819

**5  TREWYN GARDEN**
St Ives
**TEL:** 01736 794 937

**6  WYEVALE GARDEN CENTRE**
Nut Lane, Hayle
**TEL:** 01736 753 731

**7  PARADISE PARK**
Hayle, St Ives
**TEL:** 01736 757 407

**8  HARDY EXOTICS NURSERY**
Gilly Lane, Whitecross, Penzance, Cornwall,
TR20 8BZ.
**TEL:** 01736 740 660
*Hardy Exotics grows the largest collection of exotic-looking plants in the UK. A fascinating nursery with plenty of advice on hand. All plants are hardiness-rated.*
**OPEN:** Open all year. Call for opening times.
**SPECIALITIES:** Bamboos, Conservatory plants, Exotic plants, Herbaceous plants, Shrubs.
**FACILITIES:** Credit cards, Dogs allowed, Own gift tokens, Sell plants, Toilets.

**9  LITTLE TREASURES**
Wheal Treasure, Horsedowns
**TEL:** 01209 831 978

**10  T B WAKEFIELD**
The Nurseries, Higher Skewes, Camborne
**TEL:** 01209 831 402

**11  CRANHAN NURSERIES**
Newmill, Penzance
**TEL:** 01736 362 897

**12  TRENGWAINTON GARDEN, NATIONAL TRUST**
Madron, Penzance
**TEL:** 01736 362 297

Wild Garden

**13  TREVARNO ESTATE GARDENS & THE NATIONAL MUSEUM OF GARDENING**
Trevarno Manor, Sithney, Helston, Cornwall,
TR13 0RU.
**TEL:** 01326 574 274
**EMAIL:** enquiry@trevarno.fsnet.co.uk

*Unforgettable gardening experience, beautiful Victorian and Georgian gardens with the splendid fountain garden conservatory, unique range of crafts and the amazing National Museum of Gardening.*
**OPEN:** Open all year. Closed Chrismas & Boxing Day.
**ENTRY COSTS:** £4.50, Child: £1.50 Under 5 free, OAPs: £3.95, Disabled £2.50.
**SPECIALITIES:** Comprehensive range of Trevarno crafts.
**FACILITIES:** Wheelchair access, Toilets, Coffee shop, Dogs allowed, Sell plants.

**14  TREREIFE GARDEN**
Penzance
**TEL:** 01736 362 750

**15  TREWIDDEN GARDEN & NURSERY**
Penzance, Cornwall, TR20 8TT.
**TEL:** 01736 362 087
**EMAIL:** info@trewiddengarden.co.uk
**WEB:** www.trewidden.co.uk
*Trewidden is steeped in history and natural beauty. Famous for camellias and a display of reputedley the oldest tree ferns in the country.*
**OPEN:** Telephone for opening times.
**ENTRY COSTS:** £3, Child: Under 16s free.
**SPECIALITIES:** Camellias, Exotic plants, Ferns, Hardy plants, Magnolias.
**FACILITIES:** Sell plants, Toilets.

**16  TREVENA CROSS NURSERIES**
Breage, Helston
**TEL:** 01736 763 880

**17  GWEEK NURSERIES**
Parc Bottom, Gweek, Helston
**TEL:** 01326 221311

**18  FLAMBARDS VICTORIAN VILLAGE GARDEN**
Helston
**TEL:** 01326 573 404

**19  TRELOWARREN**
Mawgan, Helston
**TEL:** 01326 221 661

**20  THE OLD WITHY GARDEN NURSERY**
Cury Cross Lanes, Helston
**TEL:** 01326 240 817

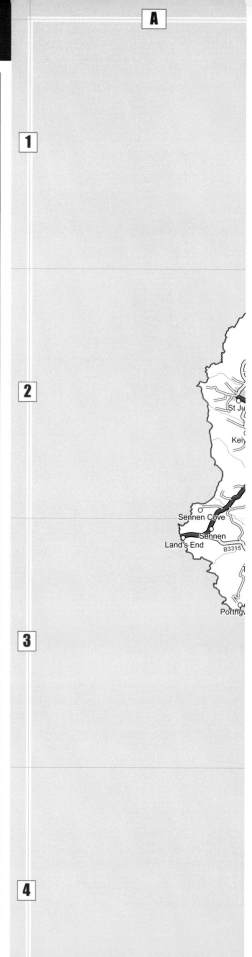

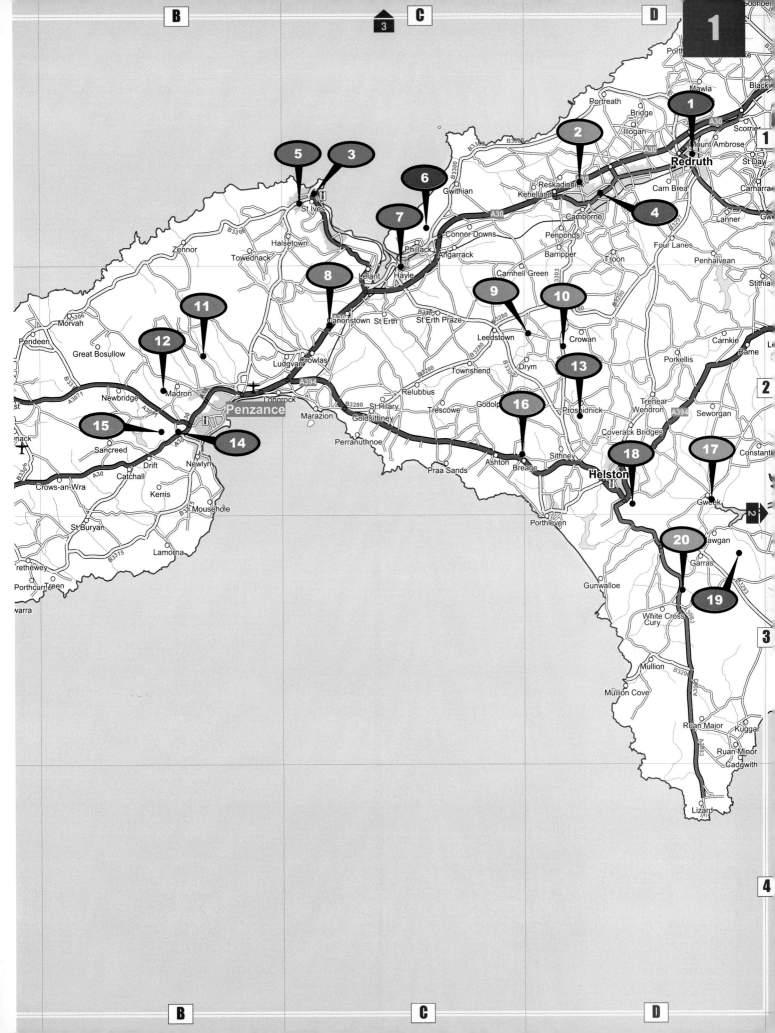

**1** **TREWITHEN GARDENS & NURSERIES**
Grampound Road, Truro
TEL: 01726 883 647

**2** **PROBUS GARDENS**
Probus, Truro
TEL: 01726 882 597

**3** **CREED HOUSE**
Creed, Grampound
TEL: 01872 530 372

**4** **PENTEWAN VALLEY NURSERY**
Pentewan Road, St Austell
TEL: 01726 842 360

**5** **LOST GARDENS OF HELIGAN**
Pentewan, St Austell
TEL: 01726 845 100

**6** **BOSVIGO PLANTS AND GARDEN**
Bosvigo Lane, Truro
TEL: 01872 275 774

**7** **FLOWERPOT NURSERIES**
Unit 6, 20-21 Pannier Market, Lemon Quay, Truro
TEL: 01872 261 494

**8** **ROSELAND HOUSE NURSERY**
Chacewater, Truro
TEL: 01872 560 451

**9** **SUNNY CORNER NURSERIES & GARDEN CENTRE**
The Square, Chacewater, Truro
TEL: 01872 560 084

**10** **TREGOTHNAN NURSERY**
Estate Office, Tregothnan, Truro
TEL: 01872 520 584

**11** **CARNON DOWNS GARDEN CENTRE**
Quenchwell Road, Carnon Downs, Truro
TEL: 01872 863 058

**12** **TRELISSICK GARDEN, NATIONAL TRUST**
Feock, Truro
TEL: 01872 862 090

**13** **BURNCOOSE GARDEN & NURSERIES**
Gwennap, Redruth
TEL: 01209 860 316

**14** **CHURCHTOWN NURSERY**
Perranarworthal, Truro
TEL: 01872 863033

**15** **CORNISH GARDEN CENTRE**
Perranarworthal, Truro
TEL: 01872 864380

**16** **FOX ROSEHILL GARDENS**
Melville Road, Falmouth
TEL: 01326 319 377

**17** **FALMOUTH GARDEN CENTRE**
Swanpool Road, Golden Bank, Falmouth
TEL: 01326 315 404

**18** **FIR TREE FARM NURSERY**
Tresahor, Constantine, Falmouth
TEL: 01326 340 593

**19** **CARWINION GARDENS**
Mawnam Smith, Falmouth
TEL: 01326 250 258

**20** **MEUDON HOTEL & GARDENS**
Mawnam Smith, Falmouth
TEL: 01326 250 541

**21** **TOWAN CAMELLIAS AT CARWINION**
Mawnan Smith, Falmouth
TEL: 01326 251 115

**22** **TREBAH GARDEN TRUST**
Mawnan Smith, Falmouth, Cornwall, TR11 5JZ.
TEL: 01326 250 448
EMAIL: mail@trebah-garden.co.uk
WEB: www.trebah-garden.co.uk

*Stunningly beautiful subtropical ravine garden running down to a private beach on Helford river. A riot of colour and scent throughout the year.*
OPEN: Open daily 10.30-5 (last admission).
ENTRY COSTS: £4.50, Child: £2.50 Under 5's free, OAPs: £4, Disabled: £2.50, RHS members: Free.
FACILITIES: Toilets, Credit cards, Wheelchair access, Restaurant, Dogs allowed, Child area, Coffee shop, Sell plants, Gift shop, HTA gift tokens.

**23** **GLENDURGAN GARDEN, NATIONAL TRUST**
Helford River, Mawnam Smith, Fairford
TEL: 01326 250 906

**24** **MYRTLE NURSERY**
High Lane, Manaccan, Cornwall, TR12 6HT.
TEL: 01326 231 604
*Visit our nursery then take a stroll around our garden and lake followed by a cream tea in our tea room. What better way to enjoy a few hours?*
OPEN: Thu-Mon: 10-5. Tea room: Easter-Oct 10-5.
SPECIALITIES: Comprehensive range, Fuchsias, Hanging baskets, Hardy plants, Shrubs.
FACILITIES: Coffee shop, Own gift tokens, Sell plants, Toilets, Wheelchair access.

Flower baskets

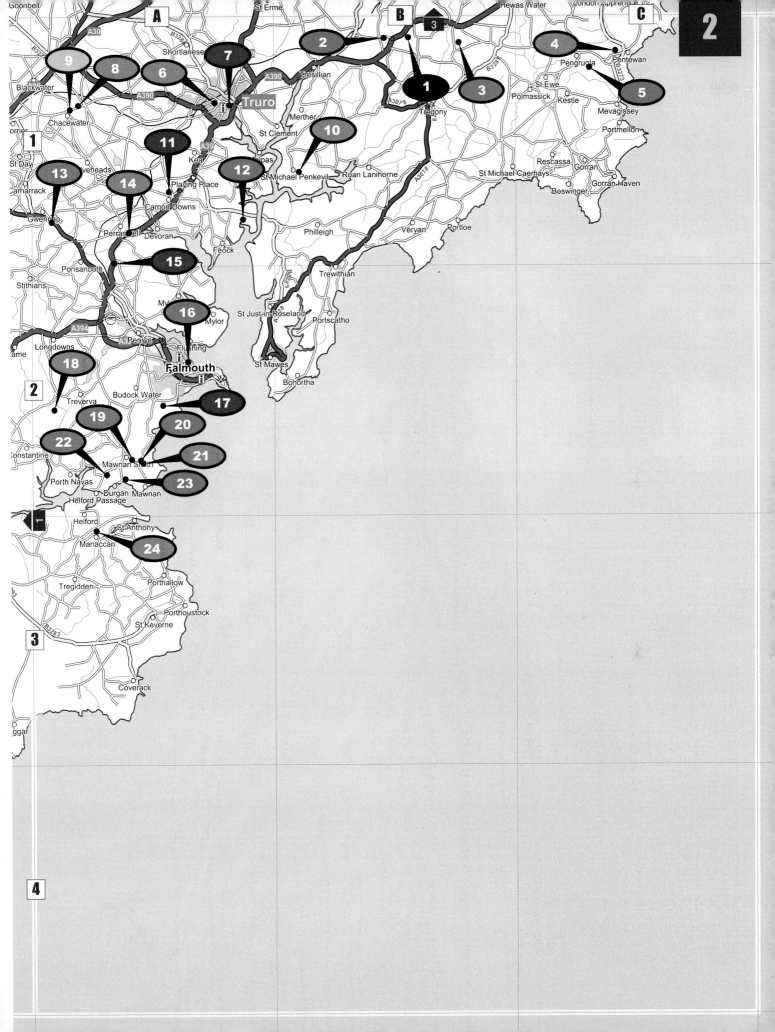

**1  BRUALLEN NURSERY**
Trewennen Lane, St Teath, Bodmin
**Tel:** 01208 850 650

**2  LONG CROSS VICTORIAN GARDENS**
Trelights, Port Isaac
**Tel:** 01208 880 243

**3  THE OLD MILL HERBARY**
Helland Bridge, Bodmin
**Tel:** 01208 841 206

**4  TRELAWNEY GARDEN LEISURE**
Sladesbridge, Wadebridge
**Tel:** 01208 812 966

**5  PENCARROW**
Washaway, Bodmin
**Tel:** 01208 841 369

**6  JAPANESE GARDEN & BONSAI NURSERY**
St Mawgan Village, Newquay
**Tel:** 01637 860 116

**7  BODMIN PLANT & HERB NURSERY**
Laveddon Mill, Bodmin
**Tel:** 01208 72 837

**8  LANHYDROCK, NATIONAL TRUST**
Lanhydrock, Bodmin
**Tel:** 01208 733 20

**9  PORTH VEOR FUCHSIAS**
54 Arundel Way, Newquay
**Tel:** 01637 877 208

**10  MERLIN GARDEN SUPPLIES**
3 St Georges Road, Newquay
**Tel:** 01637 879 100

**11  DUCHY OF CORNWALL NURSERY**
Cott Road, Lostwithiel
**Tel:** 01208 872 668

**12  NEWQUAY GARDEN CENTRE**
Little Trethiggey, Quintrell Downs, Newquay
**Tel:** 01637 872 199

**13  TRERICE, NATIONAL TRUST**
Kestle Mill, Newquay
**Tel:** 01637 875 404

**14  EDEN PROJECT**
Bodelva, St Austell
**Tel:** 01726 222 900

**15  PINE LODGE GARDEN & NURSERY**
Cuddra, Holmbush, St Austell
**Tel:** 01726 735 00

**16  WYEVALE GARDEN CENTRE**
Par Moor Road, Plymouth
**Tel:** 01726 814 854

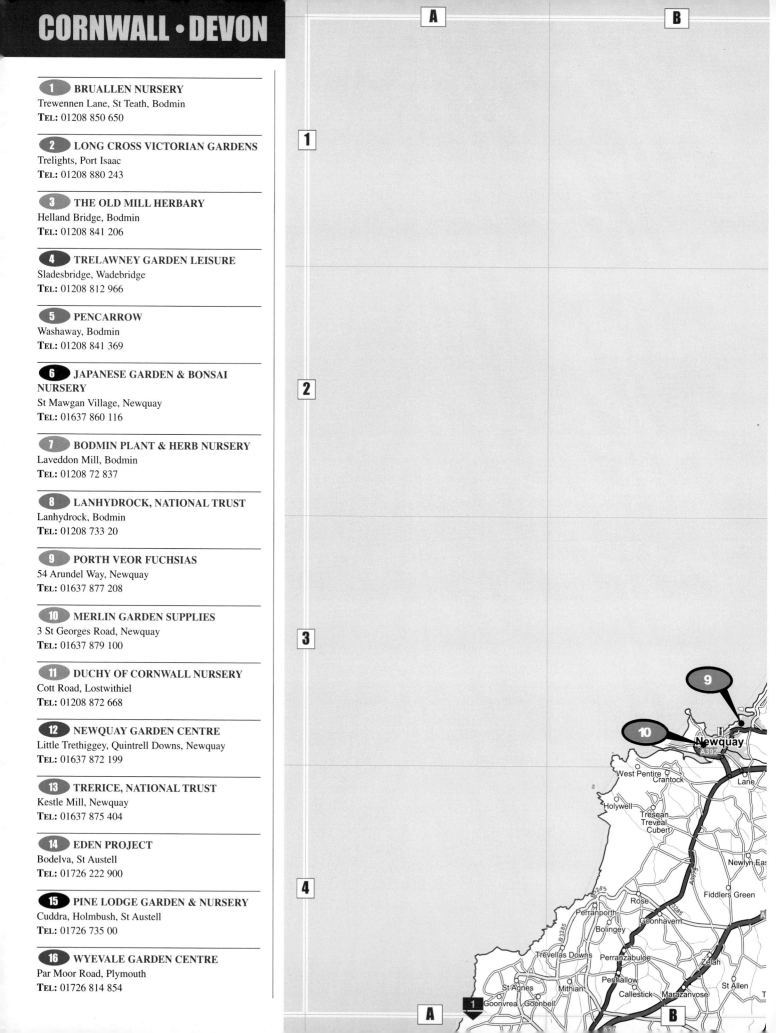

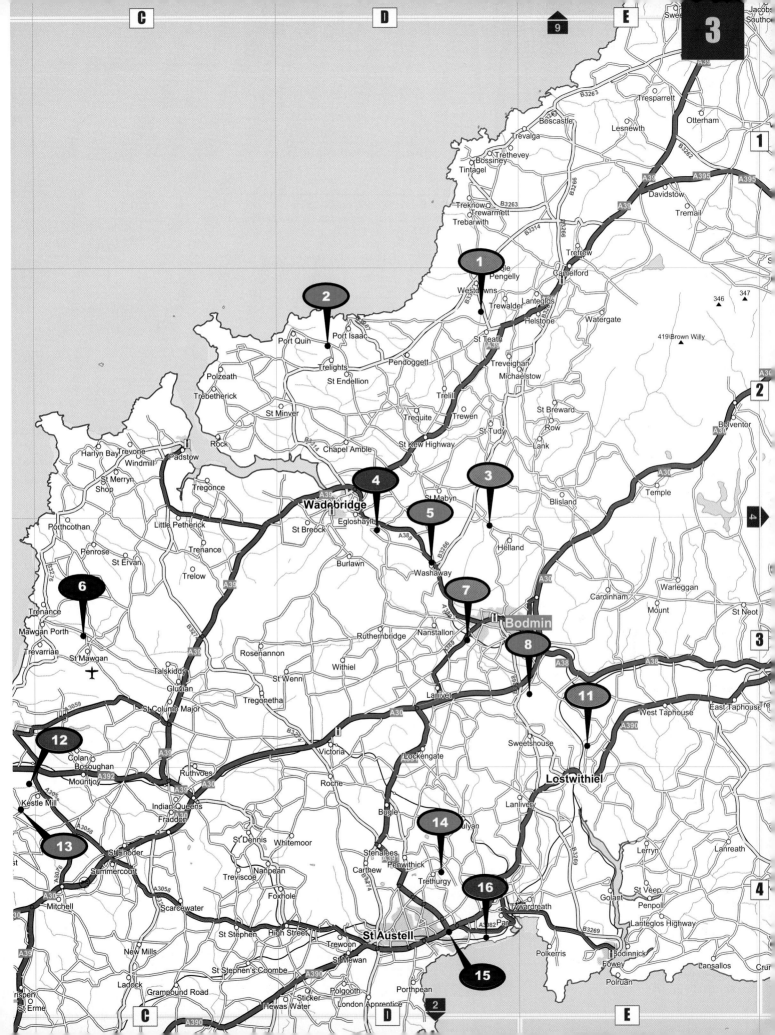

**1  HIGURASHI BONSAI**
Henford, Ashwater
TEL: 01409 211 137

**2  THORNDON CROSS NURSERY**
Whincote, Thorndon Cross, Okehampton
TEL: 01837 861 347

**3  LYDFORD ALPINE NURSERY**
2 Southern Cottages, Lydford, Okehampton
TEL: 01822 820 398

**4  BOYTON NURSERY & GARDEN CENTRE**
Braggs Hill, Boyton, Launceston
TEL: 01566 776 474

**5  ROWDEN GARDENS**
Rowden, Brentor, Tavistock
TEL: 01822 810 275

**6  ENDSLEIGH GARDENS NURSERY**
Milton Abbot, Tavistock
TEL: 01822 870 235

**7  ENDSLEIGH HOUSE AND GARDENS**
Endsleigh House, Milton Abbot
TEL: 01822 870 248

**8  KAMINSKI HOME & GARDEN CENTRE**
17b Parkwood Road, Tavistock
TEL: 01822 613 147

---

**9  TRECANNA NURSERY**
Rose Farm, Latchley, Gunnislake, Cornwall, PL18 9AX.
TEL: 01822 834 680
EMAIL: mark@trecanna.com
WEB: www.trecanna.com
*A new Cornish nursery specialising in fragrant plants, crocosmia, helianthemums, sempervivums and unusual perennials. Wide choice, garden settings, superb views over the Tamar Valley.*
OPEN: Mar 29-Oct 19: Fri-Sat & BH's 10-5.
SPECIALITIES: Bulbs, Grasses, Herbaceous plants, Rock plants, Themed gardens.
FACILITIES: Dogs allowed, Plant guarantee, Sell plants, Toilets.

---

**10  COCKINGTON NURSERY**
Callington
TEL: 01579 370 977

**11  COTEHELE, NATIONAL TRUST**
St Dominick, Saltash
TEL: 01579 351 346

**12  BUCKLAND ABBEY, NATIONAL TRUST**
Yelverton
TEL: 01822 853 607

**13  GARDEN HOUSE**
Buckland Monachorum, Yelverton
TEL: 01822 854 769

**14  MARISTOW NURSERY GARDENS**
Roborough, Plymouth
TEL: 01752 736 779

**15  GOLDENBANK NURSERY & GARDEN CENTRE**
Plymouth Road, Liskeard
TEL: 01579 348 622

**16  CATCHFRENCH MANOR GARDENS**
St Germans, Saltash
TEL: 01503 240 759

**17  PLYMOUTH GARDEN CENTRE**
Fort Austin Avenue, Crownhill, Plymouth
TEL: 01752 771 820

**18  MEADOW COTTAGE PLANTS**
Pitt Hill, Ivybridge
TEL: 01752 894 532

**19  NARKURS NURSERY**
The Cottage, Narkurs, Torpoint
TEL: 01503 250 379

**20  ENDSLEIGH GARDEN & LEISURE**
Ivybridge
TEL: 01752 898 989

**21  ANTONY WOODLAND GARDEN, NATIONAL TRUST**
Near Antony House, Torpoint
TEL: 01752 812 364

**22  SALTRAM, NATIONAL TRUST**
Plymton, Plymouth
TEL: 01752 336 546

**23  STANBOROUGH GARDEN CENTRE**
Haye Road, Elberton, Plymouth
TEL: 01752 403 240

**24  MOUNT EDGCUMBE HOUSE & GARDENS**
Cremyll, Torpoint
TEL: 01752 822 236

**25  SUNRIDGE NURSERIES**
Worston, Yealmpton, Plymouth
TEL: 01752 880 438

**26  OTTER NURSERIES OF PLYMOUTH**
Chittleburn Hill, Brixton, Plymouth
TEL: 01752 405 422

**27  POUNSLEY PLANTS**
Pounsley Combe, Spriddlestone, Brixton
TEL: 01752 402 873

**28  RIVERFORD PLANT CENTRE**
Riverford at Kitley, Yealmpton, Plymouth
TEL: 01752 880 925

Rockery

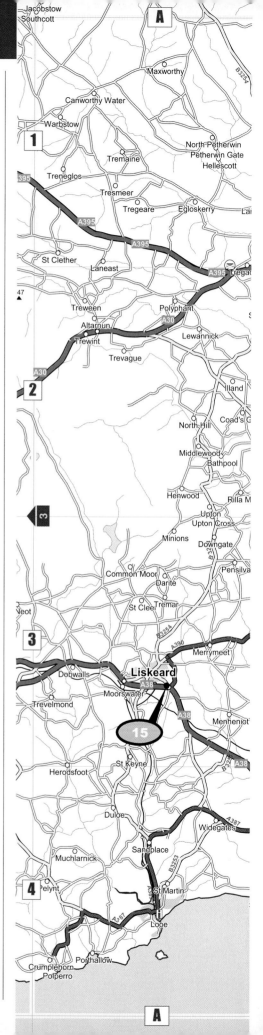

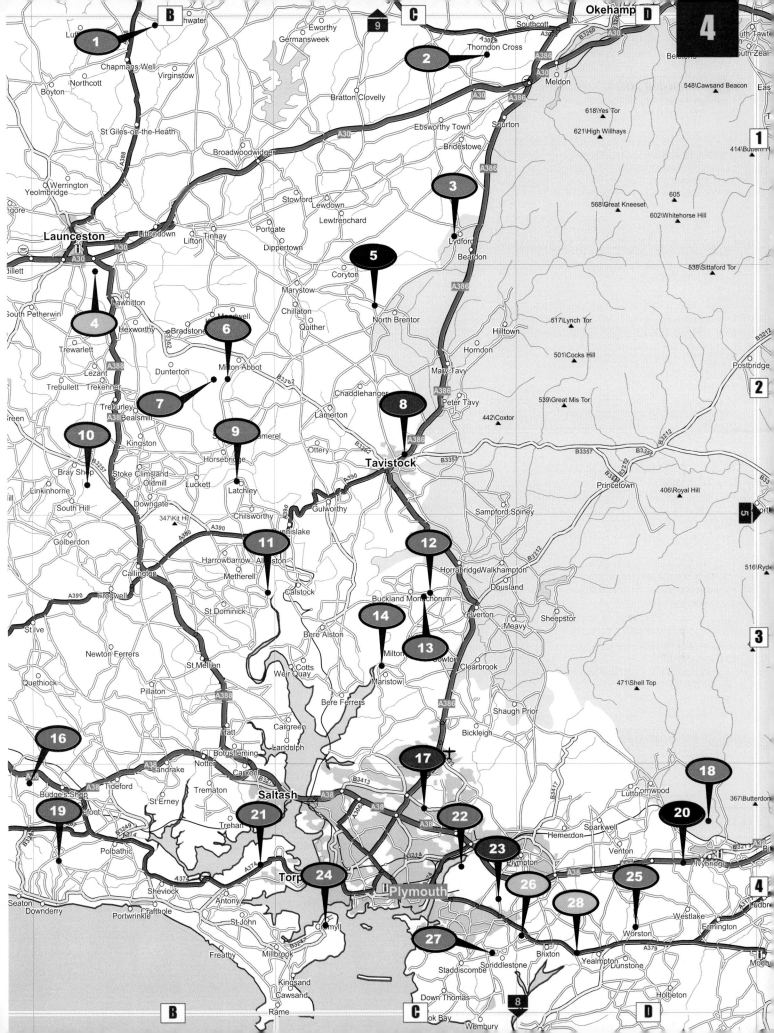

**1 EXETER UNIVERSITY GARDENS**
Streatham Farm, Prince of Wales Road, Exeter
**TEL:** 01392 263 059

**2 ST BRIDGET NURSERIES & GARDEN CENTRE**
Sidmouth Road, Clyst St Mary, Exeter
**TEL:** 01392 876 281

**3 SPRINGWELL NURSERY**
Old Ide Lane, Ide, Exeter
**TEL:** 01392 410 545

**4 ST BRIDGET NURSERIES & GARDEN CENTRE**
Old Rydon Lane, Exeter
**TEL:** 01392 873 672

**5 CASTLE DROGO, NATIONAL TRUST**
Drewsteignton, Exeter
**TEL:** 01647 433 306

**6 SEABROOK GARDEN CENTRE**
Topsham Road, Exeter
**TEL:** 01392 875 070

**7 THE PLANTSMAN NURSERY**
North Wonson Farm, Throwleigh, Okehampton
**TEL:** 01647 231 699

**8 STRAWBERRY HILL NURSERY**
Dunsford, Exeter
**TEL:** 01647 253 297

**9 MYTHIC GARDEN**
Stone Farm, Chagford, Newton Abbot
**TEL:** 01647 231 311

**10 STONE LANE GARDENS**
Stone Farm, Chagford, Newton Abbot
**TEL:** 01647 231 311

**11 TEIGN VALLEY NURSERY**
Bridford Mills, Bridford, Exeter
**TEL:** 01647 252 654

**12 PEVERIL CLEMATIS NURSERY**
Christow, Exeter
**TEL:** 01647 252 937

**13 POWDERHAM CASTLE**
Powderham, Kenton, Exeter
**TEL:** 01626 890 243

**14 BROAD OAK NURSERIES**
Mowlish Lane, Kenton, Exeter
**TEL:** 01626 890 034

**15 THE ROCK NURSERY**
Station Hill, Chudleigh, Newton Abbot
**TEL:** 01626 852 134

**16 ORCHID PARADISE**
Burnham Nurseries, Forches Cross, Newton Abbot
**TEL:** 01626 352 233

**17 JACK'S PATCH GARDEN CENTRE**
Bishopsteignton, Teignmouth
**TEL:** 01626 776 996

**18 BUCKFAST NURSERY**
Unit 29, Market Hall, Market Street, Newton Abbot
**TEL:** 01626 201 009

**19 PLEASANT VIEW NURSERY AND GARDEN**
Two Mile Oak, Denbury, Newton Abbot
**TEL:** 01803 813 388

**20 TORBAY AQUATIC CENTRE**
St Marychurch Road, Newton Abbot
**TEL:** 01803 873 663

**21 TORBAY PALM FARM**
St Marychurch Road, Coffinswell, Newton Abbot
**TEL:** 01803 872 800

**22 ELMCROFT GARDENS**
Old Newton Road, Kingskerwell, Newton Abbot
**TEL:** 01803 872 526

**23 BRAMLEY LODGE GARDEN NURSERY**
Beech Tree Lane, Ipplepen, Newton Abbot
**TEL:** 01803 813 265

**24 PLANT WORLD GARDENS & NURSERY**
St Marychurch Road, Newton Abbot
**TEL:** 01803 872 939

**25 FERMOY'S GARDEN CENTRE & FARM SHOP**
Totnes Road, Ipplepen, Newton Abbot
**TEL:** 01803 813 504

**26 HILL HOUSE NURSERY AND GARDEN**
Landscove, Ashburton, Newton Abbot
**TEL:** 01803 762 273

**27 KERSWELL GARDEN CENTRE**
Newton Road, Torquay
**TEL:** 01803 872 124

**28 GILBERTS PET & GARDEN CENTRE**
40 Fore Street, St Marychurch, Torquay
**TEL:** 01803 329 149

**29 OTTER NURSERIES & GARDEN CENTRE**
250 Babbacombe Road, Torquay
**TEL:** 01803 214 294

**30 STAVERTON BRIDGE NURSERY**
Staverton, Totnes
**TEL:** 01803 762 678

**31 DARTINGTON HALL**
Dartington, Totnes
**TEL:** 01803 862 367

**32 CIDER PRESS PLANT CENTRE**
Shinners Bridge, Dartington, Totnes
**TEL:** 01803 864 171

**33 DEVON VIOLET NURSERY**
Rattery, South Brent
**TEL:** 01364 643 033

**34 PAIGNTON ZOO AND BOTANICAL GARDENS**
Totnes Road, Paignton, Devon, TQ4 7EU.
**TEL:** 01803 697 500
**EMAIL:** info@paigntonzoo.org.uk
**WEB:** www.paigntonzoo.org.uk

*Paignton Zoo's redevelopment programme has transformed the zoo into a unique environmental park, featuring plants and animals from some of the world's threatened habitats.*
**OPEN:** Apr-Oct:: 10-6. Nov-Mar: 10-5. Closed Christmas Day.
**ENTRY COSTS:** £8, Child: £5.75, OAPs: £6.50, Family: £24.70.
**SPECIALITIES:** Aviary, Exotic plants, Fruit & fruit trees, Gifts, Palms.
**FACILITIES:** Restaurant, Coffee shop, Wheelchair access, Credit cards, Toilets, Gift shop, Child area, Coffee shop, Pushchair friendly.

**35 LONGCOMBE NURSERY & GARDEN CENTRE**
Longcombe Cross, Longcombe, Totnes
**TEL:** 01803 863 098

**36 TORBAY GARDEN CENTRE**
Brixham Road, Paignton
**TEL:** 01803 559 768

**37 SAMUEL DOBIE & SON**
Long Road, Paignton
**TEL:** 01803 696 411

**38 BRIXHAM HOME PET & GARDEN SUPPLIES**
10 Greenswood Road, Brixham
**TEL:** 01803 854 410

**39 GREENWAY HOUSE & GARDENS, NATIONAL TRUST**
Churston Ferrers, Brixham
**TEL:** 01803 842 382 / 843 235

**40 COLETON FISHACRE HOUSE & GARDEN, NATIONAL TRUST**
Coleton, Kingswear, Dartmouth
**TEL:** 01803 752 466

**41 M G M NURSERIES**
Brent Road, Loddiswell, Kingsbridge
**TEL:** 01548 550 754

Fungi

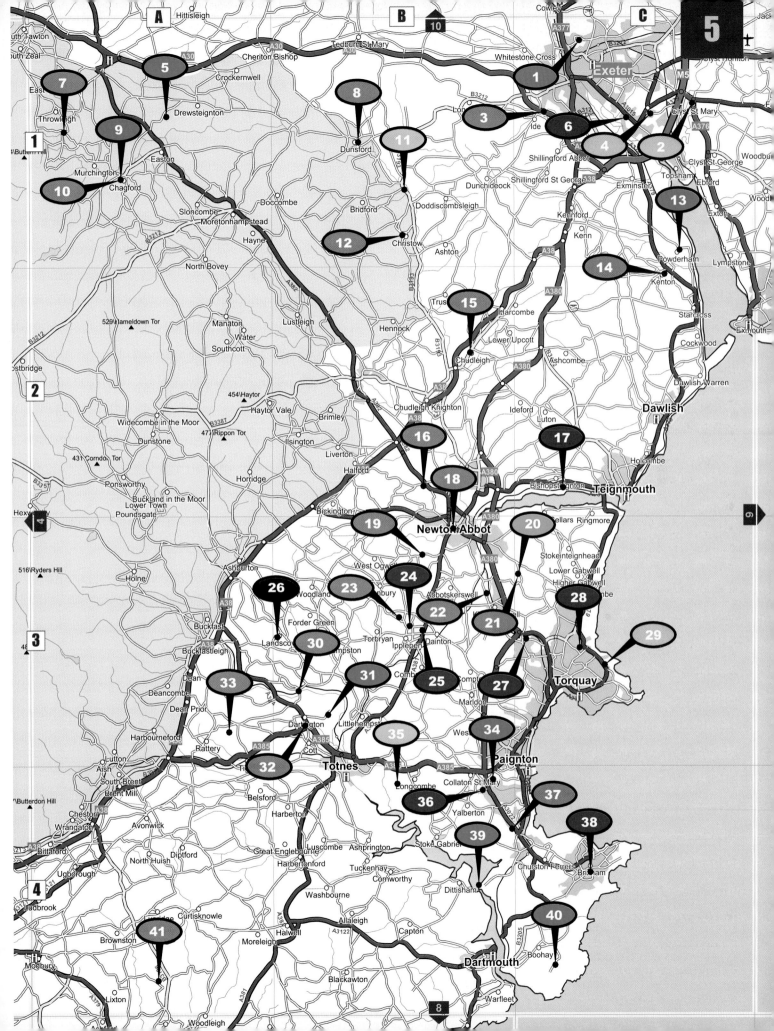

DEVON    DORSET

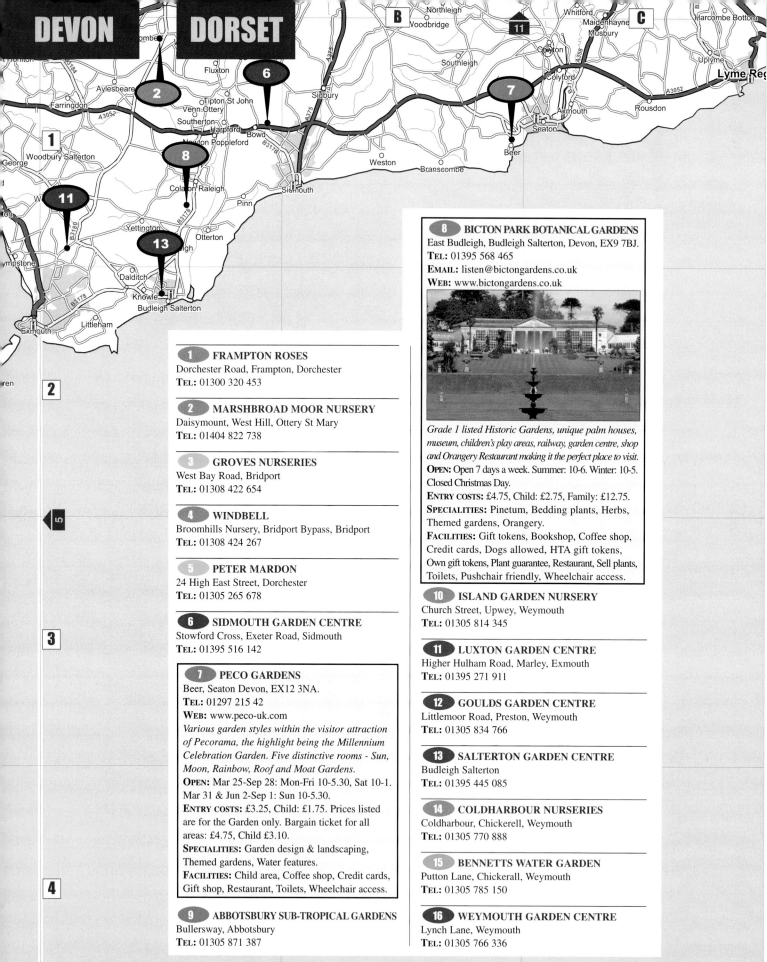

**1  FRAMPTON ROSES**
Dorchester Road, Frampton, Dorchester
TEL: 01300 320 453

**2  MARSHBROAD MOOR NURSERY**
Daisymount, West Hill, Ottery St Mary
TEL: 01404 822 738

**3  GROVES NURSERIES**
West Bay Road, Bridport
TEL: 01308 422 654

**4  WINDBELL**
Broomhills Nursery, Bridport Bypass, Bridport
TEL: 01308 424 267

**5  PETER MARDON**
24 High East Street, Dorchester
TEL: 01305 265 678

**6  SIDMOUTH GARDEN CENTRE**
Stowford Cross, Exeter Road, Sidmouth
TEL: 01395 516 142

**7  PECO GARDENS**
Beer, Seaton Devon, EX12 3NA.
TEL: 01297 215 42
WEB: www.peco-uk.com
*Various garden styles within the visitor attraction of Pecorama, the highlight being the Millennium Celebration Garden. Five distinctive rooms - Sun, Moon, Rainbow, Roof and Moat Gardens.*
OPEN: Mar 25-Sep 28: Mon-Fri 10-5.30, Sat 10-1. Mar 31 & Jun 2-Sep 1: Sun 10-5.30.
ENTRY COSTS: £3.25, Child: £1.75. Prices listed are for the Garden only. Bargain ticket for all areas: £4.75, Child £3.10.
SPECIALITIES: Garden design & landscaping, Themed gardens, Water features.
FACILITIES: Child area, Coffee shop, Credit cards, Gift shop, Restaurant, Toilets, Wheelchair access.

**9  ABBOTSBURY SUB-TROPICAL GARDENS**
Bullersway, Abbotsbury
TEL: 01305 871 387

**8  BICTON PARK BOTANICAL GARDENS**
East Budleigh, Budleigh Salterton, Devon, EX9 7BJ.
TEL: 01395 568 465
EMAIL: listen@bictongardens.co.uk
WEB: www.bictongardens.co.uk

*Grade 1 listed Historic Gardens, unique palm houses, museum, children's play areas, railway, garden centre, shop and Orangery Restaurant making it the perfect place to visit.*
OPEN: Open 7 days a week. Summer: 10-6. Winter: 10-5. Closed Christmas Day.
ENTRY COSTS: £4.75, Child: £2.75, Family: £12.75.
SPECIALITIES: Pinetum, Bedding plants, Herbs, Themed gardens, Orangery.
FACILITIES: Gift tokens, Bookshop, Coffee shop, Credit cards, Dogs allowed, HTA gift tokens, Own gift tokens, Plant guarantee, Restaurant, Sell plants, Toilets, Pushchair friendly, Wheelchair access.

**10  ISLAND GARDEN NURSERY**
Church Street, Upwey, Weymouth
TEL: 01305 814 345

**11  LUXTON GARDEN CENTRE**
Higher Hulham Road, Marley, Exmouth
TEL: 01395 271 911

**12  GOULDS GARDEN CENTRE**
Littlemoor Road, Preston, Weymouth
TEL: 01305 834 766

**13  SALTERTON GARDEN CENTRE**
Budleigh Salterton
TEL: 01395 445 085

**14  COLDHARBOUR NURSERIES**
Coldharbour, Chickerell, Weymouth
TEL: 01305 770 888

**15  BENNETTS WATER GARDEN**
Putton Lane, Chickerall, Weymouth
TEL: 01305 785 150

**16  WEYMOUTH GARDEN CENTRE**
Lynch Lane, Weymouth
TEL: 01305 766 336

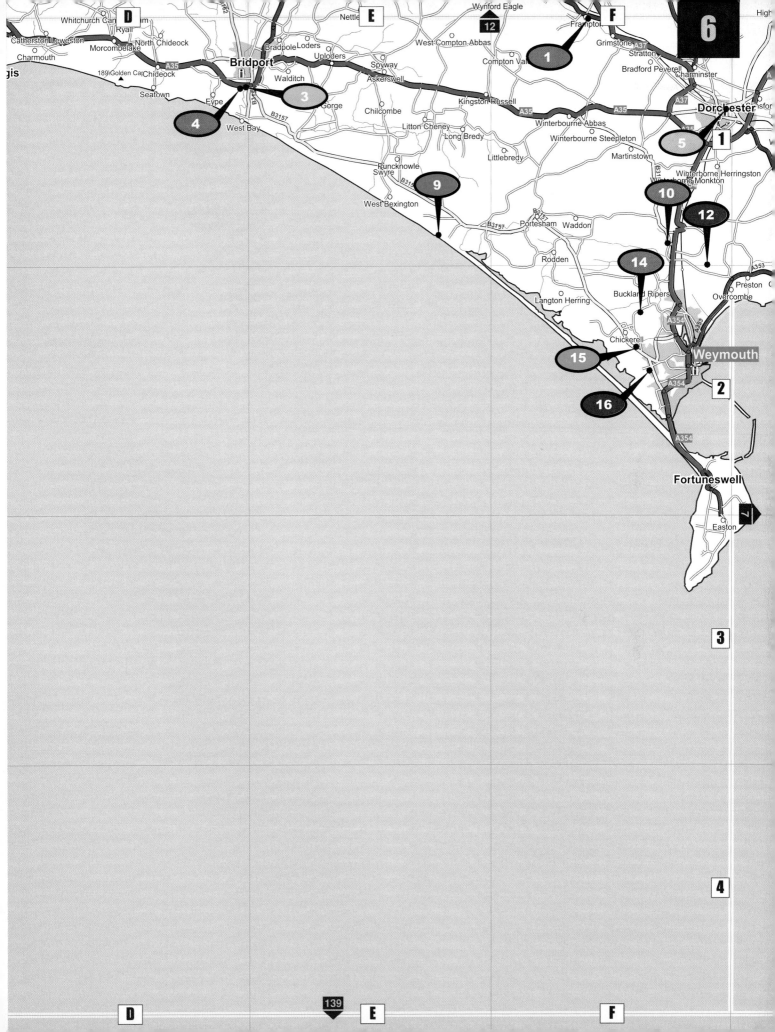

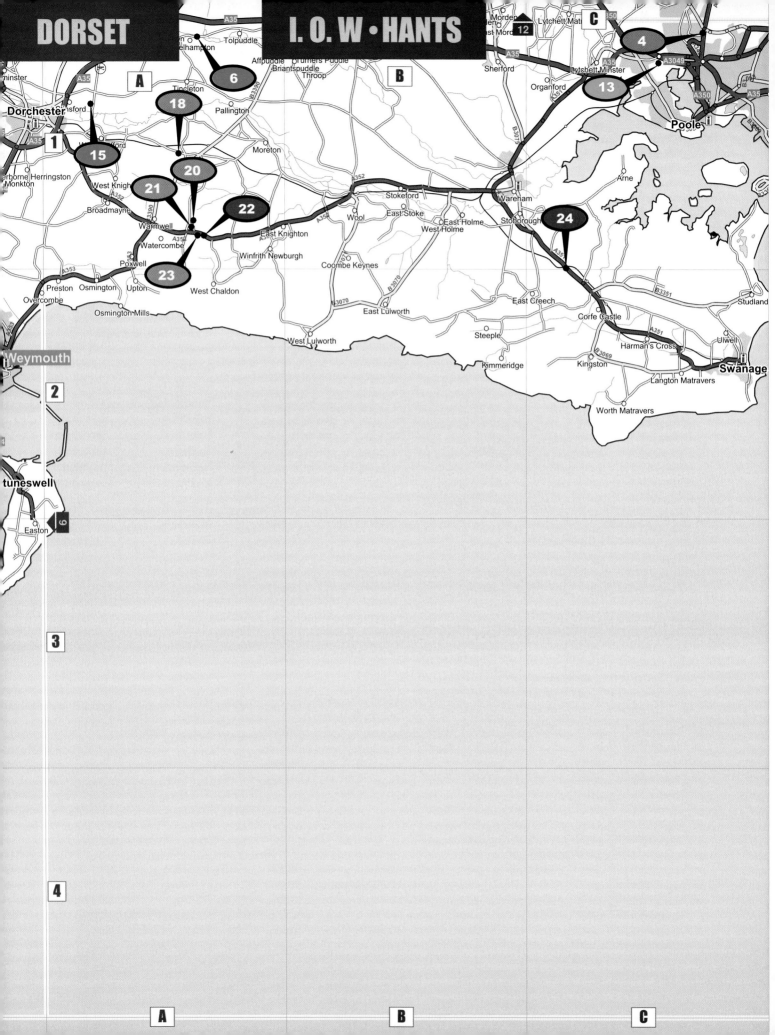

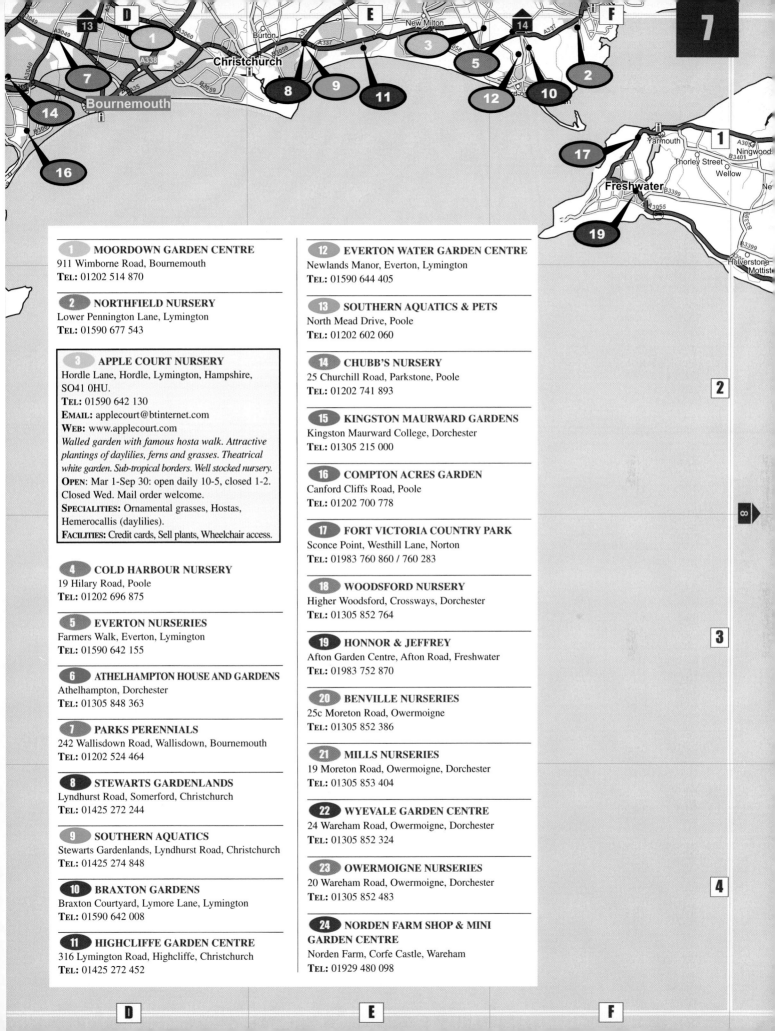

**7**

**1  MOORDOWN GARDEN CENTRE**
911 Wimborne Road, Bournemouth
TEL: 01202 514 870

**2  NORTHFIELD NURSERY**
Lower Pennington Lane, Lymington
TEL: 01590 677 543

**3  APPLE COURT NURSERY**
Hordle Lane, Hordle, Lymington, Hampshire,
SO41 0HU.
TEL: 01590 642 130
EMAIL: applecourt@btinternet.com
WEB: www.applecourt.com
*Walled garden with famous hosta walk. Attractive
plantings of daylilies, ferns and grasses. Theatrical
white garden. Sub-tropical borders. Well stocked nursery.*
OPEN: Mar 1-Sep 30: open daily 10-5, closed 1-2.
Closed Wed. Mail order welcome.
SPECIALITIES: Ornamental grasses, Hostas,
Hemerocallis (daylilies).
FACILITIES: Credit cards, Sell plants, Wheelchair access.

**4  COLD HARBOUR NURSERY**
19 Hilary Road, Poole
TEL: 01202 696 875

**5  EVERTON NURSERIES**
Farmers Walk, Everton, Lymington
TEL: 01590 642 155

**6  ATHELHAMPTON HOUSE AND GARDENS**
Athelhampton, Dorchester
TEL: 01305 848 363

**7  PARKS PERENNIALS**
242 Wallisdown Road, Wallisdown, Bournemouth
TEL: 01202 524 464

**8  STEWARTS GARDENLANDS**
Lyndhurst Road, Somerford, Christchurch
TEL: 01425 272 244

**9  SOUTHERN AQUATICS**
Stewarts Gardenlands, Lyndhurst Road, Christchurch
TEL: 01425 274 848

**10  BRAXTON GARDENS**
Braxton Courtyard, Lymore Lane, Lymington
TEL: 01590 642 008

**11  HIGHCLIFFE GARDEN CENTRE**
316 Lymington Road, Highcliffe, Christchurch
TEL: 01425 272 452

**12  EVERTON WATER GARDEN CENTRE**
Newlands Manor, Everton, Lymington
TEL: 01590 644 405

**13  SOUTHERN AQUATICS & PETS**
North Mead Drive, Poole
TEL: 01202 602 060

**14  CHUBB'S NURSERY**
25 Churchill Road, Parkstone, Poole
TEL: 01202 741 893

**15  KINGSTON MAURWARD GARDENS**
Kingston Maurward College, Dorchester
TEL: 01305 215 000

**16  COMPTON ACRES GARDEN**
Canford Cliffs Road, Poole
TEL: 01202 700 778

**17  FORT VICTORIA COUNTRY PARK**
Sconce Point, Westhill Lane, Norton
TEL: 01983 760 860 / 760 283

**18  WOODSFORD NURSERY**
Higher Woodsford, Crossways, Dorchester
TEL: 01305 852 764

**19  HONNOR & JEFFREY**
Afton Garden Centre, Afton Road, Freshwater
TEL: 01983 752 870

**20  BENVILLE NURSERIES**
25c Moreton Road, Owermoigne
TEL: 01305 852 386

**21  MILLS NURSERIES**
19 Moreton Road, Owermoigne, Dorchester
TEL: 01305 853 404

**22  WYEVALE GARDEN CENTRE**
24 Wareham Road, Owermoigne, Dorchester
TEL: 01305 852 324

**23  OWERMOIGNE NURSERIES**
20 Wareham Road, Owermoigne, Dorchester
TEL: 01305 852 483

**24  NORDEN FARM SHOP & MINI
GARDEN CENTRE**
Norden Farm, Corfe Castle, Wareham
TEL: 01929 480 098

# DEVON · ISLE OF WIGHT

**1** **OSBORNE HOUSE, ENGLISH HERITAGE**
York Avenue, East Cowes
TEL: 01983 200 022

**2** **BARTON MANOR**
Whippingham, East Cowes
TEL: 01983 280 676

**3** **RYDE HOUSE NURSERY**
Binstead Road, Ryde
TEL: 01983 565 650

**4** **LUSHINGTON GARDEN CENTRE**
Lushington Hill, Wootton Bridge
TEL: 01983 882 216

**5** **LYNWOOD GARDEN CENTRE**
Fairlee Road, Newport
TEL: 01983 526 618

**6** **FOREST VIEW NURSERY**
Forest Road, Newport
TEL: 01983 530 675

**7** **MEDINA GARDEN CENTRE**
Staplers Road, Wootton
TEL: 01983 883 430

**8** **BUSY BEE PLANT CENTRE**
Brading Road, Ryde
TEL: 01983 811 096

**9** **WHITEFIELD FOREST**
Brading Road, Ryde
TEL: 01983 614 388

**10** **HUNNEYHILL AQUATICS**
Vicarage Walk, Newport
TEL: 01983 825 577

**11** **RINGWOOD NURSERIES**
Yarmouth Road, Ningwood, Yarmouth
TEL: 01983 760 376

**12** **OASIS**
Carpenters Road, Brading
TEL: 01983 613 760

**13** **MORTON MANOR**
Brading, Sandown
TEL: 01983 406 168

**14** **BRADING ROMAN VILLA**
Morton Old Road, Brading
TEL: 01983 406 223

**15** **HASELEY MANOR**
Arreton, Newport
TEL: 01983 865 420

**16** **THOMPSON'S PLANT & GARDEN CENTRE**
Watery Lane, Newchurch, Sandown
TEL: 01983 865 292

**17** **HIGHWOOD NURSERIES**
Newport Road, Rookley
TEL: 01983 721 011

**18** **HONNOR & JEFFREY**
Dalverton Garden Centre, Newport Road, Sandown
TEL: 01983 868 602

**19** **NEWCHURCH NURSERIES**
Springbank Nursery, Winford Road, Newchurch
TEL: 01983 865 444

**20** **JUBILEE GARDEN CENTRE**
Newport Road, Branston, Sandown
TEL: 01983 865 562

**21** **DEACONS NURSERY**
Moor View, Godshill
TEL: 01983 840 750

**22** **AQUASCAPE**
1 Merryl Lane, Godshill
TEL: 01983 840 268

**23** **APPULDURCOMBE HOUSE, ENGLISH HERITAGE**
Wroxall, Ventnor
TEL: 01983 852 484

**24** **LITTLE HERMITAGE**
St Catherines Down, Ventnor
TEL: 01983 730 512

**25** **VENTNOR BOTANIC GARDEN**
Undercliff Drive, Ventnor
TEL: 01983 855 397

**26** **ALSTON NURSERY**
Alston Gate, Malborough, Kingsbridge
TEL: 01548 561 947

**27** **OVERBECKS MUSEUM & GARDEN, NATIONAL TRUST**
Sharpitor, Salcombe
TEL: 01548 842 893

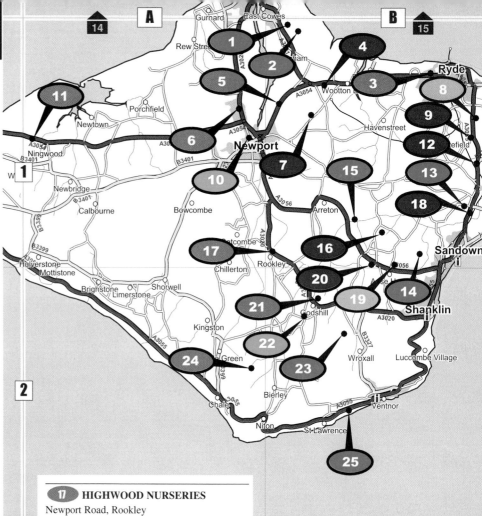

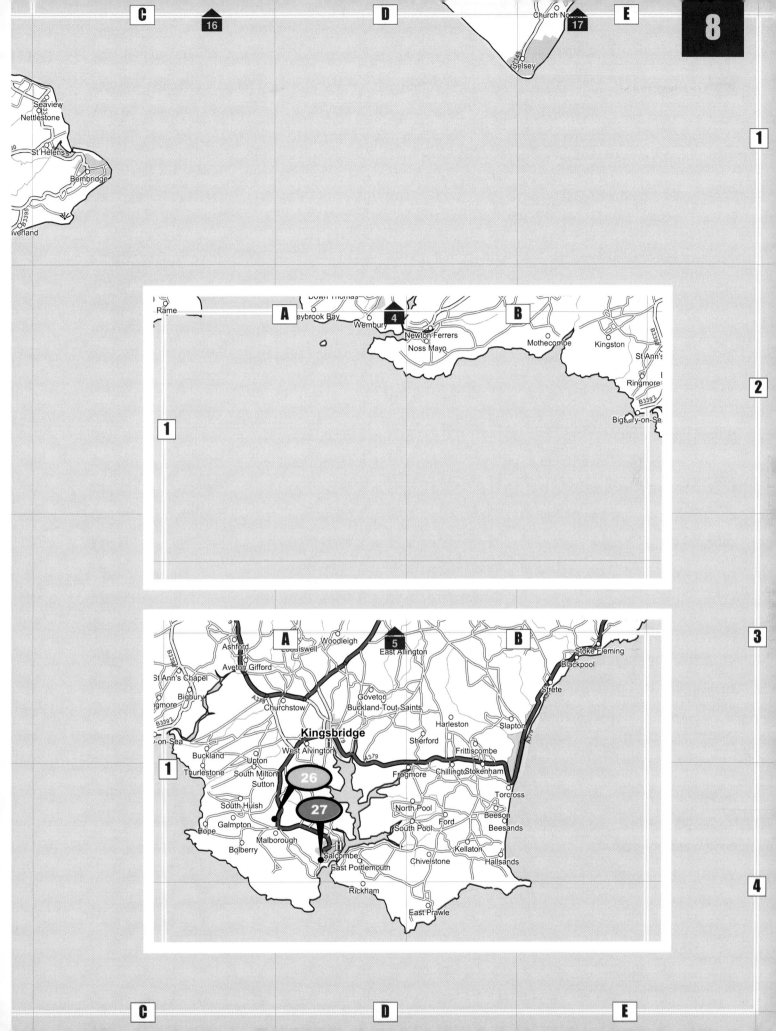

# DEVON · CORNWALL

**1 ARLINGTON COURT, NATIONAL TRUST**
Arlington, Barnstaple     TEL: 01271 850 296

**2 MARWOOD HILL GARDENS**
Marwood Hill, Barnstaple     TEL: 01271 342 528

**3 SANDY LANE FARM NURSERY**
Burrows Close, Braunton     TEL: 01271 812 288

**4 BANBURY'S GARDEN CENTRE**
Strand Lane, Ashford, Barnstaple
    TEL: 01271 342 880

**5 SCOTT'S CLEMATIS**
Birchbrook, Birch Lane, Landkey
    TEL: 01271 831 032

**6 ST JOHN'S GARDEN CENTRE**
St John's Lane, Newport, Barnstaple
    TEL: 01271 343 884

**7 TAPELEY PARK**
Tapeley House, Instow     TEL: 01271 342 558

**8 THE SECRET GARDEN**
2a Cross Street, Northam, Bideford
    TEL: 01237 474 403

**9 BIDEFORD GARDEN CENTRE**
Clovelly Industrial Estate, Clovelly Road, Bideford
    TEL: 01237 424 348

**10 HARTLAND ABBEY**
Cuckoo Wood Cottage, Hartland, Bideford
    TEL: 01237 441 264

**11 DOCTON MILL**
Lymebridge, Hartland, Bideford
    TEL: 01237 441 369

**12 GLEBE COTTAGE PLANTS**
Pixie Lane, Warkleigh, Umberleigh
    TEL: 01769 540 554

**13 M & M PLANTS**
Lloret, Chittlehamholt, Umberleigh
    TEL: 01769 540 448

**14 ROSEMOOR GARDEN, ROYAL HORTICULTURAL SOCIETY**
Great Torrington     TEL: 01805 624 067

**15 KENWITH NURSERY**
Blinsham, Torrington, Great Torrington
    TEL: 01805 603 274

**16 GNOME RESERVE AND WILDFLOWER GARDEN**
West Putford, Bradworthy     TEL: 0870 845 9012

**17 FERNWOOD NURSERY**
Peters Marland, Torrington     TEL: 01805 601 446

**18 CHAPEL FARM HOUSE NURSERY**
Halwill Junction, Beaworthy     TEL: 01409 221 594

**19 RAINBOW GARDEN CENTRE**
Treskinnick Cross, Poundstock, Bude
    TEL: 01288 361 898

**20 BOSTOCK GARDEN CENTRE**
North Road, Okehampton     TEL: 01837 532 48

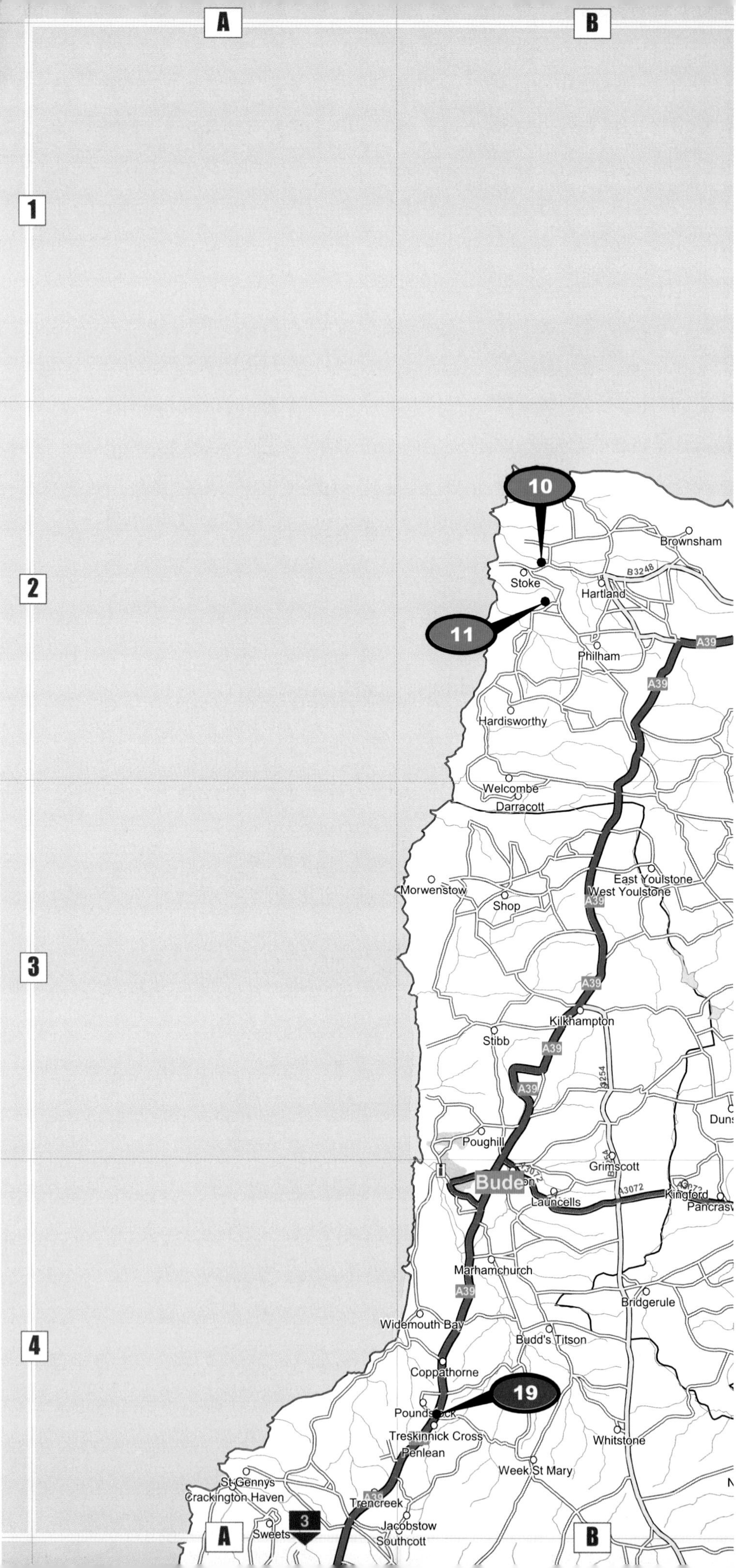

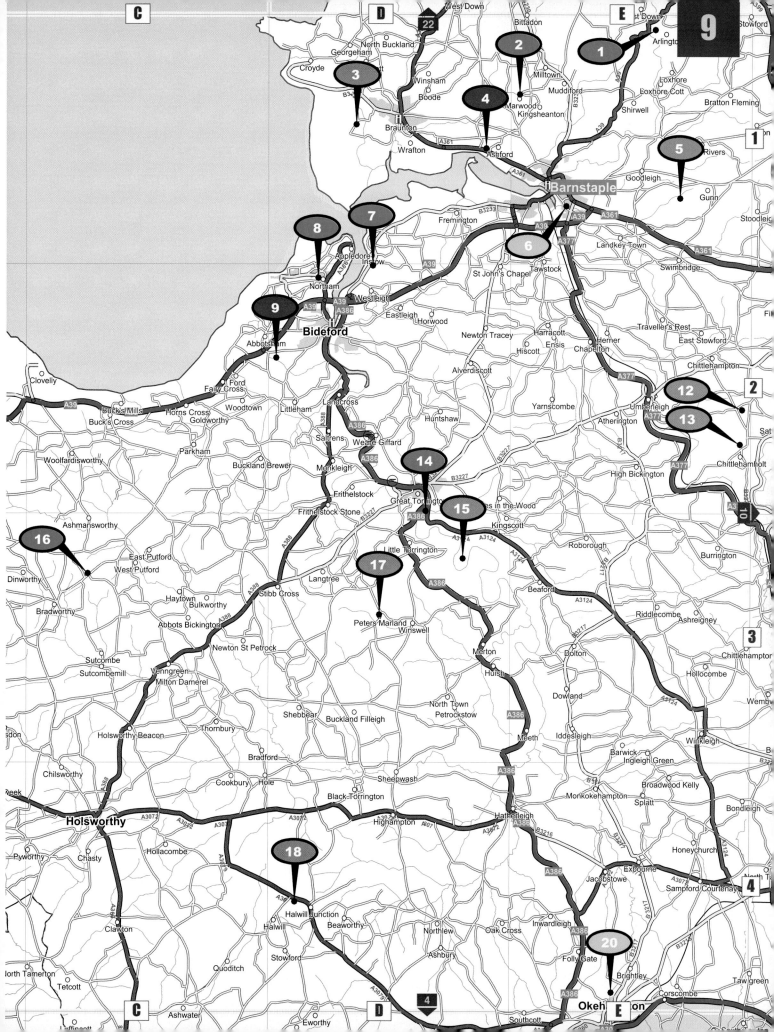

**1** CAMFORD NURSERIES
Woodford, Williton, Taunton
TEL: 01984 640 522

**2** ELWORTHY COTTAGE PLANTS
Elworthy, Lydeard-St-Lawrence, Taunton
TEL: 01984 656 427

**3** NORTH STREET GARDEN CENTRE
6 North Street, Wiveliscombe, Taunton
TEL: 01984 623 256

**4** ASH MOOR NURSERY
Rose Ash, South Molton
TEL: 01884 860 355

**5** SAMPFORD SHRUBS
Sampford Peverell, Tiverton
TEL: 01884 821 164

**6** KNIGHTSHAYES COURT, NATIONAL TRUST
Bolham, Tiverton
TEL: 01884 254 665

**7** SOUTH WEST CARNIVOROUS PLANTS
2 Rose Cottages, Culmstock, Cullompton
TEL: 01884 841 549

**8** TURNPIKE NURSERIES
Leonard Moor Cross, Uffculme, Cullompton
TEL: 01884 840 980

**9** WITHLEIGH NURSERIES
Withleigh, Tiverton
TEL: 01884 253 351

**10** EGGESFORD GARDENS
Eggesford, Chulmleigh
TEL: 01769 580 250

**11** WATER GARDENS
Highcroft, Mooren, Chulmleigh
TEL: 01837 83 566

**12** DULFORD NURSERIES
Cullompton
TEL: 01884 266 361

**13** THORNHAYES NUSERY
St Andrews Wood, Dulford, Cullompton
TEL: 01884 266 746

**14** BOW AQUATIC CENTRE
Burston, Bow, Crediton
TEL: 01363 824 38

**15** EDWIN TUCKER & SONS
Commercial Road, Crediton
TEL: 01363 772 202

**16** KILLERTON HOUSE, NATIONAL TRUST
Broadclyst, Exeter
TEL: 01392 881 345

**17** FEEBERS HARDY PLANTS
1 Feeber Cottage, Westwood, Exeter
TEL: 01404 822 118

**18** OTTER NURSERIES GARDEN CENTRE
Gosford Road, Ottery St Mary, Devon, EX11 1LZ.
TEL: 01404 815 815
EMAIL: otter@otternurseries.co.uk
WEB: www.otternurseries.co.uk
*One of the best garden centres in the country is a family run business in beautiful East Devon, with an acre under cover.*
OPEN: Mon-Sat 9-5.30, Sun 10.30-4.30. Closed Easter Sunday, Christmas & Boxing Day.
SPECIALITIES: Bedding plants, Garden & conservatory furniture, Greenhouses & sheds, Hardy plants, Terracotta pots.
FACILITIES: Bookshop, Coffee shop, Credit cards, Gift shop, HTA gift tokens, Own gift tokens, Plant guarantee, Pushchair friendly, Restaurant, Sell plants, Toilets, Wheelchair access.

**19** BERNAVILLE NURSERIES
Three Horse Shoes, Cowley, Exeter
TEL: 01392 851 326

**20** BOW AQUATIC CENTRE
Bernaville Nurseries, Cowley, Exeter
TEL: 01392 851 823

Quaking Grass

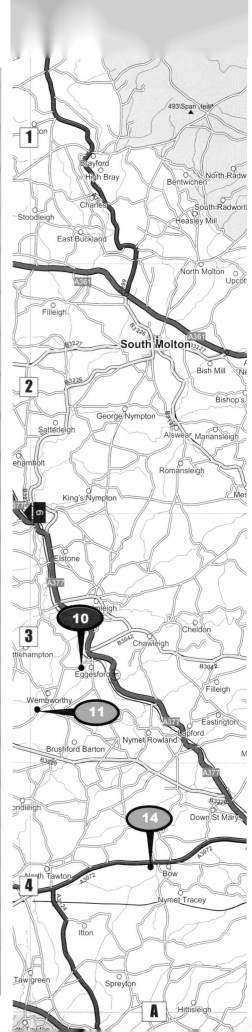

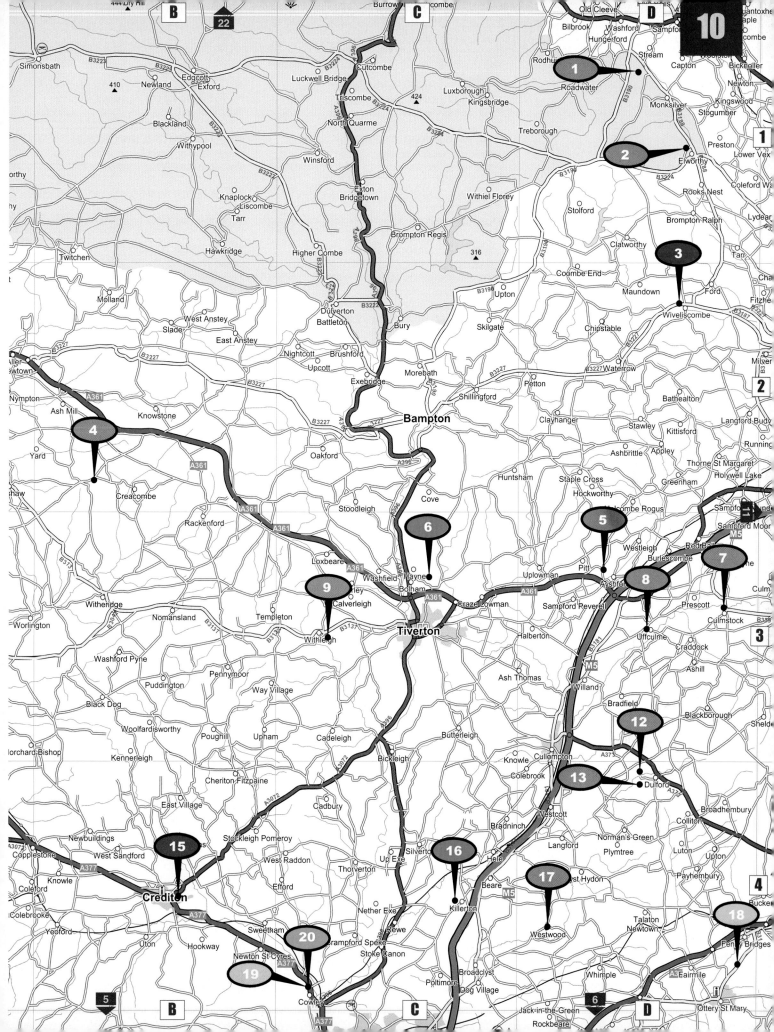

**1** CANNINGTON COLLEGE HERITAGE GARDENS
Cannington, Bridgwater
**TEL:** 01278 655 200

**2** HALSWAY NURSERIES
Crowcombe, Taunton
**TEL:** 01984 618 243

**3** BOWER FLOWERS
East Bower, Bridgend
**TEL:** 01278 423 845

**4** TRINITY NURSERIES
Broadway, Bridgewater
**TEL:** 01278 422 897

**5** TRISCOMBE NURSERIES
West Bagborough, Taunton
**TEL:** 01984 618 267

**6** ASHFIELD COURT NURSERIES
Farringdon, North Petherton
**TEL:** 01278 663 438

**7** GREENWAY NURSERY
Mount Fancy, Cheddon Fitzpaine, Taunton
**TEL:** 01823 412 681

**8** HESTERCOMBE GARDENS
Cheddon Fitzpaine, Taunton
**TEL:** 01823 413 923

**9** MONKTON ELM GARDEN & PET CENTRE
Monkton Elm, West Monkton, Taunton
**TEL:** 01823 414 104

**10** KELWAYS NURSERY AND PLANT CENTRE
Barrymore Farm, Langport
**TEL:** 01458 250 521

**11** WYEVALE GARDEN CENTRE
Pen Elm, North Fitzwarren, Taunton
**TEL:** 01823 323 777

**12** HIGH ELMS NURSERIES
Broad Lane, North Curry, Taunton
**TEL:** 01823 490 306

**13** AVERY PLANT CENTRE
Silk Mills Road, Taunton
**TEL:** 01823 288 324

**14** ST JOHN'S GARDEN CENTRE
Priory Way, Barnstaple
**TEL:** 01823 336 279

**15** BROADLEIGH GARDENS NURSERY
Bishops Hull, Taunton
**TEL:** 01823 286 231

**16** BROOKFIELD FARM SHOP & NURSERY
Brookfield Farm, Ruishton Lane, Ruishton, Taunton
**TEL:** 01823 443 333

**17** DEANE GARDEN SHOPS
29 North Street, Taunton
**TEL:** 01823 337 768

**18** BARN CLOSE NURSERIES
Barn Close, Henlade, Taunton
**TEL:** 01823 443 507

**19** GREENSHUTTERS NURSERIES
Milehill, Fivehead, Taunton
**TEL:** 01460 281 265

**20** MALLET COURT NURSERY
Curry Mallet, Taunton
**TEL:** 01823 480 748

**21** BLACKDOWN NURSERIES & GARDEN CENTRE
2 Hockholler, West Buckland, Wellington
**TEL:** 01823 661 699

**22** CHELSTON NURSERIES
Chelston, Wellington
**TEL:** 01823 662 007

**23** FOXMOOR FLOWER TOWER
Foxmoor Nurseries, Chelston, Wellington
**TEL:** 01823 661 662

**24** HATCH COURT
Hatch Beauchamp, Taunton
**TEL:** 01823 480 120

**25** SUE STRICKLAND PLANTS
The Poplars, Isle Brewers, Taunton
**TEL:** 01460 281 454

**26** WELLINGTON PET, GARDEN & FARM STORE
10-10a High Street, Wellington
**TEL:** 01823 662 914

**27** EAST LAMBROOK MANOR GARDENS
East Lambrook, South Petherton
**TEL:** 01460 240 328

**28** BARRINGTON COURT & GARDEN, NATIONAL TRUST
Barrington, Ilminster
**TEL:** 01460 241 938

**29** LYNASH NURSERIES
Wall Ditch Lane, Merriott
**TEL:** 01460 777 64

**30** STREET ASH NURSERY & PLANT CENTRE
Street Ash, Chard
**TEL:** 01460 234 582

**31** SCOTTS NURSERIES
Higher Street, Merriott
**TEL:** 01460 723 06

**32** GRANVILLES NURSERY
Hazlebury Road, Merriott, Crewkerne
**TEL:** 01460 778 44

**33** LOWER SEVERALLS GARDEN & NURSERY
Crewkerne
**TEL:** 01460 732 34

**34** GLENFIELD ORGANIC COMPOST
Puddletown, Haselbury Plucknett, Crewkerne
**TEL:** 01460 732 51

**35** CHARD GARDEN CENTRE
Cuttifords Door, Chard
**TEL:** 01460 630 88

**36** KINGSFIELD CONSERVATION NURSERY
Broadenham Lane, Winsham, Chard
**TEL:** 01460 300 70

**37** FORDE ABBEY
Chard
**TEL:** 01460 221 290

**38** R D UNUSUAL PLANTS
Homelea Farm, Chard Road, Tytherleigh
**TEL:** 01460 220 206

**39** NICKY'S ROCK GARDEN NURSERY
Broadhayes, Stockland, Honiton
**TEL:** 01404 881 213

**40** NURSERY OF MINIATURES
Hutgate Road, Honiton
**TEL:** 01404 426 17

**41** HALE LANE NURSERY
Honiton
**TEL:** 01404 427 11

**42** BURROW FARM GARDENS
Dalwood, Axminster
**TEL:** 01404 831 285

**43** SLADES COUNTRYWISE
Turks Head, Exeter Road, Honiton
**TEL:** 01404 427 20

**44** HUNTERS CROFT NURSERY
Raymonds Hill, Charmouth Road, Axminster
**TEL:** 01297 333 66

**45** SINCLAIR GARDEN NURSERY
Maes-y-Haf, Yawl Hill Lane, Uplyme
**TEL:** 01297 443 079

Dahlia

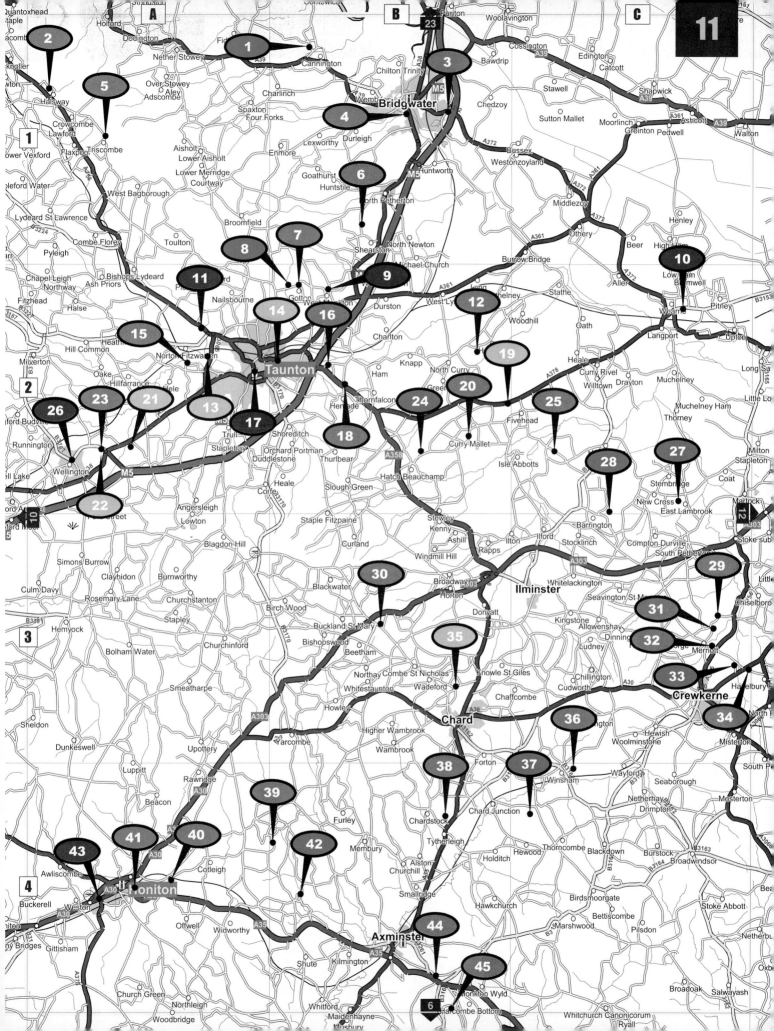

**1** **PEAR TREE COTTAGE PLANTS**
Pear Tree Cottage, Prestleigh, Shepton Mallet
TEL: 01749 831 487

**2** **SWEET ACRE NURSERY**
Godney Road, Glastonbury
TEL: 01458 834 602

**3** **ST ANNE'S NURSERY**
Havyatt, Glastonbury
TEL: 01458 832 720

**4** **STOURHEAD, NATIONAL TRUST**
Stourton, Warminster
TEL: 01747 841 152

**5** **STOURTON HOUSE**
Stourton, Warminster
TEL: 01747 840 417

**6** **HADSPEN GARDEN & NURSERY**
Hadspen House, Castle Cary
TEL: 01749 813 707

**7** **LITTLETON MONOCOT NURSERY**
St. Michaels, Littleton, Somerton
TEL: 01458 272 356

**8** **ABBEY PLANTS**
Chiffchaffs, Chaffeymoor, Bourton
TEL: 01747 840 841

**9** **MILTON GARDEN PLANTS**
Milton on Stour, Gillingham
TEL: 01747 822 484

**10** **PLANTWORLD NURSERY**
Kendalls Lane, Milton on Stour, Gillingham
TEL: 01747 824 015

**11** **DAYSPRING NURSERY**
Quarr, Buckthorn Weston, Gillingham
TEL: 01747 823 030

**12** **SCATS COUNTRYSTORES**
Station Road, Gillingham
TEL: 01747 824 933

**13** **WILLIAMS NURSERY**
L A Williams & Son, Station Road, Stalbridge
TEL: 01963 362 355

**14** **BRINSMORE GARDENS**
Tintinhull Road, Yeovil
TEL: 01935 411 000

**15** **MONTACUTE HOUSE, NATIONAL TRUST**
Montacute, Yeovil
TEL: 01935 823 289

**16** **CASTLE GARDENS PLANT CENTRE**
Castleton, Sherborne
TEL: 01935 814 633

**17** **SHERBOURNE CASTLE**
New Road, Sherborne
TEL: 01935 813 182

**18** **GOLDEN ACRES NURSERY**
Alvington Lane, Alvington, Yeovil
TEL: 01935 475 613

**19** **TINTINHULL HOUSE GARDEN, NATIONAL TRUST**
Farm Street, Tintinhull, Yeovil
TEL: 01935 822 545

**20** **NORTH PERROTT GARDEN CENTRE**
North Perrott, Crewkerne
TEL: 01460 770 90

**21** **DORSET WATER LILY**
Yeovil Road, Halstock, Yeovil, Dorset, BA22 9RR.
TEL: 01935 891 668
*Specialist growers of waterlilies, marginals and associated herbaceous plants. Wide selection of tropical waterlillies and other exotic water plants. Consultancy service available.*
OPEN: Mar-Oct: Mon & Fri 9.30-4.
SPECIALITIES: Water plants, Aquatics, Exotic plants.
FACILITIES: Sell plants.

**22** **DIGWELL NURSERY**
Red Lion Yard, Market Place, Blandford Forum
TEL: 01258 454 714

**23** **MINTERNE GARDENS**
Minterne Magna, Dorchester
TEL: 01300 341 370

Tranquil garden

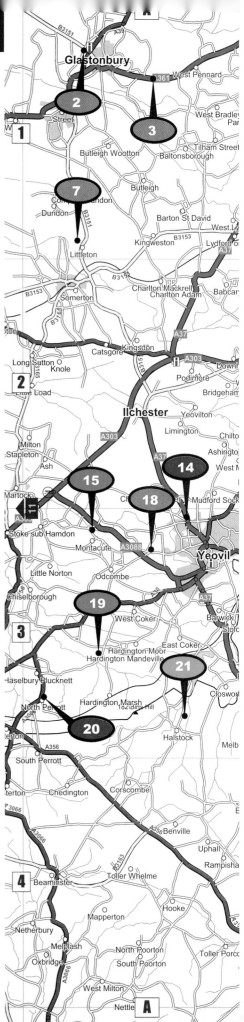

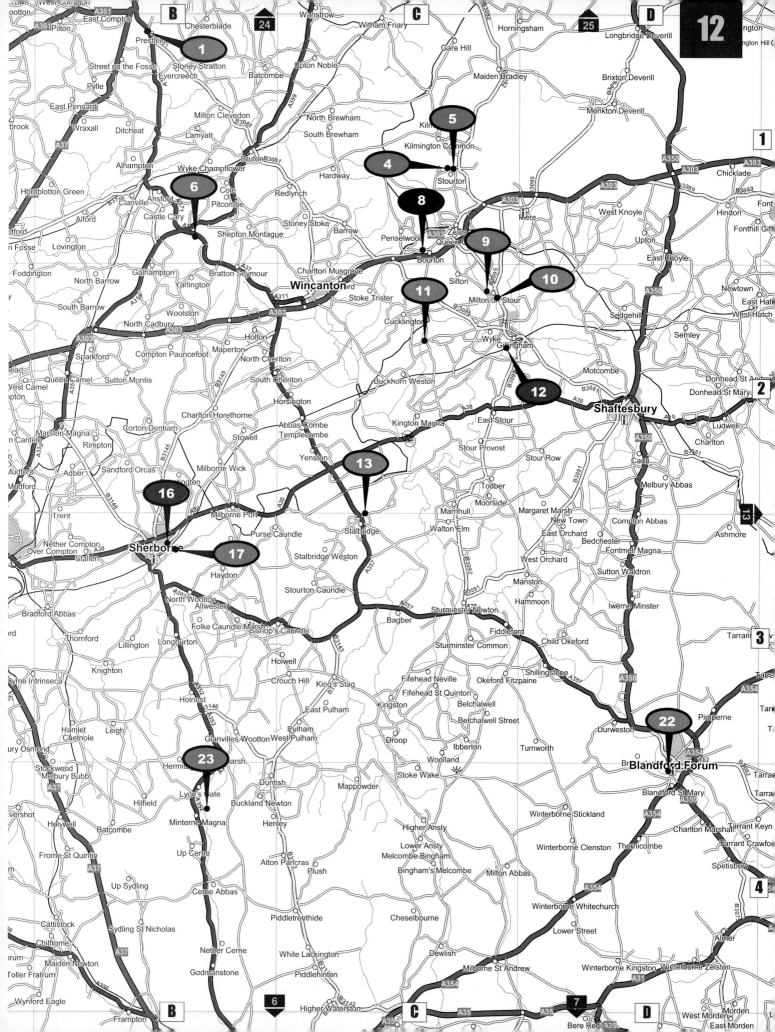

GARDEN CENTRE
GARDEN & NURSERY

● NURSERY & GARDEN CENTRE
● WATER GARDEN SPECIALIST

**1** **HEALE GARDENS & PLANT CENTRE**
Heale House, Middle Woodford, Salisbury
**TEL:** 01722 782 504

**2** **PORTWAY PLANTS**
The Portway, Old Sarum, Salisbury
**TEL:** 01722 337 192

**3** **WILTON HOUSE**
Wilton, Salisbury
**TEL:** 01722 746 720

**4** **SCATS COUNTRYSTORES**
Churchfields Road, Salisbury
**TEL:** 01722 336 886

**5** **THE ROYAL GLOUCESTERSHIRE, BERKSHIRE AND WILTSHIRE REGIMENT MUSEUM**
The Wardrobe, 58 The Close, Salisbury
**TEL:** 01722 414 536

**6** **MOMPESSON HOUSE**
The Close, Salisbury
**TEL:** 01722 335 659

**7** **SOUCHEZ NURSERIES**
86 Britford Lane, Salisbury
**TEL:** 01722 336 777

**8** **OLD WARDOUR CASTLE, ENGLISH HERITAGE**
Tisbury, Salisbury
**TEL:** 01747 870 487

**9** **LARMER TREE GARDENS**
Tollard Royal, Salisbury
**TEL:** 01725 516 228

**10** **DRYSDALE NURSERY**
Bowerwood Road, Fordingbridge
**TEL:** 01425 653 010

**11** **WOLVERCROFT WORLD OF PLANTS**
Fordingbridge Road, Alderholt, Fordingbridge
**TEL:** 01425 652 437

**12** **HORTON VALE NURSERY**
Horton Heath, Horton, Wimborne
**TEL:** 01202 813 473

**13** **GLOBAL ORANGE GROVES UK**
Horton Road, Horton Heath, Wimborne
**TEL:** 01202 826 244

**14** **HOLLY HEDGE NURSERIES**
Verwood Road, Three Legged Cross, Wimborne
**TEL:** 01202 822 447

**15** **BRACKENDALE NURSERIES**
Horton Road, Three Legged Cross, Wimborne
**TEL:** 01202 822 349

**16** **KOI SHOP AQUATIC CENTRE**
John Brown Garden Centre, Ringwood Road, Three Legged Cross
**TEL:** 01202 823 042

**17** **THREE LEGGED CROSS GARDEN CENTRE**
Ringwood Road, Three Legged Cross, Wimborne
**TEL:** 01202 822 203

**18** **LITTLEBANKS NURSERY**
Green Lane, Crow, Ringwood
**TEL:** 01425 461 658

**19** **J B TURNER**
Stanford House, Three Cross Road, Wimborne
**TEL:** 01202 892 266

**20** **STEWARTS COUNTRY GARDEN CENTRE**
God's Blessing Lane, Broomhill, Wimborne
**TEL:** 01202 882 462

**21** **SHELLEY NURSERIES**
77 Pinehurst Road, West Moors, Ferndown
**TEL:** 01202 873 283

**22** **KINGSTON LACY, NATIONAL TRUST**
Wimborne Minster
**TEL:** 01202 883 402

**23** **WYEVALE GARDEN CENTRE**
Wimbourne Road West, Stapehill, Wimborne
**TEL:** 01908 281 161

**24** **STAPEHILL ABBEY CRAFTS & GARDENS**
276 Wimborne Road West, Stapehill, Ferndown
**TEL:** 01202 861 686

**25** **BARTHELMY & CO**
262 Wimborne Road West, Stapehill, Wimborne
**TEL:** 01202 874 283

**26** **PRIEST'S HOUSE MUSEUM AND GARDEN**
23-27 High Street, Wimborne
**TEL:** 01202 882 533

**27** **KNOLL GARDENS & NURSERY**
Hampreston, Ferndown, Wimborne
**TEL:** 01202 873 931

**28** **TREHANE CAMELLIA NURSERY**
Stapehill Road, Hampreston, Wimborne
**TEL:** 01202 873 490

**29** **HASKINS GARDEN CENTRE**
Ham Lane, Longham, Ferndown, Dorset, BH22 9DG.
**TEL:** 01202 591 919
**WEB:** www.haskins.co.uk

*Gardeners have enjoyed the fruits of Haskins labour since 1882. Gardens can bring so much pleasure - our aim is to make sure that pleasure lasts.*
**OPEN:** Mon-Sat 9-6, Sun 10-5. Closed Easter Sun, Christmas & Boxing Day.
**SPECIALITIES:** Bedding plants, Furniture, Gifts, Hardy plants, Pet centre.
**FACILITIES:** Bookshop, Child area, Coffee shop, Credit cards, Dogs allowed, Gift shop, HTA gift tokens, Own gift tokens, Plant guarantee, Pushchair friendly, Restaurant, Sell plants, Toilets, Wheelchair access.

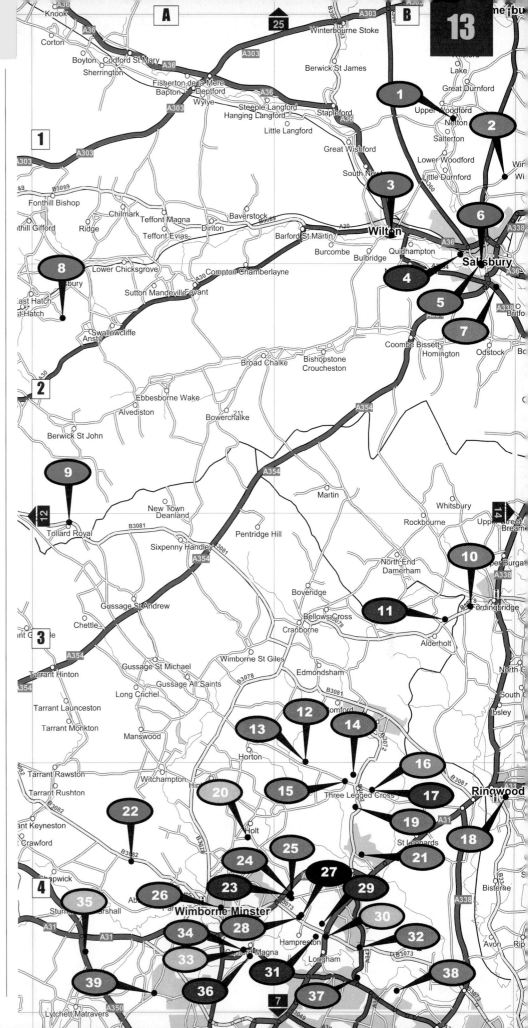

**30** PLOWMANS GARDEN NURSERY & PLANT CENTRE
392 Christchurch Road, West Parley, Ferndown
TEL: 01202 582 169

**31** GOLDEN ACRES NURSERY
359 Christchurch Road, West Parley, Ferndown
TEL: 01202 570 033

**32** COPPINS PLANT CENTRE
Christchurch Road, Dudsbury, Ferndown
TEL: 01202 574 665

**33** OAKS GARDEN CENTRE
Queen Anne Drive, Merley, Wimborne
TEL: 01202 603 322

**34** BEECROFT NURSERIES
Queen Anne Drive, Merley, Wimborne
TEL: 01202 693 705

**35** WOODLANDS THE SPECIALIST PLANT CENTRE
Blandford Road, Lytchett Matravers, Poole
TEL: 01258 857 163

**36** CANFORD PARK GARDEN CENTRE
Magna Road, Wimborne    TEL: 01202 577 770

**37** CHERRY TREE NURSERY
Off New Rd Roundabout, Northbourne, Bournemouth
TEL: 01202 593 537

**38** R R & M P LEWIS
The Gardens, Muscliffe Lane, Bournemouth
TEL: 01202 510 429

**39** NAKED CROSS NURSERIES
Waterloo Road, Corfe Mullen, Wimborne
TEL: 01202 693 256

Phlox

**1** **LONGSTOCK PARK NURSERY**
Longstock, Stockbridge
**Tel:** 01264 810 894

**2** **HOUGHTON LODGE GARDENS**
Hampshire Hydroponicum, Houghton, Stockbridge
**Tel:** 01264 810 912

**3** **MOTTISFONT ABBEY & GARDEN, NATIONAL TRUST**
Mottisfont, Romsey
**Tel:** 01794 340 757

**4** **TEST VALLEY NURSERY**
Stockbridge Road, Timsbury, Romsey
**Tel:** 01794 368 881

**5** **MACGREGORS PLANTS FOR SHADE**
Carters Clay Road, Lockerly, Romsey
**Tel:** 01794 340 256

**6** **SIR HAROLD HILLIER GARDENS & ARBORETUM**
Jermyns Lane, Ampfield, Romsey
**Tel:** 01794 368 787

**7** **HILLIER PLANT CENTRE**
Jermyns Lane, Braishfield, Romsey
**Tel:** 01794 368 407

**8** **CHOICE PLANTS**
Stockbridge Road, Timsbury, Romsey
**Tel:** 01794 368 895

**9** **CEDAR NURSERIES**
Sandy Lane, Belbins, Romsey
**Tel:** 01794 368 375

**10** **COURTENS GARDEN CENTRE**
Romsey Road, Whiteparish, Salisbury
**Tel:** 01794 884 489

**11** **POCOCKS ROSES**
Jermyns Lane, Ampfield, Romsey
**Tel:** 01794 367 500

**12** **GANGER FARM**
Jermyn's Lane, Romsey, Hampshire, SO51 0QA.
**Tel:** 01794 513 345
**Email:** gangerfarm@farming.co.uk
**Web:** www.gangerfarm.co.uk
*Family-run PYO for strawberries, raspberries, tayberries, loganberries, black and redcurrants, gooseberries and a wide range of fresh vegetables.*
**Open:** Jun-Sep: 10-6. Closed Mon after strawberry season has finished.
**Specialities:** Fruit & fruit trees, Vegetables.
**Facilities:** Toilets, Dogs allowed.

**13** **MILLWATER GARDENS**
Mill Lane, Romsey
**Tel:** 01794 513 444

**14** **WORLD OF WATER**
Stockbridge Road, Romsey
**Tel:** 01794 515 923

**15** **DANDY'S NURSERY**
Dandy's Ford Lane, Sherfield English, Romsey
**Tel:** 01794 324 398

**16** **HILLIER GARDEN CENTRE**
Botley Road, Romsey
**Tel:** 01794 513 459

**17** **LANDFORD TREES**
Landford Lodge, Landford, Salisbury, Wiltshire, SP5 2EH.
**Tel:** 01794 390 808
**Email:** tree@landfordtrees.co.uk
**Web:** www.landfordtrees.co.uk
*700+ varieties of quality ornamental and forestry trees. Visitors welcome weekdays.*
**Open:** Open daily.
**Specialities:** Hedging, Yews, Trees.
**Facilities:** Sell plants.

**18** **BROADLANDS**
Broadlands Park, Romsey
**Tel:** 01794 505 010

**19** **GOLDEN ACRES NURSERY**
Southampton Road, Landford, Salisbury
**Tel:** 01794 390 319

**20** **B & W NURSERIES**
Salisbury Road, Plaitford, Romsey
**Tel:** 01794 232 28

**21** **HEATHERLEA NURSERIES**
New Road, Salisbury
**Tel:** 01794 322 567

**22** **PAULTONS NURSERY AND PLANT CENTRE**
Romsey Road, Ower, Southampton
**Tel:** 023 8081 3776

**23** **SPENCER COTTAGE NURSERY**
Nursling Street, Nursling, Southampton
**Tel:** 023 8073 9352

**24** **ABBEY GARDEN CENTRE**
Southampton Road, Cadnam, Southampton
**Tel:** 023 8081 2240

**25** **POPS PLANTS**
Greenfield Farm, North Gorley, Fordingbridge
**Tel:** 01725 511 421

**26** **FURZEY GARDENS**
Minstead, Lyndhurst
**Tel:** 023 8081 2464

**27** **FURZEY GARDENS NURSERY**
Minstead Lodge, Minstead, Lyndhurst
**Tel:** 023 8081 2464

**28** **GUYS NURSERY & GARDEN CENTRE**
Forest Corner, Ringwood
**Tel:** 01425 473 113

**29** **FAIRWEATHER'S GARDEN CENTRE**
High Street, Beaulieu, Brockenhurst
**Tel:** 01590 612 307

**30** **HOLLY BUSH GARDEN CENTRE**
Setley, Brockenhurst
**Tel:** 01590 622 839

**31** **MACPENNYS NURSERIES**
154 Burley Road, Bransgore, Christchurch
**Tel:** 01425 672 348

**32** **SPINNERS GARDEN**
School Lane, Boldre, Lymington
**Tel:** 01590 673 347

**33** **BECKHEATH NURSERIES**
East End, Lymington
**Tel:** 01590 626 620

**34** **SCATS COUNTRYSTORES**
Sway Road, Mount Pleasant Lane, Lymington
**Tel:** 01590 676 633

**35** **BASHLEY PLANT CENTRE**
Bashley Common Road, New Milton
**Tel:** 01425 612 442

Golden Tiara

**36** REDCLIFFE GARDEN CENTRE

Bashley Road, Bashley, New Milton
TEL: 01425 614 210

**37** LYMINGTON PLANT CENTRE

Pitmore Lane, Pennington, Lymington
TEL: 01590 682 611

**38** GARDEN COTTAGE NURSERY

New Lane, Bashley, New Milton
TEL: 01425 613 029

**39** AGARS NURSERY

Agars Lane, Hordle, Lymington
TEL: 01590 683 703

**40** STEVEN BAILEY

Silver Street, Sway, Lymington
TEL: 01590 682 227

**41** FAIRWINDS GARDEN CENTRE

126 High Street, Lymington
TEL: 01590 677 022

**42** SADLERS GARDENS

31 Rawley Road, Pennington, Lymington
TEL: 01590 672 728

**1** **HOOKER'S GARDEN CENTRE**
Main Road, Littleton, Winchester
**Tel:** 01962 880 292

**2** **SCATS COUNTRYSTORES**
Easton Lane, Winchester
**Tel:** 01962 863 007

**3** **GREAT HALL**
Castle Avenue, Winchester
**Tel:** 01962 846 476

**4** **WINCHESTER PET & AQUATIC CENTRE**
Hillier Garden Centre, Romsey Road, Winchester
**Tel:** 01962 856 753

**5** **HILLIER GARDEN CENTRE**
Romsey Road, Winchester
**Tel:** 01962 842 288

**6** **WATER MEADOW NURSERY & HERB FARM**
Water Meadows, Cheriton, Alresford
**Tel:** 01962 771 895

**7** **BLACKTHORN NURSERY**
Kilmeston, Arlesford
**Tel:** 01962 771 796

**8** **GEORGE BECKETT NURSERIES**
Compton Nursery, Compton, Winchester
**Tel:** 01962 713 732

**9** **BRAMBRIDGE PARK GARDEN CENTRE**
Kiln Lane, Brambridge, Eastleigh
**Tel:** 01962 713 707

**10** **GREENACRES NURSERY**
Green Lane, Ampfield, Romsey
**Tel:** 01794 512 409

**11** **SANDYFIELDS NURSERIES**
Main Road, Colden Common, Winchester
**Tel:** 01962 712 218

**12** **HANGER NURSERIES**
Thompsons Lane, Owslebury, Winchester
**Tel:** 01962 777 531

**13** **WYEVALE GARDEN CENTRE**
Winchester Road, Fair Oak, Eastleigh
**Tel:** 023 8060 0392

**14** **FIELDFARE OF FARE OAK**
Winchester Road, Fair Oak, Eastleigh
**Tel:** 023 8060 0541

**15** **CONIGER NURSERIES**
Bishopstoke Road, Eastleigh
**Tel:** 023 8061 2385

**16** **ALLINGTON NURSERY**
Allington Lane, Fair Oaks, Eastleigh
**Tel:** 023 8060 0182

**17** **TREETOPS NURSERY**
Allington Lane, Fair Oak, Eastleigh
**Tel:** 023 8060 0782

**18** **ARTURI'S GARDEN CENTRE**
Allington Lane, Fair Oak, Eastleigh
**Tel:** 02380 602 234

**19** **ORCHARDLEIGH NURSERIES**
Botley Road, Bishops Waltham, Southampton
**Tel:** 01489 892 687

**20** **WEST END NURSERY**
Burnetts Lane, West End, Southampton
**Tel:** 023 8047 0595

**21** **JOBS COTTAGE NURSERIES**
Durley Hall Lane, Durley, Southampton
**Tel:** 01489 860 456

**22** **HASKINS GARDEN CENTRE**
Gaters Hill, Mansbridge Road, West End,
Southampton, Hampshire, SO18 3HW.
**Tel:** 023 8047 2324
**Web:** www.haskins.co.uk

*Gardeners have enjoyed the fruits of Haskins labour since 1882. Gardens can bring so much pleasure - our aim is to make sure that pleasure lasts.*
**Open:** Mon-Sat 9-6, Sun 10-5. Closed Easter Sun, Christmas & Boxing Day.
**Specialities:** Bedding plants, Hardy plants, Water plants, Furniture, Gifts.
**Facilities:** Toilets, Credit cards, Wheelchair access, Gift tokens, Dogs allowed, Bookshop, Child area, Coffee shop, Plant guarantee, Gift shop, HTA gift tokens, Own gift tokens, Pushchair friendly, Restaurant, Sell plants.

**23** **HILLIER GARDEN CENTRE**
Woodhouse Lane, Botley, Southampton
**Tel:** 01489 782 306

**24** **FAMILY TREES**
The Tree Nursery, Sandy Lane, Shedfield
**Tel:** 01329 834 812

**25** **UPLANDS NURSERIES**
Winchester Street, Botley, Southampton
**Tel:** 01489 782 069

**26** **BELMONTE COTTAGE NURSERIES**
Botley Road, Shedfiled, Southampton
**Tel:** 01329 832 319

**27** **LODGE HILL NURSERY**
Lodge Hill, Newtown, Wickham
**Tel:** 01329 834 753

**28** **TUDOR HOUSE MUSEUM GARDEN**
Cultural Services, Civic Centre, Southampton
**Tel:** 023 8063 5904

**29** **PARK PLACE FARM NURSERY**
Titchfield Lane, Wickham
**Tel:** 01329 834 991

**30** **MUD ISLAND NURSERIES**
Southwick Road, Wickham, Fareham
**Tel:** 01329 834 407

**31** **MOUNT FOLLY NURSERIES**
Southwick Road, Wickham
**Tel:** 01329 832 294

**32** **SILVER SPRINGS NURSERIES**
Fontley Road, Titchfield, Fareham
**Tel:** 01329 842 114

**33** **GARSONS**
Fontley Road, Titchfield, Fareham, Hampshire, PO15 6QX.
**Tel:** 01329 844 336
**Email:** mail@garsons.co.uk
**Web:** www.garsons.co.uk

*A modern garden centre with restaurant, gift shop, farm shop and comprehensive choice of plants and garden furniture. Excellent pet shop and camping centre.*
**Open:** Open 7 days a week. Summer: Mon-Sat 9-6, Sun 11-5. Winter: Mon-Sat 9-5, Sun 11-5 Sun. Closed Christmas & Boxing Day.
**Specialities:** Pot plants, Shrubs.
**Facilities:** Toilets, Credit cards, Wheelchair access, Restaurant, Gift tokens, Dogs allowed, Bookshop, Child area, Coffee shop, Plant guarantee, Farm shop, Gift shop, HTA gift tokens, Pushchair friendly, Sell plants.

**34** **HAMBROOKS GARDEN CENTRE**
135 Southampton Road, Titchfield, Fareham
**Tel:** 01489 572 285

**35** **LEYDENE GARDENS NURSERY**
122 Segensworth Road, Titchfield, Fareham
**Tel:** 01329 843 899

**36** **ABBEY GARDEN CENTRE**
Mill Lane, Titchfield, Fareham
**Tel:** 01329 842 225

**37** **MEDINA NURSERIES**
46 Brook Lane, Warsash, Southampton
**Tel:** 0802 902 200

**38** **ST MARGARET'S FUCHSIA NURSERY**
St Margarets Lane, Titchfield, Fareham
**Tel:** 01329 846 006

**39** **EXBURY GARDENS**
Exbury, Southampton
**Tel:** 023 8089 8625

Water lily

**1  VALLEY NURSERIES**
Basingstoke Road, Alton
TEL: 01420 549 700

**2  COUNTRY MARKET**
Malthouse & Osborne Farms, Kingsley, Borden
TEL: 01420 477 582

**3  ROSE COTTAGE NURSERY**
Rose Cottage, Kingsley Common, Bordon
TEL: 01420 489 071

**4  EASTFIELD PLANT CENTRE**
Paice Lane, Medstead, Alton
TEL: 01420 563 640

**5  GARTHOWEN GARDEN CENTRE & NURSERIES**
Alton Lane, Four Marks, Alton
TEL: 01962 773 225

**6  GILBERT WHITE'S HOUSE & GARDEN**
The Wakes, Selborne
TEL: 01420 511 275

**7  BLACKMOOR NURSERY**
Blackmoor, Liss
TEL: 01420 473 141

**8  OAKLEIGH NURSERIES**
Petersfield Road, Monkwood, Alresford
TEL: 01962 773 344

**9  LANGLEY BOXWOOD NURSERY**
Rake, Liss, Hampshire, GU33 7JL.
TEL: 01730 894 467
EMAIL: sales@boxwood.co.uk
WEB: www.boxwood.co.uk

*Specialist nursery for box and yew hedging and topiary. Many varieties of box, national collection of Buxus.*
OPEN: Mon-Fri 9-4.30, Sat 10-4.
SPECIALITIES: Hardy plants, Shrubs, Box hedges, Hedging, Topiary.
FACILITIES: Sell plants.

**10  PRINCES GARDEN CENTRE**
London Road, Rake, Liss
TEL: 01730 894 011

**11  HILLIER GARDEN CENTRE**
Farnham Road, Liss, Petersfield
TEL: 01730 892 196

**12  LISS PET & AQUATIC CENTRE**
Hillier Garden Centre, Farnham Road, Liss
TEL: 01730 894 135

**13  PETERSFIELD PHYSIC GARDEN**
16 High Street, Petersfield
TEL: 01730 233 371

**14  AYLINGS GARDEN CENTRE**
Trotton Rogate, Petersfield, Hampshire, GU31 5ES.
TEL: 01730 813 621
EMAIL: sales@aylingsgardencentre.co.uk
*Very large range of trees, shrubs, conifers, specimen plants, herbaceous plants, pot plants, pots and compost.*
OPEN: Mon-Sat 8-5, Sun 10.30-4.30.
SPECIALITIES: Clematis, Garden machinery, Gifts, Herbaceous plants, Terracotta pots.
FACILITIES: Toilets, Wheelchair access, Credit cards, Gift tokens, Dogs allowed, Coffee shop, Gift shop, HTA gift tokens, Pushchair friendly.

**15  BIRCHFLEET NURSERY**
Greenfields, Nyewood, Petersfield
TEL: 01730 821 636

**16  UPPARK, NATIONAL TRUST**
South Harting, Petersfield
TEL: 01730 825 415

**17  QUEEN ELIZABETH COUNTRY PARK**
Gravel Hill, Horndean, Waterlooville
TEL: 023 9259 5040

**18  RUMSEY GARDENS NURSERIES**
117 Drift Road, Clanfield, Waterlooville
TEL: 023 9259 3367

**19  RUSTLINGS NURSERIES**
104 Catherington Lane, Waterlooville
TEL: 023 9259 4832

**20  KEYDELL NURSERIES**
Havant Road, Horndean, Waterlooville
TEL: 023 9259 3839

**21  STANSTED PARK GARDEN CENTRE**
Stansted Park, Rowland's Castle
TEL: 023 9241 3090

**22  GARDEN IN MIND**
Stansted Park, Rowland's Castle
TEL: 023 9241 3149

**23  STAUNTON COUNTRY PARK**
Middle Park Way, Havant
TEL: 023 9245 3405

**24  EAST ASHLING NURSERIES**
Lye Lane, East Ashling, Chichester
TEL: 01243 575 523

**25  WYEVALE GARDEN CENTRE**
Bartons Road, Havant
TEL: 023 9245 6200

**26  HAYWARDS CARNATIONS**
The Chace Gardens, 141 Stakes Road, Waterlooville
TEL: 023 9226 3047

**27  BEACHLANDS NURSERY**
Newells Lane, West Ashling, Chichester
TEL: 01243 573 117

**28  BARRY'S BLOOMING BASKETS**
112 Main Road, Emsworth
TEL: 01243 379 929

**29  GREENACRE NURSERY**
Main Road, Chidham, Chichester, West Sussex, PO18 8TP.
TEL: 01243 572 441
*Growing bedding, fuchsias, geraniums, hanging baskets and tubs, shrubs, climbers and shop.*
OPEN: Open daily 9.30-5.
SPECIALITIES: Fuchsias.
FACILITIES: Credit cards, Wheelchair access, Pushchair friendly.

**30  THE GARDEN PLACE**
Main Road, Bosham, Chichester
TEL: 01243 573 696

**31  FISHBOURNE ROMAN PALACE & GARDENS**
Salthill Road, Fishbourne, Chichester
TEL: 01243 785 859

**32  APULDRAM ROSES**
Apuldram Lane, Dell Quay, Chichester
TEL: 01243 785 769

**33  CEDAR NURSERY**
Birdham Road, Chichester
TEL: 01243 782 666

**34  MEADOW FARM NURSERY**
Woodgason Lane, Northney, Hayling Island
TEL: 023 9246 1570

**35  WOPHAMS LANE NURSERY**
Wophams Lane, Birdham, Chichester
TEL: 01243 512 862

**36  RICHARDSON'S NURSERY**
Burdham Straight, Chichester
TEL: 01243 512 087

Pansies

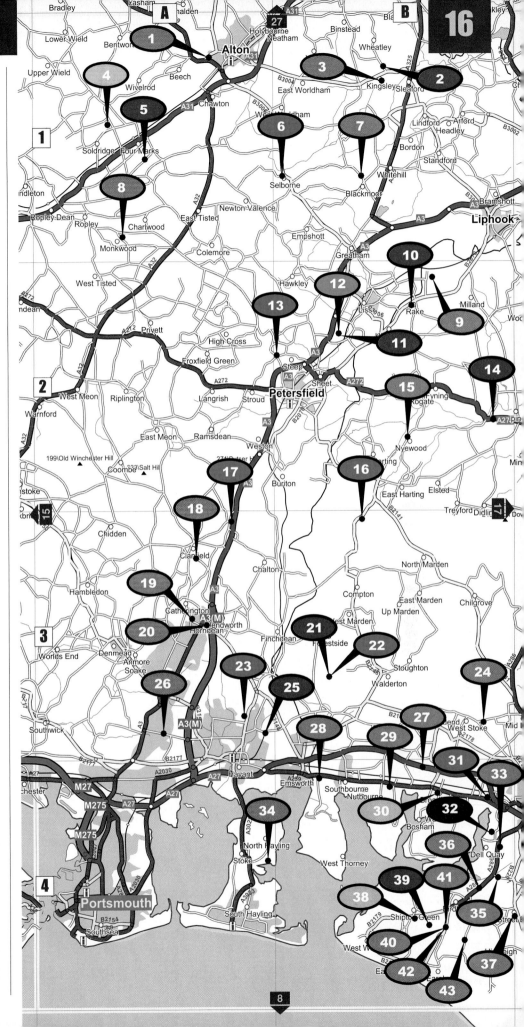

**1　WINKWORTH ARBORETUM, NATIONAL TRUST**
Hascombe Road, Godalming　**Tel:** 01483 208 477

**2　HYDON NURSERIES**
Clock Barn Lane, Hydon Heath, Godalming
**Tel:** 01483 860 252

**3　WHEELER STREET NURSERY**
Wheeler Lane, Witley, Godalming　**Tel:** 01428 682 638

**4　NOTCUTTS GARDEN CENTRE**
Guildford Road, Cranleigh　**Tel:** 01483 274 222

**5　MILLAIS NURSERIES**
Crosswater Farm, Churt, Farnham　**Tel:** 01252 792 698

**6　SWEETWATER NURSERY**
Sweetwater Farm, Culmer Lane, Witley
**Tel:** 01428 682 211

**7　GARDENING WORLD**
Haslemere Road, Godalming　**Tel:** 01293 883 237

**8　GREEN STOP GARDEN CENTRE**
Haslemere Road, Brook, Godalming
**Tel:** 01428 682 913

**9　WYEVALE GARDEN CENTRE**
Horsham Rd, Alfold, Cranleigh　**Tel:** 01403 752 359

**10　RAMSTER GARDENS**
Ramster, Chiddingfold　**Tel:** 01428 654 167

**11　STRIKERS NURSERIES**
2 New Building, Shillinglee, Godalming
**Tel:** 01428 708 167

**12　LOXWOOD CONIFER NURSERIES**
Guildford Road, Loxwood　**Tel:** 01403 753 389

**13　MRS JANE SADLER**
Ingrams Cottage, Wiseborough Green, Billingshurst
**Tel:** 01403 700 234

**14　ROTHERHILL NURSERIES & GARDEN CENTRE**
Stedham, Midhurst　**Tel:** 01370 813 687

**15　PETWORTH HOUSE AND PARK**
Petworth　**Tel:** 01798 342 207

---

**16　MURRELLS NURSERY**
Broomers Hill Lane, Pulborough, West Sussex, RH20 2DU
**Tel:** 01798 875 508

*Extensive range (including unusual varieties) of shrubs, herbaceous, bedding and basket plants, trees and fruit trees. House and conservatory plants.*
**Open:** Open 7 days a week. Summer: Mon-Sat 9-5.30, Sun 10-4. Winter: Mon-Sat 9-5. Closed Easter Sun, Christmas, Boxing & New Years Day.
**Specialities:** Climbers, Shrubs, Bonsai, Geraniums, Herbs.
**Facilities:** Credit cards, HTA gift tokens, Sell plants

---

**17　THE CITRUS CENTRE**
West Mare Lane, Marehill, Pulborough
**Tel:** 01798 872 786

**18　WYEVALE GARDEN CENTRE**
Stopham Road, Pulborough　**Tel:** 01798 872 981

**19　P VERHEUL**
Sylvan Nurseries, West Chillington Road, Pulborough　**Tel:** 01798 813 567

**20　PARHAM ELIZABETHAN HOUSE AND GARDENS**
Parham Park, Pulborough　**Tel:** 01903 744 888

**21　HILLSIDE NURSERIES**
A29, Bury, Pulborough　**Tel:** 01798 831 325

**22　WEALD & DOWNLAND OPEN AIR MUSEUM**
Singleton, Chichester　**Tel:** 01243 811 363

---

**23　WEST DEAN GARDENS**
West Dean, Chichester, West Sussex, PO18 0QZ.
**Tel:** 01243 818 210
**Email:** gardens@westdean.org.uk
**Web:** www.westdean.org.uk
*Highly acclaimed restored Victorian walled Kitchen Garden. Sixteen Victorian Glasshouses and cold-frames. Herbaceous borders, specimen trees and 300' Harold Peto designed pergola hosting climbers.*
**Open:** May-Sep: 11-5. Mar-Apr & Oct: 10.30-5.
**Entry costs:** £4.50, Child: £2, OAPs: £4, Family: £11.
**Specialities:** Climbers, Fruit & fruit trees, Greenhouses & sheds, Hardy plants, Shrubs.
**Facilities:** Coffee shop, Credit cards, Gift shop, Restaurant, Toilets, Wheelchair access.

---

**24　PUMPKIN COTTAGE**
4 Top Road, Slindon, Arundel　**Tel:** 01243 814 219

**25　ALDINGBOURNE COUNTRY CENTRE**
Blackmill Lane, Norton, Chichester
**Tel:** 01243 542 075

---

**26　ARUNDEL ARBORETUM**
Scotland Barn, Chichester Road, Arundel, West Sussex, BN18 0AD.
**Tel:** 01903 883 251
**Email:** arundel-arboretum@hinge.mistral.co.uk
*Extensive range of specialist trees 4ft-20ft. Shrubs and conifers. Deliveries and planting undertaken. Advice given.*
**Open:** Mon-Fri 8-5, Sat-Sun 10-4. Closed Christmas and New Year.
**Specialities:** Hardy plants, Shrubs, Trees, Topiary.
**Facilities:** Credit cards, Dogs allowed, Sell plants.

---

**27　DENMANS GARDEN**
Denmans, Fontwell, Arundel　**Tel:** 01243 542 808

**28　MAUDLIN NURSERY**
Westhampnett, Chichester　**Tel:** 01243 773 024

**29　SHOPWHYKE NURSERIES & SUPPLIES**
Shopwhyke Road, Chichester　**Tel:** 01243 783 123

**30　HIGHFIELD & SUNNYSIDE NURSERIES**
Yapton Rd, Barnham, Bognor Regis　**Tel:** 01243 553 062

---

**31　TORRI NURSEY**
Old Mead Road, Littlehampton　**Tel:** 01903 717 140

**32　P PERELLA**
Glen Villa Chalet, Old Mead Road, Littlehampton
**Tel:** 01903 713 305

**33　MANOR NURSERY**
Yapton Road, Barnham　**Tel:** 01243 552 028

**34　LILLIES NURSERY & CARAVAN PARK**
Yapton Road, Barnham, Bognor Regis
**Tel:** 01243 552 081

**35　CROFTWAY NURSERY**
Yapton Road, Barnham, Bognor Regis
**Tel:** 01243 552 121

**36　ARCHITECTURAL PLANTS**
Lidsey Road Nursery, Woodgate, Chichester
**Tel:** 01243 545 008

**37　BRICK KILN NURSERY & GARDEN CENTRE**
Bognor Road, Chichester　**Tel:** 01243 531 700

**38　FAIRHAVEN PLANTS**
Toddington Lane, Lyminster, Littlehampton
**Tel:** 01903 725 642

**39　WESTHOLME NURSERIES**
Toddington Lane, Littlehampton　**Tel:** 01903 714 845

**40　MANOR NURSERY**
High Street, Angmering　**Tel:** 01903 785 123

**41　WYEVALE GARDEN CENTRE**
Bognor Road, Merston, Chichester
**Tel:** 01243 789 276

---

**42　HASKINS ROUNDSTONE GARDEN CENTRE**
Roundstone Bypass, Angmering, West Sussex, BN16 4BD.
**Tel:** 01903 776 481
**Web:** www.roundstonegardencentre.co.uk

*Gardeners have enjoyed the fruits of Haskins labour since 1882. Gardens can bring so much pleasure - our aim is to make sure that pleasure lasts.*
**Open:** Mon-Sat 9-6, Sun 10-5. Closed Easter Sun, Christmas & Boxing Day.
**Specialities:** Bedding plants, Furniture, Gifts, Hardy plants, Pet centre.
**Facilities:** Bookshop, Coffee shop, Credit cards, Dogs allowed, Gift shop, HTA gift tokens, Own gift tokens, Plant guarantee, Pushchair friendly, Restaurant, Sell plants, Toilets, Wheelchair access.

---

**43　LOWERTREES NURSERY**
Roundstone By-pass, Angmering
**Tel:** 01903 770 457

**44　CINDERS LANE NURSERY**
Bilsham Road, Yapton　**Tel:** 01243 552 555

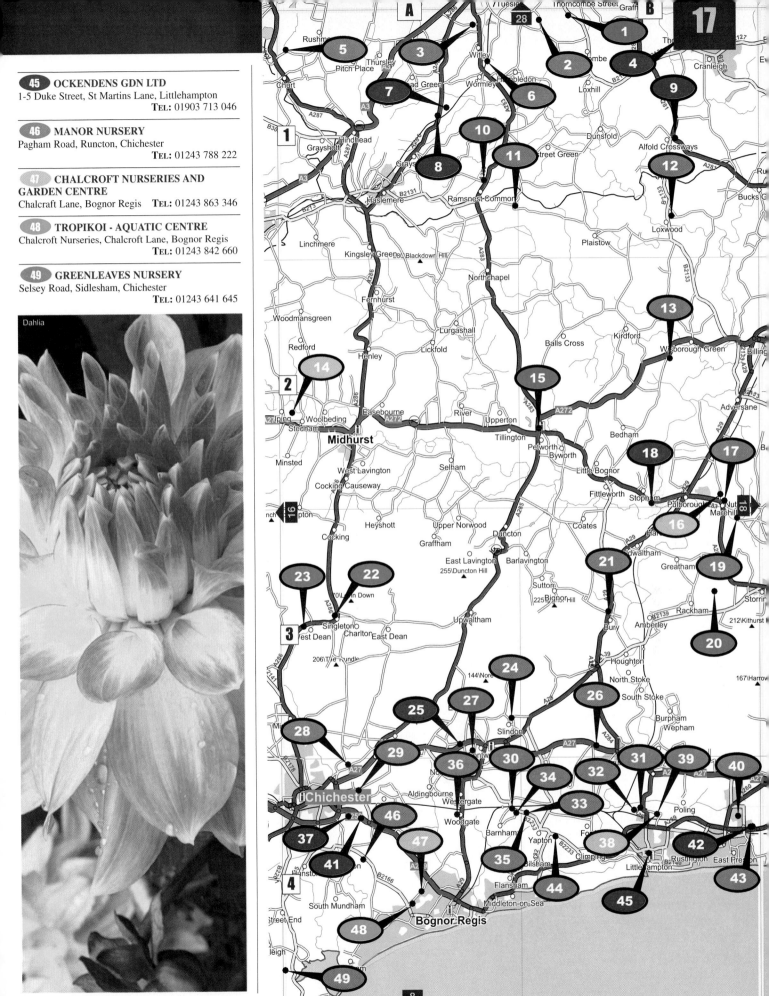

**45** OCKENDENS GDN LTD
1-5 Duke Street, St Martins Lane, Littlehampton
**TEL:** 01903 713 046

**46** MANOR NURSERY
Pagham Road, Runcton, Chichester
**TEL:** 01243 788 222

**47** CHALCROFT NURSERIES AND GARDEN CENTRE
Chalcraft Lane, Bognor Regis **TEL:** 01243 863 346

**48** TROPIKOI - AQUATIC CENTRE
Chalcroft Nurseries, Chalcroft Lane, Bognor Regis
**TEL:** 01243 842 660

**49** GREENLEAVES NURSERY
Selsey Road, Sidlesham, Chichester
**TEL:** 01243 641 645

Dahlia

**1   OCKLEY COURT FARM**
Ockley Court, Dorking   TEL: 01306 711 160

**2   BURSTOW NURSERIES**
Antlands Lane, Shipley Bridge, Horley
TEL: 01293 771 942

**3   NEWLAKE GARDENS**
West Park Road, Copthorne, Crawley
TEL: 01342 712 332

**4   WYEVALE GARDEN CENTRE**
Copthorne Road, Pound Hill, Crawley
TEL: 01293 883 3311

**5   SQUIRE'S GARDEN CENTRE CHEALS**
Horsham Road, Crawley   TEL: 01293 522 101

**6   BUCHAN COUNTRY PARK**
Horsham Road, Crawley   TEL: 01293 542 088

**7   KINGSFOLD NURSERY PLANT CENTRE**
Dorking Road, Kingsfold, Horsham
TEL: 01306 627 614

**8   BROOKSIDE CACTUS NURSERY**
Bognor Road, Horsham   TEL: 01403 790 996

**9   NEWBRIDGE NURSERIES**
Billingshurst Road, Broadbridge Heath, Horsham
TEL: 01403 272 686

**10   CAMELIA BOTNAR GARDEN & CRAFT CENTRE**
Littleworth Lane, West Grinstead, Horsham
TEL: 01403 864 773

**11   HIGH BEECHES WOODLAND & WATER GARDENS**
High Beeches, Handcross   TEL: 01444 400 589

**12   HIGH BEECHES NURSERY**
Handcross, Haywards Heath   TEL: 01444 401 398

**13   HILLIER GARDEN CENTRE**
Brighton Road, Horsham   TEL: 01403 210 113

**14   HORSHAM WATER GARDEN CENTRE**
Hillier Garden Centre, Brighton Road, Horsham
TEL: 01403 268 152

**15   NYMANS GARDEN, NATIONAL TRUST**
Handcross, Haywards Heath   TEL: 01444 400 321

**16   OAKDEAN NURSERY**
Sedgwick Lane, Horsham   TEL: 01403 252 897

**17   HOWARDS OF HORSHAM**
Nursery Centre, Handcross Road, Horsham
TEL: 01403 891 255

**18   WYEVALE GARDEN CENTRE**
London Road, Handcross   TEL: 01444 400 725

**19   LEONARDSLEE GARDENS**
Lower Beeding, Horsham, West Sussex, RH13 6PP.
TEL: 01403 891 212
EMAIL: gardens@leonardslee.com
WEB: www.leonardslee.com

*Peaceful 240-acre valley with seven beautiful lakes. Spectacular rhododendrons and azaleas in spring, fine trees, summer wildflowers and autumn tints. Wallabies, deer and wildlife. Rock garden, fascinating bonsai.*
OPEN: Apr-Oct: 9.30-6.
ENTRY COSTS: £5-£7, Child: £3.
SPECIALITIES: Rhododendrons and azaleas, Bonsai, Water features, Wild flowers.
FACILITIES: Toilets, Restaurant, Coffee shop, Sell plants, Gift shop, Bookshop.

**20   SCATS COUNTRYSTORES**
Frenches Corner, Billingshurst, West Sussex, RH14 9LR.
TEL: 08451 304 030
EMAIL: billingshurst.countrystore@scats.co.uk
WEB: www.scatscountrystores.co.uk

*SCATS Countrystores has 20 stores across southern England. Products include garden furniture and equipment, country clothing, DIY, animal feeds, pet food and accessories and equestrian sundries.*
OPEN: Mon-Sat 8-5.
SPECIALITIES: Sundries, Bedding plants, Furniture, Pot plants.
FACILITIES: Credit cards, HTA gift tokens, Own gift tokens, Pushchair friendly, Sell plants, Wheelchair access.

**21   COOMBLAND GARDENS NURSERY**
Coombland, Coneyhurst, Billingshurst
TEL: 01403 741 727

**22   BOLNEY NURSERY**
Cowfold Road, Bolney
TEL: 01444 881 784

**23   MAYFIELD NURSERY**
West Chiltington Lane, Broadford Bridge, Billingshurst
TEL: 01403 741 224

**24   A ARCHER-WILLS**
Broadford Bridge Road, West Chiltington, Pulborough
TEL: 01798 813 204

**25   WINDMILL NURSERY**
High Hatch Lane, Goddards Green, Hassocks
TEL: 01273 834 696

**26   OLD BARN NURSERIES**
Dial Post, A24, Horsham, West Sussex, RH13 8NR.
TEL: 01403 710 000
EMAIL: info@old-barn.co.uk
WEB: www.old-barn.co.uk
*Attractive garden centre. Large outdoor areas and award winning houseplants. Garden and conservatory furniture. Sundries and gifts. Lunch or snacks available in the Old Barn.*

OPEN: Mon-Sat 9-6, Sun 10.30-4.30.
Barn: Mon-Sat 9-6, Sun 9-4.30.
SPECIALITIES: House plants, Shrubs, Furniture, Christmas displays.
FACILITIES: Toilets, Credit cards, Wheelchair access, Restaurant, Coffee shop, Plant guarantee, Gift shop, HTA gift tokens, Own gift tokens, Pushchair friendly.

**27   THE VILLAGE NURSERIES**
Sinnocks, West Chiltington, Pulborough
TEL: 01798 813 040

**28   CHURCHFIELD FARM**
West Chiltington, Pulborough   TEL: 0800 783 3879

**29   ALLWOOD BROS**
London Road, Hassocks   TEL: 01273 844 229

**30   BLACKGATE LANE NURSERY**
Blackgate Lane, Pulborough   TEL: 01798 872 923

**31   HOLLY GATE CACTUS NURSERY & GARDEN**
Billingshurst Road, Ashington   TEL: 01903 892 930

**32   CHANCTONBURY NURSERIES**
Rectory Lane, Ashington, Pulborough
TEL: 01903 892 870

**33   LANCASTERS NURSERY**
West End Lane, Henfield   TEL: 01273 493 913

**34   STONEPOUND NURSERY**
Brighton Road, Hassocks   TEL: 01273 843 754

**35   SOUTH DOWNS GARDEN CENTRE**
Brighton Road, Hassocks   TEL: 01273 845 232

**36   HOLE STREET NURSERIES**
Hole Street, Ashington   TEL: 01903 892 897

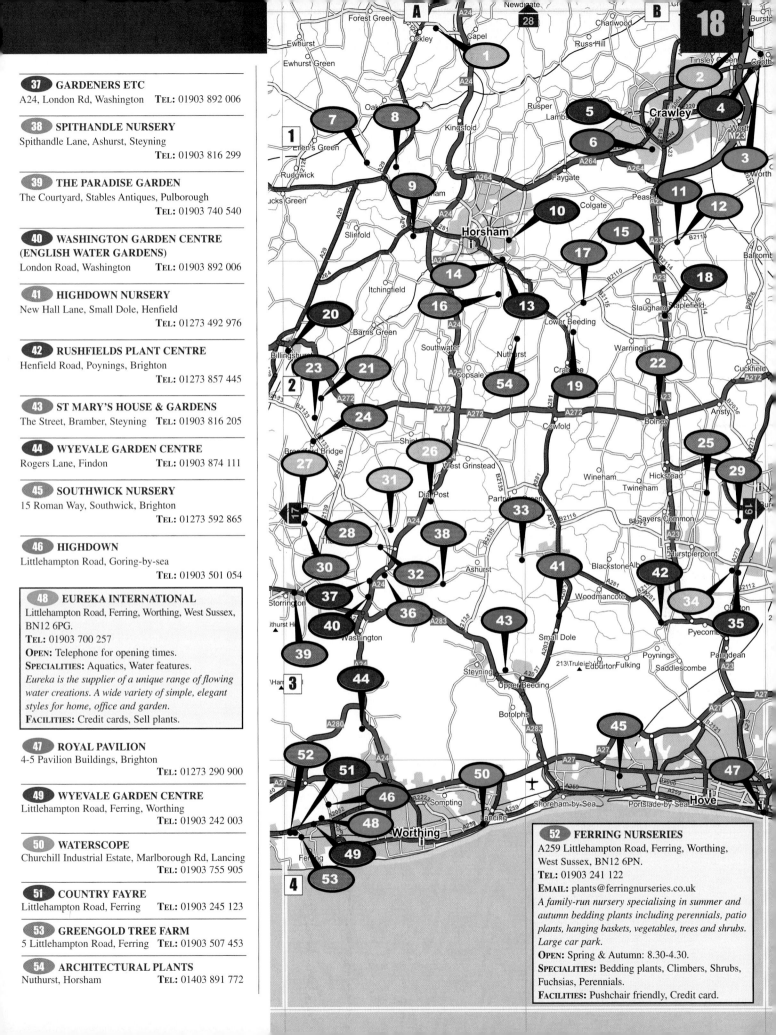

**37** GARDENERS ETC
A24, London Rd, Washington **TEL:** 01903 892 006

**38** SPITHANDLE NURSERY
Spithandle Lane, Ashurst, Steyning
**TEL:** 01903 816 299

**39** THE PARADISE GARDEN
The Courtyard, Stables Antiques, Pulborough
**TEL:** 01903 740 540

**40** WASHINGTON GARDEN CENTRE
(ENGLISH WATER GARDENS)
London Road, Washington **TEL:** 01903 892 006

**41** HIGHDOWN NURSERY
New Hall Lane, Small Dole, Henfield
**TEL:** 01273 492 976

**42** RUSHFIELDS PLANT CENTRE
Henfield Road, Poynings, Brighton
**TEL:** 01273 857 445

**43** ST MARY'S HOUSE & GARDENS
The Street, Bramber, Steyning **TEL:** 01903 816 205

**44** WYEVALE GARDEN CENTRE
Rogers Lane, Findon **TEL:** 01903 874 111

**45** SOUTHWICK NURSERY
15 Roman Way, Southwick, Brighton
**TEL:** 01273 592 865

**46** HIGHDOWN
Littlehampton Road, Goring-by-sea
**TEL:** 01903 501 054

**48** EUREKA INTERNATIONAL
Littlehampton Road, Ferring, Worthing, West Sussex,
BN12 6PG.
**TEL:** 01903 700 257
**OPEN:** Telephone for opening times.
**SPECIALITIES:** Aquatics, Water features.
*Eureka is the supplier of a unique range of flowing
water creations. A wide variety of simple, elegant
styles for home, office and garden.*
**FACILITIES:** Credit cards, Sell plants.

**47** ROYAL PAVILION
4-5 Pavilion Buildings, Brighton
**TEL:** 01273 290 900

**49** WYEVALE GARDEN CENTRE
Littlehampton Road, Ferring, Worthing
**TEL:** 01903 242 003

**50** WATERSCOPE
Churchill Industrial Estate, Marlborough Rd, Lancing
**TEL:** 01903 755 905

**51** COUNTRY FAYRE
Littlehampton Road, Ferring **TEL:** 01903 245 123

**53** GREENGOLD TREE FARM
5 Littlehampton Road, Ferring **TEL:** 01903 507 453

**54** ARCHITECTURAL PLANTS
Nuthurst, Horsham **TEL:** 01403 891 772

**52** FERRING NURSERIES
A259 Littlehampton Road, Ferring, Worthing,
West Sussex, BN12 6PN.
**TEL:** 01903 241 122
**EMAIL:** plants@ferringnurseries.co.uk
*A family-run nursery specialising in summer and
autumn bedding plants including perennials, patio
plants, hanging baskets, vegetables, trees and shrubs.
Large car park.*
**OPEN:** Spring & Autumn: 8.30-4.30.
**SPECIALITIES:** Bedding plants, Climbers, Shrubs,
Fuchsias, Perennials.
**FACILITIES:** Pushchair friendly, Credit card.

**1  SOUTHON PLANTS**
The Nursery, Mutton Hill, Lingfield  TEL: 01342 870 150

**2  SNOWHILL PLANT & GARDEN CENTRE**
Snow Hill Lane, Copthorne, Crawley  TEL: 01342 712 545

**3  ORCHARD NURSERY**
Holtye Rd, East Grinstead  TEL: 01342 311 657

**4  HAMMERWOOD PARK**
Forest Row, East Grinstead  TEL: 01342 850 594

**5  LAURENCE HOBBS ORCHIDS**
Hophurst Lane, Crawley Down  TEL: 01342 715 142

**6  PERRYHILL NURSERIES LTD**
Hartfield, East Sussex, TN7 4JP.
TEL: 01892 770 377
EMAIL: sales@perryhillnurseries.co.uk
WEB: www.perryhillnurseries.co.uk

*GA OFFER*

*You can find us one mile north of Hartfield on the B2026. Over 5000 varieties of plants, we believe we have the widest range in the South-East, including the rare and unusual.*
OPEN: Mar-Oct: 9-5. Nov-Feb: 9-4.30.
SPECIALITIES: Climbers, Perennials, Roses, Shrubs, Trees.
FACILITIES: Credit cards, Wheelchair access, HTA gift tokens, Own gift tokens, Sell plants.

**7  GROOMBRIDGE PLACE GARDENS**
Groombridge, Tunbridge Wells  TEL: 01892 863 999

**8  HELLYER'S GARDEN PLANTS**
Wallage Lane, Crawley  TEL: 01342 718 280

**9  IMBERHORNE LANE NURSERY**
Imberhorne Lane, East Grinstead, West Sussex, RH19 1TZ.
TEL: 01342 321 175
EMAIL: gardenexpert@btinternet.com
WEB: www.imberhornelanenursery.co.uk
*An environmentally friendly plant nursery growing a wide range of shrubs, herbaceous, climbers and bedding. We stock a comprehensive range of eco friendly composts and mulches.*
OPEN: Mar-Nov: 9-5. Dec-Feb: 10-4.
SPECIALITIES: Bedding plants, Climbers, Shrubs, Herbaceous plants, Camellias.
FACILITIES: Credit cards, Wheelchair access, Plant guarantee, Sell plants, Pushchair friendly.

**10  WORLD OF WATER**
Turners Hill Rd, Worth, Crawley  TEL: 01293 883 237

**13  STANDEN HILLSIDE GARDEN, NATIONAL TRUST**
East Grinstead  TEL: 01342 323 029

**14  BIRCH FARM HARDY PLANT NURSERY**
Graveye Estate, East Grinstead  TEL: 01342 810 236

**15  GEMA NURSERY**
Lye Green, Crowborough  TEL: 01892 864 682

**16  CASABLANCA NURSERIES**
Colemans Hatch, Hartfield  TEL: 01342 824 064

**11  POTS AND PITHOI**
The Barns, East Street, Turners Hill, West Sussex, RH10 4QQ.
TEL: 01342 714 793
EMAIL: info@pots-and-pithoi.co.uk
WEB: www.pots-and-pithoi.co.uk

*Largest selection in the world of handmade terracotta pots from Crete. For garden, terrace, patio, conservatory and water features. Prices from £10-£750.*
OPEN: Open 7 days a week. Summer: 10-5. Winter: 10-4. Closed Christmas-New Year & Jan: Sat-Sun.
SPECIALITIES: Terracotta pots.
FACILITIES: Toilets, Credit cards, Wheelchair access, Gift tokens, Own gift tokens, Gift shop, Pushchair friendly.

**12  PLANTS 'N' GARDENS**
World of Water, Turners Hill Road, Worth, Crawley, West Sussex, RH10 4PE.
TEL: 01293 882 992
EMAIL: paul@plantsandgardens.freeserve.co.uk
WEB: www.plantsandgardens.org.uk

*Picturesque woodland setting with extensive display gardens. Wide range of perennials, shrubs and climbers. Ability to source unusual, rare plants.*
OPEN: Open 7 days a week. Summer: Mon-Sat 9-6. Winter: Mon-Sat 9-5, Sun 10.30-4.30.
SPECIALITIES: Japanese maples, Ferns, Ornamental grasses.
FACILITIES: Toilets, Credit cards, Wheelchair access, Dogs allowed.

**17  ROYAL MIRES NURSERY**
Lye Green, Crowborough  TEL: 01892 668 850

**18  MOORLANDS**
Friar's Gate, Crowborough  TEL: 01892 652 474

**19  COURTLANDS NURSERIES**
Sharpthorne, East Grinstead  TEL: 01342 810 780

**20  OAKHURST NURSERY**
Mardens Hill, Crowborough  TEL: 01892 653 273

**22  WAKEHURST PLACE, NATIONAL TRUST**
Ardingly, Haywards Heath  TEL: 01444 892 701

**23  STONEHURST ORCHID & CAMELLIA NURSERY**
Ardingly, Haywards Heath  TEL: 01444 892 488

**24  ROCKINGTON NURSERY**
Blackness Road, Crowborough  TEL: 01892 654 083

**25  THE MILLBROOK GARDEN COMPANY**
Jarvis Brook, Crowborough  TEL: 01474 331135

**21  WYCH CROSS NURSERIES LTD**
Wych Cross, Forest Row, East Sussex, RH18 5JW.
TEL: 01342 822 705
EMAIL: roses@wychcross.co.uk
WEB: www.wychcross.co.uk
*Independent garden centre with Britain's biggest selection of roses - 1400 varieties. Larger than average selection of shrubs and other plants. Excellent refreshments at The Hybrid Tea Room.*
OPEN: Mon-Sat 9-5.30. Closed Sun, Christmas, Boxing & New Year's Day.
SPECIALITIES: Roses, Shrubs, Garden & conservatory furniture.
FACILITIES: Credit card, Own gift tokens.

**26  NUTLIN NURSERY**
Nutley, Uckfield  TEL: 01825 712 670

**27  ASHDOWN FOREST GARDEN CENTRE & NURSERY**
Duddleswell, Uckfield  TEL: 01825 712 300

**28  BORDE HILL GARDEN**
Balcombe Road, Haywards Heath, West Sussex, RH16 1XP.
TEL: 01444 450 326
EMAIL: info@bordehill.co.uk
WEB: www.bordehill.co.uk
*Winner of 2 prestigious awards. Historic botanical garden with rare trees and shrubs, created in the 1890's. Tranquil and intimate garden 'rooms' offer all year colour.*
OPEN: Open daily 10-6 (or dusk).
ENTRY COSTS: £5.50, Child: £3, OAPs: £5, Family: £15.
SPECIALITIES: Rhododendrons and azaleas, Aquatics, Roses, Herbaceous plants, Glasshouses.
FACILITIES: Toilets, Credit cards, Wheelchair access, Restaurant, Gift shop, Dogs allowed, Child area, Coffee shop.

**29  BLOOMS OF BORDE HILL**
Borde Hill, Haywards Heath  TEL: 01444 414 151

**30  SHEFFIELD PARK GARDEN, NT**
Sheffield Park, Uckfield  TEL: 01825 790 231

**31  WILDERNESS WOOD**
Hadlow Down, Uckfield  TEL: 01825 830 509

**32  OAST FARM**
Buxted, Uckfield  TEL: 01825 733 446

**33  CABBAGES & KINGS**
Hadlow Down, Uckfield  TEL: 01825 830 552

**34  SCAYNES HILL NURSERY**
Haywards Heath  TEL: 01444 831 673

**36  BLACKBOYS NURSERY**
Blackboys, Uckfield  TEL: 01825 890 858

**37  STAVERTON NURSERY**
Eastbourne Road, Halland  TEL: 01825 840 249

**38  CHUBBS NURSERY**
Cooksbridge, Lewes  TEL: 01273 400 218

**39  BENTLEY WILDFOWL & MOTOR MUSEUM & GARDENS**
Halland, Lewes  TEL: 01825 840 573

**41  MCBEAN'S ORCHIDS**
Cooksbridge, Lewes  TEL: 01273 400 228

**42  CLAYHILL NURSERIES**
Uckfield Rd, Ringmer, Lewes  TEL: 01273 812 409

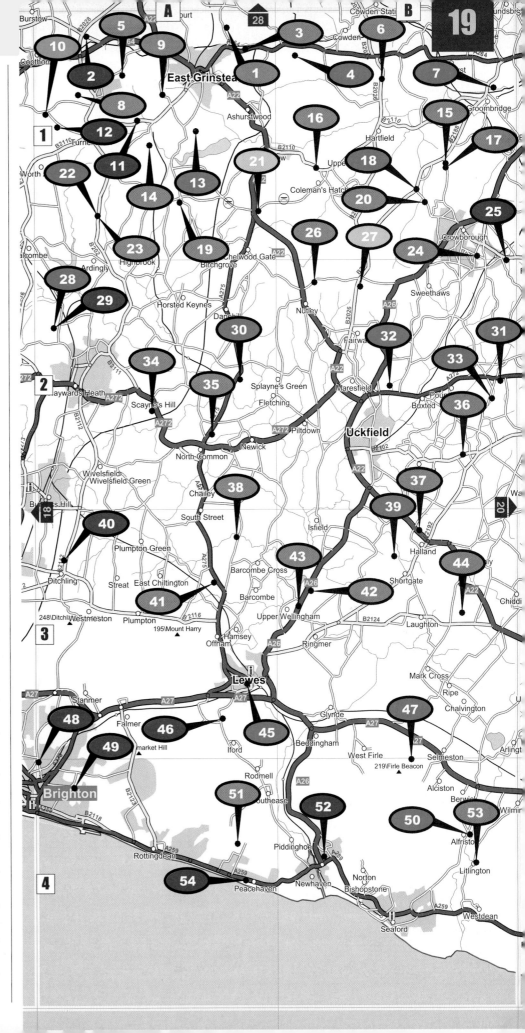

**35** **WARRENORTH NURSERY**

East Grinstead Road, North Chailey, East Sussex, BN8 4JD.

**TEL:** 01825 723 266

*Fuchsia & non-hardy geranium specialist. Breeders & suppliers of quality plants.*

**OPEN:** Tue-Sun & BH Mon, 9.30-5.

**SPECIALITIES:** Fuchsias, Geraniums.

**FACILITIES:** Wheelchair access, Plant guarantee, Sell plants.

**40** **GARDEN PRIDE GARDEN CENTRE**

Common Lane, Ditchling, East Sussex, BN6 8TP.

**TEL:** 01273 846 844

**EMAIL:** info@gardenpride.co.uk

**WEB:** www.gardenpride.co.uk

*Large garden centre stocking quality plants, specimen trees, furniture and unusual gifts. Pet, aquatic and craft shops together with popular coffee shop.*

**OPEN:** Mon-Sat 9-6, Sun 10.30-4.30. Closed Easter Sun, Christmas & Boxing Day.

**SPECIALITIES:** Gifts, Furniture, Perennials, Shrubs, Terracotta pots.

**FACILITIES:** Toilets, Credit cards, Wheelchair access, Restaurant, Gift tokens, Dogs allowed, Bookshop, Child area, Coffee shop, Gift shop, HTA gift tokens, Own gift tokens, Plant guarantee, Pushchair friendly, Sell plants.

**43** **GOLDCLIFF NURSERIES**

The Holdings, Uckfield Rd, Lewes **TEL:** 01273 814 949

**44** **WALLACE PLANTS**

B2124 Lewes Road, Laughton **TEL:** 01323 811 729

**45** **LEWES CASTLE AND BARBICAN HOUSE MUSEUM**

169 High Street, Lewes **TEL:** 01273 486 290

**46** **WYEVALE GARDEN CENTRE**

Newhaven Rd, Kingston, Lewes **TEL:** 01273 473 510

**47** **CHARLESTON**

Firle, Lewes **TEL:** 01323 811 626

**48** **EASTWOODS GARDEN CENTRE**

253 Ditchling Road, Brighton **TEL:** 01273 505 058

**49** **WYEVALE GARDEN CENTRE**

Warren Road, Brighton **TEL:** 01273 607 888

**50** **ALFRISTON CLERGY HOUSE, NT**

The Tye, Alfriston **TEL:** 01323 870 001

**51** **LOUVAIN ORGANIC NURSERIES**

66 Telscombe Rd, Peacehaven **TEL:** 01273 608 755

**52** **PARADISE PARK**

Avis Road, Newhaven **TEL:** 01273 616 000

**53** **LITLINGTON NURSERY**

Litlington **TEL:** 01323 871 211

**54** **POPLETT OF PEACEHAVEN**

170-174 South Coast Rd, Peacehaven **TEL:** 01273 583 133

**1** NOTCUTTS GARDEN CENTRE
Tonbridge Road, Pembury, Tunbridge Wells
TEL: 01892 822 636

**2** KINGS TOLL NURSERY
Maidstone Road, Matfield, Tonbridge
TEL: 01892 824 474

**3** MARLE PLACE GARDENS
Brenchley, Tonbridge
TEL: 01892 722 304

**4** PLANTBASE
Charcott Holm Farm, Hadlow, Tonbridge
TEL: 01892 891 453

**5** WYEVALE GARDEN CENTRE
Eridge Road, Tunbridge Wells
TEL: 01892 515 234

**6** BROADWATER PLANTS
Fair View Lane, Langton Green, Tunbridge Wells, Kent, TN3 9JP.
TEL: 01892 534 760
EMAIL: broadwater@coblands.co.uk
WEB: www.broadwaterplants.co.uk
*Specialist working nursery, growing ericaceous plants, rhododendrons (to specimen sizes), Azaleas, Acers, Camellias, Pieris plus other rare and unusual plants that should be more widely grown.*
OPEN: Jul-Sep, Mon-Fri 9-4. Oct-Jun, Mon-Sat 9-4.
SPECIALITIES: Camellias, Japanese maples, Magnolias, Rhododendrons and azaleas, Shrubs.
FACILITIES: Credit cards, Sell plants.

**7** OWL HOUSE GARDENS
Mount Pleasant, Lamberhurst, Tunbridge Wells
TEL: 01892 891 290

**8** FINCHCOCKS
Goudhurst
TEL: 01580 211 702

**9** FLOWER POWER
The Nursery, Frant Road, Tunbridge Wells
TEL: 01892 510 190

**10** SCOTNEY CASTLE GARDEN, NATIONAL TRUST
Lamberhurst, Tunbridge Wells
TEL: 01892 891 081

**11** GREENCAP NURSERY
Sleepers Stile Road, Lower Cousley Road, Wadhurst, East Sussex, TN5 6QX.
TEL: 01892 782 685
EMAIL: greencapnursery@aol.com
WEB: www.villagenet.co.uk
*Hanging baskets, bedding plants, shrubs, trees, unusual rustic planters, obelisks, terracotta pots. Also landscape design and building.*
OPEN: Open daily 10-5 (seasonal variations).
SPECIALITIES: Hanging baskets.
FACILITIES: Wheelchair access, Dogs allowed, Child area, Plant guarantee.

**12** BEDGEBURY NATIONAL PINETUM
Goudhurst, Cranbrook
TEL: 01580 211 044

**13** SUSSEX COUNTRY GARDENS
Eastbourne Road, Mark Cross, Crowborough, East Sussex, TN6 3PJ.
TEL: 01892 852 828
*Extensive ranges of plants, terracotta, stoneware and garden sundries. Hardwood and conservatory furniture. Statuary. Fish and aquatics centre. Expert and friendly advice.*
OPEN: Mon-Sat 9-5.30, Sun 10-5. Closed Easter Sun, Christmas & Boxing Day.
SPECIALITIES: Bedding plants, Garden & conservatory furniture, Water plants, Herbaceous plants, Shrubs.
FACILITIES: Credit cards, Wheelchair access, Gift tokens, Dogs allowed, HTA gift tokens, Sell plants, Pushchair friendly, Coffee shop.

**14** PASHLEY MANOR GARDENS
Ticehurst, Wadhurst
TEL: 01580 200 888

**15** THE NISHIKIGOI CENTRE
Hawkhurst Fish Farm, Hastings Road, Hawkhurst
TEL: 01580 754 030

**16** KING JOHN'S LODGE
Sheepstreet Lane, Etchingham
TEL: 01580 819 232

**17** MERRIMENTS GARDENS & NURSERY
Hawkhurst Road, Hurst Green, East Sussex, TN19 7RA.
TEL: 01580 860 666
EMAIL: markbuchele@beeb.net
WEB: www.merriments.co.uk

*This is a garden of extraordinary intensity. The colour composition is remarkable for its imaginative flair and daring. An experience of sheer delight that will remain in the mind forever.*
OPEN: Nursery: open daily. Garden: Apr-Oct.
ENTRY COSTS: £3.50, Child: £2, OAPs: £3.50.
SPECIALITIES: Garden & conservatory furniture, Alpines, Hardy plants, Roses, Ornamental grasses.
FACILITIES: Toilets, Credit cards, Wheelchair access, Restaurant, Gift tokens, Dogs allowed, Bookshop, Coffee shop, Gift shop, HTA gift tokens, Own gift tokens, Sell plants.

**18** MOYSES NURSERIES
Five Ashes, Mayfield
TEL: 01435 872 375

**19** BATEMAN'S, NATIONAL TRUST
Burwash, Etchingham
TEL: 01435 882 302

**20** OAKDENE ALPINE NURSERY
Street End Lane, Broad Oak, Heathfield, East Sussex, TN21 8TU.
TEL: 01435 864 382

*Oakdene Alpine Nursery offers a wide range of alpines and woodland plants for the experienced and non-experienced enthusiast. The nursery is situated in an area of outstanding natural beauty.*
OPEN: Wed-Sat 9-5, Sun by appt only. Gardens: open office hours & for the National Garden Scheme.
ENTRY COSTS: £2.50, Child: Free.
SPECIALITIES: Woodland plants, Alpines, Herbaceous plants.
FACILITIES: Sell plants.

**21** OLD ORCHARD NURSERY
Burwash Common, Burwash
TEL: 01435 882 060

**22** BROAD OAK GARDEN CENTRE
Broad Oak, Heathfield
TEL: 01435 865 045

**23** THORPE GARDENS
Little London Road, Horam, Heathfield
TEL: 01435 812 455

**24** A P NURSERY
Vines Cross, Heathfield
TEL: 01435 812 965

**25** SUNNY RISE NURSERIES
North Trade Road, Battle
TEL: 01424 772 685

**26** UCKHAM LANE NURSERY
Caldbec Hill, Battle
TEL: 01424 772 919

**27** ROSSLOW ROSES
North Street Farm, North Street, Hellingly
TEL: 01323 440 888

**28** LIME CROSS NURSERY
Herstmonceux, Hailsham, East Sussex, BN27 4RS.
TEL: 01323 833 229
EMAIL: LimeCross@aol.com
*Well stocked plant centre with a strong emphasis on conifers, trees, shrubs and herbaceous, also includes an attractively laid out small pinetum. Catalogue available on request.*
OPEN: Mon-Sat 8.30-5, Sun 10-4. Closed Dec 25-Jan 3.
SPECIALITIES: Wide selection of conifers.
FACILITIES: Credit cards, HTA gift tokens, Sell plants.

**29** COOPERS CROFT NURSERIES
New Road, Herstmonceux, Hailsham
TEL: 01323 832 151

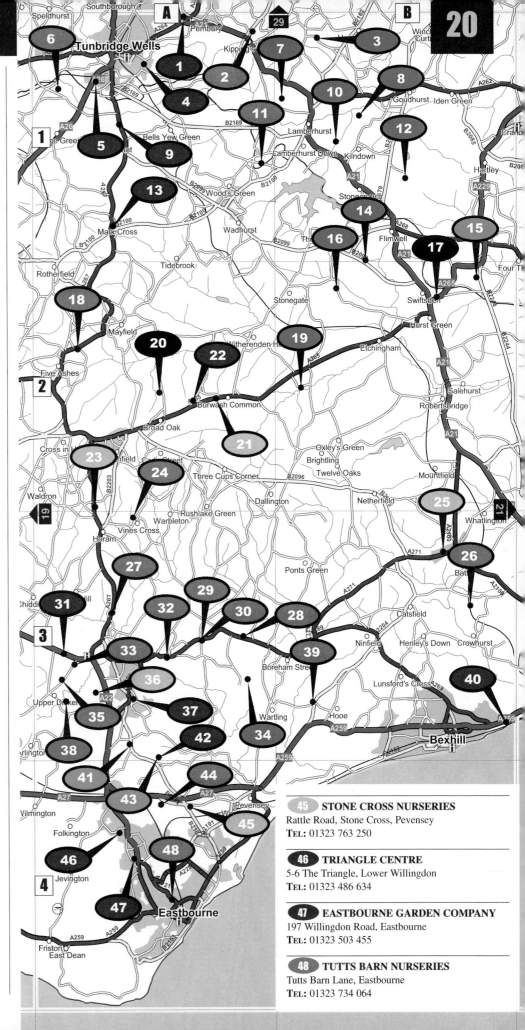

**30 NEW ROAD NURSERIES**
New Road, Amberstone, Hailsham
TEL: 01323 846 577

**31 WYEVALE GARDEN CENTRE**
Lower Dicker, Hailsham
TEL: 01323 844 834

**32 USUAL & UNUSUAL PLANTS**
Onslow House, Magham Down, Hailsham,
East Sussex, BN27 1PL.
TEL: 01323 840 967
EMAIL: jennie@onslow.clara.net
*A small nursery specialising in the best perennials
available, produced in low numbers to ensure the
widest range. Plants produced on site. Show garden
being created.*
OPEN: Mar-Oct: Wed-Sat 9.30-5.30.
SPECIALITIES: Hardy plants, Herbaceous plants,
Ornamental grasses, Perennials.
FACILITIES: Plant guarantee.

**33 COLDHARBOUR NURSERY**
Coldharbour Road, Lower Dicker, Hailsham
TEL: 01323 846 753

**34 HERSTMONCEUX CASTLE GARDENS
& GROUNDS**
Herstmonceux Castle, Hailsham
TEL: 01323 833 816

**35 ROBINS NURSERY**
Coldharbour Road, Upper Dicker, Hailsham
TEL: 01323 844 734

**36 HEMPSTEAD NURSERIES**
Hempstead Lane, Hailsham
TEL: 01323 843 183

**37 TENDRING GARDEN SHOP**
26 High Street, Hailsham
TEL: 01323 840 600

**38 MICHELHAM PRIORY**
Upper Dicker, Hailsham
TEL: 01323 844 224

**39 UPLANDS FUCHSIA NURSERY**
Hooe, Ninfield, Battle
TEL: 01424 844 846

**40 WYEVALE GARDEN CENTRE**
Bexhill Road, St Leonards On Sea, Hastings
TEL: 01424 443 414

**41 WORLD OF WATER**
Ersham Road, Hailsham
TEL: 01323 442 400

**42 HILLIER GARDEN CENTRE**
Hailsham Road, Stone Cross, Pevensey
TEL: 01323 763 240

**43 CROFT WATER GARDENS & AQUATICS**
Glyndley Garden Centre, Hailsham Road, Pevensey
TEL: 01323 847 868

**44 DITTONS NURSERY**
Dittons Road, Stone Cross, Pevensey
TEL: 01323 488 188

**45 STONE CROSS NURSERIES**
Rattle Road, Stone Cross, Pevensey
TEL: 01323 763 250

**46 TRIANGLE CENTRE**
5-6 The Triangle, Lower Willingdon
TEL: 01323 486 634

**47 EASTBOURNE GARDEN COMPANY**
197 Willingdon Road, Eastbourne
TEL: 01323 503 455

**48 TUTTS BARN NURSERIES**
Tutts Barn Lane, Eastbourne
TEL: 01323 734 064

# E SUSSEX · KENT

**1** **BRIDGE FARM FLOWERS**
Bridge Farm, Lyminge, Folkestone
TEL: 01303 863 625.

**2** **BUMBLES NURSERY**
Tolehurst Farm, Frittenden, Cranbrook, Kent,
TN17 2BN.
TEL: 01580 720 940

*Specialist growers of perennials, huge selection of
roses, large range of trees and shrubs. Extensive
selection of pots from around the world at factory
prices.*
**OPEN:** Open daily 8.30-5. Closed Christmas &
Boxing Day.
**SPECIALITIES:** Perennials, Terracotta pots.
**FACILITIES:** Credit cards, HTA gift tokens,
Pushchair friendly, Sell plants, Toilets,
Wheelchair access.

**3** **LEE'S NURSERY**
Pot Kilne Lane, High Halden, Ashford
TEL: 01233 850 456

**4** **OLDBURY NURSERIES**
Brissenden Green, Bethersden, Ashford
TEL: 01233 820 416

**5** **GREENWAYS GARDEN CENTRE**
Ashford Road, Bethersden, Bethersden
TEL: 01233 820 526

**6** **STONE OAK NURSERY**
Flood Street, Mersham, Ashford
TEL: 01233 720 925

**7** **1580 GARDEN CENTRE**
Sissinghurst Road, Biddenden, Ashford
TEL: 01580 292 600

**8** **BIDDENDEN NURSERIES**
Sissinghurst Road, Biddenden
TEL: 01580 292 100

**9** **SISSINGHURST CASTLE GARDEN,
NATIONAL TRUST**
Sissinghurst, Cranbrook
TEL: 01580 710 700

**10** **NEWINGREEN NURSERIES**
Ashford Road, Newingreen, Hythe
TEL: 01303 260 863

**11** **WYEVALE GARDEN CENTRE**
Ingles Meadow, Jointon Road, Folkestone
TEL: 01303 258 100

**12** **PORT LYMPNE WILD ANIMAL PARK**
Lympne, Hythe
TEL: 01303 264 647

**13** **LONGACRE NURSERIES**
St Mary's Road, West Hythe, Hythe
TEL: 01303 265 444

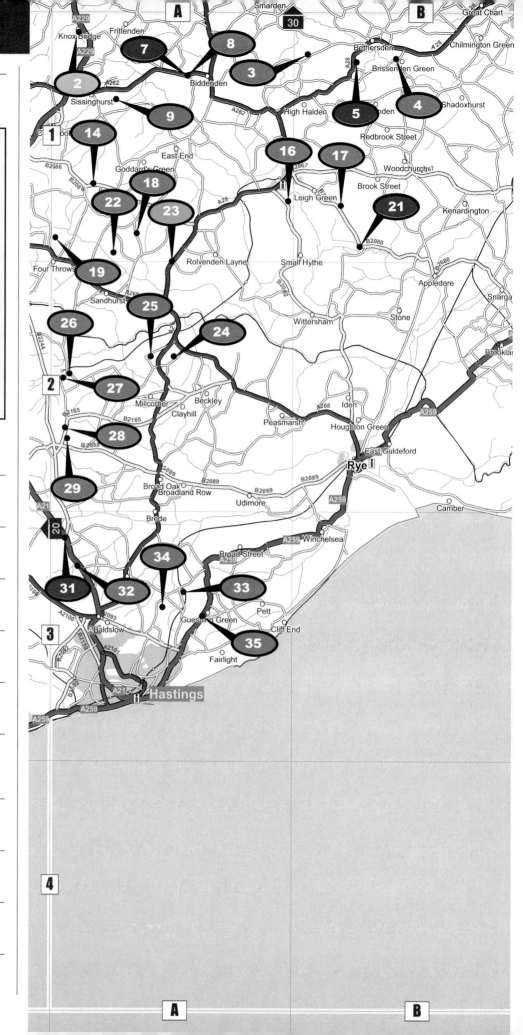

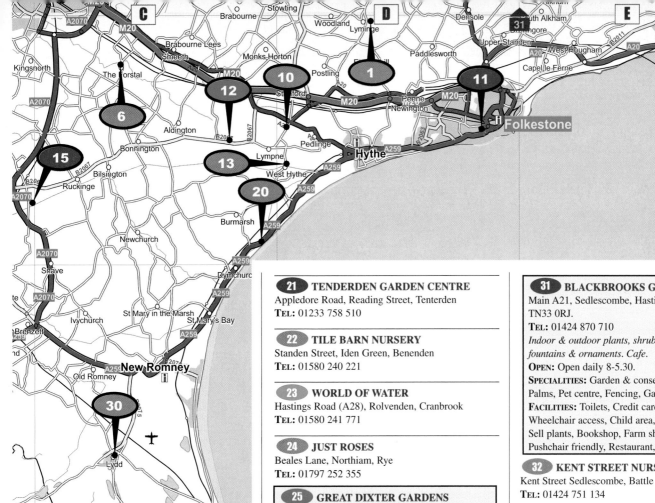

**21 TENDERDEN GARDEN CENTRE**
Appledore Road, Reading Street, Tenterden
TEL: 01233 758 510

**22 TILE BARN NURSERY**
Standen Street, Iden Green, Benenden
TEL: 01580 240 221

**23 WORLD OF WATER**
Hastings Road (A28), Rolvenden, Cranbrook
TEL: 01580 241 771

**24 JUST ROSES**
Beales Lane, Northiam, Rye
TEL: 01797 252 355

**25 GREAT DIXTER GARDENS**
Northiam, Rye, East Sussex, TN31 6PH.
TEL: 01797 252 878
EMAIL: office@greatdixter.co.uk
WEB: www.greatdixter.co.uk
*Home of gardening writer, Christopher Lloyd, boasting a variety of topiary, meadows, ponds and the famous Long Border and Exotic Garden. Free parking.*
OPEN: Apr 1-Oct 29: Tue-Sun & BH 2-5.
ENTRY COSTS: £4.50, Child: £1.
SPECIALITIES: Bedding plants, Climbers, Hardy plants, Pot plants, Shrubs.
FACILITIES: Toilets, Credit cards, Bookshop, Wheelchair access.

**26 BODIAM NURSERY**
Ockham House, Bodiam, Robertsbridge
TEL: 01580 830 649

**27 BODIAM BONSAI**
Ewhurst Green, Robertsbridge
TEL: 01580 830 644

**28 ED'S NURSERY**
Sunflower Gardens, Staplecross
TEL: 01580 830 701

**29 STAPLECROSS SHRUB CENTRE**
Brambles Cripps Corner, Robertsbridge
TEL: 01580 830 678

**30 SOUTHCOTT NURSERY**
South Street, Lydd, Romney Marsh
TEL: 01797 321 848

**31 BLACKBROOKS GARDEN CENTRE**
Main A21, Sedlescombe, Hastings, East Sussex, TN33 0RJ.
TEL: 01424 870 710
*Indoor & outdoor plants, shrubs, trees, fish, ponds, fountains & ornaments. Cafe.*
OPEN: Open daily 8-5.30.
SPECIALITIES: Garden & conservatory furniture, Palms, Pet centre, Fencing, Garden buildings.
FACILITIES: Toilets, Credit cards, Coffee shop, Wheelchair access, Child area, HTA gift tokens, Sell plants, Bookshop, Farm shop, Gift shop, Pushchair friendly, Restaurant, Plant guarantee.

**32 KENT STREET NURSERIES**
Kent Street Sedlescombe, Battle
TEL: 01424 751 134

**33 LODGE NURSERY**
Cottage Lane, Westfield, Hastings
TEL: 01424 870 186

**34 ROTHERVIEW NURSERY**
Ivyhouse Lane, Three Oaks, Hastings, East Sussex, TN35 4NP.
TEL: 01424 756 228
EMAIL: rotherview@btinternet.com

*A wide range of alpines available. We sell handmade hypertufa troughs empty and planted. An extensive Camelia range including autumn flowering Sasanquas.*
OPEN: Open 7 days a week. Summer: 9.30-4.30. Winter: 10-3.
SPECIALITIES: Alpines, Hardy plants, Camellias, Ferns, Grasses.
FACILITIES: Toilets, Wheelchair access, Plant guarantee, Sell plants.

**35 HARBOROUGH NURSERIES**
The Thorne (Rye Road), Guestling, Hastings
TEL: 0142 814 220

**14 ASHENDEN NURSERY**
Cranbrook Road, Benenden, Cranbrook
TEL: 01580 241 792

**15 WYEVALE GARDEN CENTRE**
Hamstreet, Ashford
TEL: 01233 732 988

**16 HOPES GROVE NURSERIES**
Hope Grove Farm, Smallhythe Road, Tenterden
TEL: 01580 765 600

**17 PINECOVE NURSERIES**
Appledore Road, Tenterden
TEL: 01580 765 429

**18 LAURELS NURSERY**
Dingleden, Benenden
TEL: 01580 240 463

**19 THE WALLED NURSERY**
St Ronans, Water Lane, Hawkhurst
TEL: 01580 752425

**20 COUNTRY FLOWERS WILDFLOWER NURSERY**
62 Lower Sands, Dymchurch, Romney Marsh
TEL: 01303 873 052

**1  BRYNCETHIN NURSEY**
Mount Pleasant, Bryncethin, Bridgend
TEL: 01656 862 379

**2  THE GARDEN OUTLET**
Designer Outlet Wales, The Derwen, Bridgend
TEL: 01656 651 413

**3  WYEVALE GARDEN CENTRE**
Village Farm Industrial Estate, Bridgend
TEL: 01656 741 443

**4  PENCOED COLLEGE GARDEN CENTRE**
Bridgend
TEL: 01656 302 600

**5  CROSSROADS GARDEN CENTRE**
Junction 35, M4, Pencoed, Bridgend
TEL: 01656 861 100

**6  SINGLETON GARDEN CENTRE**
Greenknowe, Coychurch, Bridgend
TEL: 01656 658 201

**7  WALTERS PET & GARDEN STORES LTD**
14 Cowbridge Road, Bridgend
TEL: 01656 652 410

**8  BORDERVALE PLANTS**
Nantyderi, Sandy Lane, Ystradowen
TEL: 01446 774 036

**9  MUSEUM OF WELSH LIFE**
St Fagans, Cardiff
TEL: 029 2057 3500

**10  CROSS FARM NURSERIES**
Cross Farm, Pentre Meyrick, Cowbridge
TEL: 01446 774 053

**11  HURRANS GARDEN CENTRE**
High Street, Cowbridge
TEL: 01446 775 053

**12  P WHELAN**
Cae'r Delyn, St Hilary, Cowbridge
TEL: 01446 772 888

**13  DYFFRYN BOTANIC GARDEN**
St Nicholas, Cardiff
TEL: 029 2059 3328

**14  THE GARDEN CENTRE**
Boverton Road, Boverton, Llantwit Major
TEL: 01446 792 105

**15  BROAD STREET GARDEN CENTRE**
Barry Town Station Site, Broad Street, Barry
TEL: 01446 720 333

**16  PLANTWISE NURSERIES**
Kibsworthy Farm, Barbrook, Lynton
TEL: 01598 753 766

**17  HELE BAY GARDEN CENTRE**
25 Watermouth Road, Ilfracombe
TEL: 01271 862 873

**18  SILVER DALE NURSERIES**
Shute Lane, Combe Martin, Ilfracombe
TEL: 01271 882 539

**19  WEST SOMERSET GARDEN CENTRE**
Mart Road, Minehead, Somerset, TA24 5BJ.
TEL: 01643 703 612
EMAIL: wsgardencentre@compuserve.com
WEB: www.westsomersetgardencentre.co.uk

*Friendly atmosphere with a good selection of shrubs and bedding grown in our own nursery. You will be pleasantly surprised.*
OPEN: Mon-Sat 8-5, Sun 10-4.
SPECIALITIES: Water plants, Palms, Shrubs, Trees, Garden buildings.
FACILITIES: Toilets, Credit cards, Wheelchair access, Restaurant, Gift tokens, Coffee shop, Plant guarantee, HTA gift tokens, Own gift tokens.

**20  DUNSTER CASTLE, NATIONAL TRUST**
Dunster, Minehead
TEL: 01643 821 314

**21  COTSWOLD HARDY PLANTS**
Wibble Farm, West Quantoxhead, Taunton
TEL: 01984 632 303

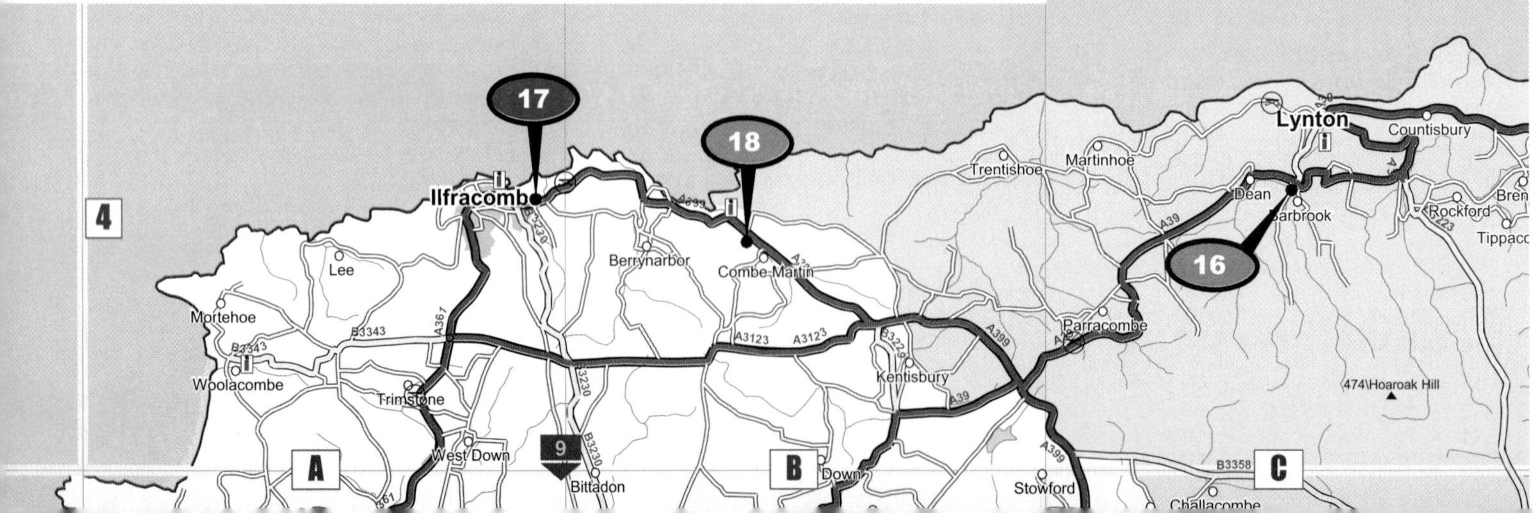

4

A  9  B  C

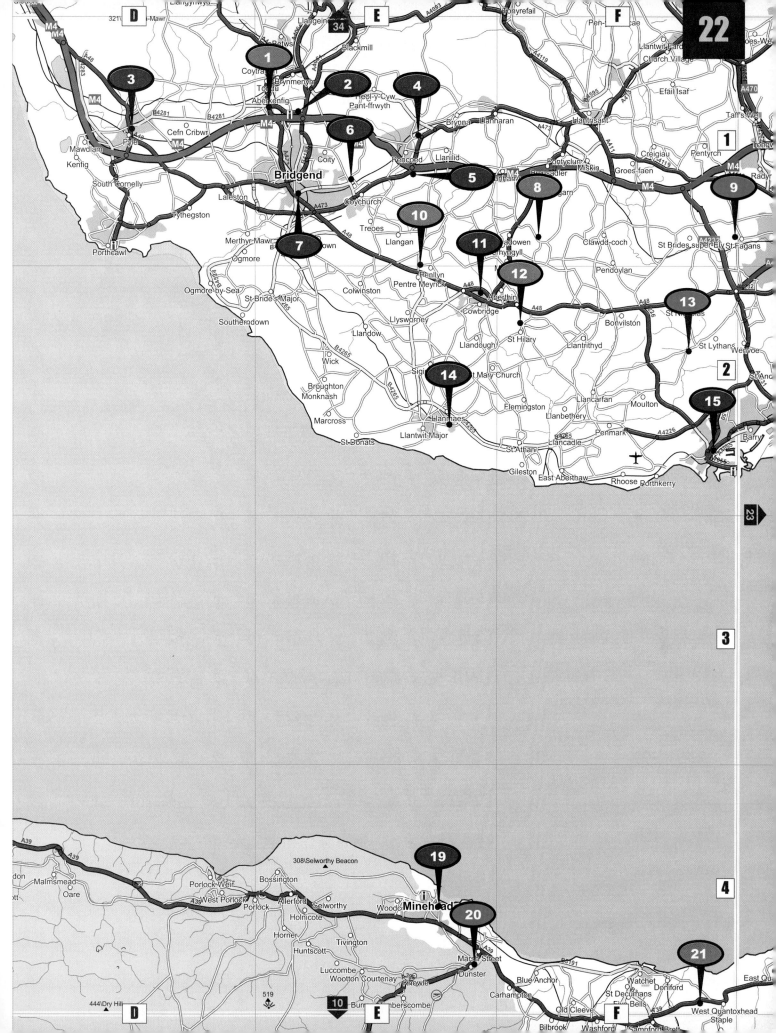

**1 CAERPHILLY GARDEN CENTRE**
Penrhos, Nantgarw, Cardiff    TEL: 029 2086 1511

**2 TREDEGAR HOUSE & PARK**
Newport    TEL: 01633 815 880

**3 WYEVALE GARDEN CENTRE**
Newport Road, Castleton, Cardiff
TEL: 01633 680 002

**4 J DEEN & SONS**
Dutch Nursery in Wales, Junction 30, M4, Cardiff Gate
TEL: 029 2077 7050

**5 JARDINERIE**
Newport Road, St Mellons, Cardiff
TEL: 029 2077 7977

**6 PUGHS GARDEN CENTRE**
Tynant Nursery, Morganstown, Cardiff
TEL: 02920 842 017

**7 CEFN ONN PARK**
Cherry Orchard Road, Lisvane, Cardiff
TEL: 029 2087 2000

**8 BLAISE CASTLE HOUSE**
Henbury, Bristol    TEL: 0117 950 6789

**9 HENLEAZE GARDEN SHOP**
146-148 Henleaze Road, Bristol  TEL: 01179 620 418

**10 MOORES PET & GARDEN STORES**
72 Shirehampton Road, Stoke Bishop, Bristol
TEL: 0117 987 2738

**11 BRACKENWOOD GARDEN CENTRE**
131 Nore Road, Portishead, Bristol
TEL: 01275 843 484

**12 ALL SEASONS GARDEN CENTRE**
99 Clive Street, Grangetown, Cardiff
TEL: 029 2025 5337

**13 BRACKENWOOD PLANT CENTRE**
Pill Road, Abbots Leigh, Bristol  TEL: 01275 375 292

**14 GARAWAYS GARDEN CENTRE**
Chantry Road, Clifton, Bristol  TEL: 0117 973 3402

**15 BRISTOL ZOO GARDENS**
Clifton, Bristol    TEL: 0117 970 6176

**16 UNIVERSITY OF BRISTOL BOTANIC GARDEN**
North Road, Leigh Woods, Bristol
TEL: 0117 973 3682

**17 STYLE GARDENS**
Port Road, Wenvoe, Cardiff    TEL: 029 2059 3888

**18 BRYNHEULOG NURSERIES**
St Andrews Road, Wenvoe, Cardiff
TEL: 029 2059 3375

**19 RIVERSIDE GARDEN CENTRE**
Clift House Road, Southville, Bristol
TEL: 0117 966 7535

**20 TICKENHAM GARDEN CENTRE**
Smallway, Congresbury    TEL: 01934 838 237

**21 GLEN BROOK BONSAI NURSERY**
Tickenham, Clevedon    TEL: 01275 858 596

**22 ASHTON COURT ESTATE**
Long Ashton, Bristol    TEL: 0117 963 9174

**23 BRYNAWEL GARDEN CENTRE**
Cross Common Road, Penarth  TEL: 029 2070 2660

**24 ALEXANDRA PARK**
Beach Road, Penarth    TEL: 029 2070 4617

**25 BONSAI IN BRISTOL**
47 Bedminster Down Road, Bedminster, Bristol
TEL: 0117 902 5641

**26 NATIONAL COLLECTION OF PASSIFLORA**
Greenholm Nurseries Ltd, Kingston Seymour, Clevedon
TEL: 01934 833 350

**27 CLEEVE NURSERY**
Main Road, Cleeve, Bristol    TEL: 01934 832 134

**28 CADBURY GARDEN & LEISURE**
Smallway, Congresbury    TEL: 01934 875 700

**29 ARNE HERBS**
Limeburn Nurseries, Limeburn Hill, Chew Magna
TEL: 01275 333 399

**30 CHEW VALLEY TREES**
Winford Road, Chew Magna, Bristol
TEL: 01275 333 752

**31 WESTON WATERSCAPES**
21 Rendcomb Close, Weston-Super-Mare
TEL: 01934 620 129

**32 MANSFIELD NURSERIES**
Mansfield Avenue, Weston-Super-Mare
TEL: 01934 627 916

**33 GROVE NURSERIES**
Lower Langford, Langford, Bristol
TEL: 01934 862 848

**34 BLAGDON WATER GARDENS**
Bath Road, Upper Langford
TEL: 01934 852 973

**35 LITTLE CREEK NURSERY**
39 Moor Road, Banwell, Weston-Super-Mare
TEL: 01934 823 739

**36 HUTTON GARDEN CENTRE**
Banwell Road, Hutton, Weston-Super-Mare
TEL: 01934 822 795

**37 BURRINGTON COOMBE GARDEN CENTRE**
Burrington Coombe, Burrington, Bristol
TEL: 01761 462 570

**38 BANWELL GARDEN CENTRE**
Castle Hill, Banwell    TEL: 01934 822 246

**39 WEST HARPTREE NURSERY**
Bristol Road, West Harptree    TEL: 01761 221 370

**40 NETHERCOTT NURSERIES**
Cheddar Rd, Clewer, Wedmore  TEL: 01934 742 881

**41 BURNHAM GARDEN CENTRE**
Pier Street, Burnham-on-sea    TEL: 01278 792 262

**42 MILL COTTAGE PLANTS**
The Mill, Henley Lane, Wookey  TEL: 01749 676 966

**43 THE FLOWER BOWER**
Shurton, Stogursey, Bridgwater  TEL: 01278 732 134

**44 BROWNE'S GARDEN CENTRE**
Woodford Lane, Wells    TEL: 01749 673 050

**45 WILLOWS GARDEN CENTRE**
Shapwick Road, Westhay, Glastonbury
TEL: 01458 860 060

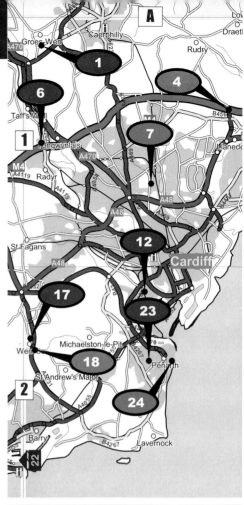

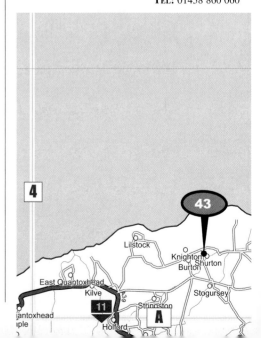

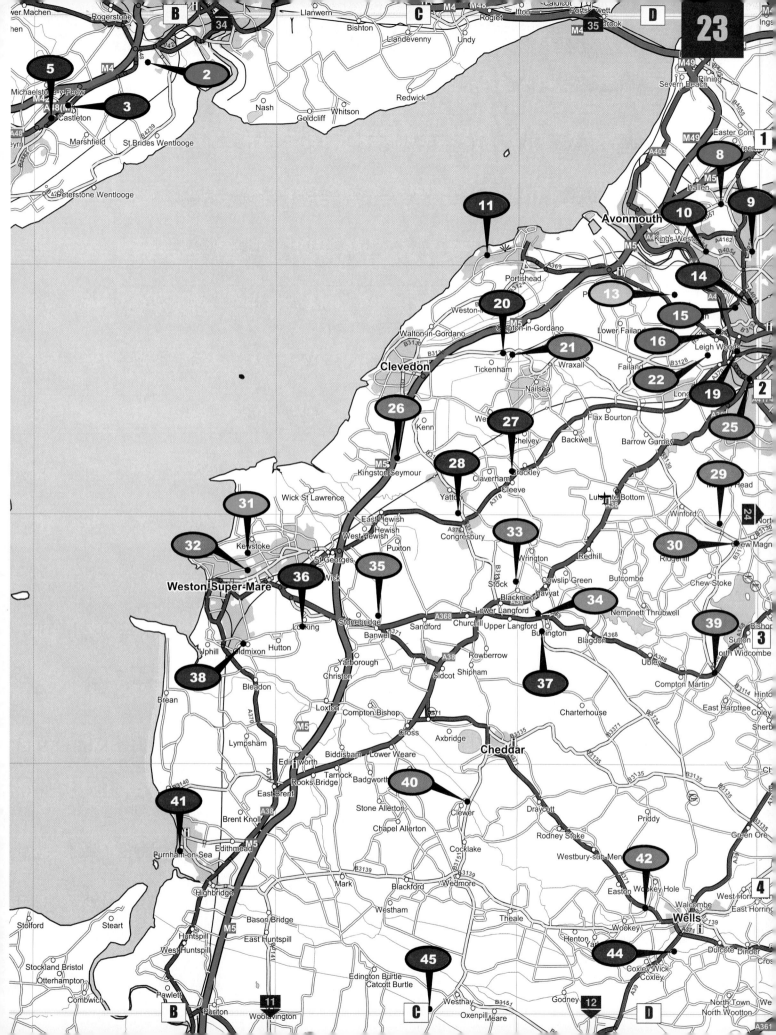

**1  HORTHAM NURSERIES**
Hortham Lane, Almondsbury, Bristol
**TEL:** 01454 613 468

**2  PARKERS GARDEN & AQUATIC CENTRE**
Wotton Road, Iron Acton, Bristol
**TEL:** 01454 228 761

**3  ALMONDSBURY GARDEN CENTRE**
Over Lane, Almondsbury, Bristol
**TEL:** 01454 457 300

**4  ALMONDSBURY AQUATIC CENTRE**
Almondsbury Garden Centre, Overlane, Almondsbury
**TEL:** 01454 201 118

**5  SANDAY'S NURSERY**
Over Lane, Almondsbury
**TEL:** 01454 615 076

**6  C S LOCKYER (FUCHSIAS)**
70 Henfield Road, Coalpit Heath, Bristol
**TEL:** 01454 772 219

**7  ELMWOOD FARM NURSERIES**
The Hollows, Coalpit Heath, Bristol
**TEL:** 0117 956 1495

**8  AQUA STORE**
542 Filton Avenue, Horfield, Bristol
**TEL:** 0117 969 2345

**9  POUND HILL GARDEN & PLANT CENTRE**
West Kington, Chippenham, Wiltshire, SN14 7JG.
**TEL:** 01249 783 880
**EMAIL:** poundhillplants@westkingtonnurseries.co.uk
**WEB:** www.poundhillplants.co.uk
*Themed rooms of romantic English planting with structure of clipped hedging, stone walls and extensive topiary. Unusual plants and topiary are available in the plant centre adjacent.*

**OPEN:** Mar-Oct: 2-5.
**ENTRY COSTS:** £2.50, Child: free.
**SPECIALITIES:** Comprehensive range.
**FACILITIES:** Wheelchair access, Coffee shop, Gift shop, HTA gift tokens.

**10  DYRHAM PARK, NATIONAL TRUST**
Chippenham
**TEL:** 0117 937 2501

**11  BRECKLANDS NURSERY**
Syston Lane, Webbs Heath, Bristol
**TEL:** 0117 961 0554

**12  SPECIAL PLANTS**
Greenways Lane, Cold Ashton, Chippenham
**TEL:** 01225 891 686

**13  ALAN PHIPPS CACTI**
62 Samuel White Road, Hanham, Bristol
**TEL:** 0117 960 7591

**14  JARRETT NURSERY**
Barry Road, Oldland Common, Bristol
**TEL:** 0117 932 3112

**15  FONTHILL GARDEN CENTRE**
Bath Road, Bitton, Bristol
**TEL:** 0117 932 3110

**16  AVON AQUATICS**
Jarretts Garden Centre, Bath Road, Bristol
**TEL:** 0117 932 7659

**17  WYEVALE GARDEN CENTRE**
Hicks Gate, Keynsham, Bristol
**TEL:** 01179 778 945

**18  WHITEGATE NURSERIES**
Stockwood Hill, Keynsham, Bristol
**TEL:** 0117 986 2653

**19  POPLAR NURSERIES**
The Batch, Bath
**TEL:** 01225 858 658

**20  BATHFORD NURSERIES**
Box Road, Bath
**TEL:** 01225 858 188

**21  BATH AQUATICS**
14 Brookside House, Weston, Bath
**TEL:** 01225 426 878

**22  NORTON NURSERY & GARDEN CENTRE**
Norton Lane, Whitchurch, Bristol
**TEL:** 01275 832 296

**23  HILLSIDE COTTAGE PLANTS**
Hilllside, Gibbet Lane, Whitchurch
**TEL:** 01275 837 505

**24  GEORGIAN GARDEN**
Gravel Walk, Bath
**TEL:** 01225 477 752

**25  BATH BOTANIC GARDENS / ROYAL VICTORIA PARK**
Royal Victoria Park, Bath
**TEL:** 01225 482 624

**26  CLAVERTON MANOR**
Claverton, Bath
**TEL:** 01225 460 503

**27  PRIOR PARK GARDEN CENTRE**
Prior Park Road, Widcombe
**TEL:** 01225 427 175

**28  BLACKMORE & LANGDON**
Stanton Nursery, Pensford, Bristol
**TEL:** 01275 332 300

**29  HILLIER GARDEN CENTRE**
Whiteway Road, Bath
**TEL:** 01225 421 162

**30  PRIOR PARK LANDSCAPE GARDEN, NATIONAL TRUST**
Ralph Allen Drive, Bath
**TEL:** 01225 833 422

**31  DOWNSIDE NURSERIES**
Upper Westwood, Bradford on Avon
**TEL:** 01225 862 392

**32  THE PETO GARDEN**
Iford Manor, Bradford on Avon
**TEL:** 01225 863 146

**33  MEADGATE FARM NURSERIES**
Weekesley Lane, Timsbury, Bath
**TEL:** 01761 470 344

**34  RODE TROPICAL BIRD GARDENS**
Rode, Bath
**TEL:** 01373 830 326

**35  R T HERBS**
Kilmersdon, Bath
**TEL:** 01761 435 470

Magnolia

**36** **NORTON GREEN GARDEN CENTRE**
Wells Road, Stratton-on-the-Fosse, Bath
TEL: 01761 232 137

**37** **BRICKHOUSE FARM NURSERY**
Brickhouse Farm, Holcombe, Bath
TEL: 01761 232 558

**38** **MEADOWS NURSERY**
5 Rectory Cottages, Mells, Frome
TEL: 01373 813 025

**39** **SLIPPS GARDEN CENTRE**
Butts Hill, Frome
TEL: 01373 467 013

**40** **ROCKY MOUNTAIN NURSERY**
Masbury, Wells
TEL: 01749 841 014

**41** **SOMERSET COUNTY ENTERPRISES GARDEN CENTRE**
Manor Road, Marston Trading Centre, Frome
TEL: 01373 453 094

**42** **LONGLEAT**
Warminster
TEL: 01985 844 400

**43** **THE WALLED GARDEN NURSERY**
Cock Road, Horningsham
TEL: 01985 845 004

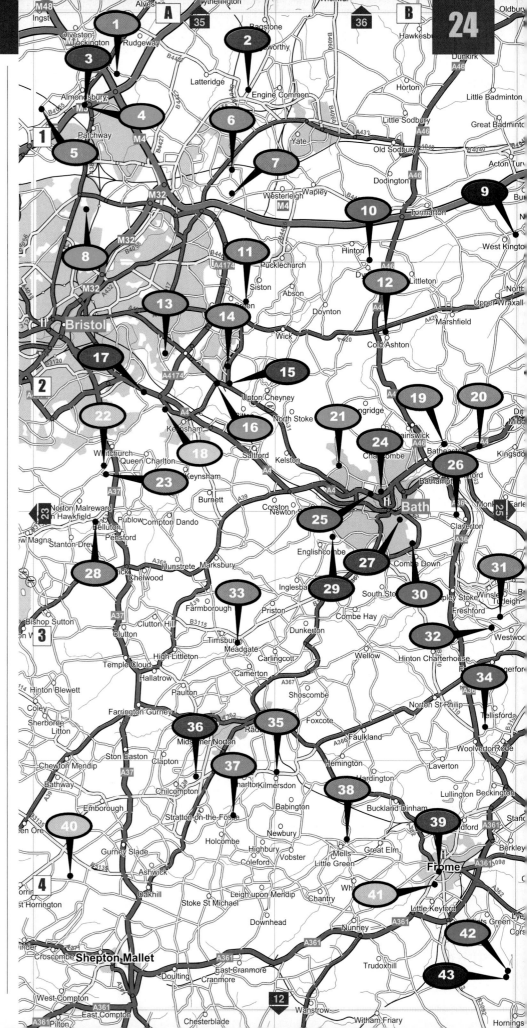

# HAMPSHIRE · SOMERSET · WILTSHIRE

**1** **ABBEY HOUSE GARDENS**
Market Cross, Malmesbury
TEL: 01666 822 212

**2** **FOXLEY ROAD NURSERIES**
Foxley Road, Malmesbury
TEL: 01666 822 171

**3** **SHERSTON PARVA NURSERY**
Malmesbury Road, Malmesbury
TEL: 01666 841 066

**4** **TOOMERS' STONE LANE GARDEN CENTRE**
Stone Lane, Lydiard Millicent, Swindon
TEL: 01793 771 766

**5** **ARGYLE GARDEN & PET SUPPLIES**
Cirencester Way, Argyle Street, Swindon
TEL: 01793 520 827

**6** **WORLD OF WATER**
Jardinerie Garden Centre, Hay Lane, Swindon
TEL: 01793 853 097

**7** **JARDINERIE**
Hay Lane, Wroughton, Swindon
TEL: 01793 852 736

**8** **BREACH LANE NURSERY**
Upper Green Hill, Wooton Bassett, Swindon
TEL: 01793 854 660

**9** **POUND HILL PLANTS**
West Kington, Chippenham
TEL: 01249 782 822

**10** **ARISTONE**
Allington Farm Shop, Allington, Chippenham
TEL: 01249 659 920

**11** **BENCROFT GARDENS**
Bremhill, Calne
TEL: 01249 740 324

**12** **BLOUNTS COURT NURSERIES**
Blounts Court, Studley, Calne
TEL: 01249 812 103

**13** **CORSHAM COURT**
Corsham
TEL: 01249 701 610

**14** **BOWOOD HOUSE AND GARDENS**
Bowood House, Derry Hill, Calne
TEL: 01249 812 102

**15** **AVEBURY MANOR & GARDEN, NATIONAL TRUST**
Marlborough
TEL: 01672 539 250

**16** **WHITEHALL GARDEN CENTRE**
Corsham Road, Lacock, Chippenham
TEL: 01249 730 204

**17** **LACOCK ABBEY**
Lacock, Chippenham
TEL: 01249 730 227

**18** **BOTANIC NURSERY**
Bath Road, Atworth, Melksham
TEL: 01225 706 597

**19** **LEWDEN GARDEN CENTRE**
Bath Road, Shaw, Melksham
TEL: 01225 702 345

**20** **PINE TREE NURSERY**
Conscience Lane, Rowde, Devizes
TEL: 01380 722 899

**21** **ROWDE MILL NURSERY**
Rowde, Devizes
TEL: 01380 723 016

**22** **COURTS GARDEN, NATIONAL TRUST**
Holt, Trowbridge
TEL: 01225 782 340

**23** **TOWNSENDS GARDEN CENTRE**
Bath Road, Devizes
TEL: 01380 723 722

**24** **WESTDALE NURSERIES**
Holt Road, Bradford on Avon
TEL: 01225 863 258

**25** **WOODBOROUGH GARDEN CENTRE**
Nursery Farm, Woodborough, Pewsey
TEL: 01672 851 249

**26** **J C GARDENS**
Marsh Road, Hilperton Marsh, Trowbridge
TEL: 01225 776 556

**27** **TROWBRIDGE GARDEN CENTRE**
288 Frome Road, Trowbridge
TEL: 01225 763 927

**28** **PARHAM BUNGALOW PLANTS**
Parham Lane, Market Lavington, Devizes
TEL: 01380 812 605

**29** **VICARAGE LANE NURSERIES**
The Sands, Easterton, Devizes
TEL: 01380 812 332

**30** **HEATHER BANK NURSERY**
1 High Street, Littleton Panell, Devizes
TEL: 01380 812 739

**31** **MEAD NURSERY**
Brokerswood, Westbury
TEL: 01373 859 990

**32** **GRANBY GARDEN CENTRE**
32 Astor Crescent, Ludgershall, Andover
TEL: 01264 790 275

**33** **BARTERS PLANT CENTRE**
Barters Farm Nurseries, Chapmanslade, Westbury
TEL: 01373 832 694

**34** **LAKESIDE GARDEN CENTRE**
Crockerton Shopping Centre, Crockerton, Warminster
TEL: 01985 217 413

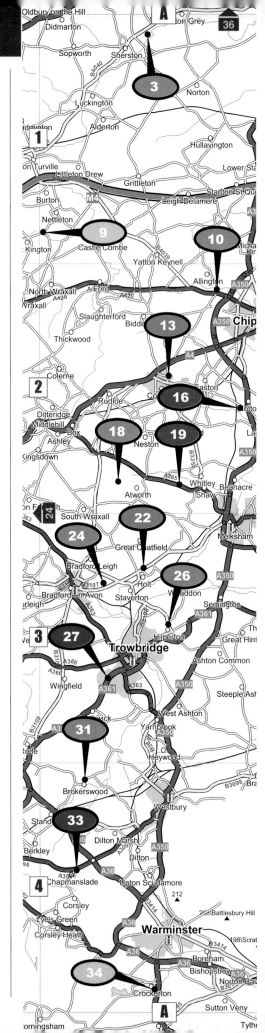

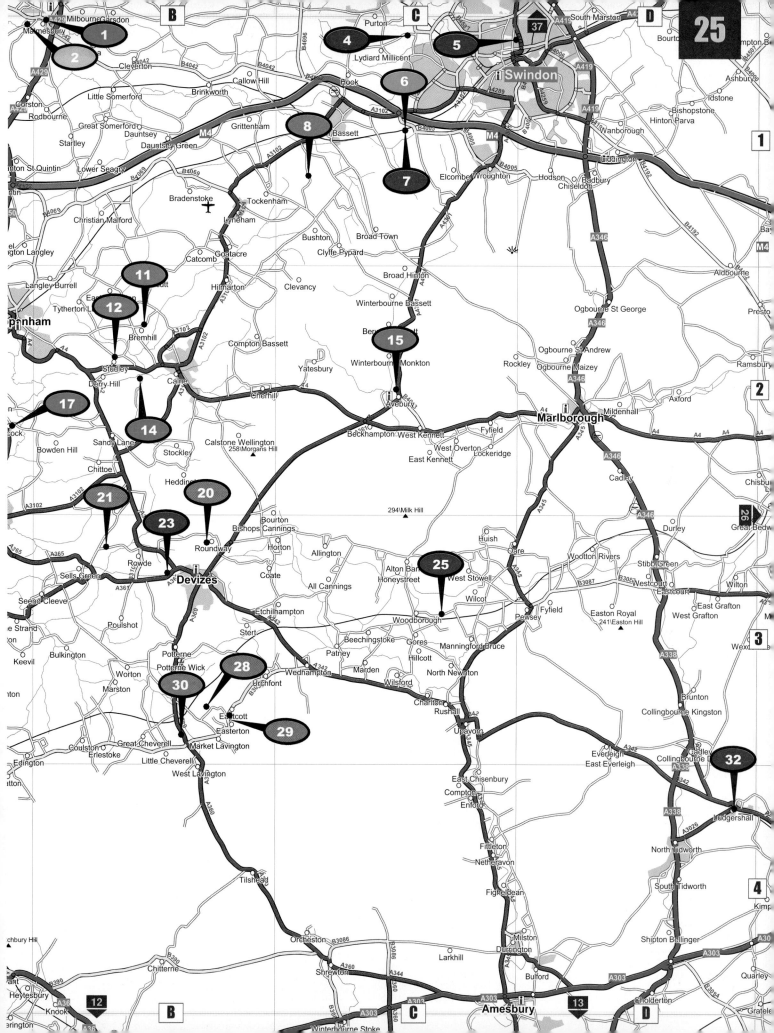

**1   WYEVALE GARDEN CENTRE**
Newbury Road, Chilton, Didcot
TEL: 01235 833 900

**2   ASHDOWN HOUSE, NATIONAL TRUST**
Lambourn
TEL: 01488 725 84

**3   GATEHAMPTON FUCHSIAS**
Gatehampton Farm, Goring, Reading
TEL: 01491 872 894

**4   BASILDON PARK, NATIONAL TRUST**
Lower Basildon, Reading
TEL: 0118 984 3040

**5   LIVING RAINFOREST**
Wyld Court Hall, Hampstead Norreys, Newbury,
TEL: 01635 202 444

**6   DAI-ICHI BONSAI**
Priors Court Road, Hermitage, Thatcham
TEL: 01635 200 667

**7   AQUASCAPE**
Hillier Garden Centre, Priors Court Road, Hermitage
TEL: 01635 202 300

**8   HILLIER GARDEN CENTRE**
Priors Court Road, Hermitage, Thatcham
TEL: 01635 200 442

**9   WOODSIDE FARM NURSERY**
Priors Court Road, Hermitage, Thatcham
TEL: 01635 201 561

**10   GLENVALE NURSERIES**
Hungerford Lane, Southend Bradfield, Reading,
Berkshire, RG7 6JH.
TEL: 0118 974 4006
EMAIL: eric@glenvalesagehost.co.uk
*Open 7 days a week for a full range of plants.*
OPEN: Open 7 days a week. Summer: Mon-Sat 9-5.30,
Sun 10-4. Winter: Mon-Sat 9-5, Sun 10-1.
SPECIALITIES: Bedding plants, Roses, Seeds, Bulbs,
Shrubs.
FACILITIES: Credit cards, Toilets, Wheelchair access,
Gift tokens, Plant guarantee, HTA gift tokens,
Sell plants, Pushchair friendly.

**11   WYEVALE GARDEN CENTRE**
4a Bath Road, Hungerford
TEL: 01488 682 916

**12   HAMSTEAD GROWERS LTD**
Red Hill, Hamstead Marshall, Newbury, Berkshire,
RG20 0JG.
TEL: 01635 254 091
EMAIL: hg@kwgl.co.uk
*PYO fruit and vegetables. Farm shop of personally
selected produce. Flowers and floristry department.
Bedding plants.*
OPEN: Mon-Sat 8-5.30. Sep-May: Sun 10-1.
PYO: Jun-Aug: Sun 10-4.30.
SPECIALITIES: Bedding plants, Vegetables, Floristry,
Hanging baskets, Stone ornaments.
FACILITIES: Toilets, Wheelchair access, Credit cards,
Pushchair friendly, Sell plants.

**13   COTTAGE GARDEN PLANTS**
9 Buckingham Road, Newbury
TEL: 01635 319 41

**14   WHITE TOWER NURSERY**
Aldermaston Village, Reading, Berkshire, RG7 4LD.
TEL: 0118 971 2123
EMAIL: crissy@whitetowernursery.freeserve.co.uk
*Family nursery growing herbaceous, tender and
hardy plants, shrubs, winter & summer baskets.
Floral work to order.*
OPEN: Open daily 9-6 or dusk if earlier. Closed
Christmas & Boxing Day.
SPECIALITIES: Bedding plants, Herbaceous perennials..
FACILITIES: Credit cards, Dogs allowed.

**15   FOXGROVE PLANTS**
Foxgrove Farm, Enborne, Newbury
TEL: 01635 405 54

**16   YEW TREE GARDEN CENTRE**
Ball Hill, Newbury
TEL: 01635 255 250

**17   DARLING BUDS OF MAY**
Newbury Road, Headley, Thatcham
TEL: 01635 269 308

**18   LAKESIDE GARDEN CENTRE**
Brimpton Common Road, Brimpton Common,
Tadley, Berkshire, RG7 4RT.
TEL: 01189 814 138
*Established family run garden centre with a vast
range of plants for beginners to experts. Discount
for senior citizens on Tuesdays. Delivery service
available.*
OPEN: Open 7 days a week. Summer: Mon-Sat 9-5.30,
Sun 10.30-4.30. Winter: Mon-Sat 9-5, Sun 10.30-4.30.
Closed Christmas, Boxing & New Years Day.
SPECIALITIES: Aquatics, Pet centre, Bedding plants,
Hanging baskets, Terracotta pots.
FACILITIES: Sell plants, Credit cards, Toilets,
HTA gift tokens, Plant guarantee, Pushchair friendly.

**19   PENWOOD NURSERIES LTD**
The Drove, Penwood, Burghclere, Newbury,
Berkshire, RG20 9EW.
TEL: 01635 254 366
*Growers of beautiful trees, shrubs, roses and
herbaceous plants. Extensive range of unusual
and grafted stock always available. Hedging
and fruit trees in season. Rural Setting.*
OPEN: Mon-Sat 9-5, Sun 10-4.
SPECIALITIES: Trees, Shrubs, Roses, Herbaceous plants.
FACILITIES: Sell plants.

**20   HOLLINGTON HERB GARDEN**
The Walled Garden, Woolton Hill, Newbury
TEL: 01635 253 908

**21   THE COTTAGE GARDEN CENTRE**
Newbury Road, Kingsclere, Newbury
TEL: 01635 297 979

**22   GREENACRES NURSERY**
Aldermaston Road, Pamber Green, Basingstoke
TEL: 01256 850 470

**23   HIGHCLERE CASTLE AND GARDENS**
Highclere, Newbury
TEL: 01635 253 210

**24   ELM PARK GARDEN CENTRE**
Aldermaston Road, Pamber End, Tadley
TEL: 01256 850 587

**25   HARDY'S COTTAGE GARDEN PLANTS**
Priory Lane, Freefolk, Whitchurch
TEL: 01256 896 533

**26   WYEVALE GARDEN CENTRE**
Winchester Road, North Waltham, Basingstoke
TEL: 01256 397 155

**27   WYEVALE GARDEN CENTRE**
Salisbury Road, Andover
TEL: 01264 710 551

Aeonium

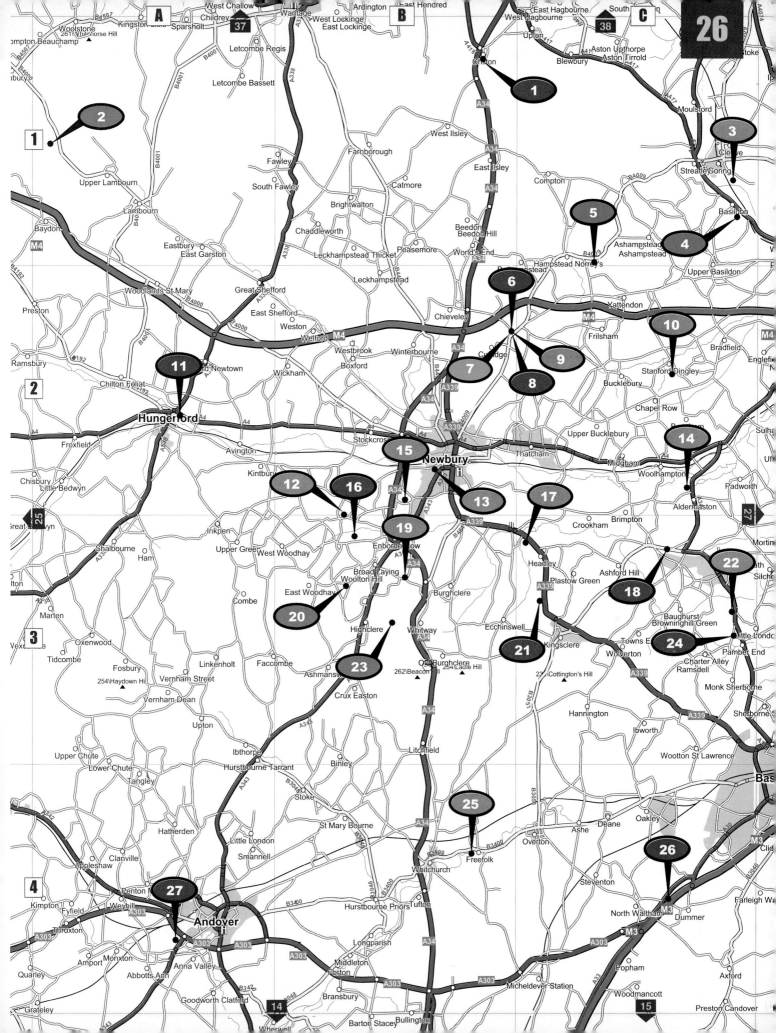

**1  HAYDEN NURSERIES**
Bishop Lane, Marlow          **TEL:** 01628 484 855

**2  TOAD HALL GARDEN CENTRE**
Marlow Rd, Henley on Thames  **TEL:** 01491 574 615

**3  GREYS COURT, NATIONAL TRUST**
Rotherfield Greys, Henley on Thames
                              **TEL:** 01491 628 529

**4  WOODCOTE GARDEN CENTRE**
Reading Road, Woodcote, Reading
                              **TEL:** 01491 680 335

**5  BERKSHIRE COLLEGE OF AGRICULTURE PLANT CENTRE**
Hall Place, Burchetts Green, Maidenhead
                              **TEL:** 01628 824 444

**6  ENGBERS NURSERY & GARDEN CENTRE**
Harpsden Woods, Harpsden, Henley on Thames
                              **TEL:** 0118 940 3078

**7  THE HERB FARM**
Peppard Road, Reading        **TEL:** 0118 972 4220

**8  WATERFIELD NURSERY**
Collins End, Goring Heath, Reading
                              **TEL:** 01491 681 541

**9  LADD'S GARDEN VILLAGE**
Bath Road, Hare Hatch, Reading, Berkshire, RG10 9SE.
**TEL:** 01189 404 794
*Centre with wide range of stock.*
**OPEN:** Open 7 days a week. Summer: Mon-Sat 9-6, Sun 10.30-4.30. Winter: 9-5.30. Closed Christmas & Boxing Day.
**SPECIALITIES:** Comprehensive range.
**FACILITIES:** Credit cards, Dogs allowed, Gift tokens, Plant guarantee, Sell plants, Toilets, Wheelchair access.

**10  AQUASPLASH**
Ladds Garden Village, Bath Road, Hare Hatch, Reading, Berkshire, RG10 9SB.
**TEL:** 0118 940 4188
**EMAIL:** ptataqua@aol.com
**WEB:** www.aquasplash-online.co.uk
*Aquasplash can cater for all your aquatic needs from aquariums to fish ponds. Full range of pumps, filters, pond liners and plants are always in stock.*
**OPEN:** Mon-Sat 9-5.30, Sun 10.30-4.30. Closed Christmas, Boxing & New Years Day.
**SPECIALITIES:** Aquatics.
**FACILITIES:** Credit cards, Own gift tokens, Pushchair friendly, Sell plants, Toilets, Wheelchair access.

**11  WYEVALE GARDEN CENTRE**
Hare Hatch, Twyford, Reading  **TEL:** 01189 403 933

**12  BERRY BROOK GARDEN CENTRE**
Henley Rd, Playhatch, Reading  **TEL:** 0118 948 4794

**13  H W HYDE & SON**
New Road, Ruscombe, Reading  **TEL:** 0118 934 0011

**14  COUNTRY HOMES AND GARDENS**
Henley Road, Playhatch, Reading, Berkshire, RG4 9RB.
**TEL:** 0118 948 4445
**EMAIL:** playhatch@countryhomesandgardens.co.uk
**WEB:** www.countryhomesandgardens.co.uk
*One of the county's leading garden centres with a vast range of plants, garden and conservatory furniture, gifts and garden goods. Free local delivery - please phone for details.*
**OPEN:** Mon-Sat 9-6, Sun 10-4.
**SPECIALITIES:** Comprehensive range of landscape materials for trade and retail customers.
**FACILITIES:** Credit cards, Dogs allowed, Plant guarantee, Toilets, Wheelchair access, HTA gift tokens.

**15  PRIMROSE NURSERY**
London Rd, Harehatch, Reading  **TEL:** 0118 9404 288

**16  ROTHERSTONE PLANTS**
70 Long Lane, Tilehurst, Reading  **TEL:** 0118 961 5889

**17  BARN FARM NURSERIES**
Wokingham Road, Hurst        **TEL:** 01734 321 008

**18  ENGLEFIELD GARDEN CENTRE**
The Street, Englefield, Theale  **TEL:** 0118 930 4898

**19  ENGLEFIELD HOUSE**
Englefield Estate Office, Englefield, Reading
**TEL:** 0118 930 2221 (0118 930 2504 - office)

**20  COUNTRY NURSERIES & GARDEN CENTRE**
Reading Road, Winnersh, Reading, Berkshire, RG41 5HG.
**TEL:** 0118 977 2141
**WEB:** www.countryhomesandgardens.co.uk
*One of the county's leading garden centres with a vast range of plants many grown on site, garden and conservatory furniture, gifts and garden goods.*
**OPEN:** Mon-Sat 9-6, Sun 10-4.
**SPECIALITIES:** Bedding plants, Hanging baskets, Fuchsias, Geraniums, Patio plants.
**FACILITIES:** Credit cards, Dogs allowed, HTA gift tokens, Plant guarantee, Pushchair friendly, Toilets, Wheelchair access.

**21  WYEVALE GARDEN CENTRE**
Forrest Rd, Binfield, Bracknell  **TEL:** 01344 869 456

**22  ASHRIDGE MANOR NURSERIES**
Forect Road, Wokingham       **TEL:** 0118 977 0730

**23  RURAL CRAFTS**
374 Reading Road, Winnersh, Wokingham
                              **TEL:** 01734 790 000

**24  LAURELS PLANT CENTRE**
29 Hyde End Lane, Ryeish Green, Reading
                              **TEL:** 0118 988 3792

**25  PUDDING LANE NURSERY**
Reading Rd, Arborfield, Reading  **TEL:** 0118 976 1048

**26  WORLD OF WATER**
166 Hyde End Road, Shinfield, Reading
                              **TEL:** 0118 988 5492

**27  GROVELANDS GARDEN CENTRE**
166 Hyde End Road, Shinfield, Reading,
                              **TEL:** 0800 074 7195

**28  CHANDLERS FARM NURSERY**
Grazeley Green, Reading      **TEL:** 01734 832 015

**29  HENRY STREET GARDEN CENTRE**
Swallowfield Road, Arborfield, Reading
                              **TEL:** 0118 976 1223

**30  WYEVALE GARDEN CENTRE**
Heathlands Road, Wokingham   **TEL:** 0118 977 3055

**31  BROOKSIDE NURSERY**
Church Road, Swallowfield, Reading
                              **TEL:** 0118 988 4122

**32  WELLINGTON COUNTRY PARK AND DAIRY MUSEUM**
Odiham Rd, Riseley, Reading  **TEL:** 0118 932 6444

**33  CHOBHAM NURSERIES**
Bagshot Road, Chobham        **TEL:** 01276 858 252

**34  SOUTHVIEW NURSERIES**
Chequers Lane, Eversley Cross Hook
                              **TEL:** 0118 973 2206

**35  SANDHURST GARDEN CENTRE**
Yorktown Road, Sandhurst     **TEL:** 01252 872 294

**36  PETER TRENEAR NURSERIES**
Chequers Lane, Eversley Cross, Hook
                              **TEL:** 0118 973 2300

**37  WHITEWATER NURSERY**
Hound Green, Mattingley, Hook  **TEL:** 01189 326 487

**38  D H  WATER GARDENS**
Wyevale Garden Centre, Wildmoor Lane, Sherfield-on-Loddon, Basingstoke, Hampshire, RG27 0HA.
**TEL:** 01256 882 019

*Hampshire aquatic superstore for every indoor and outdoor need. Maintenance, installation and landscaping available.*
**OPEN:** Mon-Sat 9.30-5.30, Sun 10.30-4.30. Closed Christmas Day & Easter Sun.
**SPECIALITIES:** Aquatics.
**FACILITIES:** Toilets, Credit cards, Wheelchair access, Restaurant, Gift tokens, Dogs allowed, Coffee shop, Own gift tokens, Pushchair friendly.

**39  SCATS COUNTRYSTORES**
Wildmoor Lane, Sherfield-on-Loddon, Basingstoke
                              **TEL:** 0870 0119 254

**40  WYEVALE GARDEN CENTRE**
Wildmoor Lane, Sherfield on Loddon
                              **TEL:** 01256 882 239

**41  VICARAGE HILL NURSERY**
Hartley Wintney, Basingstoke  **TEL:** 01252 842 523

**42  WEST GREEN HOUSE GARDEN, NT**
West Green, Hartley Wintney   **TEL:** 01252 844 611

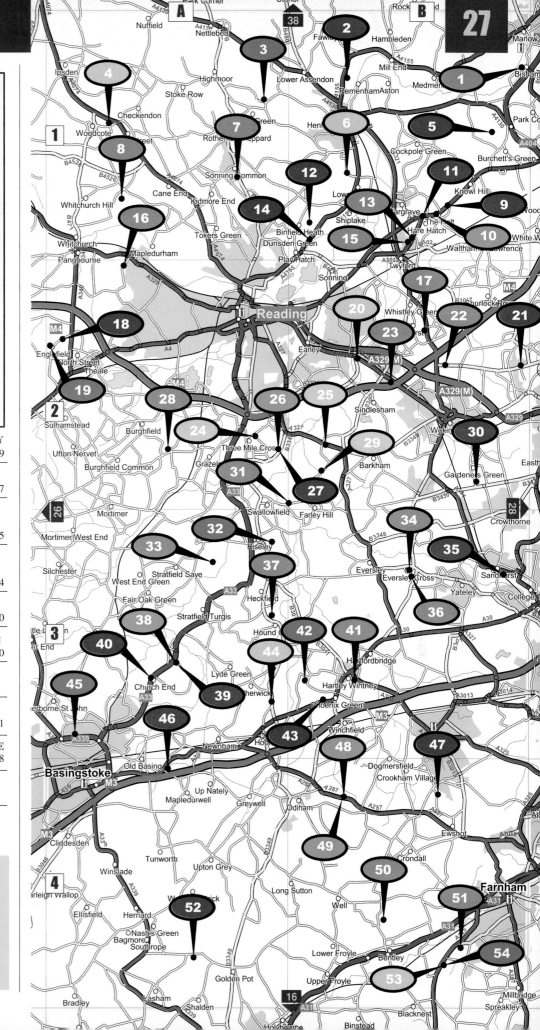

### 43 COACH HOUSE GARDEN CENTRE

London Road, Hartley Wintney, Hook, Hampshire, RG27 8HY.

**GA OFFER**

**TEL:** 01252 842 400

**EMAIL:** coach_house@hotmail.com

**WEB:** www.acegardens.co.uk

*Friendly, family run centre. Fabulous furniture for the garden and conservatories. Large covered plant area. Nursery fresh plants, shrubs and trees. Excellent coffee shop within outdoor terrace.*

**OPEN:** Mon-Fri 8.30-6, Sat 9-6, Sun 10.30-4.30. Closed Easter Sun, Christmas, Boxing & New Years Day.

**SPECIALITIES:** Christmas trees, Garden & conservatory furniture, Shrubs, Turf.

**FACILITIES:** Toilets, Credit cards, Wheelchair access, Gift tokens, Bookshop, Child area, Coffee shop, Gift shop.

### 44 HOOK GARDEN CENTRE & NURSERY
Reading Road, Hook   **TEL:** 01256 762 739

### 45 VYNE
Sherborne St John, Basingstoke **TEL:** 01256 881 337

### 46 CONKERS GARDEN CENTRE
London Road, Hatch, Basingstoke
**TEL:** 01256 840 515

### 47 REDFIELDS GARDEN CENTRE
Ewshot Lane, Church Crookham, Fleet
**TEL:** 01252 624 444

### 48 WYCHWOOD WATERLILY FARM
Farnham Road, Odiham, Hook **TEL:** 01256 702 800

### 49 ODIHAM WATERLILY COLLECTION
Farnham Road, Odiham, Hook **TEL:** 01256 702 800

### 50 GREEN FARM PLANTS
Bury Court, Bentley, Farnham **TEL:** 01420 232 02

### 51 GARDEN STYLE
Wrecclesham Hill, Farnham **TEL:** 01252 735 331

### 52 AVENUE NURSERIES GARDEN CENTRE
The Avenue, Lasham, Alton **TEL:** 01256 381 648

### 53 FOREST LODGE GARDEN CENTRE
Holt Pound, Farnham **TEL:** 01420 232 75

### 54 BIRDWORLD
Forest Lodge Garden Centre, Holt Pound, Farnham
**TEL:** 01420 221 40

**1  GROVELAND NURSERY**
Clay Tye Road, Upminster    TEL: 01708 222 528

**2  HIGH HOUSE GARDEN CENTRE**
Ockendon Road, Upminster    TEL: 01708 222 181

**3  NORTHWICK GARDEN CENTRE**
Canvey Road, Canvey Island    TEL: 01268 692 595

**4  CORNELL'S GARDEN CENTRE**
36a Fobbing Road, Corringham, Stanford le Hope
TEL: 01375 642 118

**5  THURROCK GARDEN CENTRE**
South Road, South Ockendon    TEL: 01708 851 991

**6  SMITHS ORCHARD GARDEN CENTRE**
70 Chadwell Road, Grays    TEL: 01375 372 195

**7  TILBURY FORT**
No 2 Office Block, The Fort, Tilbury
TEL: 01375 858 489

**8  SPRINGHEAD NURSERIES LTD**
Watling Street, Southfleet, Gravesend
TEL: 01474 361 370

**9  SWALLOW AQUATICS**
Station Road, Southfleet, Gravesend
TEL: 01474 561 123

**10  THE MILLBROOK GARDEN COMPANY**
Station Road, Southfleet, Gravesend
TEL: 01474 331 135

**11  HAWLEY GARDEN CENTRE**
Hawley Road, Hawley, Dartford, Kent, DA2 7RB.
TEL: 01322 224 108
EMAIL: hawleygardenctr@aol.com

*Family run centre with large range of bedding plants, shrubs, garden sundries and much more! Aquatic centre also on site. Large FREE car park.*
OPEN: Mon-Sat 8-6, Sun 10.30-4.30.
SPECIALITIES: Bedding plants, Climbers, Rhododendrons and azaleas, Roses, Shrubs.
FACILITIES: Toilets, Wheelchair access, Gift tokens, Bookshop, Coffee shop, Own gift tokens, HTA gift tokens.

**12  WATERLAND**
Dillywood Lane, Hisham, Rochester
TEL: 01634 719 889

**13  ROCHESTER CASTLE**
The Keep, Rochester    TEL: 01634 402 276

**14  SHORNE WOOD COUNTRY PARK**
Brewers Rd, Shorne, Gravesend  TEL: 01474 823 800

**15  RIVERSIDE FUCHSIAS**
Gravel Road, Sutton at Hone, Dartford, Kent, DA4 9HQ.
TEL: 01322 863 891
*National Collection and 5,000 varieties of fuchsias. 1,000 varieties of geraniums, hardy & erodrums. Penstemons.*
OPEN: Tue-Sun 9-5. Closed Christmas & Boxing Day.
SPECIALITIES: Fuchsias.
FACILITIES: Wheelchair access, Toilets, Credit cards, Dogs allowed.

**16  SCALERS HILL NURSERY**
Scalers Hill, Cobham, Gravesend
TEL: 01474 822 856

**17  WALNUT HILL NURSERIES**
Walnut Hill Road, Longfield Hill, Gravesend
TEL: 01474 704 859

**18  WOODLAND NURSERIES & GARDEN CENTRE**
Ash Lane, Sevenoaks    TEL: 01474 852 788

**19  ROSIE'S GARDEN PLANTS**
Rochester Road, Aylesford    TEL: 01622 715 777

**20  MILLYARD NURSERIES**
The Garden Shop Millyard, Swan Street, West Malling
TEL: 01732 875 545

**21  IGHTHAM PLANT CENTRE**
Borough Green Road, Ightham, Kent, TN15 9JA.
TEL: 01732 884 726
EMAIL: info@forwardnurseries.co.uk
WEB: www.hedgingdirect.co.uk
*Fully stocked plant centre specialising in specimens and hedging and ivies.*
OPEN: Open daily.
SPECIALITIES: Hedging, Ivies.
FACILITIES: Sell plants, Credit cards, Dogs allowed, HTA gift tokens, Plant guarantee.

**22  GREAT COMP GARDEN & NURSERY**
Comp Lane, Platt, Borough Green, Kent, TN15 8QS.
TEL: 01732 882 669 / 886 154
EMAIL: william.dyson@ukgateway.net
WEB: www.greatcomp.co.uk

*Seven-acre 'plantsman's paradise' surrounding 17th century manor. Enormous collection of choice and unusual plants from all over the globe, many of which are available at the nursery.*
OPEN: Apr-Oct: 11-6.
ENTRY COSTS: £3.50, Child: £1, OAPs: £3.50.
SPECIALITIES: Perennials.
FACILITIES: Toilets, Coffee shop, Wheelchair access, Restaurant, Sell plants, Pushchair friendly, Gift shop.

**23  G REUTHE NURSERIES**
Sevenoaks Road, Seal, Sevenoaks
TEL: 01732 810 694

**24  CROMAR NURSERY**
North Pole, Wateringbury, Maidstone
TEL: 01622 812 380

**25  DESIGNER PLANTS**
Back Lane, Ightham, Sevenoaks, Kent, TN15 9AU.
TEL: 01732 885 700
EMAIL: dp@coblands.co.uk
WEB: www.coblands.co.uk
*Specialist herbaceous nursery with other plants which will tempt the garden designers. Select "Nursery Fresh" from our vast range of perennials both the usual and the unusual.*
OPEN: Mon-Fri 9-4. Other times, telephone to confirm opening times.
SPECIALITIES: Alpines, Ferns, Geraniums, Ornamental grasses, Perennials.
FACILITIES: Credit cards, Plant guarantee, Sell plants.

**26  WINDMILL NURSERY**
The Street, Mereworth, Maidstone
TEL: 01622 813 330

**27  BIJOU NURSERIES**
Tonbridge Road, Wateringbury, Maidstone
TEL: 01622 812 278

**28  PLAXTOL NURSERIES**
The Spoute, Plaxtol, Sevenoaks  TEL: 01732 810 550

**29  IGHTHAM MOTE, NATIONAL TRUST**
Ivy Hatch, Sevenoaks    TEL: 01732 810 378

**30  DOWNDERRY NURSERY**
Pillar Box Lane, Hadlow, Tonbridge
TEL: 01732 810 081

**31  OLD WALLED GARDEN**
Oxonhoath, Hadlow    TEL: 01732 810 012

**32  RALPH'S NURSERY & FARM SHOP**
Wierton Road, Boughton Monchelsea, Maidstone
TEL: 01622 743 851

**33  BOUGHTON MONCHELSEA PLACE**
Church Hill, Boughton Monchelsea, Maidstone
TEL: 01622 743 120

**34  BROOKSIDE GARDEN CENTRE**
Seven Mile Lane, East Peckham, Tonbridge, Kent, TN12 5JG.
TEL: 01622 871 250
EMAIL: brooksidegckent@ukonline.co.uk
WEB: www.brooksidegardencentre.co.uk
*Large independent centre est. 1968. A wide range of trees, shrubs, conifers, perennials, alpines, bedding and house plants. Aquatics.*
OPEN: Mon-Fri 8.30-5.30. Closed Christmas & Boxing Day.
SPECIALITIES: Shrubs, Pet centre.
FACILITIES: Toilets, Credit cards, Wheelchair access, Gift tokens, Bookshop, Coffee shop, Plant guarantee, HTA gift tokens, Pushchair friendly, Sell plants.

**35** **G & S SMALLHOLDINGS**
Wheelers Lane, Linton, Maidstone
**TEL:** 01622 744 273

**36** **HADLOW COLLEGE PLANT CENTRE**
Hadlow College, Hadlow, Tonbridge
**TEL:** 01732 853 211

**37** **YALDING ORGANIC GARDENS**
Benover Rd, Yalding, Maidstone **TEL:** 01622 814 650

**38** **GATE HOUSE FARM NURSERY**
Coldharbour Lane, Hildenborough, Tonbridge
**TEL:** 01732 832 180

**39** **FOUR SEASONS BONSAI NURSERY &**
**RHINO ROCK GARDENS**
Snoll Hatch Rd, East Peckham **TEL:** 01622 872 403

**40** **DE JAGER & SONS**
The Nurseries, Marden **TEL:** 01622 831 235

**41** **WYEVALE GARDEN CENTRE**
Maidstone Road, Paddock Wood, Tonbridge
**TEL:** 01892 835 777

**42** **HAYESDEN HERB & HONEY FARM**
Upper Hayesden Lane, Upper Hayesden, Tonbridge
**TEL:** 01732 353 421

**43** **SPELDHURST NURSERIES**
Langton Road, Speldhurst, Tunbridge Wells
**TEL:** 01892 862 682

# dig
# deeper

## Get
## more
## information
## from

www.gardenersatlas.co.uk

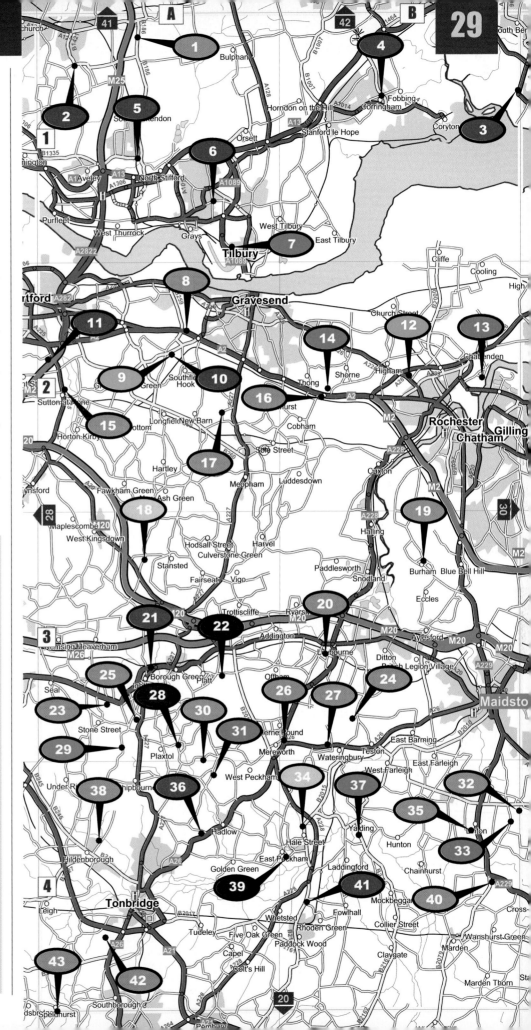

**1** OASIS
42 Greenwood Avenue, South Benfleet
Tel: 01268 757 666

**2** LEIGH GARDEN & TIMBER SUPPLIES
1 Ligham Court Drive, Leigh on Sea
Tel: 01702 474 376

**3** HOMELEIGH NURSERY
Ratcliffe Highway, Rochester   Tel: 01634 250 235

**4** STONES NURSERY
Halfway Road, Minster on Sea, Sheerness
Tel: 01795 580 411

**5** BRAMBLEDOWN GARDEN CENTRE
Lower Road, Minster on Sea, Sheerness
Tel: 01795 877 977

**6** WAVERLEY NURSERIES
622 Lower Rainham Road, Rainham, Gillingham
Tel: 01634 232 520

**7** SUE HARTFREE
25 Crouch Hill Court, Lower Halstow, Sittingbourne
Tel: 01795 842 426

**8** HOLYWELL LANE NURSERIES
Holywell Lane, Upchurch, Sittingbourne
Tel: 01795 842 335

**9** KNOWLER NURSERY
143 Berengrave Lane, Rainham, Gillingham
Tel: 01634 361 631

**10** BERENGRAVE NURSERIES
61 Berengrave Lane, Rainham, Gillingham
Tel: 01634 363 412

**11** GORE HOUSE NURSERY
London Road, Newington, Sittingbourne
Tel: 01795 842 365

**12** W H CARTER & SON
34 Borstal Hill, Whitstable   Tel: 01227 272 903

**13** OAKLANDS NURSERIES
24 London Road, Newington, Sittingbourne
Tel: 01795 842 173

**14** ULTIMATE KOI
Colourpack Plant Centre, Lower Hartlip Road, Sittingbourne
Tel: 01795 841 300

**15** BREDHURST NURSERY
Dunn Street, Bredhurst, Gillingham
Tel: 01634 386 444

**16** MERESBOROUGH NURSERY
Meresborough Road, Rainham, Gillingham
Tel: 01634 231 639

**17** WYEVALE GARDEN CENTRE
Elm Court, Capstone Road, Gillingham
Tel: 01634 813 778

**18** MEADOW GRANGE NURSERY
Honey Hill, Blean, Whitstable   Tel: 01227 471 205

**19** WYEVALE GARDEN CENTRE
Norton Crossroads, London Road, Norton
Tel: 01795 521 549

**20** THE BONSAI SHOP
London Road, Teynham, Sittingbourne
Tel: 01795 522 466

**21** SHILLINGHURST NURSERY
Oad St, Borden, Sittingbourne   Tel: 01795 842 446

**22** VALE NURSERY
Hayes Lane, Stockbury Lane, Sittingbourne
Tel: 01795 844 004

**23** A & E BRIDGEN & SON LTD
Ospringe Nursery, Brogdale Road, Faversham
Tel: 01795 532 433

**24** MACKNADE GARDEN CENTRE
Canterbury Road, Faversham   Tel: 01795 531 213

**25** BROGDALE HORTICULTURAL TRUST
Brogdale Road, Faversham   Tel: 01795 535 286

**26** COPTON ASH SPECIALIST NURSERY
105 Ashford Road, Faversham   Tel: 01795 535 919

**27** MOUNT EPHRAIM GARDENS
Staple Street, Hernhill, Faversham
Tel: 01227 751 496

**28** WYEVALE GARDEN CENTRE
Upper Harbledown, Canterbury   Tel: 01227 454 264

**29** DODDINGTON PLACE GARDENS
Doddington, Sittingbourne   Tel: 01795 886 101

**30** NOTCUTTS GARDEN CENTRE
Newnham Court Bearsted Road, Maidstone
Tel: 01622 739 944

**31** LONGACRE NURSERY
Perrywood, Selling, Faversham   Tel: 01227 752 254

**32** POTTED GARDEN NURSERY
Ashford Road, Bearsted, Maidstone
Tel: 01622 737 801

**33** PILGRIM HOUSE HERBS
Coles Dane, Stede Hill, Maidstone
Tel: 01622 859 371

**34** LEEDS CASTLE
Maidstone   Tel: 01622 765 400

**35** RUMWOOD NURSERIES AND GARDEN CENTRE
Sutton Road, Langley, Maidstone
Tel: 01628 614 77

**36** COOKOO BOX NURSERY
63 Charlesford Avenue, Kingswood, Maidstone
Tel: 01622 844 866

**37** PLEASANT VIEW GARDEN CENTRE
Plough Wents Road, Maidstone   Tel: 01622 844 872

**38** BEECH COURT GARDENS
Canterbury Road, Challock Ashford
Tel: 01233 740 735

**39** VICTORIANA NURSERY GARDENS
Challock, Ashford
Tel: 01233 740 480

**40** WARMLAKE NURSERY & FARM SHOP
North Street, Sutton Valence, Maidstone
Tel: 01622 844 000

**41** CROFTERS NURSERY
Church Hill, Charing Heath, Ashford
Tel: 01233 712 798

**42** CHURCH HILL COTTAGE GARDENS AND NURSERY
Church Hill, Charing Heath, Ashford
Tel: 01233 712 522

**43** OLANTIGH GARDEN NURSERIES
Little Olantigh Road, Wye, Ashford
Tel: 01233 812 248

**44** GRAFTY GARDEN CENTRE
Grafty Green, Maidstone
Tel: 01622 858 800

**45** HEADCORN FLOWER CENTRE & VINEYARD
Grigg Lane, Headcorn
Tel: 01622 890 250

**46** BYBROOK BARN GARDEN CENTRE
Canterbury Road, Ashford
Tel: 01233 631 959

**47** IDEN CROFT HERBS
Frittenden Road, Staplehurst
Tel: 01580 891 432

**48** MADRONA NURSERY
Pluckley Road, Bethersden, Ashford, Kent, TN26 3DD.
Tel: 01233 820 100
*Unusual, rare and new plant varieties displayed on a spectacular and unique nursery site. Catalogue available.*
Open: Mid Mar-end Oct: Sat-Tue 10-5.
Specialities: Ferns, Grasses, Perennials, Shrubs, Trees.
Facilities: Toilets, Credit cards, Wheelchair access, Gift tokens, Own gift tokens.

**49** WYEVALE GARDEN CENTRE
Hythe Road, Willesborough, Ashford
Tel: 01233 502 136

**50** THE COTTAGE GARDEN
Cranbrook Road, Staplehurst
Tel: 01580 891 312

**51** BEAN PLACE NURSERY
52 Gladstone Road, South Willesborough, Ashford
Tel: 01233 631 550

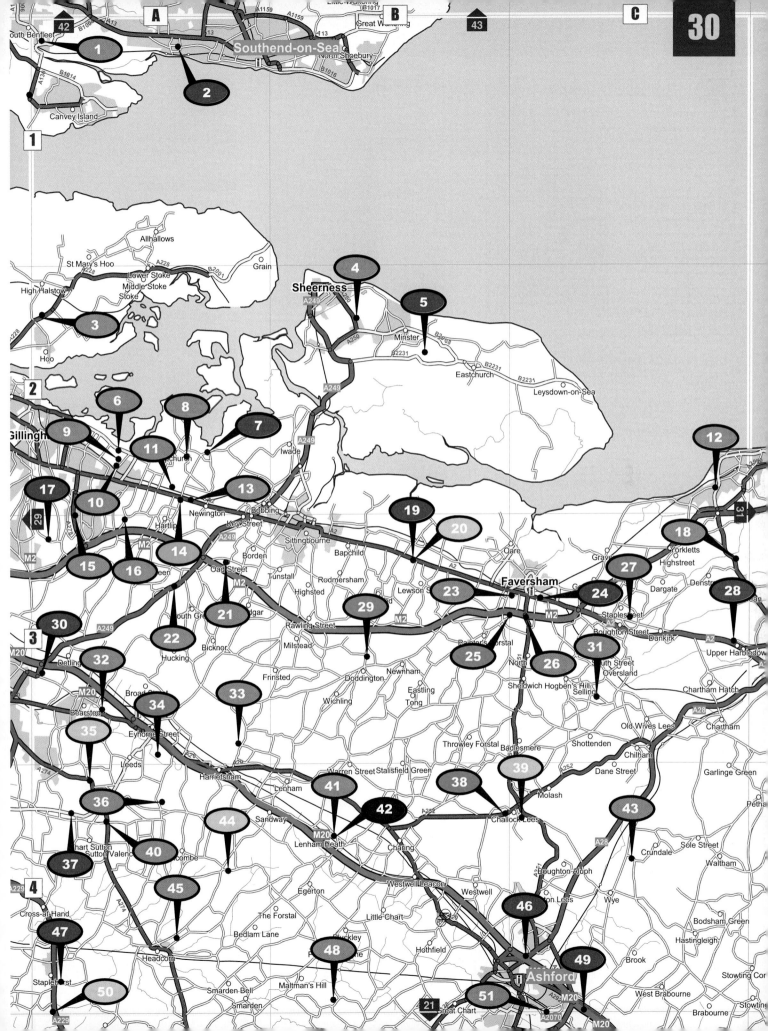

### 1  EAST NORTHDOWN FARM & GARDENS

Margate, Kent, CT9 3TS.
**TEL:** 01843 862 060
**EMAIL:** friend.northdown@ukonline.co.uk
**WEB:** www.botanyplants.co.uk
*Family nursery specialising in plants for coastal and chalky areas, farmhouse gardens with familiar and unusual plants suited to local conditions.*
**OPEN:** Open daily 10-5.
**ENTRY COSTS:** Free.
**SPECIALITIES:** Water plants, Ornamental grasses, Bamboos, Perennials, Shrubs, Trees.
**FACILITIES:** Toilets, Credit cards, Gift tokens, Child area, Farm shop, Sell plants.

### 2  KINGSGATE & KENVER NURSERIES

George Hill Road, Kingsgate, Broadstairs
**TEL:** 01843 604 407

### 3  CROFTERS GARDENING STORE

42 Station Road, Westgate-on-Sea
**TEL:** 01843 836 286

### 4  GROVE NURSERY

The Grove, Westgate-on-Sea
**TEL:** 01843 835 988

### 5  NICKY'S NURSERY

33 Fairfield Road, Broadstairs
**TEL:** 01843 601 897

### 6  VINCENT NURSERIES

47 Eddington Lane, Herne Bay
**TEL:** 01227 375 806

### 7  ROSEMARY NURSERY

Manston Road, Margate
**TEL:** 01843 823 282

### 8  JOHNSONS NURSERY

Thanet Way, Whitstable
**TEL:** 01227 793 763

### 9  WYEVALE GARDEN CENTRE

Hereson Road, Ramsgate
**TEL:** 01843 592 393

### 10  BUSHEYFIELDS NURSERY

Herne Common, Herne Bay
**TEL:** 01227 375 415

### 11  FOXHILL NURSERY

Foxhill, Sturry, Canterbury
**TEL:** 01227 713 012

### 12  ROSEWOOD DAYLILIES

70 Deansway Avenue, Sturry, Canterbury
**TEL:** 01227 711 071

---

### 13  PRESTON NURSERY

The Street, Preston Next Wingham, Canterbury, Kent, CT3 1ED.
**TEL:** 01227 722 250
**EMAIL:** tim-offord@supanet.com
*An attractive family run nursery, specialising in trees and specimen palms, bamboos, topiary, tree ferns, large pots.*
**OPEN:** Open daily 10-5.
**SPECIALITIES:** Trees, Bamboos, Topiary, Shrubs, Palms.
**FACILITIES:** Toilets, Credit cards, Wheelchair access, Gift tokens, Dogs allowed, HTA gift tokens.

### 14  SAUNDERS HOUSE NURSERY

Saunders Lane, Ash, Canterbury
**TEL:** 01304 812 092

### 15  ARCHERS LOW NURSERY

Ash Road, Sandwich
**TEL:** 01304 613 150

### 16  WYEVALE GARDEN CENTRE

Stour Valley Business Park, Chartham, Canterbury
**TEL:** 01227 731 033

### 17  MERRYFIELD NURSERIES

Stodmarsh Road, Canterbury
**TEL:** 01227 462 602

### 18  WINGHAM COUNTRY MARKET

The Depot, Sgatterling, Canterbury
**TEL:** 01227 720 567

### 19  PICKARD'S MAGNOLIA GARDENS

Stodmarsh Road, Canterbury
**TEL:** 01227 463 951

### 20  LAYHAM GARDEN CENTRE

Lower Road, Staple, Canterbury, Kent, CT3 1LH.
**TEL:** 01304 813 267
**EMAIL:** layham@gcstaple.fsnet.co.uk
*Specialist rose growers as well as offering a wide selection of shrubs, trees, conifers and herbaceous plants.*
**OPEN:** Open daily 9-5. Closed Dec 24-Jan 2.
**SPECIALITIES:** Garden & conservatory furniture, Roses, Shrubs, Trees, Herbaceous plants.
**FACILITIES:** Toilets, Credit cards, Wheelchair access, Gift tokens, Coffee shop, Dogs allowed, HTA gift tokens, Sell plants.

### 21  TREVORS NURSERY

Dover Road, Sandwich
**TEL:** 01304 614 377

### 22  SOUTH EAST WATER GARDENS

Dover Road, Sandwich
**TEL:** 01304 614 963

### 23  SUMMERFIELD NURSERIES

Barnsole Road, Staple
**TEL:** 01304 812 549

---

### 24  MARTINS NURSERY

Poison Cross Nursery, Eastry, Sandwich
**TEL:** 01304 611 262

### 25  HIGHAM PARK & GARDENS

Higham Park, Bridge, Canterbury
**TEL:** 01227 830 830

### 26  GOODNESTONE PARK GARDENS

Goodnestone, Canterbury
**TEL:** 01304 840 107

### 27  WALMER NURSERY

19-21 Dover Road, Walmer, Deal
**TEL:** 01304 375 277

### 28  THOMPSON'S PLANT & GARDEN CENTRE

Stone Street, Petham, Canterbury
**TEL:** 01227 700 449

### 29  WALMER CASTLE & GARDENS, ENGLISH HERITAGE

Kingsdown Road, Walmer, Deal
**TEL:** 01304 364 288

### 30  ORCHARD NURSERIES

Stone Street, Petham, Canterbury
**TEL:** 01227 700 375

### 31  RINGWOULD ALPINES

Dover Road, Ringwould, Deal
**TEL:** 01304 360 034

### 32  BLAKENEY HOUSE NURSERIES

Osier Grounds, Agester Lane, Denton
**TEL:** 01227 831 800

### 33  GARDEN PLANTS

Victory Road, St Margarets at Cliffe, Dover
**TEL:** 01304 853 225

### 34  PINES GARDEN

Beach Road, St Margaret's Bay, Dover
**TEL:** 01304 852 764

### 35  KERSNEY ABBEY AND RUSSELL GARDENS

Alkham Valley Road, Temple Ewell, Dover
**TEL:** 01304 872 434

### 36  ELWIN F END

32 Lower Road, Temple Ewell, Dover
**TEL:** 01304 822 541

### 37  FARTHING COMMON PLANT CENTRE

Stone Street, Lyminge, Folkestone
**TEL:** 01303 863 438

### 38  MACFARLANES NURSERY & GARDEN CENTRE

Swingfield, Folkestone
**TEL:** 01303 844 244

### 39  DOUR GARDENS & AQUATIC CENTRE

Charlton Green, Dover
**TEL:** 01304 201 101

### 40  ALKHAM VALLEY GARDEN CENTRE

Alkham Valley Road, South Alkham, Dover
**TEL:** 01303 893 351

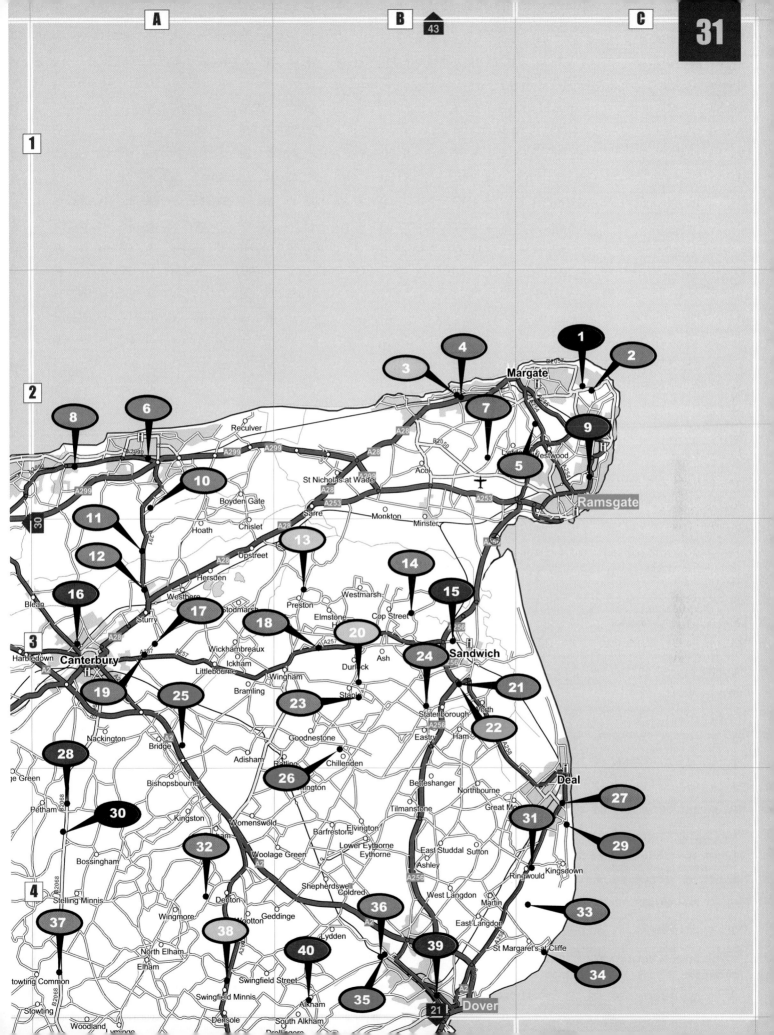

# SOUTH WALES

**1** THE PERENNIAL NURSERY
St. Davids, Haverfordwest
TEL: 01437 721 954

**2** LITTLE RHYNDASTON NURSERIES
Hayscastle, Haverfordwest
TEL: 01437 710 656

**3** HILTON COURT GARDENS AND CRAFT
Roch, Haverford West
TEL: 01437 710 262

**4** MOOR FARM NURSERY
Pont-Y-Fenni, Whitland
TEL: 01994 240 335

**5** PICTON CASTLE
Haverfordwest
TEL: 01437 751 326

**6** TAVERNSPITE GARDEN CENTRE
Tavernspite, Whitland
TEL: 01834 831 671

**7** COLBY WOODLAND GARDEN,
NATIONAL TRUST
Amroth, Narberth
TEL: 01834 811 885

**8** ST ISHMAEL'S NURSERIES
Haverfordwest
TEL: 01646 636 343

**9** HONEYBOROUGH GARDEN CENTRE
Honeyborough Ind Est, Neyland, Milford Haven
TEL: 01646 601 943

**10** STAMMERS GARDENS
Stammers Road, Saundersfoot
TEL: 01834 813 766

---

**11** UPTON CASTLE GARDENS
Cosheton, Pembroke Dock, Pembrokeshire, SA72 4SE.
TEL: 01646 651 782
EMAIL: enquiries@carewcastle-pembrokeshirecoast.org.uk
WEB: www.pembrokeshire.org.uk
*37 acre gardens noted for rhododendrons,
camellias and magnolias, containing 250 different
species of trees and shrubs alongside formal
terraces, herbaceous borders, rose gardens
and a medieval chapel.*
OPEN: Mar 29-end Oct; Sun-Fri 10-4.30.
ENTRY COSTS: £1.20, Child: 60p, OAPs: £1.20,
Family: £3.00 .
SPECIALITIES: Rhododendrons and azaleas,
Roses, Shrubs, Trees, Herbaceous plants.
FACILITIES: Toilets, Dogs allowed.

---

**12** PEMBROKE GARDEN CENTRE
Slade Cross, Cosheston, Pembroke Dock
TEL: 01646 622 488

**13** BUSH SCHOOL CASH & CARRY
NURSERY
Bush Hill, Pembroke
TEL: 01646 681 780

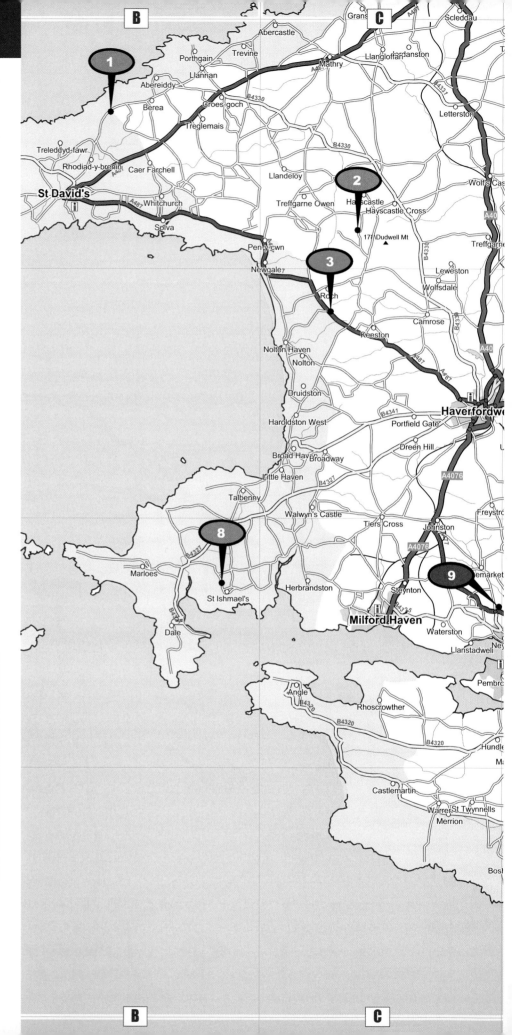

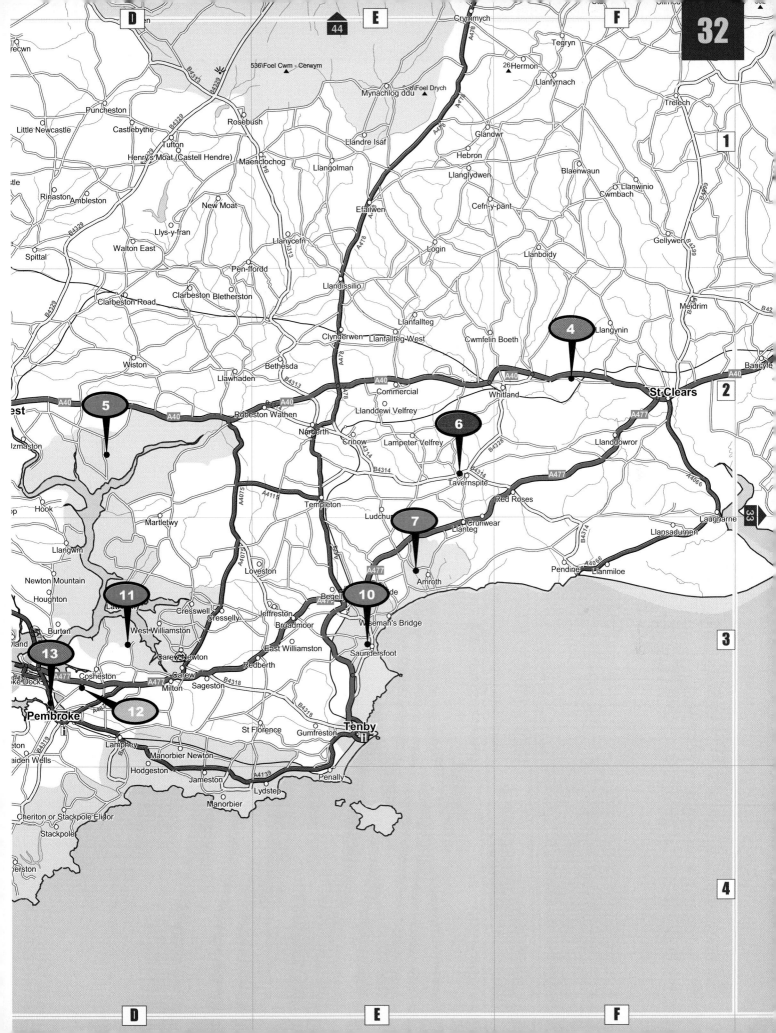

# SOUTH WALES

**1** **CILWERN PLANTS**
Cilwern, Talley, Llandeilo
**TEL:** 01558 685 526

**2** **ALLTYFERIN NURSERY**
Nantgaredig, Carmarthen
**TEL:** 01267 290 367

---

**3** **ABERGLASNEY GARDENS**
Llangathen, Carmarthen, Carmarthenshire, SA32 8QH.
**TEL:** 01558 668 998
**EMAIL:** info@aberglasney.org.uk
**WEB:** www.aberglasney.org.uk

*Set in the Tywi Valley, the gardens have first class horticultural qualities and a mysterious history, destined to become one of the most fascinating gardens in the UK.*
**OPEN:** Apr-Oct: 10-6 (last admission 5). Nov-Dec: Mon-Fri & 1st Sun of month, 10.30-3.
**ENTRY COSTS:** £5, Child: £2.50 Under 5s Free, OAPs: £4, Family: £12.
**SPECIALITIES:** Walled garden, Woodland plants, Exotic plants, Hardy plants, Lilies.
**FACILITIES:** Toilets, Credit cards, Wheelchair access, Restaurant, Own gift tokens, Pushchair friendly.

---

**4** **WYEVALE GARDEN CENTRE**
Myrtle Hill, Pensam, Carmarthen
**TEL:** 01267 221 363

**5** **NATIONAL BOTANIC GARDENS OF WALES**
Middleton Hall, Llanarthne
**TEL:** 01558 668 768

**6** **PONTARDDULAIS GARDEN CENTRE**
Alltygraban Road, Pontarddulais, Swansea
**TEL:** 01792 882 561

**7** **BRYNCOCH NURSERY**
The Beaches, Bryncoch
**TEL:** 01792 812 175

**8** **ROSE VILLA NURSERY**
43 Cwmrhydyceirw Road, Morriston, Swansea
**TEL:** 01792 772 602

**9** **WYEVALE GARDEN CENTRE**
Bynea, Llanelli
**TEL:** 01554 772 189

**10** **BETTS NURSERIES**
Cadoxton Road, Neath
**TEL:** 01639 632 746

**11** **WYEVALE GARDEN CENTRE**
Enterprise Park, Llansamlet, Swansea
**TEL:** 01792 310 052

**12** **FFORESTMILL GARDEN CENTRE**
Pontardulais Road, Fforestfach, Swansea
**TEL:** 01792 580 005

**13** **SWANSEA PLANTASIA**
Parc Tawe, Swansea
**TEL:** 01792 474 555

**14** **SINGLETON BOTANIC GARDENS**
Singleton Park, Swansea
**TEL:** 01792 302 420

**15** **BLACKHILLS NURSERIES**
Blackhills Lane, Fairwood, Swansea
**TEL:** 01792 280 520

**16** **CLYNE GARDENS**
Mill Lane, Blackpill, Swansea
**TEL:** 01792 401 737

**17** **GOWER GARDEN CENTRE**
Nicholston, Gower, Swansea
**TEL:** 01792 371 615

**18** **CASH HARDWARE STORES**
13-15 Newton Road, Mumbles, Swansea
**TEL:** 01792 368 187

Daisy

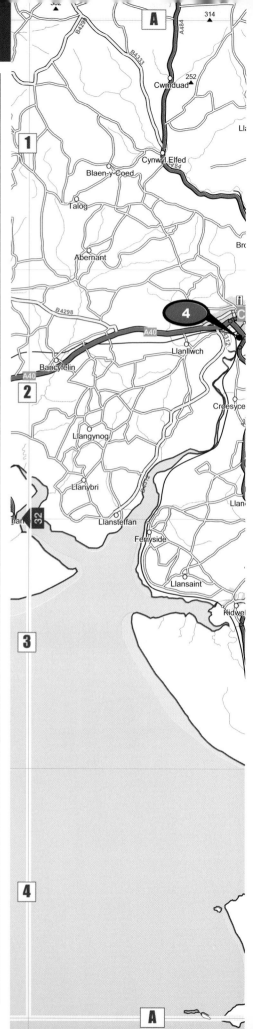

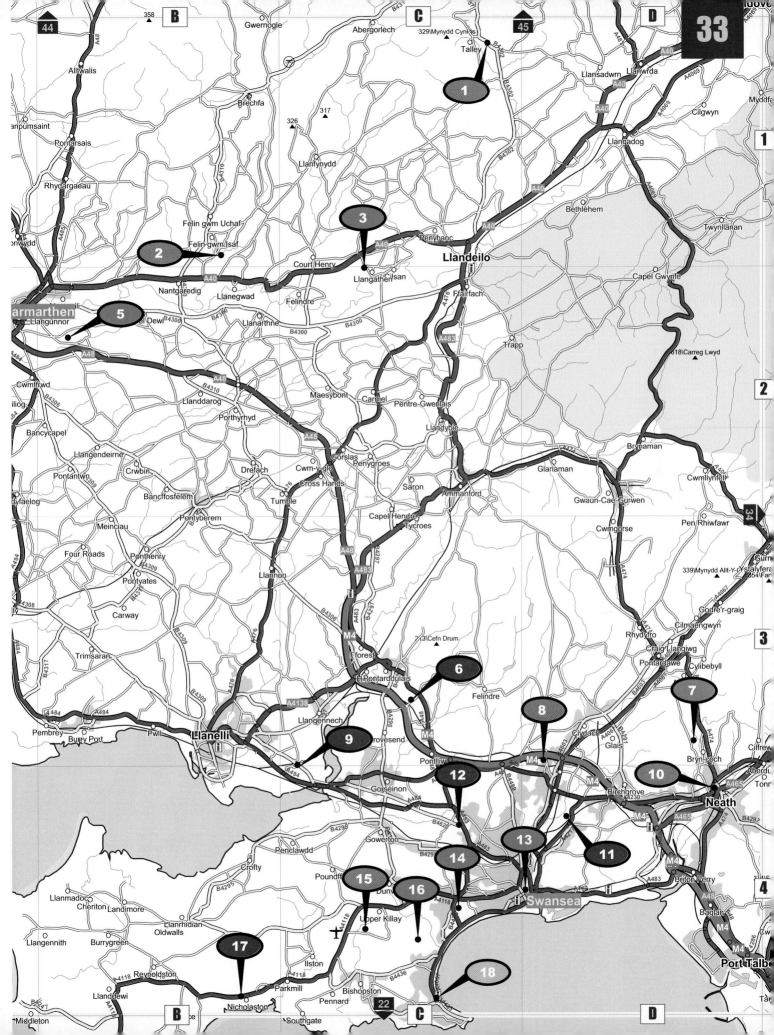

# SOUTH WALES

**1**   **HERBS AT MYDDFAI**
Beiliglas, Myddfai, Llandovery
**Tel:** 01550 720 494

**2**   **THE GARDEN CENTRE**
53 High Street, Brecon
**Tel:** 01874 625 913

**3**   **TRETOWER COURT**
Tretower, Crickhowell
**Tel:** 01874 730 279

**4**   **RED CASTLE NURSERIES**
Cross Ash, Abergavenny
**Tel:** 01873 821 232

**5**   **WOODLANDS SUPPLIES & SERVICES**
The Gardeners Garden Centre, Brooklands,
Abergavenny
**Tel:** 01873 855 431

**6**   **EVESHAM GARDENS**
Llanfoist, Abergavenny
**Tel:** 01873 853 839

**7**   **CORNER SHOP GARDEN CENTRE**
1 Church Crescent, Beaufort, Ebbw Vale
**Tel:** 01495 303 951

**8**   **PENPERGWM PLANTS**
Penpergwm Lodge, Abergavenny
**Tel:** 01873 840 422

**9**   **WILLOWS GARDEN CENTRE**
The Willows, Abercarnaid Ind Est, Merthyr Tydfil
**Tel:** 01685 384 415

**10**   **THE SECRET GARDEN**
Pentwyn Farm, Mamhilad, Pontypool
**Tel:** 01495 785 237

**11**   **GORDON'S NURSERY**
1 Cefnpennar Cottages, Cefnpennar, Mountain Ash
**Tel:** 01443 474 593

**12**   **SUNNINGDALE GARDEN CENTRE**
St Davids Wood, Woodfieldside, Blackwood
**Tel:** 01495 228 015

**13**   **PUGHS GARDEN CENTRE**
Treherbert Road Nursery, Croesyceiliog, Cwmbran
**Tel:** 01633 484 004

**14**   **WOODFIELDS PLANT & NURSERY CENTRE**
Derwen Deg, Twyn Road, Hengoed
**Tel:** 01443 812 773

**15**   **AQUAJARDIN**
Hurrans Garden Centre, Catsash Road, Newport
**Tel:** 01633 413 587

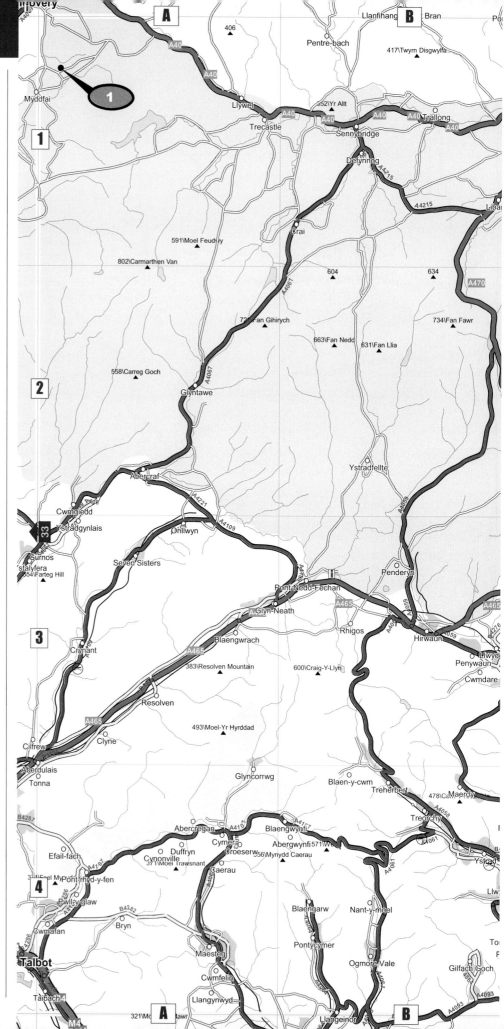

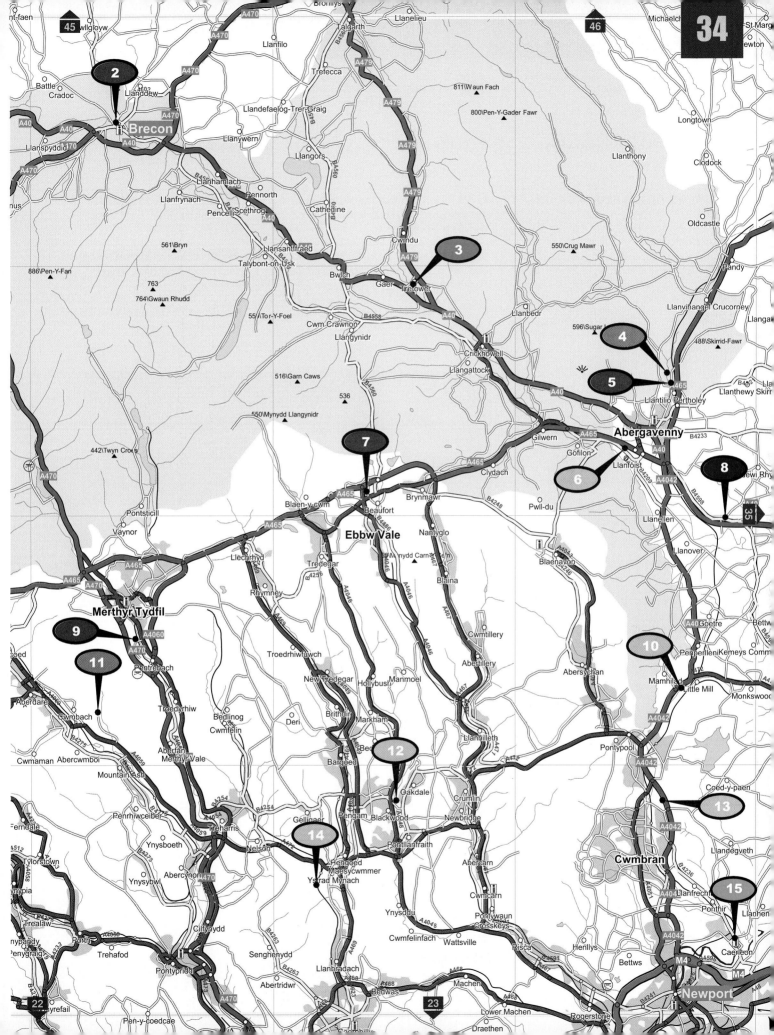

# GLOUCS · HEREFORD · S WALES

○ GARDEN
○ GARDEN CENTRE
● GARDEN & NURSERY
○ NURSERY
○ NURSERY & GARDEN CENTRE
○ WATER GARDEN SPECIALIST

**1 ABBEY DORE GARDEN**
Abbey Dore, Hereford
**TEL:** 01981 240 419

**2 HOW CAPLE COURT GARDENS**
How Caple, Hereford
**TEL:** 01989 740 626

**3 PENGETHLEY NURSERY & GARDEN CENTRE**
Peterstowe, Harewood End
**TEL:** 01989 730 284

**4 GREEN'S LEAVES**
Leba Orchard, Lea Bailey, Ross on Wye
**TEL:** 01989 750 303

**5 SPLENDOURS OF THE ORIENT**
Jubilee Park, Symonds Yat West, Herefordshire, HR9 6DA.
**TEL:** 01600 890 668
**EMAIL:** info@orientalsplendour.co.uk
**WEB:** www.orientalsplendour.co.uk
*We welcome visitors of all ages to browse round our unique oriental centre, garden, fairytaleland with butterflies, birds and plants and Thimbles Cafe and chocolate shop.*
**OPEN:** Jan-Mar: 10-4. Apr-Sep: 10-6. Oct-Dec: 10-5.
**ENTRY COSTS:** Oriental Garden: Free. Fairytaleland: £2.
**SPECIALITIES:** Water features, Ornaments, Bamboos, Garden & conservatory furniture.
**FACILITIES:** Child area, Coffee shop, Pushchair friendly, Wheelchair access, Credit cards, Gift shop, Toilets.

**6 39 STEPS**
Grove Cottage, Forge Hill, Lydbrook
**TEL:** 01594 860 544

**7 PYGMY PINETUM NURSERIES**
Cannop Cross Roads, Speech House Road, Coleford
**TEL:** 01594 833 398

**8 MILLBROOK NURSERY & GARDEN CENTRE**
Mitchel Troy, Monmouth
**TEL:** 01600 713 770

**9 COLEFORD GARDEN CENTRE**
Lambsquay Road, Milkwall, Coleford
**TEL:** 01594 832 700

**10 RAGLAN GARDEN CENTRE**
Old Abergavenny Road, Usk
**TEL:** 01291 690 751

**11 COINROS NURSERY**
Clements End, Coleford
**TEL:** 01594 562 610

**12 UNUSUAL PLANTS**
Mork Road, St Briavels, Lydney
**TEL:** 01594 530 561

**13 LYDNEY GARDEN & AQUATIC CENTRE**
15 High Street, Lydney
**TEL:** 01594 842 121

**14 WYE VALLEY PLANTS**
The Nurtons, Tintern, Chepstow
**TEL:** 01291 689 253

**15 USK LEIRE**
The Nurseries, Llanbadoc, Usk
**TEL:** 01291 673 603

**16 MOUNT PLEASANT NURSERY**
Mount Pleasant Farm, Rockhampton, Berkeley
**TEL:** 01454 260 348

**17 EASTWOOD GARDEN PLANT CENTRE**
The Gardens, Eastwood Park, Wotton under Edge
**TEL:** 01454 260 288

**18 PARKWALL GARDEN CENTRE**
Crick, Near Chepstow, Caldicot
**TEL:** 01291 424 585

**19 PENHOW NURSERIES**
St Brides Netherwent, Penhow
**TEL:** 01633 400 419

**20 SUNNYSIDE NURSERIES**
Chepstow Road, Langstone, Newport
**TEL:** 01633 412 411

**21 THORNBURY GARDEN SHOP**
The Courtyard, High Street, Bristol
**TEL:** 01454 419 350

**22 HURRANS GARDEN CENTRE**
Catsash Road, Langstone, Newport
**TEL:** 01633 413 355

**23 WYEVALE GARDEN CENTRE**
Milbury Heath, Wotton under Edge
**TEL:** 01454 412 247

Anemone

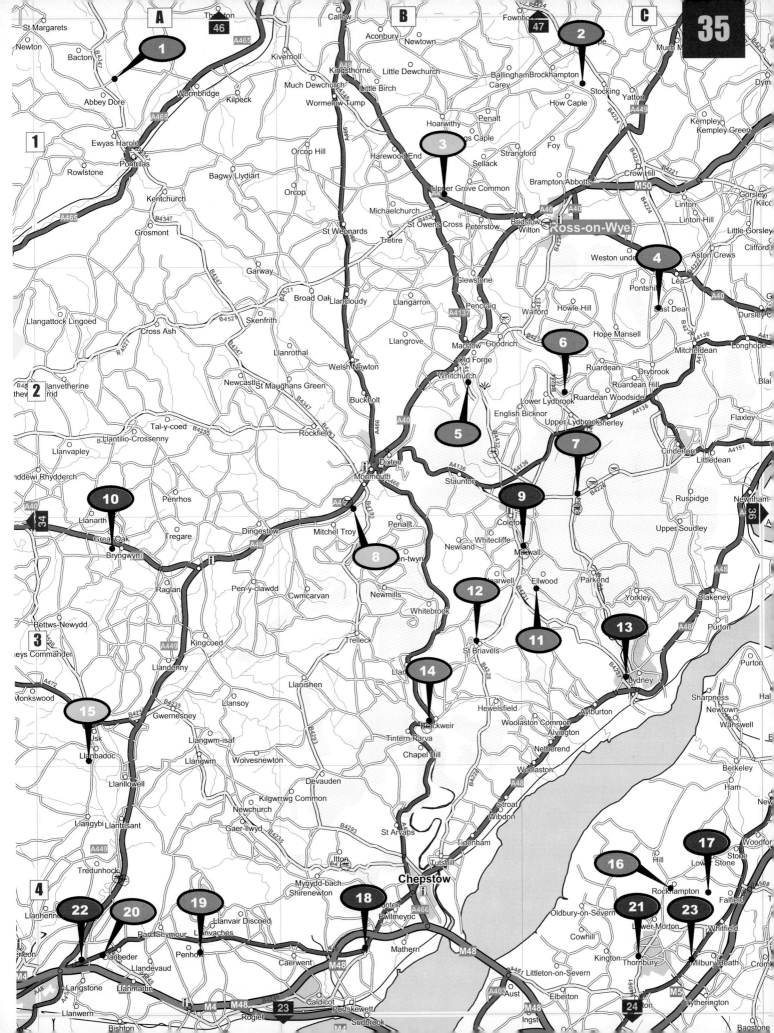

GARDEN
GARDEN CENTRE
GARDEN & NURSERY

NURSERY
NURSERY & GARDEN CENTRE
WATER GARDEN SPECIALIST

**1 CHRIS PATTINSON**
Brookend, Pendock
TEL: 01531 650 480

**2 TINPENNY PLANTS**
Tinpenny Farm, Fiddington, Tewkesbury
TEL: 01684 292 668

**3 NOMADS FUCHSIAS & PELARGONIUM SPECIALISTS**
West Warren Farm, Cheltenham
TEL: 01242 604 304

**4 GOTHERINGTON NURSERIES**
Gretton Road, Gotherington, Cheltenham
TEL: 01242 676 722

**5 HOO HOUSE NURSERY**
Hoo House, Gloucester Road, Tewkesbury
TEL: 01684 293 389

**6 THE GARDEN NURSERY**
Evesham Road, Bishops Cleeve, Cheltenham
TEL: 01242 674 695

**7 SUDELEY CASTLE & GARDENS**
Winchcombe, Cheltenham
TEL: 01242 602 308

**8 BONSAI WORLD OF CHELTENHAM**
Two Hedges Road, Woodmancote, Cheltenham
TEL: 01242 674 389

**9 ROSES COUNTRY FAYRE**
52 Ledbury Road, Newent
TEL: 01531 821 242

**10 STANBORO LANE NURSERIES**
Stanboro Road, Tewesbury, Cheltenham
TEL: 01242 681 115

**11 JARDINERIE**
Evesham Road, Cheltenham
TEL: 01242 672 560 / 672 153

**12 THUYA ALPINE NURSERY**
Glebelands, Gloucester Road, Hartpury
TEL: 01452 700 548

**13 BROOK FARM PLANTS**
Boulsdon Lane, Newent
TEL: 01531 822 534

**14 BEDDING PLANT CENTRE**
Chelt Nurseries, Tewksbury Road, Cheltenham
TEL: 01242 680 366

**15 BARBRIDGE NURSERIES**
Tewksbury Road, Cheltenham
TEL: 01242 680 277

**16 BARBERS BRIDGE NURSERIES**
Tibberton Corner, Barbers Bridge, Gloucester
TEL: 01452 790 443

**17 HURRANS GARDEN CENTRE**
Cheltenham Road East, Churchdown, Gloucester
TEL: 01452 712 232

**18 TELLING & COATES**
64a Church Street, Charlton Kings, Cheltenham
TEL: 01242 514 472

**19 VALLEY ROUNDABOUT NURSERIES**
Badgeworth Road, Cheltenham
TEL: 01452 713 102

**20 CHELTENHAM POT & PLANT CENTRE**
Kidnappers Lane, Leckhampton, Cheltenham
TEL: 01242 513 401

**21 GLEBE GARDEN NURSERY**
Kidnappers Lane, Leckhampton, Cheltenham
TEL: 01242 521 001

**22 THE COUNTRY GARDEN CENTRE**
Ross Road, Huntley, Gloucester
TEL: 01452 830 229

**23 DAWN NURSERIES**
Main Road, Shurdington, Cheltenham
TEL: 01242 862 877

**24 FAIRVIEW NURSERY**
Chapel Lane, Churcham, Gloucester
TEL: 01452 750 436

**25 BARTON HARDWARE & GARDEN SHOP**
217 Barton Street, Gloucester
TEL: 01452 524 601

**26 WYEVALE GARDEN CENTRE**
Shurdington Road, Brockworth
TEL: 01452 862 334

**27 SHURDINGTON NURSERIES**
Whitelands Lane, Shurdington, Cheltenham
TEL: 01242 863 738

**28 QUEDGELEY GARDEN CENTRE**
73 Bristol Road, Quedgeley
TEL: 01452 500 576

**29 WESTBURY COURT GARDEN, NATIONAL TRUST**
Westbury Court, Westbury-on-Severn
TEL: 01452 760 461

**30 JARDINERIE**
Bath Road, Haresfield, Gloucester
TEL: 01452 721 081

**31 SPOONBED NURSERY**
Rococo Garden, Painswick
TEL: 01452 814 242

**32 PAINSWICK ROCOCO GARDEN**
Painswick House, Painswick
TEL: 01452 813 204

**33 MISERDEN NURSERY**
Miserden, Stroud
TEL: 01285 821 638

**34 HIGHFIELD NURSERIES**
School Lane, Whitminster
TEL: 01452 741 444

**35 WORLD OF WATER**
Highfield Garden Centre, Whitminster
TEL: 01452 741 414

**36 HIGHFIELD GARDEN CENTRE**
Bristol Road, Whitminster, Gloucester
TEL: 01452 740 266

**37 WYEVALE GARDEN CENTRE**
Ebley Road, Stonehouse, Stroud
TEL: 01453 823 846

**38 SPINNYWELL NURSERY**
Waterlane, Oakridge, Bisley
TEL: 01452 770 092

**39 W G GEISSLER**
Winsford, Kingston Road, Slimbridge
TEL: 01453 890 340

**40 SELSLEY HERB FARM**
Waterlane, Selsley, Stroud
TEL: 01453 766 682

**41 WYEVALE GARDEN CENTRE**
Waterside Garden Centre, Avening Road, Nailsworth
TEL: 01453 833 989

**42 HUNTS COURT**
North Nibley, Dursley
TEL: 01453 547 440

**43 MARSHALL'S MALMAISON**
4 The Damsells, Tetbury
TEL: 01666 502 589

**44 WESTONBIRT ARBORETUM PLANT CENTRE**
Westonbirt Arboretum, Westonbirt, Tetbury
TEL: 01666 880 544

**45 ARCHFIELD NURSERY**
Kingswood, Wotton under Edge
TEL: 01454 294 216

**46 NURDENS GARDEN CENTRE**
Crudwell Road, Malmesbury
TEL: 01666 822 809

Daisy

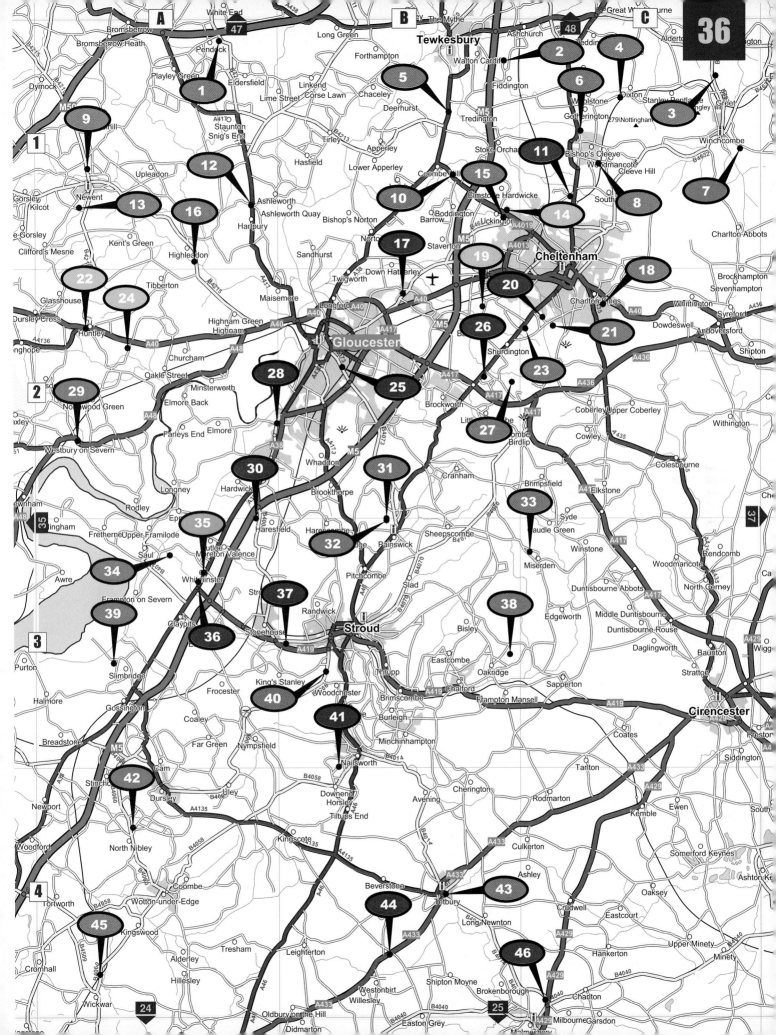

**1  BATSFORD GARDEN CENTRE**
Batsford, Moreton in Marsh
TEL: 01386 700 409

**2  TODDINGTON GARDEN CENTRE**
Toddington Railway Yard, Toddington, Cheltenham
TEL: 01242 621 314

**3  FOSSEWAY FARM NURSERY**
Stow Road, Moreton in Marsh
TEL: 01608 651 757

**4  WYATTS**
Hillbarn Farm, Great Rollright, Chipping Norton
TEL: 01608 684 990

**5  COMPTON LANE NURSERIES**
Little Compton, Moreton in Marsh
TEL: 01608 674 578

**6  APPLEGARTH NURSERIES**
Hardy Plant Centre, Banbury Road, Chipping Norton
TEL: 01608 641 642

**7  A R PONTIN**
Lidstone Nurseries, Lidstone Chipping Norton
TEL: 01608 677 382

**8  ROUSHAM HOUSE**
Steeple Aston, Bicester
TEL: 01869 347 110

**9  PEBBLY HILL FARM NURSERY**
Icomb Road, Bledington, Chipping Norton
TEL: 01608 659 851

**10  COTSWOLD GARDEN CENTRE & FARMSHOP**
Wyck Hill, Stow-on-the-Wold
TEL: 01451 830 216

**11  Q GARDEN COMPANY**
Wyck Hill, Stow-on-the-Wold
TEL: 01451 830 216

**12  BLENHEIM PALACE**
Woodstock, Oxford
TEL: 01993 811 325

**13  HILLTOP GARDEN CENTRE**
Witney Road, Ramsden, Chipping Norton
TEL: 01993 868 403

**14  SHERBOURNE GARDENS**
Sherbourne, Cheltenham
TEL: 01451 844 522

**15  FIELDFARE NURSERIES & GARDEN CENTRE**
Church Road, Church Hanborough
TEL: 01993 882 663

**16  FREELAND NURSERIES**
Wroslyn Road, Freeland, Witney
TEL: 01993 881 430

**17  THE BURFORD GARDEN COMPANY**
Shilton Road, Burford
TEL: 01993 823 117

**18  WHITEHILL FARM NURSERY**
Whitehill Farm, Burford
TEL: 01993 823 218

**19  CASSSINGTON NURSERIES**
Yarnton Road, Cassington, Witney
TEL: 01865 882 550

**20  A G O AQUATICS**
Unit 3, The Old Saw Mill, Cirencester
TEL: 01285 750 307

---

**21  BARNSLEY HOUSE GARDEN**
Barnsley House, Barnsley, Cirencester,
Gloucestershire, GL7 5EE.
TEL: 01285 740 561
EMAIL: cverey@barnsleyhouse.freeserve.co.uk
WEB: www.opengarden.co.uk
*Family home of the late Rosemary Verey. Enjoy your stay and visit amongst blossoms and bulbs, mixed beds, features, lawns and wilderness.*
OPEN: Feb-Dec: Mon, Wed-Sat 10-5.30.
ENTRY COSTS: £4, Child: Free, OAPs: £3.50.
SPECIALITIES: Bedding plants, Climbers, Garden & conservatory furniture, Hardy plants, Themed gardens.
FACILITIES: Coffee shop, Gift shop, Sell plants, Toilets, Wheelchair access.

---

**22  LECHLADE GARDEN CENTRE**
Fairford Road, Warrens Cross, Lechlade
TEL: 01367 252 372

**23  FROSTS MILLETS FARM**
Milletts Farm Gdn Centre, Kingston Road, Abingdon
TEL: 01865 391 923

**24  MARCHAM PLANTS**
Hyde Farm Nurseries, Abingdon Road, Abingdon
TEL: 01865 391 054

**25  BUSCOT PARK**
Faringdon
TEL: 01367 240 786

**26  STEVENTON ROAD NURSERY**
Steventon Road, East Hanney, Wantage
TEL: 01235 868 828

**27  RICHARD MATHEWS**
7 Harwell Road, Sutton Courtenay, Abingdon
TEL: 01235 847 194

**28  SEVEN ACRES NURSERY**
Faringdon Road, Stanford in the Vale, Faringdon
TEL: 01367 718 266

**29  BROADSTONE NURSERIES**
13 The Nursery, High Street, Abingdon
TEL: 01235 847 557

**30  WYEVALE GARDEN CENTRE**
Hyde Road, Stratton St Margaret, Swindon
TEL: 01793 822 224

**31  CHARLTON PARK GARDEN CENTRE**
Charlton Road, Wantage
TEL: 01235 772 700

**32  OLD CHURCH HOUSE**
2 Priory Road, Wantage
TEL: 01235 762 785

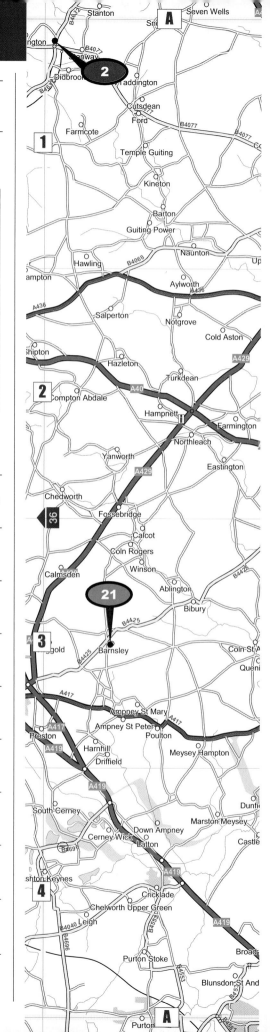

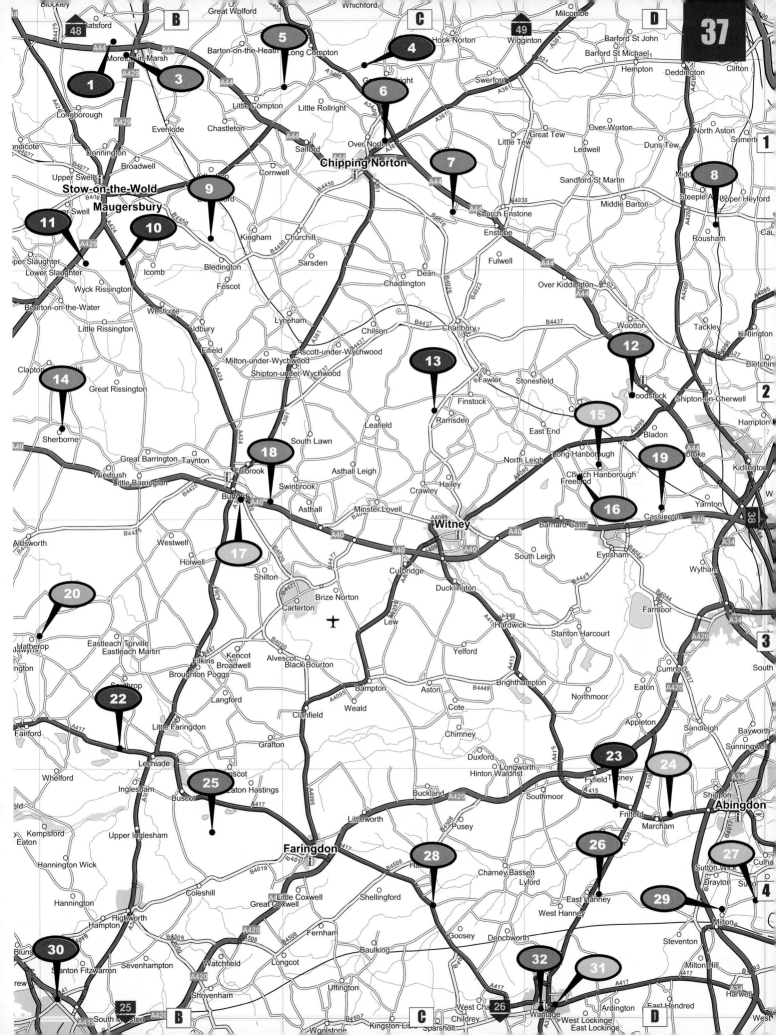

- GARDEN
- GARDEN CENTRE
- GARDEN & NURSERY
- NURSERY
- NURSERY & GARDEN CENTRE
- WATER GARDEN SPECIALIST

**1  BUCKINGHAM NURSERIES & GARDEN CENTRE**
Tingewick Road, Buckingham
TEL: 0845 345 6269

**2  BARR'S NURSERIES**
Bletchley Road, Thornborough, Buckingham
TEL: 01280 816 855

**3  PRESTON BISSETT NURSERIES & COUNTRY SHOP**
Bushey Lane, Preston Bissett
TEL: 01280 848 038

**4  FOUR ACRE NURSERY**
Station Road, Mursley, Milton Keynes
TEL: 01296 720 791

**5  BLOOMS OF BICESTER**
Oxford Road, Bicester
TEL: 01869 242 248

**6  PLANTASIA**
Bicester Garden Centre, Oxford Road, Bicester
TEL: 01869 325 455

**7  WORLD OF WATER**
Bicester Garden Centre, Oxford Road, Bicester
TEL: 01869 322 489

**8  BICESTER GARDEN & PET CENTRE**
Oxford Road, Bicester
TEL: 01869 242 248

**9  WADDESDON MANOR, NATIONAL TRUST**
Aylesbury
TEL: 01296 651 226

**10  BERNWODE PLANTS**
Kingswood Lane, Ludgershall, Aylesbury
TEL: 01844 237 415

**11  SUMMERTOWN GARDEN CENTRE**
200-202 Banbury Road, Oxford
TEL: 01865 554 956

**12  S WEST & SONS**
74 Windmill Road, Oxford
TEL: 01865 763 556

**13  WATERPERRY GARDENS**
Wheatley, Oxford
TEL: 01844 339 226

**14  OXFORD BOTANIC GARDENS**
Rose Lane, Oxford
TEL: 01865 276 920

**15  LOWER ICKNIELD FARM NURSERIES**
Lower Icknield Way, Great Kimble, Aylesbury
TEL: 01844 343 436

**16  WYEVALE GARDEN CENTRE**
57 London Road, Wheatley, Oxford
TEL: 01865 873 057

**17  MILL VIEW NURSERY**
Ladder Hill, Wheatley, Oxford
TEL: 01865 873 488

**18  ASKETT NURSERIES**
Aylesbury Road, Askett, Princes Risborough
TEL: 01844 274 635

**19  LASHLAKE NURSERIES**
Chinnor Road, Towersey, Thame
TEL: 01844 212 392

**20  WYEVALE GARDEN CENTRE**
Southern by-pass, South Hinksey, Oxford
TEL: 01865 326 066

**21  BOUNDRY FARM SHOP AND NURSERY**
Wheatley Road, Garsington, Oxford
TEL: 01865 361 311

**22  Q GARDEN COMPANY**
Thame Road, Chinnor
TEL: 01844 353 540

**23  NOTCUTTS GARDEN CENTRE**
Nuneham Courtenay, Oxford
TEL: 01865 343 454

**24  HARCOURT ARBORETUM**
Oxford Lodge, Peacock Gate, Nuneham Courtenay
TEL: 01865 343 501

**25  NEWINGTON NURSERIES**
Newington, Wallingford
TEL: 01865 400 533

**26  THE WALLED GARDEN**
2 Castle Road, Shirburn, Watlington
TEL: 01491 612 882

**27  JARDINERIE**
Studley Green, Stokenchurch, High Wycombe
TEL: 01494 483 761

**28  WEST WYCOMBE GARDEN CENTRE**
Chorley Road, West Wycombe, High Wycombe
TEL: 01494 438 635

**29  WEST WYCOMBE PARK, NATIONAL TRUST**
West Wycombe
TEL: 01628 488 675

**30  CUCKOO PEN NURSERY**
St. Helen's Avenue, Benson, Wellingborough
TEL: 01491 835 971

**31  SHEARDS GARDEN CENTRE**
High Road, Brightwell-Cum-Sotwell, Wallingford
TEL: 01491 836 277

**32  NOTCUTTS GARDEN CENTRE**
Clay Lane, Booker, Near Marlow
TEL: 01494 532 532

**33  SPRINGLEA NURSERY**
Springlea, Seymour Plain, Marlow
TEL: 01628 473 366

Roses

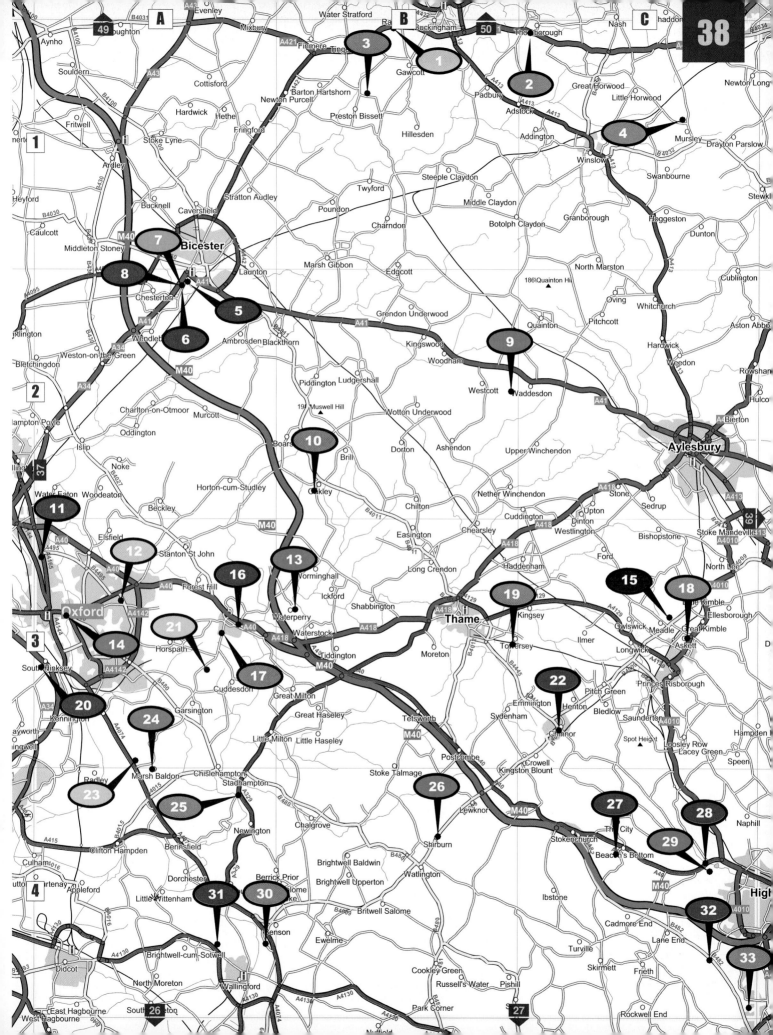

**1 FLITTVALE GARDEN CENTRE & NURSERY**
Flitwich Road, Westoning  TEL: 01525 712 484

**2 HILLCREST NURSERY**
Bedford Road, Holwell, Hitchin TEL: 01462 712 636

**3 CHILTERN AQUATICS**
Westoning Road, Harlington  TEL: 01525 873 070

**4 POPLARS NURSERY GARDEN CENTRE**
Harlington Road, Toddington, Dunstable
TEL: 01525 872 017

**5 GROVE ROAD GARDEN CENTRE**
20 Grove Road, Hitchin  TEL: 01462 451 519

**6 PAUL BROMFIELD AQUATICS**
Maydencroft Lane, Gosmore, Hitchin
TEL: 01462 457 399

**7 LEIGHTON BUZZARD GARDEN CENTRE**
Hockliffe Rd, Leighton Buzzard TEL: 01525 854 938

**8 ASCOTT, NATIONAL TRUST**
Wing, Leighton Buzzard  TEL: 01296 688 242

**9 GARDEN SCENE**
The Rye, Eaton Bray, Dunstable TEL: 01525 220 104

**10 STOCKWOOD CRAFT MUSEUM & GARDENS**
Stockwood Park, Farley Hill, Luton
TEL: 01582 738 714

**11 WYEVALE GARDEN CENTRE**
Dunstable Rd, Caddington, Luton TEL: 01582 457 313

**12 SHAW'S CORNER, NATIONAL TRUST**
Ayot St Lawrence, Welwyn  TEL: 01438 820 307

**13 L W PLANTS**
23 Wroxham Way, Harpenden  TEL: 01582 768 467

**14 STUDHAM NURSERY**
Clements End Road, Studham, Dunstable
TEL: 01582 872 958

**15 TOWNSEND NURSERY**
96 Townsend Lane, Harpenden  TEL: 01582 713 083

**16 HARPENDEN GARDEN CENTRE**
9 Amenbury Lane, Harpenden  TEL: 01582 764 679

**17 GODLY'S ROSES**
Redding Lane, Redbourn, St Albans
TEL: 01582 792 255

**18 FOUR ACRES NURSERY**
Hemel Hempstead Road, Dagnall, Berkhamsted
TEL: 01442 842 838

**19 WYEVALE GARDEN CENTRE**
Bulbourne Road, Tring  TEL: 01442 891 393

**20 WYEVALE GARDEN CENTRE**
Broadwater Gdn Centre, Gt. Gaddesden, Hemel H'stead
TEL: 01442 231 284

**21 EMERALD VALLEY NURSERY**
Thrift Cottage, Park Road, Tring TEL: 01442 891 213

**22 CARPENTER'S NURSERY**
106 St Albans Road, Sandridge, St Albans
TEL: 01727 853 340

**23 WYEVALE GARDEN CENTRE**
Aylesbury Road, Wendover, Aylesbury
TEL: 01296 623 116

**24 HILLIER GARDEN CENTRE**
Leighton Buzzard Road, Piccotts End, Hemel H'stead
TEL: 01442 242 637

**25 LITTLE HEATH FARM NURSERY**
Little Heath Lane, Potten End, Berkhamsted
TEL: 01442 864 951

**26 CAPITAL GARDENS LTD**
The Old Iron Works, High Street, Berkhamsted
TEL: 01442 863 159

**27 NOTCUTTS GARDEN CENTRE**
Hatfield Road, Smallford, St Albans
TEL: 01727 853 224

**28 SEEDS BY SIZE**
45 Crouchfield, Boxmoor, Hemel Hempstead
TEL: 01442 251 458

**29 TUNFIELD NURSERY**
Hogg Lane, Ashley Green, Chesham
TEL: 01442 865 552

**30 SHEPHERD NURSERY**
Chartridge, Chesham  TEL: 01494 775 688

**31 AYLETT NURSERIES**
North Orbital Road, London Colney, St Albans
TEL: 01727 822 255

**32 WYEVALE GARDEN CENTRE**
North Orbital Road, St Albans  TEL: 01727 825 815

---

**33 GARDENS OF THE ROSE**
Royal National Rose Society, Chiswell Green,
St Albans, Hertfordshire, AL2 3NR.
TEL: 01727 850 461
EMAIL: mail@rnrs.org.uk
WEB: www.roses.co.uk
*Famous rose garden with over 30,000 roses both old and new. Landscaped garden setting with over 100 different varieties of clematis along with other companion planting.*
OPEN: Jun 1-Sep 29: Mon-Sat 9-5, Sun & BH 10-6.
ENTRY COSTS: £4, Child: £1.50 (5-15), OAPs: £3.50.
SPECIALITIES: Roses, Clematis.
FACILITIES: Coffee shop, Credit cards, Dogs allowed, Gift shop, Sell plants, Toilets, Wheelchair access, Pushchair friendly.

---

**34 BURSTON ROSE & GARDEN CENTRE LTD**
North Orbital Road, Chiswell Green, St Albans
TEL: 01727 832 444

**35 HERTFORDSHIRE FISHERIES**
Burston Nurseries, North Orbital Road, St. Albans
TEL: 01727 833 960

**36 WYEVALE GARDEN CENTRE**
Tower Hill, Chipperfield  TEL: 01442 834 364

**37 GARDEN SCENE**
Chapelcraft, Chipperfield, Kings Langley
TEL: 01923 262 492

**38 SOUTH HEATH GARDEN CENTRE & NURSERY LTD (B N SPENCER)**
Meadow Lane, South Heath, Great Missenden
TEL: 01494 863 269

**39 SHENLEY PARK**
Radlett Lane, Radlett  TEL: 01923 852 629

**40 THE GARDEN NURSERY**
39 London Rd, Shenley, Radlett TEL: 01923 854 955

**41 HYRONS TREES**
The Green, Sarratt, Rickmansworth
TEL: 01923 263 000

**42 THE CONIFER NURSERY**
Hare Lane Nursery, Little Kingshill, Great Missenden
TEL: 01494 862 086

**43 CHESLYN HOUSE**
54 Nascot Wood Rd, Watford  TEL: 01923 235 946

**44 PLANTS DIRECT**
Roundbush, Aldenham, Watford TEL: 01923 850 809

**45 CHANDLERS CROSS GARDEN CENTRE**
Firtree Hill, Chandlers Cross, Rickmansworth
TEL: 01923 261 219

**46 BLACKETTS NURSERIES**
Rousebarn Lane, Chandlers Cross, Rickmansworth
TEL: 01923 265 743

**47 CHENIES AQUATICS**
The Van Hage Garden Company, Chenies, Rickmansworth
TEL: 01494 764 549

**48 THE VAN HAGE GARDEN COMPANY**
Chenies, Rickmansworth  TEL: 01494 764 545

**49 D & J NURSERIES**
The Green, Croxley Green, Rickmansworth
TEL: 01923 779 799

**50 HUGHENDEN MANOR, NATIONAL TRUST**
High Wycombe  TEL: 01494 755 573

**51 ROWAN NURSERIES GARDEN CENTRE**
Gorelands Lane, Chalfont St Giles TEL: 01494 872 335

**52 FIELD GROVE NURSERY**
Hammersley Lane, Penn, High Wycombe
TEL: 01494 816 754

**53 HAZELTONE GARDENS**
Sandy Lane, Northwood  TEL: 020 8421 5977

**54 KILN NURSERIES**
Common Road, Stanmore  TEL: 020 8954 4628

**55 CARPENDERS PARK NURSERY**
Little Oxhey Lane, Watford  TEL: 020 8420 1959

**56 JACQUES ARMAND**
The Nurseries, Clamp Hill, Stanmore
TEL: 020 8420 7110

**57 WYEVALE GARDEN CENTRE**
Headstone Lane, Harrow  TEL: 020 8428 3408

**58 WYEVALE GARDEN CENTRE**
London Road, Beaconsfield  TEL: 01494 672 522

**59 HASTE HILL NURSERIES**
Fore Street, Eastcote, Pinner  TEL: 01895 674 896

**60 DENHAM COURT NURSERY**
Denham Court Drive, Denham  TEL: 01895 832 035

**61 WYEVALE GARDEN CENTRE**
Pump Lane South, Little Marlow, Marlow
TEL: 01628 482 716

**62 PLATATION GARDEN CENTRE**
Kenton Road, Harrow  TEL: 020 8423 2073

**63 EASTCOTE GARDEN CENTRE**
216 Field End Rd, Eastcote, Pinner TEL: 020 8868 9911

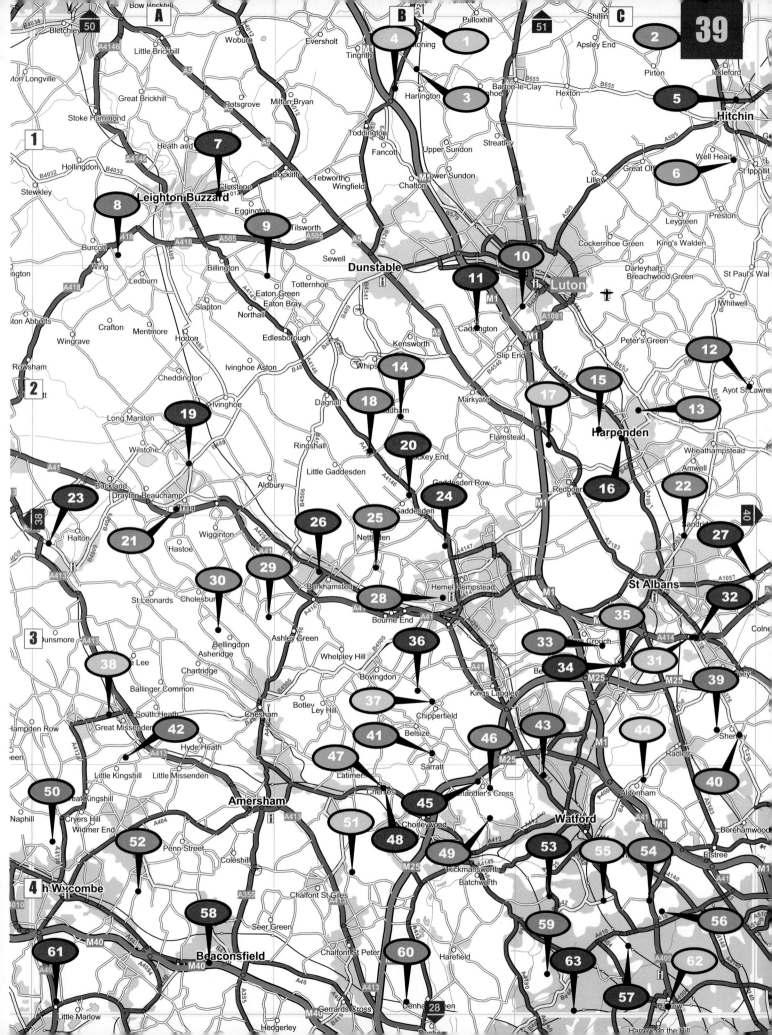

**1 MILL END NURSERY**
Mill End, Rushden, Buntingford
TEL: 01763 288 434

**2 THE ROSE GARDENS**
Cambridge Road, Hitchin
TEL: 01426 420 402

**3 WYEVALE GARDEN CENTRE**
Cambridge Road, Hitchin
TEL: 01462 434 027

**4 PIONEER NURSERY**
Baldock Lane, Willian, Letchworth
TEL: 01462 675 858

**5 STEVENAGE GARDEN CENTRE**
North Road, Stevenage
TEL: 01438 312 660

**6 KNEBWORTH HOUSE AND COUNTRY PARK**
Knebworth Park, Knebworth
TEL: 01438 813 825

**7 THE VAN HAGE GARDEN COMPANY**
Bragbury Lane, Bragbury End, Stevenage
TEL: 01438 811 777

**8 VANSTONE PARK GARDEN CENTRE**
B656 Hitchin Road, Codicote, Hitchin
TEL: 01438 820 412

**9 HOPLEYS PLANTS**
High Street, Much Hadham
TEL: 01279 842 509

**10 WATTON NURSERY**
Ware Road, Hereford
TEL: 01920 830 944

**11 WYEVALE GARDEN CENTRE**
High Street, Codicote
TEL: 01438 820 433

**12 PRIORSWOOD CLEMATIS NURSERY**
Priorswood, Widbury Hill, Ware
TEL: 01920 461 543

**13 THE PET AND GARDEN CENTRE**
5 Howardsgate, Welwyn Garden City
TEL: 01707 320 577

**14 THE VAN HAGE GARDEN COMPANY**
Great Amwell, Ware
TEL: 01920 870 811

**15 RIVERSIDE GARDEN CENTRE**
Lower Hatfield Road, Hertford
TEL: 01992 501 502

**16 THE AQUATIC WAREHOUSE**
Birchall Lane, Colgreen, Hertford
TEL: 01707 391 196

**17 THE GARDEN OUTLET**
Unit 50 (Level 1), The Galleria Shopping Centre, Hatfield
TEL: 01707 272 932

**18 HATFIELD HOUSE**
Hatfield Park, Hatfield
TEL: 01707 262 823

**19 BONNIES OAK GARDEN CENTRE**
Water Lane, Roydon, Harlow
TEL: 01279 792 231

**20 THREE DEE'S NURSERY**
Reeves Lane, Roydon, Harlow
TEL: 01279 793 417

**21 ROYDON HAMLET WATER GARDENS**
Tylers Road, Roydon Hamlet, Harlow
TEL: 01279 792 235

**22 KINGLEA PLANT CENTRE**
Sedge Green, Nazeing, Waltham Abbey
TEL: 01992 470 460

**23 RHODES & ROCKLIFFE**
2 Nursery Road, Nazeing
TEL: 01992 463 693

**24 KINGFISHER NURSERIES & GARDEN CENTRE**
White Stubbs Lane, Bayford, Hertford
TEL: 01992 511 611

**25 HOE LANE NURSERY**
Hoe Lane, Nazeing, Waltham Abbey
TEL: 01992 892 181

**26 BRYNFIELD NURSERY**
610 Goffs Lane, Goffs Oak, Waltham Cross
TEL: 01707 873 311

**27 CROWN HILL NURSERY**
Crown Hill, Upshire, Waltham Abbey
TEL: 01992 700 877

**28 WYEVALE GARDEN CENTRE**
Cattlegate Road, Crews Hill, Enfield
TEL: 020 8367 0422

**29 THE AQUATIC WAREHOUSE**
Culver Nurseries, Cattlegate Road, London
TEL: 020 8363 3600

**30 POTTERS BAR NURSERY**
The Ridgeway, Potters Bar
TEL: 01707 658 444

**31 CULVER GARDEN CENTRE**
Cattlegate Road, Enfield
TEL: 020 8366 0701

**32 SPRINGTIME NURSERIES ENFIELD**
Cattlegate Road, Crews Hill, Enfield
TEL: 020 83679 326

**33 ST SIMON'S NURSERY**
Cattlegate Road, Enfield
TEL: 020 8366 4404

**34 THE CHELSEA GARDENER**
Cattlegate Road, Crews Hill, Enfield
TEL: 020 8367 3377

**35 WOLDENS NURSERIES AND GARDEN CENTRE**
Cattlegate Road, Enfield
TEL: 020 8363 7003

**36 BROWN'S GARDEN CENTRE**
Theobalds Park Road, Crews Hill, Enfield
TEL: 020 8367 1741

**37 SPRING TIME NURSERIES**
Cattlegate Road, Enfield
TEL: 020 8367 9326

**38 CAPEL MANOR**
Bullsmoor Lane, Enfield
TEL: 020 8366 4442

**39 WOODLANDS NURSERY**
Theobalds Park Road, Enfield
TEL: 020 8363 9371

**40 WILDWOODS WATER GARDENS LTD**
Theobalds Park Road, Enfield
TEL: 020 8366 0243

**41 CREWS HILL GARDENING CLUB**
Within Park View Nurseries, Crewes Hill, Enfield
TEL: 020 8367 9406

**42 MYDDELTON HOUSE GARDENS**
Myddelton House, Bulls Cross, Enfield
TEL: 01992 717 711

**43 A J MILLS**
Clock House Nursery, Forty Hill, Enfield
TEL: 020 8363 1016

**44 NORTHFIELD NURSERIES**
Sewardstone Road, Chingford, London
TEL: 020 8529 0367

**45 WYEVALE GARDEN CENTRE**
Dancers Hill Road, Bentley Heath, Barnet
TEL: 020 8440 4734

**46 CHAPELFIELD NURSERY**
Sewardstone Road, Chingford, London
TEL: 020 8529 1840

**47 SANTA MARIA NURSERIES**
Daws Hill, Chingford, London
TEL: 020 8524 0385

**48 FOREST NURSERIES**
Nursery Road, Loughton
TEL: 020 8508 1377

**49 COTTAGE GARDEN NURSERY**
Barnet Road, Arkley, Barnet
TEL: 020 8441 8829

**50 KING EASTON**
Station Road, Winchmore Hill, London
TEL: 020 8886 8783

**51 FINCHLEY NURSERIES**
Burton Hole Lane, Mill Hill, London
TEL: 020 8959 2124

**52  HURRANS NURSERY**
175 New Road, Chingford, London
Tel: 020 8529 1898

**53  ARNOS PARK**
Bowes Road, New Southgate, London
Tel: 020 8368 2779

**54  WYEVALE GARDEN CENTRE**
Daws Lane, Mill Hill, London
Tel: 020 8906 4255

**55  REDBRIDGE GARDEN CENTRE**
152 Snakes Lane East, Woodford Green
Tel: 020 8532 9000

**56  ALEXANDRA PALACE GARDEN CENTRE**
Alexandra Palace, London
Tel: 020 8444 2555

**58  FINCHLEY MANOR GARDEN CENTRE**
120 East End Road, Finchley, London
Tel: 020 8349 1228

**59  CAPITAL GARDENS LTD TEMPLE FORTUNE GARDEN CENTRE**
788a Finchley Road, Finchley, London
Tel: 020 8455 5363

**60  CAPITAL GARDENS LTD HIGHGATE GARDEN CENTRE**
1 Townsend Yard, Highgate High Street, London
Tel: 020 8340 1041

**61  KENWOOD HOUSE**
Hampstead Lane, Hampstead, London
Tel: 020 8348 1286

Geranium

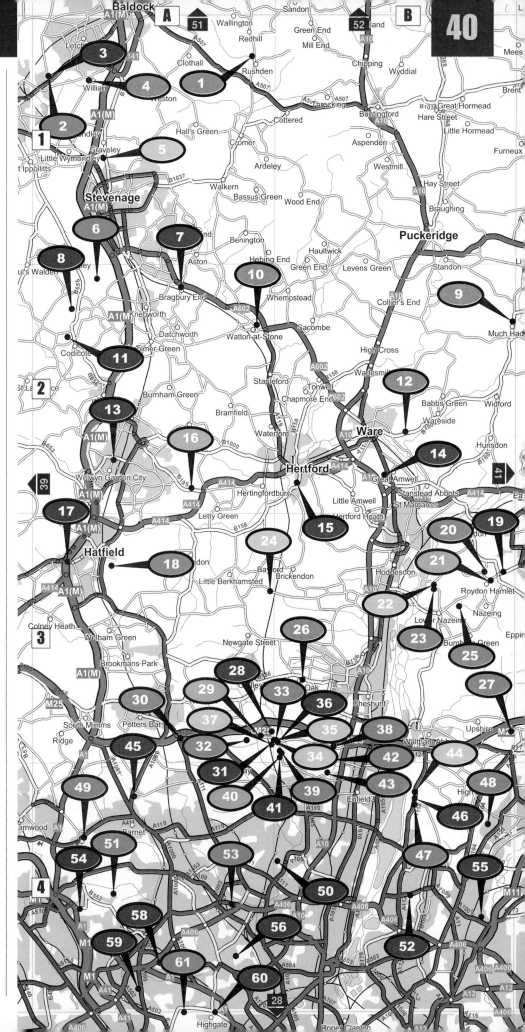

**1** **F W WHYMAN**
Hill Green, Clavering, Saffron Walden
**TEL:** 01799 550 568

**2** **SNOWHILL NURSERY**
Snow Hill, Great Easton, Dunmow
**TEL:** 01371 870 030

**3** **BROOKSIDE GARDEN CENTRE**
Bran End, Stebbing, Dunmow
**TEL:** 01371 856 999

**4** **CHAPEL END NURSERY**
Chapel End, Broxted, Dunmow
**TEL:** 01279 850 771

**5** **EASTON LODGE, THE FORGOTTEN GARDENS**
Little Easton, Great Dunmow
**TEL:** 01371 876 979

**6** **G MARIS & SON**
Garden Centre, Dunmow Road, Bishop's Stortford
**TEL:** 01279 870 472

**7** **LANGTHORNS PLANTERY**
Little Canfield, Dunmow, Essex, CM6 1TD.
**TEL:** 01371 872 611
*World famous nursery with an eye for the rare and spectacular. Large variety of interesting plants available all year round.*
**OPEN:** Open daily 10-5 (or dusk if earlier). Closed Christmas fortnight.
**SPECIALITIES:** Shrubs, Trees, Herbaceous plants, Climbers, Roses.
**FACILITIES:** Credit cards, Wheelchair access, Own gift tokens, Sell plants, Plant guarantee, Pushchair friendly.

**8** **OAKRIDGE NURSERY**
Redricks Lane, Sawbridgeworth
**TEL:** 01279 641 078

**9** **HARLOW GARDEN CENTRE**
Canes Lane, Hastingwood, Harlow
**TEL:** 01279 419 039

**10** **REDRICKS NURSERY**
Vicarage Lane, North Weald, Epping
**TEL:** 01992 524 570

**11** **HAPPY GROW**
High Road, Thornwood
**TEL:** 01992 575 387

**12** **GREENBROOK NURSERY**
Wyses Road, Highwood, Chelmsford
**TEL:** 01245 248 871

**13** **ARGENTS LTD (THE NURSERIES)**
Highwood Road, Edney Common, Chelmsford
**TEL:** 01245 248 630

**14** **WYEVALE GARDEN CENTRE**
Langford Bridge, Ongar Road, Brentwood
**TEL:** 01277 365 485

**15** **WAYSIDE AQUATICS**
5 Blackmore Road, Hook End, Doddinghurst
**TEL:** 01277 823 603

**16** **INGATESTONE GARDEN CENTRE**
Roman Road, Ingatestone
**TEL:** 01277 353 268

**17** **CROWTHER NURSERIES**
160 Ongar Road, Abridge, Romford
**TEL:** 01708 688 479

**18** **SHEILA CHAPMAN CLEMATIS**
Ongar Road, Abridge, Romford
**TEL:** 01708 688 090

**19** **SOW & GROW NURSERY**
Ongar Road, Pilgrims Hatch, Brentwood
**TEL:** 01277 375 252

**20** **HUTTON GARDEN CENTRE**
Rayleigh Road, Hutton, Brentwood
**TEL:** 01277 633 515

**21** **HUNTERS CHASE GARDEN CENTRE**
Rayleigh Road, Hutton, Brentwood
**TEL:** 01277 623 793

**22** **BILLERICAY NURSERIES**
London Road, Billericay
**TEL:** 01277 622 083

**24** **TOMLINS NURSERY**
Mascals Lane, Brentwood
**TEL:** 01277 214 883

**25** **JENNIKINGS GARDEN CENTRE**
210-212 Manor Road, Chigwell
**TEL:** 020 8501 2328

**23** **TISBURYS AQUATIC CENTRE**
Spice Pits Farm, Church Road, Noak Hill, Romford, Essex, RM4 1LD.
**TEL:** 01708 341 376
**EMAIL:** tisburysaquatics@freenet.co.uk

*A family run business established in 1950. Everything for the pond and tropical fish enthusiast. Extensive show areas indoors and outdoors. Expert friendly advice.*
**OPEN:** Open daily 9-5. Closed Christmas & Boxing Day.
**SPECIALITIES:** Aquatic plants, Fish, Waterfalls.
**FACILITIES:** Bookshop, Credit cards, Own gift tokens, Pushchair friendly, Sell plants, Toilets, Wheelchair access.

**26** **CHIGWELL NURSERY**
245 High Road, Chigwell
**TEL:** 020 8500 2690

**27** **BRENTWOOD GARDEN CENTRE**
Vicarage Close, Brentwood
**TEL:** 01277 262 303

**28** **HILLCREST NURSERIES**
A128 Brentwood Road, Ingrave, Brentwood
**TEL:** 01277 810 385

**29** **GREENHOUSE WATERGARDENS**
87 Chase Cross Road, Romford
**TEL:** 01708 726 726

Aster

**30 WYEVALE GARDEN CENTRE**

Nags Head Lane, Upminster Common
TEL: 01708 342 469

**31 ELMSTEAD NURSERIES**

Whalebone Lane North, Romford
TEL: 020 8597 9020

**32 WARLEY ROSE GARDENS LTD**

Warley Street, Great Warley, Brentwood
TEL: 01277 221 966

**33 NORTH STREET GARDEN CENTRE**

North Street, Romford
TEL: 01708 737 585

**34 CHO KEE**

Cho Farm, Southend Arterial Rd, Upminster
TEL: 01708 346 927

**35 COUNTY PARK NURSERY**

Essex Gardens, 384 Wingletye Lane, Hornchurch
TEL: 01708 445 205

**36 FUTURE GARDEN HYDROPONICS**

26a Woodford Avenue, Ilford
TEL: 020 8550 7310

**37 ELMHURST NURSERIES**

369 Front Lane Cranham, Upminster
TEL: 01708 640 668

**38 CROW LANE**

15 Crow Lane, Romford
TEL: 01708 724 833

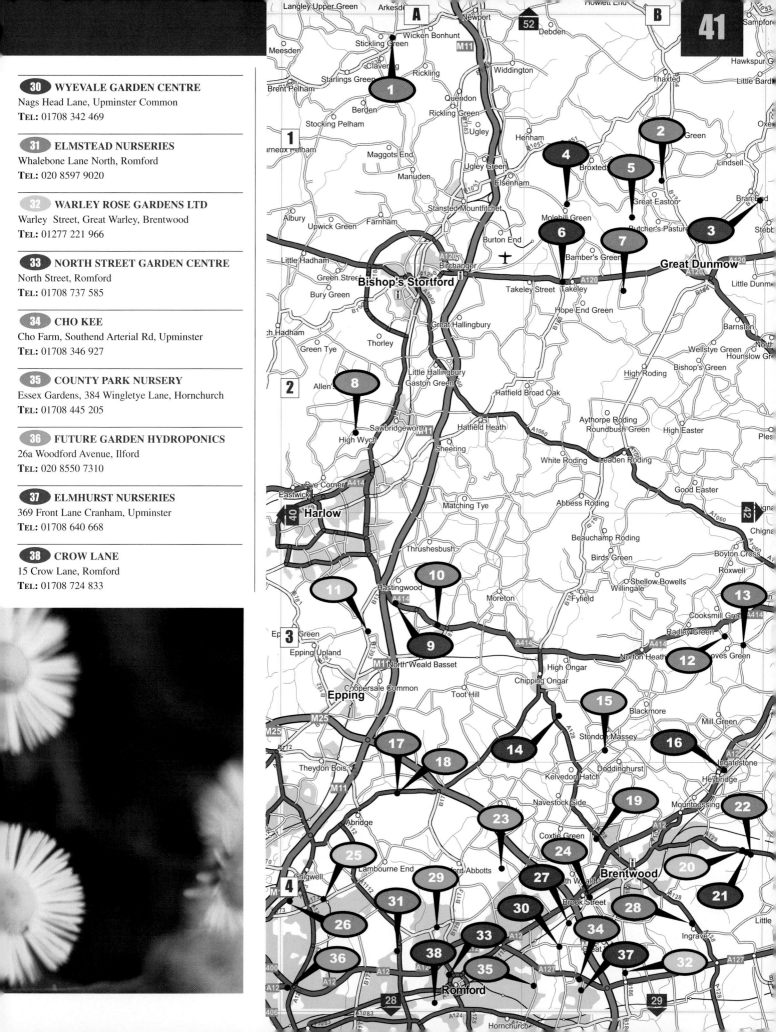

**1   N F & M C KEMPSTER**
Walthams Cross, Great Bardfield, Braintree
**TEL:** 01371 810 125

**2   ROBINSON BROS**
Tey Road, Earls Colne, Colchester
**TEL:** 01787 223 775

**3   BARDFIELD TREES**
Great Lodge, Great Bardfield, Braintree
**TEL:** 01371 810 776

**4   BOURNE BROOK NURSERIES**
Greenstead Green, Halstead
**TEL:** 01787 472 900

**5   BAYTREE FARM SHOP & GARDEN CENTRE**
Coggeshall Road, Braintree
**TEL:** 01376 344 301

**6   MARKS HALL ARBORETUM**
Marks Hall, Coggeshall, Colchester
**TEL:** 01376 563 796

**7   WORLD OF WATER**
The Dutch Nursery, West Street, Coggeshall
**TEL:** 01376 563 836

**8   WYEVALE GARDEN CENTRE**
Cressing Road, Braintree
**TEL:** 01376 553 043

---

**9   PERRYWOOD NURSERIES**
Kelvedon Road, Inworth, Tiptree, Essex, CO5 9SX.
**TEL:** 01376 570 777
*Large nursery and garden centre. Outstanding range of plants and a wide selection of gardening products. Delightful coffee shop serving homemade food. Rural setting.*
**OPEN:** Mon-Sat 8.30-5. Sun: Mar-Oct 9-5, Nov-Feb 10-4.
**SPECIALITIES:** Shrubs, Trees, House plants, Terracotta pots, Perennials.
**FACILITIES:** Toilets, Credit cards, Wheelchair access, Gift tokens, Coffee shop, Bookshop, Gift shop, HTA gift tokens, Pushchair friendly, Sell plants.

---

**10   OLD MILL HOUSE GARDEN NURSERY**
Guithavon Valley, Witham
**TEL:** 01376 512 396

**11   ROBIN SAVILL CLEMATIS SPECIALIST**
2 Bury Cottages, Bury Road, Pleshey
**TEL:** 01245 237 380

**12   FOUR SEASONS**
126 Newland Street, Witham
**TEL:** 01376 308 002

**13   MAYPOLE PET & GARDEN CENTRE**
Maypole Road, Wickham Bishops, Witham
**TEL:** 01621 892 411

**14   WOODHOUSE NURSERY**
Main Road, Boreham, Chelmsford
**TEL:** 01245 381 781

**15   JEWELS GARDEN CENTRE**
Hodges Cottage, Colchester Road, Springfield
**TEL:** 01245 460 878

**16   WYEVALE GARDEN CENTRE**
Homelands Retail Park, Cuton Hall Lane, Springfield
**TEL:** 01245 466 466

**17   AUSFERN UK**
Sedge Green, Nazing, Waltham Abbey
**TEL:** 01992 465 074

**18   HANGING GARDENS NURSERIES**
15 Further Meadow, Writtle, Chelmsford
**TEL:** 01245 421 020

**19   WRITTLE ROAD NURSERY**
7 Writtle Road, Chelmsford
**TEL:** 01245 265 655

**20   CLARENOUNT NURSERIES**
Bryants Lane, Woodham Mortimer, Maldon
**TEL:** 01245 222 643

**21   ABERCORN PLANT & GARDEN CENTRE**
Beehive Lane, Chelmsford
**TEL:** 01245 257 398

**22   C J SKILTON AQUARIST**
Great Gibcracks Chase, Butts Green, Sandon
**TEL:** 01245 400 535

**23   HORSESHOE NURSERIES**
White Elm Road, Danbury, Chelmsford
**TEL:** 01245 223 789

**24   WESTVIEW NURSERIES**
Main Road, Bicknacre, Chelmsford
**TEL:** 01245 324 171

**25   STOCKBROOK FARM SHOP & NURSERY**
Stock Road, Stock, Ingatestone
**TEL:** 01277 840 046

**26   HYDE HALL, THE ROYAL HORTICULTURAL SOCIETY**
Rettendon, Chelmsford
**TEL:** 01245 400 256

**27   HILLTOP NURSERY**
Dowsetts Lane, Ramsden Heath, Billericay
**TEL:** 01268 710 529

**28   PLANTOME NURSERIES & GARDEN CENTRE**
Woodham Road, Battlesbridge, Wickford
**TEL:** 01245 320 263

**29   BUSHUKAN BONSAI**
Ricbra, Lower Road, Hockley
**TEL:** 01702 201 029

**30   ENGLISH GARDEN NURSERY**
15 Abbey Road, Billericay
**TEL:** 01277 654788

**31   NEWHALL NURSERIES**
Lower Road, Hockley
**TEL:** 01702 205 355

**32   FAIRWAYS GARDEN CENTRE**
Hullbridge Road, Rayleigh
**TEL:** 01702 230 795

**33   ALPHA GARDEN CENTRE**
238 London Road, Wickford
**TEL:** 01268 766 093

**34   VIEW GARDENS**
Chelmsford Road, Rawreth, Wickford
**TEL:** 01268 761 337

**35   GLENCREST SEATEX LTD**
10 Heron Avenue, Wickford
**TEL:** 01268 769 641

**36   READ'S NURSERY**
99 Rawreth Lane, Rayleigh
**TEL:** 01268 785 893

**37   ESSEX AQUASCAPES**
Lindon Common Road, Little Burstead, Billericay
**TEL:** 01277 655 669

**38   SWALLOW AQUATICS**
Aqualife & Water Garden Centre, London Road, Rayleigh
**TEL:** 01268 781 265

**39   RAWAL PINDI NURSERY**
66 Main Road, Hawkwell, Hockley
**TEL:** 01702 206 244

**40   POTASH GARDEN CENTRE**
9 Main Road, Hawkwell, Hockley
**TEL:** 01702 201 120

**41** SUMMERHILL NUSERY & GARDEN CENTRE

Pipps Hill Road North, Arterial Road, Billericay
TEL: 01268 521 052

**42** ALTONS GARDEN CENTRE

Arterial Road, North Benfleet, Wickford
TEL: 01268 726 421

**43** BASILDON GARDEN & MOWER CENTRE

Nevendon Road, Basildon
TEL: 01268 523 515

**44** POT SHOP GARDEN CENTRE

Rear of 91 High Street, Rayleigh
TEL: 01268 770 083

**45** WOODSIDE GARDEN CENTRE

Arterial Road, Rayleigh
TEL: 01268 770 492

**46** WYEVALE GARDEN CENTRE

Eastwood Road, Rayleigh
TEL: 01702 527 331

**47** MANSFIELD NURSERIES

Eastwood Rise, Eastwood, Leigh on Sea
TEL: 01702 525 410

**48** FOUR SEASONS PLANT CENTRE

Southend Road, Rochford
TEL: 01702 541 454

**49** MANOR GARDENS

Pound Lane, Pitsea, Basildon
TEL: 01268 726 287

**50** COTTAGE GARDEN NURSERIES

573 Prince Avenue, West-Cliff-On-Sea
TEL: 01702 352 191

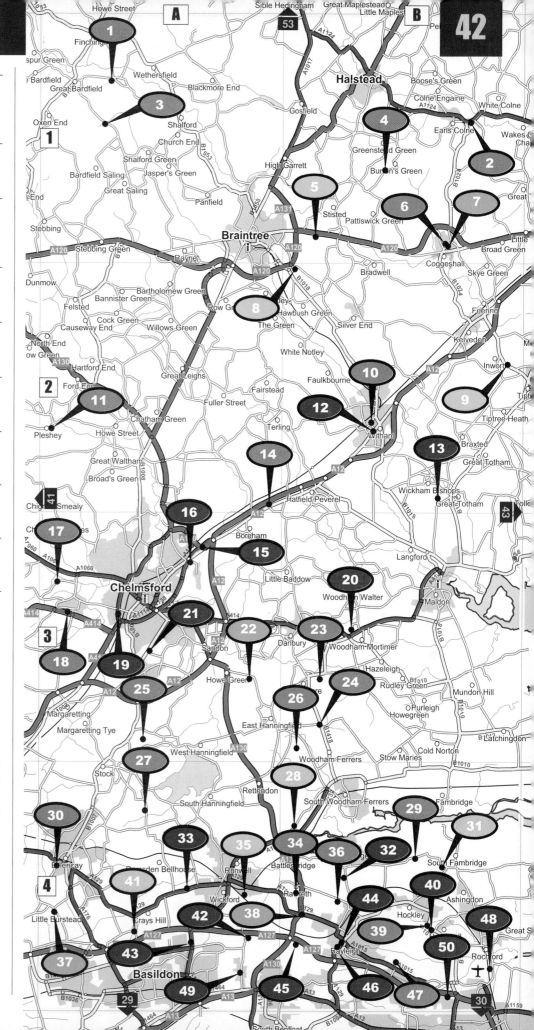

Poppies

● GARDEN
● GARDEN CENTRE
● GARDEN & NURSERY
○ NURSERY
○ NURSERY & GARDEN CENTRE
○ WATER GARDEN SPECIALIST

**1** **HEARTS DELIGHT NURSERY**
Long Road, Lawford, Manningtree
**TEL:** 01206 392 539

**2** **FILLPOTS NURSERY**
52 Straight Road, Boxted, Colchester
**TEL:** 01206 272 389

**3** **SOW & SOW NURSERIES**
Horkesley Road, Colchester
**TEL:** 01206 273 300

**4** **THE COTTAGE GARDEN**
Langham Road, Boxted, Colchester
**TEL:** 01206 272 269

**5** **OAKVIEW NURSERIES**
Dead Lane, Ardleigh, Colchester
**TEL:** 01206 231 134

**6** **NOTCUTTS GARDEN CENTRE**
Station Road, Ardleigh
**TEL:** 01206 230 271

**7** **HULL FARM NURSERY**
Spring Valley, Ardleigh, Colchester
**TEL:** 01206 230 045

**8** **SPRING VALLEY NURSERIES**
Spring Valley Lane, Ardleigh, Colchester
**TEL:** 01206 230 238

**9** **MILL RACE NURSERY**
New Road, Aldham, Colchester
**TEL:** 01206 242 521

**10** **BLENHEIM NURSERIES**
Bromley Road, Ardleigh, Colchester
**TEL:** 01206 870 605

**11** **BARNPLANTS**
Turkey Cock Lane, Lexden Heath, Colchester
**TEL:** 01206 210 486

**12** **WYEVALE GARDEN CENTRE**
342 London Road, Stanway, Colchester
**TEL:** 01206 213 050

**13** **ROLTS NURSERY & GARDEN CENTRE**
Clacton Road, Elmstead, Colchester
**TEL:** 01206 822 427

**14** **BETH CHATTO GARDENS**
Clacton Road, Elmstead Market, Colchester
**TEL:** 01206 822 007

**15** **PONDLIFE**
Poplar Nurseries, Coggeshall Road, Colchester
**TEL:** 01206 212 310

**16** **POPLAR NURSERIES**
Coggeshall Road, Marks Tey, Colchester
**TEL:** 01206 210 374

**17** **HOMESTEAD NURSERIES**
Thorpe Road, Weeley, Clacton-on-Sea
**TEL:** 01255 830 967

**18** **BLOOMFIELD GARDEN CENTRE**
241 Berechurch Hall Road, Colchester
**TEL:** 01206 575 941

**19** **BLACKWELL NURSERY**
Fingringhoe Road, Rowhedge, Colchester
**TEL:** 01206 729 121

**20** **HILLTOP NURSERIES**
Clacton Road, Weeley, Clacton-on-Sea
**TEL:** 01255 830 325

**21** **FRINTON ROAD NURSERY**
158-164 Frinton Road, Kirby Cross, Frinton-on-Sea
**TEL:** 01255 674 838

**22** **CHINA MAROC BONSAI**
Station Road, Thorrington, Colchester
**TEL:** 01206 250 547

**23** **HONEYPOT FARM**
Rectory Road, Weeley Heath, Clacton-on-Sea
**TEL:** 01255 830 181

**24** **THE GARDEN OUTLET**
Unit 1, Clacton Common Factory Shopping Centre,
Clacton-on-Sea
**TEL:** 01924 827 065

**25** **GARDEN WORLD**
6 High Street, Brightlingsea, Colchester
**TEL:** 01206 303 868

**26** **CLACTON GARDEN CENTRE**
St Johns Road, Clacton-on-Sea
**TEL:** 01255 425 711

**27** **MAYFLOWER NURSERY & GARDEN CENTRE**
Mill Road, Mayland, Chelmsford
**TEL:** 01621 740 269

**28** **L S MUMMERY NURSERIES**
Barling Road, Great Wakering, Southend-on-Sea
**TEL:** 01702 219 278

**29** **BONSAI AT MORLEY'S**
Morley Garden Centre, Great Wakering,
Southend-on-Sea
**TEL:** 01702 584 441

**30** **MORLEY NURSERIES**
Southend Road, Great Wakering, Southend-on-Sea
**TEL:** 01702 585 668

Gerber Daisy

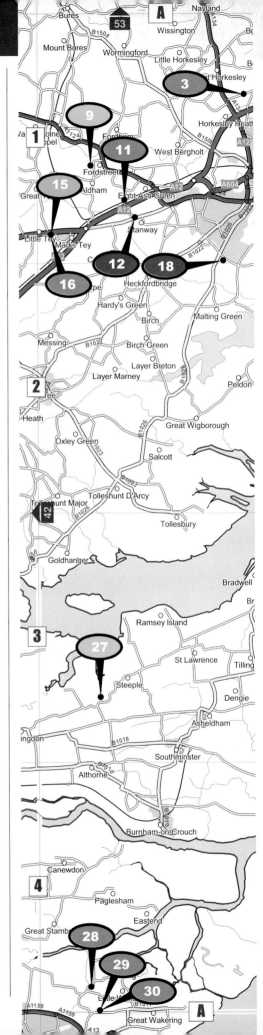

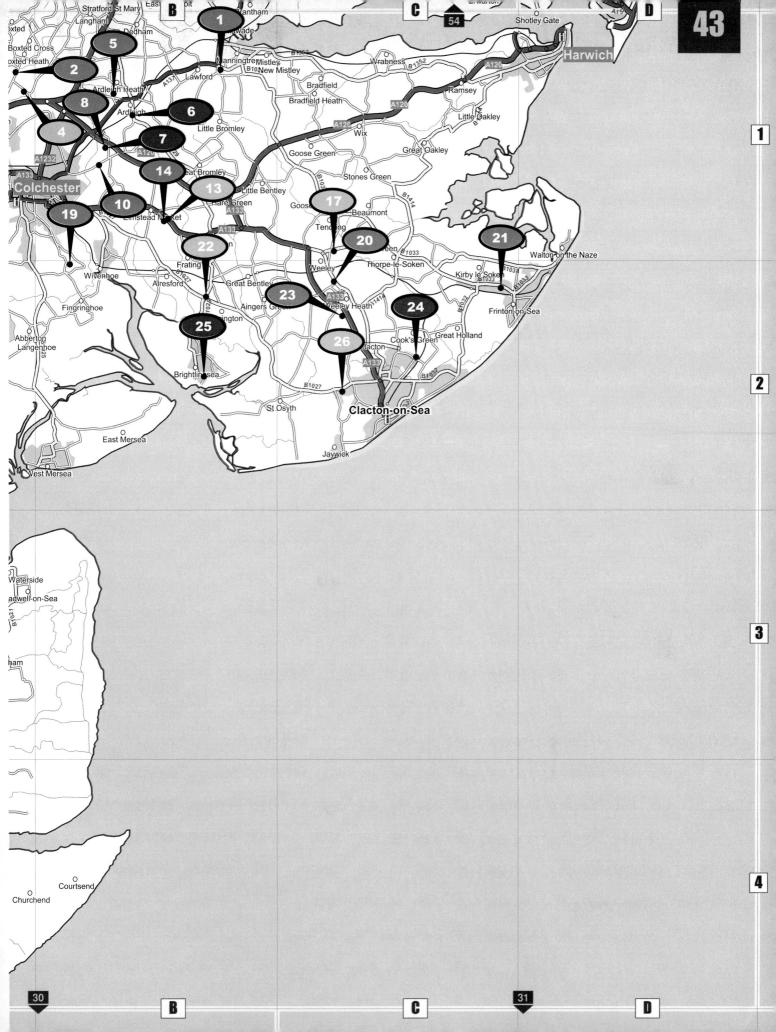

# S WALES

● GARDEN
● GARDEN CENTRE
● GARDEN & NURSERY
● NURSERY
● NURSERY & GARDEN CENTRE
● WATER GARDEN SPECIALIST

**1** **LLANARTH GARDEN CENTRE**
Pontfaen, Llanarth
TEL: 01545 580 271

**2** **THE WALLED GARDEN AT PIGEONSFORD**
Llangranog, Llandysul
TEL: 01239 654 360

**3** **GWYNFOR GROWERS**
Gwynfor, Pontgarreg, Llandysul
TEL: 01239 654 151

**4** **CAE HIR**
Cribyn, Lampeter
TEL: 01570 470 839

**5** **BRONDESBURY PARK GARDEN CENTRE**
Brondesbury Park, Aberystwyth Road, Cardigan
TEL: 01239 615 300

**6** **PENRALLT FARM NURSERY**
Moylegrove, Cardigan
TEL: 01239 881 295

**7** **PENLAN PERENNIALS**
Penlan Farm, Penrhwpal, Llandysul
TEL: 01239 851 244

**8** **GWASTOD NURSERY**
Prengwyn, Llandysul
TEL: 01545 590 479

**9** **FARMYARD NURSERIES**
Farmyard Farm, Llandysul, Carmarthen
TEL: 01559 363 389

**10** **TREFHEDYN GARDEN CENTRE**
Bridge Street, Newcastle Emlyn
TEL: 01239 710 292

**11** **TY RHOS TREES**
Ty Rhos, Velindre, Crymych
TEL: 01239 820 701

**12** **NEW INN NURSERIES**
Blaenffos, Boncath
TEL: 01239 841 215

**13** **PENLAN-UCHAF FARM GARDENS**
Gwaun Valley, Fishguard
TEL: 01348 881 388

**14** **MANOROWEN WALLED GARDEN**
Manorowen, Fishguard
TEL: 01348 872 168

**15** **ANTHONY'S NURSERY**
Glasfryn Farm, Cefn Road, Fishguard
TEL: 01348 874 034

**16** **MOORLAND COTTAGE PLANTS**
Rhyd-y-Groes, BrynBerian, Crymych
TEL: 01239 891 363

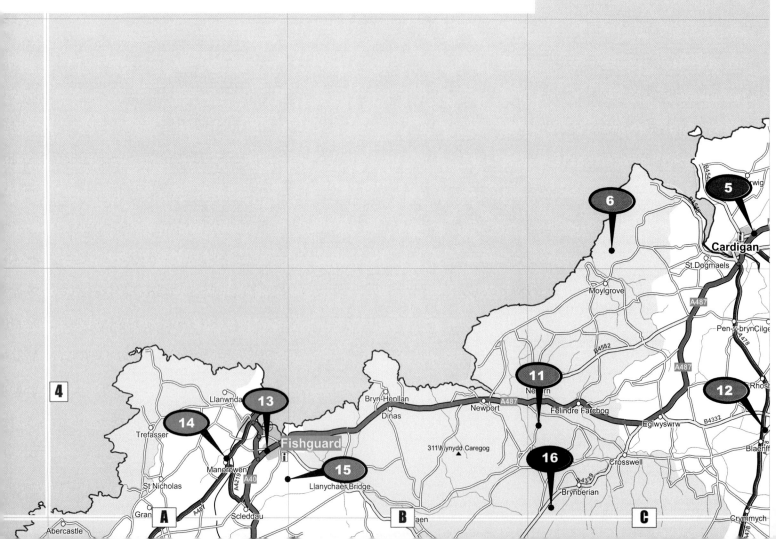

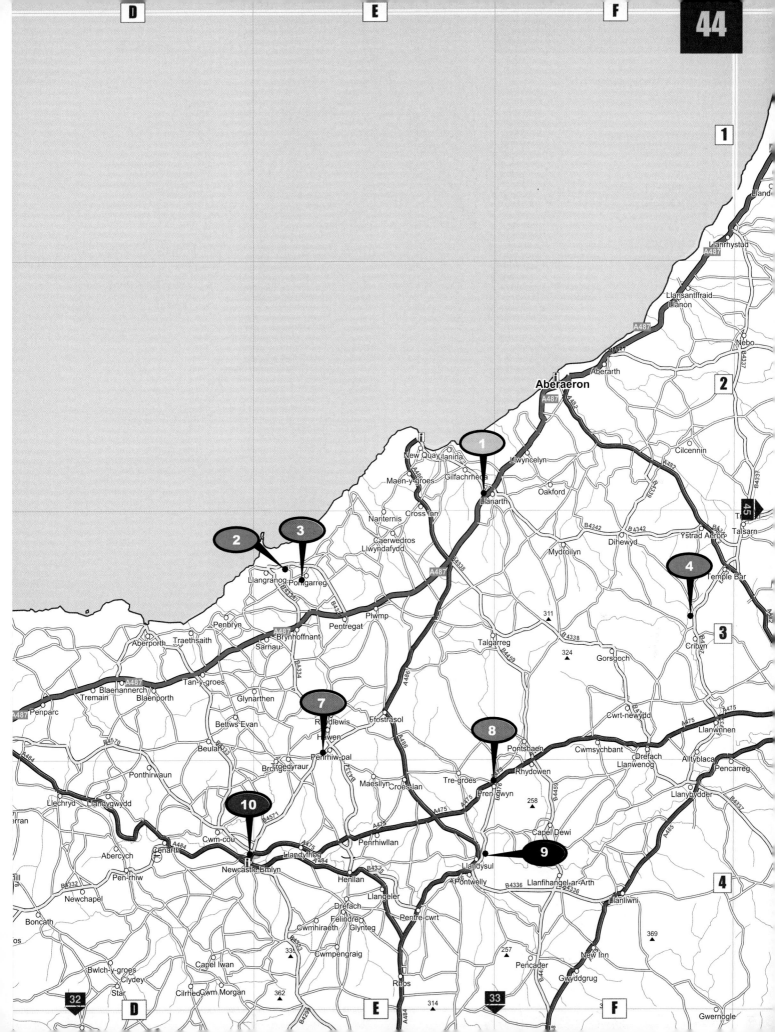

# SOUTH WALES

**1  SWN Y GWYNT NURSERIES**
Nantmel, Llandrindod Wells
**TEL:** 01597 823 798

**2  MIDWAY NURSERIES**
Penybont, Llandrindod Wells
**TEL:** 01597 851 662

**3  ROBERT'S GARDEN CENTRE**
Barley Mow, Lampeter
**TEL:** 01570 422 756

**4  RHANDIRMWYN PLANTS**
8 Pannau Street, Rhandirmwyn, Llandovery
**TEL:** 01550 760 220

**5  LLANDOVERY PET & GARDEN CENTRE**
Llangadog Road, Llandovery
**TEL:** 01550 720 029

Bird of Paradise

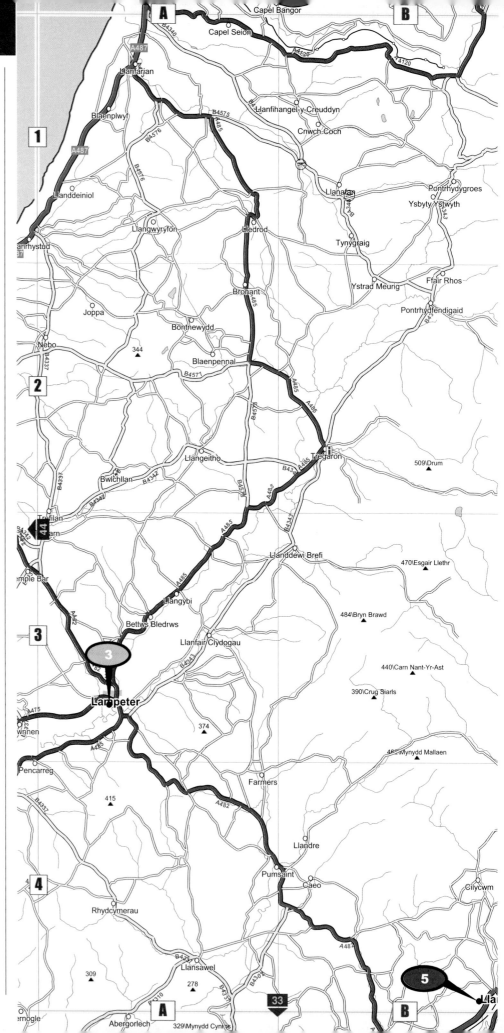

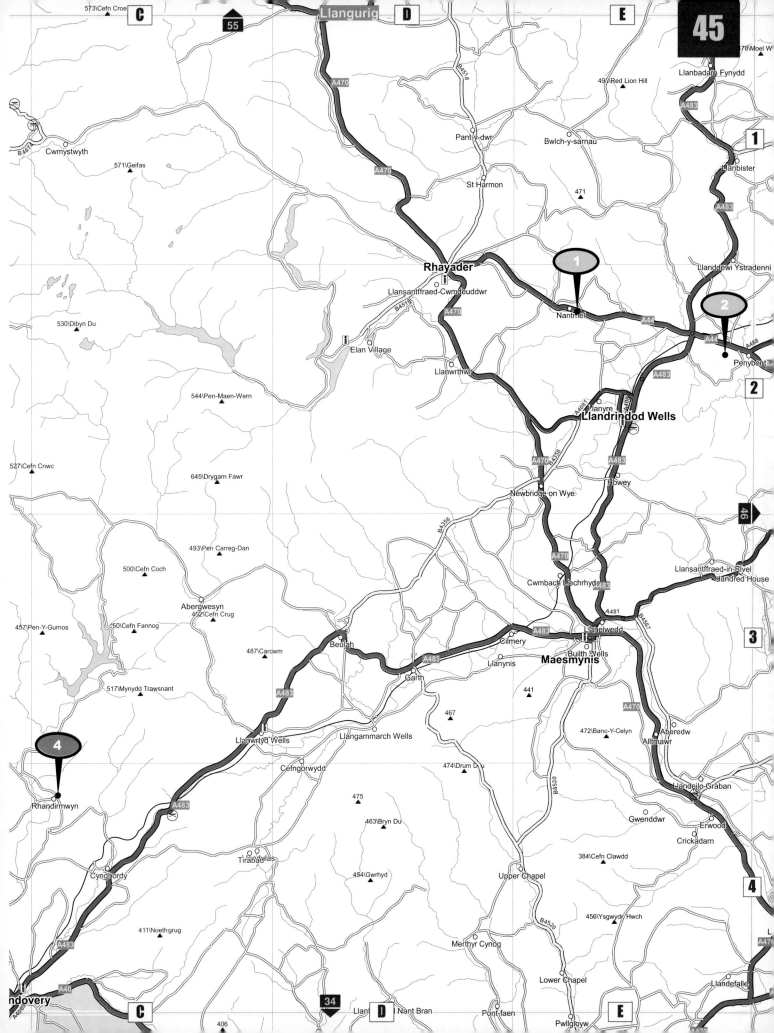

**1** **JOHN CLAYFIELD**
Llanbrook Alpine Nursery, Hopton Castle, Clunton
Tel: 01547 530 298

**2** **BUCKNELL NURSERIES**
The Nurseries, Bucknell
Tel: 01547 530 606

**3** **LINGEN NURSERY & GARDENS**
Lingen, Bucknell
Tel: 01544 267 720

**4** **CROFT CASTLE, NATIONAL TRUST**
Croft, Leominster
Tel: 01568 780 246

**5** **THE OLD VICARAGE NURSERY**
Lucton, Leominster
Tel: 01568 780 538

**6** **BRYAN'S GROUND GARDENS**
Letchmoor Lane, Stapleton, Presteigne
Tel: 01544 260 001

**7** **WHIMBLE NURSERY & GARDEN**
Kinnerton, Presteigne
Tel: 01547 560 413

**8** **BERRINGTON HALL, NATIONAL TRUST**
Leominster
Tel: 01568 615 721

**9** **STOCKTON BURY GARDENS**
Stockton Bury, Kimbolton, Leominster
Tel: 01568 613 432

**10** **ORNAMENTAL TREE NURSERY**
Cobnash, Kingsland
Tel: 01568 708 016

**11** **HERGEST CROFT GARDENS**
Ridgebourne, Kington
Tel: 01544 230 160

**12** **LYONSHALL NURSERIES AND GARDEN CENTRE**
Lyonshall, Kington
Tel: 01544 340 214

**13** **HAMPTON COURT**
The Van Kampen Gardens, Hope-under-Dinmore, Leominster
Tel: 01568 797 777

**14** **CHENNELS GATE GARDENS & NURSERY**
Chennels Gate, Eardisley
Tel: 01544 327 288

**15** **WEIR GARDEN, NATIONAL TRUST**
Swainshill, Hereford
Tel: 01981 590 697

**16** **QUEEN'S WOOD ARBORETUM**
Dinmore Hill, Leominster
Tel: 01568 798 320

**17** **DINMORE MANOR**
Dinmore, Hereford
Tel: 01432 830 322

**18** **ARROW COTTAGE GARDEN**
Weobley
Tel: 01544 318 468

**19** **QUEENSWOOD GARDEN CENTRE**
Wellington, Hereford
Tel: 01432 830 880

**20** **BROBURY GARDENS**
Brobury
Tel: 01981 500 229

**21** **THREE ACRE NURSERIES**
Wyatt Road, Cross Keys, Hereford
Tel: 01432 820 471

**22** **KENCHESTER WATER GARDENS**
Church Road, Lyde, Hereford
Tel: 01432 270 981

**23** **WYEVALE GARDEN CENTRE**
Kings Acres Road, Hereford
Tel: 01432 266 261

**24** **THE OLD RAILWAY LINE NURSERY**
Three Cocks, Brecon, Powys, LD3 0SG.
Tel: 01497 847 055
Email: clearynursery@aol.com

*Family established business of over 10 years catering for all your gardening requirements and floral tributes.*
**Open:** Open 7 days a week. Summer: Mon-Sat 8.30-5.30, Sun 9.30-5.30. Winter: Mon-Sat 8.30-5.30, Sun 10-5. Closed Christmas week.
**Specialities:** Comprehensive range.
**Facilities:** Toilets, Credit cards, Wheelchair access, Gift tokens, Gift shop, HTA gift tokens, Own gift tokens, Sell plants, Pushchair friendly, Coffee shop, Dogs allowed.

My Angel

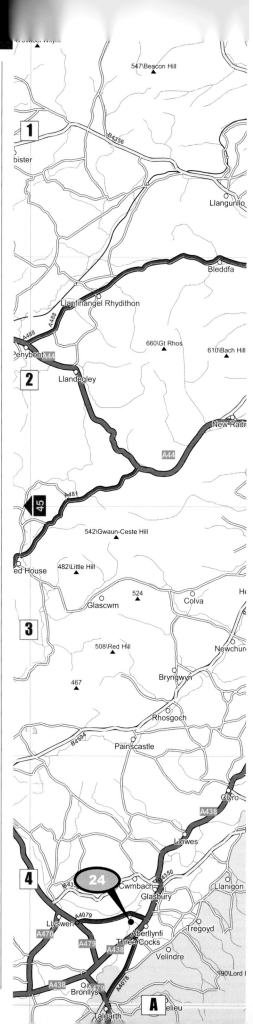

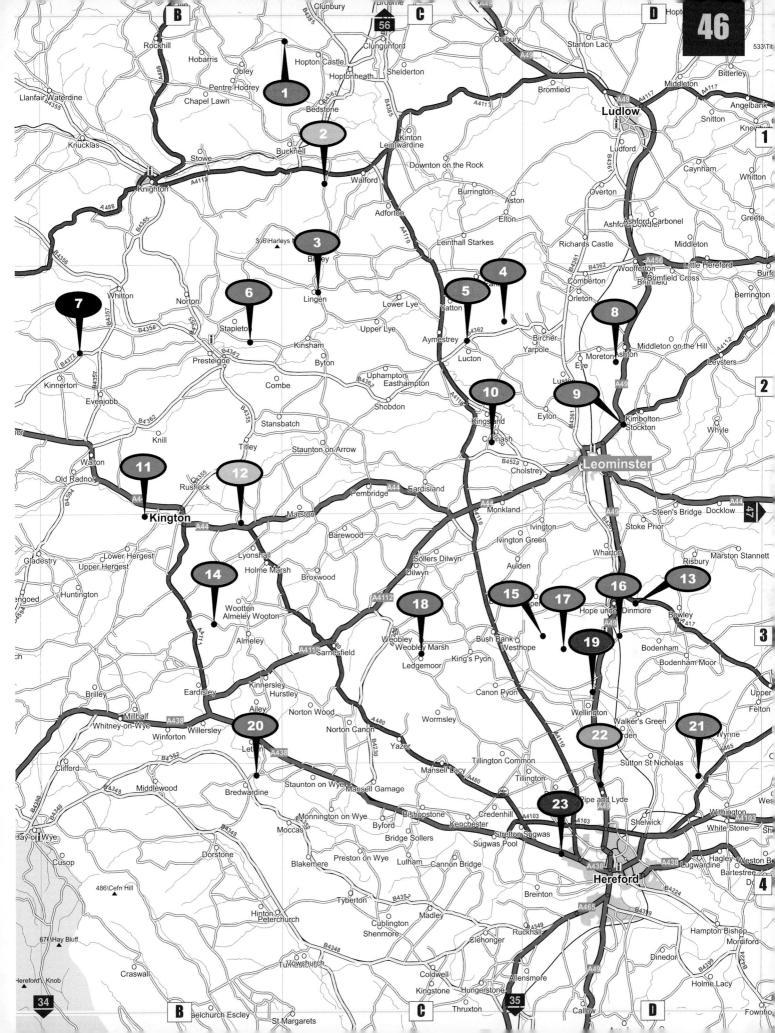

**1** **BODENHAM ARBORETUM & EARTH CENTRE**
Wolverley, Kidderminster
TEL: 01562 850 382

**2** **HURRANS GARDEN CENTRE**
Kidderminster Road South, West Hagley
TEL: 01562 700 511

**3** **SUNSET NURSERIES**
Waggon Lane, Kidderminster
TEL: 01562 700 672

**4** **BARNETT HILL GARDEN CENTRE**
Worcester Road, Clent, Stourbridge
TEL: 01562 700 308

**5** **STONE HOUSE COTTAGE NURSERIES**
Stone, Kidderminster
TEL: 01562 699 02

**6** **GARDEN THYME NURSERY**
Blackmans Stitch, Longbank, Bewdley
TEL: 01299 400 658

**7** **HARVINGTON HALL**
Harvington, Kidderminster
TEL: 01562 777 846

**8** **EVERGREEN CONIFER CENTRE**
Tenbury Road, Rock, Kidderminster
TEL: 01299 266 581

**9** **BOURNEWOOD NURSERY**
Lickhill Road North, Stourport on Severn
TEL: 01299 828 988

**10** **FUCHSIAVALE NURSERIES**
Worcester Road, Torton, Kidderminster, Worcestershire, DY11 7SB.
TEL: 01299 251162
EMAIL: fuchsiavaleuk@yahoo.co.uk
*Winners of many awards. Nearly 200 varieties of Fuchsias available together with an unusual range of pelagoniums, shrubs and bedding plants.*
OPEN: Open daily.
SPECIALITIES: Fuchsias.
FACILITIES: Credit cards, Pushchair friendly, Wheelchair access, Sell plants.

**11** **CREATIVE LANDSCAPES GARDENS & NURSERIES**
Whitlenge House Cottage, Whitlenge Lane, Kidderminster
TEL: 01299 250720

**12** **COOKS GARDEN CENTRE**
26 Worcester Road, Stourport on Severn
TEL: 01299 826 169

**13** **COTTAGE HERBARY**
Mill House, Boraston, Tenbury Wells
TEL: 01584 781 575

**14** **BURFORD HOUSE GARDENS**
Tenbury Wells, Tenbury Wells
TEL: 01584 810 777

**15** **TREASURES OF TENBURY**
Burford House Tenbury Wells
TEL: 01584 810 777

**16** **MULU NURSERIES**
Burford House, Tenbury Wells
TEL: 01584 811 592

**17** **BISHOPSWOOD NURSERY**
Bishopswood, Crossway Green, Stourport on Severn
TEL: 01299 251 208

**18** **WEBBS OF WYCHBOLD**
Wychbold, Droitwich, Worcestershire, WR9 0DG.
TEL: 01527 860 000
WEB: www.webbsofwychbold.co.uk

*Fifty acres of gardening, leisure and pleasure. Whether you are looking for a rare plant or a family day out, Webbs is the place to come.*
OPEN: Apr-Sep: Mon-Fri 9-8, Sat & BH Mon 9-6, Sun 10.30-4.30. Oct-Mar: Mon-Sat 9-6, Sun 10.30-4.30.
SPECIALITIES: Comprehensive range, House plants, Shrubs, National Collection, Paving, gates, railings & fencing.
FACILITIES: Bookshop, Child area, Coffee shop, Credit cards, Gift shop, HTA gift tokens, Own gift tokens, Plant guarantee, Pushchair friendly, Restaurant, Sell plants, Toilets, Wheelchair access.

**19** **PERHILL NURSERIES**
Worcester Road, Great Witley
TEL: 01299 896 329

**20** **WITLEY COURT, ENGLISH HERITAGE**
Worcester Road, Great Witley, Worcester
TEL: 01299 896 636

**21** **EASTGROVE COTTAGE GARDEN NURSERY**
Sankyns Green, Shrawley, Little Witley
TEL: 01299 896 389

**22** **KYRE PARK GARDENS**
Kyre Park, Tenbury Wells
TEL: 01885 410 247

**23** **RICKARD'S HARDY FERNS**
Kyre Park Gardens, Kyre, Tenbury Wells
TEL: 01885 410 282

**24** **WORCESTER GARDEN CENTRE**
Droitwich Road, Worcester
TEL: 01905 451231

**25** **GARDEN AT THE ELMS NURSERY**
Frenchlands Lane, Lower Broadheath
TEL: 01905 640 841

**26** **SPRINGRIDGE NURSERIES**
Springridge, Old Turnpike Road, Worcester
TEL: 01905 381 451

**27** **WINTERGREEN NURSERIES**
Bringsty Common, Worcester
TEL: 01886 821 858

**28** **LAYLOCKS NURSERIES**
Bromyard Road, Cotheridge, Worcester
TEL: 01905 429 212

**29** **ST PETERS GARDEN CENTRE**
Pear Tree Farm, Broomhall, Worcester
TEL: 01905 357 595

**30** **HURRANS GARDEN CENTRE**
Hereford Road, Leigh Sinton
TEL: 01886 832 462

**31** **ACTON BEAUCHAMP ROSES**
The Tynnings, Acton Beauchamp, Worcester
TEL: 01531 640 433

**32** **MILL LANE NURSERIES**
Mill Lane, Drakes Broughton, Pershore
TEL: 01905 841 650

**33** **MADRESFIELD NURSERY & GARDEN CENTRE**
Jennet Tree Lane, Madresfield, Malvern
TEL: 01684 574 066

**34** **GRANGE FARM NURSERY**
Guarlford, Malvern
TEL: 01684 562 544

**35** **PICTON GARDEN AND THE OLD COURT NURSERIES**
Walwyn Road, Colwall, Malvern
TEL: 01684 540 416

**36** **MEREBROOK WATER PLANTS**
Merebrook Farm, Hanley Swan, Worcester
TEL: 01684 310 950

**37** **OLD COURT NURSERIES**
Walwyn Road, Colwall, Malvern
TEL: 01684 540 416

**38** **EARLS CROOME NURSERY & GARDEN CENTRE**
Worcester Road, Earls Croome, Worcester
TEL: 01684 592 143

**39** **BEACONS NURSERIES**
Tewkesbury Road, Eckington, Pershore
TEL: 01386 750 359

**40** **LEDBURY'S SECRET GARDEN CENTRE**
58 The Homend, Ledbury
TEL: 01531 636 087

**41** **RUSHFIELDS OF LEDBURY**
Ross Road, Ledbury
TEL: 01531 632 004

**42** **EASTNOR GARDEN PLANTS**
Eastnor, Ledbury
TEL: 01531 635 982

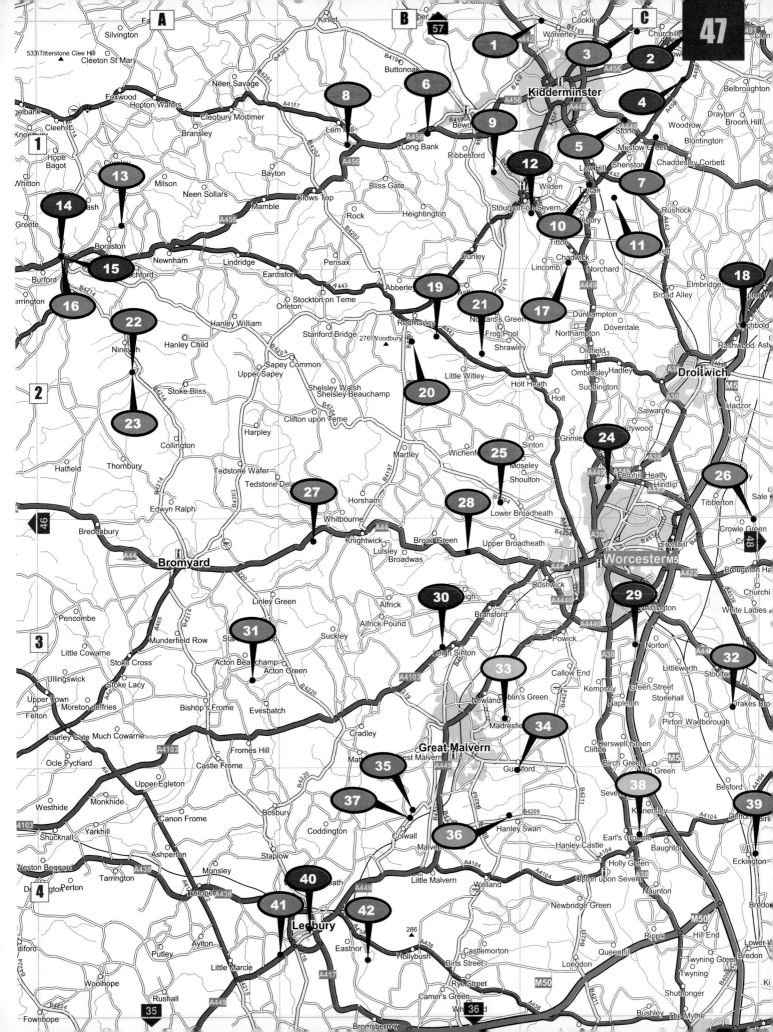

**1 JARDINERIE**
Kenilworth Road, Hampton in Arden, Solihull
**TEL: 01675 442 866**

**2 WOOLMANS GARDEN CENTRE**
72 Solihull Road, Shirley, Solihull
**TEL: 0121 744 3094**

**3 WASELEY HILLS COUNTRY PARK**
Gannow Green Lane, Rubery, Birmingham
**TEL: 01562 710 025**

**4 WYEVALE GARDEN CENTRE**
Hampton Rd, Eastcote, Solihull **TEL: 01675 442 031**

**5 A CALDICOTT & SON**
The Nursery, 50 Lovelace Avenue, Solihull
**TEL: 0121 705 747**

**6 NOTCUTTS GARDEN CENTRE**
Stratford Road, Shirley, Solihull **TEL: 0121 744 4501**

**7 BEECHCROFT NURSERIES & GARDEN CENTRE**
Madeley Road, Belbroughton, Stourbridge
**TEL: 01562 710 358**

**8 HOLLYWOOD GARDENS & PETS**
73 May Lane, Hollywood, Birmingham
**TEL: 01564 826 843**

**9 TREADMILL NURSERY**
Tythebarn Lane, Shirley, Solihull **TEL: 0121 744 6954**

**10 WYNDLEY GARDEN CENTRE**
Warwick Rd, Knowle, Solihull **TEL: 01564 777 106**

**11 FOUR ASHES NURSERIES**
Four Ashes Rd, Dorridge, Solihull **TEL: 01564 773 019**

**12 AMBLESIDE GARDEN CENTRE**
Norton Lane, Earlswood, Solihull **TEL: 01564 703 553**

**13 EARLSWOOD NURSERIES**
Forshaw Heath Road, Earlswood, Solihull
**TEL: 01564 702 749**

**14 KINGFISHER NURSERIES**
Catshill, Bromsgrove **TEL: 01527 835 084**

**15 OSCROFT'S DAHLIAS**
Woodside, Warwick Rd, Solihull **TEL: 01564 782 450**

**16 BADDESLEY CLINTON, NATIONAL TRUST**
Rising Lane, Baddesley Clinton Village, Solihull
**TEL: 01564 783 294**

**17 LITTLE HEATH GARDEN CENTRE**
Little Heath Lane, Lickey End, Bromsgrove
**TEL: 01527 878 174**

**18 PACKWOOD HOUSE, NATIONAL TRUST**
Lapworth, Solihull **TEL: 01564 782 024**

**19 WYEVALE GARDEN CENTRE**
Alcester Rd, Burcot, Bromsgrove **TEL: 01527 873 470**

**20 BARNCLOSE NURSERY**
Old Warwick Road, Shrewley, Warwick
**TEL: 01926 843 502**

**21 HILLIER GARDEN CENTRE**
Henley Road, Mappleborough Green, Studley
**TEL: 01527 852 266**

**22 BADGER NURSERIES PLANT CENTRE**
Birmingham Road, Mappleborough Green, Studley
**TEL: 01527 852 631**

**23 HATTON PLANT CENTRE**
Dark Lane, Hatton, Warwick **TEL: 01926 843 370**

**24 BOTANY BAY NURSERIES**
Edgioake Lane, Astwood Bank, Redditch
**TEL: 01527 893 885**

**25 COUGHTON COURT**
Alcester **TEL: 01789 400 777**

**26 WYEVALE GARDEN CENTRE**
Warwick Rd, Stratford-upon-Avon **TEL: 01789 734 200**

**27 RIDGEWAY NURSERIES**
Evesham Rd, Cookhill, Alcester **TEL: 01527 894 111**

**28 MARY ARDEN'S HOUSE**
Station Road, Wilmcote, Stratford-upon-Avon
**TEL: 01789 204 016**

**29 CHARLECOTE PARK, NATIONAL TRUST**
Charlecote, Wellesbourne, Warwick **TEL: 01789 470 277**

**30 CHARLECOTE FRUIT & FLOWERS**
Dog Kennel Close, Charlecote, Warwick
**TEL: 01789 842 674**

**31 SHAKESPEARE BIRTHPLACE**
Henley St, Stratford-upon-Avon **TEL: 01789 204 016**

**32 BANCROFT GARDENS**
Waterside, Stratford Upon Avon **TEL: 01789 260 631**

**33 DUDFIELD'S PLANT CENTRE**
Tavern Lane, Shottery, Stratford-upon-Avon
**TEL: 01789 292 689**

**34 ANNE HATHAWAY'S COTTAGE & GARDEN SHOP**
Cottage Lane, Shottery, Stratford-upon-Avon
**TEL: 01789 204 016**

**35 NASH'S HOUSE & NEW PLACE**
Chapel Street, Stratford-upon-Avon **TEL: 01789 204 016**

**36 HALL'S CROFT**
Old Town, Stratford-upon-Avon **TEL: 01789 204 016**

**37 AVON VALLEY GARDEN CENTRE**
Banbury Rd, Stratford-upon-Avon **TEL: 01789 414 383**

**38 HILLER GARDEN & PLANT CENTRE**
Dunnington Heath Farm, Dunnington, Alcester
**TEL: 01789 490 991**

**39 CRABTREE FARM NURSERIES**
3 Stratford Road, Bidford on Avon, Alcester
**TEL: 01789 773 497**

**40 WOODFIELD BROTHERS**
Wood End, Clifford Chambers, Stratford-upon-Avon
**TEL: 01789 205 618**

**41 NEW INN LANE NURSERIES**
Pitchill, Evesham **TEL: 01386 870 073**

**42 WAYSIDE NURSERIES**
Clifford Garden Centre, Campden Road,
Stratford-upon-Avon **TEL: 01789 205 745**

**43 MILL LANE NURSERIES**
Mill Lane, Cleeve Prior, Evesham **TEL: 01789 773 231**

**44 FOREST FARM**
Allens Hill, Pinvin, Pershore **TEL: 01386 552 240**

**45 AVON AQUATICS**
Sweet Knowle Farm, Preston On Stour,
Stratford-upon-Avon **TEL: 01789 450 638**

**46 FIBREX NURSERIES**
Honeybourne Road, Pebworth, Stratford-upon-Avon
**TEL: 01789 720 788**

**47 THREE SPRINGS NURSERY**
Defford Road, Pershore **TEL: 01386 555 476**

**48 SIDING NURSERIES**
Offenham Road, Offenham, Evesham
**TEL: 01386 493 47**

**49 BLACKWELL FUCHSIA NURSERY**
Woodbine Cottage, Blackwell, Shipston on Stour
**TEL: 01608 682 531**

**50 COTSWOLD GARDEN FLOWERS**
Sands Lane, Badsey, Evesham **TEL: 01386 422 829**

**51 BIRLINGHAM NURSERIES**
Birlingham, Pershore **TEL: 01386 750 668**

**52 HIDCOTE MANOR GARDEN, NATIONAL TRUST**
Hidcote Bartrim, Chipping Camden **TEL: 01386 438 333**

**53 BOWERS HILL NURSERY**
Willersley Road, Badsey, Evesham **TEL: 01386 832 124**

**54 ERNEST WILSON MEMORIAL GARDEN**
High Street, Leas Bourne, Chipping Camden
**TEL: 01386 840 884**

**55 BARN HOUSE**
152 High Street, Broadway **TEL: 01386 858 633**

**56 ORCHARD VIEW NURSERIES**
Orchard View, Evesham Road, Broadway
**TEL: 01386 852 346**

**57 CHARLES F ELLIS**
Nursery Oak Piece, Stanway Road, Stanston
**TEL: 01386 584 077**

**58 FOUR COUNTIES NURSERY & GARDEN SUPPLIES**
Burmington Road, Todenham, Moreton in Marsh
**TEL: 01608 650 522**

**59 MILL DENE**
Blockley, Moreton in Marsh **TEL: 01386 700 457**

**60 BATSFORD ARBORETUM**
Batsford Park, Batsford, Moreton in Marsh
**TEL: 01386 701 441**

**61 SNOWSHILL MANOR, NATIONAL TRUST**
Snowshill, Broadway **TEL: 01386 852 410**

**62 BATSFORD NURSERY**
Batsford, Moreton in Marsh **TEL: 01386 700 409**

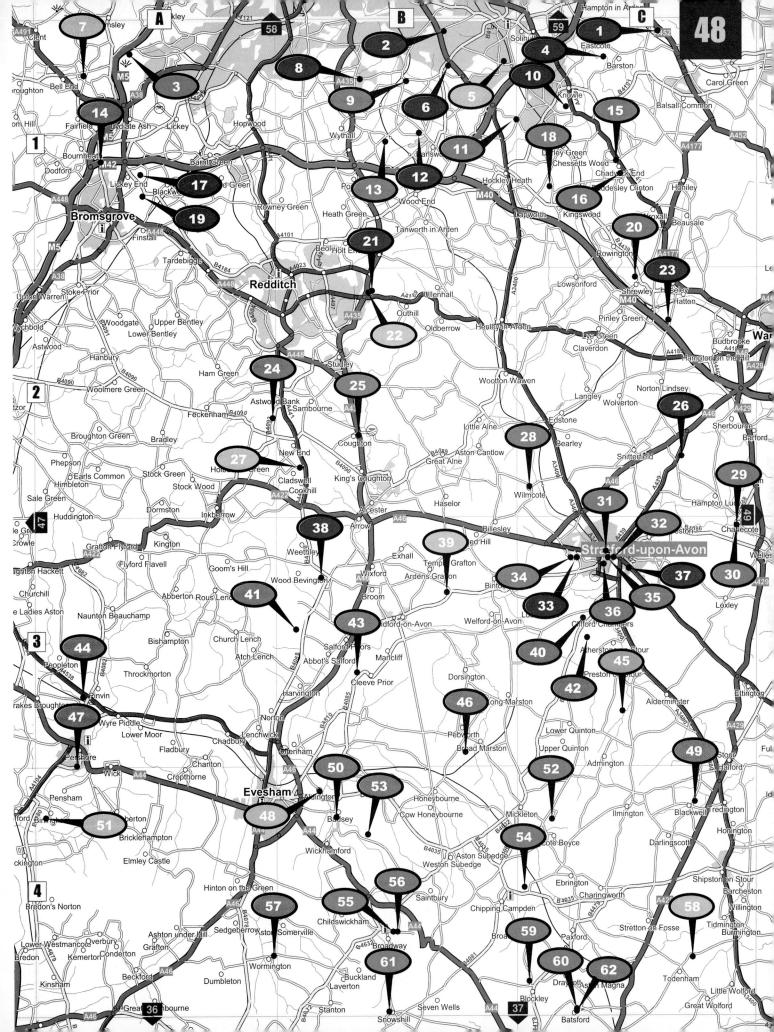

**1 COOMBE COUNTRY PARK**
Brinklow Road, Binley, Coventry
TEL: 024 7645 3720

**2 OAK FARM NURSERY**
Brinklow Road, Coventry
TEL: 024 7645 4658

**3 AVONDALE COTTAGE PERENNIALS**
3 Avondale Road, Coventry
TEL: 024 7667 3662

**4 OAKDALE ROSE & GARDEN CENTRE**
Oakdale Nurseries, Rugby Road, Coventry
TEL: 024 7654 2151

**5 WYEVALE GARDEN CENTRE**
Kings Newnham Road, Church Lawford, Rugby
TEL: 024 7654 2319

**6 UNIVERSITY OF WARWICK GARDENS**
Gibbet Hill Road, Coventry
TEL: 024 7652 3523

**7 TEBBS GARDEN CENTRE**
59-69 Hillmorton Road, Rugby
TEL: 01788 542 997

**8 BLOOMS OF RUGBY**
Bernhards Garden Centre, Bilton Road, Rugby
TEL: 01788 522 345

**9 RYTON ORGANIC GARDENS**
Ryton on Dunsmore, Coventry
TEL: 024 7630 3517

**10 SMITH'S NURSERIES**
Twelve Ash Lodge, Stoneleigh Road, Coventry
TEL: 024 7630 3382

**11 BUNGALOW NURSERIES**
65 London Road, Stretton on Dunsmore, Rugby
TEL: 01788 810 505

**12 TEBBS CRICK LODGE NURSERIES**
West Haddon Road, Crick
TEL: 01788 824 154

**13 JUST PLANTS**
25 Talisman Square, Kenilworth
TEL: 01926 853 311

**14 GUEST FOR PLANTS**
Queens Road, Kenilworth
TEL: 01926 852 759

**15 BERNHARDS RUGBY NURSERIES**
The Straight Mile, Rugby
TEL: 01788 521 177

**16 STONELEIGH GARDEN**
Stoneleigh Abbey Kenilworth
TEL: 01926 858 585

**17 VILLAGE FARM NURSERIES**
Onley Lane, Barby, Rugby
TEL: 01788 891 608

**18 WAPPENBURY HALL ESTATE NURSERY**
Wappenbury Hall, Wappenbury, Leamington Spa
TEL: 01926 633 251

**19 A D & N WHEELER**
Pye Court, Willoughby, Rugby
TEL: 01788 890 341

**20 WARWICK NURSERIES**
Woodloes Lane, Guys Cliffe, Warwick
TEL: 01926 492 273

**21 JEPHSON GARDENS**
Leamington Spa
TEL: 01926 450 000

**22 HURRANS GARDEN CENTRE**
Myton Road, Leamington Spa
TEL: 01926 881 122

**23 WARWICK CASTLE**
Castle Hill, Warwick
TEL: 01926 406 600

**24 THE MASTER'S GARDEN**
Lord Leycester Hospital, 60 High Street,
Warwick, Warwickshire, CV34 4BH.
TEL: 01926 491 422
*Historic walled garden including Norman Arch,
Nileometer and Millennium Knot Garden behind
medieval timber frame buildings. Featured in
many tv programmes and magazines. Tea rooms.*
OPEN: Mar 18-Sep 30: Tue-Sun & BH: 10-4.30.
ENTRY COSTS: £1.50, Child: Free.
SPECIALITIES: Themed gardens.
FACILITIES: Toilets, Coffee shop, Sell plants.

**25 BRIDGE NURSERY**
Tomlow Road, Stockton, Rugby
TEL: 01926 812 737

**26 WHILTON LOCKS GARDEN CENTRE**
Whilton Locks, Whilton, Daventry
TEL: 01327 842 727

**27 DUNCAN'S PET & GARDEN CENTRE**
10 Warwick Road, Wellesbourne, Warwick
TEL: 01789 841 847

**28 CANONS ASHBY HOUSE, NATIONAL TRUST**
Canons Ashby, Daventry
TEL: 01327 860 044

**29 FARNBOROUGH GARDEN CENTRE**
Southam Road, Farnborough, Banbury
TEL: 01295 690 479

**30 BARN FARM PLANTS**
Wardington, Banbury
TEL: 01295 758 080

**31 UPTON HOUSE, NATIONAL TRUST**
National Trust, Banbury
TEL: 01295 670 266

**32 D A CHESTER HOME NURSERIES**
Sulgrave Road, Greatworth, Banbury
TEL: 01295 768 141

**33 BROOK COTTAGE**
Well Lane, Alkerton, Banbury
TEL: 01295 670 303

**34 PURELY PLANTS**
Turnpike Hill, Main Road, Middleton Cheney
TEL: 01295 812 735

**35 WROXTON ABBEY**
Wroxton, Banbury
TEL: 01295 730 551

**36 HURRANS GARDEN CENTRE**
Compton Road, Banbury
TEL: 01295 266 300

**37 GREENFINGERS GARDEN CENTRE**
Market House Courtyard, Market Place, Brackley
TEL: 01280 701 677

**38 PURELY PLANTS**
Mill Lane, Kings Sutton, Banbury
TEL: 01295 812 735

**39 PLANTA EXOTICA**
11 Heath Close, Banbury
TEL: 01295 721 989

**40 SWALLOW'S NURSERY**
Finmere Road, Brackley
TEL: 01280 847 721

Walled garden

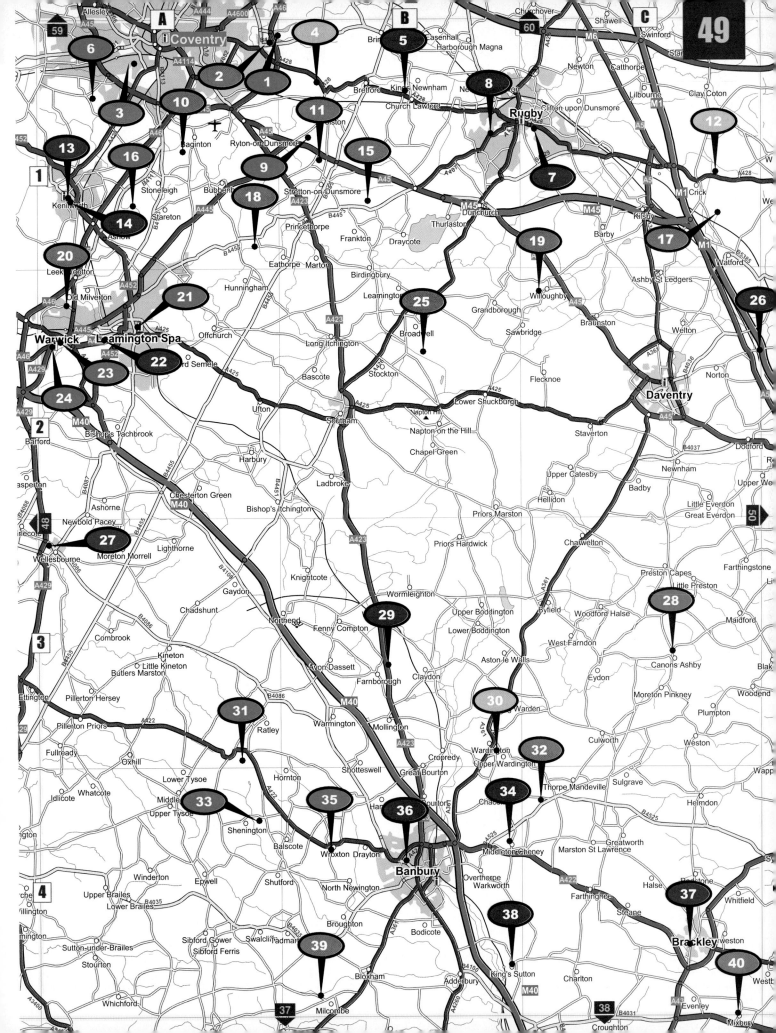

**1 SUNNYVALE FARM NURSERIES**
Sunnyvale Farm, Harrington, Northampton
TEL: 01604 686 608

**2 EVERGREEN NURSERIES**
Mawsley Lane, Loddington, Kettering
TEL: 01536 712 177

**3 ISE GARDEN CENTRE**
Warkton Lane, Kettering
TEL: 01536 519 792

**4 LAMPORT HALL GARDENS**
Lamport Hall, Lamport, Northampton
TEL: 01604 686 272

**5 BOSWORTH NURSERIES & GARDEN CENTRE**
110 Finedon Road, Burton Latimer, Kettering
TEL: 01536 722 635

**6 COTTESBROOKE HALL & GARDENS**
Cottesbrooke Hall, Cottesbrooke, Northampton
TEL: 01604 505 808

**7 COTON MANOR GARDENS**
Guilsborough, Northampton
TEL: 01604 740 219

**8 PLANTSMAN**
West Haddon Nurseries, Northampton Road, Northampton
TEL: 01788 510 206

**9 HILLSIDE FARM NURSERIES**
Hillside Farm, Harrowden Lane, Wellingborough
TEL: 01933 681 076

**10 CEDAR NURSERIES**
Poplar Farm, Holcot, Northampton
TEL: 01604 781 267

**11 THE WATER GARDEN**
Greenacres, Finedon Road, Wellingborough
TEL: 01933 271 870

---

**12 HADDONSTONE SHOW GARDENS**
The Forge House, Church Lane, East Haddon, Northampton, Northamptonshire, NN6 8DB.
TEL: 01604 770 711
EMAIL: info@haddonstone.co.uk
WEB: www.haddonstone.co.uk.
*View Haddonstone's classic garden ornaments in the walled manor gardens and the new jubilee garden, including urns, fountains, sundials, statuary, balustrading and follies.*
OPEN: Mon-Fri 9-5.30. Closed BH & Christmas.
ENTRY COSTS: Free
SPECIALITIES: Fountains, Ornaments, Stone ornaments, Water features.
FACILITIES: Toilets, Credit cards, Own gift tokens, Wheelchair access.

---

**13 HOLDENBY HOUSE & GARDENS**
Holdenby, Northampton
TEL: 01604 770 074

**14 GAGGINI'S PLANT CENTRE**
Glebe House, Glebe Road, Northampton
TEL: 01604 812 371

**15 THE PLANT NURSERY**
Sandy Hill Lane, Moulton, Northampton
TEL: 01604 491 941

**16 ROB'S NURSERY**
Castle Hill View, Church Street, Northampton
TEL: 01604 495 073

**17 WYEVALE GARDEN CENTRE**
Millers Lane, Wellingborough
TEL: 01933 273 728

**18 SYWELL COUNTRY PARK**
Washbrook Lane, Ecton, Northampton
TEL: 01604 810 970

**19 CRAMDEN NURSERY**
Harborough Road North, Northampton
TEL: 01604 846 246

**20 RAVENSTHORPE NURSERY**
6 East Haddon Road, Ravensthorpe
TEL: 01604 770 548

**21 WYEVALE GARDEN CENTRE**
Harlestone Road, Harlestone Heath, Northampton
TEL: 01604 751 346

**22 PODINGTON GARDEN CENTRE**
High Street, Podington, Wellingborough
TEL: 01933 353 656

**23 GOLBY'S GARDEN CENTRE**
Tollgate Way, Duston, Northampton
TEL: 01604 752 155

**24 BLISS LANE NURSERY**
34 Bliss Lane, Flore, Northampton
TEL: 01327 340 918

**25 CASTLE ASHBY GARDENS**
Castle Ashby, Northampton
TEL: 01604 696 696

**26 BILLING GARDEN CENTRE**
The Causeway, Great Billing, Northampton
TEL: 01604 404 550

**27 DELAPRE ABBEY**
London Road, Northampton
TEL: 01604 761 074

**28 WYEVALE GARDEN CENTRE**
Newport Pagnell Road, Wootton, Northampton
TEL: 01604 765 725

**29 C W WARWICK**
Bedford Road East, Yardley Hastings, Northampton
TEL: 01604 696 241

**30 D F & C M YOUNGS**
33 Northampton Road, Blisworth, Northampton
TEL: 01604 858 574

**31 BELL PLANTATION**
Plantation House, Watling Street, Towcester
TEL: 01327 354 126

**32 GREEN LANE NURSERIES**
Brackley Road, Towcester
TEL: 01327 350 593

**33 ALDERTON PLANT NURSERY**
Spring Lane, Alderton, Towcester
TEL: 01327 811 253

**34 WYEVALE GARDEN CENTRE**
Junction Avebury Blvd & Secklow Gate, Milton Keynes
TEL: 01908 604 011

**35 STOWE GARDENS, NATIONAL TRUST**
Buckingham
TEL: 01280 822 850

**36 WYEVALE GARDEN CENTRE**
Newport Road, Woburn Sands, Milton Keynes
TEL: 01908 281 161

**37 FROSTS WOBURN SANDS**
Newport Road, Woburn Sands, Milton Keynes
TEL: 01908 583 511

**38 CUCKOO SPIT NURSERIES**
Walnut Tree Farm, Walton Road, Milton Keynes
TEL: 01908 698 341

**39 THE FISH HOUSE**
18 Watling Street, Fenny Stratford, Milton Keynes
TEL: 01908 377 336

Liatris

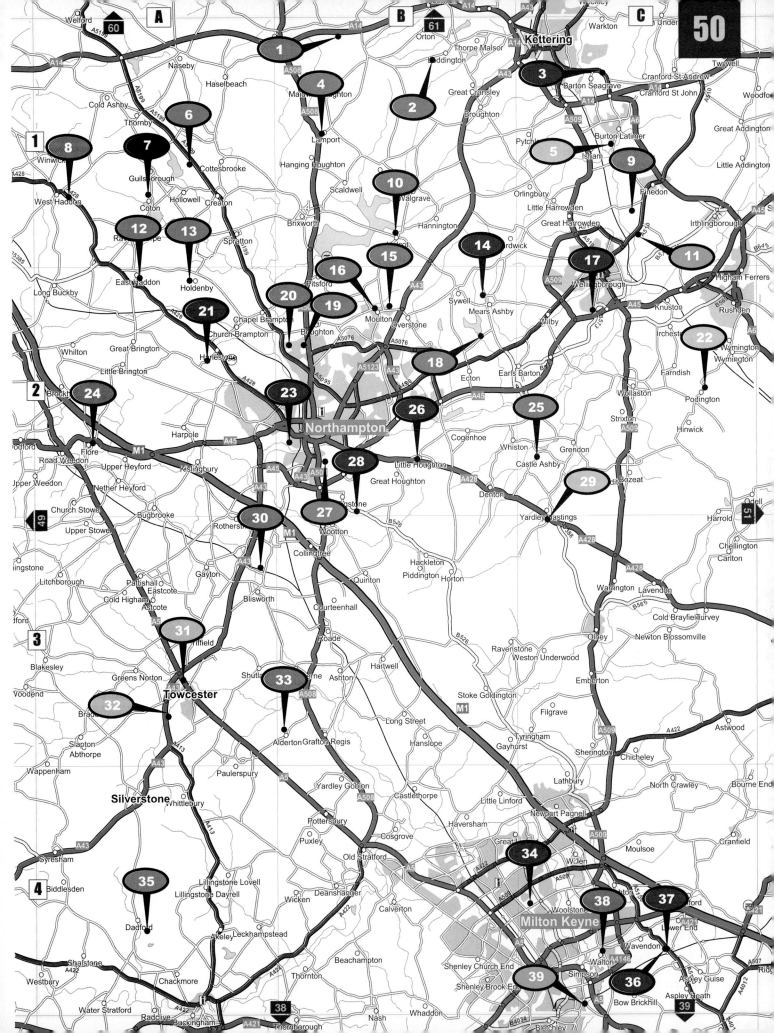

**1  HOMEFIELDS NURSERY**
Station Road, Catworth, Huntingdon
**TEL:** 01832 710 428

**2  HUNTINGTON GARDEN & LEISURE**
Banks End, Wyton, Huntingdon
**TEL:** 01480 433 349

**3  BRAMPTON GARDEN CENTRE**
Buckden Road, Brampton, Huntingdon
**TEL:** 01480 453 048

**4  TURF MAZE**
The Green, Hilton, Huntingdon
**TEL:** 01480 830 137

**5  ROOKERY FARM NURSERIES**
5 Rookery Road, Bedford
**TEL:** 01480 213 506

**6  BLUEBELL NURSERIES**
Roxton Road, Chawston, Bedford
**TEL:** 01480 216 934

**7  MILTON ERNEST GARDEN CENTRE**
Radwell Road, Milton Ernest, Bedford
**TEL:** 01234 823 033

**8  ROXTON GARDEN CENTRE**
Bedford Road, Roxton
**TEL:** 01480 212 701

**9  WARESLEY PARK GARDEN CENTRE & NURSERIES**
Gamlingay Road, Waresley, Sandy
**TEL:** 01767 650 249

**10  SEDDINGTON NURSERIES**
Great North Road, Seddington, Sandy
**TEL:** 01767 680 983

**11  ASTERBY AND CHALKCROFT NURSERY**
The Ridgeway, Blunham
**TEL:** 01767 640 148

**12  FROSTS WILLINGTON**
Willington Garden Centre, Sandy Road, Bedford
**TEL:** 01234 838 777

**13  THE LODGE NATURE RESERVE**
The RSPB, Potton Road, Sandy, Bedfordshire, SG19 2DL.
**TEL:** 01767 680 541
**EMAIL:** thelodge@rspb.org.uk
**WEB:** www.rspb.org.uk
*The organically maintained gardens around the mansion boast large specimen trees, spreading rhododendron, an azalea walk, wisteria, a long herbaceous bed and wildlife garden.*
**OPEN:** Mon-Fri 9-9 or dusk if earlier, Sat-Sun 10-9 or dusk if earlier.
**ENTRY COSTS:** £3, Child: £1, OAPs: £1.50, Family: £6.
**SPECIALITIES:** Bluebells, Herbaceous border, Lavender, Trees.
**FACILITIES:** Credit cards, Gift shop, Bookshop, Toilets, Wheelchair access.

**14  COTTAGE FARM NURSERIES**
312 Cople Road, Cardington, Bedford
**TEL:** 01234 838 383

**15  GROWING CARPETS**
Christmas Tree House, High Street, Royston
**TEL:** 01763 852 705

**16  FIR SCREEN NURSERIES**
Broom Road, Stanford, Biggleswade
**TEL:** 01462 811 264

**17  LANGFORD NURSERIES & GARDEN CENTRE**
Henlow Road, Langford, Biggleswade
**TEL:** 01462 700 791

**18  MCGRATH NURSERIES**
The A507, Maulden Bypass, Maulden
**TEL:** 01525 862 124

**19  STAPLES NURSERIES**
Fordfield Road, Millbrook, Bedford
**TEL:** 01525 405 484

**20  BICKERDIKES GARDEN CENTRE**
Norton Road, Norton, Letchworth
**TEL:** 01462 673 333

**21  TAPP'S GARDEN CENTRE**
Wallington Road, Baldock
**TEL:** 01462 896 302

Gerber Daisy

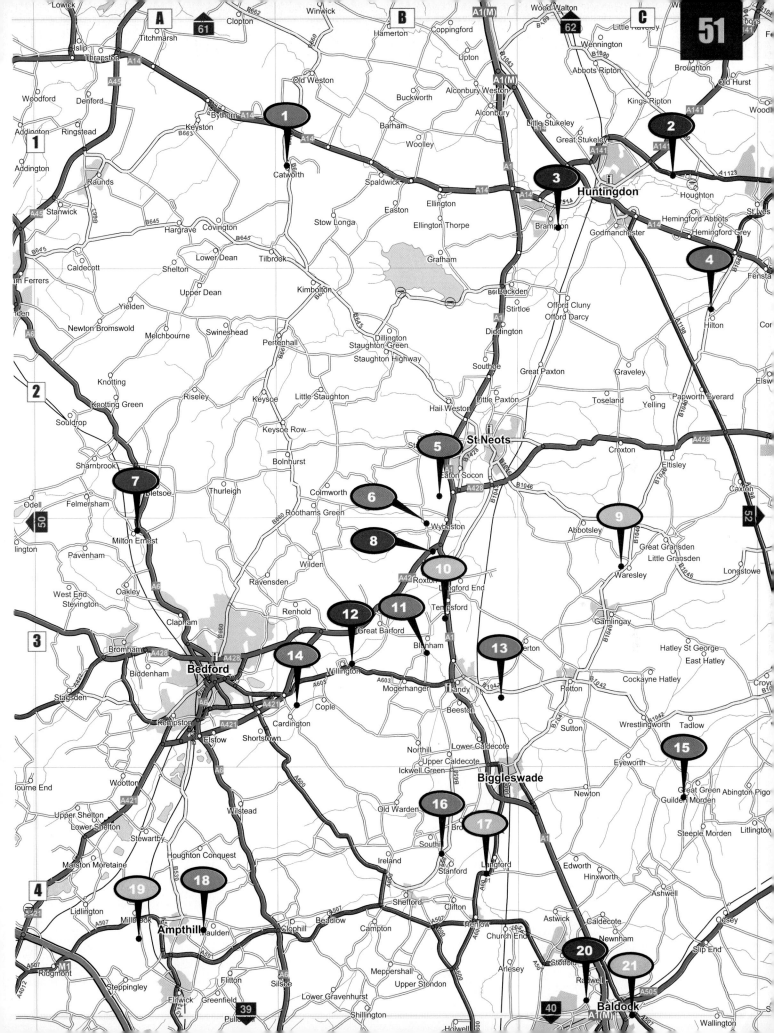

**1 PARKHALL NURSERIES & GARDEN CENTRE**
Parkhall Road, Somersham, Huntingdon
TEL: 01487 840 397

**2 PEMBROKE FARM NURSERY**
Pembroke Farm Nursery, Barway, Ely
TEL: 01353 722 903

**3 SOHAM NURSERIES & GARDEN CENTRE**
67 East Fen Common, Soham, Ely
TEL: 01353 720 848

**4 TWENTYPENCE GARDEN CENTRE**
Twentypence Road, Wilburton, Ely
TEL: 01353 740 024

**5 TRIANGLE FARM NURSERY**
Angle Common, Soham, Ely
TEL: 01353 720 313

**6 FORDHAM NURSERY**
Market Street, Fordham, Ely
TEL: 01638 720 455

**7 THE PLANT PLACE**
2 Mill Road, Fen Drayton, Cambridge
TEL: 01954 232 699

**8 MAY'S GARDEN CENTRE**
Windmill Hill, Exning, Newmarket
TEL: 01638 577 261

**9 LONGFIELDS NURSERY**
Oakington Road, Cottenham
TEL: 01223 234 929

**10 OAKINGTON GARDEN CENTRE**
Dry Drayton Road, Oakington, Cambridge
TEL: 01223 234 818

**11 CAMBRIDGE GARDEN PLANTS**
The Lodge, Clayhithe Road, Horningsea
TEL: 01223 861 370

**12 ANSELLS GARDEN CENTRE**
High Street, Horningsea, Cambridge
TEL: 01223 860 320

**13 ANGLESEY ABBEY, GARDEN AND LODE MILL**
Lode, Cambridge
TEL: 01223 811 200

**14 CLARE COLLEGE FELLOWS' GARDEN**
Trinity Lane, Cambridge
TEL: 01223 333 200

**15 CAMBRIDGE UNIVERSITY BOTANIC GARDEN**
Cory Lodge, Bateman Street, Cambridge, Cambridgeshire, CB2 1JF.
TEL: 01223 336 265
EMAIL: enquiries@botanic.cam.ac.uk
WEB: www.botanic.cam.ac.uk

*Forty acres of beautifully landscaped gardens and glasshouses displaying the amazing diversity of the plant kingdom. Colour and interest all year. Entrance on Bateman Street. Nine National Collections*
OPEN: Nov-Jan: 10-4. Feb: 10-5. Mar-Sep: 10-6. Oct: 10-5. Closed Dec 25-Jan 1.
ENTRY COSTS: £2.50, Child: £2 Under 5s free, OAPs: £2.
SPECIALITIES: Herbaceous plants, Pinetum, Woodland plants, Alpines.
FACILITIES: Toilets, Coffee shop, Gift shop, Pushchair friendly, Wheelchair access.

**16 SAUNDERS NURSERIES**
11 West Street, Comberton, Cambridge
TEL: 01223 262 268

**17 SCOTSDALE NURSERY & GARDEN CENTRE**
120 Cambridge Road, Great Shelford, Cambridge
TEL: 01223 842 777

**18 PADLOCK CROFT**
Padlock Road, West Wratting, Cambridge
TEL: 01223 290 383

**19 ALL YEAR NURSERY**
51 North Road, Great Abington, Cambridge
TEL: 01223 893 218

**20 CROSSING HOUSE GARDEN**
Meldreth Road, Shepreth, Royston
TEL: 01763 261 071

**21 COUNTRY HOMES AND GARDENS**
Dunsbridge Turnpike, Shepreth, Royston, Hertfordshire, SG8 6RD.
TEL: 01763 260 412
EMAIL: royston@countryhomesandgardens.co.uk
WEB: www.countryhomesandgardens.co.uk
*One of the county's leading garden centres with a vast range of plants, garden and conservatory furniture, gifts and garden goods. Free local delivery - please phone for details.*
OPEN: Mon-Sat 9-6, Sun 10-4.
SPECIALITIES: Comprehensive range of landscape materials for trade and retail customers.
FACILITIES: Bookshop, Coffee shop, Credit cards, Dogs allowed, Plant guarantee, Restaurant, Toilets, Wheelchair access, HTA gift tokens.

**22 PHILLIMORE GARDEN CENTRE**
Cambridge Road, Melbourn, Royston
TEL: 01763 260 537

**23 ICKLETON GARDEN CENTRE & AQUATICS**
Frogge Street, Ickleton, Saffron Walden
TEL: 01799 530 911

**24 BURY LANE FARM SHOP & NURSERY**
Melbourn, Royston
TEL: 01763 260 418

**25 MARDEN COTTAGE NURSERY**
1 Marden Cottage, Old North Road, Kneesworth
TEL: 01763 244 457

**26 BEECHES NURSERY**
Village Centre, Ashdon, Saffron Walden
TEL: 01799 584 362

**27 SPRINGWELL NURSERIES**
Walden Road, Little Chesterford, Saffron Walden
TEL: 01799 530 959

**28 AUDLEY END HOUSE, ENGLISH HERITAGE**
Audley End, Saffron Walden
TEL: 01799 522 399

**29 AUDLEY END ORGANIC KITCHEN GARDEN**
Audley End House, Saffron Walden
TEL: 01799 522 842

**30 GARDEN CENTRE AT SAFFRON WALDEN**
Thaxted Road, Saffron Walden
TEL: 01799 527 536

**31 MANOR NURSERIES**
Thaxted Road, Wimbish, Saffron Walden
TEL: 01799 513 481

**32 R & R SAGGERS**
Waterloo House, High Street, Newport
TEL: 01799 540 858

Gay Princess

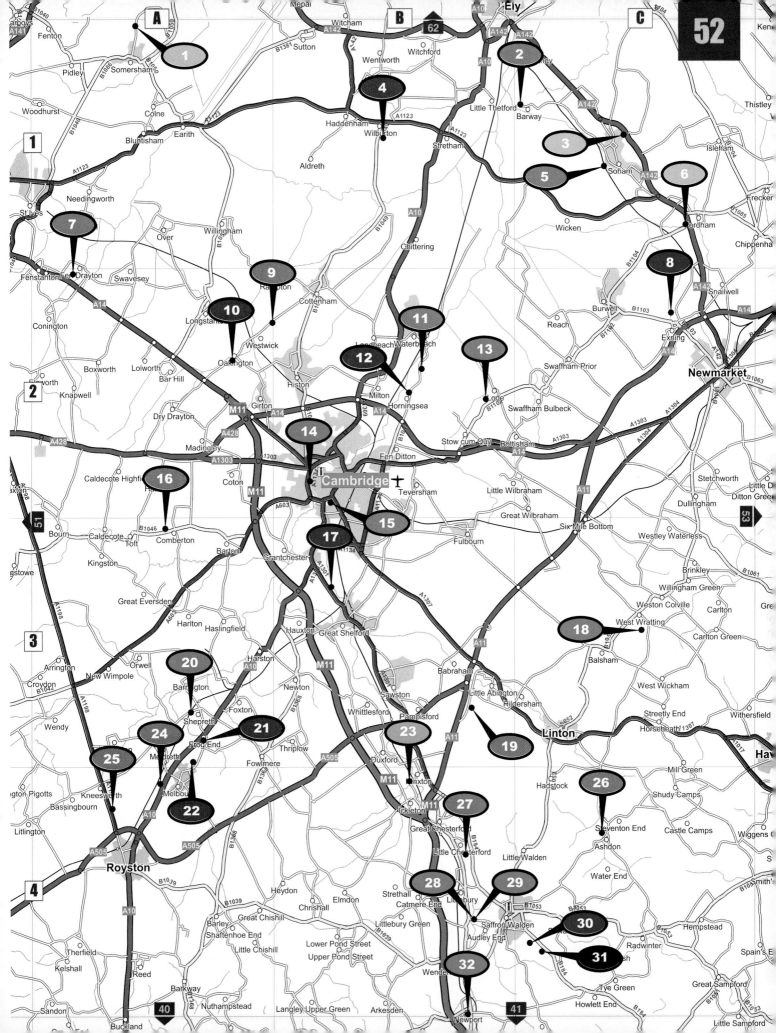

**1** WAVENY WATER GARDENS
Park Road, Diss
TEL: 01379 642 697

**2** THE PLANT CENTRE
Park Road, Diss
TEL: 01379 644 171

**3** HILL CREST NURSERIES
Barningham Road, Stanton, Bury St Edmunds
TEL: 01359 250 327

**4** WYKEN HALL
Stanton, Bury St Edmunds
TEL: 01359 250 287

**5** GARDINER'S HALL PLANTS
Braiseworth, Eye
TEL: 01379 678 285

**6** DOGWOOD NURSERY
Risby Barn, South Street, Bury St Edmunds
TEL: 01284 811 055

**7** POTASH NURSERY
Cow Green, Bacton, Stowmarket
TEL: 01449 781 671

**8** MARLOWS DIY & GARDEN CENTRE
Hollow Road, Bury St Edmunds
TEL: 01284 763 155

**9** MILL'S FARM PLANTS & GARDENS
Norwich Road, Mendlesham, Stowmarket
TEL: 01449 766 425

**10** ABBEY GARDENS
Angel Hill, Bury St Edmunds
TEL: 01284 757 490

**11** ROUGHAM HALL NURSERIES
Ipswich Road, Rougham, Bury St Edmunds
TEL: 01359 270 577

**12** WYEVALE GARDEN CENTRE
Rougham Road, Bury St Edmunds
TEL: 01284 755 818

**13** BEYTON NURSERIES
Tostock Road, Beyton, Bury St Edmunds
TEL: 01359 270 800

**14** WOOLPIT NURSERIES
Woolpit, Bury St Edmunds
TEL: 01359 240 370

**15** ICKWORTH PARK & GARDEN, NATIONAL TRUST
The Rotunda, Ickworth, Horringer
TEL: 01284 735 270

**16** NAREY'S GARDEN CENTRE
Eden Nurseries, Bury Road, Stowmarket
TEL: 01449 612 559

**17** HARVEYS GARDEN PLANTS
Bradfield St George, Bury St Edmunds
TEL: 01284 386 777

**18** MARTINS NURSERIES
Smallwood Green, Bradfield St George,
Bury St Edmunds
TEL: 01449 737 698

**19** LAVENHAM GUILDHALL OF CORPUS CHRISTI, NATIONAL TRUST
Market Place, Lavenham, Sudbury
TEL: 01787 247 646

**20** HEDGEROWS FARM SHOP & NURSERY
Hedgerows Farm, Brent Eleigh, Sudbury
TEL: 01787 247 772

**21** DAIRY FARM NURSERY
Lower Dairy Farm, Bramford, Ipswich
TEL: 01473 833 359

**22** HOLLOW TREES FARM SHOP
Hollow Trees, Semer, Hadleigh
TEL: 01449 741 247

**23** MELFORD HALL, NATIONAL TRUST
Long Melford, Sudbury
TEL: 01787 880 286

**24** CLAREMONT NURSERY
Back Road (A1071), Hintlesham
TEL: 07702 083 378

**25** WYEVALE GARDEN CENTRE
Newton Road, Chilton, Sudbury
TEL: 01787 373 628

**26** ESSEX & SUFFOLK KOI
Bolton Garden Centre, Birdbrook, Halstead
TEL: 01440 788 007

**27** GREEN LAWNS BONSAI
The Nursery, Hadleigh Road, Boxford
TEL: 01787 210 501

**28** BY-PASS NURSERIES
Capel St Mary Garden Centre, London Road,
Capel St Mary
TEL: 01473 310 604

**29** FRANCES MOUNT PERENNIAL PLANTS
1 Steps Farm, Polstead, Colchester
TEL: 01206 262 811

**30** PARADISE CENTRE
Twinstead Road, Lamarsh, Bures
TEL: 01787 269 449

**31** HEDINGHAM CASTLE
Castle Hedingham, Halstead
TEL: 01787 460 261

**32** THE PLACE FOR PLANTS
East Bergholt Place, East Bergholt
TEL: 01206 299 224

**33** SPAINS HALL FOREST NURSERY
Spains Hall Farmhouse, Spains Hall Road, Braintree
TEL: 01371 810 156

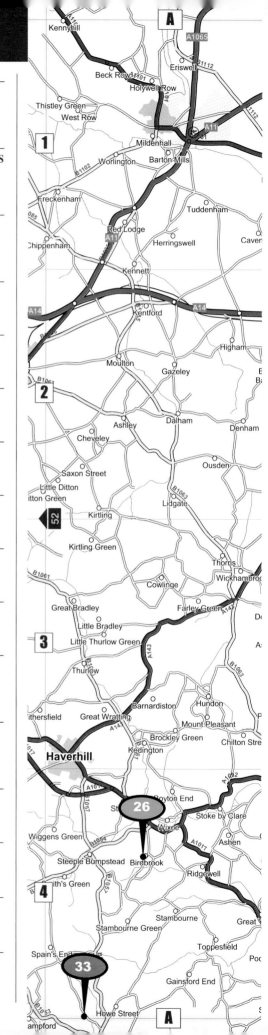

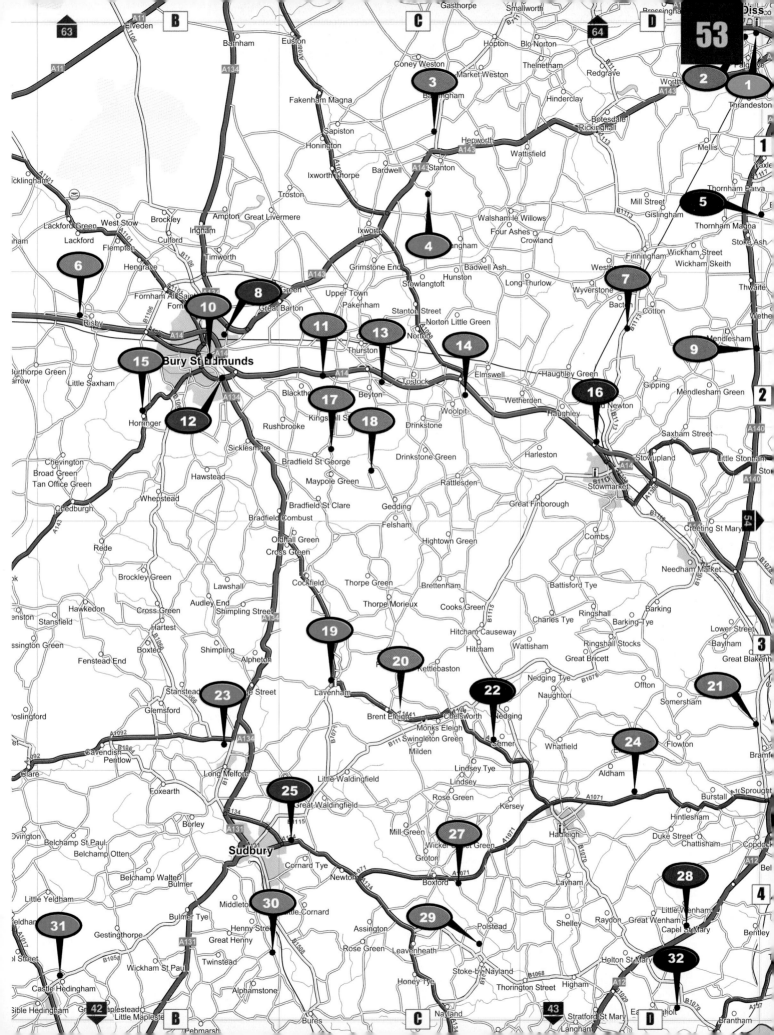

**1  DISS GARDEN CENTRE**
Victoria Road, Diss
TEL: 01379 642 873

**2  HOLTON ROAD GARDEN CENTRE**
36 Holton Road, Halesworth
TEL: 01986 872 761

**3  GOLDBROOK PLANTS**
Hoxne, Eye
TEL: 01379 668 770

**4  WOOTTENS PLANTS**
Blackheath, Wenhaston, Halesworth
TEL: 01502 478 258

**5  WRIGHT'S ROSES**
Broadview Bungalow, The Street, Woodbridge
TEL: 01379 388 162

**6  BRIDGE NURSERIES**
Bridge House Dunwich, Saxmundham
TEL: 01728 648 850

**7  ASKERS HILL GARDEN CENTRE**
Little Street, Yoxford, Saxmundham
TEL: 01728 668 237

**8  WHITE HALL PLANTS**
Southolt Road, Worlingworth
TEL: 01728 628 490

**9  LAUREL FARM HERBS**
Main Road, Kelsale, Saxmundham
TEL: 01728 668 223

**10  PARK GREEN NURSERIES**
Wetheringsett, Stowmarket
TEL: 01728 860 139

**11  FRAMLINGHAM CASTLE**
Framlingham
TEL: 01728 724 189

**12  LEISTON GARDEN CENTRE**
8-10 Abbey Road, Leiston
TEL: 01728 830 123

**13  DEBEN VALLEY NURSERIES**
Thorpe Lane, Ashfield
TEL: 01728 860 559

**14  MICKFIELD WATERGARDEN CENTRE**
Debenham Road, Mickfield, Stowmarket
TEL: 01449 711 336

**15  THE WALLED GARDEN**
Park Road, Benhall, Saxmundham
TEL: 01728 602 510

**16  GARNETTS GARDENS**
Fen Nursery, The Street, Woodbridge
TEL: 01728 724 589

**17  STONHAM BARNS GARDEN CENTRE**
Pettaugh Road, Stonham Aspal, Stowmarket
TEL: 01449 711 103

**18  LADYBIRD NURSERIES**
Gromford Lane, Snape, Saxmundham
TEL: 01728 688 289

**19  HELMINGHAM HALL GARDENS**
Helmingham Hall, Helmingham, Stowmarket
TEL: 01473 890 363

**20  EXOTIC GARDEN CO.**
Hall Farm, Saxmundham Road, Aldeburgh
TEL: 01728 454 456

**21  SISKIN PLANTS**
Davey Lane, Charsfield, Woodbridge
TEL: 01473 737 567

**22  OTLEY HALL**
Hall Lane, Otley, Ipswich
TEL: 01473 890 264

**23  TLC BOTANICA**
Chantry Farm, Campsy Ashe, Wickham Market
TEL: 01728 747 113

**24  CROWN NURSERY**
High Street, Ufford, Woodbridge
TEL: 01394 460 755

**25  N J SCOTT FARM SHOP & NURSERY**
Glencoe, Church Lane, Ipswich
TEL: 01473 830 331

**26  L SWANN NURSERY**
Eyke Road, Bromswell, Woodbridge
TEL: 01394 382 698

**27  WYEVALE GARDEN CENTRE**
Grundisburgh Road, Woodbridge
TEL: 01394 380 022

**28  NOTCUTTS GARDEN CENTRE**
Ipswich Road, Woodbridge
TEL: 01394 445 400

**29  LAUREL FARM GARDEN CENTRE**
Laurel Farm, Henley Road, Ipswich
TEL: 01473 215 984

**30  HOME MEADOWS NURSERY**
Top Street, Woodbridge
TEL: 01394 382 419

**31  FIRECREST TREES AND SHRUBS**
Hall Road, Little Bealings, Woodbridge
TEL: 01473 625 937

**32  VICTORIA NURSERIES**
Westerfield Road, Ipswich
TEL: 01473 253 980

**33  CHRIS LING GARDEN SCENE**
9 Beardmoor Park, Martlesham Heath, Ipswich
TEL: 01473 610 926

**34  WYVALE GARDEN CENTRE**
39 West Gate, Ipswich
TEL: 01473 288 198

**35  BOURNE GARDEN CENTRE**
Wherstead Road, Ipswich
TEL: 01473 691 567

**36  STATION NURSERIES**
2 Cordys Lane, Trimley St Mary, Felixstowe
TEL: 01394 283 518

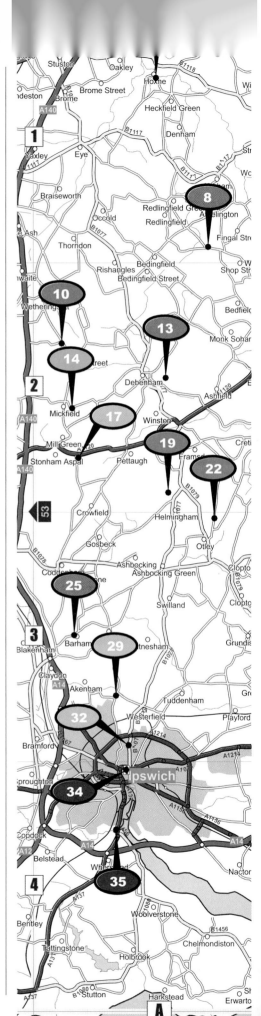

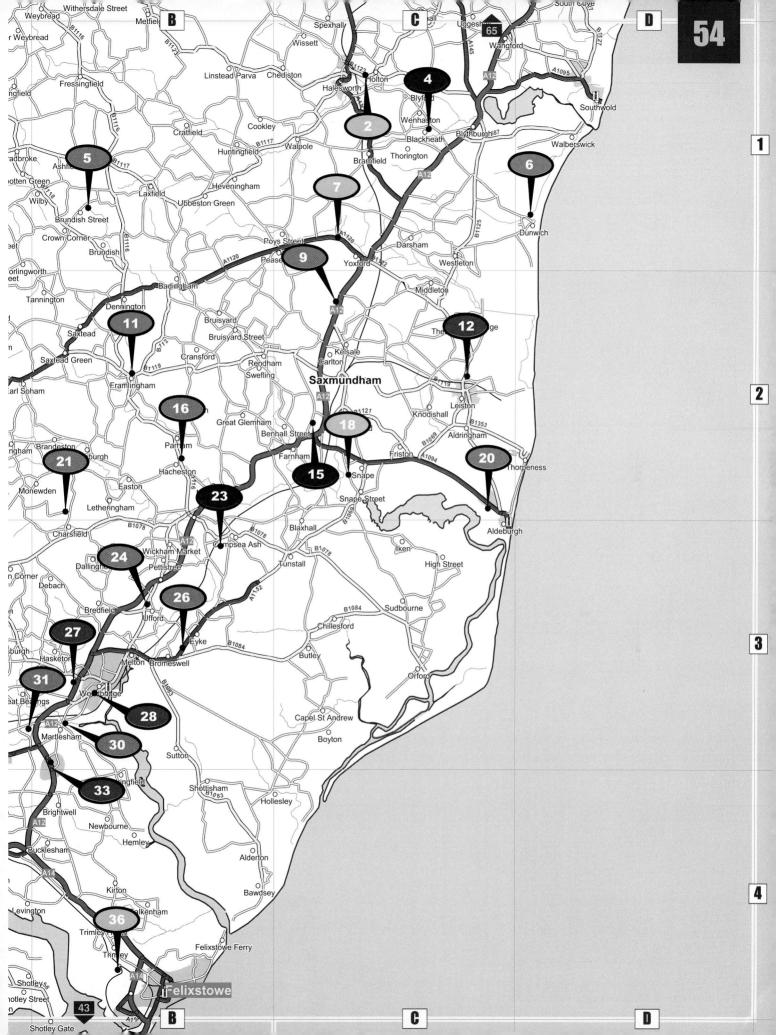

# POWYS · CEREDIGION

**1   ROSEMARY'S FARMHOUSE NURSERY**
Llwn-y-Moel-Gau, Llanfihangel, Llanfyllin
**TEL:** 01691 648 196

**2   BANWY VALLEY NURSERY**
Foel, Welshpool
**TEL:** 01938 820 281

**3   CEFN VAENOR NURSERIES**
Capel Dewi, Aberystwyth
**TEL:** 01970 820 019

Fungi

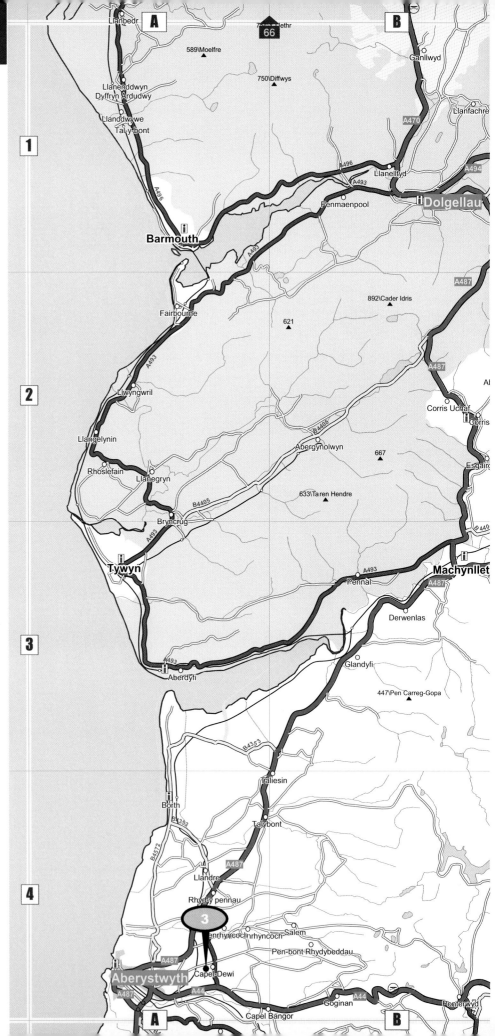

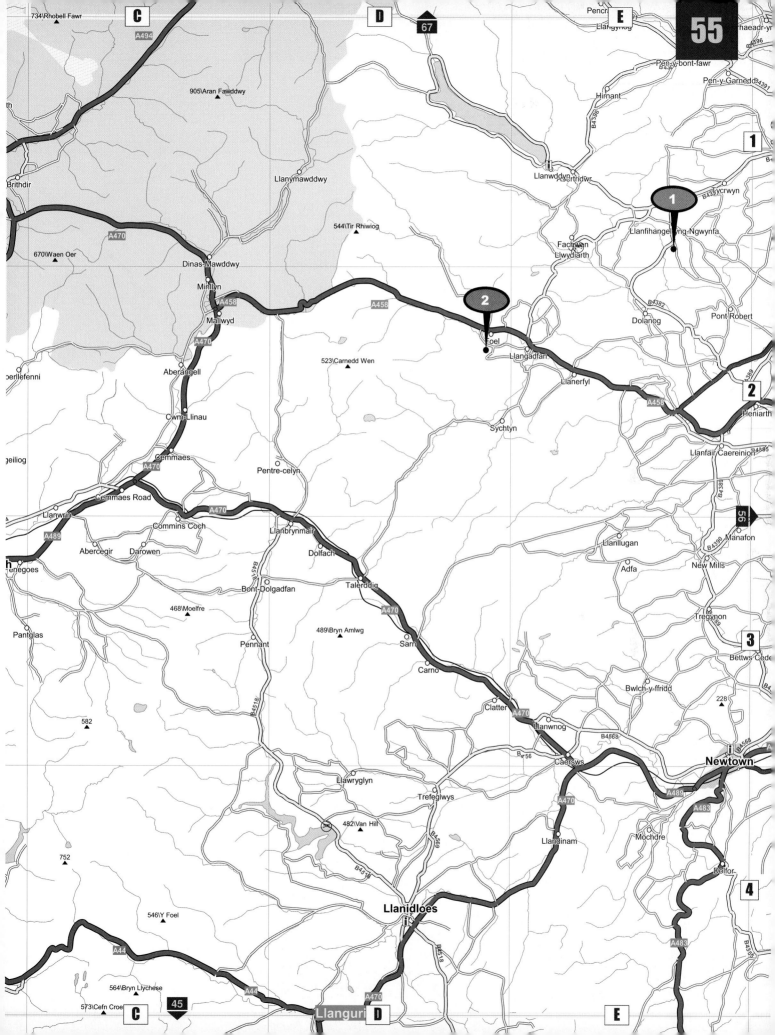

**1** **P F STUBBS**
The Nursery, Weston Lullingfield, Shrewsbury
**TEL:** 01939 260 307

**2** **SHAWBURY GARDEN CENTRE &
FRUIT FARM**
Edgebolton, Shawbury, Shrewsbury
**TEL:** 01939 251 173

**3** **COUNTRY GARDEN PLANT CENTRE**
Black Birches, Hadnall, Shrewsbury
**TEL:** 01939 210 380

**4** **HALL FARM NURSERY**
Vicarage Lane, Kinnerley, Oswestry
**TEL:** 01691 682 135

**5** **MERTON NURSERIES**
Merton, Holyhead Road, Bicton
**TEL:** 01743 850 773

**6** **DERWEN GARDEN CENTRE**
Guilsfield, Welshpool, Powys, SY21 9PH.
**TEL:** 01938 553 015
**EMAIL:** Kathy@derwengardencentre.co.uk
**WEB:** www.derwengardencentre.co.uk

*Unique atmosphere, ideal for an enjoyable day
out. Exceptional range of plants, complimented by
pottery, stoneware and statuary. Stunning decorative
gift ware. Licensed cafe.*
**OPEN:** Wed-Mon 10-6, Tue 2-6. Closed Christmas
& New Year.
**SPECIALITIES:** Comprehensive range.
**FACILITIES:** Bookshop, Child area, Coffee shop, Credit cards,
Gift shop, HTA gift tokens, Own gift tokens, Pushchair friendly,
Restaurant, Sell plants, Toilets, Wheelchair access.

**7** **OAK COTTAGE WALLED HERB
GARDEN**
Pimhill Organic Farm Shop, Harmer Hill
**TEL:** 01939 210 219

**8** **PERCY THROWER'S GARDENING &
LEISURE**
Oteley Road, Shrewsbury
**TEL:** 01743 352 311

**9** **SUTTON GRANGE NURSERY**
Oteley Road, Shrewsbury
**TEL:** 01743 355 201

**10** **EMSTREY GARDEN CENTRE**
Emstry, Shrewsbury
**TEL:** 01743 356 012

**11** **ATTINGHAM PARK, NATIONAL TRUST**
Shrewsbury
**TEL:** 01743 708 123

**12** **DOBBIES GARDEN WORLD**
Bayston Hill, Shrewsbury
**TEL:** 01743 874 261

**13** **DINGLE NURSERIES & GARDEN**
Frochas, Welshpool, Powys, SY21 9JD.
**TEL:** 01938 555 145
**EMAIL:** retail@dinglenurseries.co.uk
**WEB:** www.dinglenurseries.co.uk

*Set in the heart of mid-Wales, the nursery, alongside
the famous and stunning four acre garden contains
a huge range of quality, well priced plants.*
**OPEN:** Wed-Mon 9-5. Closed Christmas week.
**ENTRY COSTS:** £2, Child: free. Admission charge
for garden only.
**SPECIALITIES:** Trees, Shrubs, Hedging,
Herbaceous plants, Rare plants.
**FACILITIES:** Toilets, Dogs allowed, Sell plants,
Wheelchair access, Credit cards, HTA gift tokens,
Own gift tokens, Pushchair friendly.

**14** **SEVERNDALE NURSERIES**
Wroxeter Lane, Cross Houses, Shrewsbury
**TEL:** 01743 761 212

**15** **POWIS CASTLE GARDENS,
NATIONAL TRUST**
Welshpool
**TEL:** 01938 551 920

**16** **LOWER SPRING NURSERY**
Kenley, Shrewsbury
**TEL:** 01952 510 589

**17** **ABERMULE NURSERY GARDENS**
Kerry Road, Abermule, Montgomery
**TEL:** 01686 630 203

**18** **STOKESAY CASTLE, ENGLISH HERITAGE**
Stokesay
**TEL:** 01588 672 544

Clivea

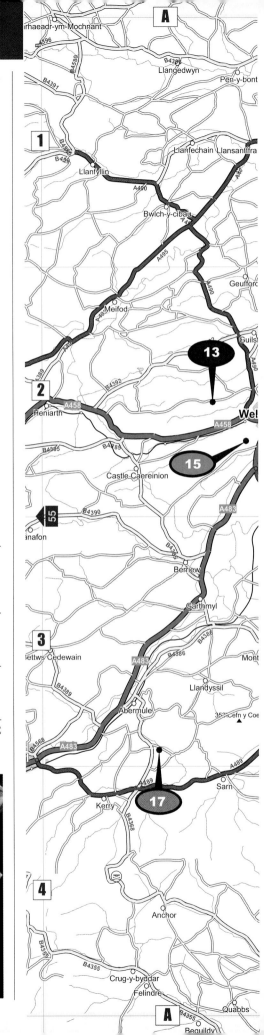

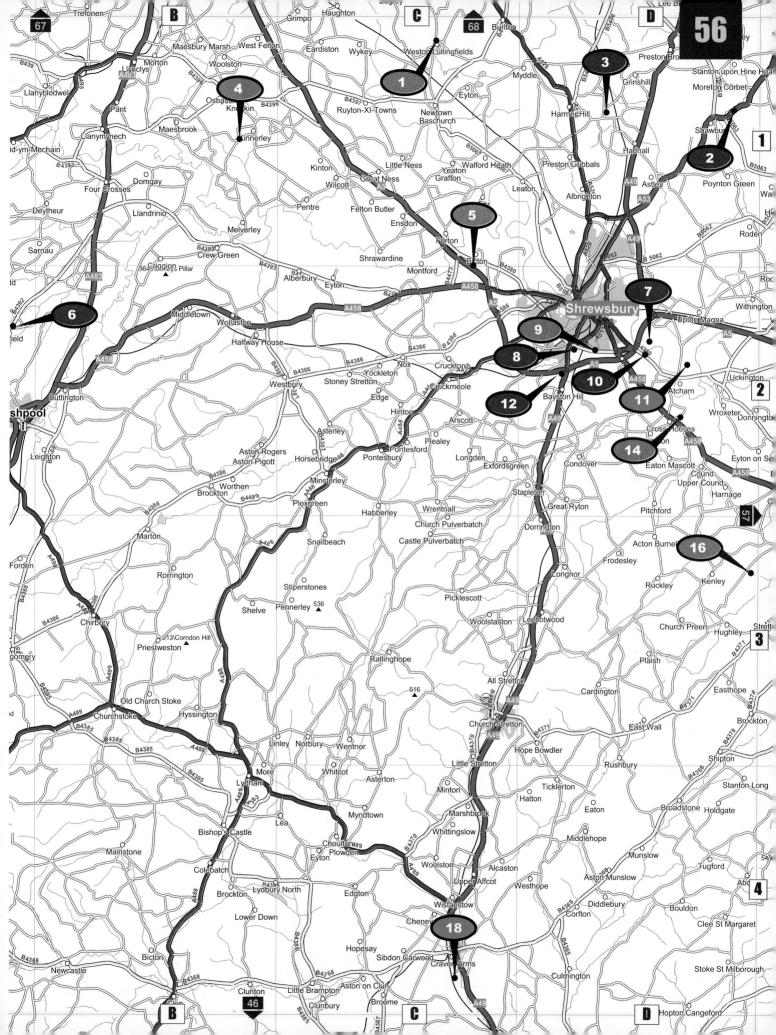

**1 PRIORY GARDEN CENTRE**
18-22 Corporation Street, Stafford
TEL: 01785 246 363

**2 BARLOW NURSERIES**
Aylesland House, Cheswardine Road, Pickstock
TEL: 01952 550 933

**3 SANDSTONES COTTAGE GARDEN PLANTS**
58 Bolas Heath, Great Bolas, Telford
TEL: 01952 541 657

**4 MILDENE NURSERY**
Tibberton Road, Great Bolas, Telford
TEL: 01952 541 314

**5 PLOUGH FARM NURSERIES**
Plough Farm, Forton Road, Newport
TEL: 01952 810 915

**6 MILLINGTONS GARDEN CENTRE**
101 High Street, Newport
TEL: 01952 811 190

**7 FOSTER GARDEN CENTRE**
Oak Lane, Bradley, Stafford
TEL: 01785 780 208

**8 WYEVALE GARDEN CENTRE**
Station Road, Donnington, Telford
TEL: 01952 677 733

**9 BLOOMSBURY NURSERY**
Bloomsbury, Shifnal
TEL: 01952 691 203

**10 STANELLI GARDEN CENTRE**
Bungham Road, Penkridge, Stafford
TEL: 01785 712 387

**11 WATKINS NURSERIES & GARDEN CENTRE**
Apley Castle Gardens, Apley, Telford
TEL: 01952 242 393

**12 WREKIN FARM & GARDEN CENTRE**
Bridge Road, Wellington, Telford
TEL: 01952 641 342

**13 COTTAGE ROSE GARDENS**
Woodlands House, Garden Lane, Stretton
TEL: 01785 840 217

**14 TAFS**
St Georges, Telford
TEL: 01952 620 184

**15 DOBBIES GARDEN WORLD**
Saxon Cross, Watling Street, Gailey
TEL: 01902 791 555

**16 BOSCOBEL HOUSE, ENGLISH HERITAGE**
Boscobel Lane, Bishopswood, Stafford
TEL: 01902 850 244

**17 GRANGE FARM GARDEN CENTRE**
Stirchley Road, Stirchley, Telford
TEL: 01952 594 346

**18 COVEN HEATH NURSERY**
Shaw Hill Lane, Coven Heath, Wolverhampton
TEL: 01902 783 670

**19 WYEVALE GARDEN CENTRE**
Newport Road, Albrighton, Wolverhampton
TEL: 01902 374 200

**20 DAVID AUSTIN ROSES**
Bowling Green Lane, Albrighton, Wolverhampton
TEL: 01902 376 300

**21 OAKEN NURSERIES**
Shop Lane, Oaken, Wolverhampton
TEL: 01902 842 200

**22 BISHTONS NURSERY**
Posenhall, Benthall, Broseley
TEL: 01952 883 766

**23 HARLEY NURSERY**
Harley
TEL: 01952 510 241

**24 CODSALL AND WERGS GARDEN CENTRE**
Wergs Hall Road, Codsall, Wolverhampton
TEL: 01902 842 461

**25 WENLOCK PRIORY, ENGLLISH HERITAGE**
6 The Bull Ring, Much Wenlock
TEL: 01952 727 466

**26 MIDLANDSCAPES BUILDING & GARDEN CENTRE**
13 Birches Barn Road, Bradmore, Wolverhampton
TEL: 01902 334 242

**27 DIMMINGSDALE GARDEN CENTRE**
Ebstree Road, Lower Penn, Wolverhampton
TEL: 01902 765 040

**28 LEALANS NURSERIES & GARDEN CENTRE**
Bridgnorth Road, Shipley, Pattingham
TEL: 01902 700 209

**29 GARDENLANDS GARDEN & LEISURE**
Bridgnorth Road, Shipley, Wolverhampton
TEL: 01902 700 508

**30 PAVILION GARDEN CENTRE**
Bridgnorth Road, Shipley, Wolverhampton
TEL: 01902 701 001

**31 RUDGE HEATH NURSERIES**
Pattingham, Wolverhampton
TEL: 01746 710 462

**32 HILLVIEW HARDY PLANTS**
Worfield, Bridgenorth
TEL: 01746 716 454

**33 BEACON NURSERY & GARDEN CENTRE**
Rowan Road, Sedgley, Dudley
TEL: 01902 882 933

**34 WHITECROSS GARDEN CENTRE**
Orton Lane, Wombourne, Wolverhampton
TEL: 01902 895 055

**35 SANDIACRE FARM SHOP & NURSERIES**
Himley Lane, Himley, Dudlley
TEL: 01902 893 542

**36 ASHWOOD NURSERIES**
Ashwood Lower Lane, Ashwood, Kingswinford
TEL: 01384 401 996

**37 BEECHWOOD BONSAI NURSERY**
Wolverhampton Road, Prestwood, Stourbridge
TEL: 01384 877 847

**38 HANBURY NURSERIES**
43 Worcester Street, Stourbridge
TEL: 01384 395 179

**39 GOBBETT NURSERY**
Farlow, Kidderminster
TEL: 01746 718 276

Sea Aeres

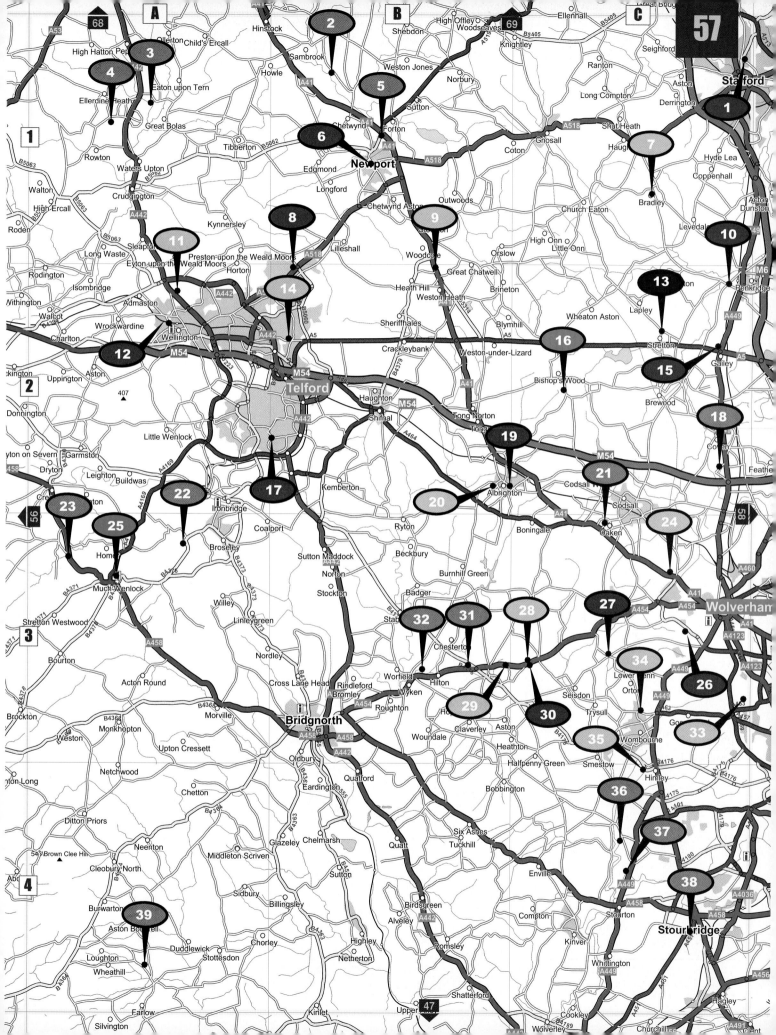

**1  ROSEACRE NURSERY AND GARDEN CENTRE**
Main Road, Great Haywood, Stafford
TEL: 01889 882 288

**2  SHUGBOROUGH ESTATE, NATIONAL TRUST**
Milford, Stafford
TEL: 01889 881 388

**3  BROMLEY HAYES GARDEN CENTRE**
Shaw Lane, Riley Hill, Lichfield
TEL: 01543 472 230

**4  COUNTRY LADY NURSERY**
Lilac Cottage, Chapel Lane, Gentleshaw
TEL: 01543 675 520

**5  OLBARR NURSERIES**
Western By-Pass (A51), Lichfield
TEL: 01543 262 805

**6  THE ORANGE TREE**
Wheel Lane, Lichfield
TEL: 01543 258 158

**7  ERASMUS DARWIN CENTRE**
Darwin House, Beacon Street, Lichfield
TEL: 01543 306 260

**8  HATHERTON AQUATICS AND NURSERIES**
Watling Street, Cannock
TEL: 01543 466 423

**9  WILLOW VALE GARDEN CENTRE**
185 Hednesford Road, Brownhills West, Walsall
TEL: 01543 275 082

**10  KINGSWOOD NURSERIES**
105 Norton Lane, Great Wyrley, Walsall
TEL: 01922 418 291

**11  G ELWELL NURSERIES**
Wolverhampton Road, Cheslyn Hay, Walsall
TEL: 01922 412 674

**12  FISHERS FARM GARDEN CENTRE**
Upper Landywood Lane, Cheslyn Hay, Walsall
TEL: 01922 413 681

**13  DE-RIDDER NURSERIES**
35 Bentons Lane, Walsall
TEL: 01922 413 542

**14  WESTWOOD NURSERIES**
Muckley Corner, Lichfield
TEL: 01543 373 347

**15  HOLLYBUSH GARDEN CENTRE AND AQUARIA**
Warstine Road, Shareshill, Wolverhampton
TEL: 01922 418 050

**16  GRASMERE GARDEN CENTRE**
Lichfield Road, Brownhills, Walsall
TEL: 01543 372 927

**17  FOSTER GARDEN CENTRE**
Birmingham Road, Shenstone, Lichfield
TEL: 01543 480 095

**18  MOSELEY OLD HALL, NATIONAL TRUST**
Moseley Old Hall Lane, Fordhouses, Wolverhampton
TEL: 01902 782 808

**19  RAILSWOOD NURSERIES**
Railswood Drive, Pelsall, Walsall
TEL: 01922 691 563

**20  WESTCROFT NURSERIES**
Westcroft Farm Drive, Cannock Road, Westcroft
TEL: 01902 724 796

**21  WYEVALE GARDEN CENTRE**
Chester Road, Aldridge, Walsall
TEL: 01922 451 401

**22  WYNDLEY GARDEN CENTRE**
Lichfield Road, Sutton Coldfield
TEL: 01213 084 646

**23  THREE CROWNS GARDEN CENTRE**
Sutton Road, Aldridge, Walsall
TEL: 01922 454 557

**24  PACIFIC NURSERIES**
Chester Road, Aldridge, Walsall
TEL: 0121 353 4017

**25  GLEN VIEW NURSERY**
41 Little Hardwick Road, Walsall
TEL: 0121 353 7578

**26  VALLEY NURSERIES**
297 Erdington Road, Aldridge, Walsall
TEL: 01922 456 060

**27  ASHFURLONG NURSERIES**
Tamworth Road, Four Oaks, Sutton Coldfield
TEL: 0121 308 0530

**28  SUTTON PARK**
Blackroot Hill, Sutton Park, Sutton Coldfield
TEL: 0121 354 1916

**29  HALL'S GARDEN SUPPLIES**
211 Chester Road, New Oscott, Sutton Coldfield
TEL: 0121 355 7701

**30  PETS & GARDENS**
372-376 Birmingham Rd, Wylde Green, Sutton Coldfield
TEL: 0121 373 1491

**31  SEDGLEY ROAD AQUARIUM**
72-74 Sedgley Road, Woodsetton, Dudley
TEL: 01902 670 098

**32  GRAVELLY LANE GARDEN CENTRE**
1-5 Gravelly Lane, Erdington, Birmingham
TEL: 0121 384 2847

**33  HIRONS GARDEN CENTRE**
212 Wellington Road, Handsworth, Birmingham
TEL: 0121 356 5185

**34  THE LITTLE GARDEN CENTRE**
97-101 Bromford Lane, West Bromwich
TEL: 0121 553 4048

**35  D HARVEY & CO**
7 North Street, Dudley
TEL: 01384 253 200

**36  CASTLE BROMWICH HALL GARDENS**
Chester Road, Castle Bromwich, Birmingham
TEL: 0121 749 4100

**37  HALL'S GARDEN SUPPLIES**
207-209 Chester Road, Castle Bromwich, Birmingham
TEL: 01217 473 046

Tulips

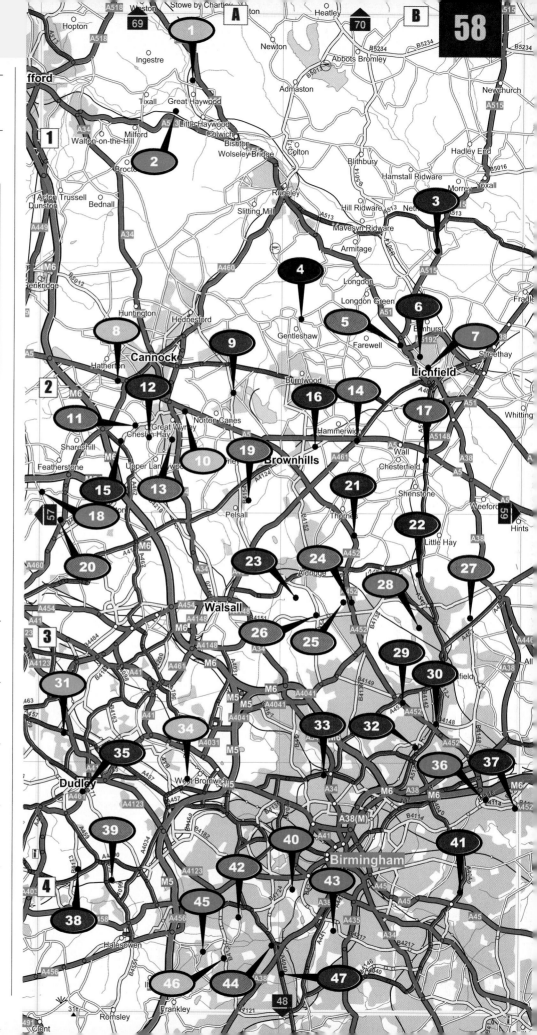

**1  F M HEATH & SON**

Woodhouse Farm Nurseries, Woodhouses, Melbourne, Derbyshire, DE73 1DN.
TEL: 01332 862 645

*Small friendly family-run nursery. Fresh home grown vegetables. Vegetable plants, composts, bedding plants, hanging baskets, alpines, shrubs, stoneware.*
OPEN: Open daily 9-5. Closed Dec 25-Jan 2.
SPECIALITIES: Alpines, Bedding plants, Seeds, Bulbs, Hardy plants.
FACILITIES: Toilets, Wheelchair access, Dogs allowed, Farm shop, Own gift tokens, Pushchair friendly, Sell plants.

**2  BRETBY NURSERIES**
Bretby Lane, Burton upon Trent
TEL: 01283 703 355

**3  MARSHMENTS GARDEN CENTRE**
Forest Road, Burton upon Trent
TEL: 01283 562 499

**4  BYRKLEY PARK**
Rangemore, Burton upon Trent
TEL: 01283 716 467

**5  C E STONEHOUSE**
19 Derby Street, Burton upon Trent
TEL: 01283 563 693

**6  WALLED GARDEN NURSERY**
The Sett, Bretbury Park, Burton upon Trent
TEL: 01283 211 531

**7  CALKE ABBEY, NATIONAL TRUST**
Ticknall
TEL: 01332 863 822

**8  STAUNTON HAROLD NURSERIES**
Ashby
TEL: 01332 862 769

**9  GARDEN KING GARDEN CENTRE**
Park Road, Newhall, Swadlincote
TEL: 01283 550 516

**10  SAGE GARDEN PRODUCTS & NURSERY**
41 Sandcliffe Road, Midway, Swadlincote
TEL: 01283 217 377

**11  BARTON FIELDS PATIO & GARDEN CENTRE**
Litchfield Road, Bartin-Under-Nebowood, Burton upon Trent
TEL: 01283 711 288

**12  STANTON DALE NURSERIES**
Dale Cottage Farm, Stanton Dale, Ashbourne
TEL: 01538 308 384

**13  STANTON NURSERIES**
44 Woodland Road, Stanton, Burton upon Trent
TEL: 01283 214 144

**14  BLUEBELL ARBORETUM & NURSERY**
Annwell Lane, Smisby, Ashby de la Zouch
TEL: 01530 413 700

**15  CHAPMAN'S NURSERIES**
Burton Road, Rosliston, Swadlincote
TEL: 01283 564 353

**16  CASTLE NURSERIES**
71 Mount Pleasant Road, Castle Gresley, Swadlincote
TEL: 01283 221 733

**17  NATIONAL FOREST PLANT CENTRE**
Bath Yard, Bath Lane, Swadlincote
TEL: 01283 558 140

**18  GROTTO FARM NURSERY**
Main Street, Overseal, Swadlincote
TEL: 01283 760 277

**19  GRANGEWOOD GARDEN CENTRE**
Lullington Road, Netherseal, Swadlincote
TEL: 01283 762 026

**20  S & S PERENNIALS**
24 Main Street Normanton le Heath
TEL: 01530 262 250

**21  T PICKERING & SONS**
89 Bosworth Road, Measham, Swadlincote
TEL: 01530 270 377

**22  JACKSON'S NURSERIES**
Hillcrest, Clifton Campville, Tamworth
TEL: 01827 373 307

**23  WILLOW BROOK NURSERIES**
Shadows Lane, Congerstone, Nuneaton
TEL: 01827 880 305

**24  WOODLANDS GRANGE NURSERY**
Off Plantation Lane, Hopwas, Tamworth
TEL: 01827 541 444

**25  FLORASCAPE**
Bonehill Road, Tamworth
TEL: 01827 588 58

**26  BELGRAVE NURSERIES & FLOWERS**
Greta Nova, Wilnecote Lane, Tamworth
TEL: 01827 289 516

**27  PLANTERS GARDEN CENTRE**
Woodlands Farm, Trinity Road, Freasley
TEL: 01827 251 511

**28  DURNO'S NURSERY**
Old Holy Lane, Whittington, Atherstone
TEL: 01827 713 233

**29  KINGSBURY GARDEN CENTRE**
Tamworth Road, Kingsbury, Tamworth
TEL: 01827 875 103

**30  DOBBIES GARDEN WORLD**
Nuneaton Road, Atherstone
TEL: 01827 715 511

**31  NEWLAND NURSERIES**
Coppice Lane, Middleton, Tamworth
TEL: 0121 308 7197

**32  OAKS NURSERIES**
326 Weddington Road, Nuneaton
TEL: 024 7638 4550

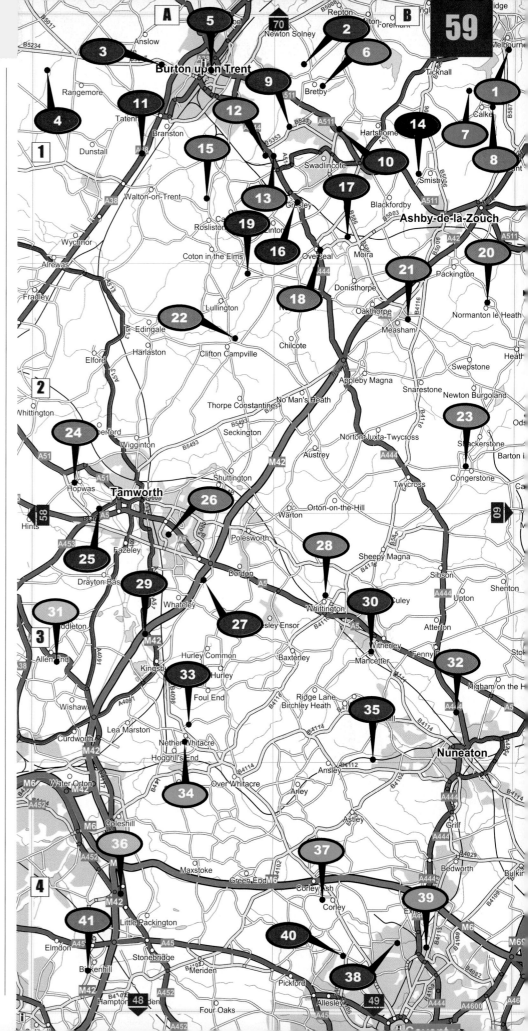

## 33 WHITACRE GARDEN CENTRE
Tamworth Road, Nether Whitacre, Coleshill
**TEL:** 01675 481 306

## 34 WORLD OF WATER
Whitacre Garden Centre, Tamworth Road, Nether Whitacre
**TEL:** 01675 481 144

## 35 ALPINE LANDSCAPES
Garden Centre, Kingswood Road, Nuneaton
**TEL:** 024 7635 0052

## 36 MELBICKS GARDEN & LEISURE
Chester Road, Coleshill, Birmingham
**TEL:** 0121 782 2683

## 37 CORLEY NURSERY & CORLEY KOI AQUATICS
Church Lane, Corley, Coventry
**TEL:** 01676 540 101

## 38 DALE'S
315 Holbrook Lane, Coventry
**TEL:** 024 7666 5050

## 39 HYDROPONICS CENTRE
994 Foleshill Road, Coventry
**TEL:** 024 7668 8586

## 40 WYEVALE GARDEN CENTRE
Brownshill Green Road, Allesley, Coventry
**TEL:** 024 7633 3998

## 41 BRACEYS NURSERIES
Catherine de Barnes Lane, Bickenhill, Solihull
**TEL:** 01675 442 587

Rose

# LEICS · WEST MIDS · DERBYS

○ **GARDEN**
○ **GARDEN CENTRE**
○ **GARDEN & NURSERY**
○ **NURSERY**
○ **NURSERY & GARDEN CENTRE**
○ **WATER GARDEN SPECIALIST**

**1 SIX ACRE NURSERIES**
Loughborough Road, Costock, Loughborough
TEL: 01509 856 079

**2 MELBOURNE HALL GARDENS**
Melbourne TEL: 01332 862 502

**3 PRIORY NURSERIES**
Hall Farm, Breedon-on-the-Hill, Derby
TEL: 01332 862 406

**4 GRANGE GARDEN CENTRE**
Sysonby Grange House, Melton Road, Asfordby Hill
TEL: 01664 812 012

**5 BEACON VIEW NURSERY**
126-128 Cotes Road, Barrow on Soar, Loughborough
TEL: 01509 412 787

**6 LOUGHBOROUGH ROAD NURSERIES**
103 Loughborough Road, Quorn, Loughborough
TEL: 01509 416 680

**7 SOAR VALLEY NURSERIES**
263 Loughbrorough Road, Loughborough
TEL: 01509 412 681

**8 REARSBY ROSES**
Melton Rd, Rearsby, Leicester TEL: 0116 260 1211

**9 KAYES GARDEN NURSERY**
1700 Melton Road, Rearsby TEL: 01664 424 578

**10 DERRY'S NURSERIES**
Main Street, Cossington TEL: 01509 812 815

**11 ROWENA GARDEN CENTRE**
Loughborough Road, Rothley, Leicester
TEL: 0116 237 6500

**12 HEATHER LANE NURSERIES**
Heather Lane, Ravenstone, Coalville
TEL: 01530 832 101

**13 GOSCOTE NURSERIES**
Syston Road, Cossington, Leicestershire, LE7 4UZ.
TEL: 01509 812 121
EMAIL: sales@goscote.co.uk
WEB: www.goscote.co.uk

*Over 2,000 varieties of hardy trees, shrubs, Japanese maples, conifers, fruit, climbers, alpines, heathers, herbaceous plants, many rare or unusual.*
OPEN: Open daily. Closed Christmas-New Year.
SPECIALITIES: Comprehensive range.
FACILITIES: Wheelchair access, Credit cards, Toilets.

**14 ULVERSCROFT GRANGE NURSERY**
Priory Lane, Ulverscroft, Markfield
TEL: 01530 243 635

**15 M B R GREEN**
174 Leicester Road, Ibstock TEL: 01530 260 061

**16 SUNNYSIDE GARDEN CENTRE HOUSE**
Sunnyside, Leicester Rd, Ibstock TEL: 01530 263 418

**17 RECTORY FIELD NURSERY**
Wanlip, Leicester TEL: 0116 267 4613

**18 TED BROWN UNUSUAL PLANTS**
1 Croftway, Markfield, Leicester TEL: 01530 244 517

**19 BARKBY VILLAGE NURSERY**
Queniborough Road, Barkby, Leicester
TEL: 0116 260 3600

**20 BROOKSIDE NURSERIES**
129 Cropston Road, Anstey, Leicester
TEL: 0116 236 4564

**21 BRADGATE NURSERIES**
Bradgate Garden Buildings, 538 Bradgate Road,
Newtown Linford TEL: 01530 242 985

**22 BIRSTALL AQUARIA & WATERGARDENS**
27 Sibson Rd, Birstall, Leicester TEL: 0116 267 6121

**23 JOHN SMITH & SON**
Thornton Nurseries, Thornton, Coalville
TEL: 01530 230 331

**24 COUNTY GARDENS**
Gorse Close, Tilton Lane, Billesdon
TEL: 0116 259 6248

**25 JAMES COLES & SONS**
624 The Nurseries, Uppingham Road, Leicester
TEL: 0116 241 8394

**26 CRAIGHILL NURSERIES**
Craighill Road, Knighton, Leicester
TEL: 0116 270 7065

**27 UNIVERSITY OF LEICESTER BOTANIC GARDEN**
Beaumont Hall, Stoughton Drive, Oadby
TEL: 0116 271 7725

**28 HAWGRIP NURSERIES**
Hawgrip, Seine Lane, Enderby TEL: 0116 284 8227

**29 PALMERS GARDEN CENTRE**
St Johns, Narborough, Leicester TEL: 0116 286 3323

**30 MOZART HOUSE NURSERY GARDEN**
84 Central Avenue, Wigston TEL: 0116 288 9548

**32 GREENACRES NURSERY**
Ashby Rd, Stapleton, Leicester TEL: 01455 290 878

**33 HILLVIEW NURSERY**
Croft Lane, Thurlaston, Leicester TEL: 01455 888 393

**34 ECOB'S GARDEN CENTRE**
Horsewell Lane, Wigston TEL: 0116 288 3627

**35 CHAMNEY GARDEN CENTRE**
Lutterworth Rd, Blaby, Leicester TEL: 0116 277 7020

**36 GLEBE GARDEN CENTRE**
Foston Road, Countesthorpe, Leicester
TEL: 0116 277 1570

**37 KIBWORTH GARDEN CENTRE**
Fleckney Road, Kibworth, Leicester
TEL: 0116 279 2754

**31 WOODLANDS NURSERIES**
Ashby Road, Stapleton, Hinckley, Leicestershire,
LE9 8JE.
TEL: 01455 291 494
WEB: www.woodlandsnurseries.co.uk

*Make it a day out at the Midlands premier garden centre. Extensive site packed with quality plants and garden products. Winner of the Best Midlands Garden Centre Award.*
OPEN: Mar-Sep: Mon-Sat 9-6. Oct-Nov: Mon-Fri 9-5.
Dec: Mon-Fri 9-6. Jan-Feb: Mon-Fri 9-5. All year:
Sun 10.30-4.30.
SPECIALITIES: Bedding plants, Furniture, Grasses,
Hardy plants, Herbaceous plants, Christmas decorations.
FACILITIES: Bookshop, Credit cards, Gift shop,
HTA gift tokens, Pushchair friendly, Restaurant,
Sell plants, Toilets, Wheelchair access, Coffee shop.

**38 MOORE'S NURSERY**
Leicester Rd, Fleckney, Leicester TEL: 0116 240 2289

**39 PETER PLANTS**
Hinckley Rd, Sapcote, Leicester TEL: 01455 274 049

**40 GLEN STEWART NURSERY**
Melton Road, East Langton, Market Harborough
TEL: 01858 545 466

**41 CHARLIE BROWN'S GARDEN CENTRE**
33 Dunton Road, Broughton Astley, Leicester
TEL: 01455 282 310

**42 3 POTS NURSERY**
51 Newstead Avenue, Burbage, Hinckley
TEL: 01455 632 716

**43 ASHBY PARVA NURSERIES**
Ashby Parva, Lutterworth TEL: 01455 209 225

**44 ULLESTHORPE GARDEN & AQUATICS CENTRE**
Willowbrough House, The Green, Leire
TEL: 01455 202 144

**45 TEALBY FARM NURSERY**
Mill Lane, Gilmorton, Lutterworth
TEL: 01455 558 771

**46 A & A THORP**
Bungalow No 5, Main Street, Theddingworth
TEL: 01858 880 496

**47 WITHYBROOK NURSERIES**
Overstone Road, Withybrook, Coventry
TEL: 01455 220 297

**48 HILLTOP GARDEN CENTRE**
Shilton Lane, Shilton, Coventry TEL: 024 7661 4752

**49 GANDY'S ROSES**
North Kilworth Lutterworth TEL: 01858 880 398

**50 CLIPSTON NURSERY**
Naseby Road, Clipston, Market Harborough
TEL: 01858 525 567

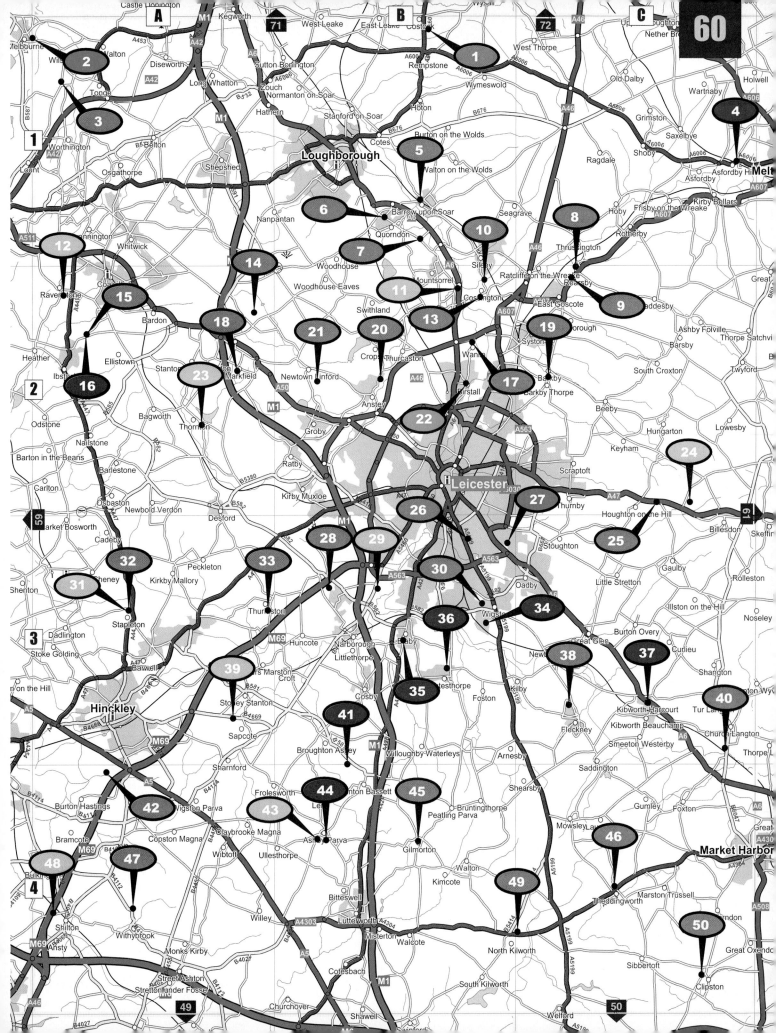

**1 SOUTHFIELD NURSERIES**
Bourne Road, Morton, Bourne
**TEL:** 01778 570 168

**2 GRIMSTHORPE CASTLE PARK & GARDENS**
Grimsthorpe, Bourne
**TEL:** 01778 591 205

**3 WOODVIEW NURSERY**
50 South Road, Bourne
**TEL:** 01778 422 508

**4 RASELL'S NURSERIES**
Station Road, Little Bytham, Grantham
**TEL:** 01780 410 345

**5 THE HERB NURSERY**
Thistleton, Oakham
**TEL:** 01572 767 658

**6 GREETHAM GARDEN CENTRE**
Oakham Road, Greetham, Oakham
**TEL:** 01572 813 100

**7 BARSNDALE GARDENS**
Exton Avenue, Oakham
**TEL:** 01572 813 200

**8 WATERSIDE GARDEN CENTRE**
King Street, Baston, Peterborough
**TEL:** 01778 560 000

**9 BARNSDALE PLANTS & GARDENS**
Exton Avenue, Oakham
**TEL:** 01572 813 200

**10 GATES NURSERIES & GARDEN CENTRE**
Somerby Road, Cold Overton, Oakham
**TEL:** 01664 454 309

**11 STAMFORD GARDEN & LEISURE CENTRE**
Casterton Hill, Stamford
**TEL:** 01780 765 656

**12 WOTHORPE NURSERIES**
Kettering Road, Wothorpe, Stamford
**TEL:** 01780 763 268

**13 BURGHLEY HOUSE**
Stamford
**TEL:** 01780 752 451

**14 RUTLAND WATER GARDEN NURSERY**
Lyndon Road, Manton, Oakham
**TEL:** 01572 737 711

**15 BARN GARDEN & AQUATIC CENTRE**
Gunthorpe Road, Preston Parkway, Peterborough
**TEL:** 01733 320 134

**16 WINGWELL NURSERY**
Top Street, Wing, Oakham
**TEL:** 01572 737 727

**17 PARNWELL PLANTS**
152 Fulbridge Road, Peterborough
**TEL:** 01733 572 688

**18 THORPE HALL**
Thorpe Road, Longthorpe, Peterborough
**TEL:** 01733 330 060

**19 THORPE HALL PLANT CENTRE**
Thorpe Hall, Thorpe Road, Longthorpe
**TEL:** 01733 334 443

**20 BEDE HOUSE**
Bluecoat Lane, Lyddington, Uppingham
**TEL:** 01572 822 438

**21 FLETTON GARDEN & POND CENTRE**
102 High Street, Fletton, Peterborough
**TEL:** 01733 703 285

**22 NOTCUTTS GARDEN CENTRE**
Oundle Road, Orton Waterville, Peterborough
**TEL:** 01733 234 600

**23 BLOOMS OF ELTON**
Elton Hall, Elton, Peterborough
**TEL:** 01832 280 058

**24 DEENE PARK**
Deene, Corby
**TEL:** 01780 450 278

**25 KIRBY HALL, ENGLISH HERITAGE**
Deene, Corby
**TEL:** 01536 203 230

**26 LONGRIDGE NURSERIES**
Ashley Road, Middleton, Market Harborough
**TEL:** 01536 771 323

**27 A1 CHERRIASH GARDEN CENTRE & SUPPLIES**
109 North Street, Stilton, Peterborough
**TEL:** 01733 241 653

**28 THE GROWING GARDEN**
Barnwell Road, Oundle, Peterborough,
Cambridgeshire, PE8 5PB.
**TEL:** 01832 273 478
**EMAIL:** info@growinggarden.co.uk
**WEB:** www.growinggarden.co.uk
*We are a garden centre and nursery, who also manufacture garden buildings, together with a wide variety of other wooden products. We can also custom build items.*
**OPEN:** Jan-Feb: Fri-Sun. Mar-Dec: Tue-Sat 10-5, Sun 10.30-4.30.
**SPECIALITIES:** House plants, Herbaceous plants, Perennials, Shrubs.
**FACILITIES:** Toilets, Credit cards, Gift tokens, HTA gift tokens, Own gift tokens, Pushchair friendly, Sell plants, Wheelchair access.

**29 TANDEE NURSERY**
Barnwell Road, Thurning, Oundle
**TEL:** 01832 293 755

**30 GEDDINGTON GARDENS HARDY PLANT NURSERY**
The Spinney, Grafton Road, Geddington
**TEL:** 01536 461 020

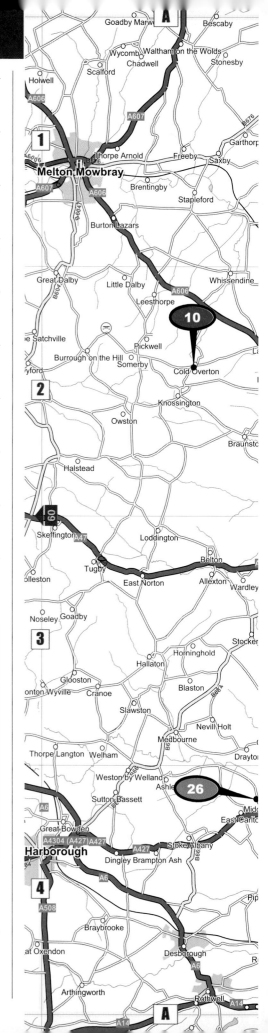

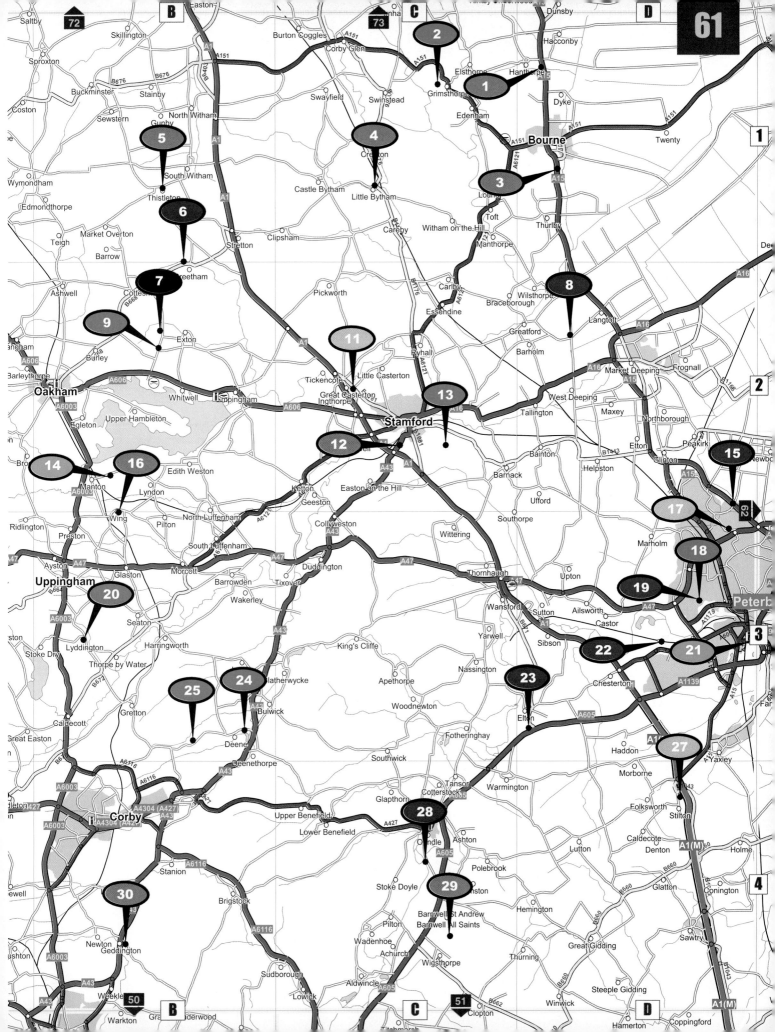

**1  SPALDING TROPICAL FOREST**
Glenside North, Pinchbeck, Spalding
TEL: 01775 710 882

**2  GLENSIDE NURSERIES**
Glenside South, West Pinchbeck, Spalding
TEL: 01775 640 520

**3  BAYTREE NURSERIES & GARDEN CENTRE**
High Road, Weston, Spalding
TEL: 01406 370 242

**4  SABAN GARDEN CENTRE**
Fleet Road, Holbeach, Spalding
TEL: 01406 422 942

**5  TOM THUMB GARDEN CENTRE & PETSTORE**
210 Spalding Road, Pinchbeck, Spalding
TEL: 01775 722 726

**6  C GREGORY ROSES**
Rose Tweed Nursery, 101 Broadgate, Weston
TEL: 01406 371 633

**7  SPRINGFIELDS SHOW GARDENS**
Camelgate, Spalding
TEL: 01775 724 843

**8  AYSCOUGHFEE HALL MUSEUM AND GARDENS**
Churchgate, Spalding
TEL: 01775 725 468

**9  NIMMERDOR NURSERIES**
Monks House Lane, Spalding
TEL: 01775 722 437

**10  ORNAMENTAL CONIFERS**
22 Chapel Road, Terrington St Clement, King's Lynn
TEL: 01553 828 874

**11  AFRICAN VIOLET CENTRE**
71 Station Road, Terrington St Clement, King's Lynn
TEL: 01553 828 374

**12  MOAT ROAD NURSERY**
7 Moat Road, King's Lynn
TEL: 01553 828 723

**13  LESLEY MARSHALL**
Islington Lodge Cottage, Tilney All Saints,
King's Lynn
TEL: 01553 765 103

**14  EAU BRINK CACTUS NURSERY**
Eau Brink Road, King's Lynn
TEL: 01553 617 635

**15  JUNIPER GARDEN CENTRE**
Sutton Road, Tydd Gote, Tydd
TEL: 01945 420 672

**16  GRASMERE PLANTS**
Grasmere, School Road, Terrington St John
TEL: 01945 880 514

**17  CHOICE LANDSCAPES PRIORY FARM NURSERY**
101 Salts Road, West Walton, Wisbech
TEL: 01945 585 051

**18  PECKOVER HOUSE & GARDEN, NATIONAL TRUST**
North Brink, Wisbech
TEL: 01945 583 463

**19  ELGOOD'S BREWERY**
North Brink, Wisbech
TEL: 01945 583 160

**20  PARKSIDE NURSERIES**
Ingleby, Cromwell Road, Wisbech
TEL: 01945 582 448

**21  TRAMWAYS GARDEN CENTRE**
Outwell Road, Emneth, Wisbech
TEL: 01945 466 187

**22  GOLDINGS**
Hall Road, Outwell, Wisbech
TEL: 01945 772 802

**23  WHISPERING TREES NURSERY**
West Way, Winbotsham, King's Lynn
TEL: 01366 388 752

**24  BAYS NURSERY**
49 Downham Road, Outwell, Wisbech
TEL: 01945 773 929

**25  DOWNHAM GARDEN CENTRE**
14 Railway Road, Downham Market
TEL: 01366 382 384

**26  BENELL PLANTS**
Rowan, Stone Cross, Downham Market
TEL: 01366 388 407

**27  TWO ACRES NURSERY**
Wisbech Road, Downham Market

**28  ORCHARD NURSERIES,**
Orchard Place, Flint House Road , Threeholes
TEL: 01354 638 613

**29  DENTS FARM SHOP & GARDEN CENTRE**
Steels Drove, West Fen, Downham Market
TEL: 01366 385 661

**30  WESTFIELD NURSERIES**
Station Road, Whittlesey, Peterborough
TEL: 01733 206 688

**31  D J'S THE GARDENER'S DREAM**
134 London Road, Chatteris
TEL: 01354 693 937

**32  BRANDS OF ELY**
42-44 Market Street, Ely
TEL: 01353 663 463

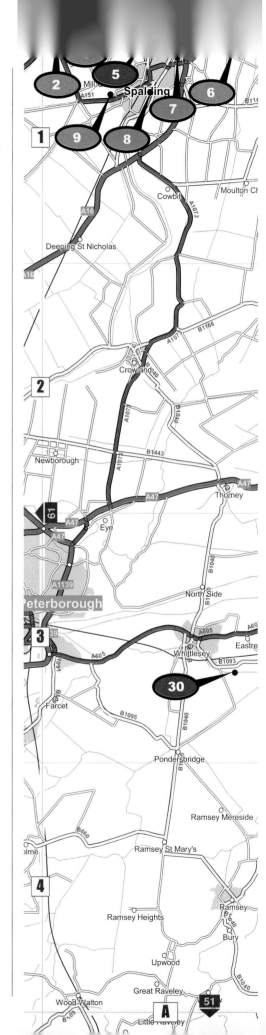

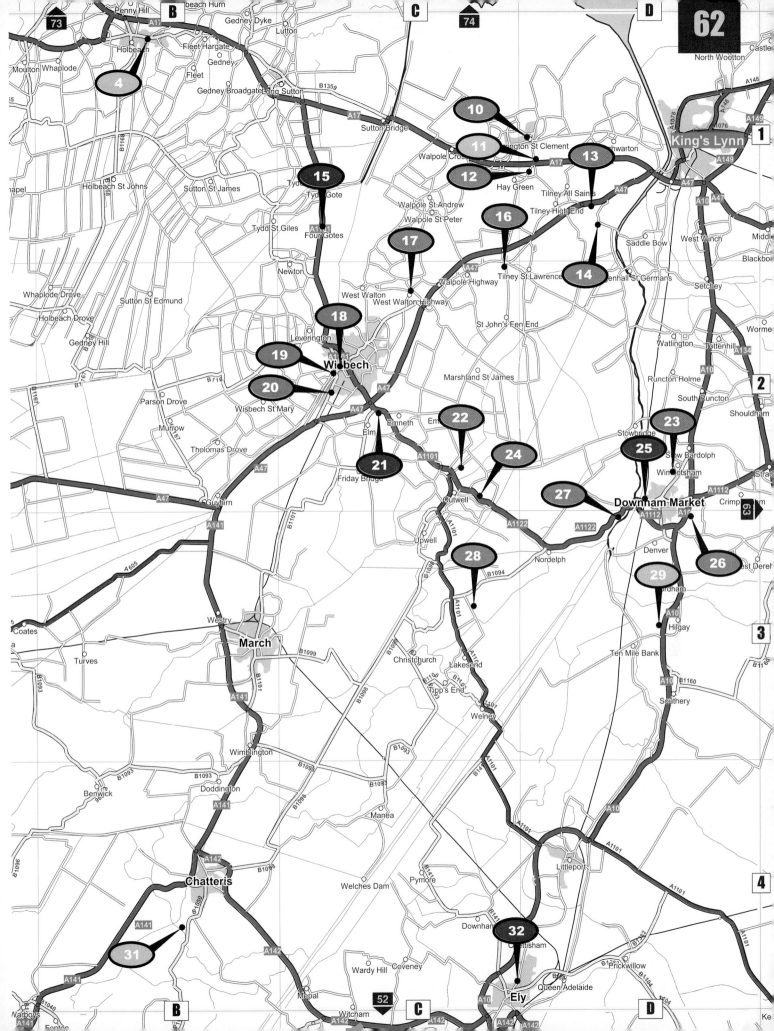

**1** **CONGHAM HALL HERB GARDEN**
Lynn Road, Grimston, King's Lynn
**Tel:** 01485 600 250

**2** **WEST ACRE GARDENS**
West Acre, King's Lynn
**Tel:** 01760 755 562

**3** **NORFOLK HERBS**
Blackberry Farm, Dillington, Dereham
**Tel:** 01362 860 812

**4** **CASTLE ACRE PRIORY, ENGLISH HERITAGE**
Back Lane, Stocks Green, Castle Acre
**Tel:** 01760 755 394

**5** **SWANTON ROAD NURSERIES**
Swanton Road, Dereham
**Tel:** 01362 697 156

**6** **RIVERSIDE GARDEN CENTRE**
Swaffham Road, Dereham
**Tel:** 01362 698 722

**7** **READS NURSERIES**
Old Hall Nurseries, Dumpling Green, Dereham
**Tel:** 01362 693 102

**8** **CHALK FARM NURSERY**
A47, Near Swaffham
**Tel:** 01760 338 760

**9** **NIDUS GARDEN CENTRE**
153 Shipdham Road, Toftwood, Dereham
**Tel:** 01362 695 686

**10** **BRECKLAND NURSERIES**
Dereham Road, Yaxham, Dereham
**Tel:** 01362 696 750

**11** **NECTON GARDEN CENTRE**
Tuns Road, Necton, Swaffham
**Tel:** 01760 723 612

**12** **OXBURGH HALL & GARDEN, NATIONAL TRUST**
Oxburgh, Swaffham
**Tel:** 01366 328 258.

**14** **MAGPIES**
Green Lane, Mundford, Thetford
**Tel:** 01842 878 496

**15** **LYNFORD ARBORETUM**
Lynford Road, Mundford, Thetford
**Tel:** 01842 810 271

**13** **WALNUT TREE GARDEN NURSERY**
Flymoor Lane, Rocklands, Attleborough, Norfolk, NR17 1BP.
**Tel:** 01953 488 163
**Email:** jimnclare@aol.com
**Web:** www.walnut-tree-garden-nursery.co.uk
*A family run nursery offering a comprehensive range of garden plants including many unusual varieties, especially herbaceous perennials and trees.*
**Open:** Feb-Nov: Tue-Sun & BH 9-6.
**Specialities:** Perennials, Herbaceous plants, Trees.
**Facilities:** Credit cards, Plant guarantee, Toilets, Sell plants, Own gift tokens.

**16** **SWALLOW AQUATIC**
Aqualife & Water Garden Centre, Harling Road, East Harling
**Tel:** 01953 718 184

**17** **GARBOLDISHAM GARDEN CENTRE**
Oakdene, Hopton Road, Garboldisham
**Tel:** 01953 681 326

Rose

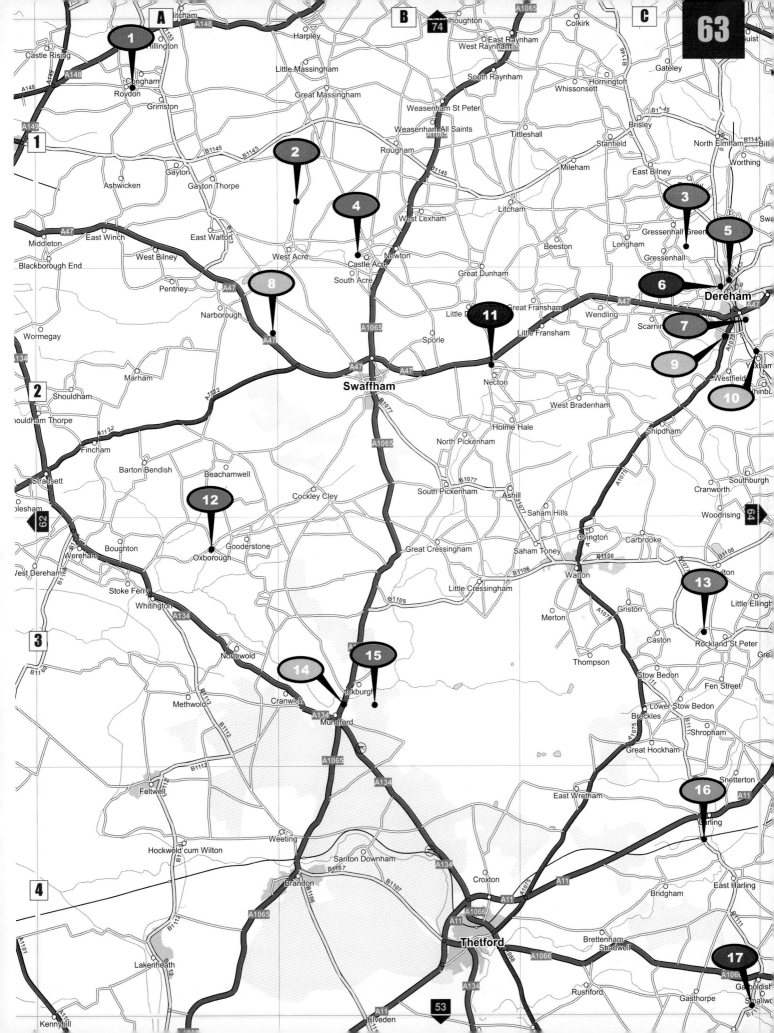

**1 WOODGATE NURSERY**
Woodgate, Cawston Road, Aylsham
TEL: 01263 731 510

**2 AYLSHAM GARDEN CENTRE**
Norwich Road, Aylsham
TEL: 01263 735 001

**3 SIMPSONS NURSERY**
62 High Street, Thorpe Market Road, Marsham
TEL: 01263 731 999

**4 BAWDESWELL GARDEN CENTRE**
Norwich Road, Bawdeswell, East Dereham
TEL: 01362 688 387

**5 ROMANTIC GARDEN NURSERY**
The Street, Swannington
TEL: 01603 261 488

**6 BLACKROW NURSERIES**
Short Thorn Road, Stratton Strawless, Norwich
TEL: 01603 754 878

**7 FELTHORPE FOREST NURSERY**
Felthorpe, Norwich
TEL: 01603 754 553

**8 TAVERHAM GARDEN & CRAFT CENTRE**
Fir Covert Road, Taverham
TEL: 01603 860 522

**9 BOTANICUS**
The Nurseries, Ringland Lane, Old Costessey
TEL: 01603 742 063

**10 URBAN JUNGLE**
The Nurseries, Ringland Lane, Old Costessy
TEL: 01603 744 997

**11 SEVEN ACRES NURSERY**
Common Road, East Tuddenham, Norwich
TEL: 07703 347 014

**12 PLANTATION GARDEN**
4 Earlham Road, Norwich
TEL: 01603 621 868

**13 D M PHOB**
Hill House, Watton Road, Little Melton
TEL: 01603 810 214

**14 NOTCUTTS GARDEN CENTRE**
Daniels Road, Norwich
TEL: 01603 453 155

**15 THORNCROFT CLEMATIS NURSERY**
The Lings, Reymerston, Norwich
TEL: 01953 850 407

**16 IPSWICH ROAD GARDEN CENTRE**
120 Ipswich Road, Norwich
TEL: 01603 507 800

**17 DOWNHAM PLANT CENTRE**
Tuttles Lane East, Wymondham
TEL: 01953 607 133

**18 BOBBIN BROS**
Roadside Nurseries, Main Road, Swardeston
TEL: 01508 570 286

**19 HOMESTEAD NURSERIES**
Tuttlers Lane East, Wymondham
TEL: 01953 606 797

**20 LODGE FARM NURSERIES**
Brick Kiln Lane, Swainsthorpe
TEL: 01508 471 104

**21 ROOTS N SHOOTS**
The Turnpike, Norwich Road, Fudenhall
TEL: 01508 488 101

**22 TROPICAL BUTTERFLY WORLD**
Great Ellingham, Attleborough, Norfolk, NR17 1AW.
TEL: 01953 453 175
EMAIL: gegcuk@hotmail.com
WEB: www.tropicalbutterflyworld.com
*Lush tropical gardens with vibrant floating butterflies. You will feel as if you have travelled to another part of the world. Superb garden centre, gift and coffee shop.*
OPEN: Mon-Sat 10-5, Sun 11-5.
ENTRY COSTS: £4, Child: £2.75, OAPs: £2.75.
SPECIALITIES: Bedding plants, Christmas trees, Maze, Pot plants, Terracotta pots.
FACILITIES: Child area, Coffee shop, Credit cards, Gift shop, Own gift tokens, HTA gift tokens, Pushchair friendly, Sell plants, Toilets, Wheelchair access, Bookshop, Plant guarantee.

**23 FOUNDRY NURSERIES**
Hempnall, Norwich
TEL: 01508 498 263

**24 PETER BEALE'S ROSES**
London Road, Attleborough
TEL: 01953 454 707

**25 TALL TREES NURSERY**
New Buckenham Road, Old Buckenham
TEL: 01953 860 412

**26 PULHAM MARKET GARDEN CENTRE**
Ipswich Road, Pulham Market, Diss
TEL: 01379 676 418

**27 P W PLANTS**
Sunnyside, Heath Road, Kenninghall
TEL: 01953 888 212

**28 BLACKSMITH'S COTTAGE NURSERY**
Langmere Road, Langmere, Dickleburgh
TEL: 01379 740 982

**29 PLANTSMAN'S PREFERENCE**
Church Road, South Lopham, Diss
TEL: 01953 688 194

**30 FOGGY BOTTOM**
Bressingham, Diss
TEL: 01379 688 402

### 31 BLOOMS WATER GARDENS,
Bressingham, Diss, Norfolk, IP22 2AB.
**Tel:** 01379 688 551

*Quality aquatic superstore for every need, indoor and outdoor. Maintenance, installation, landscaping available.*
**Open:** Mon-Sat 9.30-6, Sun 9.30-4.30.
**Specialities:** Aquatics.
**Facilities:** Credit cards, Dogs allowed, Gift shop, Own gift tokens, Sell plants, Wheelchair access, Pushchair friendly.

### 32 BLOOMS OF BRESSINGHAM
Bressingham, Diss
**Tel:** 01379 688 585

### 33 DELL GARDEN
Bressingham Steam Museum & Garden,
Bressingham, Diss
**Tel:** 01379 687 585

Tulips

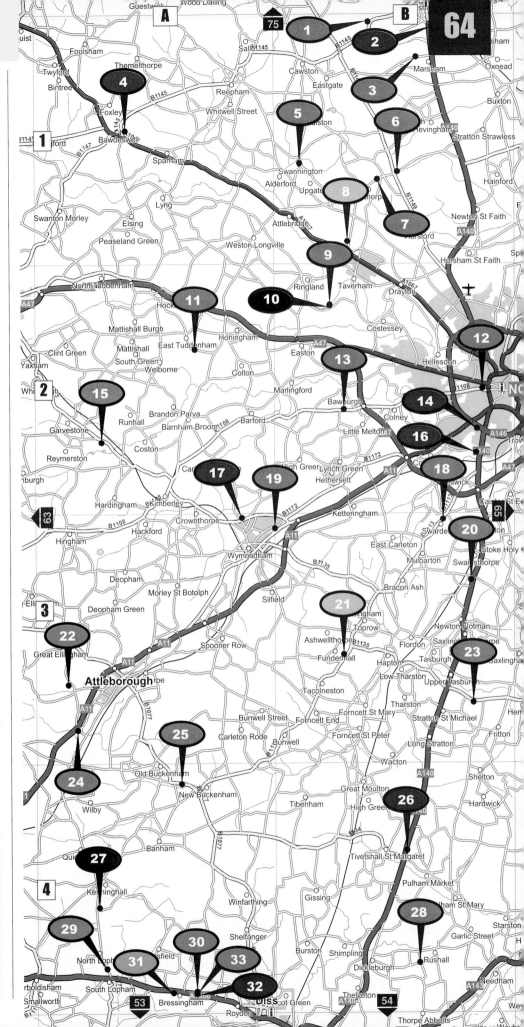

**1  A G MEALE & SONS**
Wayford Nurseries, Stalham, Norwich
**TEL:** 01692 580 226

**2  P & A PLANT SUPPLIES**
The Nursery, The Street, Norwich
**TEL:** 01692 580 424

**3  HICKLING HEATH NURSERY**
Nursery Cottage, Sutton Road, Hickling
**TEL:** 01692 598 513

**4  HOVETON HALL GARDENS**
Wroxham, Norwich
**TEL:** 01603 782 798

**5  SCRATBY GARDEN CENTRE**
Beach Road, Scratby, Great Yarmouth
**TEL:** 01493 730 950

**6  FAIRHAVEN GARDEN TRUST**
2 Wymers Lane, South Walsham, Norwich
**TEL:** 01603 270 449

**7  CROWFOOT NURSERIES**
Honeycombe Road, Salhouse, Norwich
**TEL:** 01603 720 116

**8  THRIGBY HALL WILDLIFE GARDENS**
Filby, Great Yarmouth
**TEL:** 01493 369 477

**9  M GOULD**
The Gardens, Acle Road, South Walsham
**TEL:** 01493 750 549

**10  WYEVALE GARDEN CENTRE**
Blue Boar Lane, Sprowston, Norwich
**TEL:** 01603 412 239

**11  MOUSEHOLD GARDEN CENTRE**
63 Mousehold Lane, Norwich
**TEL:** 01603 413 272

**12  BRITISH WILD FLOWER PLANTS**
Burlingham Gardens, 31 Main Road, North Burlingham
**TEL:** 01603 716 615

**13  MOULTON NURSERIES**
Reedham Road, Moulton St Mary, Acle
**TEL:** 01493 750 458

**14  HIGHWAY NURSERIES**
Loddon Road, Framlingham Pigot, Norwich
**TEL:** 01508 494 665

**15  BELTON NURSERIES**
35 Station Road South, Belton, Great Yarmouth
**TEL:** 01493 780 494

**16  GREEN PASTURES NURSERY**
Mill Road, Berghapton, Norwich
**TEL:** 01508 480 734

**17  POTS OF PLANTS**
2 Alberta Piece, Church Road, Alpington
**TEL:** 01508 494 480

**18  MIDWAY NURSERIES**
Yarmouth Road, Corton, Lowestoft
**TEL:** 01502 730 419

**19  SOMERLEYTON HALL AND GARDENS**
Somerleyton, Lowestoft
**TEL:** 01502 730 224

**20  B BEEVOR**
Hillfield Nursery, Mill Lane, Thorpe next Haddiscoe
**TEL:** 01508 548 306

**21  HOLLY GARDENS NURSERIES**
Flixton Road, Blundeston, Lowestoft
**TEL:** 01502 730 648

**22  RAVENINGHAM HALL GARDENS**
Raveningham, Norwich
**TEL:** 01508 548 222

**23  READS NURSERY**
Hales Hall, Loddon
**TEL:** 01508 548 395

**24  HALES HALL**
Loddon
**TEL:** 01508 548 395

**25  THREE WILLOWS GARDEN CENTRE**
Bardolph Road, Bungay
**TEL:** 01986 893 834

**26  WINTER FLORA**
Hall Farm, London Road, Weston
**TEL:** 01502 713 346

**27  ASHLEY NURSERIES & GARDEN CENTRE**
London Road, Kessingland, Lowestoft
**TEL:** 01502 740 264

Gerber Daisy with Baby's Breath

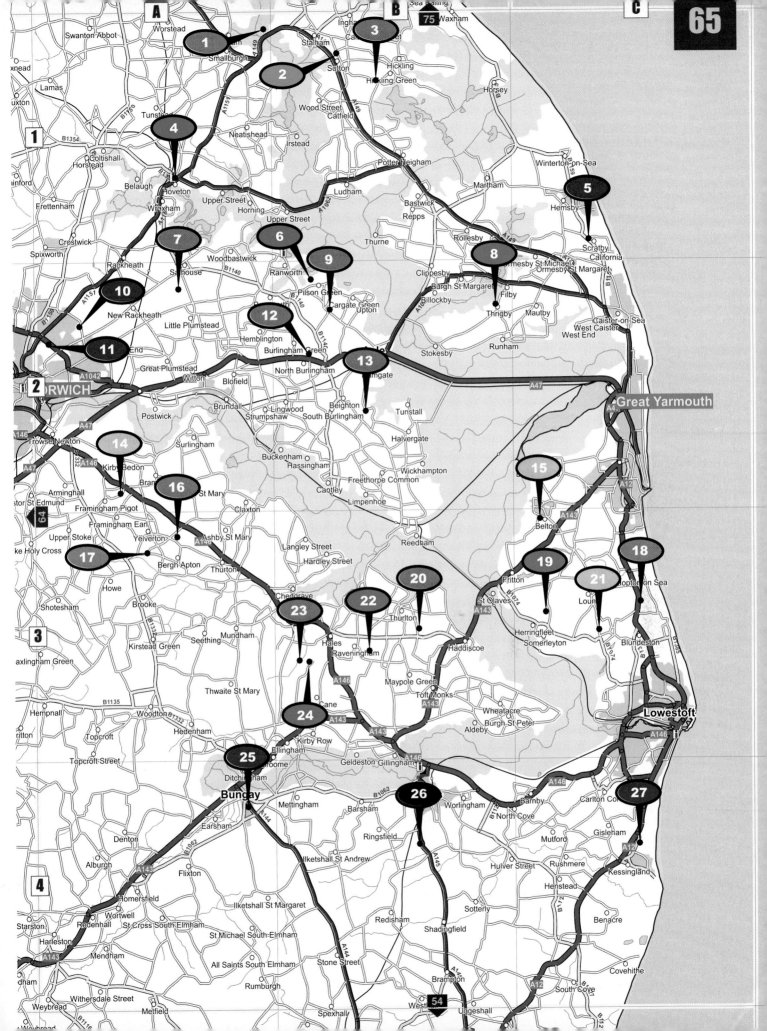

# NORTH WALES

**1  PLANTASIA**
Star, Gaerwen
TEL: 01248 717 797

**2  HOLLAND ARMS GARDEN CENTRE**
Gaerwen
TEL: 01248 421 655

**3  TREBWORTH NURSERIES**
Trebworth Road, Bangor
TEL: 01248 354 282

**4  PLAS NEWYDD, NATIONAL TRUST**
Llanfairpwyll, Anglesey
TEL: 01248 714 795

**5  MARY'S ACRE**
Garreg Lwyd, Dwyran, Llanfairpwllgwyngyll
TEL: 01248 430 536

**6  CRUG FARM PLANTS**
Crug Farm, Griffiths Crossing, Caernarfon,
Gwynedd, LL55 1TU.
TEL: 01248 670 232
EMAIL: bleddyn+sue@crug-farm.co.uk
WEB: www.crug-farm.co.uk
*Crug Farm Plants has an outstanding and unrivalled
selection of plants, located in one of the most beautiful
areas of North Wales.*
OPEN: End Feb-end Sep: Thurs-Sun & BH 10-6.
ENTRY COSTS: Free.
SPECIALITIES: Climbers, Geraniums, Herbaceous
plants, National Collection, Woodland plants.
FACILITIES: Credit cards, Own gift tokens, Sell plants,
Toilets, Wheelchair access.

**7  SEIONT NURSERIES**
Caer Glyddyn, Pontrug, Rhosbodrual
TEL: 01286 672 524

**8  FRON GOCH**
Pant Road, Llanfaglan, Caernarfon
TEL: 01286 672 212

**9  GLYNLLIFION**
Clynnog Road, Llandwrog, Caernarfon
TEL: 01286 830 222

**10  PLAS BRONDANW GARDENS**
Llanfrothen, Panrhyndeudreath
TEL: 01766 770 484

**11  PLAS TAN-Y-BWLCH**
Maentwrog
TEL: 01766 590 324

**12  BRON EIFION NURSERY**
Bron Eifion, Criccleth
TEL: 01766 522 890

**13  PORTMEIRION**
Penrhyndeudraeth
TEL: 01766 770 228

**14  PLAS YN RHIW, NATIONAL TRUST**
Rhiw, Pwllheli
TEL: 01758 780 219

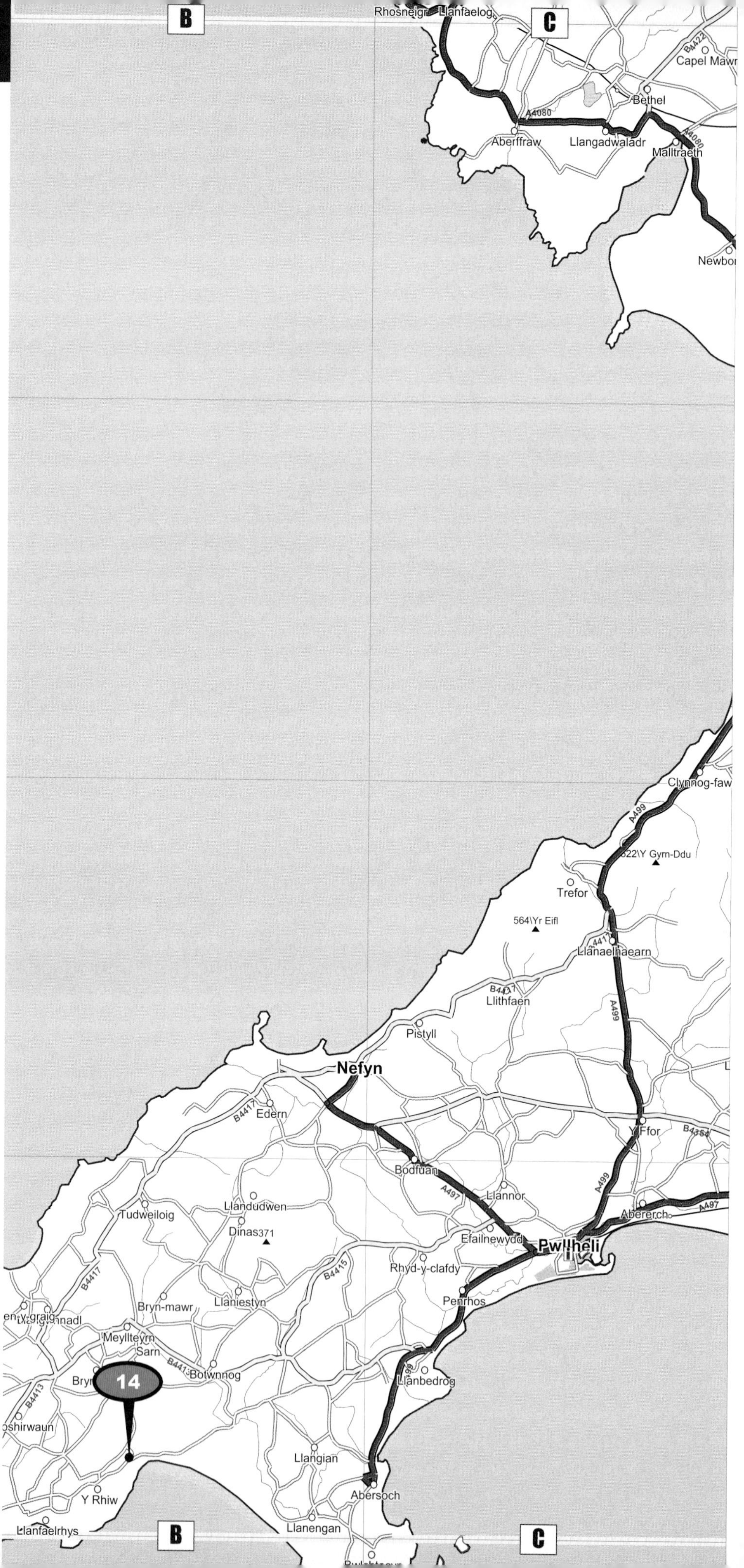

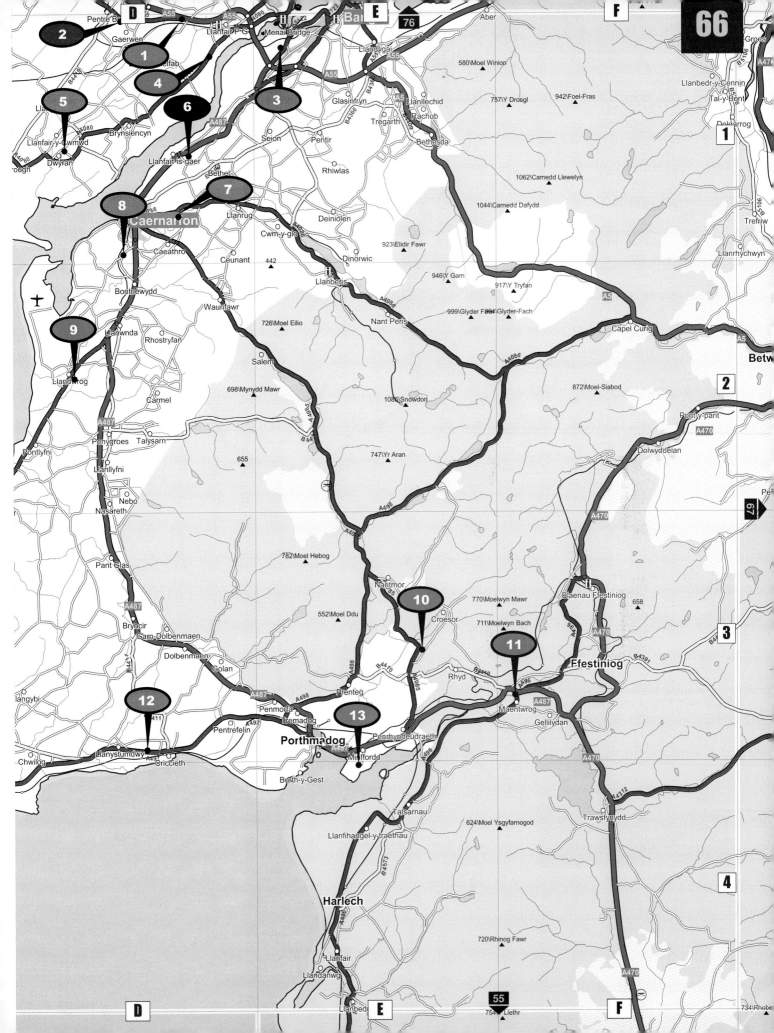

**1 ABERWHEELER NURSERIES**
Mold Road, Bodfari, Denbigh   TEL: 01745 710 673

**2 DALESIDE NURSERY**
Gladstone Way, Hawarden   TEL: 01244 532 041

**3 GREEN FINGERS GARDEN CENTRE**
Rhyl Road, Denbigh   TEL: 01745 815 279

**4 GWYDIR CASTLE**
Llanrwst   TEL: 01492 641 687

**5 SEVEN OAKS GARDEN CENTRE**
Lon Parcwr Business Estate, Ruthin
   TEL: 01824 702 567

**6 GWYDIR PLANTS**
Plas Muriau, Betws-y-coed   TEL: 01690 750 379

**7 CARLTON GARDEN CENTRE**
Pinfold Lane, Llay Industrial Estate, Llay
   TEL: 01978 852 896

**8 SPECTRUM HOME & GARDEN CENTRE**
Mold Road, Cefn-Y-Bedd, Wrexham
   TEL: 01978 760 634

**9 FRENDALE HOME & GARDEN CENTRE**
Berse Road, Caego, Wrexham   TEL: 01978 751 946

**10 WATERWAYS GARDEN CENTRE**
Holt Road, Llan-Y-Pwll, Wrexham
   TEL: 01978 660 289

**11 ERDDIG, NATIONAL TRUST**
Wrexham   TEL: 01978 355 314

**12 GLYNDWR PLANTS**
Tafarn Bric, Corwen   TEL: 01490 413 313

**13 CELYN VALE EUCALYPTUS NURSERIES**
Allt Y Celyn, Carrog, Corwen   TEL: 01490 430 671

**14 CHIRK CASTLE, NATIONAL TRUST**
Chirk, Wrexham   TEL: 01691 777 701

**15 MORETON PARK GARDEN CENTRE**
Gledrid, Chirk, Wrexham, Shropshire, LL14 5DG.
TEL: 01691 777 722

*A purpose built garden centre for all your gardening
and gift ideas. Delivery service available - please
call for details.*
OPEN: Mon-Sat 9-6, Sun 10.30-4.30.
SPECIALITIES: Aquatics, Floristry, Shrubs, Trees,
BBQs and furniture.
FACILITIES: Toilets, Credit cards, Wheelchair access,
Restaurant, Gift tokens, Bookshop, Child area,
Coffee shop, Plant guarantee.

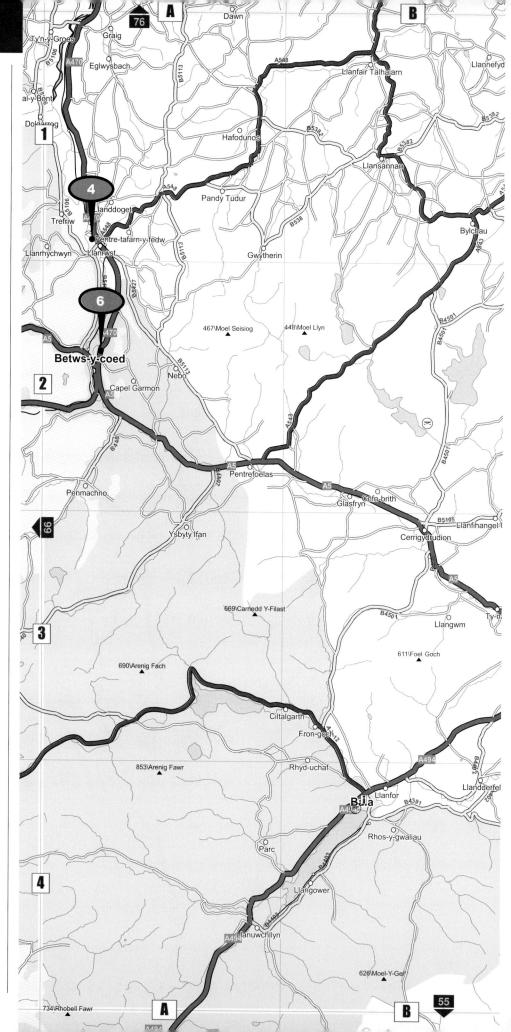

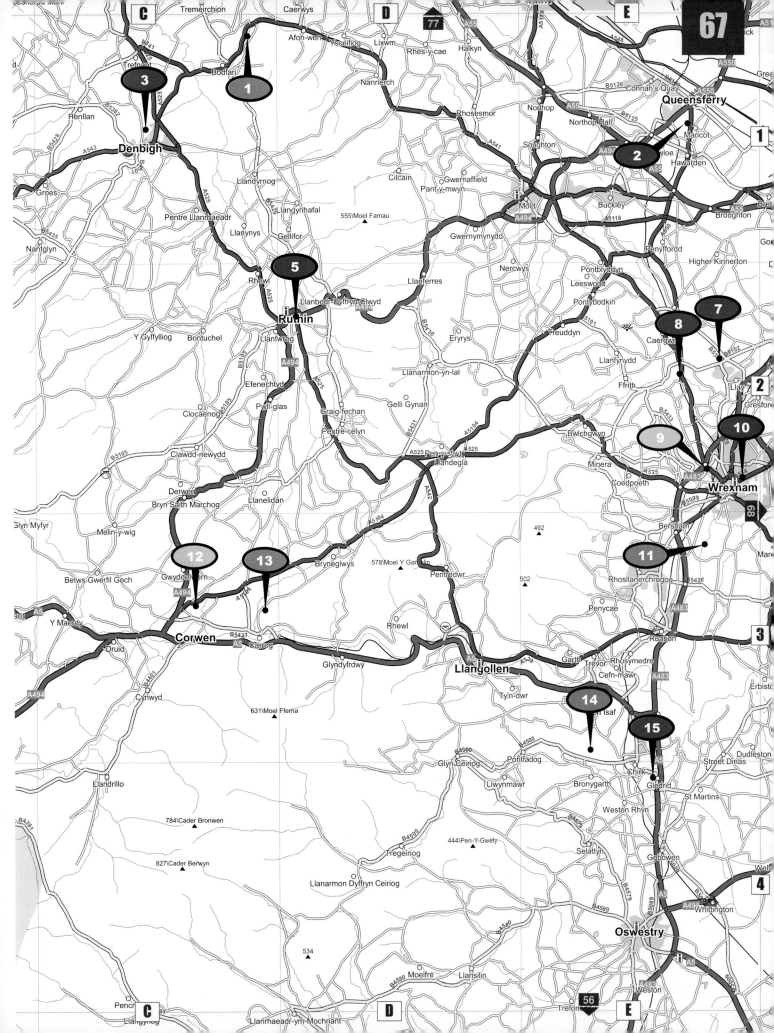

**1 OLD VICARAGE GARDEN CENTRE**
Chester Road, Dunham Hill, Frodsham
Tel: 01244 300 805

**2 K'S NURSERY AND GARDEN CENTRE**
Coalpit Lane, Chester
Tel: 01244 880 468

**3 STONYFORD COTTAGE NURSERY**
Stonyford Lane, Cuddington, Northwich
Tel: 01606 888 128

**4 GARDENLAND GARDEN CENTRE**
Blakemere Craft Centre, Chester Road, Northwich
Tel: 01606 888 312

**5 CHESHIRE WATERLIFE**
Lake Mere Craft Centre, Chester Road, Northwich
Tel: 01606 882 223

**6 OAK TREE FARM NURSERIES**
Fiddlers Lane, Saughall, Chester
Tel: 01244 880 895

**7 CHESTER ZOO**
Upton-by-Chester, Chester
Tel: 01244 380 280

**8 CHESTER ROAD NURSERY**
Kelsall, Tarporley
Tel: 01829 752 333

**9 C & K JONES**
Goldenfields Nursery, Barrow Lane, Tarvin
Tel: 01829 740 663

**10 CHESHIRE HERBS**
Fourfields, Forest Road, Tarporley
Tel: 01829 760 578

**11 WYEVALE GARDEN CENTRE**
Forest Road, Tarporley
Tel: 01829 760 433

**12 BEECHMOOR NURSERIES**
Whitchurch, Great Boughton, Chester
Tel: 01244 336 922

**13 OKELL'S NURSERIES**
Duddon Heath, Tarporley
Tel: 01829 741 512

**14 GROSVENOR GARDEN CENTRE**
Wrexham Road, Belgrave, Chester
Tel: 01244 682 856

**15 NANNEY'S BRIDGE NURSERY**
Church Minshall, Nantwich
Tel: 01270 522 239

**16 MINSHULL'S NURSERY**
Eardswick Lane, Bradfield Green, Crewe
Tel: 01270 522 482

**17 WATERWAYS GARDEN CENTRE**
Chester Road, Lavister, Rossett
Tel: 01244 571 064

**18 QUEEN'S PARK, CREWE**
Victoria Avenue, Wistaton Road, Crewe
Tel: 01270 537 239

**19 CREWE ROAD NURSERIES**
209 Crewe Road, Willaston, Nantwich
Tel: 01270 624 245

**20 STAPELEY WATER GARDENS**
London Road, Stapeley, Nantwich
Tel: 01270 623 868

**21 BROMAC NURSERY**
Little Porters Hill Farm, Frith Lane, Wrenbury
Tel: 01270 780 319

**22 PLASSEY PLANTS**
Plassey, Eyton, Wrexham
Tel: 01978 780 788

**23 SPRINGWOOD NURSERIES**
3 Steel Road, Tilstock, Whitchurch
Tel: 01948 880 397

**24 HEATHWOOD NURSERIES**
The Meadows, Higher Heath, Whitchurch
Tel: 01948 840 120

**25 BALMER GROVE PLANTS**
Bayston Hill Nurseries, Welshampton
Tel: 01948 710 403

**26 HILLCREST CONIFERS**
Salisbury Road, Market Drayton
Tel: 01630 652 088

**27 ELLESMERE ROAD ORGANIC NURSERY**
Shrewsbury Road, Cockshutt, Ellesmere
Tel: 01939 270 270

**28 HAWKSTONE HISTORIC PARK & FOLLIES**
Weston-under-Redcastle, Shrewsbury
Tel: 01939 200 611

**29 HODNET HALL**
Hodnet, Market Drayton
Tel: 01630 685 202

Dutch Iris

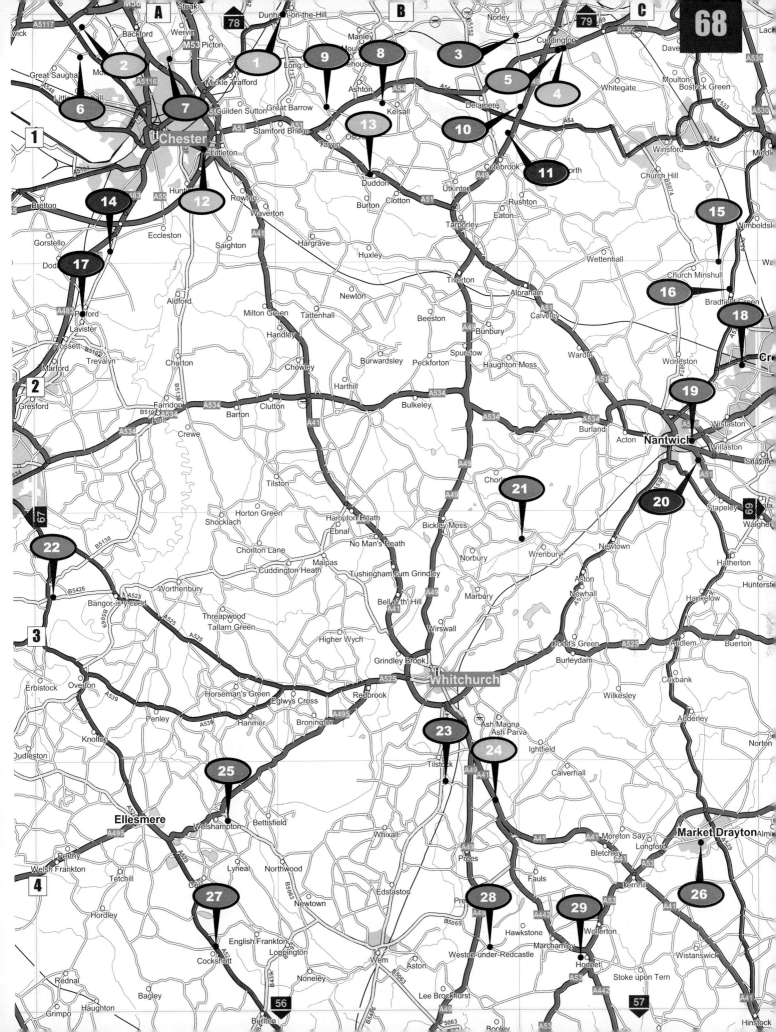

**1  GRANADA ARBORETUM**
Jodrell Bank, Holmes Chapel, Macclesfield
TEL: 01477 571 339

**2  MACCLESFIELD GARDEN CENTRE**
Bullocks Lane, Off Byrons Lane, Macclesfield
TEL: 01625 618 933

**3  HILLS GARDEN CENTRE**
London Road, Allostock, Knutsford
TEL: 01565 722 567

**4  GAWSWORTH HALL**
Macclesfield
TEL: 01260 223 456

**5  HOLLAND'S NURSERIES**
Maley Pole Farm, Gawsworth, Macclesfield
TEL: 01260 223 362

**6  BOOSEY'S GARDEN CENTRE**
Newton Bank, Middlewich
TEL: 01606 832 324

**7  WALNUT TREE NURSERIES**
Walnut Tree Farm, Plant Lane, Moston
TEL: 01270 526 248

**8  D J M NURSERY**
Newcastle Road, Astbury, Congleton
TEL: 01260 275 032

**9  ASTBURY MEADOW GARDEN CENTRE**
Newcastle Road (A34), Astbury, Congleton
TEL: 01260 276 466

**10  CONGLETON GARDEN CENTRE**
Moss Road, Astbury, Congleton
TEL: 01260 270 010

**11  BIDDULPH GRANGE GARDEN**
Biddulph Grange, Biddulph, Stoke-on-Trent
TEL: 01782 517 999

**12  LITTLE MORETON HALL**
Newcastle Road, Congleton
TEL: 01260 272 018

**13  RODE HALL**
Church Lane, Scholar Green, Congleton
TEL: 01270 873 237

**14  JACKSONS GARDEN CENTRE**
Tunstall Road, Knypersley, Stoke-on-Trent
TEL: 01782 513 405

**15  Q GARDEN**
Garden Centre Shop, 2 Church Street, Leek
TEL: 01538 383 114

**16  KNYPERSLEY HALL GARDEN CENTRE**
Conway Road, Knypersley, Stoke-on-Trent
TEL: 01782 512 766

**17  BARNCROFT NURSERIES**
Dunwood Lane, Longsdon, Leek
TEL: 01538 384 310

**18  FLOWER POT GARDEN CENTRE**
Crewe Road, Radwat Green, Alsager
TEL: 01270 884 207

**19  FORD GREEN HALL**
Ford Green Road, Smallthorne, Stoke-on-Trent
TEL: 01782 233 195

**20  KERRY HILL NURSERIES**
Eaves Lane, Bucknall, Stoke-on-Trent
TEL: 01782 302 498

**21  BRIDGEMERE GARDEN WORLD**
Bridgemere, Nantwich, Cheshire, CW5 7QB.
TEL: 01270 521 100
EMAIL: info@bridgemere.co.uk
WEB: www.bridgemere.co.uk

# BRIDGEMERE
## GARDEN WORLD

*Britain's largest garden centre with 4,000 different plant varieties. Over two acres of beautiful gardens, restaurants, childrens play area and parking for 1000 cars.*
OPEN: Open 7 days a week. Summer: 8-8. Winter: 8-6. Closed Christmas & Boxing Day.
SPECIALITIES: Comprehensive range, Furniture, Hanging baskets, House plants, Perennials.
FACILITIES: Toilets, Credit cards, Wheelchair access, Restaurant, Coffee shop, Gift tokens, Bookshop, Gift shop, Child area, Sell plants, Plant guarantee, Coffee shop, HTA gift tokens, Own gift tokens, Pushchair friendly.

**22  ROSE FARM NURSERIES**
Whitmore Road, Newcastle under Lyme
TEL: 01782 637 522

**23  NORTHWOOD GARDEN CENTRE**
Clayton Road, Clayton, Newcastle under Lyme
TEL: 01782 635 081

**24  WEST HOLME NURSERIES**
Ireland's Cross London Road, Woore
TEL: 01630 647 829

**25  TRENTHAM PARK GARDENS**
Stone Road, Stoke-on-Trent
TEL: 01782 657 341

**26  COUNTRY CABIN**
10 Holding, Cocknage, Stoke-on-Trent
TEL: 01782 327 429

**27  DOROTHY CLIVE GARDEN**
Willoughbridge, Market Drayton, Shropshire, TF9 4EU.
TEL: 01630 647 237
WEB: www.dorothyclivegarden.co.uk
*This romantic garden is home to choice and unusual plants in informal settings. An alpine scree, water features and a spectacular woodland garden are just some of the delights.*
OPEN: Mar 28-Oct 31: 10-5.30.
ENTRY COSTS: £3.20, Child: £1 Under 11's free, OAPs: £2.70.
SPECIALITIES: Rhododendrons and azaleas, Herbaceous plants, Perennials, Water features, Shrubs.
FACILITIES: Toilets, Wheelchair access, Coffee shop.

**28  BARLASTON NURSERIES**
Old Road, Barlaston, Stoke-on-Trent
TEL: 01782 373 960

**29  TRENT NURSERIES**
56 Tittensor Road, Tittensor, Stoke-on-Trent
TEL: 01782 372 395

**30  ROCK LANE NURSERY**
Mucklestone, Market Drayton
TEL: 01843 862 060

**31  HEATHER'S ROSES**
Heather Nursery, Moss Lane, Hilderstone
TEL: 01889 505 345

**32  HIGH FARM NURSERIES**
High Farm, Nobut Road, Church Leigh
TEL: 01889 502 252

**33  BURY BANK PLANT CENTRE**
P&M Edwards, Bury Bank Nurseries, Bury Bank
TEL: 01782 296 353

**34  FLETCHER'S GARDEN AND LEISURE CENTRE**
Bridge Farm, Stone Road, Eccleshall
TEL: 01785 851 057

**35  JOHNSON HALL NURSERIES**
Johnson Hall, Eccleshall, Stafford
TEL: 01785 850 400

**36  AMERTON GARDEN CENTRE**
Stow by Chartley, Amerton, Stafford
TEL: 01889 271 998

**37  BRIDGEFORD GARDEN CENTRE**
Newport Road, Great Bridgeford, Stafford
TEL:

**38  GREENHEART PLANTS**
Hopton Hall Lane, Hopton, Stafford
TEL: 01785 257 975

Frangipani

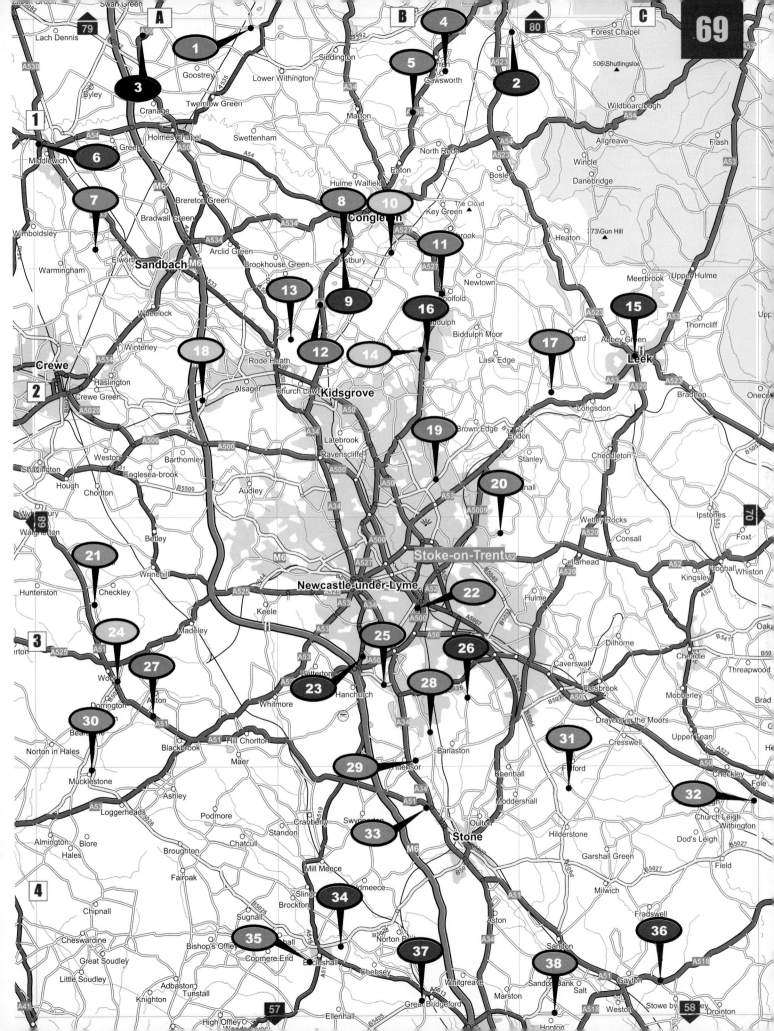

**1  GLENHYRST NURSERIES**
Vincent Crescent, Brampton, Chesterfield
TEL: 01246 566 632

**2  CHATSWORTH**
Edensor, Bakewell
TEL: 01246 582 204

**3  CHATSWORTH GARDEN CENTRE**
Calton Lees, Beeley, Matlock
TEL: 01629 734 004

**4  HADDON HALL**
Estate Office, Bakewell
TEL: 01629 812 855

**5  GARDEN CENTRES OF EXCELLENCE**
Nottingham Road, Tansley, Matlock
TEL: 01629 580 500

**6  FOREST NURSERIES**
Oddford Lane, Two Dales, Matlock
TEL: 01629 733 225

**7  KNABB HALL NURSERIES**
Knabb Hall Lane, Tansley, Matlock
TEL: 01629 554 61

**8  JAMES SMITH NURSERIES**
Stretton Road, Tansley, Matlock
TEL: 01629 583 036

**9  MATLOCK GARDEN WATER LIFE & PET CENTRE**
Nottingham Road, Tansley, Matlock
TEL: 01629 580 500

**10  LORNA CROSS NURSERY**
3 Cliff Villas, Tansley, Matlock
TEL: 01629 583 207

**11  CROMFORD GARDEN CENTRE**
Derby Road, Cromford, Matlock
TEL: 01629 824 990

**12  WESSINGTON GARDEN CENTRE**
Matlock Road, Wessington, Alfreton
TEL: 01773 832 517

**13  TISSINGTON NURSERY**
Tissington, Ashbourne
TEL: 01335 390 650

**14  OLD HALL NURSERY**
Old Hall Farm, Leek
TEL: 01538 308 257

**15  ILAM PARK, NATIONAL TRUST**
Ilam, Ashbourne
TEL: 01335 350 245

**16  BROADHOLME LANE FARM NURSERY**
Broadholme Lane, Belper
TEL: 01773 823 517

**17  CALLWOOD NURSERY**
Belper Road, Bargate, Belper
TEL: 01773 824 771

**18  FAIRWAYS GARDEN CENTRE**
Clifton, Ashbourne
TEL: 01335 347 900

**19  BIRCHWOOD FARM NURSERY**
Portway, Coxbench
TEL: 01332 880 685

**20  ALTON TOWERS**
Alton, Stoke-on-Trent
TEL: 0990 204 060

**21  DERBY GARDEN CENTRE**
Alfreton Road, Little Eaton, Derby
TEL: 01332 831 666

**22  KEDLESTON HALL, NATIONAL TRUST**
Derby
TEL: 01332 842 191

**23  MEYNELL LANGLEY GARDENS**
Langley Hall, Kirk Langley, Ashbourne
TEL: 01332 824 358

**24  MARKEATON GARDEN CENTRE & NURSERY**
Markeaton Lane, Derby
TEL: 01332 292 554

**25  ALLARDS PLANT CENTRE**
20-23 The Meadows, Chequers Road, Derby
TEL: 01332 205 135

**26  DERBY ARBORETUM**
Arboretum Square, Derby
TEL: 01332 716 644

**27  HELDON NURSERIES**
Ashbourne Road, Spath, Uttoxeter
TEL: 01889 563 377

**28  DEVONSHIRE NURSERIES**
13 Devonshire Drive, Mickelover
TEL: 01332 513 211

**29  GRANGECRAFT GARDEN CENTRE**
Hospital Lane, Mickleover, Mickelover
TEL: 01332 510 951

**30  SUDBURY HALL, NATIONAL TRUST**
Sudbury, Ashbourne
TEL: 01283 585 305

**31  WYEVALE GARDEN CENTRE**
Burton Road, Findern, Derby
TEL: 01332 514 268

**32  FIRS FARM NURSERY**
Firs Farm, Scropton Road, Derby
TEL: 01283 520 331

**33  SAMUEL JACKSON GROWERS**
The Glasshouse, Lowers Lane, Derby
TEL: 01332 700 800

**34  SLATER'S GARDENS**
Dovecliffe Road, Stretton, Burton upon Trent
TEL: 01283 565 650

Lotus

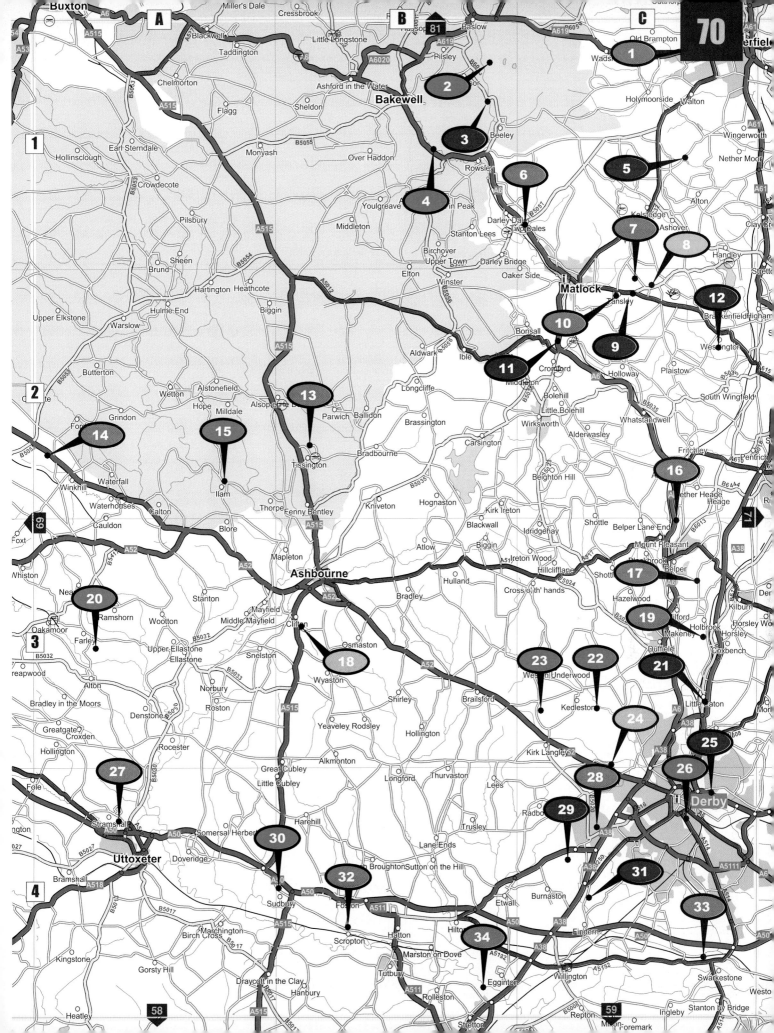

**1 ROSE'S GARDEN CENTRE**
Chesterfield Road, Arkwright Town, Chesterfield
**TEL:** 01246 551 627

**2 FIVE ACRE KOI SUPPLIES**
Five Acre Kennels, Chesterfield Road, Duckmanton
**TEL:** 01246 240 350

**3 BOLSOVER CASTLE, ENGLISH HERITAGE**
Bolsover
**TEL:** 01246 823 349

**4 THORESBY TREE & SHRUB NURSERY**
The Old Gardens, Thoresby Park, Perlthorpe
**TEL:** 01623 824 885

**5 FOURWAYS NURSERY**
Rotherham Road, Bolsover, Chesterfield
**TEL:** 01246 241 317

**6 CHESTERFIELD AQUATICS**
Mansfield Road, Hasland, Chesterfield
**TEL:** 01246 558 444

**7 PLANTWORLD**
Old Manor Nurseries, Mansfield Road,
Temple Normanton
**TEL:** 01246 850 336

**8 GLAPWELL NURSERIES**
Bolsover Road, Glapwell, Chesterfield
**TEL:** 01623 812 191

**9 THE HERB GARDEN**
Hall View Cottage, Hardstoft, Pilsley
**TEL:** 01246 854 268

**10 HARDWICK OLD HALL, ENGLISH HERITAGE**
Doe Len, Chesterfield
**TEL:** 01246 850 431

**11 SPENCER'S**
Fernlea, 83a Clay Lane, Chesterfield
**TEL:** 01246 862 628

**12 OILWELL NURSERY**
Oilwell Nursery, Chesterfield Road, Tibshelf
**TEL:** 01773 874 321

**13 SHERWOODS GARDEN CENTRE**
7-9 Sherwood Hall Road, Mansfield
**TEL:** 01623 624 923

**14 DALESTORTH GARDEN CENTRE**
Dalestorth House, Skegby Lane, Skegby
**TEL:** 01623 557 817

**15 WESTFIELD GARDEN CENTRE**
Beck Lane, Skegby, Sutton in Ashfield
**TEL:** 01623 554 515

**16 GREENHILLS GARDEN CENTRE**
Greenhills Farm, Cauldwell Road, Sutton in Ashfield
**TEL:** 01623 554 418

**17 CARNFIELD HALL GARDEN & CRAFT CENTRE**
Carnfield Hill, South Normanton, Alfreton
**TEL:** 01773 834 577

**18 THE GARDEN OUTLET**
Building 2 Derbyshire Designer Outlet Village,
Mansfield Road, South Normanton
**TEL:** 01773 545 066

**19 WILBOURN'S GARDEN CENTRE**
Station Street, Kirkby-in-Ashfield, Nottingham
**TEL:** 01623 753 100

**20 NEWSTEAD ABBEY PARK**
Newstead Abbey, Ravenshead
**TEL:** 01623 455 900

**21 SHIRLEY NURSERIES**
Mansfield Road, Papplewick
**TEL:** 0115 963 2677

**22 GREENWOOD BONSAI STUDIO & GARDENS**
Ollerton Road, Arnold, Nottingham
**TEL:** 0115 920 5757

**23 REUBEN SHAW & SON**
Hollydean Nurseries, More Green, Langley Mill
**TEL:** 01773 714 326

**24 RAVENSDALE NURSERY**
7a Midland Road, Heanor
**TEL:** 01773 712 431

**25 FLORALANDS GARDEN CENTRE**
Catfoot Lane, Lambley, Nottingham
**TEL:** 0115 926 8137

**26 GREENACRES NURSERY**
322 Spring Lane, Nottingham
**TEL:** 0115 926 2951

**27 LAMBLEY AQUATICS**
Floralands Garden Centre, Catfoot Lane, Lambley
**TEL:** 0115 926 2545

**28 SHIPLEY GARDEN CENTRE**
Hassock Lane North, Shipley, Heanor
**TEL:** 01773 713 596

**29 BROOKFIELDS GARDEN & LEISURE CENTRE**
431 Mapperley Plains, Arnold, Nottingham
**TEL:** 0115 926 8200

**30 NOEL CLAY GARDEN CENTRE**
Gin Close Way, Awsworth
**TEL:** 0115 938 4544

**31 ANDERSEN'S NURSERY**
Awsworth Lane, Cossall, Nottingham
**TEL:** 0115 930 1884

**32 HILLTOP NURSERIES**
166 Lambley Lane, Gedling, Nottingham
**TEL:** 0115 961 2054

**33 COLLINWOOD NURSERIES**
5 Colville Villas, Nottingham
**TEL:** 01625 582 272

**34 GROWING SENSE**
40a St Peter's Street, Nottingham
**TEL:** 0115 978 3228

**35 WOODLANDS GARDEN CENTRE**
Nottingham Road, Trowell Moor, Nottingham
**TEL:** 0115 928 3200

**36 DALE ABBEY PLANTS**
Hagg Lane, Dale Abbey, Ilkeston
**TEL:** 0115 932 2728

Sunflower

**37  TROWELL GARDEN CENTRE**
Stapleford Road, Trowell
TEL: 0115 932 6920

**38  WOLLATON PARK**
Wollaton Road, Wollaton, Nottingham
TEL: 0115 915 3900

**39  HEWTHORN HERBS & WILD FLOWERS**
Simkins Farm, Adbolton Lane, West Bridgford
TEL: 01602 812 861

**40  LOCKO NURSERIES**
144 Locko Road, Spondon, Derby
TEL: 01332 672 304

**41  PIKES OAK FARM NURSERIES**
Oak Farm, Willoughby Road, Keyworth
TEL: 0115 937 5352

**42  BARDILLS ROSES**
Toton Lane, Stapleford, Nottingham
TEL: 0115 949 0019

**43  SALLEY GARDENS**
32 Lansdowne Drive, West Bridgford
TEL: 0115 923 3878

**44  LANES GARDEN CENTRE**
Breaston Lane, Risley, Draycott
TEL: 0115 939 7128

**45  COVENT GARDEN NURSERIES**
135 Victoria Avenue, Borrowash, Derby
TEL: 01332 673 549

**46  COLLYER'S NURSERIES**
Nottingham Road, Borrowash, Derby
TEL: 01332 662 035

**47  WHEATCROFT**
Landmere Lane, Edwalton, Nottingham
TEL: 0115 921 6060

**48  ELVASTON CASTLE COUNTRY PARK**
Elvaston, Thulston, Derby
TEL: 01332 571 342

**49  ECOPLANTS**
Flawforth Lane, Ruddington
TEL: 0115 9211 054

**50  FIELD HOUSE ALPINES**
Leake Road, Gotham, Nottingham
TEL: 0115 983 0278

**51  DONINGTON NURSERIES**
Kings Mills, Park Lane, Castle Donington
TEL: 01332 853 004

**52  BAILIFFS MEAD NURSERIES**
67 High Street, Castle Donington, Derby
TEL: 01332 810 245

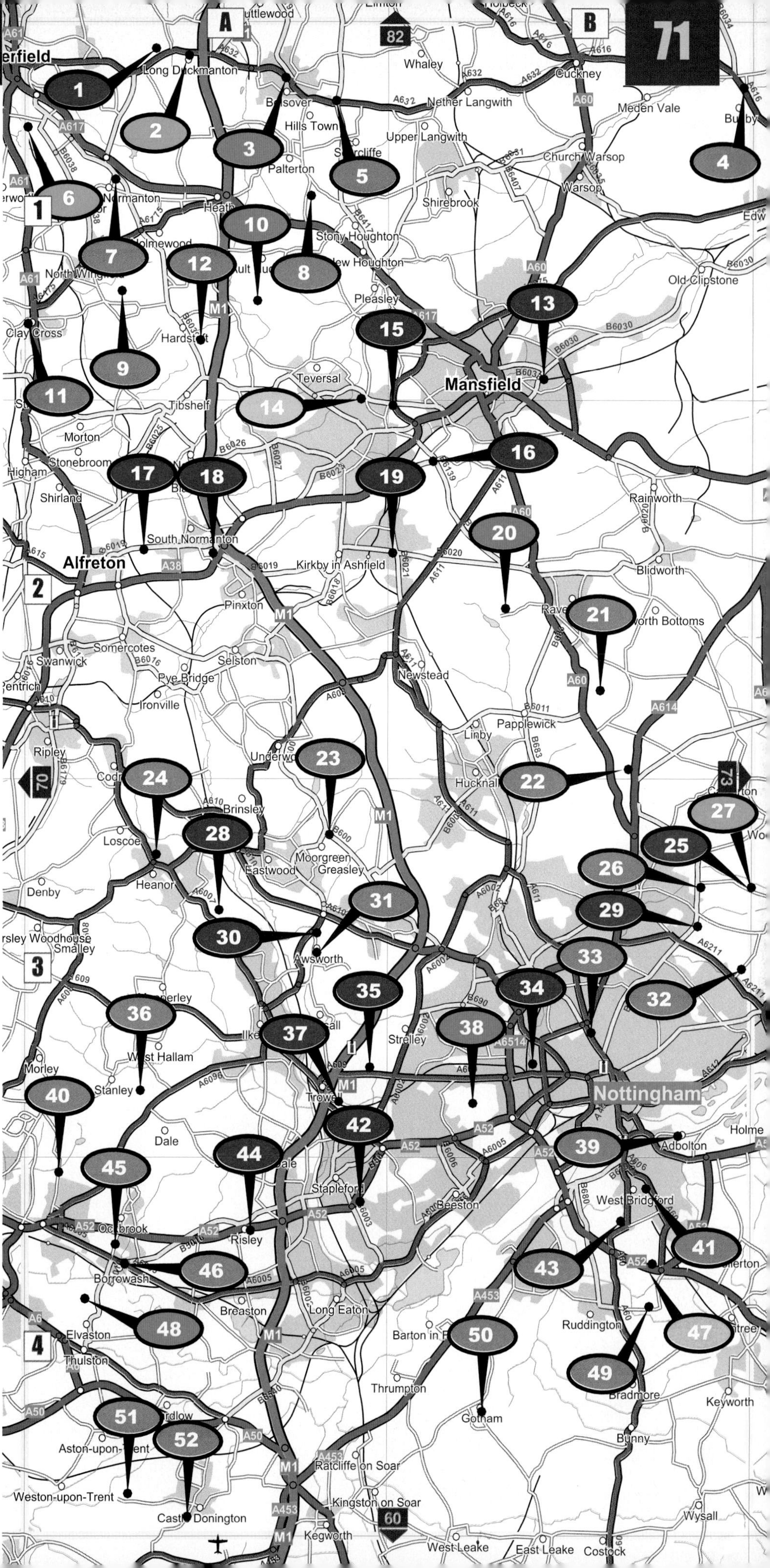

**1  EASTFIELD NURSERIES**
Eastfield Farm, Lincoln Road, Tuxford
TEL: 01777 870 341

**2  WALESBY GARDEN CENTRE**
Brake Road, Walesby, Newark
TEL: 01623 860 382

**3  PLANTLAND GARDEN CENTRE**
Moorland Centre, Tritton Road, Lincoln
TEL: 01522 500 588

**4  WHISBY WATER AND GARDEN CENTRE**
Whisby Road, Lincoln
TEL: 01522 685 395

**5  RUFFORD ABBEY & COUNTRY PARK**
The Sawmill, Rufford, Newark
TEL: 01623 822 944

**6  PENNELLS GARDEN CENTRE**
Newark Road, South Hykeham, Lincoln
TEL: 01522 880 033

**7  WADDINGTON NURSERIES**
123 Station Road, Waddington, Lincoln
TEL: 01522 720 220

**8  NORWELL NURSERIES**
Woodhouse Road, Norwell, Newark
TEL: 01636 636 337

**9  DALESTORTH NURSERIES**
Cockett Lane, Farnsfield, Newark
TEL: 01623 883 187

**10  SLACKS ROSES**
Farnsfield, Newark
TEL: 01623 621 058

**11  WONDERLAND GARDEN CENTRE**
White Post, Farnsfield, Newark
TEL: 01623 883 395

**12  REG TAYLOR GARDEN CENTRE**
Corkhill Lane, Normanton, Southwell
TEL: 01636 813 184

**13  H  MERRYWEATHER & SON**
The Garden Centre, Halam Road, Southwell
TEL: 01636 813 204

**14  CRINK LANE NURSERIES**
Crink Lane, Fiskerton Road, Southwell
TEL: 01636 812 706

**15  SOUTHWELL GARDEN CENTRE**
Fiskerton Road, Southwell
TEL: 01636 812 886

**16  DANNY-LYP GARDEN CENTRE**
41 Sibcy Lane, Balderton, Newark
TEL: 01636 674 840

**17  MILL HILL PLANTS**
Mill Hill House, Elston Lane, East Stoke
TEL: 01636 525 460

**18  WORLD OF WATER**
Timmermans Garden Centre, Lowdham Lane,
Woodborough
TEL: 0115 966 3333

**19  TIMMERMANS GARDEN CENTRE**
Lowdham Lane, Woodborough, Nottingham
TEL: 0115 966 4033

**20  LILY VALE NURSERIES**
Park Lane, Lambley, Nottingham
TEL: 0115 931 3506

**21  AQUATIC CENTRE**
Main Road, Bulcote, Nottingham
TEL: 0115 931 2986

**22  TALL TREES GARDEN CENTRE**
Main Road, Bulcote, Nottingham
TEL: 0115 931 2356

**23  ORCHARD NURSERIES**
Tow Lane, Foston, Grantham
TEL: 01400 281 354

**24  BRIDGFORD GARDEN WATER LIFE
& PET CENTRE**
Fosse Road, East Bridgford
TEL: 01949 200 55

**25  DOWNTOWN GARDEN CENTRE**
Gonerby Moor Roundabout, A1, Grantham
TEL: 01476 512 333

**26  BELTON HOUSE**
Belton, Grantham
TEL: 01476 566 116

**27  BELTON HOUSE, NATIONAL TRUST**
Grantham
TEL: 01476 566 116

**28  STRAGGLETHORPE NURSERIES**
Radcliffe on Trent
TEL: 01602 332 158

**29  CLAPTONS CONSERVATORY &
GARDEN CENTRE**
Union Street, Grantham
TEL: 01476 564 728

**30  IVOR THOMPSON NURSERIES**
82 Cotgrave Lane, Tollerton, Nottingham
TEL: 0115 937 2360

**31  NATURESCAPE WILDFLOWER FARM**
Coach Gap Lane, Langar
TEL: 01949 860 592

**32  BELVOIR CASTLE**
Belvoir, Grantham
TEL: 01476 870 262

**33  MOORES NURSERIES**
156 Melton Road, Stanton on the Wolds, Nottingham
TEL: 0115 937 3717

Rose

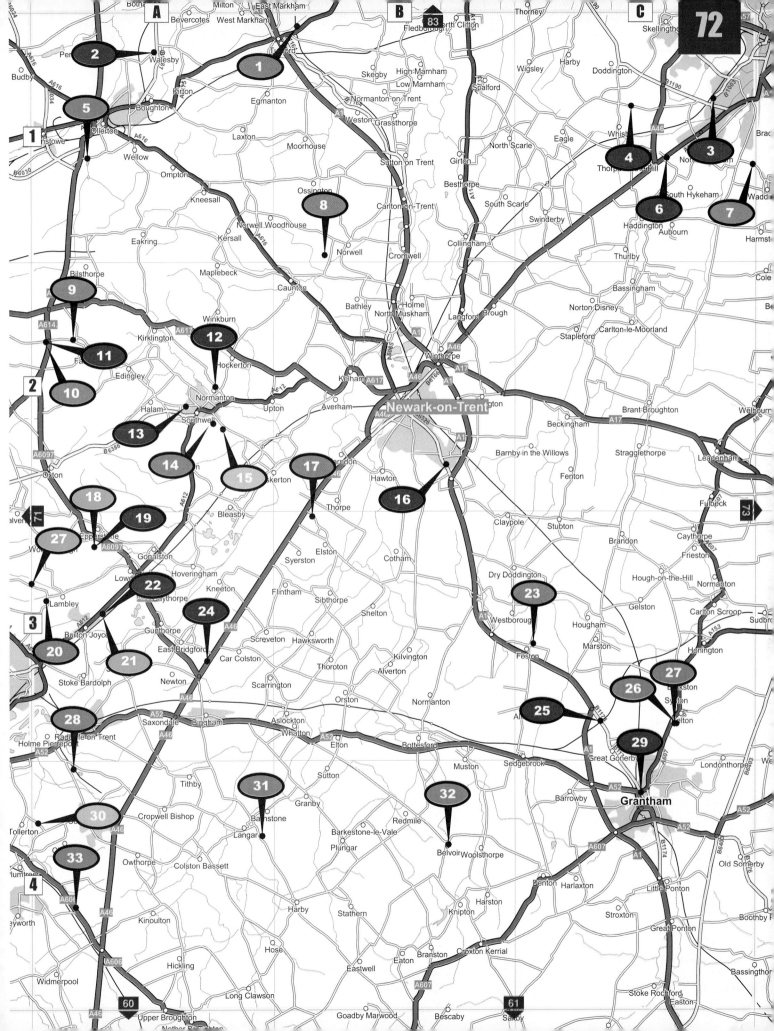

**1  PATIO PLANTING BY HAZEL**
Unit 6 Cobb Hall Yard, St. Pauls Lane, Lincoln
TEL: 01522 536 573

**2  JOHN DAWBER GARDEN**
The Lawn, Union Road, Lincoln
TEL: 01522 873 622

**3  SIR JOSEPH BANKS CONSERVATORY**
The Lawn, Union Road, Lincoln
TEL: 01522 873 622

**4  LINCOLN CATHEDRAL**
Castle Hill, Lincoln
TEL: 01522 544 544

**5  CROWDERS GARDEN CENTRE**
Lincoln Road, Thimbleby, Horncastle
TEL: 01507 525 252

**6  BARN NURSERY**
Five Mile Lane, Washingborough
TEL: 01522 793 727

**7  CONTENTED GARDENER**
The Garden House, 42 Wragby Road, Bardney
TEL: 01526 397 307

**8  HOLMDALE HOUSE GARDEN**
55 High Street, Martin, Lincoln
TEL: 01526 378 838

**9  CHOICE PLANTS**
83 Halton Road, Spilsby
TEL: 0788 791 3704

**10  EAST KEAL EARLS CROOME**
Main Road, East Keal, Spilsby
TEL: 01790 752 396

**11  ERMINE COTTAGE NURSERY**
Heath Road, Coleby, Lincoln
TEL: 01522 810 396

**12  BLANKNEY KOI & GARDEN CENTRE**
Martin Road, Blankney, Lincoln
TEL: 01526 378 880

**13  DORRINGTONS GARDEN CENTRE**
Dorrington Fen, Dorrington, Lincoln
TEL: 01526 832 529

**14  SHENLEA NURSERIES**
Main Road, Sibsey, Boston
TEL: 01205 750 424

**15  RUSKINGTON GARDEN CENTRE**
White House Farm, Newton Lane, Ruskington
TEL: 01526 833 022

**16  ANWICK GARDEN CENTRE**
Old Manor Farm, Anwick, Sleaford
TEL: 01526 832 277

**17  WESTHOLME NURSERIES**
The Gride, Old Leake, Boston
TEL: 01205 870 202

**18  MAURICE ROWE**
106 Horncastle Road, Boston
TEL: 01205 363 567

**19  MARWOOD HOUSE NURSERY**
Marwood House, High Ferry Lane, Sibsey
TEL: 01205 750 336

**20  JOHNSONS GARDEN CENTRE**
Wainfleet Road, Boston
TEL: 01205 636 408

**21  GLENHURST CACTUS NURSERY**
Station Road, Swineshead, Boston
TEL: 01205 820 314

**22  BELTON GARDEN CENTRE**
Belton, Grantham
TEL: 01476 563 700

**23  RAINBOW GARDEN & AQUATIC CENTRE**
Grange Farm, London Road, Kirton
TEL: 01205 723 555

**24  UNITY HOUSE NURSERY AND GARDEN CENTRE**
Unity House, Sutterton, Boston
TEL: 01205 460 213

**25  ANGLIAN GARDENS**
20 Gosberton Road, Surfleet, Spalding
TEL: 01775 680 760

**26  BIRCHGROVE GARDEN CENTRE**
Surfleet Road, Pinchbeck, Spalding
TEL: 01775 680 490

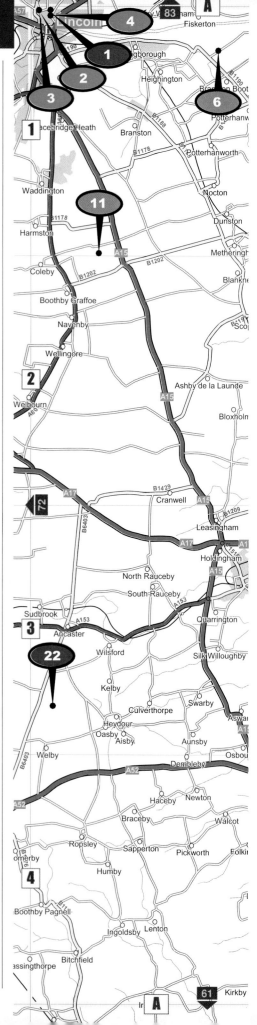

Water Lily

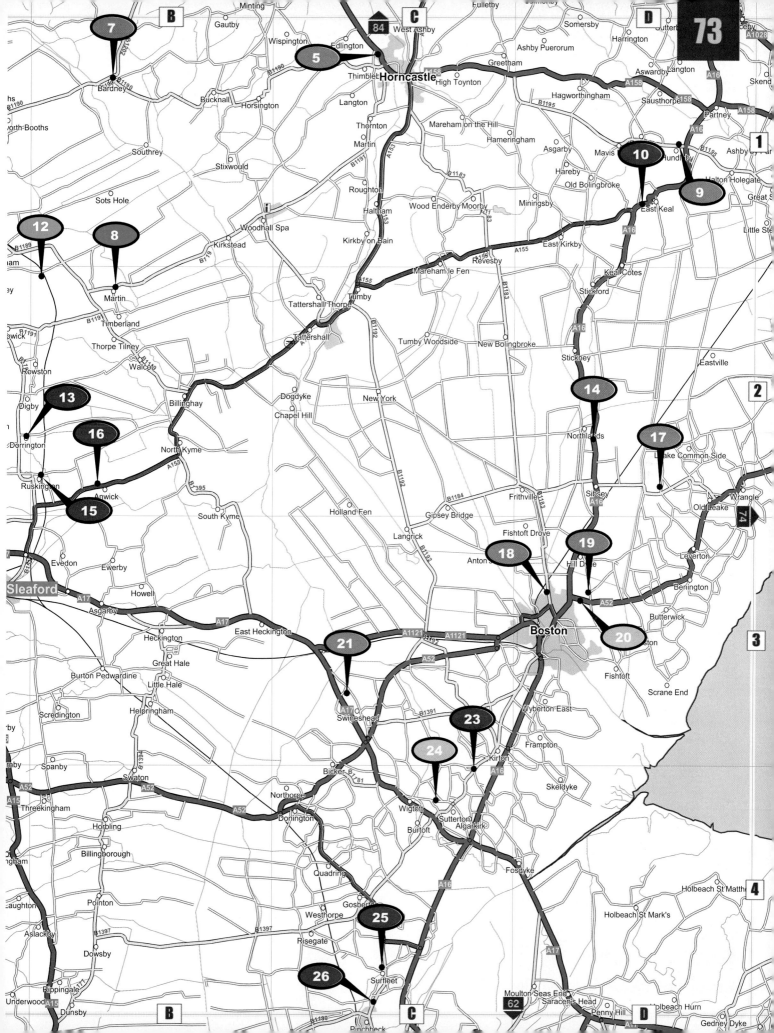

# NORFOLK · LINCS

**1**  **CHAPEL GARDEN CENTRE**
Skegness Road, Chapel St Leonards, Skegness
**TEL:** 01754 873 558

**2**  **THE PLANT LOVERS**
Candlesby House, Candlesby, Spilsby
**TEL:** 01754 890 256

**3**  **LYNDHURST GARDEN CENTRE**
Burgh-le-Marsh, Skegness
**TEL:** 01754 810 295

**4**  **HOLKHAM NURSERY GARDENS**
Holkham Park, Holkham, Wells-next-the-Sea
**TEL:** 01328 711 636

**5**  **STUBBINGS - THE GARDEN SHOP**
Market Place, Burnham Market
**TEL:** 01328 730 668

**6**  **NORFOLK LAVENDER**
Caley Hill, Heacham, King's Lynn
**TEL:** 01485 570 384

**7**  **CREAKE PLANT CENTRE**
Nursery View, Leicester Road, South Creake
**TEL:** 01328 823 018

**8**  **FAKENHAM GARDEN CENTRE**
Mill Road, Hempton, Fakenham
**TEL:** 01328 863 380

**9**  **SANDRINGHAM HOUSE, MUSEUM
AND COUNTRY PARK**
Sandringham, King's Lynn
**TEL:** 01553 772 675

**10**  **PENSTHORPE WATERFOWL PARK**
Pensthorpe Waterfowl Trust, Pensthorpe, Fakenham
**TEL:** 01328 851 465

Frangipani

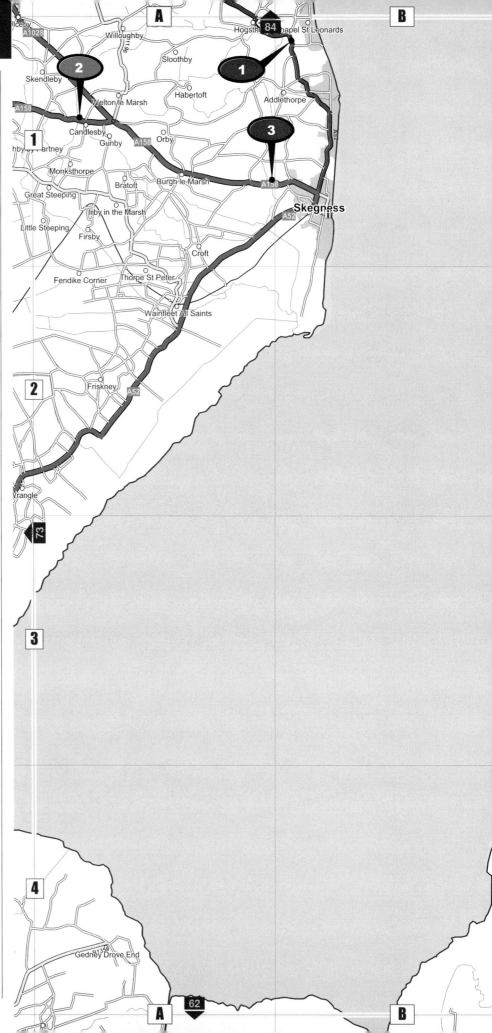

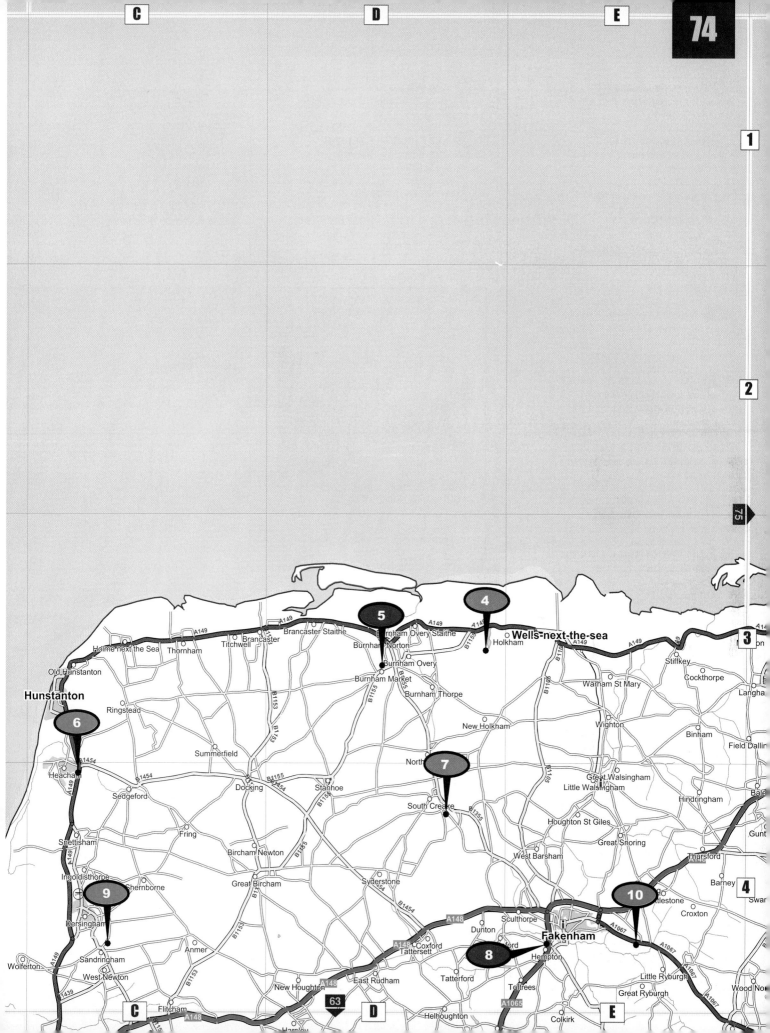

### 1  CLEY NURSERIES
Rectory Hill Nursery, Holt Road, Cley
**TEL:** 01263 740 892

### 2  BAKERS OF HOLT
8 Market Place, Holt
**TEL:** 01263 712 244

### 3  PRIORY MAZE & GARDENS
Beeston Regis, Sheringham
**TEL:** 01263 822 986

### 4  SHERINGHAM PARK, NATIONAL TRUST
Sheringham
**TEL:** 01263 823 778

### 5  NATURAL SURROUNDINGS
Centre for Wildlife Gardening & Conservation, Bayfield Estate, Holt
**TEL:** 01263 711 091

### 6  EMCY GARDEN & LEISURE
Weybourne Road, Kelling, Holt
**TEL:** 01263 713 126

### 7  OVERSTRAND COTTAGE GARDEN CENTRE
6 Mundesley Road, Overstrand, Cromer
**TEL:** 01263 579 485

### 8  FOUR SEASONS
Sellbrigg Road, High Kelling, Holt
**TEL:** 01263 712 629

### 9  FELBRIGG HALL & GARDEN, NATIONAL TRUST
Felbrigg, Roughton
**TEL:** 01263 837 444

### 10  GROVELAND GARDEN CENTRE
Groveland, Thorpe Market Road, Roughton
**TEL:** 01263 833 133

### 14  MANNINGTON GARDENS
Saxthorpe, Norwich, Norfolk, NR11 7BB.
**TEL:** 01263 584 175
**WEB:** www.manningtongardens.co.uk

*Beautiful gardens surround medieval moated manor. Heritage Rose Garden, wild flowers, trees and shrubs, lake. Extensive footpath network. Playground, tearooms. Events programme.*
**OPEN:** Jun-Aug: Wed-Fri 11-5, May-Sep: Sun 12-5.
**ENTRY COSTS:** £3.00, Child: Free, OAPs: £2.50.
**SPECIALITIES:** Themed garden, Roses, Trees, Walled garden, Wild flowers.
**FACILITIES:** Child area, Coffee shop, Gift shop, Sell plants, Toilets, Wheelchair access, Own gift tokens.

### 11  EDGEFIELD NURSERIES
Norwich Road, Edgefield, Melton Constable
**TEL:** 01263 587 457

### 12  ALBY CRAFTS GARDENS
Cromer Road, Erpingham, Norwich
**TEL:** 01263 761 226

### 13  WOLTERTON HALL
Wolterton Estate, Norwich
**TEL:** 01263 584 175

### 15  WOLTERTON PARK
Erpingham, Aylsham
**TEL:** 01263 584 175

### 16  NORTH WALSHAM GARDEN CENTRE & GARDEN MACHINERY
Norwich Road, North Walsham, Norfolk, NR28 0DR.
**TEL:** 01692 402 591

*Follow 'The Rose Centre' signs for a lovely day out.*
**OPEN:** Mon-Sat 9-5.30, Sun 11-5. Closed Easter Sun & Christmas Day .
**SPECIALITIES:** Roses, House plants, Perennials, Herbs, Shrubs.
**FACILITIES:** Credit cards, Dogs allowed, Gift shop, HTA gift tokens, Pushchair friendly, Restaurant, Sell plants, Toilets, Wheelchair access, Child area, Coffee shop, Plant guarantee.

### 17  BLICKLING HALL & GARDEN, NATIONAL TRUST
Blickling
**TEL:** 01263 733 084

### 18  THE KNOT GARDEN NURSERY
Heydon Lane, Wood Dalling, Norfolk, NR11 6SA.
**TEL:** 01263 587 051
*We are one of the country's leading specialists and plant nurseries. Our areas of expertise are mature quality trees and shrubs, specimen plants, topiary and imported exotica.*
**OPEN:** Summer: Mon-Sat 9-5. Winter: Mon-Fri 9-4, Sat 10-4. Other times by appointment only.
**SPECIALITIES:** Box hedges, Japanese maples, Rhododendrons and azaleas, Topiary, Trees.
**FACILITIES:** Own gift tokens, Sell plants, Toilets, Pushchair friendly.

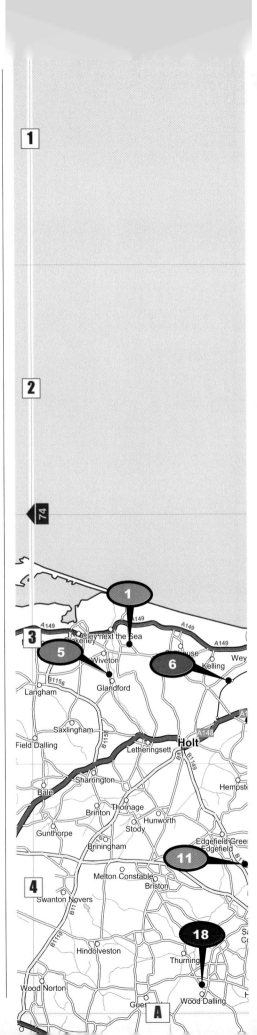

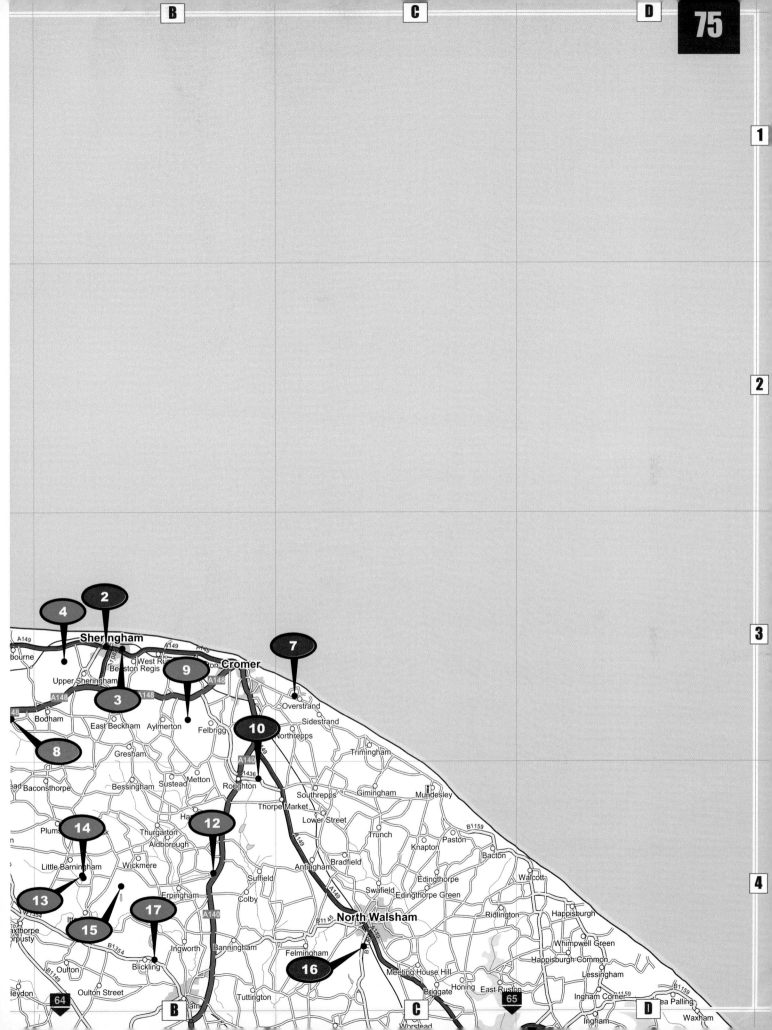

1

2

A149
Sheringham
A149
A149
West Ru...
...ton  **Cromer**
Beeston Regis
A148
Upper Sheringham
A148    A148
Bodham
East Beckham    Aylmerton    Felbrigg
48
Gresham
...ead  Baconsthorpe    Bessingham    Sustead    Metton
B1436
Roughton
Plums...    Thurgarton    Aldborough
Little Barningham    Wickmere
...xthorpe    Itt...
...rpusty
W 1354
Oulton
Oulton Street    Irmingham    Banningham
...eydon
64
B    ...ham    Tuttington

3

Overstrand
Sidestrand
Northrepps
Trimingham
Southrepps    Gimingham    Mundesley
Thorpe Market
Lower Street
Trunch    B1159
Knapton    Paston    Bacton
Bradfield
Antingham    Edingthorpe    Walcott
Suffield    Swafield    Edingthorpe Green
Colby    **North Walsham**    Ridlington    Happisburgh
B11 5
Felmingham    Whimpwell Green
Honing    East Ruston    Happisburgh-Common
Briggate    Lessingham
Meeting House Hill    A44 59
65    Ingham Corner    ...ea Palling
Worstead    C    D    Waxham
Ingham

4

Numbered markers on map: 2, 4, 7, 3, 9, 8, 10, 14, 12, 13, 17, 15, 16

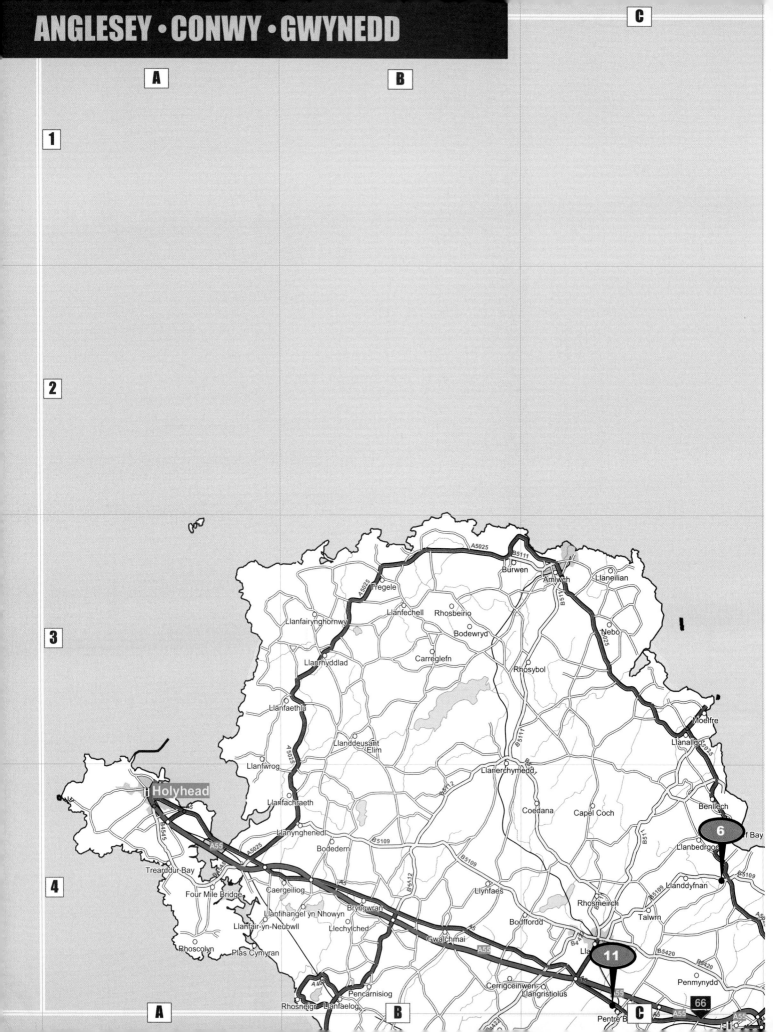

**1** SECRET GARDEN CENTRE
Old Station Yard, Oxford Road, Llandudno
Tel: 01492 872 767

**2** BATTY'S NURSERIES
Llandudno Road, Penrhyn Bay, Llandudno
Tel: 01492 549 176

**3** RHOS GARDEN CENTRE
17 Rhos Road, Rhos on Sea, Colwyn Bay
Tel: 01492 544 567

**4** GERDDI HAULFRE
Haulfre, Llangoed, Beaumaris
Tel: 01248 490 709

**5** BRYN EUR YN NURSERY
Dinerth Road, Rhos on Sea, Colwyn Bay
Tel: 01492 546 757

**6** PENTRAETH NURSERIES
Chapel Bank, Pentraeth
Tel: 01248 450 269

**7** SNOWDONIA NURSERIES
Llanrwst Road, Glan Conwy, Colwyn Bay, Conwy,
LL28 5SR.
Tel: 01492 580 703

*Family run nursery and garden centre. Quality home-grown bedding plants, extensive plant range, new coffee shop and furniture showroom.*
Open: Mon-Sat 9-5, Sun 10.30-4.30. Closed Easter Sun, Christmas & Boxing Day.
Specialities: Comprehensive range, Gifts.
Facilities: Toilets, Credit cards, Wheelchair access, Gift tokens, Dogs allowed, Coffee shop, Pushchair friendly, HTA gift tokens, Sell plants, Gift shop.

**8** BRYN MYNAN NURSERY
Bryn Mynan, Glan Conwy, Colwyn Bay
Tel: 01492 596 095

**9** ABERCONWY NURSERY
Graig, Glan Conwy, Colwyn Bay
Tel: 01492 580 875

**10** CONWY VALLEY NURSERIES
Tyn-y-Groes, Conwy
Tel: 01492 650 228

**11** HENLLYS LODGE PLANTS
Henllys Lodge, Beaumaris, Anglesey
Tel: 01248 810 106

**12** PENRHYN CASTLE, NT
Bangor
Tel: 01248 353 084

**13** BODNANT GARDENS, NT
Tal y Cafn, Colwyn Bay
Tel: 01492 650 460

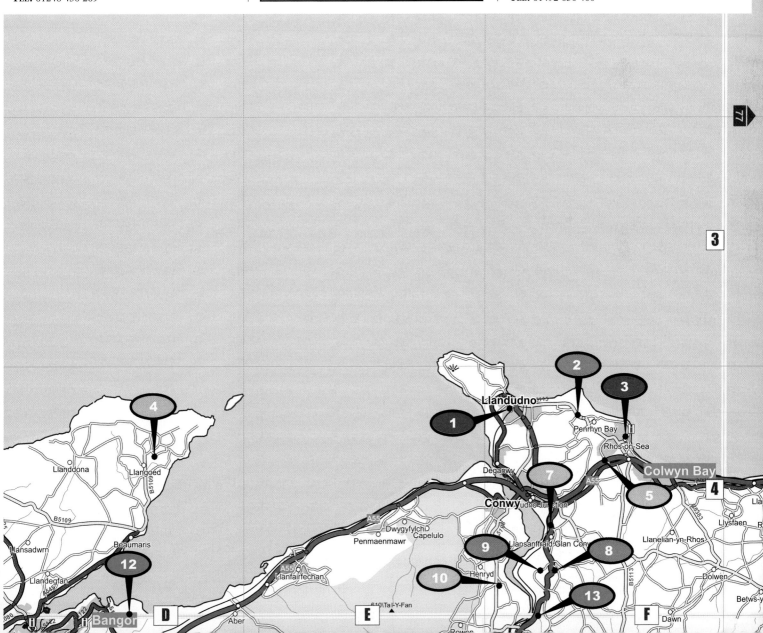

**1 FOUR SEASONS**
224a Liverpool Rd, Southport **Tel:** 01704 560 164

**2 WHITE MOSS GARDEN CENTRE**
New Cut Lane, Birkdale, Southport **Tel:** 01704 550 095

**3 FORMBY GARDEN CENTRE**
1 Cable St, Formby, Liverpool **Tel:** 01704 879 198

**4 ROSE NURSERIES**
Altcar Rd, Great Altcar, Liverpool **Tel:** 01704 878 488

**5 LADY GREEN NURSERIES & GARDEN CENTRE**
Lady Green Lane, Ince Blundell, Formby
**Tel:** 0151 929 3635

**6 W N RUSHTON**
Tanhouse Farm, Runnels Lane, Liverpool
**Tel:** 0151 924 2365

**7 BROWNMOOR NURSERIES & WATER GARDENS**
43 Brownmoor Lane, Liverpool **Tel:** 0151 928 1292

**8 TONY ALMOND DIY & GARDEN CENTRE**
52-54 South Road, Waterloo, Liverpool
**Tel:** 0151 286 2460

**9 MAGILL'S NURSERIES**
Leasowe Rd, Wallasey, Wirral **Tel:** 0151 639 6784

**10 K CROSS & SON**
Rostherne, Leasowe Rd, Moreton **Tel:** 0151 638 6240

**11 MCGREAL'S NURSERY**
Leasowe Road, Wirral **Tel:** 0151 639 0495

**12 TREVOR'S NURSERY**
Leasowe Rd, Wallasey, Leasowe **Tel:** 0151 691 0024

**13 CARR FARM GARDEN CENTRE**
Birkenhead Rd, Meols, Hoylake **Tel:** 0151 632 1457

**14 GREENFIELDS PET & AQUATIC CENTRE**
Birkenhead Rd, Meols, Wirral **Tel:** 0151 632 2582

**15 WIRRAL WATER GARDENS**
Birkenhead Rd, Meols, Wirral **Tel:** 0151 632 2222

**16 SANDY LANE NURSERIES**
1-2 Market Country Produce & Fish,
Grange Precinct, Birkenhead **Tel:** 0151 647 3137

**17 FORIZO GARDEN SHOP**
Walker Street, Higher Tranmere, Birkenhead
**Tel:** 0151 652 2275

**18 BERESFORD NURSERIES AND GARDEN CENTRE**
96 Storeton Road, Prenton, Birkenhead
**Tel:** 0151 608 1950

**19 PORT SUNLIGHT GARDEN CENTRE**
The Causeway, Port Sunlight, Wirral
**Tel:** 0151 645 6244

**20 THINGWALL NURSERIES PLANT CENTRES LTD**
Lower Thingwall Lane, Barnston, Wirral
**Tel:** 0151 648 0281

**21 JACKSONS NURSERIES & GARDEN CENTRE**
Marian, Trelawnyd, Rhyl **Tel:** 01745 570 680

**22 RABY NURSERIES**
Benty Heath Lane, Willaston, Winchester
**Tel:** 0151 327 4221

**23 SILVER BIRCH NURSERIES**
St Asaph Avenue, Kinmel Bay, Rhyl
**Tel:** 01745 351 366

**24 PARKGATE NURSERIES**
Boathouse Lane, Parkgate, Neston **Tel:** 0151 336 4178

**25 FOLLY FIELD NURSERY**
Benty Heath Lane, Hooton, Willaston
**Tel:** 0151 327 4999

**26 BARRY'S OF PENSARN**
17 Marine Rd, Pensarn, Abergele **Tel:** 01745 825 056

**27 TWO OAKS FARM NURSERY**
Hanns Hall Road, Willaston, Neston
**Tel:** 0151 336 1385

**28 NESS BOTANIC GARDENS**
Ness, Neston, South Wirral **Tel:** 0151 353 0123

**29 NORTH WALES WATER GARDENS**
St Asaph Av, Kinmel Bay, Rhyl **Tel:** 01745 338 222

**30 GORDALE GARDEN CENTRE**
Chester High Road (A540), Burton, South Wirral
**Tel:** 0151 336 2116

**31 BURTON NURSERIES & GARDEN CENTRE**
Chester High Rd, Burton, Neston **Tel:** 0151 336 2275

**32 SUNDAWN NURSERY & GARDEN CENTRE**
St Asaph Rd, Caerwys, Mold **Tel:** 01352 720 840

**33 WOODCOTE NURSERIES**
Mudhouse Lane, Burton, Wirral **Tel:** 0151 336 1894

**34 STATION HOUSE NURSERIES**
Station Road, Burton, Neston **Tel:** 0151 353 0022

---

**35 DOVECOTE NURSERIES**
Station Road, Burton, Wirral, Cheshire, CH64 5SB.
**Tel:** 0151 336 5748
**Email:** lindajones5748@hotmail.com
*Wide selection of mainly home-grown plants.*
*Extensive and increasing range of perennials.*
*Lovely, quiet, rural setting. Staff usually available*
*to offer advice.*
**Open:** Mar-Oct: daily 9-5.30. Nov-Feb: Mon-Sat 9-5,
Sun 10-4. Closed Christmas-New Year.
**Specialities:** Bedding plants, Hanging baskets,
Herbs, Perennials, Shrubs.
**Facilities:** Credit cards, HTA gift tokens, Pushchair friendly,
Sell plants, Toilets, Wheelchair access.

---

**36 OLD HALL NURSERIES**
Puddington Lane, Puddington, Neston
**Tel:** 0151 336 2320

**1** FIR TREE NURSERIES
Holmeswood Road, Holmeswood, Ormskirk
TEL: 01704 823 334

**2** RUFFORD OLD HALL, NATIONAL TRUST
Rufford, Ormskirk
TEL: 01704 821 254

**3** BIRKACRE NURSERIES & GARDEN CENTRE
Birkacre Road, Chorley
TEL: 01257 270 473

**4** WEST COAST BONSAI
Colin's Garden Centre, 49-51 Southport Road, Southport
TEL: 01704 500 304

**5** COLIN'S NURSERIES & GARDEN CENTRE
Southport Road, Southport
TEL: 01704 545 487

**6** CAUSEWAY NURSERY
Causeway Lane, Rufford, Ormskirk
TEL: 01704 893 149

**7** NELSONS FARM SHOP & NURSERY
Mossville, Burscough, Ormskirk
TEL: 01695 892 599

**8** COPPULL MOOR LANE NURSERIES
Coppull Moor Lane, Coppull, Chorley
TEL: 01257 791 804

**9** STONEY LEACH NURSERIES
40 Toogood Lane, Wrightington, Wigan
TEL: 01257 253 105

**10** TUNLEY MOSS NURSERIES
Tunley Lane, Wrightington, Wigan
TEL: 01259 423 874

**11** BRADLEY HALL NURSERIES
151 Bradley Hall Trading Estate, Standish, Wigan
TEL: 01257 427 085

**12** KIWI NURSERIES
Arbour Lane, Standish, Wigan
TEL: 01257 472 511

**13** ALAN ASHCROFT GARDEN CENTRE
Hall Lane, Lathom, Ormskirk
TEL: 01704 892 315

**14** LLOYDS NURSERIES
1 Broad lane, Downholland, Ormskirk
TEL: 0151 526 0669

**15** WARBRECK GARDEN CENTRE
Lyelake Lane, Lathom, Ormskirk
TEL: 01695 722 960

**16** CICELY'S COTTAGE PLANTS
Cicely's Cottage, 43 Elmers Green, Skelmersdale
TEL: 01695 720 790

**17** MILTON NURSERIES
Cricket Street Business Park, Prescott Street, Wigan
TEL: 01942 825 445

**18** LYDIATE BARN NURSERIES
Southport Road, Lydiate, Liverpool
TEL: 0151 520 1238

**19** NORTHWAY NURSERIES
Moss Lane, Lydiate, Liverpool
TEL: 0151 526 4191

**20** ROSE NURSERIES
Gathurst Road, Orrell, Wigan
TEL: 01942 215 605

**21** PIMBO NURSERIES & GARDEN CENTRE
30a Pimbo Lane, Upholland, Skelmersdale
TEL: 01695 622 601

**22** BILLINGE GARDEN CENTRE
Winstanley Road, Orrell, Wigan
TEL: 01695 632 317

**23** SEFTON MEADOWS GARDEN & HOME CENTRE
Sefton Lane, Maghull, Liverpool
TEL: 0151 531 6688

**24** SANDY LANE NURSERIES
Sandy Lane, Melling, Liverpool
TEL: 0151 526 3232

**25** STABLE YARD GARDEN CENTRE & BUILDERS SUPPLY
Off Church Road, Haydock, St Helens
TEL: 01744 617 307

**26** BUCKELS NURSERY
Copplehouse Lane, Liverpool
TEL: 0151 525 2712

**27** SUREGROW GARDEN CENTRE
Merton Bank Road, St Helens
TEL: 01744 727 879

**28** CROXTETH HALL COUNTRY PARK
Croxteth Hall Lane, Liverpool
TEL: 0151 228 5311

**29** JAMES WHITAKER & SONS
Liverpool Road, Prescot
TEL: 0151 426 6455

**30** C & D GARDEN & PET CENTRE
297 East Prescot Road, Knotty Ash, Liverpool
TEL: 0151 228 3143

**31** SAUNDERS NURSERIES
Windy Arbor Road, Whiston, Prescot
TEL: 0151 4266 336

**32** LANDLIFE WILDFLOWERS
National Wildflower Centre, Court Hey Park, Liverpool
TEL: 0151 737 1819

**33** WOODEND NURSERY
Warrington Road, Bold Heath, Widnes
TEL: 0151 424 4932

**34** WYEVALE GARDEN CENTRE
Mill Lane, Widnes
TEL: 0151 424 6264

**35** RIVENDELL NURSERIES & GARDEN CENTRE
Mill Lane, Widnes
TEL: 0151 423 2638

**36** WHITE MOSS NURSERY AND GARDEN CENTRE
South Lane, Widnes
TEL: 01925 721 111

**37** GATEACRE GARDEN CENTRE
Acrefield Road, Liverpool
TEL: 0151 428 6556

**38** THE NEW WIDNES HOME & GARDEN CENTRE
Birchfield Road, Widnes
TEL: 0151 424 7221

**39** VICTORIA PARK
Birchfield Road, Appleton, Widnes
TEL: 0151 423 3153

**40** OAKFIELD NURSERIES
Aldford Road, Huntington, Chester
TEL: 01244 320 731

**41** NORTON PRIORY MUSEUM AND GARDENS
Tudor Road, Manor Park, Runcorn
TEL: 01928 569 895

**42** **REYNOLDS PARK WALLED GARDEN**
Church Road, Woolton, Liverpool
TEL: 0151 724 2371

**43** **CALDERSTONE PARK**
Liverpool
TEL: 0151 225 5921

**44** **SPEKE HALL, NATIONAL TRUST**
The Walk, Liverpool
TEL: 0151 427 7231

**45** **HALE VILLAGE GARDEN CENTRE**
High Strett, Hale Village, Liverpool
TEL: 0151 425 2131

**46** **BROOKFIELD GARDEN CENTRE**
2 Weston Road, Runcorn
TEL: 01928 576 754

**47** **ROBERT GREAVES HOME & GARDEN CENTRE**
Mill Lane, Frodsham, Warrington
TEL: 01928 735 713

**48** **BURLEYDAM GARDEN CENTRE**
Chester Road, Childer Thronton, Ellesmere Port
TEL: 0151 339 3195

**49** **SYCAMORE PARK GARDEN CENTRE**
Chester Road, Great Sutton
TEL: 0151 339 1289

**50** **THE GARDEN OUTLET**
Unit 112-113, Ellesmere Port
TEL: 0151 357 3335

**51** **SINGLETON HOUSE FARM NURSERY**
Dunham-on-the-Hill, Frodsham
TEL: 01928 722 136

Clerodendrum

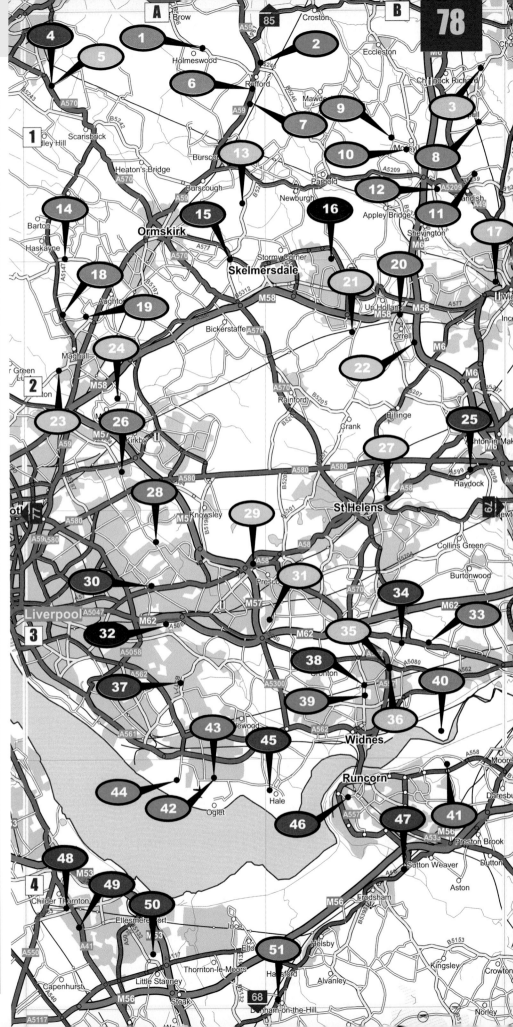

**1  SUMMERSEAT GARDEN CENTRE**
Railway Street, Bury
TEL: 01204 883 048

**2  RIVINGTON TERRACED GARDENS**
Great House Information Centre, Horwich, Bolton
TEL: 01204 691 549

**3  BRITAINS AQUATIC SUPERSTORE LTD**
225 Folds Road, Bolton
TEL: 01204 534 343

**4  HAIGH HALL GARDENS**
Haigh Country Park, Haigh, Wigan
TEL: 01942 832 895

**5  STEPHEN H SMITH'S GARDEN & LEISURE**
Radcliffe Moor Road, Bradley Fold, Bolton
TEL: 01204 529 949

**6  BARTON GRANGE GARDEN CENTRE**
Wigan Road, Bolton
TEL: 01204 660 660

**7  DARBY'S GARDEN CENTRE**
Church Street, Westhoughton, Bolton
TEL: 01942 818 430

**8  R H GILL**
Boscow Road, Little Lever, Bolton
TEL: 01204 573 195

**9  GIANTS SEAT NURSERY**
Ringley, Stoneclough, Manchester
TEL: 0161 723 3462

**10  BROADOAK PARK GARDEN CENTRE**
173 Worsley Road, Worsley, Manchester
TEL: 01617 943 377

**11  WORSLEY HALL GARDEN CENTRE**
Boothstown, Worsley, Manchester
TEL: 0161 790 8792

**13  BENTS GARDEN CENTRE & NURSERIES LTD**
Warrington Road, Glazebury, Warrington, Cheshire, WA3 5NT.
TEL: 01942 266 300
EMAIL: info@bents.co.uk
WEB: www.bents.co.uk
*Designed to inspire the expert gardener and keen amateurs alike, Bents have been nurturing all gardening needs for over 60 years with high quality, individually chosen products.*

Winners of the
**Best Garden Centre**
in the UK 2001

OPEN: Mon-Fri 8.30-8, Sat & BH 8.30-5.30, Sun 10-5.
SPECIALITIES: Garden & conservatory furniture, Gifts, Stone ornaments, Shrubs.
FACILITIES: Bookshop, Coffee shop, Credit cards, Gift shop, HTA gift tokens, Own gift tokens, Plant guarantee, Pushchair friendly, Restaurant, Sell plants, Toilets, Wheelchair access.

**12  E ROGERS**
190A Church Street, Eccles, Manchester
TEL: 01617 893 338

**14  KENYON LANE NURSERIES**
Kenyon Lane, Culcheth, Warrington
TEL: 01925 763 324

**15  BROOKEDGE NURSERIES**
Woodhouse Road, Davyhulme, Manchester
TEL: 0161 746 7300

**16  TREBARON GARDEN CENTRE**
Southworth Road, Newton le Willows
TEL: 01925 224 138

**17  CULCHETH GARDEN CENTRE**
Church Lane, Culcheth, Warrington
TEL: 01925 765 500

**18  NEWCROFT NURSERIES**
40 Newcroft Road, Urmston, Manchester
TEL: 0161 7486 036

**19  FLIXTON GARDEN CENTRE**
Carrington Road, Urmston, Manchester
TEL: 0161 748 5187

**20  BRADLEY LANE NURSERIES**
Bradley Lane, Stretford, Manchester
TEL: 0161 976 5007

**21  FERNDALE NURSERIES**
273 Glazebrook Lane, Glazebrook, Warrington
TEL: 0161 775 2977

**22  PRINCES PARK GARDEN CENTRE**
Liverpool Road, Irlam, Albury
TEL: 0161 775 0030

**23  VICARAGE BOTANICAL GARDENS**
Manchester Road, Carrington, Manchester
TEL: 0161 775 2750

**24  WARD FUCHSIAS**
5 Pollen Close, Sale
TEL: 0161 282 7434

**25  RAMSWOOD NURSERIES**
196 Manchester Road, Warrington
TEL: 01925 821 002

**26  BATTMAN & SONS**
29 Deans Gate Lane, Timperley, Altrincham
TEL: 0161 928 0556

**27  WOOLSTON GARDEN CENTRE**
1 New Cut Lane, Woolston, Warrington
TEL: 01925 822 300

**28  TOMFIELD NURSERIES**
Manchester Road, Rixton, Warrington
TEL: 0161 775 0141

**29  WYEVALE GARDEN CENTRE**
Green Lane, Timperley, Altrincham
TEL: 0161 9806 036

**30  WORLD OF WATER**
Thorley Lane, Timperley, Altrincham
TEL: 0161 903 9944

**31  DUNHAM MASSEY HALL, NATIONAL TRUST**
Altrincham
TEL: 0161 941 1025

**32  CANTILEVER GARDEN CENTRE**
Station Road, Latchford, Warrington
TEL: 01925 635 799

**33  WILLOW POOL GARDEN CENTRE**
Burford Lane, Lymm
TEL: 01925 757 827

**34  WALTON NURSERIES**
54 Burford Lane, Lymm
TEL: 01925 759 827

**35  CADDICKS CLEMATIS NURSERY**
Lymm Road, Thelwall, Warrington
TEL: 01925 757 196

**36  SPRINGBROOK NURSERIES**
Rear of Ship Inn, Chester Road, Warrington
TEL: 01925 267 085

**37  LANE END NURSERY**
Old Cherry Lane, Lymm, Warrington
TEL: 01925 752 618

**38  BELLHOUSE NURSERY**
Bellhouse Lane, Moore, Warrington
TEL: 01925 740 874

**39  WALTON HALL GARDENS**
Walton Lea Road, Higher Walton, Warrington
TEL: 01925 601 617

**40  WALTON CHRISTMAS TREE CENTRE**
Chester New Road, Higher Walton, Warrington
TEL: 01925 212 010

**41  PRIMROSE HILL NURSERIES**
Warrington Road, High Legh, Knutsford
TEL: 01925 752 635

**42  HIGH LEGH GARDEN CENTRE**
High Legh, Knutsford
TEL: 01925 756 991

**43  TATTON PARK, NATIONAL TRUST**
Knutsford
TEL: 01625 534 400

**44  ARLEY HALL NURSERY**
Arley, Great Budworth, Northwich
TEL: 01565 777 353

**45  ARLEY HALL AND GARDENS**
Arley, Great Budworth, Northwich
TEL: 01565 777 479

**46  FRYER'S NURSERIES**
Manchester Road, Knutsford
TEL: 01565 755 455

## 47 CURBISHLEY'S ROSES
Bate Heath, Aston-by-Budworth, Northwich
**TEL:** 01565 733 286

## 48 BLUEBELL COTTAGE, GARDENS AND LODGE LANE NURSERY
Lodge Lane, Dutton, Warrington
**TEL:** 01928 713 718

## 49 OLLERTON NURSERY AND PLANT CENTRE
Chelford Road, Knutsford
**TEL:** 01565 652 247

## 50 D & A WRIGHT
Earls Lane, Wincham, Northwich
**TEL:** 01565 733 503

## 51 MARBURY HALL NURSERIES
Marbury Country Park, Comberbach, Northwich
**TEL:** 01606 741 68

## 52 PARKSIDE ROSE NURSERY
Sudlow Lane, Tabley, Knutsford, Cheshire, WA16 0TP.
**TEL:** 01565 652 598
*Specialist rose growers wholesale and retail, also shrubs, trees, conifers and heathers.*
**OPEN:** Mon-Sat 8.30-12.30, Sun 10.30-12.30.
Closed 12.30-1.30.
**SPECIALITIES:** Climbers, Roses, Conifers, Heathers, Shrubs.
**FACILITIES:** Pushchair friendly, Wheelchair access, Sell plants.

## 53 HEATHFIELD NURSERY
Ullard Hall Lane, Plumley, Knutsford
**TEL:** 01565 634 361

## 54 THE HIDDEN NURSERY
Plumley Moor Road, Plumley, Knutsford
**TEL:** 01565 722 315

## 55 WEAVER VALE GARDEN CENTRE
Winnington Lane, Northwich
**TEL:** 01606 799 65

Water Garden

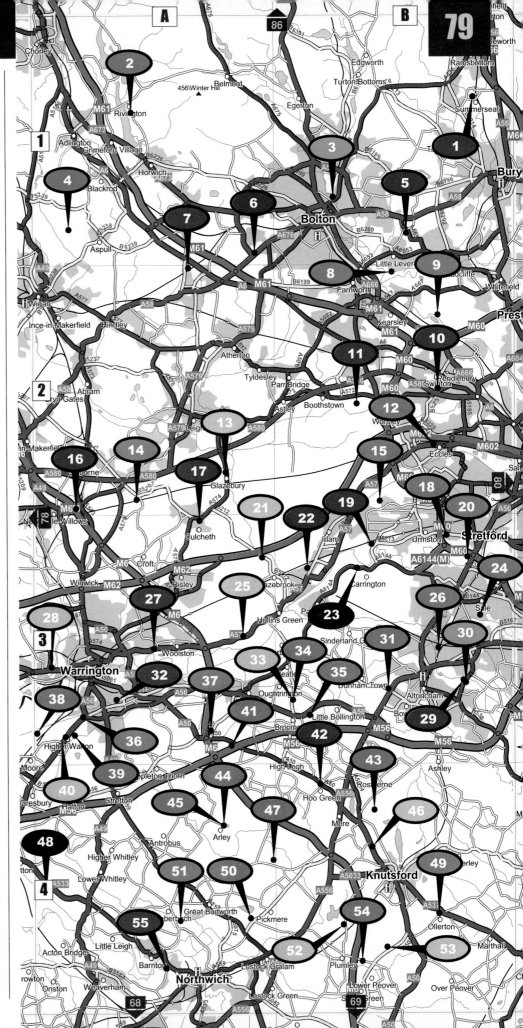

**1** MOSS BRIDGE GARDEN CENTRE

Moss Bridge Road, Kingsway, Rochdale, Lancashire, OL16 4UX.

*Specialising in volume sales of quality plants at unbeatable prices. Fantastic selection of seedlings and young plants. Importers of silk flowers etc.*

**OPEN:** Mon-Fri 9-8, Sat 9-5.30, Sun 11-5. Closed Christmas Day & Boxing Day.
**SPECIALITIES:** Artificial flowers, Bedding plants, House plants, Shrubs.
**FACILITIES:** Bookshop, Credit cards, Gift shop, HTA gift tokens, Own gift tokens, Pushchair friendly, Sell plants, Toilets, Wheelchair access.

**2** ALL-IN-ONE GARDEN CENTRE

Rochdale Road, Middleton, Manchester, Greater Manchester, M24 2RB.
**TEL:** 01706 711 711
**EMAIL:** info@allinone.co.uk
**WEB:** www.allinone.co.uk

*Visit this award winning garden centre at any time of year and marvel at the array of products and displays for your home and garden.*

**OPEN:** Open 7 days a week. Summer: Mon-Fri 9-8, Sat 9-5, Sun 10-4. Winter: Mon-Fri 9-5, Sun 10-4.
**SPECIALITIES:** Aquatics, Gifts, Hanging baskets, Pet centre, Garden & conservatory furniture.
**FACILITIES:** Bookshop, Child area, Coffee shop, Credit cards, Gift shop, HTA gift tokens, Own gift tokens, Plant guarantee, Sell plants, Toilets, Wheelchair access, Pushchair friendly.

**3** HOPWOOD ARMS FARM SHOP & GARDEN CENTRE

768 Rochdale Road, Middleton, Manchester
**TEL:** 01616 549 943

**4** STAKEHILL NURSERIES

Stakehill Lane, Middleton, Manchester
**TEL:** 0161 643 3075

**5** SHOLVERMOOR NURSERIES

Ripponden Road, Moorside, Oldham
**TEL:** 01616 245 553

**6** NEWBANK GARDEN CENTRE

Irwell Bank Farm, Bury Road, Radcliffe
**TEL:** 0161 724 0585

**7** BOOTH'S GARDEN CENTRE

Turf Lane, Royton, Oldham
**TEL:** 01706 845 337

**8** BOWLEE NURSERY

Heywood Old Road, Middleton, Manchester
**TEL:** 0161 653 9626

**9** HEATON PARK

Prestwich, Manchester, Greater Manchester, M25 2SW.
**TEL:** 0161 773 1085
**EMAIL:** heatonpark@ukonline.co.uk
**WEB:** www.manchester.gov.uk/leisure/parks

*Large horticultural centre set in formal gardens. Extensive range of plants including roses, herbaceous plants, bedding plants and hanging baskets.*

**OPEN:** Open daily 9-3.30.
**SPECIALITIES:** Bedding plants, Rhododendrons and azaleas, Roses, Shrubs, Trees.
**FACILITIES:** Toilets, Wheelchair access, Restaurant, Dogs allowed, Credit cards, Child area, Coffee shop.

**10** CLEVELAND GARDEN CENTRE

Bank Road, Crumpsall, Manchester
**TEL:** 0161 795 2244

**11** DAISY NOOK GARDEN CENTRE

Daisy Nook, Failsworth, Manchester
**TEL:** 0161 681 4245

**12** THE POND SHOP

Daisy Nook Garden Centre, Failsworth, Manchester
**TEL:** 0161 681 5742

**13** PARKER'S GARDEN CENTRE

448 Chester Road, Old Trafford, Manchester
**TEL:** 0161 877 4247

**14** AQUA TONIC

24 Arundel Street, Glossop
**TEL:** 01457 853 409

**15** CHARLESWORTH NURSERY & GARDEN CENTRE

Glossop Road, Charlesworth, Glossop
**TEL:** 01457 863 998

**16** LYMEFIELD GARDEN NURSERY

Lymefield, Broadbottom, Hyde
**TEL:** 01457 764 686

**17** ROMILEY DIY & GARDEN CENTRE

23 Compstall Road, Romiley, Stockport
**TEL:** 0161 430 3040

**18** FLETCHER MOSS

Mill Gate Lane, Didsbury
**TEL:** 0161 445 4241

**19** WYTHENSHAWE PARK & HORTICULTURAL CENTRE

Wythenshawe Road, Manchester
**TEL:** 0161 998 2117

**20** GOLDEN DAYS GARDEN CENTRE

Manchester Road, Cheadle
**TEL:** 0161 428 3098

**21** WYEVALE GARDEN CENTRE

Marple, Stockport
**TEL:** 0161 427 7211

**22** LOMAX NURSERIES

Adswood Road, Cheadle Hume, Cheadle
**TEL:** 0161 485 1824

**23** LADYRIDGE GARDEN CENTRE

Ladyridge Road, Cheadle Hulme, Cheadle
**TEL:** 0161 485 1345

**24** BRAMALL HALL

Bramall Park, Bramhall
**TEL:** 0161 485 3708

**25** PRIMROSE COTTAGE NURSERIES & GARDEN CENTRE

Ringway Road, Moss Nook, Manchester
**TEL:** 0161 437 1557

**26** BROOKSIDE GARDEN CENTRE

Macclesfield Road, Poynton
**TEL:** 01625 872 919

**27** ANDERTON'S NURSERIES

38 Hall Moss Lane, Woodford Bramhall, Stockport
**TEL:** 0161 439 8711

**28** CROFTLAND NURSERY

Altrincham Road, Styal, Wilmslow
**TEL:** 01625 539 616

**29** BARTON GRANGE GARDEN CENTRE

Chester Road, Woodford, Stockport
**TEL:** 0161 439 0745

**30** WILMSLOW GARDEN CENTRE

Manchester Road, Wilmslow
**TEL:** 01625 525 700

Sunflower

**31** **ANSELL NURSERIES**
Hall Moss Lane, Bramhall, Stockport
TEL: 0161 262 6466

**32** **LYME PARK, NATIONAL TRUST**
Disley, Stockport
TEL: 01663 762 023

**33** **MORLEY NURSERY**
Altrincham Road, Wilmslow
TEL: 01625 528 953

**34** **PARKERS MOTTRAM ST ANDREW
GARDEN CENTRE**
Lees Lane, Newton, Macclesfield
TEL: 01625 520 002

**35** **ALL SEASONS PLANT CENTRE**
9 Lees Lane, Newton, Macclesfield
TEL: 01625 523 871

**36** **NED YATES GARDEN CENTRE**
Moor Lane, Wilmslow
TEL: 01625 522 128

**37** **DUNGE VALLEY HIDDEN GARDENS**
Kettleshume, Whaley Bridge, High Peak
TEL: 01663 733 787

**38** **COLLINWOOD NURSERIES**
Mottram St Andrew, Macclesfield
TEL: 01625 582 272

**39** **HARE HILL, NATIONAL TRUST**
Over Alderley, Macclesfield
TEL: 01625 828 981

**40** **ONE HOUSE NURSERY**
Buxton New Road, Macclesfield
TEL: 01625 427 087

**41** **BRIDGEMERE AT FLORA**
Chelford Road, Henbury, Macclesfield
TEL: 01625 669 007

**42** **FIRS HERBACEOUS PERENNIALS
NURSERY**
Chelford Road, Henbury, Macclesfield
TEL: 01625 426 422

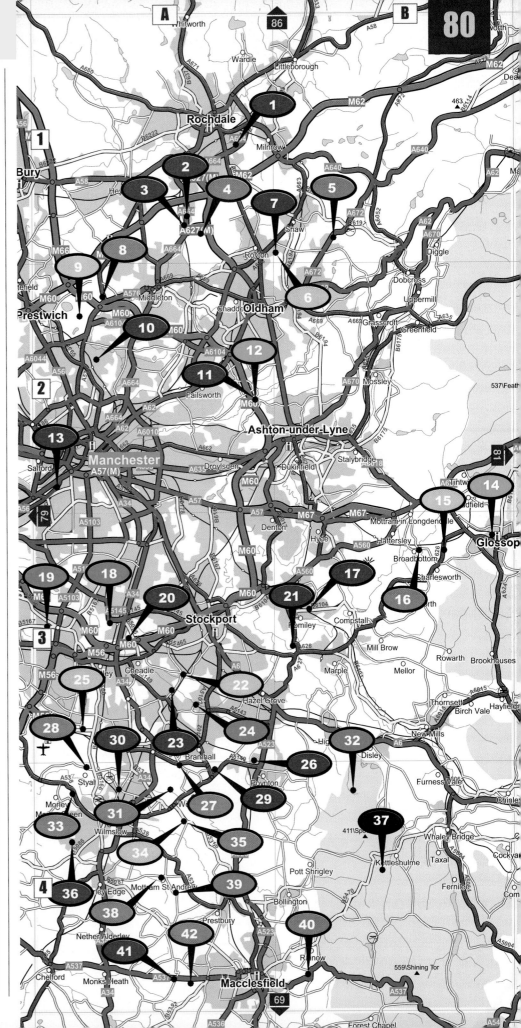

GARDEN CENTRE
GARDEN & NURSERY
● NURSERY & GARDEN CENTRE
● WATER GARDEN SPECIALIST

**1 HAMPSONS PLANT WORLD GARDEN CENTRE**
Denby Dale Road, Durkar, Wakefield
TEL: 01924 298 365

**2 HAMPSONS PLANT WORLD GARDEN CENTRE**
Long Lane, Dalton, Huddersfield
TEL: 01484 423 519

**3 COLNE VALLEY GARDEN CENTRE**
Scar Lane, Milnsbridge, Huddersfield
TEL: 01484 656 164

**4 HALL GREEN NURSERIES**
Stoney Lane, Wooley, Wakefield
TEL: 01924 259 589

**5 YORKSHIRE SCULPTURE PARK**
Bretton Hall, West Breton, Wakefield
TEL: 01924 830 302

**6 OAK DENE NURSERIES**
10 Black Lane West, Royston, Barnsley
TEL: 01226 722 253

**7 ARMITAGE'S PENNINE GARDEN CENTRE**
Huddersfield Road, Shelley
TEL: 01484 607 248

**8 CANNON HALL GARDEN CENTRE**
Bark House Lane, Cawthorne, Barnsley
TEL: 01226 790 785

**9 CANNON HALL COUNTRY PARK**
Cawthorne, Barnsley
TEL: 01226 790 270

**10 TOTTIES NURSERY**
Greenhill Bank Road, Totties, Huddersfield
TEL: 01484 683 363

**11 CLAYCLIFFE GARDEN CENTRE**
Claycliffe Road, Barugh Green, Barnsley
TEL: 01226 243 128

**12 TOM HORSFIELD, ROSE GROWER & NURSERYMAN**
Barnsley Road, Silkstone, Barnsley
TEL: 01226 790 441

**13 CUTTING EDGE MARKET GARDEN**
Knowle Road, Worsbrough, Barnsley
TEL: 01226 730 292

**14 ROYD MARKET GARDEN & NURSERIES**
Hollin Busk Lane, Sheffield
TEL: 0114 283 0525

**15 MOREHALL NURSERIES**
Morehall Lane, Bolsterstone, Sheffield
TEL: 0114 288 3239

**16 BURNCROSS NURSERIES**
235 Burncross Road, Chapeltown, Sheffield
TEL: 0114 257 0959

**17 BARLOW NURSERIES**
94 Edge Lane, Sheffield
TEL: 0114 231 3758

**18 HILLSBOROUGH WALLED GARDEN**
Middlewood Road, Sheffield
TEL: 0114 281 2167

**19 RHINEGOLD NURSERIES**
West Lane, Loxley, Sheffield
TEL: 0114 285 1487

**20 PEARSON GARDEN SUPPLIES**
Loxley Nurseries, Long Lane, Loxley
TEL: 0114 233 7134

**21 HUTTONS NURSERIES**
Long Lane, Loxley
TEL: 01742 337 134

**22 NORMANDALE NURSERIES**
66 Rodney Hill, Loxley
TEL: 0114 234 4703

**23 HIGH RIGGS NURSERY**
Uppergate Road, Stannington, Sheffield
TEL: 0114 285 4061

**24 VALLEYSIDE GARDEN CENTRE**
Bell Hagg, Manchester Road, Sheffield
TEL: 0114 230 1925

**25 THE BOTANICAL GARDENS**
Clarkehouse Road, Sheffield
TEL: 0114 273 4599

**26 W O R K**
Bents Green Workshops, Ringinglow Road, Sheffield
TEL: 0114 262 0094

**27 HOME AND GARDEN CENTRE**
237 Ringinglow Road, Sheffield
TEL: 01142 351 325

**28 HIGH PEAK GARDEN CENTRE**
Hope Road, Bamford, Hope Valley
TEL: 01433 651 484

**29 DORE MOOR NURSERY**
Brickhouse Lane, Dore, Sheffield
TEL: 0114 236 8144

**30 ABBEYDALE GARDEN CO**
Abbeydale Road South, Dore, Sheffield
TEL: 0114 236 9091

**31 HATHERSAGE NURSERIES**
Station Road, Hathersage, Hope Valley
TEL: 01433 650 886

**32 LONGDENDALE NURSERY**
Blackbrook Lane, Chapel en le Frith, High Peak
TEL: 01298 813 940

**33 FERNDALE NURSERY & GARDEN CENTRE**
Dyche Lane, Coal Aston, Dronfield
TEL: 01246 412 763

**34 NEW LEAF PLANT CENTRE**
Dyche Lane, Coal Aston, Sheffield
TEL: 01246 413 311

**35 WARD'S NURSERY & GARDEN CENTRE**
Eckington Road, Coal Aston
TEL: 01246 412 622

**36 CALVER SOUGH NURSERIES**
Hassop Road, Calver, Hope Valley
TEL: 01433 630 692

**37 DUNSTON HALL GARDEN CENTRE**
Dunston Road, Newbold, Chesterfield
TEL: 01246 268 468

**38 GARDEN SUPPLIES**
The Mill Garden Centre, Whittington Way, Chesterfield
TEL: 01246 260 718

**39 PAVILION GARDENS**
St John's Road, Buxton
TEL: 01298 231 14

**40 THE VICTORIAN GARDENS NURSERY**
Cressbrook, Buxton
TEL: 01298 871 552

**41 DIRECT CONIFER SUPPLIES**
Main Road, Unstone, Chesterfield
TEL: 01246 414 490

Earwig in Geranium

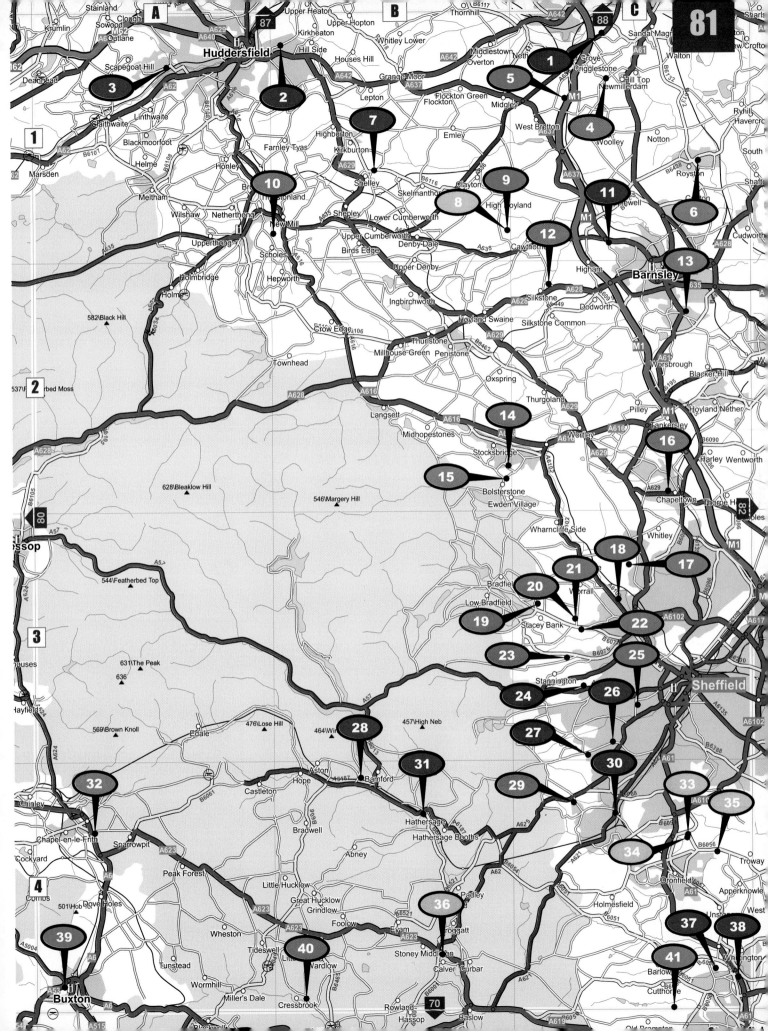

**1** JAMES LAMPREY & SONS
Pontefract Road, Ackworth, Pontefract
**TEL:** 01977 794 387

**2** NOSTELL PRIORY
Doncaster Road, Wakefield
**TEL:** 01924 863 892

**3** ACKWORTH GARDEN CENTRE
Barnsley Road, Ackworth, Pontefract
**TEL:** 01977 612 660

**4** TAYLORS CLEMATIS NURSERY
Sutton, Askern, Doncaster
**TEL:** 01302 700 716

**5** J P FOSS
Kirkby Common Farm, Brierley, Barnsley
**TEL:** 01226 711 338

**6** MARKHAM GRANGE NURSERY
Long Lands Lane, Brodsworth, Doncaster
**TEL:** 01302 722 430

**7** BRODSWORTH HALL, ENGLISH HERITAGE
Brodsworth, Doncaster
**TEL:** 01302 722 598

**8** YEW TREE GARDEN CENTRE
Doncaster Road, Barnsley
**TEL:** 01226 750 500

**9** OSCROFT NURSERIES
216 Sprotbrough Road, Doncaster
**TEL:** 01302 785 026

**10** VISCUM WATER GARDENS & AQUATICS
Doncaster Road, Barnburgh, Doncaster
**TEL:** 01709 893 265

**11** WOMBWELL AQUATICS & WATER GARDENS
52-56 Park Street, Wombwell, Barnsley
**TEL:** 01226 752 222

**12** HARLINGTON NURSERIES
100 Doncaster Road, Harlington, Doncaster
**TEL:** 01709 890 396

**13** THE GARDEN OUTLET
Unit 45, White Rose Way, Doncaster
**TEL:** 01302 366 772

**14** LLOYD WATH GARDEN CENTRE
Station Road, Wath-Upon-Deane, Rotherham
**TEL:** 01709 877 363

**16** WENTWORTH GARDEN CENTRE
Hague Lane, Wentworth, Rotherham
**TEL:** 01226 744 842

**17** OLD EDLINGTON NURSERIES
Edlington Lane, Old Edlington, Doncaster
**TEL:** 01709 868 661

**18** FOSTERS GARDEN CENTRE
Doncaster Road, Thrybergh, Rotherham
**TEL:** 01709 850 337

---

**15** STRINGER'S NURSERIES
Hollyhead Farm, Crookhill Road, Conisbrough, Doncaster, South Yorkshire, DN12 2AE.
**TEL:** 01709 863 228
**EMAIL:** info@stringers-nurseries.co.uk
**WEB:** www.stringers-nurseries.co.uk

*The one worth finding. Huge selection of trees and shrubs. Browse in our garden centre then relax in our conservatory cafe.*
**OPEN:** Open daily 9-5. Closed Christmas, Boxing & New Years Day.
**SPECIALITIES:** Shrubs, Trees.
**FACILITIES:** Toilets, Credit cards, Wheelchair access, Restaurant, Gift tokens, Child area, Coffee shop, Gift shop, HTA gift tokens, Own gift tokens, Pushchair friendly, Sell plants.

**19** MANOR GARDENS
Doncaster Road, Hooton Roberts, Rotherham
**TEL:** 01709 852 433

**20** MUNSBOROUGH NURSERIES
Munsborough Lane, Rotherham
**TEL:** 01709 551 056

**21** PLANTS OF SPECIAL INTEREST NURSERY
4 High Street, Braithwell, Rotherham
**TEL:** 01709 790 642

**22** TICKHILL GARDEN CENTRE
Bawtry Road, Tickhill, Doncaster, South Yorkshire, DN11 9EX.
**TEL:** 01302 742 134
*For the largest selection around including unusual and new varieties arriving daily, as well as Toperi bamboo and ferns and an impressive selection of fountains, furniture and containers.*
**OPEN:** Open 7 days a week. Summer: 9-6. Winter: 9-5. Closed Christmas & Boxing Day.
**SPECIALITIES:** Bedding plants, Water plants, Exotic plants, Perennials, Shrubs, Terracotta pots.
**FACILITIES:** Coffee shop, Credit cards, Gift tokens, Restaurant, Toilets, Wheelchair access, HTA gift tokens, Pushchair friendly, Sell plants.

**23** SEDGEWOOD NURSERY
2A Flanderwell Lane, Bramley, Rotherham
**TEL:** 01709 532 669

**24** B P S AQUATICS
The Crofts, Quarry Hill, Rotherham
**TEL:** 01709 820 828

**26** GODFREY'S GARDENS
Hardwick Lane, Aston, Sheffield
**TEL:** 0114 287 2447

---

**25** WAYSIDE WATER GARDENS
Doncaster Road, Oldcotes, Worksop, Nottinghamshire, S81 8HT.
**TEL:** 01909 731 367
**EMAIL:** sales@waysidewatergardens.co.uk
**WEB:** www.waysidewatergardens.co.uk

*Long established, family run watergardens, specialising in pond liners, fountains, aquatic plants, fish, pumps and filtration equipment. Highly recommended.*
**OPEN:** Mar-Sep: 10-1 & 2-6. Oct-Feb: 10-1 & 2-4. Closed Tue.
**SPECIALITIES:** Aquatics, Fountains, Water plants.
**FACILITIES:** Toilets, Credit cards, Wheelchair access, Own gift tokens.

**27** P W & H E BRADLEY
High Street, Swallownest, Sheffield
**TEL:** 0114 287 2240

**28** HODSOCK PRIORY GARDENS
Hodsock Priory, Blyth, Worksop
**TEL:** 01909 591 204

**29** COOKS RIDGEWAY NURSERIES
High Lane, Ridgeway, Sheffield
**TEL:** 0114 248 5944

**30** BIRLEY MOOR GARDEN CENTRE
27 Moor Valley, Mosborough, Sheffield
**TEL:** 0114 248 0666

Alstroemeria

## 31 THORPE SALVIN NURSERY
73 Common Road, Thorpe Salvin, Worksop
Tel: 01909 515 393

## 32 CROFT NURSERIES
South Street, Mosborough, Sheffield
Tel: 0114 248 6541

## 33 NORTHERN GARDEN SUPPLIES
Blyth Road, Oldcotes, Worksop
Tel: 01909 731 600

## 34 RENISHAW HALL GARDENS
Renishaw Hall, Renishaw Park, Sheffield
Tel: 01246 432 310

## 35 HANDLEY ROSE NURSERIES
Lightwood Road, Marsh Lane, Sheffield
Tel: 01246 432 921

## 36 SPRINGBANK NURSERIES
Westfield Lodge, Westfield Lane, Barlborough
Tel: 01246 810 393

## 37 VAN DYK GARDEN CENTRE
Worksop Road, Clowne, Chesterfield
Tel: 01246 810 236

## 38 HIGHFIELDS NURSERIES
Highfields, Chesterfield Road, Barlborough
Tel: 01246 810 636

## 39 DUKERIES GARDEN CENTRE
Welbeck, Worksop
Tel: 01909 476 506

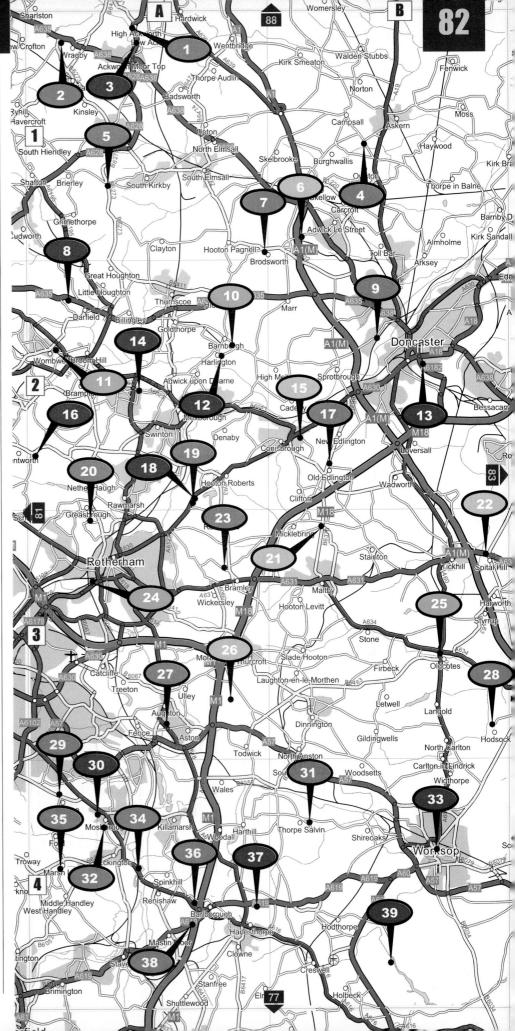

**1  NORMANBY HALL VICTORIAN WALLED GARDENS**
Normanby Park, Normanby, Scunthorpe
TEL: 01724 720 588

**2  OAKFIELD NURSERY**
Kirton Lane, Thorne, Doncaster
TEL: 01405 816 238

**3  MAYFIELD GARDEN CENTRE**
Kirton Lane, Stainforth, Doncaster
TEL: 01302 351 007

**4  ELSHAM HALL COUNTRY AND WILDLIFE PARK**
Elsham, Brigg
TEL: 01652 688 698

**5  STEPHEN H SMITH'S GARDEN & LEISURE**
Doncaster Road, Gunness, Scunthorpe
TEL: 01724 848 950

**6  SILICA LODGE GARDEN CENTRE**
Scotter Road South, Scunthorpe
TEL: 01724 282 148

**7  MENDLE NURSERY**
Holme, Scunthorpe
TEL: 01724 850 864

**8  FROSTS GARDEN CENTRE**
Bigby High Road, Brigg, Lincolnshire, DN20 9HE.
TEL: 01652 650 484
*A developing centre packed with all your gardening requirements from compost and chemicals to a range of more oriental shrubs.*
OPEN: Mon-Sat 9-5, Sun 10.30-4.30.
SPECIALITIES: Bedding plants, Herbaceous plants, Terracotta pots, Aquatics, Shrubs.
FACILITIES: Coffee shop, Credit cards, Gift shop, HTA gift tokens, Own gift tokens, Pushchair friendly, Sell plants, Toilets, Wheelchair access, Child area.

**9  GRANGE PARK AQUATICS**
Butterwick Road, Messingham, Scunthorpe
TEL: 01724 762 115

**10  ROSEHOLME NURSERY**
Roseholme Farm, Howsham, Lincoln
TEL: 01652 678 661

**11  BRANTON FARM NURSERIES**
Doncaster Road, Branton, Doncaster
TEL: 01302 538 708

**12  SCOTTER NURSERIES**
26 High Street, Scotter, Gainsborough
TEL: 01724 762 562

**13  WALKERS NURSERIES**
Mosham Road, Blaxton, Doncaster
TEL: 01302 770 325

**14  FAIR GARDENS PLANT CENTRE**
Station Road, Kirton in Lindsey
TEL: 01652 648 631

**15  PARROTTS CORNER NURSERY**
325 Bawtry Road, Doncaster
TEL: 01302 863 339

**16  BLAND TAVERN NURSERIES**
Craiselound, Haxey, Doncaster
TEL: 01427 752 267

**17  SUNNYSIDE**
Sunnyside Farm, Station Road, Gainsborough
TEL: 01427 628 240

**18  LINCLON GREEN CLEMATIS NURSERY**
Sand Lane, Osgodby, Market Rasen
TEL: 01673 828 222

**19  BAWTRY GARDEN CENTRE**
Great North Road, Bawtry, Doncaster
TEL: 01302 711 639

**20  KATHLEEN MUNCASTER FUSCHIAS**
18 Field Lane, Morton, Gainsborough
TEL: 01427 612 329

**21  MARTIN NEST NURSERIES**
Harpswell Lane, Hemswell, Gainsborough
TEL: 01427 668 369

**22  HALL FARM NURSERY**
Harpeswell, Gainsborough
TEL: 01427 668 412

**23  GAINSBOROUGH HOME AND GARDEN**
Lea Road, Gainsborough
TEL: 01427 612 004

**24  ASHKEYS NURSERY**
Great North Road, Torworth, Retford
TEL: 01777 816 202

**25  CANAL TURN NURSERIES**
Welham Road, Retford
TEL: 01777 711 449

**26  MILLFIELD NURSERIES**
Mill Lane, South Leverton, Retford
TEL: 01427 880 422

**27  MORTON HALL GARDENS**
Morton Hall, Ranby, Retford
TEL: 01777 702 530

**28  GROVE GARDEN CENTRE**
Grove, Retford
TEL: 01777 703 182

**29  KENNILWORTH NURSERIES**
London Road, Retford
TEL: 01777 703 301

**30  SCOTHERN NURSERIES**
Dunholme Road, Lincoln
TEL: 01673 862 297

**31  ORCHARD NURSERY GARDEN CENTRE**
Main Street, Laneham, Retford
TEL: 01777 228 882

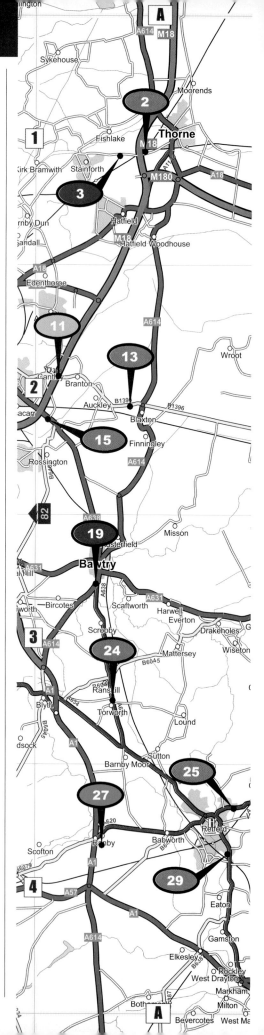

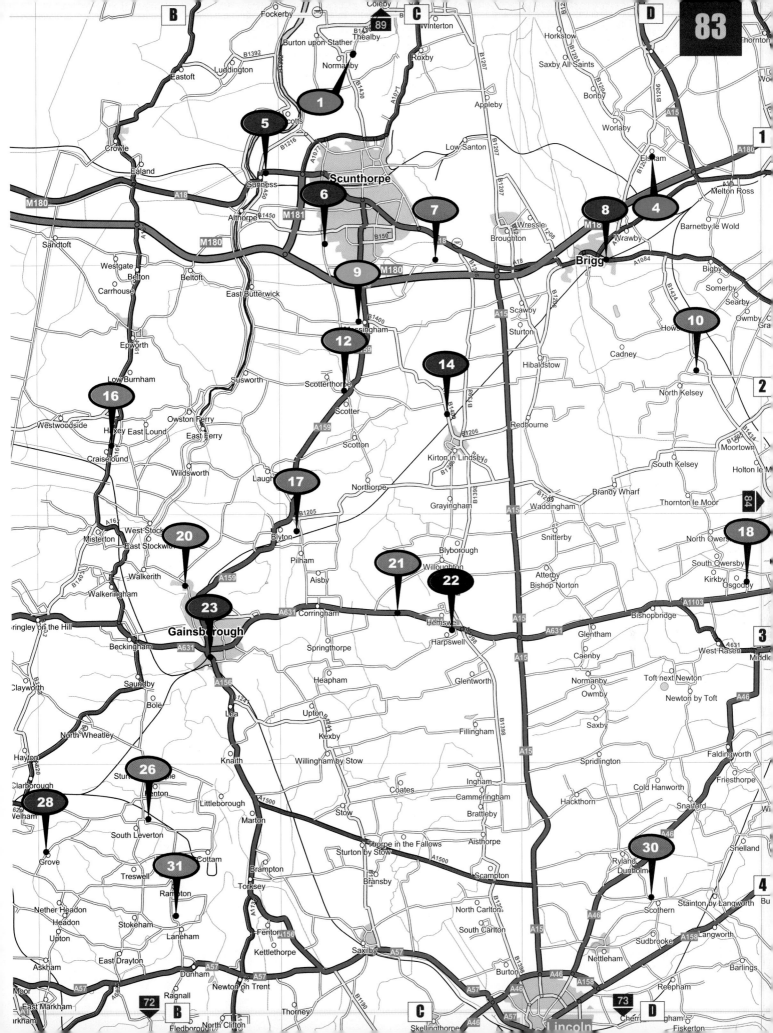

# LINCOLNSHIRE

**1  THE FERNERIES**
Killingholme Road, Ulceby
TEL: 01469 588 394

**2  WILLOW NURSERIES**
31 Cravens Lane, Habrough, Immingham
TEL: 01469 576 635

**3  LAKESIDE PLANT CENTRE AND FUCHSIA FANTASY**
Boating Lake, Kings Road, Cleethorpes
TEL: 01472 883 075

**4  THE PEOPLE'S PARK**
Welholme Road, Grimsby
TEL: 01472 323 000

**5  PENNELLS GARDEN CENTRE**
Humberston Road, Cleethorpes, Grimsby
TEL: 01472 313 600

**6  ALFORD'S GARDEN CENTRE**
Grimsby Road, Laceby, Grimsby
TEL: 01472 871 280

**7  MAKHAMS NURSERIES**
Waltham Road, Scartho, Grimsby
TEL: 01472 823 305

**8  MILLSTONE GARDEN CENTRE**
Cheapside, Waltham, Grimsby
TEL: 01472 828 150

**9  NORBURNS PLANT CENTRE**
Blenheim House, Tetney, Grimsby
TEL: 01472 815 515

**10  POTTERTON & MARTIN**
Moortown Road, Market Rasen
TEL: 01472 851 714

**11  LINCOLNFIELD NURSERIES**
Ludborough Road, North Thoresby
TEL: 01472 840 461

**12  WICKENTREE NURSERIES**
Caistor Road, Middle Rasen, Market Rasen
TEL: 01673 842 918

**13  RUSHMOOR HERBS**
Rushmoor County Park, Louth Road, Louth
TEL: 01507 327 184

**14  LOUTH GARDEN CENTRE**
Legbourne Road, Louth
TEL: 01507 605 381

**15  KENWICK FARMHOUSE NURSERY**
Kenwick Road, Louth
TEL: 01507 606 469

**16  TRUSTHORPE GARDEN CENTRE**
Sutton Road, Trusthorpe, Mablethorpe
TEL: 01507 478 191

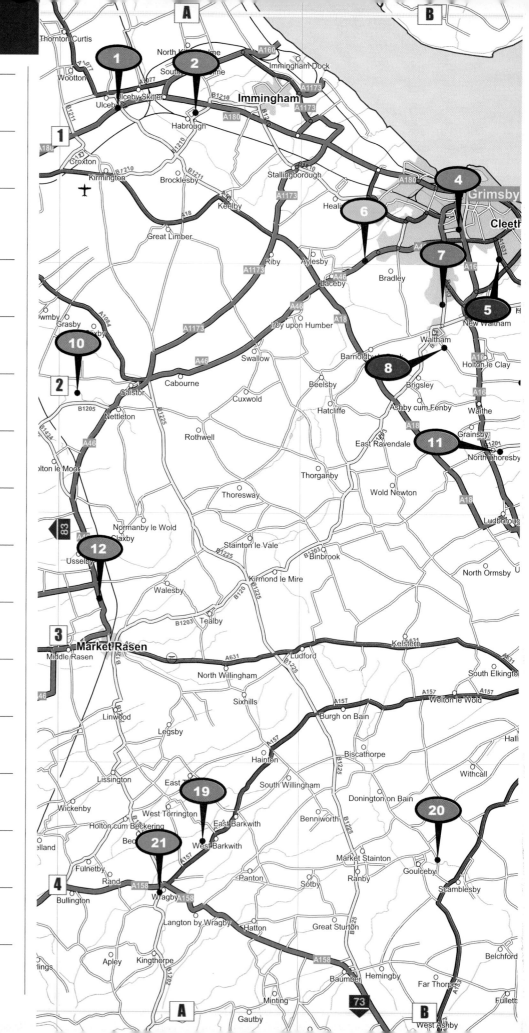

## 17 GREENWAYS GARDEN CENTRE

Gayton-Le-Marsh, Louth Road, Alford,
Lincolnshire, LN13 0NH.
**Tel:** 01507 450 336
**Email:** greenways@ntlworld.com

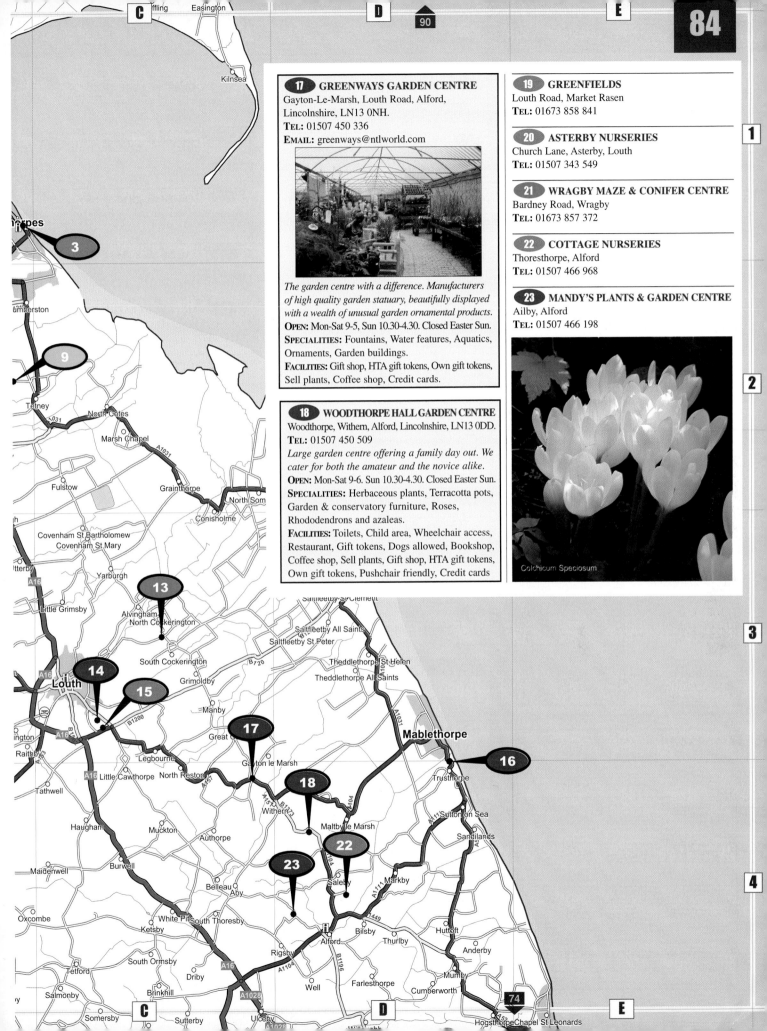

*The garden centre with a difference. Manufacturers
of high quality garden statuary, beautifully displayed
with a wealth of unusual garden ornamental products.*
**Open:** Mon-Sat 9-5, Sun 10.30-4.30. Closed Easter Sun.
**Specialities:** Fountains, Water features, Aquatics,
Ornaments, Garden buildings.
**Facilities:** Gift shop, HTA gift tokens, Own gift tokens,
Sell plants, Coffee shop, Credit cards.

## 18 WOODTHORPE HALL GARDEN CENTRE

Woodthorpe, Withern, Alford, Lincolnshire, LN13 0DD.
**Tel:** 01507 450 509
*Large garden centre offering a family day out. We
cater for both the amateur and the novice alike.*
**Open:** Mon-Sat 9-6. Sun 10.30-4.30. Closed Easter Sun.
**Specialities:** Herbaceous plants, Terracotta pots,
Garden & conservatory furniture, Roses,
Rhododendrons and azaleas.
**Facilities:** Toilets, Child area, Wheelchair access,
Restaurant, Gift tokens, Dogs allowed, Bookshop,
Coffee shop, Sell plants, Gift shop, HTA gift tokens,
Own gift tokens, Pushchair friendly, Credit cards

## 19 GREENFIELDS

Louth Road, Market Rasen
**Tel:** 01673 858 841

## 20 ASTERBY NURSERIES

Church Lane, Asterby, Louth
**Tel:** 01507 343 549

## 21 WRAGBY MAZE & CONIFER CENTRE

Bardney Road, Wragby
**Tel:** 01673 857 372

## 22 COTTAGE NURSERIES

Thoresthorpe, Alford
**Tel:** 01507 466 968

## 23 MANDY'S PLANTS & GARDEN CENTRE

Ailby, Alford
**Tel:** 01507 466 198

Colchicum Speciosum

**1 ASHTON MEMORIAL**
Williamson Park, 6 St Marks Place East, Ashton
TEL: 01772 884 444

**2 PINEWOOD GARDEN CENTRE**
Wallace Lane, Forton, Preston
TEL: 01524 792 453

**3 W ROBINSON & SONS**
Sunny Bank, Forton, Preston
TEL: 01524 791 210

**4 BEECHGROVE NURSERIES**
Station Lane, Scorton, Preston
TEL: 01524 791 286

**5 CLEGGS NURSERIES**
Hammersfield, Back Lane, Stalmine
TEL: 01253 700 250

**6 DAISY BANK GARDEN CENTRE**
172 Victoria Road West, Cleveleys
TEL: 01253 856 802

**7 HAMBLETON GARDEN CENTRE**
Bank View, Shard Lane, Hambleton
TEL: 01253 702 212

**8 BURNSIDE GARDEN CENTRE**
New Lane, Thornton Cleveleys, Blackpool,
Lancashire, FY5 5NH.
TEL: 01253 821 383
EMAIL: mail@burnside.co.uk
WEB: www.bgc.co.uk
*Established in 1950. Here
at Burnside we pride
ourselves in our courteous
and professional service
from our qualified staff
within our five acre site.*

OPEN: Mon-Sat 9-5.30,
Sun 10.30-4.30.
SPECIALITIES: House plants,
Shrubs, Water plants, Gifts,
Stone ornaments.
FACILITIES: Toilets, Credit cards, Wheelchair access,
Restaurant, Gift tokens, Bookshop, Coffee shop,
Plant guarantee, Gift shop, HTA gift tokens,
Own gift tokens, Pushchair friendly, Sell plants,
Dogs allowed.

**9 THE PLANT PLACE GARDEN CENTRE**
Fleetwood Road South, Thornton Cleveleys,
Lancashire, FY5 5NS.
TEL: 01253 856 414
*A garden centre for real gardeners. Specialising
in unusual and rare shrubs, trees, climbers and
perennials (40+ species of Japanese Maples).
Friendly staff and helpful advice.*
OPEN: Apr-Sep: 8-8. Oct-Mar: 9-5. Check times
before travelling.
SPECIALITIES: Grasses, Bamboos, Perennials,
Acers, Specimen plants.
FACILITIES: Credit cards, Dogs allowed, HTA gift tokens,
Plant guarantee, Pushchair friendly, Wheelchair access.

**10 BURTONWOOD NURSERIES**
109 Mains Lane, Poulton le Fylde
TEL: 01253 892 404

**11 STELLA MARIS NURSERY**
24 Westfield Avenue, Highfurlong, Blackpool
TEL: 01253 392 587

**12 BARTON GRANGE GARDEN CENTRE**
Garstang Road, Barton, Preston
TEL: 01772 864 242

**13 JANE LANE NURSERIES**
Jane Lane, Catforth, Preston
TEL: 01772 691 635

**14 OAK NURSERIES**
Pudding Pie Nook Lane, Goosnargh, Preston
TEL: 01772 862 828

**15 RIBBLESDALE NURSERIES AND PLANT CENTRE**
Ribblesdale, Newsham Hall Lane, Woodplumpton
TEL: 01772 863 081

**16 WILLOW BRIDGE NURSERY**
Roots Lane, Catforth, Preston
TEL: 01772 690 269

**17 CHERRY TREE LODGE NURSERY**
Roots lane, Catforth, Preston
TEL: 01772 690 561

**18 EASTWAY NURSERIES**
Eastway, Fullwood, Preston
TEL: 01772 709 511

**19 WYEVALE GARDEN CENTRE**
Preston New Road, Westby, Kirkham
TEL: 01772 684 129

**20 BLAYLOCK SHRUBS**
Lea Nurseries, Old House Lane, Blackpool
TEL: 01253 761 009

**21 BAGUELY'S THE GARDEN PEOPLE**
Midgeland Road, Marton, Blackpool
TEL: 01253 762 981

**22 PLANT EMPORIUM**
Preston New Road, Peel Corner, Blackpool
TEL: 01253 764 099

**23 CROPPER MANOR GARDEN CENTRE**
Cropper Road, Blackpool
TEL: 01253 699 987

**24 TREBARON GARDEN CENTRE**
350 Common Edge Road, Blackpool
TEL: 01253 691 368

**25 NEWTON NURSERIES**
Preston New Road, Newton, Preston
TEL: 01772 684 097

**26 DOBBIES GARDEN WORLD**
Blackpool Road, Clifton, Preston
TEL: 01772 683 844

**27 ASHTON'S NURSERY GARDENS**
Mythop Road, Lytham St Annes
TEL: 01253 736 627

**28 HAWTHORNES NURSERY**
Marsh Road, Hesketh Bank, Preston
TEL: 01772 812 379

**29 AVANT GARDEN CENTRE**
Wigan Road, Leyland, Preston
TEL: 01772 433 777

**30 EMBLEYS NURSERIES**
Liverpool Road, Much Hoole, Near Preston
TEL: 01772 612 227

**31 WORDEN PARK**
Worden Lane, Leyland
TEL: 01772 421 109

**32 CLAREMONT AQUATIC NURSERIES**
Cocker Bar Road, Leyland, Preston
TEL: 01772 421 860

**33 CHARNOCK FARM GARDEN CENTRE**
Wigan Road, Leyland, Preston
TEL: 01772 623 350

**34 BRIARLEEGARDEN CENTRE**
35 Chapel Lane, Banks, Southport
TEL: 01704 226 647

**35 TARLETON SPECIMEN PLANTS**
Gorse Lane, Tarleton, Preston
TEL: 01772 816 879

**36 BLUNDELLS NURSERIES**
68 Southport New Road, Tarleton, Preston
TEL: 01772 815 442

**37 DUNSCAR NURSERIES & GARDEN CENTRE**
118 Southport New Road, Tarleton, Preston
TEL: 01772 812 684

**38 LYNDENE NURSERIES**
143 Southport New Road, Tarleton, Preston
TEL: 01772 813 611

**39 AULDENE GARDEN CENTRE**
Southport Road, Leyland, Preston
TEL: 01772 600 271

**40 CROSTON CACTUS**
43 Southport Road, Eccleston, Chorley
TEL: 01257 452 555

**41 BOXTREE NURSERY OF CHURCHTOWN**
192 Cambridge Road, Churchtown, Southport
TEL: 01704 227 465

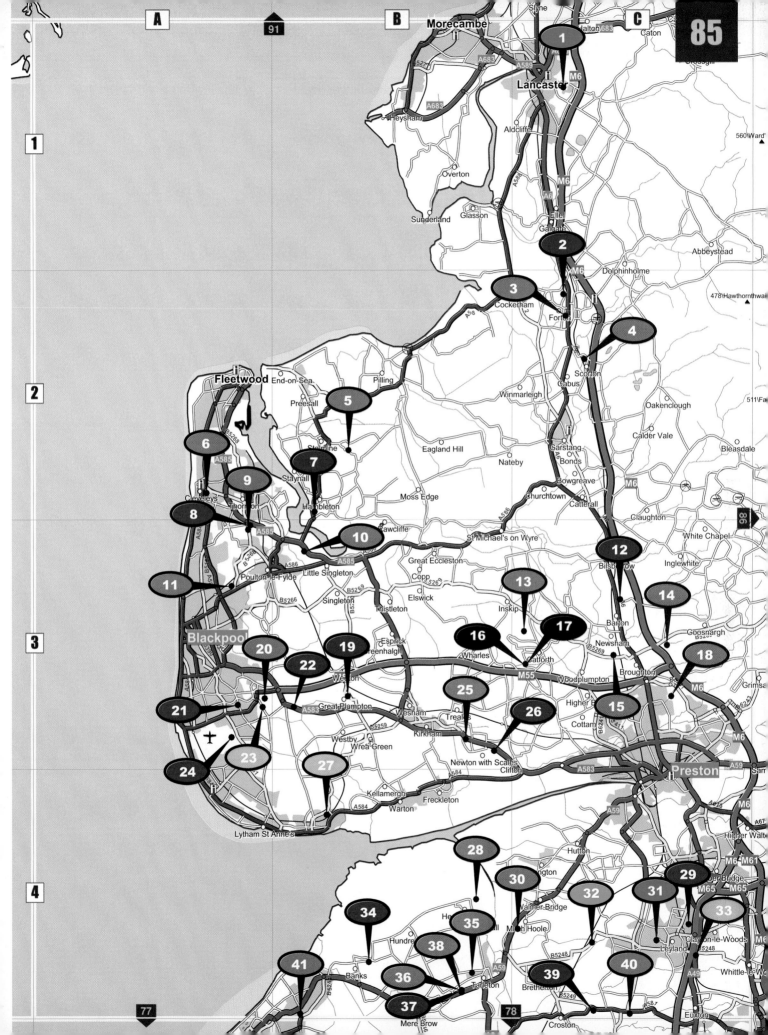

**1** **BAILEY GARDEN CENTRE**
The Bailey, Skipton
**TEL:** 01756 791 619

**2** **HOLDEN CLOUGH NURSERY**
Holden, Bolton-by-Bowland, Clitheroe
**TEL:** 01200 447 615

**3** **GARDENIA GARDEN & SHOP**
Slisden Caravan and Lesiure, Keighley Road, Silsen
**TEL:** 01535 656 351

**4** **GARDENERS CHOICE**
7a Aire Street, Cross Hills, Keighley
**TEL:** 01535 631 630

**5** **SALTERFORTH NURSERIES & LANDSCAPES**
Moor Lane, Salterforth, Barnoldswick
**TEL:** 01282 850 649

**6** **SHACKLETON GARDEN NURSERIES**
Rydal Place, Clitheroe Road, Chatburn
**TEL:** 01200 441 230

**7** **LAKESIDE GARDEN CENTRE**
Skipton Road, Foulridge, Colne
**TEL:** 01282 865 650

**8** **HEDGEROW NURSERY**
24 Braithwaite Edge Road, Keighley
**TEL:** 01535 606 531

**9** **BARKERS GARDEN CENTRE**
Whalley Road, Clitheroe
**TEL:** 01200 423 521

**10** **PENDLE HERITAGE CENTRE**
Park Hill, Barrowford, Nelson
**TEL:** 01282 661 702

**11** **TOM HANSON & SONS (BARROW NURSERIES)**
Whalley Road, Barrow, Clitheroe
**TEL:** 01254 822 145

**12** **WHALLEY NURSERIES**
The Lodge, Clitheroe Road, Whalley
**TEL:** 01254 824 990

**13** **DAWSON'S OF BRIERFIELD**
Clitheroe Road, Brierfield, Nelson
**TEL:** 01282 615 473

**14** **REEDLEY NURSERY**
Robinson Lane, Brierfield, Nelson
**TEL:** 01282 693 376

**15** **HUNTROYDE NURSERIES**
Whins Lane, Simonstone, Padiham
**TEL:** 01282 770 753

**16** **READ GARDEN CENTRE**
Accrington/Whally Road (A680), Read, Burnley
**TEL:** 01254 884 215

**17** **GAWTHORPE HALL**
Padiham, Burnley
**TEL:** 01282 771 004

**18** **SPRINGWOOD NURSERIES**
Springwood Road, Burnley
**TEL:** 01282 425 316

**19** **TOWNELEY GARDEN CENTRE**
Deerpark Nurseries, Deerpark Road, Burnley
**TEL:** 01282 424 162

**20** **SAMLESBURY BONSAI NURSERY**
The Boat House, Potters Lane, Samlesbury
**TEL:** 01772 877 213

**21** **BEARDWOOD GARDEN CENTRE**
Preston New Road, Blackburn
**TEL:** 01254 693 121

**22** **SLACK TOP ALPINES**
1 Waterloo House, Hebden Bridge
**TEL:** 01422 845 348

**23** **WITTON COUNTRY PARK**
Preston Old Road, Blackburn
**TEL:** 01254 554 23

**24** **GORDON RIGG NURSERIES LTD**
Calderbank Nurseries and Garden Centre, Walsden,
Todmorden, Lancashire, OL14 7TJ.

*Specialising in volume sales of quality plants at unbeatable prices. Fantastic selection of seedlings and young plants, importers of silk flowers etc.*
**OPEN:** Mon-Fri 9-9, Sat 9-5.30, Sun 11-5. Closed Christmas Day & Boxing Day.
**SPECIALITIES:** Seeds, Shrubs, Bedding plants, House plants, Artificial flowers.
**FACILITIES:** Bookshop, Credit cards, Gift shop, HTA gift tokens, Own gift tokens, Pushchair friendly, Sell plants, Toilets, Wheelchair access.

**25** **BROOKSIDE NURSERIES**
Roundhill Road, Accrington
**TEL:** 01706 216 491

**26** **LEABROOK NURSERIES**
Burnley Road, Rawtenstall, Rossendale
**TEL:** 01706 230 856

**27** **ARRAN NURSERIES**
Gas Street, Haslingden, Rossendale
**TEL:** 01706 227 688

**28** **FOUR SEASONS GARDEN CENTRE**
Ashton Road, Darwen
**TEL:** 01254 706 890

**29** **THAT GARDENING PLACE**
Spring Vale Road, Darwen
**TEL:** 01254 702 915

**30** **WHITWORTH GARDEN CENTRE**
Grange Road, Whitworth, Rochdale
**TEL:** 01706 853 623

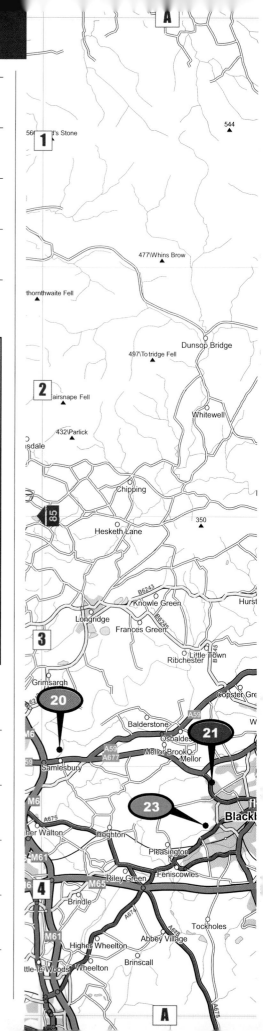

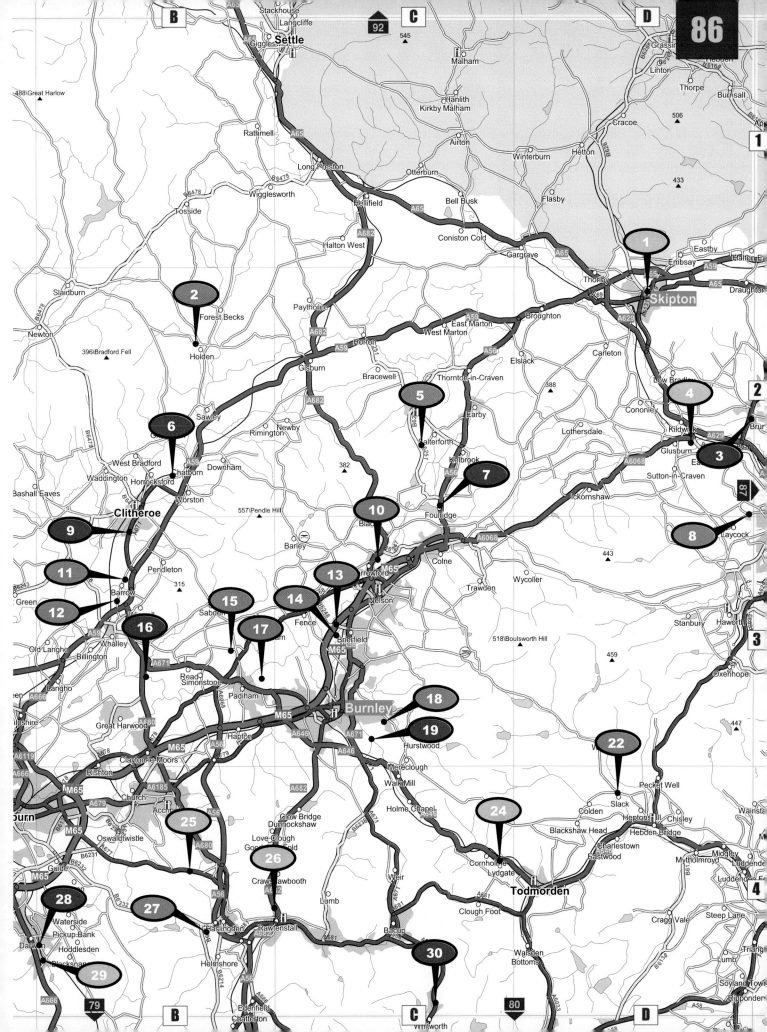

**1** **WOODLANDS COTTAGE NURSERY**
Summerbridge, Harrogate
**TEL:** 01423 780 765

**2** **PERCEVALL HALL GARDENS**
Skyreholme, Skipton
**TEL:** 01756 720 311

**3** **BLUECOAT WOOD NURSERIES**
Otley Road, Beckwithshaw, Harrogate
**TEL:** 01423 522 876

**4** **STEPHEN H SMITH'S GARDEN & LEISURE**
Wharfe Valley, Pool Road, Otley
**TEL:** 01943 462 195

**5** **ILKLEY MOOR GARDEN CENTRE**
Robin Hole, Woodhead, Ilkley
**TEL:** 01943 864 303

**6** **SWINCAR NURSERIES**
Chevin End Road, Guiseley
**TEL:** 01943 874 614

**7** **EAST RIDDLESDEN HALL, NATIONAL TRUST**
Bradford Road, Keighley
**TEL:** 01535 607 075

**8** **HIGHTREES GARDEN CENTRE**
Otley Old Road, Horsforth, Leeds
**TEL:** 01132 587 788

**9** **WOODWARD NURSERIES**
Barnsley Beck Grove, Baildon, Shipley
**TEL:** 01274 414 789

**10** **HIRSTWOOD NURSERIES**
Hirst Lane, Hirst Lock, Shipley
**TEL:** 01274 591 251

**11** **SANDY BANKS WATER LIFE**
Sandy Banks Garden Centre, Wilsden Road, Bingley
**TEL:** 01535 275 032

**12** **STEPHEN H SMITH'S GARDEN & LEISURE**
Aire Valley, Wilsden Road, Harden
**TEL:** 01535 274 653

**13** **PALMER NURSERIES**
Calverley Lane, Calverley, Pudsey
**TEL:** 01132 563 331

**14** **CARLTON NURSERIES & LANDSCAPE GARDENERS**
Cottingley Moor Road, Bingley
**TEL:** 01274 496 270

**15** **A C W GARDEN CENTRE**
Canal Road, Bradford
**TEL:** 01274 392 344

**16** **LIVING WORLD**
206 Armley Road, Leeds
**TEL:** 01132 631 509

**17** **PUDSEY PARK**
Church Lane, Pudsey
**TEL:** 01132 551 334

**18** **MOSS FARM CONIFERS**
Moss Farm, Halifax
**TEL:** 01422 245 196

**19** **TONG GARDEN CENTRE**
Tong Lane, Westgate Hill, Bradford
**TEL:** 01132 853 506

**20** **A J KEELING & SON**
North View Road, Bradford
**TEL:** 01274 682 120

**21** **BEECHES NURSERIES**
31 Back Lane, Drighlington, Bradford
**TEL:** 01132 879 077

**22** **WYEVALE GARDEN CENTRE**
Denholmegate Road, Northowram, Halifax
**TEL:** 01422 206 418

Rununculus

### 23 DOVE COTTAGE PLANTS
23 Shibden Hall Road, Halifax
**Tel:** 01422 203 553

### 24 SPEN NURSERIES
Spen Lane, Cleckheaton
**Tel:** 01274 869 282

### 25 PARK HOUSE NURSERIES
Eddercliffe Crescent, Littletown, Liversedge
**Tel:** 01274 861 500

### 26 KERSHAW'S GARDEN CENTRE
Halifax Road, Brighouse
**Tel:** 01484 713 435

### 27 WHITELEYS GARDEN CENTRE
Leeds Road, Mirfield
**Tel:** 01924 495 944

### 28 WESTFIELD NURSERIES
Shillbank Lane, Mirfield
**Tel:** 01924 498 259

### 29 ARMITAGE'S MOWER WORLD & GARDEN CENTRE
Birchencliffe Hill Road, Birchencliffe, Huddersfield
**Tel:** 01484 536 010

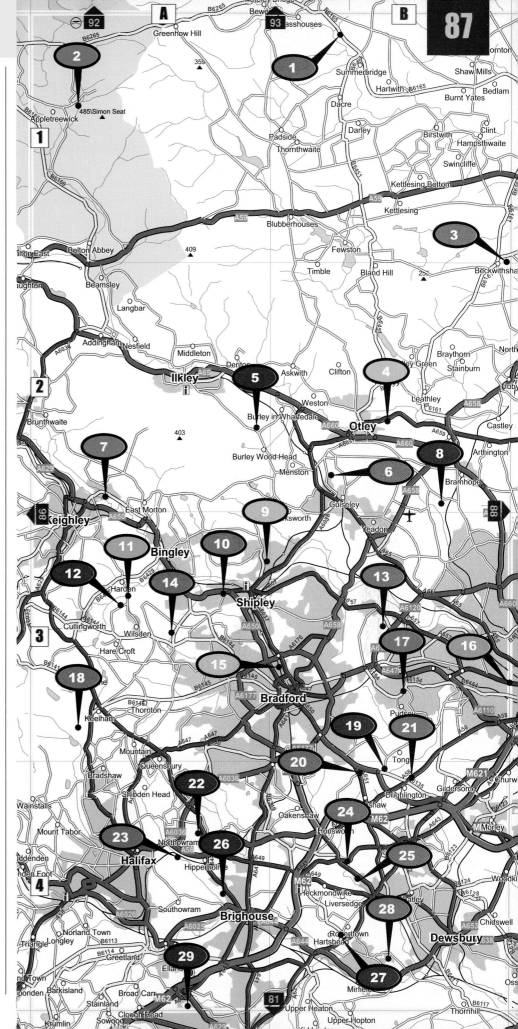

**1 ORCHARD HOUSE NURSERY**
Wormald Green, Harrogate
**Tel:** 01765 677 541

**2 WAYSIDE NURSERIES**
Minskip Road, Staveley, Knaresborough
**Tel:** 01423 340 293

**3 RIPLEY CASTLE**
Ripley, Harrogate
**Tel:** 01423 770 152

**4 DALESIDE NURSERIES**
Ripon Road, Killinghall, Harrogate
**Tel:** 01423 506 450

**5 PARK NURSERIES**
Bar Lane, Knaresborough
**Tel:** 01423 865 182

**6 M E BROWN & SONS**
Town End Farm, Mill Lane, York
**Tel:** 01904 768 247

**7 BENINGBROUGH HALL & GARDENS, NATIONAL TRUST**
Beningbrough, York
**Tel:** 01904 470 666

**8 MOOR MONKTON NURSERIES**
York Road, Moor Monkton, York
**Tel:** 01904 738 319

**9 WILLIAM STRIKE**
York Road, Knaresborough
**Tel:** 01423 865 351

**10 WIGGINTON ROAD NURSERIES**
Wigginton Road, York
**Tel:** 01904 762 250

**11 RICHARD GRIFFITHS HOUSE PLANTS**
Moorland Nurseries, Forest Moor Road, Knaresborough
**Tel:** 01423 860 672

**12 MOORLAND NURSERIES & GARDEN CENTRE**
Forest Moor Road, Knaresborough
**Tel:** 01423 866 054

**13 POTTING SHED**
Thistle Hill Nurseries, Thistle Hill, Knaresborough
**Tel:** 01423 869 949

**14 ANNAMINE NURSERIES**
Jockey Lane, Huntington, York
**Tel:** 01904 622 931

**15 HARLOW CARR BOTANICAL GARDENS**
Crag Lane, Harrogate
**Tel:** 01423 565 418

**16 WYEVALE GARDEN CENTRE**
Northfield Lane, Upper Poppleton, York
**Tel:** 01904 795 920

**17 TREASURER'S HOUSE, NT**
Minster Yard, York
**Tel:** 01904 624 247

**18 CRIMPLE VALLEY GARDEN CENTRE**
Leeds Road, Pannal, Harrogate
**Tel:** 01423 872 463

**19 MERCHANT ADVENTURERS' HALL & GARDEN**
Fossgate, York
**Tel:** 01904 654 818

**20 BRUNSWICK ORGANIC NURSERY**
Appleton Road, Bishopthorpe, York
**Tel:** 01904 701 869

**21 RIVERSIDE NURSERIES**
Linton Common, Wetherby
**Tel:** 01937 582 598

**22 GREENERY GARDEN CENTRE**
The Shopping Centre, Thorp Arch, Wetherby
**Tel:** 01937 844 778

**23 OLD MILL GARDEN CENTRE**
Leeds Road, Collingham, Wetherby
**Tel:** 01937 572 870

**24 HAREWOOD HOUSE**
Harewood, Leeds
**Tel:** 01132 886 331

**25 BRAMHAM PARK**
Wetherby
**Tel:** 01937 844 265

**26 GRIMSTON PARK NURSERIES**
Grimston Park, Grimston, Tadcaster
**Tel:** 01937 832 188

**27 STILLINGFLEET LODGE NURSERIES**
Stillingfleet
**Tel:** 01904 728 506

**28 GREENSCAPES NURSERY & GARDEN DESIGN CENTRE**
Brandon Crescent, Shadwell, Leeds
**Tel:** 01132 892 922

**29 WOLINSKI NURSERY**
Bay Horse Lane, Shadwell, Leeds
**Tel:** 01132 892 873

**32 HAYES GARDEN WORLD**
York Road, Whinmoor, Leeds, West Yorkshire, LS15 4NF.
**Tel:** 01132 731 949
**Email:** keith.laird@hayesgardenworld.co.uk
**Web:** www.hayesgardenworld.co.uk

*Here at Hayes Garden World, 4 generations of Lakeland gardening experience and expertise have culminated in an attraction that no gardener or even casual sightseer should miss.*
**Open:** Mon-Sat 9-6, Sun 11-5. Closed Easter Sun, Christmas & New Years Day.
**Specialities:** Comprehensive range.
**Facilities:** Coffee shop, Credit cards, Bookshop, Gift shop, Own gift tokens, HTA gift tokens, Plant guarantee, Sell plants, Toilets, Wheelchair access, Pushchair friendly.

**30 WILLIAM STRIKE**
Red Hall Lane, Wellington Hill, Leeds
**Tel:** 01132 657 839

**31 ROUNDHAY PARK**
Tropical World Canal Gardens, Roundhay Rd, Leeds
**Tel:** 01132 661 850

**33 HOLLIES PARK**
Westwood Lane, Leeds
**Tel:** 01132 478 361

**34 GOLDEN ACRE PARK**
Otley Road, Leeds
**Tel:** 01132 610 374

**35 WILLIAM STRIKE**
Selby Road, Swillington Common, Leeds
**Tel:** 01132 862 981

**36 LUMBY GARDEN CENTRE**
Leys House, Selby Road, South Milford
**Tel:** 01977 682 815

**37 ASHFIELD HELLEBORES, RARER PLANTS**
Ashfield House, Austfield Lane, Monk Fryston
**Tel:** 01977 682 263

**38 AQUARIUS KOI**
Quarrydene House, Quarrydene Drive, Castleford
**Tel:** 01977 668 844

**39 M G W PLANTS**
45 Potovens Lane, Lofthouse Gate, Wakefield
**Tel:** 01924 820 096

**40 GARDEN OUTLET**
Unit J2/J3 Freeport Village Glasshoughton, Carrwood Road, Castleford
**Tel:** 01977 519 238

**41 D C GRAHAM & SON**
Stranglands Lane, Ferrybridge, Knottingley
**Tel:** 01977 552 362

**42 CARR GATE NURSERIES**
Old Bradford Road, Carr Gate, Wakefield
**Tel:** 01924 823 002

**43 NEWTON HILL ALPINES**
335 Leeds Road, Newton Hill, Wakefield
**Tel:** 01924 377 056

**44 LINDHILL NURSERY**
Batley Road, Kirkhamgate, Wakefield
**Tel:** 01924 372 433

**45 VICTORIA GARDEN CENTRE**
Wayfield Road, Featherstone, Pontefract
**Tel:** 01977 701 560

**46 CROWN GARDEN CENTRE**
Doncaster Road, Whitley Bridge, Goole
**Tel:** 01977 661 643

**47 SPRING GREEN NURSERIES**
Pontefract Road, Crofton, Wakefield
**Tel:** 01924 863 859

**48 ASH VILLA NURSERIES**
Westfield Road, Horbury, Wakefield
**Tel:** 01924 274 921

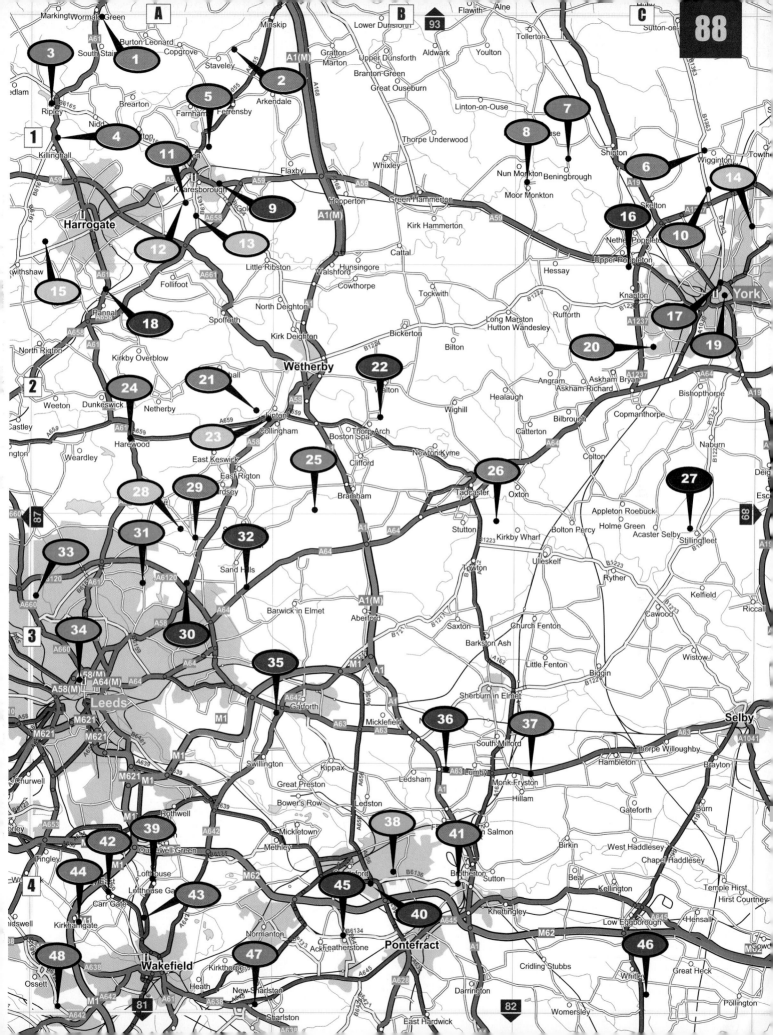

**1  FLAXTON HOUSE NURSERY**

Flaxton, York, North Yorkshire, YO60 7RJ.
TEL: 01904 468 753
*A surprisingly large nursery hidden in the peaceful country garden of Flaxton House and run by knowledgeable people who love plants.*
OPEN: Mar-Sep: Tue-Sun 10-5.
SPECIALITIES: Alpines, Climbers, Roses, Herbaceous plants, Hardy plants.
FACILITIES: Dogs allowed, Wheelchair access, Sell plants.

**2  J & D MARSTON**

Culag, Green Lane, Nafferton
TEL: 01377 254 487

**3  BELL MILLS GARDEN CENTRE**

Bell Mills, Skerne Road, Driffield
TEL: 01377 254 043

**4  DEAN'S GARDEN CENTRE**

Stockton Lane, Stockton-On-The-Forest, York
TEL: 01904 400 141

**5  ORCHARD NURSERIES**

48 Hopgrove Lane South, York
TEL: 01904 421 153

**6  LONDESBORO NURSERIES & GARDEN CENTRE**

Londesboro, Hutton Cranswick
TEL: 01377 270 272

**7  BORETREE NURSERIES**

Grimston Court, Hull Road, Grimston
TEL: 01904 488 437

**8  DAVID W SMITH GARDEN CENTRE**

Sunray, 2 Back Lane, Wilberfoss
TEL: 01759 388 863

**9  BURNBY HALL GARDENS**

The Balk, Pocklington
TEL: 01759 302 068

**10  SPRINGWELL GARDEN CENTRE**

Main Street, Wheldrake, York
TEL: 01904 448 733

**11  LANGLANDS NURSERIES & GARDEN CENTRE**

York Road, Shiptonthorpe, York, North Yorkshire, YO43 3PN.
TEL: 01430 873 426
EMAIL: info@langlands-nurseries.co.uk
WEB: www.langlands-nurseries.co.uk
*Large nurseries and garden centre open to the public. Specialist growers of fuchsias, geraniums, bedding and patio plants. Well worth a visit any time of year.*
OPEN: Mon-Sat 9-5.30, Sun 10.30-4.30.
SPECIALITIES: Bedding plants, Fuchsias, Geraniums.
FACILITIES: Toilets, Credit cards, Gift tokens, Coffee shop, Pushchair friendly, HTA gift tokens, Own gift tokens, Child area, Wheelchair access.

**12  SELBY GARDEN CENTRE**

Hull Road, Osgodby, Selby
TEL: 01757 708 658

**13  YORKSHIRE GARDEN CENTRE**

Scalby Lane, Gilberdyke, Brough
TEL: 01430 440 169

**14  OAK TREE NURSERY**

Mill Lane, Barlow, Selby
TEL: 01757 618 409

**15  CALIFORNIA GARDENS**

Boothberry Road, Howden
TEL: 01430 430 824

**16  NORDEN ALPINES**

Hirst Road, Carlton, Goole
TEL: 01405 861 348

**17  TOO HOOTS NURSERIES & GARDEN CENTRE**

Hirst Road, Carlton, Goole, East Riding of Yorkshire, DN14 9PX.
TEL: 01405 862 854
EMAIL: info@toohoots.co.uk
WEB: www.toohoots.co.uk
*Wide range of garden products, gifts and quality plants, with helpful and friendly staff offering expert advice.*
OPEN: Open 7 days a week. Summer: 9-5. Winter: 9-4.
SPECIALITIES: Hanging baskets, Comprehensive range.
FACILITIES: Child area, Credit cards, HTA gift tokens, Own gift tokens, Sell plants, Wheelchair access, Pushchair friendly, Toilets.

**18  BARTON WATER GARDENS**

Barrow Road, Barton-upon-Humber
TEL: 01652 660 291

**19  TUPLINS NURSERIES**

The Nurseries, Ferry Road, Barrow upon Humber
TEL: 01469 532 662

**20  B G PLANT NURSERY**

70 North Street, Winterton
TEL: 01724 733 695

**21  WESTSHORES NURSERIES**

82 West Street, Winterton
TEL: 01724 733 940

## Help us help you

mention the *Gardeners' Atlas* when visiting anywhere on this page

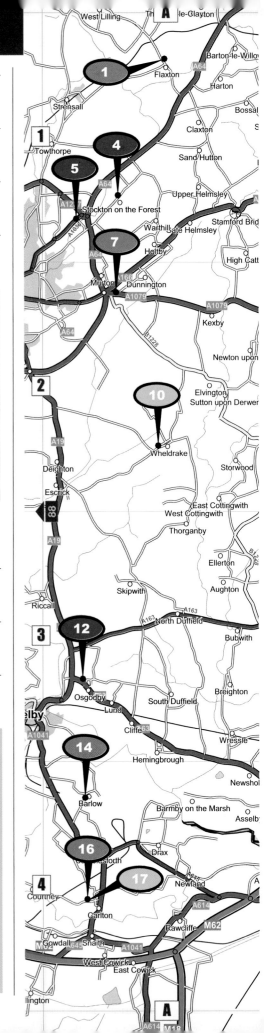

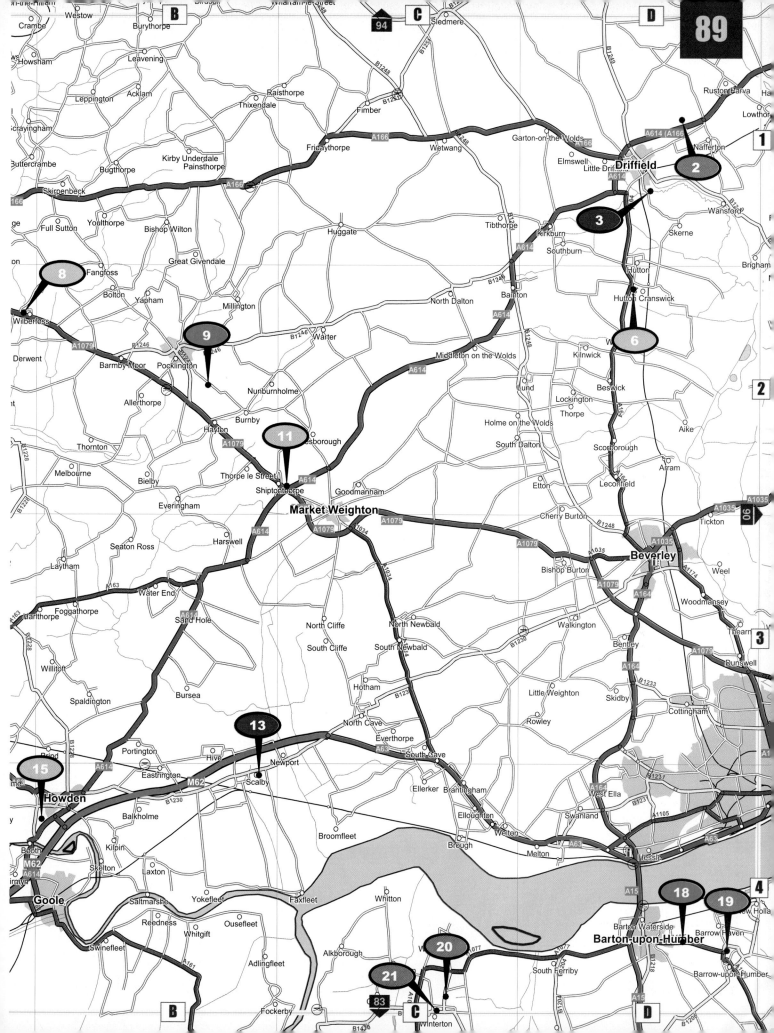

### 1  BURTON AGNES HALL GARDENS

Burton Agnes, Driffield, East Riding of Yorkshire, YO25 4NB.
**TEL:** 01262 490 324
**EMAIL:** burtonagnes@farmline.com
**WEB:** www.burton-agnes.com

*Lawns and topiary surround the Elizabethan house while the walled garden contains a riot of flowers including a maze and potage.*
**OPEN:** Apr-Oct: 11-5.
**ENTRY COSTS:** £2.40, Child: £1, OAPs: £2.15.
**SPECIALITIES:** Hardy plants, Seeds, Vegetables.
**FACILITIES:** Toilets, Credit cards, Wheelchair access, Restaurant, Dogs allowed, Child area, Plant guarantee, Coffee shop.

### 2  MIDDLE FARM NURSERIES

Main Road, Mappleton, Hornsea
**TEL:** 01964 532 542

### 3  SPRING GARDEN CENTRE

Main Street, Sigglesthorne, Hull
**TEL:** 01964 543 040

### 4  WHITE COTTAGE ALPINES

Sunnyside Nurseries, Hornsea Road, Sigglesthorne
**TEL:** 01964 542 692

### 5  LANSCAPE CENTRE

Hull Road, Skirlaugh, Hull
**TEL:** 01964 562 413

### 6  DEVINE NURSERIES & GARDEN CENTRE

Main Road, Holly, Withernsea
**TEL:** 01964 613 840

### 7  THE PALM FARM

Thornton Hall Gardens, Station Road, Thornton Curtis, Ulceby, North Lincolnshire, DN39 6XF.
**TEL:** 01469 531 232
**EMAIL:** bill@palmfarm.fsbusiness.co.uk
**WEB:** www.thepalmfarm.com

*Specialists in palms and exotics for the garden and conservatory. Unusual trees, shrubs, climbers. Palm garden and other demonstration plantings.*
**OPEN:** Open daily 2-5.
**ENTRY COSTS:** Free.
**SPECIALITIES:** Palms, Shrubs, Trees, Climbers, Exotic plants.
**FACILITIES:** Wheelchair access, Dogs allowed, Own gift tokens, Pushchair friendly, Sell plants.

Daffodil

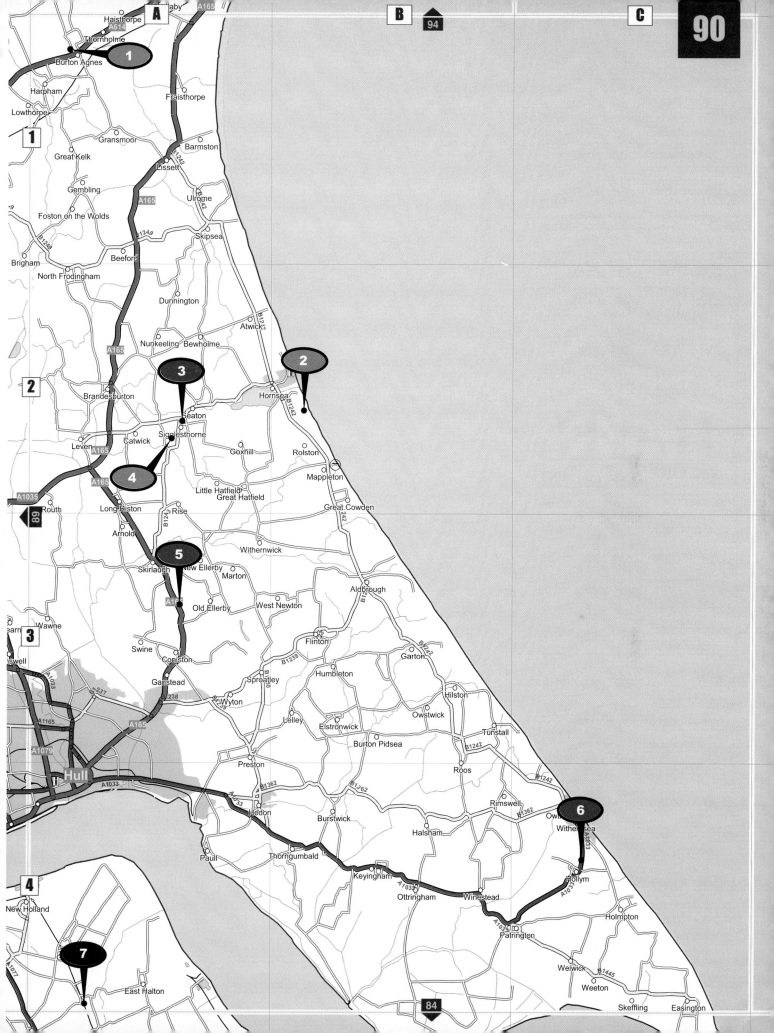

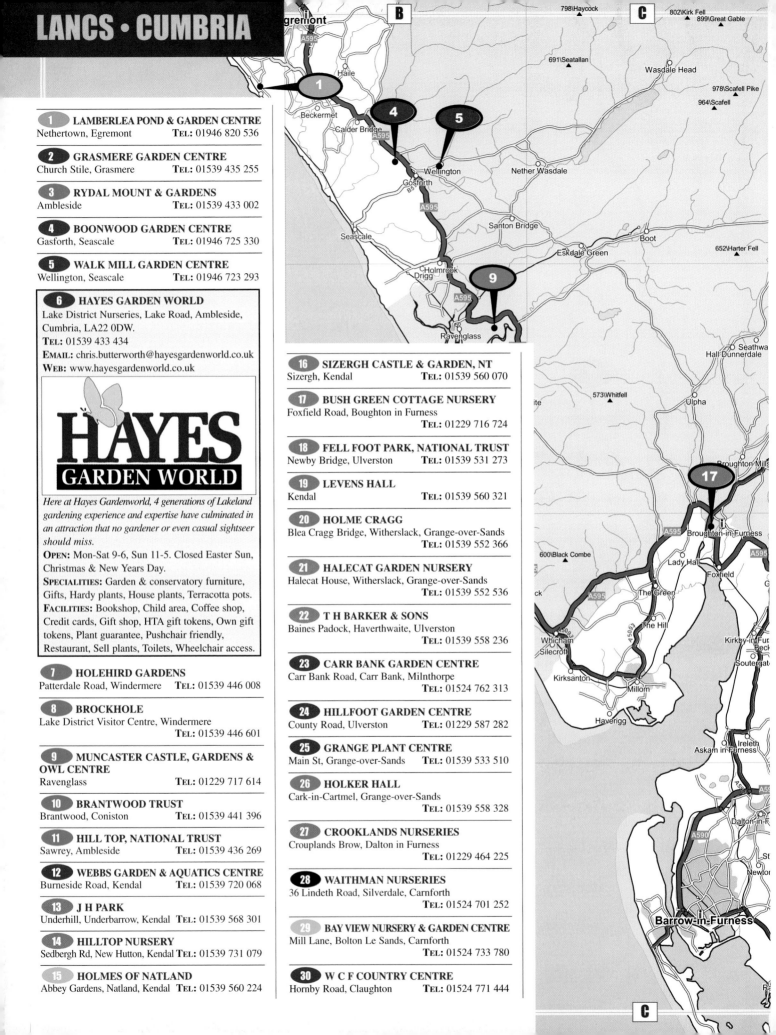

**1** **LAMBERLEA POND & GARDEN CENTRE**
Nethertown, Egremont     **Tel:** 01946 820 536

**2** **GRASMERE GARDEN CENTRE**
Church Stile, Grasmere     **Tel:** 01539 435 255

**3** **RYDAL MOUNT & GARDENS**
Ambleside     **Tel:** 01539 433 002

**4** **BOONWOOD GARDEN CENTRE**
Gasforth, Seascale     **Tel:** 01946 725 330

**5** **WALK MILL GARDEN CENTRE**
Wellington, Seascale     **Tel:** 01946 723 293

**6** **HAYES GARDEN WORLD**
Lake District Nurseries, Lake Road, Ambleside,
Cumbria, LA22 0DW.
**Tel:** 01539 433 434
**Email:** chris.butterworth@hayesgardenworld.co.uk
**Web:** www.hayesgardenworld.co.uk

# HAYES
## GARDEN WORLD

*Here at Hayes Gardenworld, 4 generations of Lakeland
gardening experience and expertise have culminated in
an attraction that no gardener or even casual sightseer
should miss.*
**Open:** Mon-Sat 9-6, Sun 11-5. Closed Easter Sun,
Christmas & New Years Day.
**Specialities:** Garden & conservatory furniture,
Gifts, Hardy plants, House plants, Terracotta pots.
**Facilities:** Bookshop, Child area, Coffee shop,
Credit cards, Gift shop, HTA gift tokens, Own gift
tokens, Plant guarantee, Pushchair friendly,
Restaurant, Sell plants, Toilets, Wheelchair access.

**7** **HOLEHIRD GARDENS**
Patterdale Road, Windermere     **Tel:** 01539 446 008

**8** **BROCKHOLE**
Lake District Visitor Centre, Windermere
    **Tel:** 01539 446 601

**9** **MUNCASTER CASTLE, GARDENS &
OWL CENTRE**
Ravenglass     **Tel:** 01229 717 614

**10** **BRANTWOOD TRUST**
Brantwood, Coniston     **Tel:** 01539 441 396

**11** **HILL TOP, NATIONAL TRUST**
Sawrey, Ambleside     **Tel:** 01539 436 269

**12** **WEBBS GARDEN & AQUATICS CENTRE**
Burneside Road, Kendal     **Tel:** 01539 720 068

**13** **J H PARK**
Underhill, Underbarrow, Kendal     **Tel:** 01539 568 301

**14** **HILLTOP NURSERY**
Sedbergh Rd, New Hutton, Kendal **Tel:** 01539 731 079

**15** **HOLMES OF NATLAND**
Abbey Gardens, Natland, Kendal **Tel:** 01539 560 224

**16** **SIZERGH CASTLE & GARDEN, NT**
Sizergh, Kendal     **Tel:** 01539 560 070

**17** **BUSH GREEN COTTAGE NURSERY**
Foxfield Road, Boughton in Furness
    **Tel:** 01229 716 724

**18** **FELL FOOT PARK, NATIONAL TRUST**
Newby Bridge, Ulverston     **Tel:** 01539 531 273

**19** **LEVENS HALL**
Kendal     **Tel:** 01539 560 321

**20** **HOLME CRAGG**
Blea Cragg Bridge, Witherslack, Grange-over-Sands
    **Tel:** 01539 552 366

**21** **HALECAT GARDEN NURSERY**
Halecat House, Witherslack, Grange-over-Sands
    **Tel:** 01539 552 536

**22** **T H BARKER & SONS**
Baines Padock, Haverthwaite, Ulverston
    **Tel:** 01539 558 236

**23** **CARR BANK GARDEN CENTRE**
Carr Bank Road, Carr Bank, Milnthorpe
    **Tel:** 01524 762 313

**24** **HILLFOOT GARDEN CENTRE**
County Road, Ulverston     **Tel:** 01229 587 282

**25** **GRANGE PLANT CENTRE**
Main St, Grange-over-Sands     **Tel:** 01539 533 510

**26** **HOLKER HALL**
Cark-in-Cartmel, Grange-over-Sands
    **Tel:** 01539 558 328

**27** **CROOKLANDS NURSERIES**
Crouplands Brow, Dalton in Furness
    **Tel:** 01229 464 225

**28** **WAITHMAN NURSERIES**
36 Lindeth Road, Silverdale, Carnforth
    **Tel:** 01524 701 252

**29** **BAY VIEW NURSERY & GARDEN CENTRE**
Mill Lane, Bolton Le Sands, Carnforth
    **Tel:** 01524 733 780

**30** **W C F COUNTRY CENTRE**
Hornby Road, Claughton     **Tel:** 01524 771 444

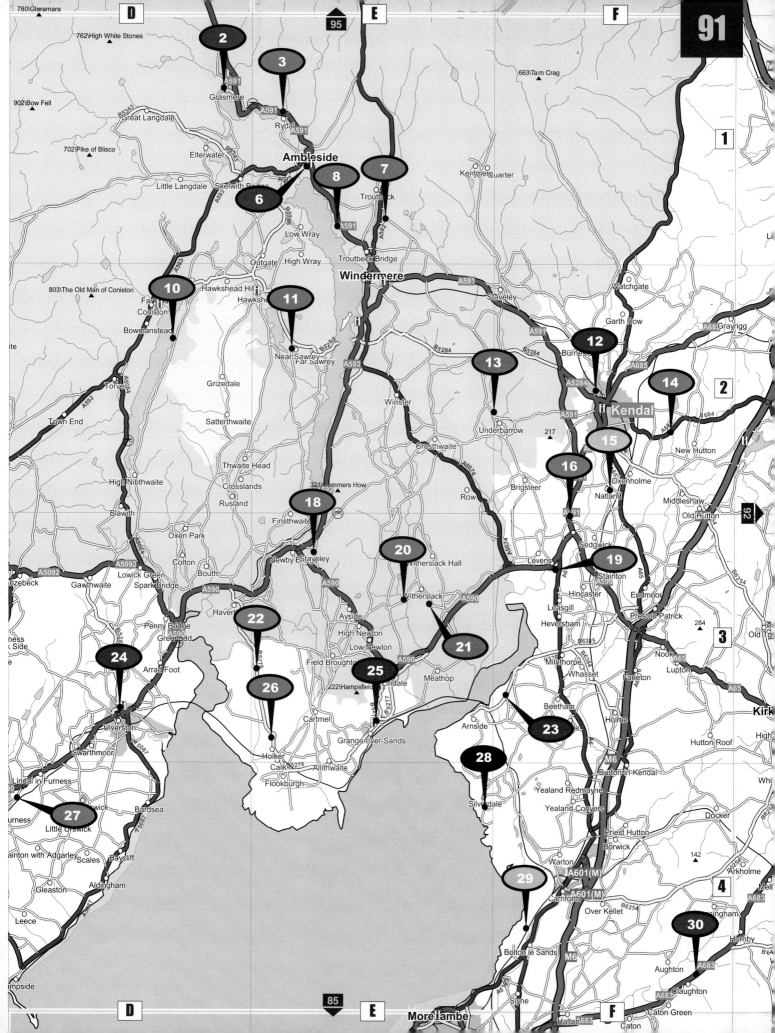

# LANCS · N. YORKS

**1  RAVENSWORTH NURSERIES**
Ravensworth, Richmond
TEL: 01325 718 370

**2  KERSHAWS NURSERIES**
Woodhall Lodge, Woodhall, Askrigg
TEL: 01969 663 652

**3  BROWNTHWAITE HARDY PLANTS**
Fell Yeat, Casterton, Kirkby Lonsdale
TEL: 01524 271 340

**4  TOLL BAR NURSERIES**
Gate House, Lower Bentham, Lancaster
TEL: 01524 261 301

Liatris

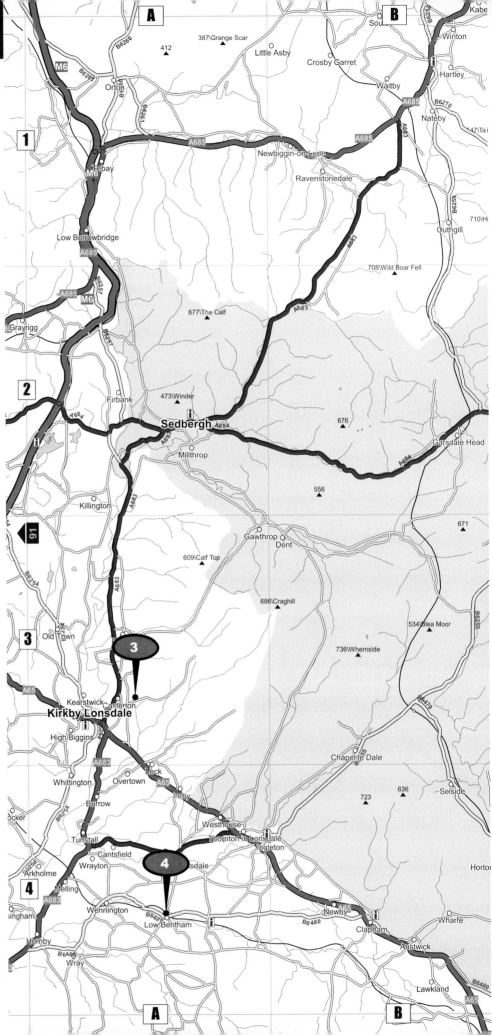

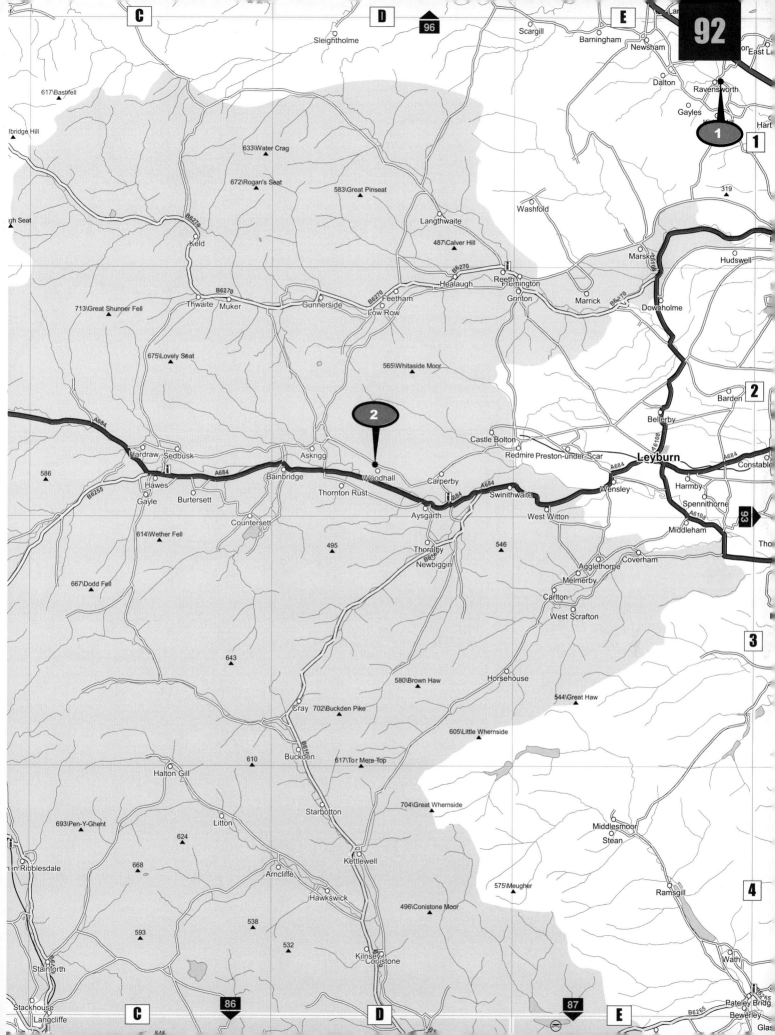

**1**   **WILLIAM STRIKE**
The Roundabout, Meadowfields, Stokesley
TEL: 01642 710 419

**2**   **BATTERSBY ROSES**
Peartree Cottage, Old Battersby, Great Ayton
TEL: 01642 723 402

**3**   **KINROSS NURSERIES**
Skutterskelfe, Yarm
TEL: 01642 710 831

**4**   **FIR TREES PELARGONIUM NURSERY**
Fir Tree Cottage, Stokesley, Middlesborough
TEL: 01642 713 066

**5**   **PADDOCK FARM NURSERIES**
West Lane, Dalton Gates, Darlington
TEL: 01325 378 286

**6**   **MILLGATE HOUSE**
Richmond
TEL: 01748 823 571

**7**   **MOUNT GRACE PRIORY, ENGLISH HERITAGE**
Saddlebridge, Northallerton
TEL: 01609 883 494

**8**   **PARWOODS NURSERY**
Darlington Road, Northallerton
TEL: 01609 760 970

**9**   **WILLIAM STRIKE**
Boroughbridge Road, Northallerton
TEL: 01609 773 694

**10**   **BURTON CONSTABLE HALL GARDENS**
Leyburn
TEL: 01677 450 428

**11**   **FAIRVIEW NURSERY**
Fairview Gardens, Aiskew, Bedale
TEL: 01677 422 256

**12**   **THORP PERROW ARBORETUM**
The Hall, Thorp Perrow, Bedale
TEL: 01677 425 323

**13**   **RIEVAULX TERRACE & TEMPLES**
Helmsley
TEL: 01439 798 340

**14**   **DUNCOMBE PARK**
Helmsley
TEL: 01439 770 213

**15**   **WHITESTONE GARDENS**
The Cactus House, Sutton Under Whitestone Cliff, Thirsk
TEL: 01845 597 467

**16**   **F A JOBLING**
Main Street, West Tanfield, Ripon
TEL: 01677 470 481

**17**   **SHANDY HALL**
Coxwold, York
TEL: 01347 868 465

**18**   **STUDLEY ROYAL GARDEN CENTRE**
Studley Roger, Ripon
TEL: 01765 604 385

**19**   **DEANSWOOD PLANTS**
Potteries Lane, Littlethorpe, Ripon
TEL: 01765 603 441

**20**   **FOUNTAINS ABBEY & STUDLEY ROYAL WATER GARDEN, NATIONAL TRUST**
Fountains, Ripon
TEL: 01765 608 888

**21**   **OLANDS GARDEN AND PLANT CENTRE**
Sawley Nursery, Risplith, Ripon, North Yorkshire, HG4 3EW.
TEL: 01765 620 622
EMAIL: olands@btconnect.com
WEB: www.olands.co.uk

*Nursery for the plant enthusiast with a two acre garden. Many choice varieties, plants for all occasions. Gardening and plant advice available.*
OPEN: Feb-Dec: 9.30-5.
ENTRY COSTS: Free.
SPECIALITIES: Perennials, Alpine, Aquatics, Climbers, Shrubs.
FACILITIES: Toilets, Credit cards, Gift tokens, Bookshop, Sell plants, Gift shop, Own gift tokens.

**22**   **NEWBY HALL AND GARDENS**
Newby Hall, Ripon
TEL: 01423 322 583

Allotment

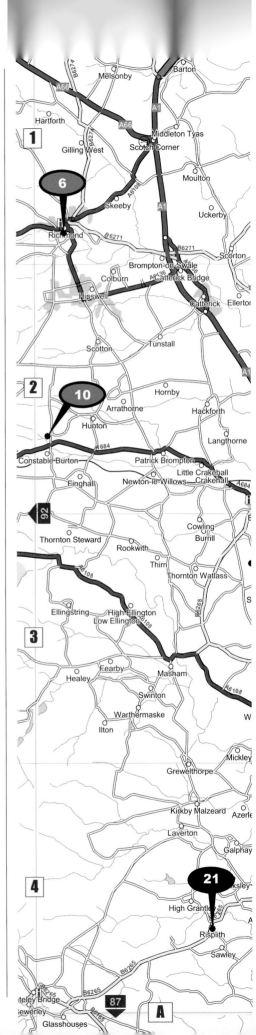

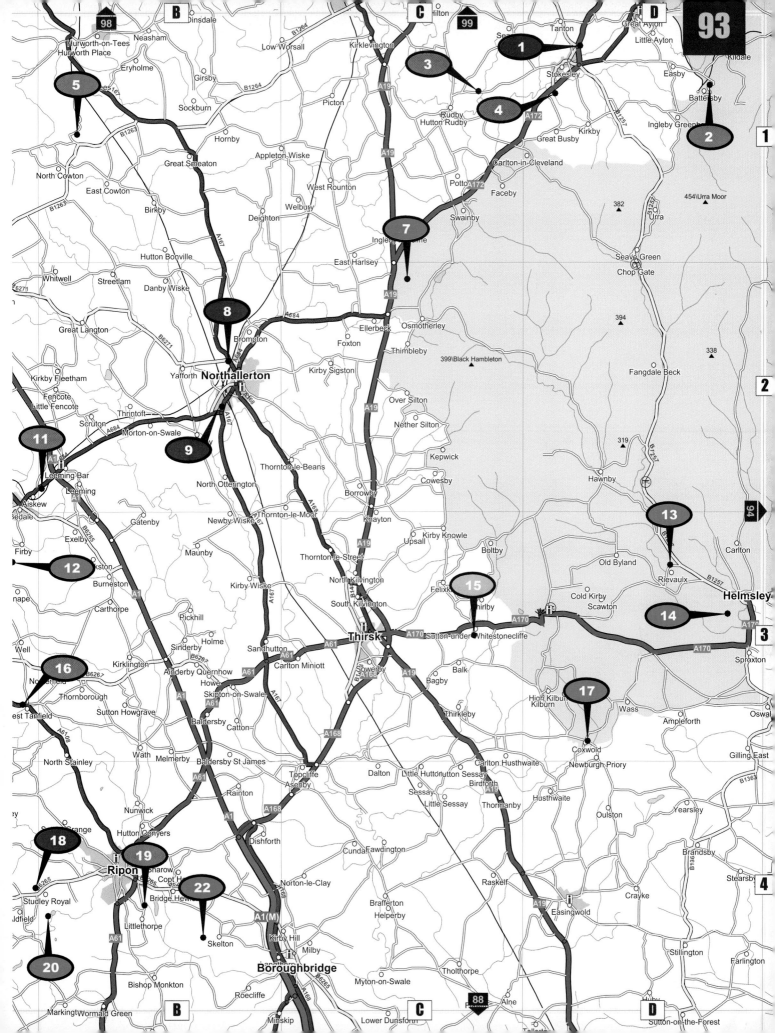

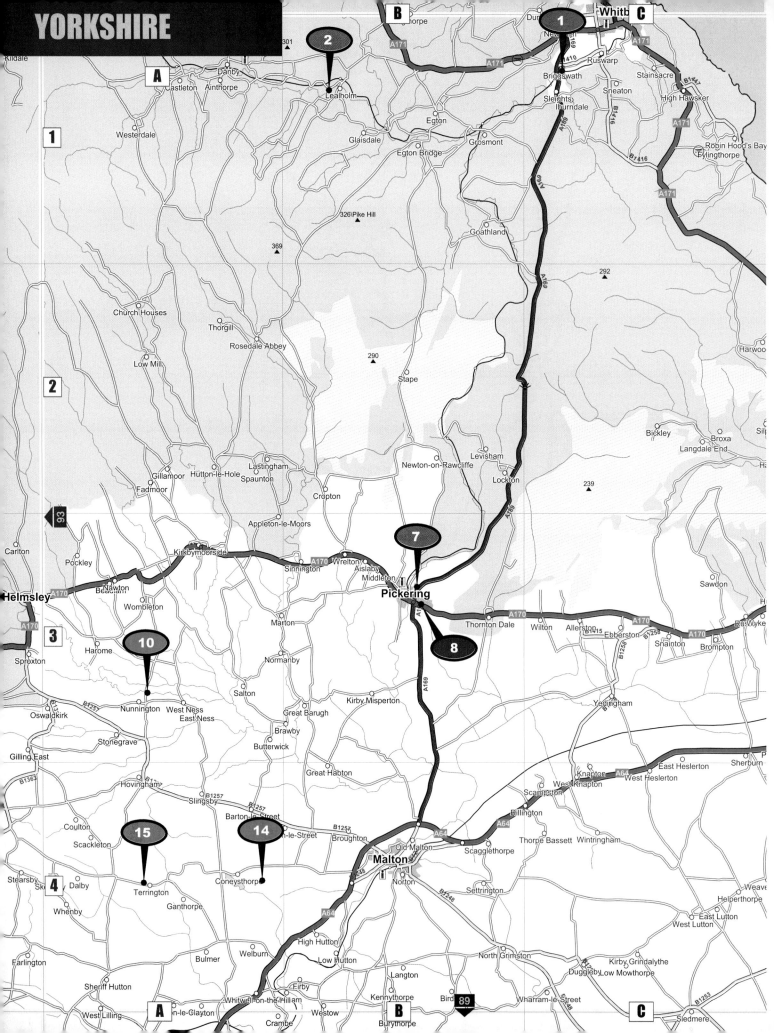

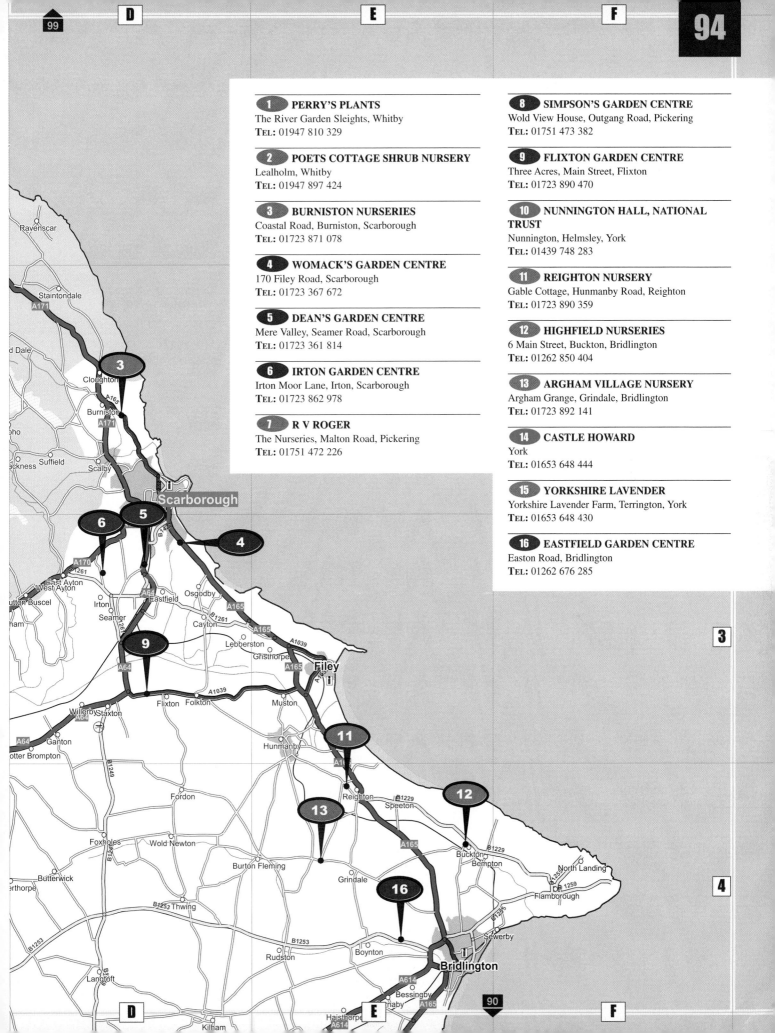

**1  PERRY'S PLANTS**
The River Garden Sleights, Whitby
TEL: 01947 810 329

**2  POETS COTTAGE SHRUB NURSERY**
Lealholm, Whitby
TEL: 01947 897 424

**3  BURNISTON NURSERIES**
Coastal Road, Burniston, Scarborough
TEL: 01723 871 078

**4  WOMACK'S GARDEN CENTRE**
170 Filey Road, Scarborough
TEL: 01723 367 672

**5  DEAN'S GARDEN CENTRE**
Mere Valley, Seamer Road, Scarborough
TEL: 01723 361 814

**6  IRTON GARDEN CENTRE**
Irton Moor Lane, Irton, Scarborough
TEL: 01723 862 978

**7  R V ROGER**
The Nurseries, Malton Road, Pickering
TEL: 01751 472 226

**8  SIMPSON'S GARDEN CENTRE**
Wold View House, Outgang Road, Pickering
TEL: 01751 473 382

**9  FLIXTON GARDEN CENTRE**
Three Acres, Main Street, Flixton
TEL: 01723 890 470

**10  NUNNINGTON HALL, NATIONAL TRUST**
Nunnington, Helmsley, York
TEL: 01439 748 283

**11  REIGHTON NURSERY**
Gable Cottage, Hunmanby Road, Reighton
TEL: 01723 890 359

**12  HIGHFIELD NURSERIES**
6 Main Street, Buckton, Bridlington
TEL: 01262 850 404

**13  ARGHAM VILLAGE NURSERY**
Argham Grange, Grindale, Bridlington
TEL: 01723 892 141

**14  CASTLE HOWARD**
York
TEL: 01653 648 444

**15  YORKSHIRE LAVENDER**
Yorkshire Lavender Farm, Terrington, York
TEL: 01653 648 430

**16  EASTFIELD GARDEN CENTRE**
Easton Road, Bridlington
TEL: 01262 676 285

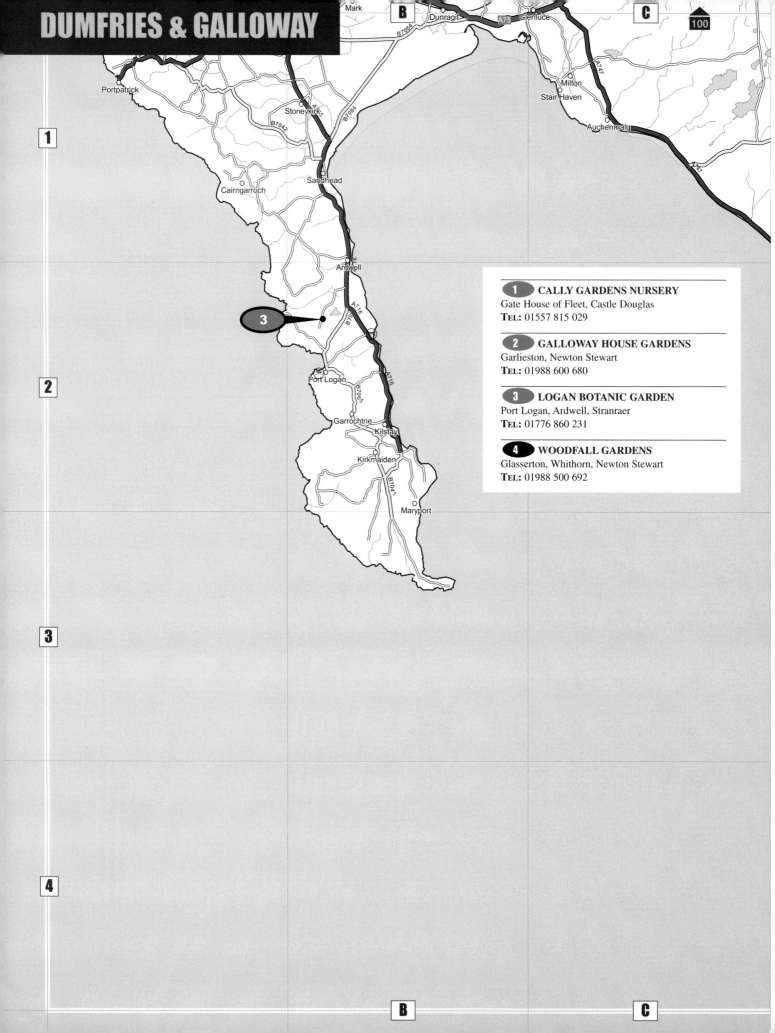

# DUMFRIES & GALLOWAY

**1 CALLY GARDENS NURSERY**
Gate House of Fleet, Castle Douglas
**TEL:** 01557 815 029

**2 GALLOWAY HOUSE GARDENS**
Garlieston, Newton Stewart
**TEL:** 01988 600 680

**3 LOGAN BOTANIC GARDEN**
Port Logan, Ardwell, Stranraer
**TEL:** 01776 860 231

**4 WOODFALL GARDENS**
Glasserton, Whithorn, Newton Stewart
**TEL:** 01988 500 692

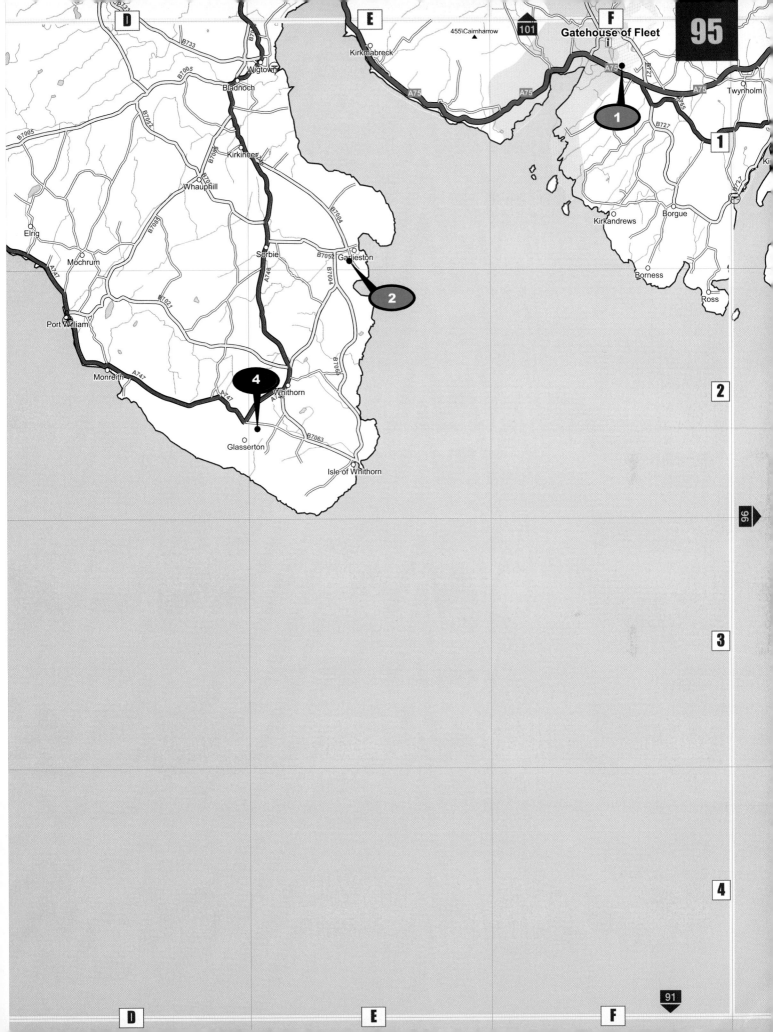

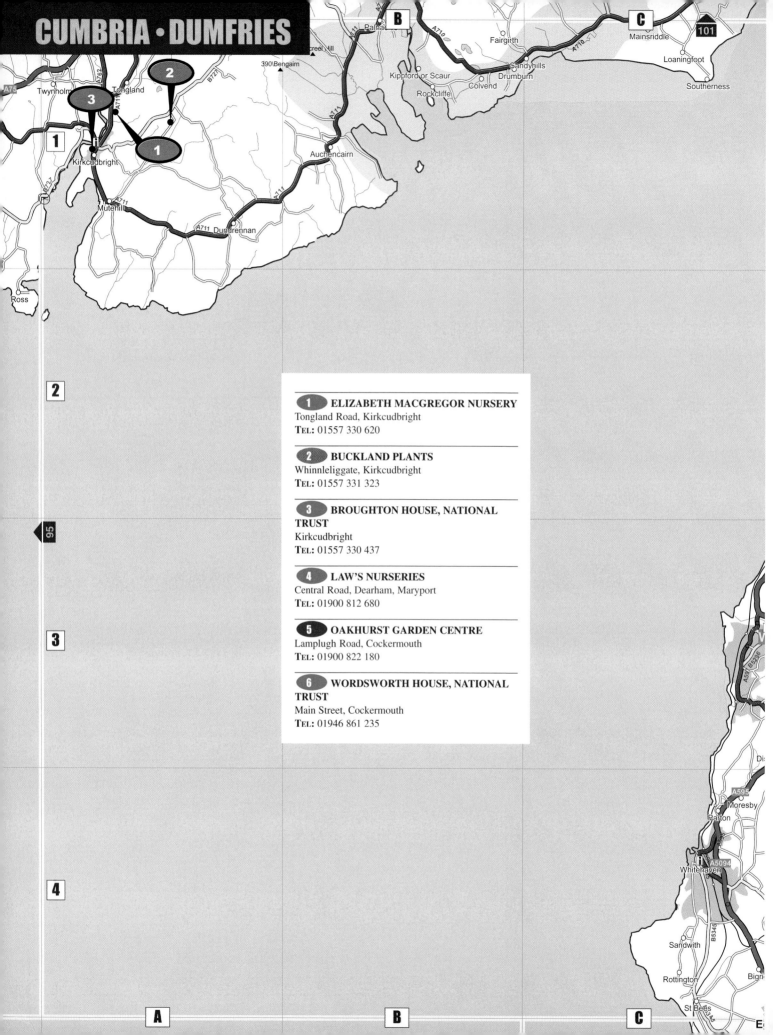

**1** **ELIZABETH MACGREGOR NURSERY**
Tongland Road, Kirkcudbright
**Tel:** 01557 330 620

**2** **BUCKLAND PLANTS**
Whinnleliggate, Kirkcudbright
**Tel:** 01557 331 323

**3** **BROUGHTON HOUSE, NATIONAL TRUST**
Kirkcudbright
**Tel:** 01557 330 437

**4** **LAW'S NURSERIES**
Central Road, Dearham, Maryport
**Tel:** 01900 812 680

**5** **OAKHURST GARDEN CENTRE**
Lamplugh Road, Cockermouth
**Tel:** 01900 822 180

**6** **WORDSWORTH HOUSE, NATIONAL TRUST**
Main Street, Cockermouth
**Tel:** 01946 861 235

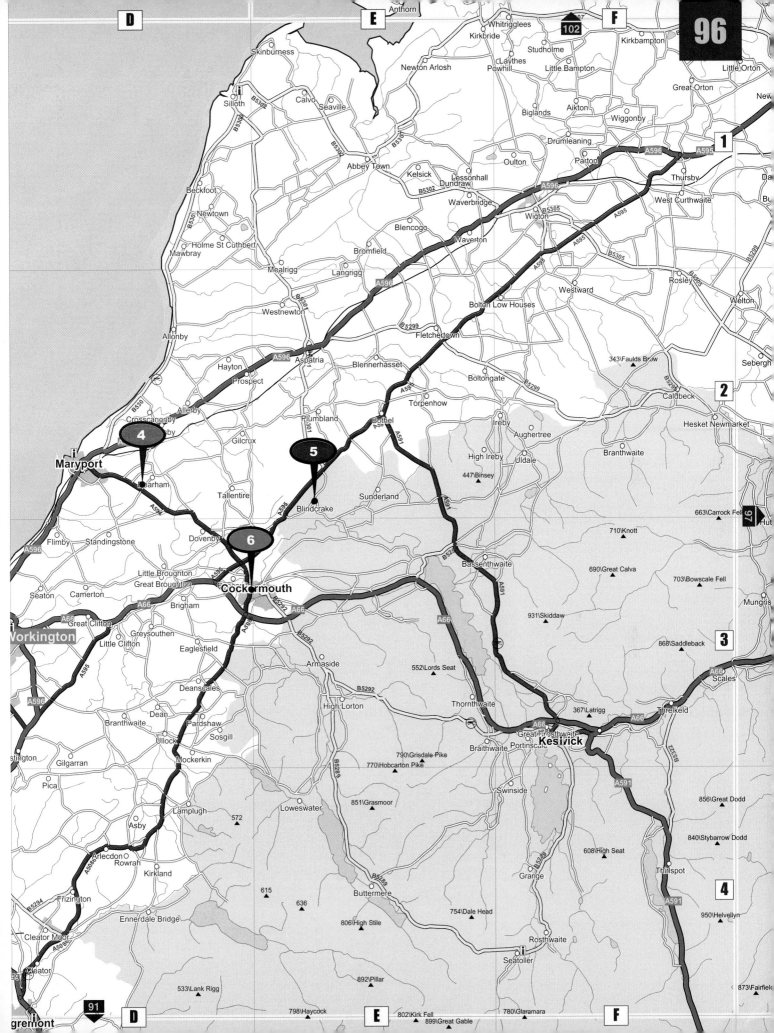

# CUMBRIA

**1**    **R LESLIE & SONS**
Durdar Road, Carlisle
TEL: 01228 521 476

**2**    **D W HICKSON & SONS**
Garden House Nurseries, Dalston, Carlisle
TEL: 01228 710 499

**3**    **PROUDPLANTS**
Shadyvale Nurseries, Ainstable, Carlisle
TEL: 01768 896 604

**4**    **HARTSIDE NURSERY GARDEN**
Alston
TEL: 01434 381 372

**5**    **THIEFSIDE GARDEN CENTRE**
Homelands, Thiefside, Calthwaite
TEL: 01768 885 073

**6**    **HUTTON-IN-THE-FOREST**
Penrith
TEL: 01768 484 449

**7**    **R & D COWIN**
Hazzeldene, Culgaith, Penrith
TEL: 01768 882 52

**8**    **ACORN BANK GARDEN**
The National Trust, Temple Sowerby, Penrith
TEL: 01768 361 893

**9**    **DALEMAIN HISTORIC HOUSE & GARDENS**
Estate Office, Penrith
TEL: 01768 486 450

**10**    **LARCH COTTAGE NURSERIES**
Melkinthorpe, Penrith
TEL: 01931 712 404

**11**    **BEECHCROFT NURSERIES**
Bongate, Appleby
TEL: 01768 351 201

# Root out

more
information from
www.gardenersatlas.co.uk

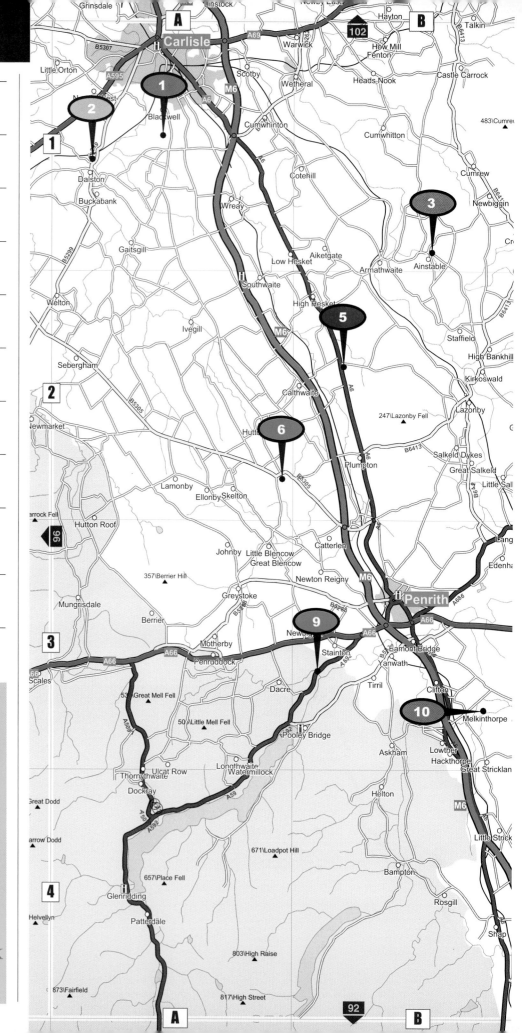

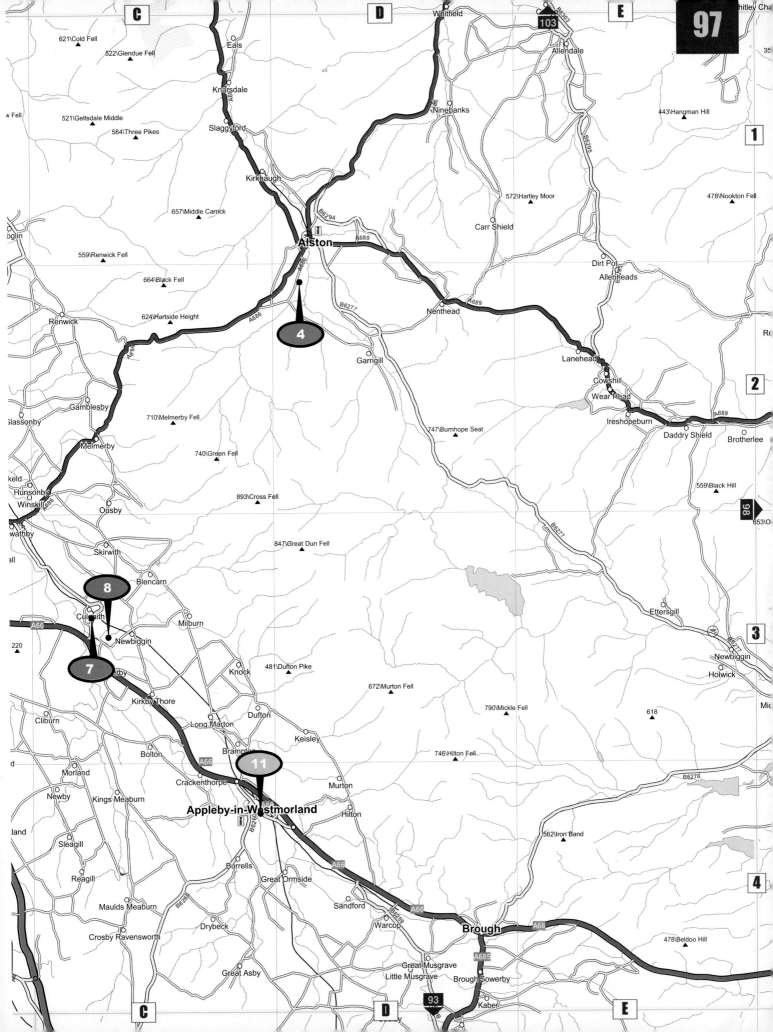

**1  BIRKHEAD'S COTTAGE GARDEN NURSERY**
Causey Arch, Sunniside, Newcastle Upon Tyne
TEL: 01207 232 262

**2  DOBBIES GARDEN WORLD**
Durham Road, Birtley
TEL: 0191 410 2556

**3  WOODLEA NURSERIES**
Woodlea, Wackerfield, Darlington
TEL: 01388 710 735

**4  THE NURSERIES**
Ebchester, Consett
TEL: 01207 560 228

**5  BEAMISH CLEMATIS NURSERY**
Burntwood Cottage, Stoney Lane, Beamish
TEL: 0191 370 0202

**6  STRIKES GARDEN CENTRE**
Burnmoor, Chester le Street
TEL: 0191 385 5154

**7  FOXWOOD GARDEN CENTRE**
Holm Hill Lane, Chester Moor, Chester le Street
TEL: 0191 389 0044

**8  ACORN NURSERY**
Bargate Bank, Ford Road, Durham
TEL: 01207 521 133

**9  LEAMSIDE NURSERIES**
Pithouse Lane, Leamside, Houghton Le Spring
TEL: 0191 512 0073

**10  A N SANDERSON & CO.**
Chestnut Cottage, Ramside, Belmont
TEL: 0191 384 2086

**11  UNIVERSITY OF DURHAM BOTANIC GARDEN**
Green Lane, Old Evlet, Durham
TEL: 0191 374 7971

**12  POPLAR TREE GARDEN CENTRE**
Hall Lane, Shincliffe, Durham
TEL: 0191 384 7553

**13  THINFORD FARM NURSERIES**
Thinford Farm, Thinford, Durham
TEL: 01740 655 704

**14  AUCKLAND PARK**
Auckland Castle, Bishop Auckland
TEL: 01388 601 627

**15  BLOSSOMS NURSERIES**
The Gardens, Windlestone Lane, Windlestone
TEL: 01388 720 216

**16  EGGLESTON HALL GARDENS**
Eggleston, Barnard Castle
TEL: 01833 650 115

**17  NINE ACRES NURSERIES**
Whinney Hill, Stockton on Tees
TEL: 01642 582 718

**18  BOWES MUSEUM**
Barnard Castle
TEL: 01833 690 606

**19  PAULS KOI & POND SUPPLIES**
Cleveland Trading Estate, Cleveland Road, Darlington
TEL: 01325 340 084

Daisy

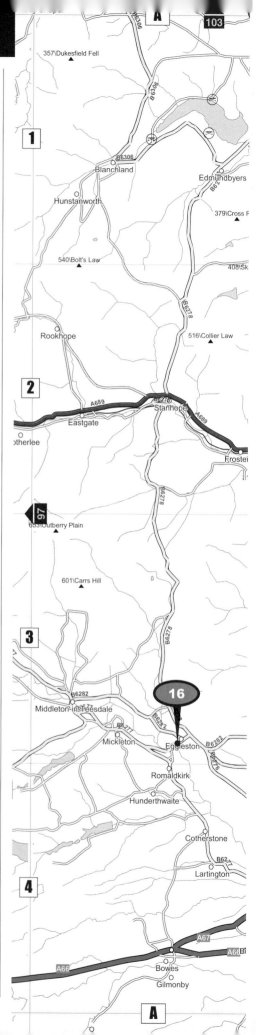

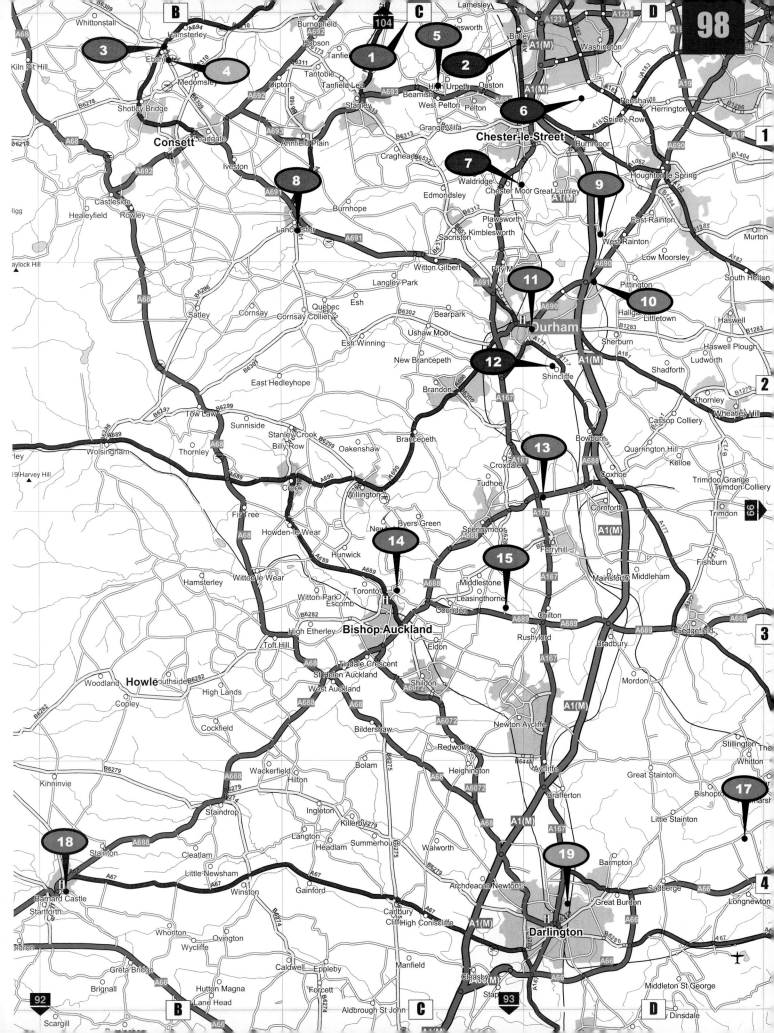

# NORTH EAST

## 1  SEATON BUILDINGS & GARDEN CENTRE
Seaton Lane, Seaton, Seaham
TEL: 0191 581 3207

## 2  HORNS GARDEN CENTRE
Dixon Estate, Shotton Colliery, Peterlee
TEL: 0191 526 2987

## 3  FOSTER & ARMSTRONG
12 Murray Street, Hartlepool
TEL: 01429 422 020

## 4  BLACKFORD NURSERIES
Stockton Road, Hartlepool
TEL: 01429 268 509

## 5  GOLDEN GATES NURSERIES
Sandy Lane West, Cleveland, Billingham
TEL: 01740 644 627

## 6  GOLDEN ACRE NURSERY
Longbeck Road, Marske-by-the-Sea, Redcar
TEL: 01642 492 332

## 7  HARPERS GARDEN CENTRE
Junction Road, Norton, Stockton on Tees
TEL: 01642 674 636

## 8  FRED HUMPHREY'S
46 The Avenue, Linthorpe, Cleveland
TEL: 01642 817 554

## 9  ORMESBY HALL, NATIONAL TRUST
Ormesby, Middlesbrough
TEL: 01642 324 188

## 10  PETER BARRATT'S GARDEN CENTRES
Yarm Road, Stockton on Tees, Cleveland, TS18 3SQ.
TEL: 01642 613 433
EMAIL: customerservices@peterbarratts.co.uk
WEB: www.peterbarratts.co.uk 
*We offer an inspirational range of quality plants, furniture, water features, terracotta, stone ornaments and gifts. Plus you can relax at the popular Cafe Jardin.*
OPEN: Open 7 days a week.
Summer: Mon-Fri 9-7, Sat 9-5.30, Sun 10.30-4.30.
Winter: Mon-Sat 9-5.30, Sun 10.30-4.30.
SPECIALITIES: Garden & conservatory furniture, Gifts, Hardy plants, Terracotta pots, Water features.
FACILITIES: Bookshop, Child area, Coffee shop, Credit cards, Gift shop, HTA gift tokens, Own gift tokens, Plant guarantee, Pushchair friendly, Restaurant, Sell plants, Toilets, Wheelchair access.

## 11  LYNDHURST NURSERIES
Ormesby Bank, Ormesby
TEL: 01642 314 547

## 12  ROWE'S NURSERIES
Priory Gardens, Bow Street, Guisborough
TEL: 01287 632 563

## 13  WINDLEBRIDGE GARDEN NURSERY
Middlesborough Road, Guisborough
TEL: 01287 635 642

## 14  PLANTARAMA GARDEN CENTRE
Sandy Flatts Lane, Ladgate Lane, Middlesbrough
TEL: 01642 320 514

## 15  CHERRY HILL NURSERIES
Stokesley Road, Hemlington, Middlesborough
TEL: 01642 590 650

## 16  ARCADIA NURSERIES
Brasscastle Lane, Nunthorpe, Middlesborough
TEL: 01642 310 782

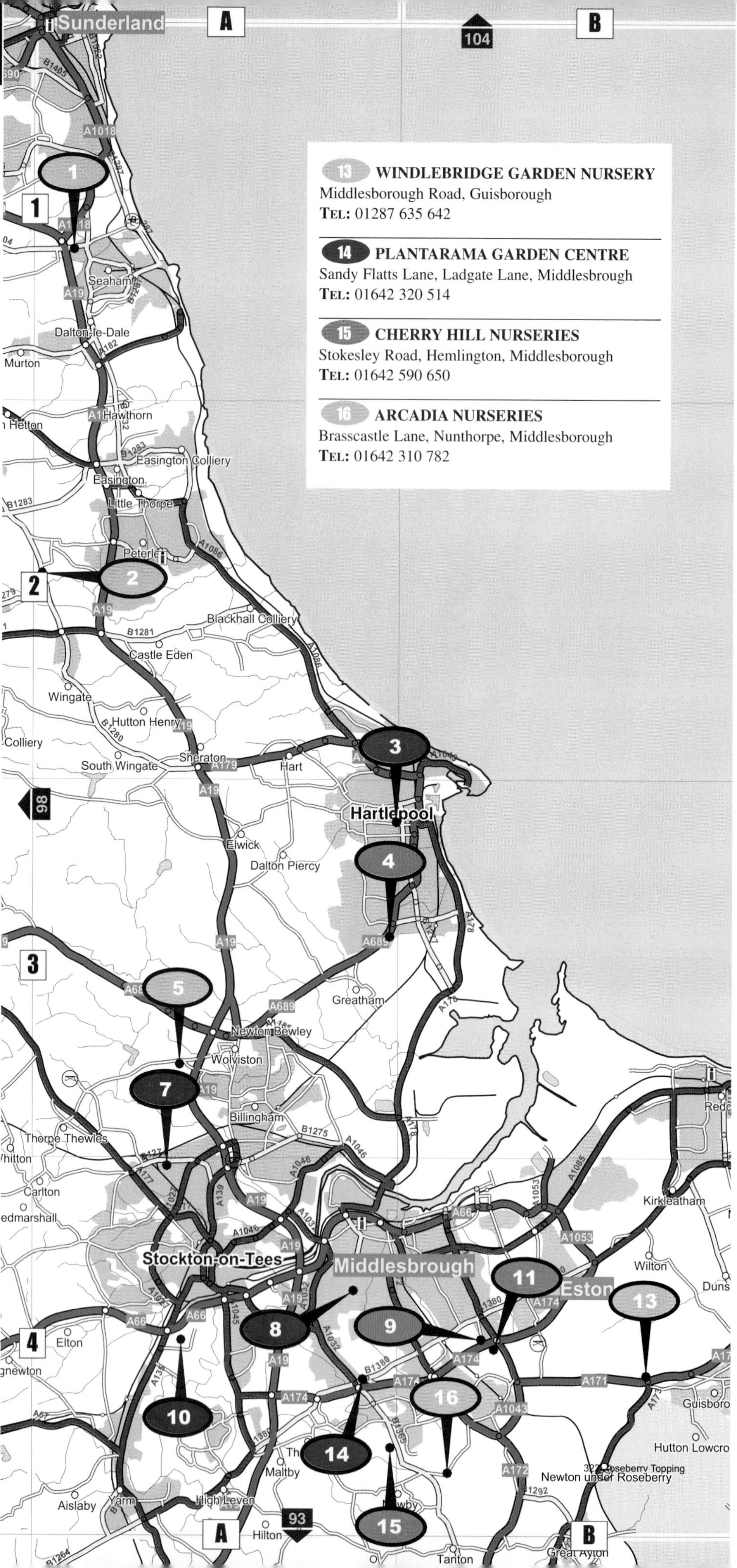

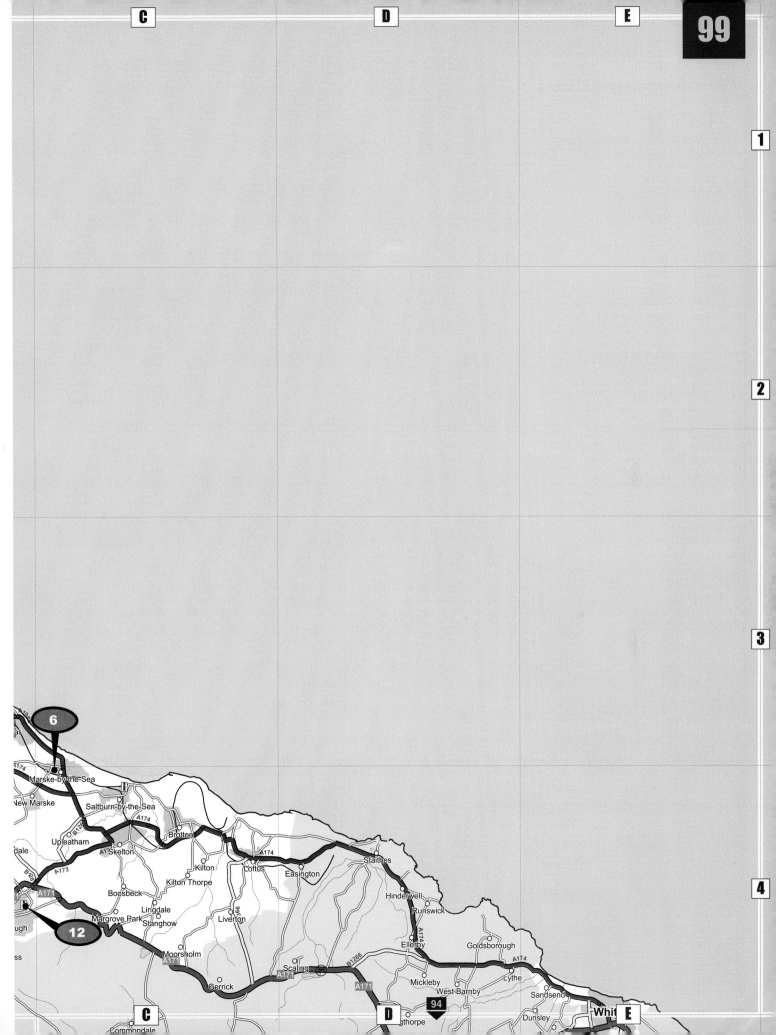

1

2

3

6

Marske-by-the-Sea

New Marske

Saltburn-by-the-Sea

A174

Upleatham

A174 Skelton

Brotton

A173

Kilton

A174 Loftus

Staithes

Boosbeck

Kilton Thorpe

Easington

A171

Lingdale

Liverton

Hinderwell

Runswick

Margrove Park

Stanghow

12

Ellerby

Goldsborough

Moorsholm

A171

A174

Scaling

B1266

Mickleby

Lythe

Gerrick

A171

West-Barnby

Sandsend

94

Dunsley

Whit

Commondale

thorpe

**1** **BARWINNOCK HERBS**
Barrhill, Girvan
**TEL:** 01465 821 338

**2** **SOLEBURN GARDEN CENTRE**
Soleburn Mill Croft, Kirkcolm, Stranraer
**TEL:** 01776 870 664

**3** **TROPIC HOUSE**
Carty Port, Newton Stewart
**TEL:** 01671 402 485

**4** **SEAFORTH NURSERIES**
Liddesdale Road, Stranraer
**TEL:** 01776 702 911

**5** **CASTLE KENNEDY GARDENS**
Stair Estates, Rephad, Stranraer, Dumfries &
Galloway, DG9 8BX.
**TEL:** 01776 702 024
**EMAIL:** ckg@stair-estates.sol.co.uk
*Landscaped gardens extending over 75 acres of*
*terraces and avenues between two natural lochs. World*
*famous for rhododendrons, azaleas and embothriums.*
*Limited access available for wheelchairs.*
**OPEN:** Easter-Sep: 10-5.
**ENTRY COSTS:** £3, Child: £1, OAPs: £2.
**SPECIALITIES:** Rhododendrons and azaleas.
**FACILITIES:** Toilets, Credit cards, Dogs allowed,
Coffee shop.

**6** **GLENWHAN GARDEN**
Dunragit, Stranraer
**TEL:** 01581 400 222

Acer

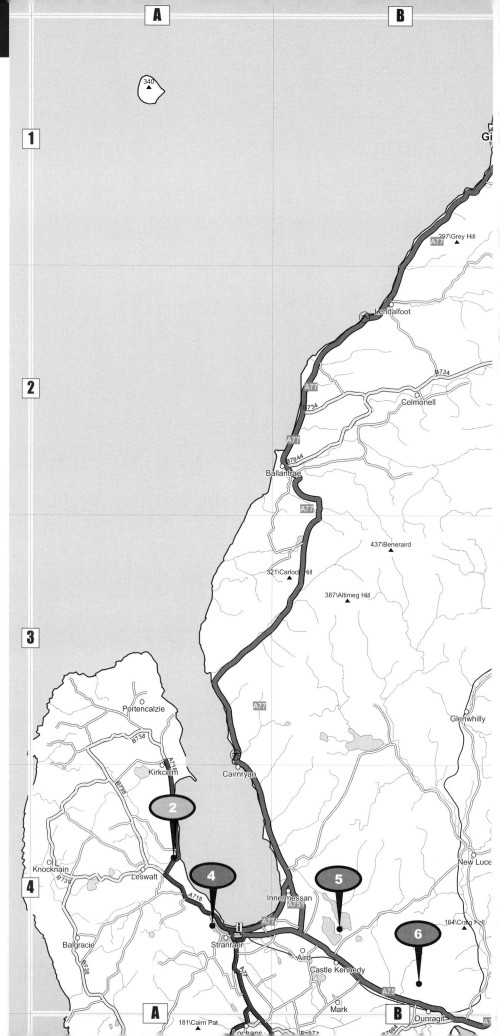

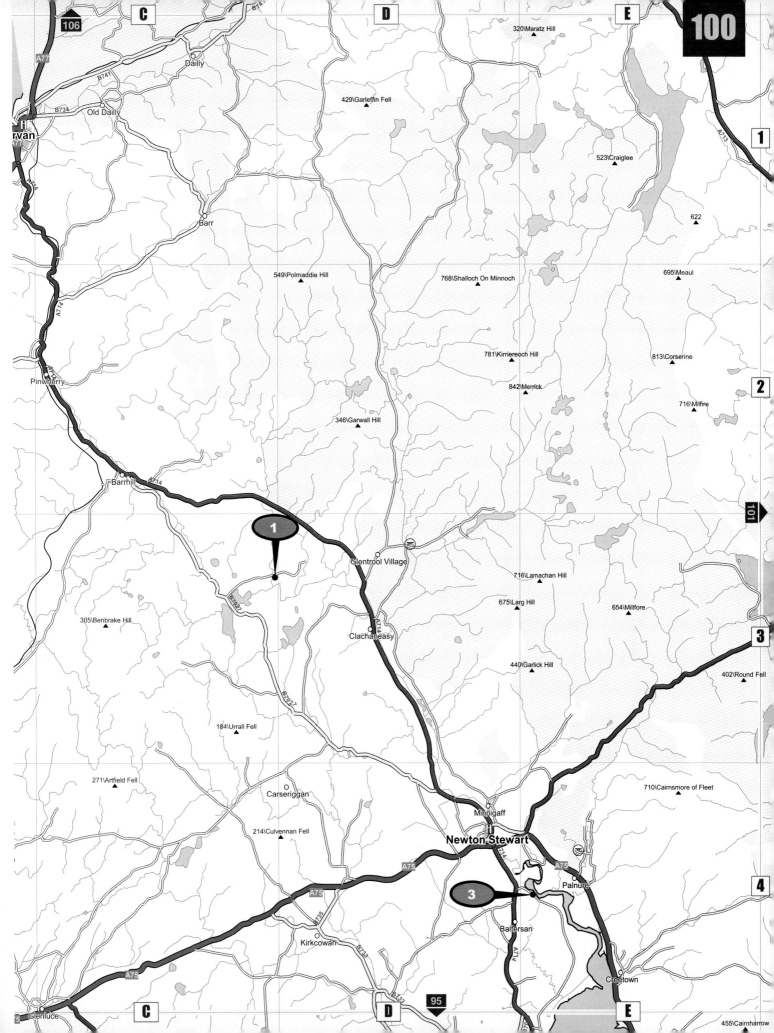

# DUMFRIES

### 1 CHARTER HOUSE NURSERY
2 Nunwood, Dumfries
TEL: 01387 720 363

### 2 TWEEDIE FRUIT TREES
Maryfield, Terregles, Dumfries
TEL: 01387 720 880

### 3 HEATHHALL GARDEN CENTRE
Edinburgh Road, Dumfries
TEL: 01387 263 101

### 4 GARDEN WISE PLANT & GARDEN CENTRE
Castle Douglas Road, Dumfries
TEL: 01387 262 654

### 5 SHEILA NORTHWAY AURICULAS
Balmaclellan, Castle Douglas
TEL: 01644 420 661

### 6 CRICHTON GARDEN CENTRE
Glencaple Road, Dumfries
TEL: 01387 266 540

### 7 CASTLE DOUGLAS GARDEN CENTRE
Castle Douglas, Kirkcudbright
TEL: 01556 503 266

### 8 THREAVE GARDEN, NATIONAL TRUST
Castle Douglas
TEL: 01556 502 575

### 9 CLIFTON PLACE GARDEN CENTRE
318 High Street, Dalbeattie
TEL: 01556 610 777

Ranunculus

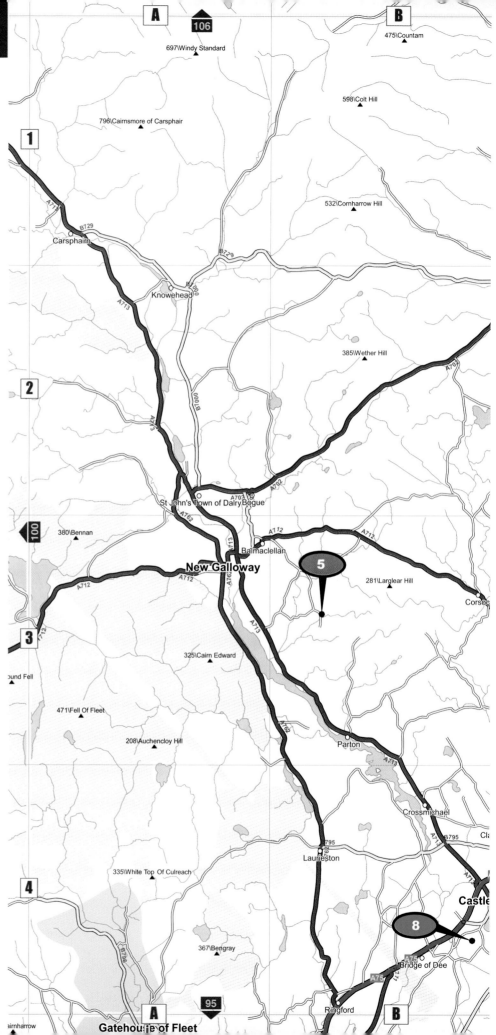

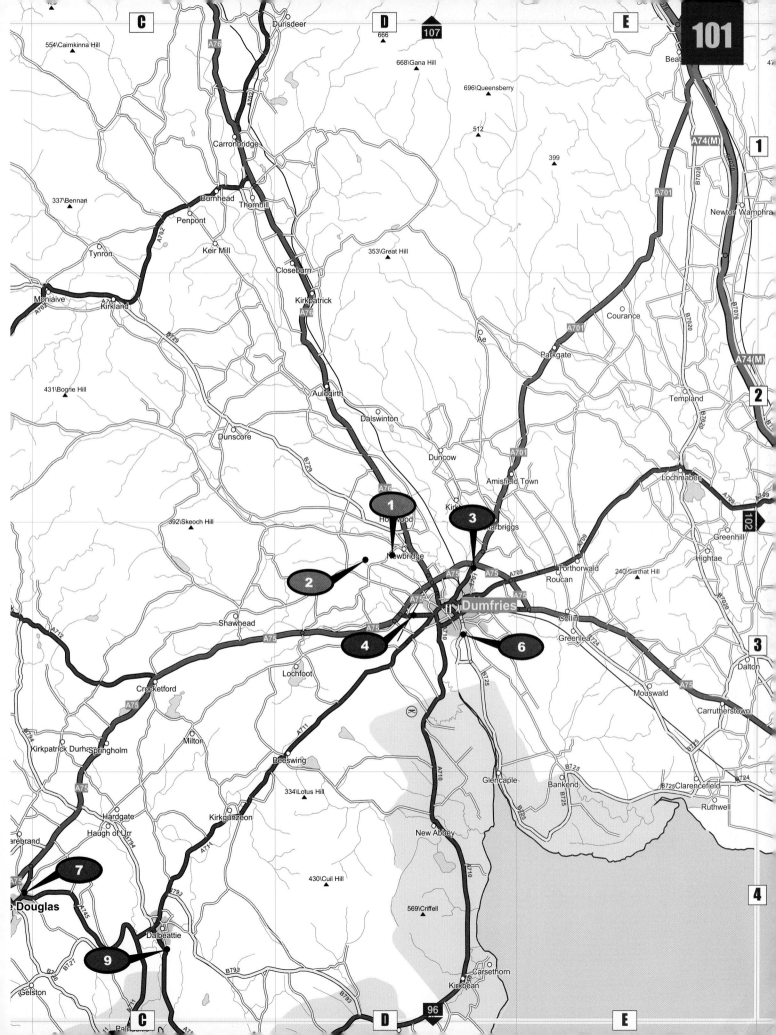

**1** **DEZ PLANTS**
Ecclefechan, Lockerbie
TEL: 01576 300 688

**2** **BRIDGE END NURSERIES**
Gretna Green
TEL: 01461 800 612

**3** **OAKABANK GARDENS**
Brampton, Carlisle
TEL: 01697 739 08

**4** **AERO NURSERIES & GARDEN CENTRE**
Harker Road Ends, Carlisle
TEL: 01228 674 612

**5** **TARN ROAD NURSERIES**
Tarn Road, Brampton
TEL: 01697 737 81

**6** **HOLME LEA NURSERY**
Holme Lea, Angerton, Kirkbride
TEL: 01697 351 688

Prickly Pear

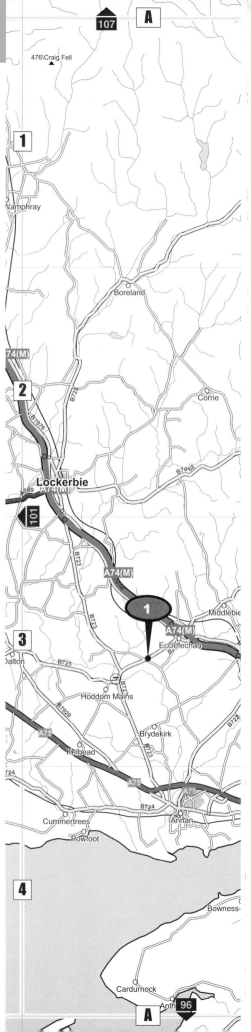

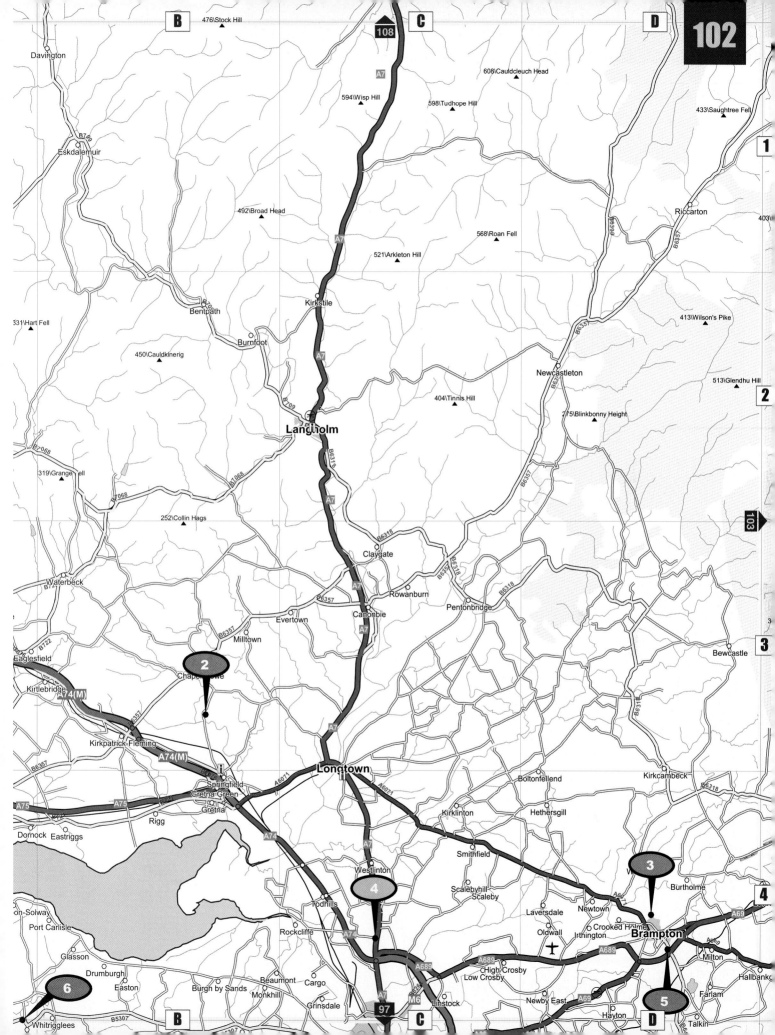

### 1 HERTERTON HOUSE GARDEN & NURSERY
Hartington, Cambo
**TEL:** 01670 774 278

### 2 WALLINGTON HALL, NATIONAL TRUST
Cambo, Morpeth
**TEL:** 01670 774 283

### 3 CHIPCHASE CASTLE NURSERY
Chipchase Castle, Wark, Hexham
**TEL:** 01434 230 083

### 4 RYAL NURSERY
East Farm Cottage, Ryal
**TEL:** 01661 886 562

### 5 HEXHAM HERBS
Chesters Walled Garden, Chollerford, Hexham
**TEL:** 01434 681 483

### 6 DOWN TO EARTH
Tyne Mills Industrial Estate, Hexham
**TEL:** 01434 600 920

Nemesia

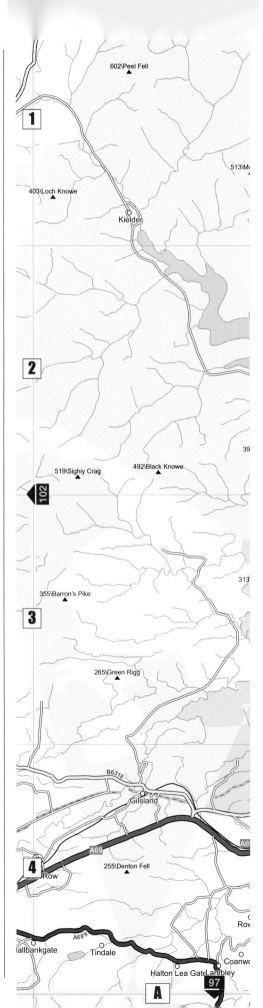

**1  CRAGSIDE HOUSE & GARDEN, NATIONAL TRUST**
Rothbury, Morpeth
TEL: 01669 620 333

**2  LONGFRAMLINGTON CENTRE FOR PLANTS**
Swarland Road, Longframlington, Morpeth
TEL: 01665 570 382

**3  HEIGHLEY GATE NURSERY & GARDEN CENTRE**
Morpeth
TEL: 01670 513 416

**4  NEW HORIZONS GARDEN CENTRE**
Saint George's Hospital, Morpeth
TEL: 01670 503 217

**5  STATION ROAD NURSERIES**
58 Station Road, Stannington, Morpeth
TEL: 01670 789 377

**6  BELSAY HALL, ENGLISH HERITAGE**
Belsay, Newcastle Upon Tyne
TEL: 01661 881 636

**7  SHAW GARDEN CENTRE**
Station Road, Cramlington
TEL: 01670 733 762

**8  KIRKLEY HALL COLLEGE GARDENS**
Ponteland
TEL: 01661 860 808

**9  LANE NURSERIES**
Callerton Lane, Ponteland, Newcastle Upon Tyne
TEL: 01661 822 333

**10  BEDE'S WORLD MUSEUM & HERB GARDEN**
Church Bank, Jarrow
TEL: 0191 489 2106

**11  DOBBIES GARDEN CENTRE**
Streethouse Farm, Ponteland
TEL: 01661 820 202

**12  CHANDLERS GARDEN CENTRE**
High Gosforth Park, Wideopen, Newcastle Upon Tyne
TEL: 0191 236 5775

**14  MANOR ROAD NURSERIES**
Manor Road, Tynemouth, North Shields
TEL: 0191 257 7264

**15  COWELLS GARDEN CENTRE**
Main Road, Woolsington, Newcastle Upon Tyne
TEL: 0191 286 3403

**16  HALLS OF HEDDON**
Westheddon Nursery, Heddon on the Wall
TEL: 01661 852 445

**17  JESMOND DENE PARK**
Millfield House, Jesmond Dene, Newcastle Upon Tyne
TEL: 0191 281 0973

**18  WYLAM NURSERIES**
End of Stephenson Terrace, Wylam
TEL: 01661 852 025

**13  PETER BARRATT'S GARDEN CENTRE**
Gosforth Park, Newcastle Upon Tyne, Tyne & Wear, NE3 5EP.
TEL: 0191 236 7111
EMAIL: customerservices@peterbarratts.co.uk
WEB: www.peterbarratts.co.uk

*We offer an inspirational range of quality plants, furniture, water features, stone ornaments, terracotta and gifts. Plus you can relax in our popular Cafe Jardin.*
OPEN: Open 7 days a week. Summer: Mon-Fri 9-7, Sat 9-5.30, Sun 10.30-4.30. Winter: Mon-Sat 9-5.30, Sun 10.30-4.30.
SPECIALITIES: Garden & conservatory furniture, Gifts, Hardy plants, Terracotta pots, Water features.
FACILITIES: Credit cards, Pushchair friendly, Wheelchair access, Sell plants, Toilets, HTA gift tokens, Own gift tokens, Gift shop, Bookshop, Coffee shop, Restaurant, Child area, Plant guarantee.

**19  HALLS OF HEDDON**
The Nursery, Ovington
TEL: 01661 832 467

**20  BENWELL NATURE PARK**
Atkinson Road, Newcastle Upon Tyne
TEL: 0191 273 2983

**21  BRADLEY NURSERY & GARDENS**
Sled Lane, Wylam
TEL: 01661 852 176

**22  BARNES GARDEN CENTRE**
Rackley Way, Whitburn
TEL: 0191 529 4423

**23  RED FOX NURSERIES**
Newcastle Road, Wardley, Gateshead
TEL: 0191 438 0821

**24  THORNLEY NURSERIES**
Hollin Hill Lane, Rowland's Gill
TEL: 01207 542 454

**25  CHEVIOT VIEW NURSERIES**
Streetgate, Sunniside, Newcastle Upon Tyne
TEL: 0191 488 1201

**26  GRANGE GARDEN CENTRE**
Thompson Road, Sunderland
TEL: 0191 548 7132

**27  GIBSIDE, NATIONAL TRUST**
Burnopfield, Gateshead, Newcastle Upon Tyne
TEL: 01207 542 255

**28  COTTAGE GARDEN NURSERY**
Hunters Lodge, Galloping Green Rd, Eighton Banks
TEL: 0191 482 0059

**29  SILVERHILLS NURSERIES**
Haggs Lane, Gateshead
TEL: 0191 487 7557

**30  CLAYS GARDEN CENTRE**
The Peel Centre, District 10 (A1231), Washington
TEL: 0191 417 7777

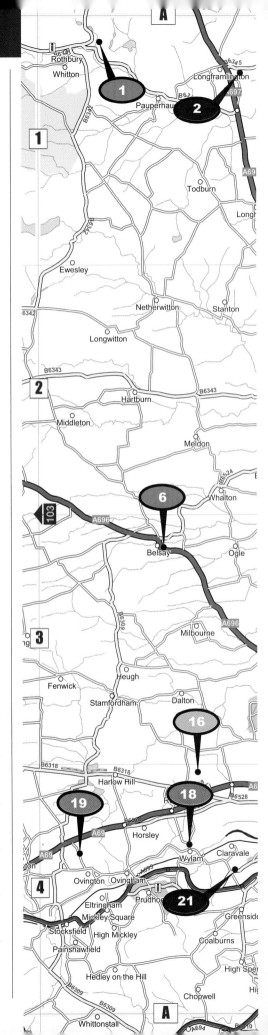

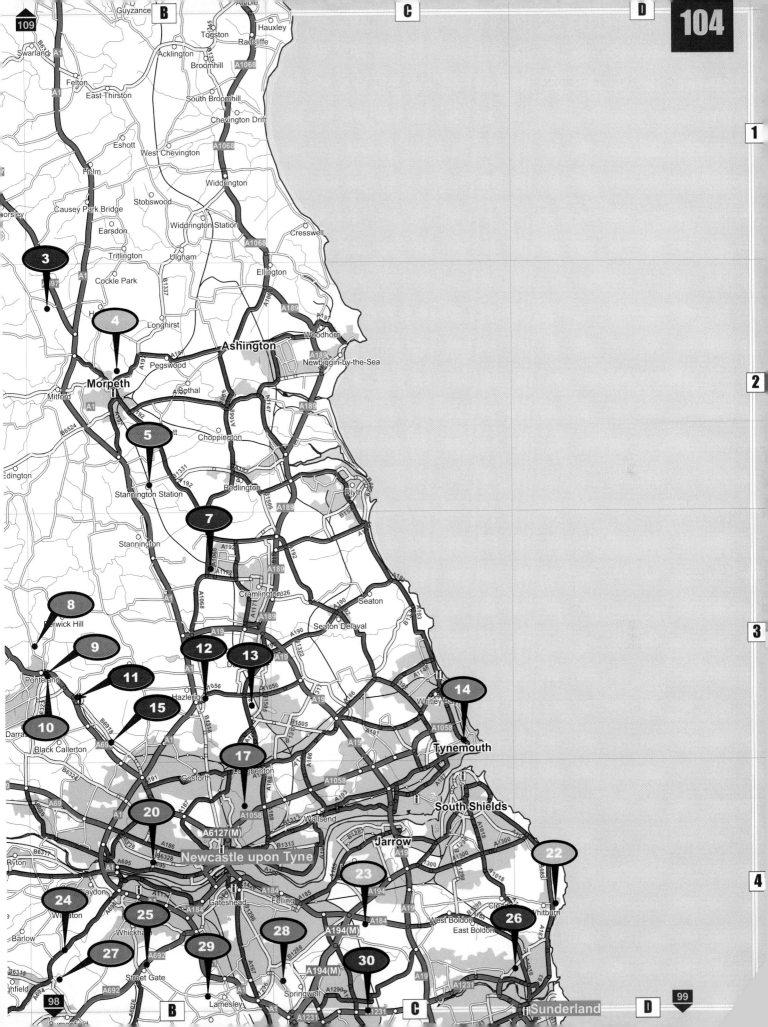

A

165\Maol Buidhe

1

B

110

C

A846

A846

Ardbeg
Lagavulin
Port Ellen  Laphroaig

**1** **ACHAMORE GARDENS**
Isle of Gigha
TEL: 01583 505 267

**2** **THE GARDEN SHOP**
6 Union Street, Campbelltown
TEL: 01586 552 653

2

3

446\Cnoc

4

428\Beinn Na Lice

A

B

C

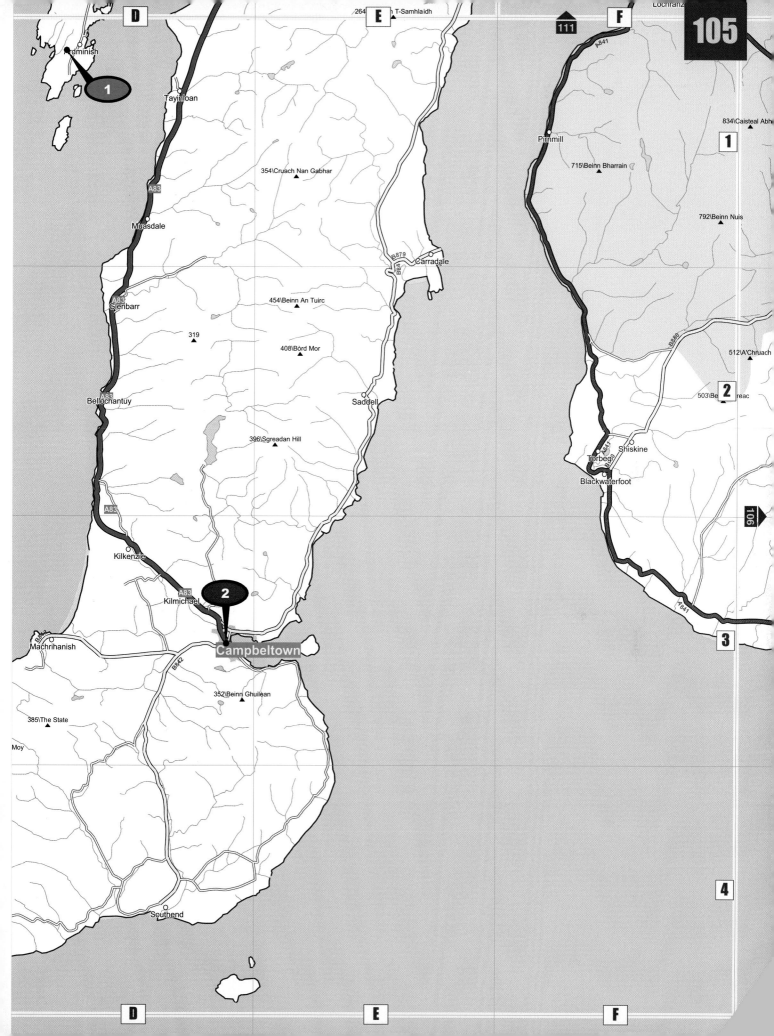

# AYRSHIRE

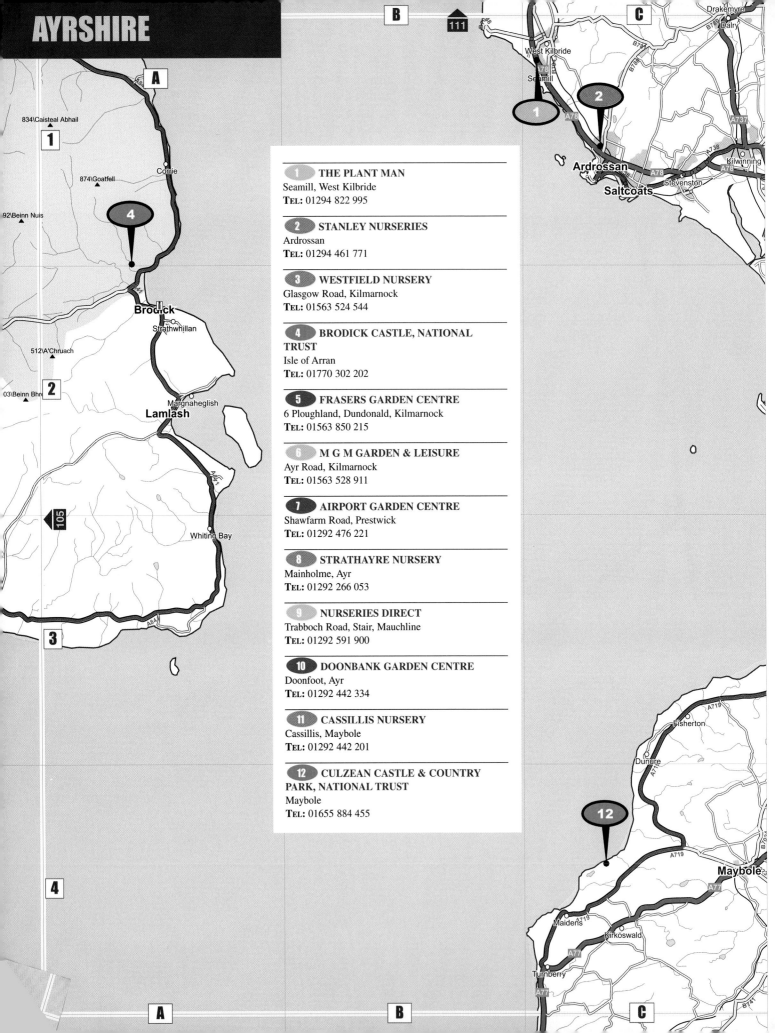

**1**   **THE PLANT MAN**
Seamill, West Kilbride
**TEL:** 01294 822 995

**2**   **STANLEY NURSERIES**
Ardrossan
**TEL:** 01294 461 771

**3**   **WESTFIELD NURSERY**
Glasgow Road, Kilmarnock
**TEL:** 01563 524 544

**4**   **BRODICK CASTLE, NATIONAL TRUST**
Isle of Arran
**TEL:** 01770 302 202

**5**   **FRASERS GARDEN CENTRE**
6 Ploughland, Dundonald, Kilmarnock
**TEL:** 01563 850 215

**6**   **M G M GARDEN & LEISURE**
Ayr Road, Kilmarnock
**TEL:** 01563 528 911

**7**   **AIRPORT GARDEN CENTRE**
Shawfarm Road, Prestwick
**TEL:** 01292 476 221

**8**   **STRATHAYRE NURSERY**
Mainholme, Ayr
**TEL:** 01292 266 053

**9**   **NURSERIES DIRECT**
Trabboch Road, Stair, Mauchline
**TEL:** 01292 591 900

**10**   **DOONBANK GARDEN CENTRE**
Doonfoot, Ayr
**TEL:** 01292 442 334

**11**   **CASSILLIS NURSERY**
Cassillis, Maybole
**TEL:** 01292 442 201

**12**   **CULZEAN CASTLE & COUNTRY PARK, NATIONAL TRUST**
Maybole
**TEL:** 01655 884 455

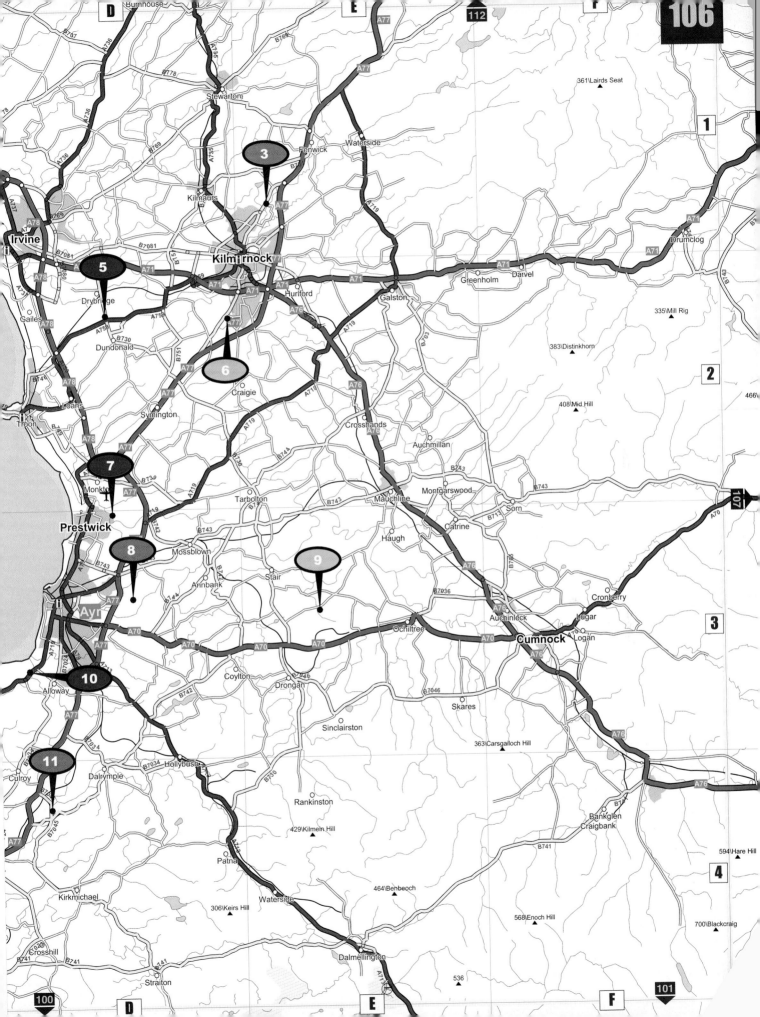

# SCOTLAND

**1** **HEADS POINT NURSERY**
Braidwood, Carluke
TEL: 01555 772 303

**2** **ROBERT JOHNSTONE PATHHEAD NURSERY**
Lesmahagow
TEL: 01698 792 264

**3** **BROUGHTON PLACE**
Broughton, Biggar
TEL: 01899 830 234

**4** **DAWYCK BOTANIC GARDEN**
Peebles
TEL: 01721 760 254

**5** **MOFFAT GARDEN CENTRE**
High Street, Moffat
TEL: 01683 220 442

**6** **CRAIGIEBURN CLASSIC PLANTS**
Moffat
TEL: 01683 221 250

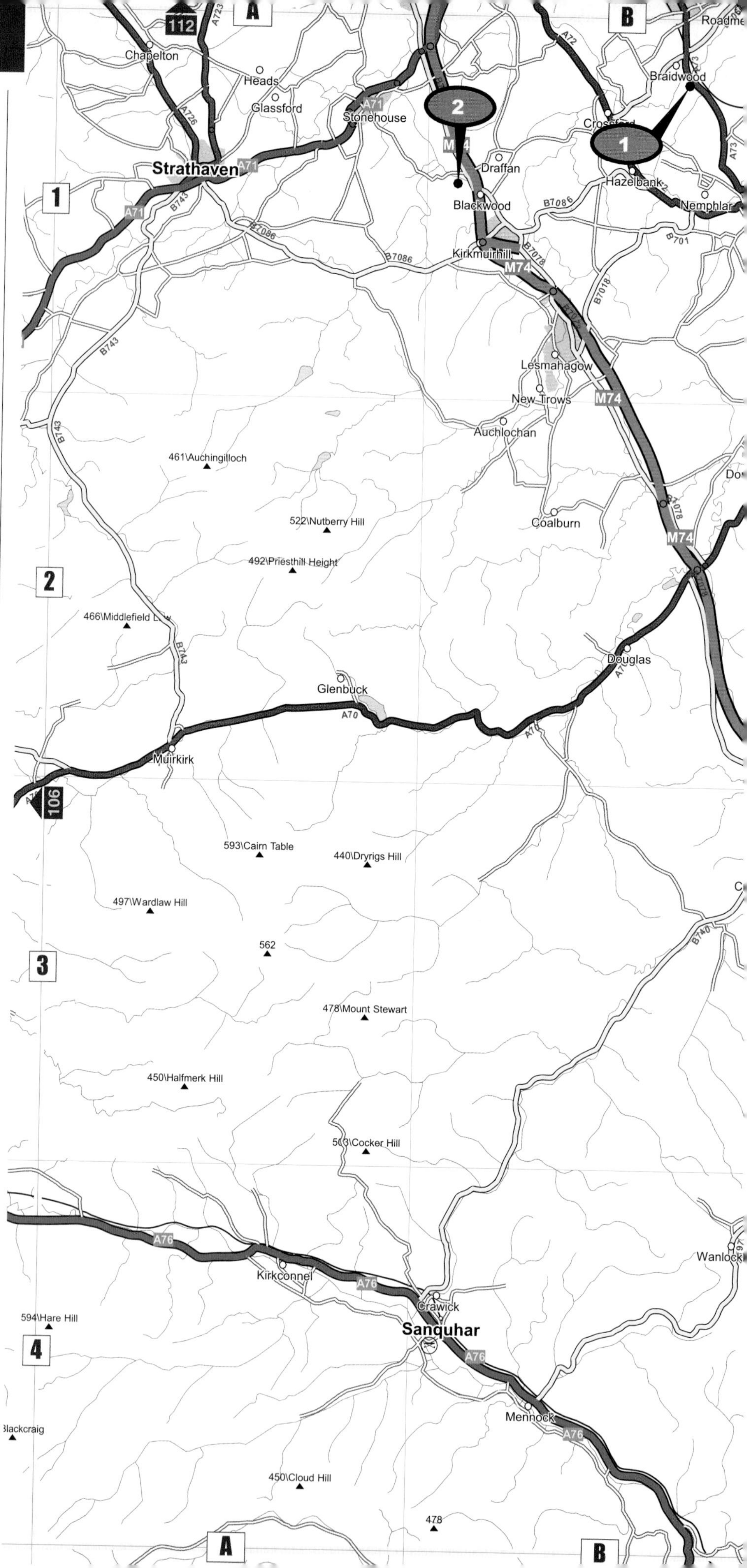

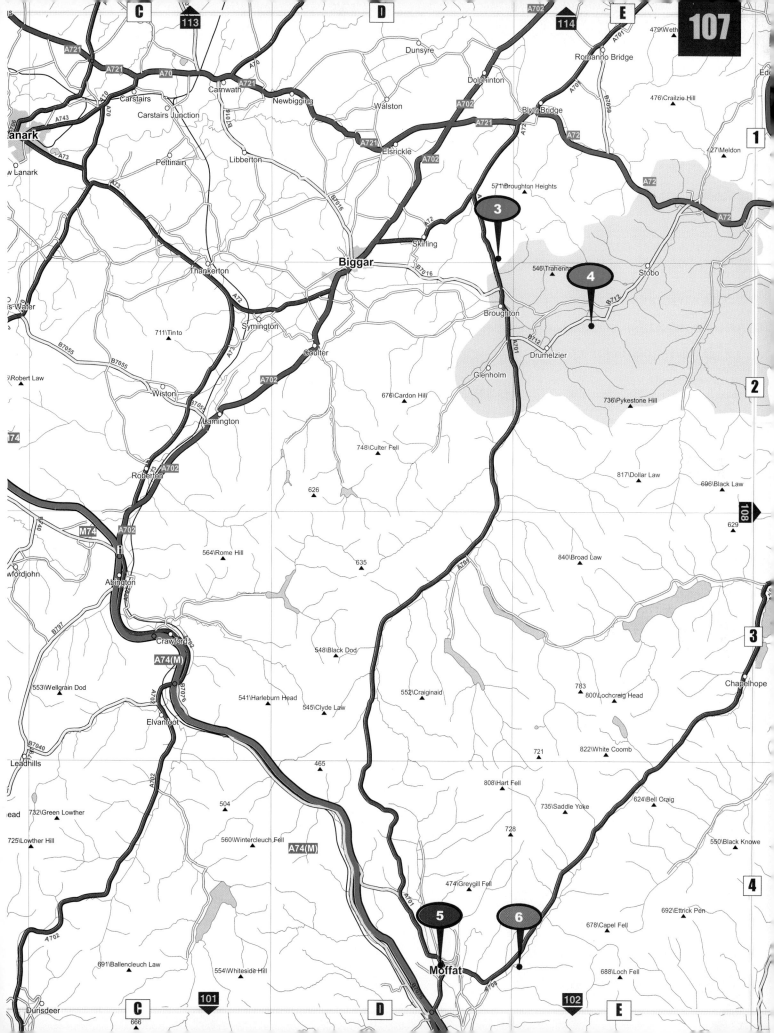

# BORDERS

**1** **MELLERSTAIN HOUSE**
Gordon
**TEL:** 01573 410 225

**2** **KAILZIE GARDENS**
Peebles
**TEL:** 01721 720 007

**3** **EILDON PLANTS**
Melrose
**TEL:** 01896 755 530

**4** **HARMONY GARDEN, N. TRUST**
Melrose
**TEL:** 01896 823 464

**5** **WAVERLEY NURSERIES**
Darnick, Melrose
**TEL:** 01896 822 257

**6** **ABBOTSFORD HOUSE & GARDENS**
Melrose
**TEL:** 01896 752 043

**7** **PRIORWOOD GARDEN, N. TRUST**
Melrose
**TEL:** 01896 822 493

**8** **ORMISTON & RENWICK**
High Street, Melrose
**TEL:** 01896 822 163

**9** **LILLIESLEAF NURSERY**
Linthill, Lillisleaf
**TEL:** 01835 870 415

**10** **WOODSIDE NURSERY**
Near Harestones Visitor Centre, Ancrum, Jedburgh
**TEL:** 01835 830 315

**11** **MONTEVIOT HOUSE GARDENS**
Jedburgh
**TEL:** 01835 830 380

**12** **JEDBURGH ABBEY, HISTORIC SCOTLAND**
Jedburgh, Borders, TD8 6JQ.
**TEL:** 01835 863 925
**WEB:** www.historic-scotland.net
*Cloister garden recreated as the monks would have had it.*
**OPEN:** Apr-Sep: 9.30-6.30.
Oct-Mar: Mon-Sat 9.30-4.30,
Sun 2-4.30.
**ENTRY COSTS:** £3.30,
Child: £1.20, OAPs: £2.50.
**SPECIALITIES:** Shrubs, Roses,
Herbs.
**FACILITIES:** Toilets, Gift shop.

**13** **HAWICK GARDEN CENTRE**
Earl Street, , Hawick
**TEL:** 01450 374 727

Water Lily

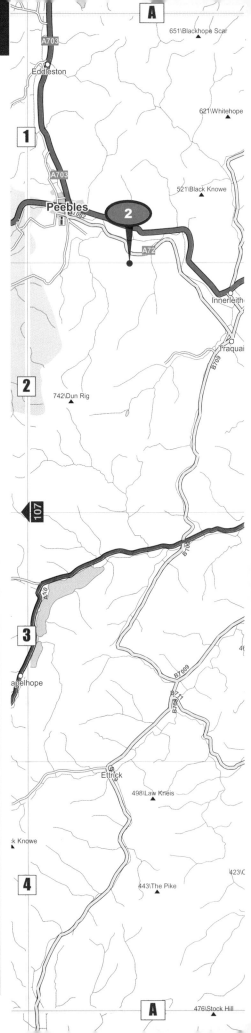

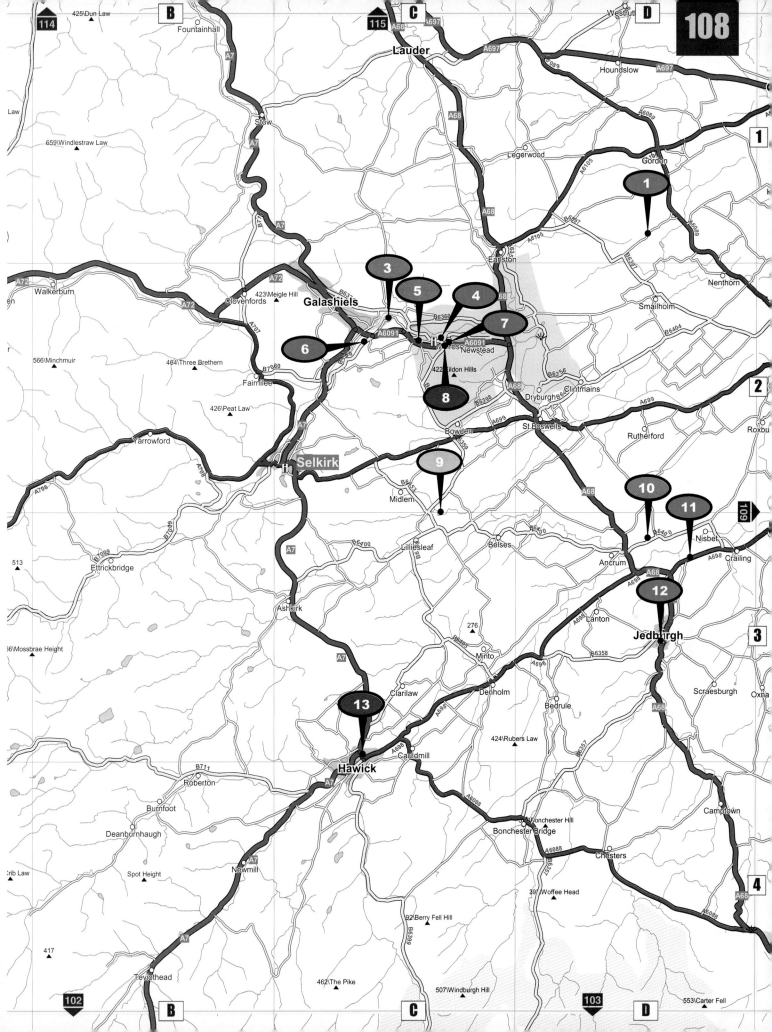

**1** **LINDISFARNE CASTLE, NATIONAL TRUST**
Holy Island, Holy Island Village, Berwick upon Tweed
TEL: 01289 389 244

**2** **HIRSEL**
Mansion House, Coldstream
TEL: 01890 882 834

**3** **STICHILL FOREST NURSERY**
Kelso
TEL: 01573 470 261

**4** **FORD NURSERY**
Ford, Berwick upon Tweed
TEL: 01890 820 379

**5** **FLOORS CASTLE**
Kelso
TEL: 01573 223 333

**6** **KLONDYKE GARDEN CENTRE**
Mayfield, Kelso
TEL: 01573 224 124

**7** **TEVIOT WATER GARDEN**
Eckford, Kelso
TEL: 01835 850 734

**8** **CHILLINGHAM CASTLE**
Chillingham
TEL: 01668 215 359

**9** **CRASTER TOWERS STABLE YARD FARM SHOP & NURSERY**
Craster Tower, Craster, Alnwick
TEL: 01665 576 898

**10** **HOWICK HALL & GARDENS**
Howick Hall, Alnwick
TEL: 01665 577 285

**11** **ALNWICK NURSERY & GARDEN CENTRE**
Denwick Lane, Alnwick
TEL: 01665 510 193

# Root out

more
information from
www.gardenersatlas.co.uk

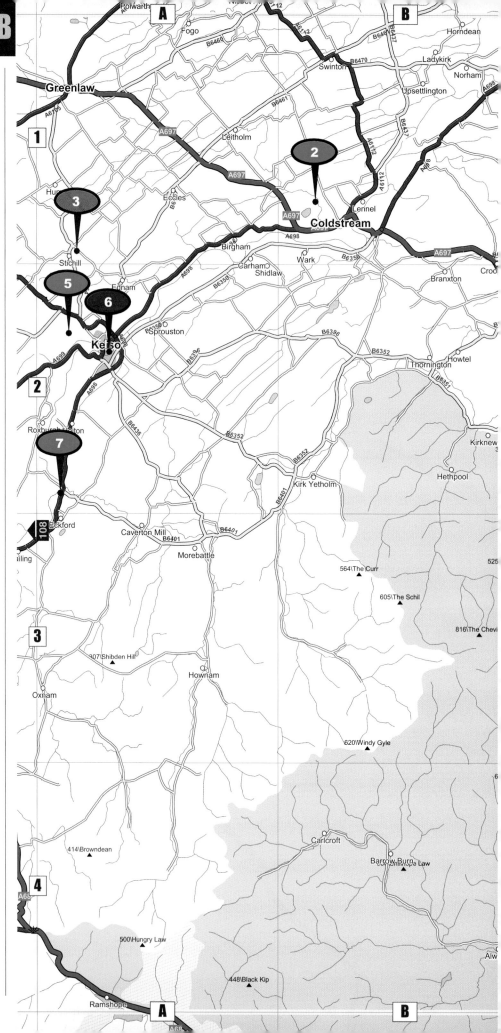

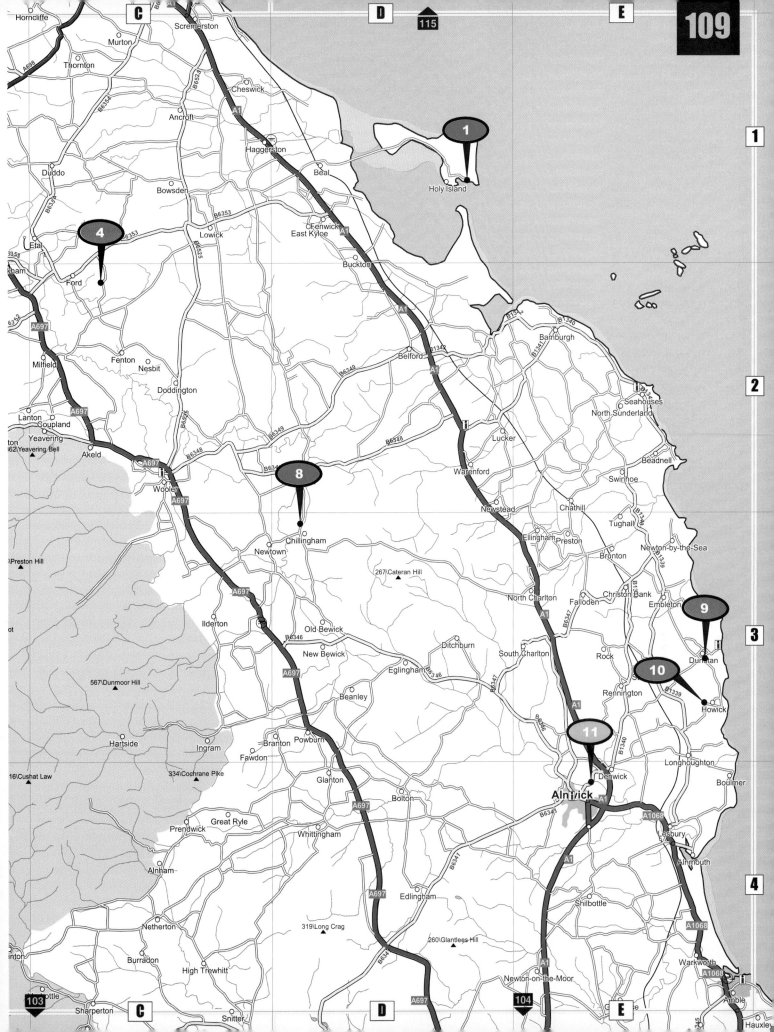

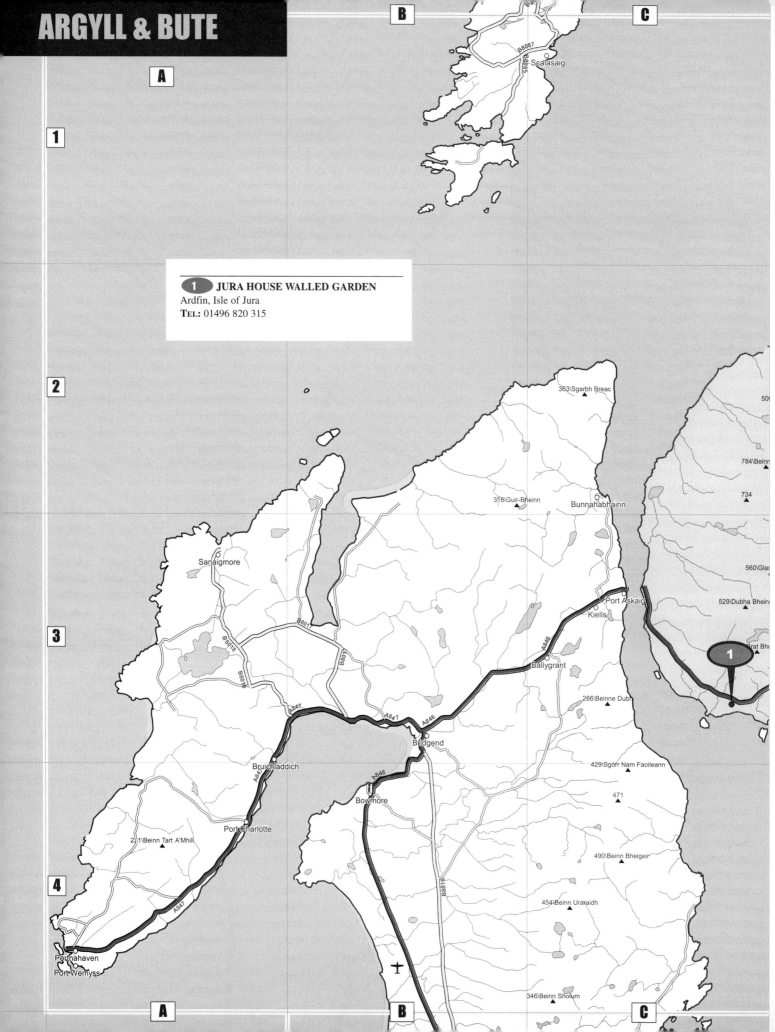

**A**

**B**

**C**

**1**

**2**

**3**

**4**

**1 JURA HOUSE WALLED GARDEN**
Ardfin, Isle of Jura
**TEL:** 01496 820 315

363\Sgarbh Breac

318\Guir-Bheinn

Bunnahabhainn

784\Beinn

734

560\Glas

529\Dubha Bheinn

Sanaigmore

Port Askaig

Kiells

rat Bhe

Ballygrant

**1**

266\Beinne Dub

Bridgend

429\Sgorr Nam Faoileann

Bruichladdich

471

Bowmore

2 1\Beinn Tart A'Mhill

Port Charlotte

490\Beinn Bheigeir

454\Beinn Uraraidh

Portnahaven

Port Wemyss

346\Beinn Sholum

Scalasaig

B8087

B8085

B8017

B8018

B8017

B8018

A847

A847

A846

A846

A846

A847

B8016

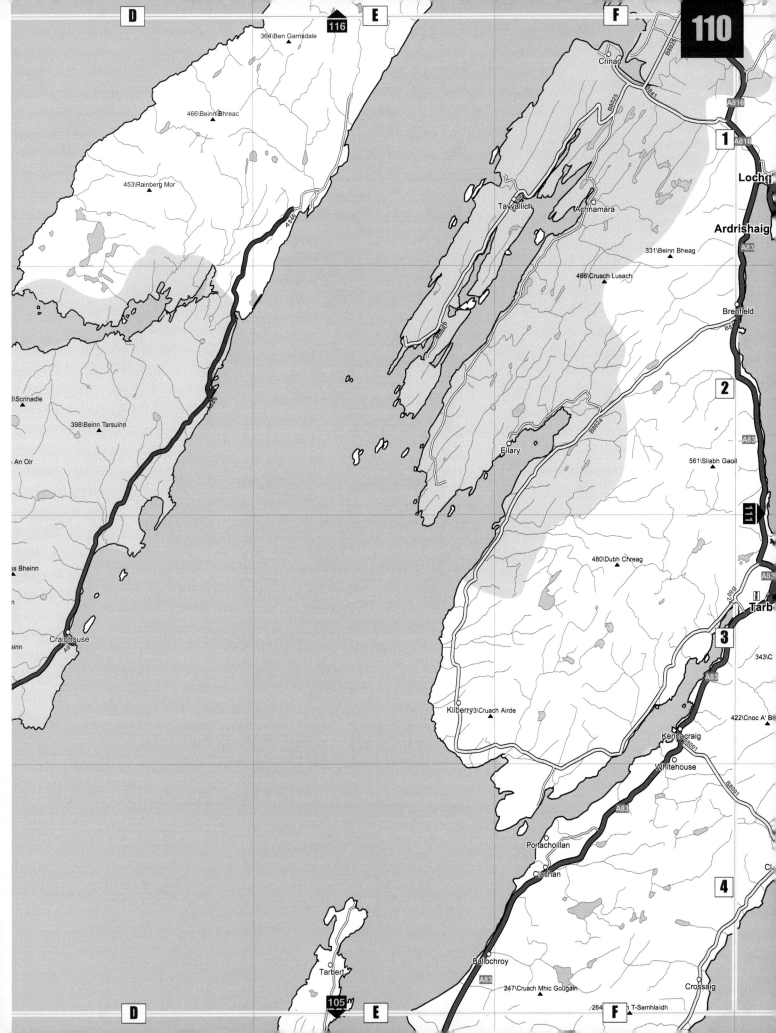

# SCOTLAND

**1** **YOUNGER BOTANIC GARDEN, BENMORE**
Dunoon, Argyll
**TEL:** 01369 706 261

**2** **BALLAGAN GARDEN CENTRE**
Gartocharn Road, Balloch, Alexandria
**TEL:** 01389 752 947

**3** **GLENARN**
Rhu, Helensburgh
**TEL:** 01436 820 493

**4** **HILL HOUSE, NATIONAL TRUST**
Helensburgh
**TEL:** 01436 673 900

**5** **DOBBIES GARDEN CENTRE**
Rhu Road Higher, Helensburgh
**TEL:** 01436 671 202

**6** **WOODEND NURSERIES**
15 West Montrose Street, Helensburgh
**TEL:** 01436 672 451

**7** **LINN BOTANIC GARDENS & NURSERY**
Cove, Helensburgh
**TEL:** 01436 842 242

**8** **GEILSTON PARK, NATIONAL TRUST**
Dumbarton
**TEL:** 01389 841 867

**9** **WALKER HOME & GARDEN CENTRE**
Dunoon
**TEL:** 01369 704 003

**10** **CARDWELL NURSERY GARDEN CENTRE**
Gourock, Inverclyde
**TEL:** 01475 521 536

**11** **FINLAYSTONE**
Langbank
**TEL:** 01475 540 285

**12** **ARDENCRAIG GARDENS**
High Craigmore, Rothesay
**TEL:** 01700 504 644

**13** **MOUNT STUART GARDENS**
Isle of Bute
**TEL:** 01700 503 877

Tea Tree Flower

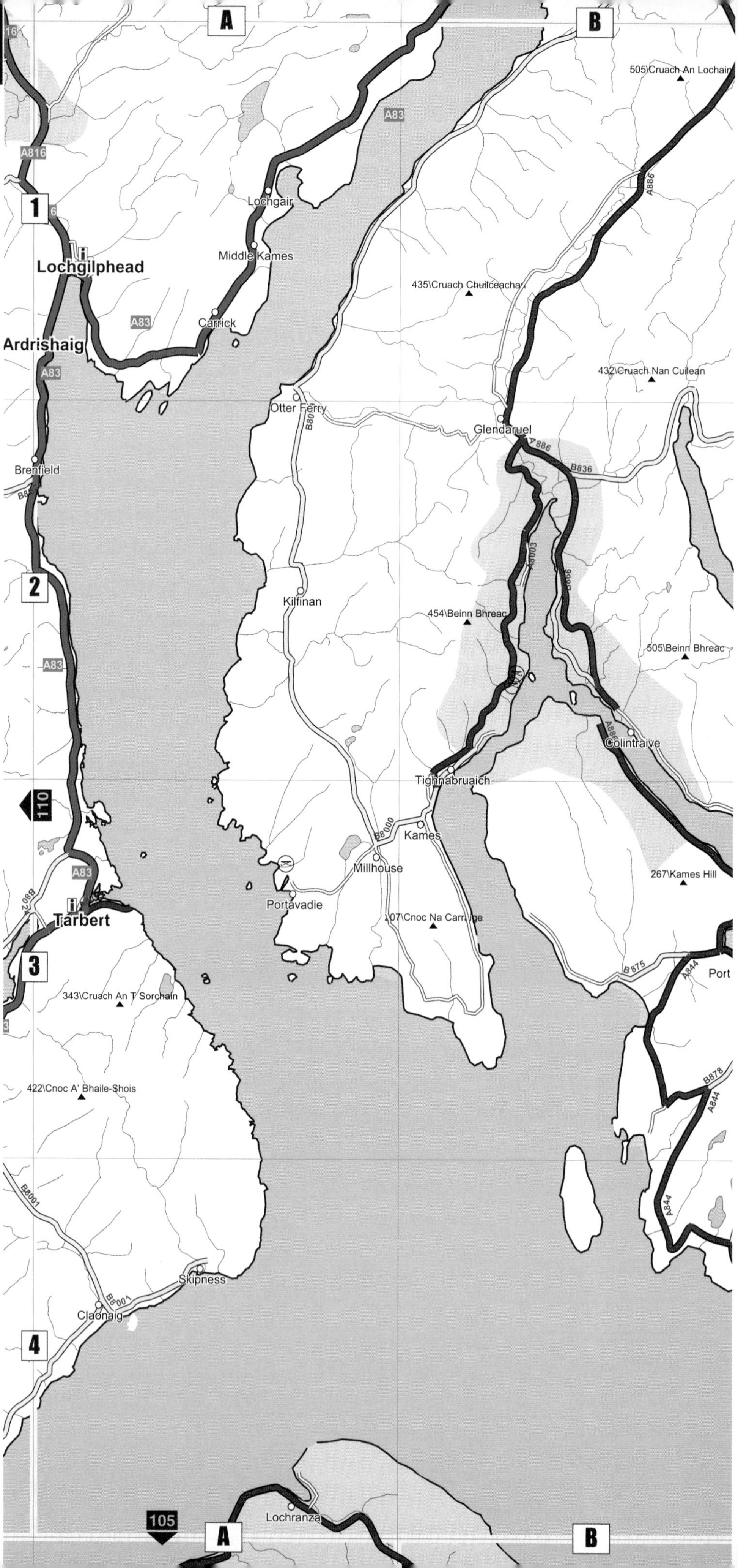

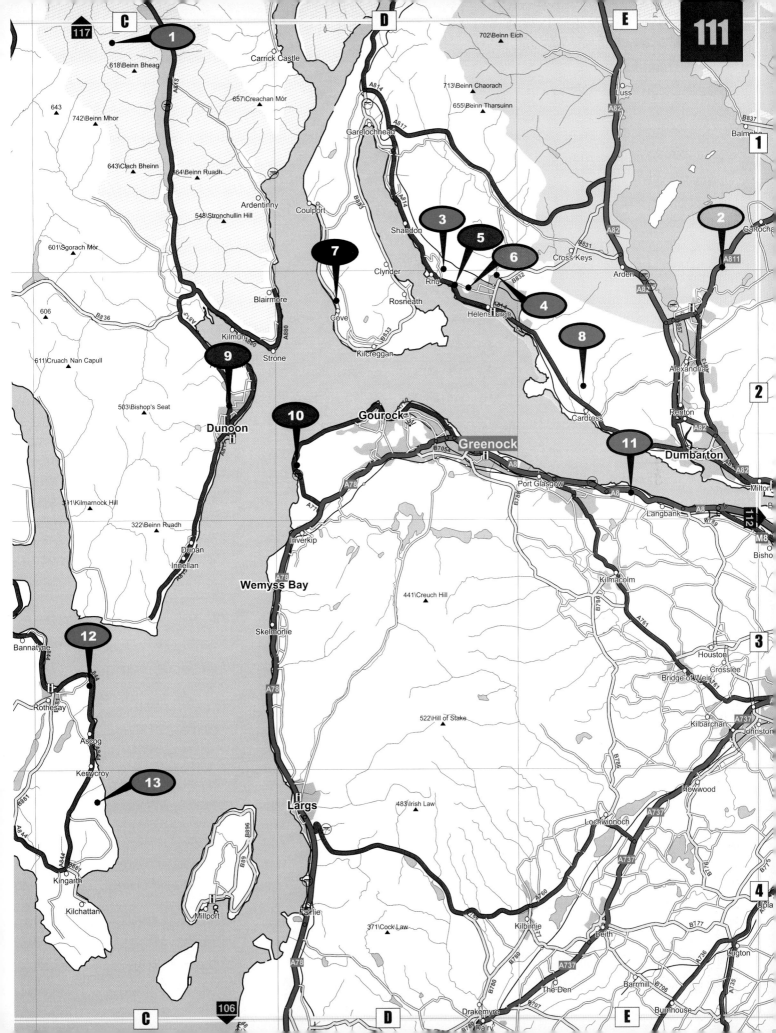

**1 HEDGEROW HERBS NURSERY & PLANT CENTRE**
Gargunnock, Stirling
TEL: 01786 860 552

**2 DOBBIES GARDEN CENTRE**
East Field Road, Westerwood, Cumbernauld
TEL: 01236 736 100

**3 BARRASTON NURSERY**
Torrance, Glasgow
TEL: 01360 620 354

**4 KLONDYKE GARDEN CENTRE**
Kirkintilloch, Glasgow
TEL: 0141 776 2001

**5 WEST CARLSTON GARDEN CENTRE**
Campsie Road, Torrance, Glasgow
TEL: 01360 620 248

**6 BALMORE NURSERIES**
Torrance, Glasgow
TEL: 01360 620 508

**7 DOBBIES GARDEN WORLD**
Boclair Road, Milngavie
TEL: 01360 620 721

**8 ERSKINE HOSPITAL GARDEN CENTRE**
Erskine Hospital, Bishopton
TEL: 0141 812 0657

**9 CRAIGEND NURSERY**
Condorrat, Cumbernauld
TEL: 01236 721 822

**10 HUNTERSHILL GARDEN & GIFT CENTRE**
Bishopbriggs
TEL: 0141 762 5100

**11 ANNIESLAND GARDEN & GIFT CENTRE**
950a Crow Road North, Glasgow
TEL: 0141 402 3551

**12 GREENHEAD NURSERY**
Inchinnan, Renfrew
TEL: 0141 812 0121

**13 LOCHEND NURSERY**
Gartcosh, Glasgow
TEL: 01236 875 800

**14 GLASGOW BOTANIC GARDENS**
Glasgow
TEL: 0141 334 2422

**15 ROUKEN GLEN GARDEN CENTRE**
18 Cauldcoats, Giffnock
TEL: 0141 620 0566

**16 IRVINES OF POLLOKSHIELDS**
128 Nithsdale Road, Glasgow
TEL: 0141 424 0357

**17 DOBBIES GARDEN CENTRE**
Hawkhead Road, Paisley
TEL: 0141 887 5422

**18 QUEENS PARK**
Glasgow
TEL: 0141 649 0331

**19 GLENROYAL NURSERY**
95 Cathcart Road, Rutherglen
TEL: 0141 647 6921

**20 BELLSHILL GARDEN CENTRE**
Reema Road, Bellshill
TEL: 01698 840 000

**21 HOLMWOOD HOUSE, NATIONAL TRUST**
Cathcart
TEL: 0141 637 2129

**22 FERENEZE GARDEN CENTRE**
Barrhead, Glasgow
TEL: 0141 881 1564

**23 ROBERTSON OF BROOMHOUSE**
Whistleberry Road, Hamilton
TEL: 01698 286 332

**24 GREENBANK GARDEN, NATIONAL TRUST**
Clarkson
TEL: 0141 616 2266

**25 PHILIPSHILL GARDEN CENTRE**
Philipshill Road, Clarkston, Glasgow
TEL: 0141 644 3638

**26 AVONHILL NURSERY SOILS & BARK SUPPLIES**
70 Carlisle Road, Hamilton
TEL: 01698 422 099

**27 BRAIDBAR NURSERIES**
Hazelden Mearns Road, Mearns Road, Glasgow
TEL: 0141 616 0007

**28 CHATELHERAULT GARDEN CENTRE**
Ferniegair, Hamilton
TEL: 01698 457 700

**29 BROOKSIDE HOMES & GARDENS**
Larkhall
TEL: 01698 886 464

**30 COTTAGE NURSERY**
Off Duke Street, Larkhall
TEL: 01698 884 511

Bearded Iris

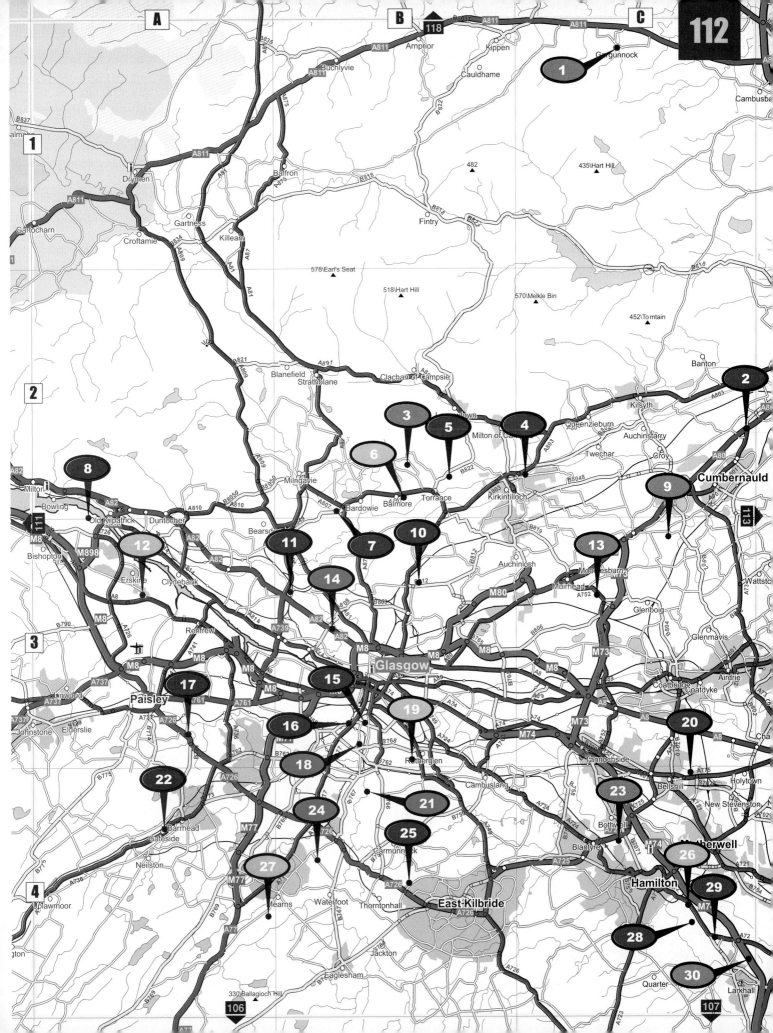

**1** STIRLING CASTLE, HISTORIC SCOTLAND

Stirling, Stirling, FK8 1EJ.
**TEL:** 01786 450 000
**WEB:** www.historic-scotland.net

*Perhaps the grandest of Scotland's castles, with outstanding architecture; the gatehouse and Great Hall of James IV, Renaissance Palace of James V and Chapel Royal of James VI. Mary Queen of Scots was crowned here.*
**OPEN:** Apr-Sep: Mon-Sun 9.30-6.30 (last entry 5.15). Oct-Mar: 9.30-5 (last entry 4.15).
**ENTRY COSTS:** £7, Child: £2, OAPs: £5.
**SPECIALITIES:** Knot, Walled garden.
**FACILITIES:** Bookshop, Coffee shop, Credit cards, Gift shop, Toilets.

**2** GREENYARDS GARDEN & PET CENTRE
Bannockburn, Stirling
**TEL:** 01786 817 369

**3** KLONDYKE GARDEN CENTRE
Glasgow Road, Whins of Milton, Stirling
**TEL:** 01786 816 167

**4** LUSCAR NURSERY
Gowkhall, Dunfermline
**TEL:** 01383 850 536

**5** HENDRY'S GARDEN CENTRE & BISTRO
Leadside, Wellwood, Dunfermline
**TEL:** 01383 733 367

**6** PINEGROVE PLANT NURSERY
Cairneyhill, Dunfermline
**TEL:** 01383 881 493

**7** FAIRLEY'S GARDEN CENTRE
Cairneyhill, Dunfermline
**TEL:** 01383 880 223

**8** CULROSS PALACE, NATIONAL TRUST
Dunfermline
**TEL:** 01383 880 359

**9** TORWOOD GARDEN CENTRE
Torwood, Larbert
**TEL:** 01324 553 152

**10** GREENYARDS GARDEN CENTRE
Carron Grove Road, Carron, Falkirk
**TEL:** 01324 555 410

**11** BONNYVIEW NURSERY
Larbert
**TEL:** 01324 562 207

**12** KLONDYKE GARDEN CENTRE
Beancross Road Polmont, Falkirk
**TEL:** 01324 717 035

**13** J B MCINTOSH
Dennyloanhead, Bonnybridge
**TEL:** 01324 840 941

**14** HOPETOUN HOUSE PRESERVATION TRUST
Hopetoun House, South Queensferry
**TEL:** 0131 331 2451

**15** HOUSE OF THE BINNS, NATIONAL TRUST
Linlithgow
**TEL:** 01506 834 255

**16** DOUGAL PHILIP
New Hopetoun Gardens, Newton Village, Broxburn
**TEL:** 01506 834 433

**17** BINNY PLANTS
Ecclesmachan, Uphall
**TEL:** 01506 858 931

**18** SOUTH LOGIE NURSERY
Westfield, Bathgate
**TEL:** 01506 631 769

**19** MILL GARDEN CENTRE
Barbauchlaw Mill, Bathgate
**TEL:** 01501 732 347

**20** AMMANDALE GARDEN CENTRE
Raw Farm Nurseries, East Calder, Livingston
**TEL:** 01506 880 018

**21** BROOMPARK PLANT CENTRE
Mid Calder, Livingston
**TEL:** 01506 881 513

**22** KLONDYKE GARDEN CENTRE
Campus Roundabout Kirkton Campus, Livingston
**TEL:** 01506 410 053

**23** FIVE SISTERS GARDEN CENTRE
Gavieside, West Calder
**TEL:** 01506 873 727

**24** POND SERVICES
Polbeth, West Calder
**TEL:** 01506 873 653

**25** RIDGEVIEW NURSERY
Crossroads, Longridge, Bathgate
**TEL:** 01501 771 144

**26** CLYDE VALLEY GARDEN CENTRE
Garrion Bridge, Larkhall
**TEL:** 01698 888 880

**27** ANDERSONS
Lanark Road, Larkhall
**TEL:** 01698 883 492

**28** GLENROSE GARDEN CENTRE
Ashgillhead Road, Ashgill, Larkhall
**TEL:** 01698 888 244

**29** GOULDING GROWERS
Dalpatrick Farm, Rosebank, Carluke
**TEL:** 01555 860 259

Water Lily

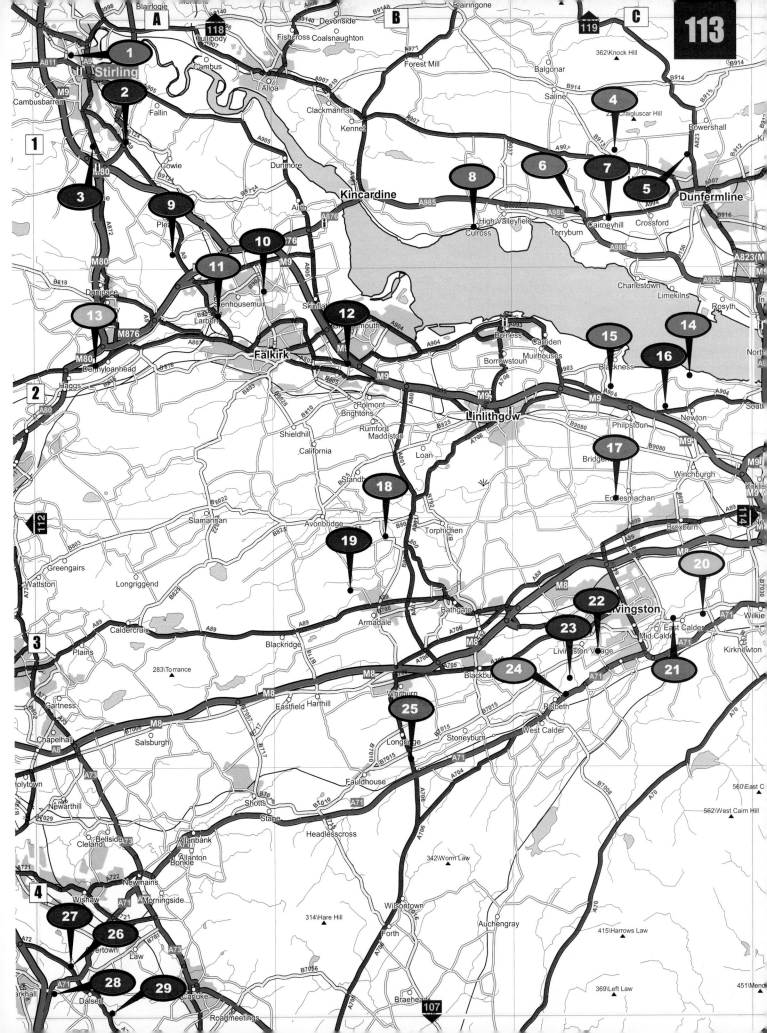

**1**  **KIRKCALDY GARDEN CENTRE**
Thornton Road, Kirkcaldy
**TEL:** 01592 652 861

**2** **LADY HELEN NURSERIES**
Cardenden, Lochgelly
**TEL:** 01592 720 740

**3** **ABERDOUR CASTLE, HISTORIC SCOTLAND**
Aberdour, Fife, KY3 0SL.
**TEL:** 01383 860 519
**WEB:** www.historic-scotland.net

*A 13th century castle built by the Douglas family. The gallery on the first floor gives an idea of how it was furnished at the time. The castle has a delightful walled garden and dovecote.*
**OPEN:** Apr-Sep: 9.30-6.30. Oct-Mar: Mon-Wed & Sat 9.30-4.30, Thu 9.30-12, Sun 2-4.30.
**ENTRY COSTS:** £2.20, Child: £0.75 Under 5s free, OAP £1.60.
**SPECIALITIES:** Walled garden.
**FACILITIES:** Gift shop, Coffee shop.

**4** **THE NURSERIES**
Middlebank Small Holdings, Dunfermline
**TEL:** 01383 413 787

**5** **DOBBIES GARDEN CENTRE**
Weston Approach Road, Dalgety Bay
**TEL:** 01383 823 841

**6** **ROYAL BOTANIC GARDEN, EDINBURGH**
Edinburgh
**TEL:** 0131 552 7171

**7** **ROUKEN GLEN GARDEN CENTRE**
18 Cauldcoats, Linlithgow
**TEL:** 01506 834 346

**8** **PRINCESS STREET GARDENS EAST AND WEST**
Edinburgh, Midlothian, EH1 3JD.
**TEL:** 0131 529 7913 or 7924
*Historic landscaped park and garden.*
**OPEN:** Open daily from dawn-dusk.
**ENTRY COSTS:** Free
**SPECIALITIES:** Bedding plants, Hardy plants, Rhododendrons and azaleas, Roses, Shrubs.
**FACILITIES:** Toilets, Wheelchair access, Dogs allowed, Child area, Coffee shop.

**9** **CONIFOX NURSERIES**
Foxhall, Kirkliston
**TEL:** 0131 333 3334

**10** **MEADOWMILL GARDEN CENTRE & NURSERY**
Meadowmill Nurseries, Tranent
**TEL:** 01875 610 664

**11** **INVERESK LODGE, NATIONAL TRUST**
Musselburgh
**TEL:** 0131 665 1855

**12** **NEWHAILES NURSERY**
Musselburgh
**TEL:** 0131 665 8291

**13** **NEWHAILES ESTATE, NATIONAL TRUST**
Musselburgh
**TEL:** 0131 665 0253

**14** **CRAIGMILLAR CASTLE, HISTORIC SCOTLAND**
Craigmillar Castle Road, Edinburgh
**TEL:** 0131 661 4445

**15** **MACPLANTS**
5 Boggs Holdings, Pencaitland
**TEL:** 01875 341 179

**16** **T H DOWNES**
38 Bridge Road, Collington, Edinburgh
**TEL:** 0131 441 2505

**17** **KLONDYKE GARDEN CENTRE**
Mortonhall, Frogston Road East, Edinburgh
**TEL:** 0131 664 8698

**18** **DOBBIES GARDEN WORLD**
Lasswade
**TEL:** 0131 663 1941

**19** **MALLENY GARDEN, NATIONAL TRUST**
Edinburgh
**TEL:** 0131 449 2283

**20** **MAYSHADE GARDEN CENTRE**
Mayshade Park, Dalkeith
**TEL:** 0131 663 1093

Alstromeria

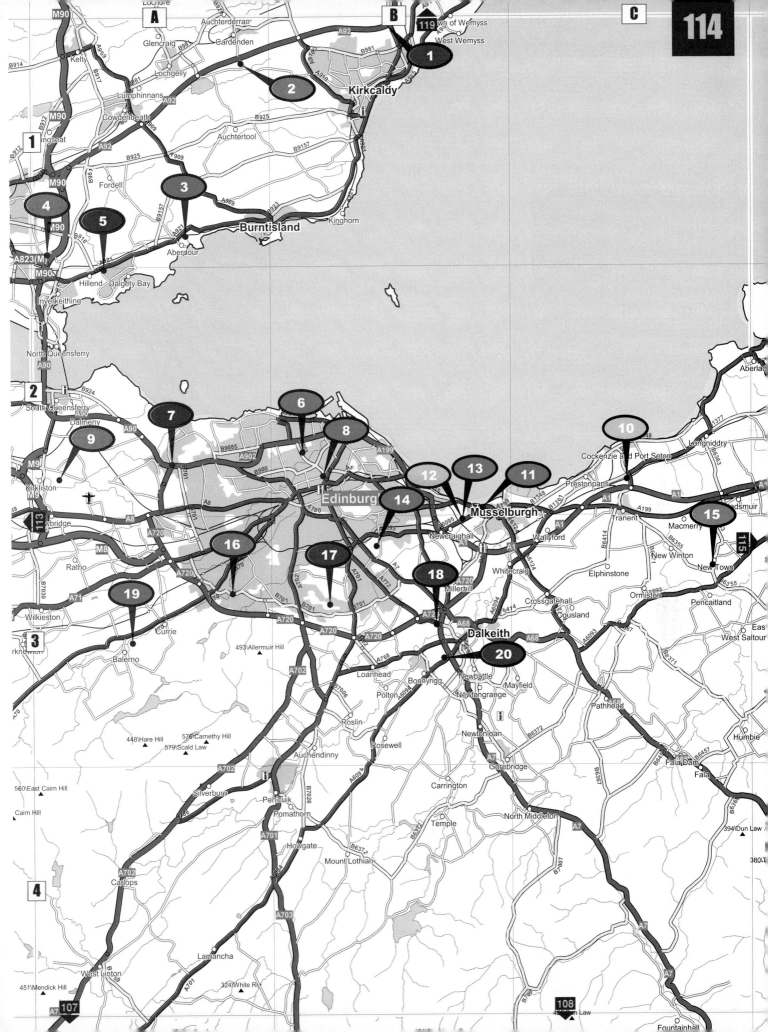

# BORDERS · E. LOTHIAN

### 1 DIRLETON CASTLE, HISTORIC SCOTLAND

Dirleton, East Lothian, EH39 5ER.
**TEL:** 01620 850 330
**WEB:** www.historic-scotland.net

*Herbaecous perennial formal gardens.*
**OPEN:** Apr-Sep: 9.30-6.30 (last admission 6), Oct-Mar: Mon-Sat 9.30-4.30 (last admission 4), Sun 2-4.30.
**ENTRY COSTS:** £2.80, Child: £1, OAPs: £2.
**SPECIALITIES:** Herbaceous plants, Perennials.
**FACILITIES:** Gift Shop.

### 2 SMEATON NURSERY GARDEN

Preston Road, East Linton
**TEL:** 01620 860 501

### 3 ROSEHALL GARDEN CENTRE

Pencaitland Road, Haddington
**TEL:** 01620 829 696

### 4 EDROM NURSERIES

Coldingham, Eyemouth
**TEL:** 01890 771 386

### 5 WAULKMILL NURSERY

Reston, Eyemouth
**TEL:** 01890 761 333

Wild Garden

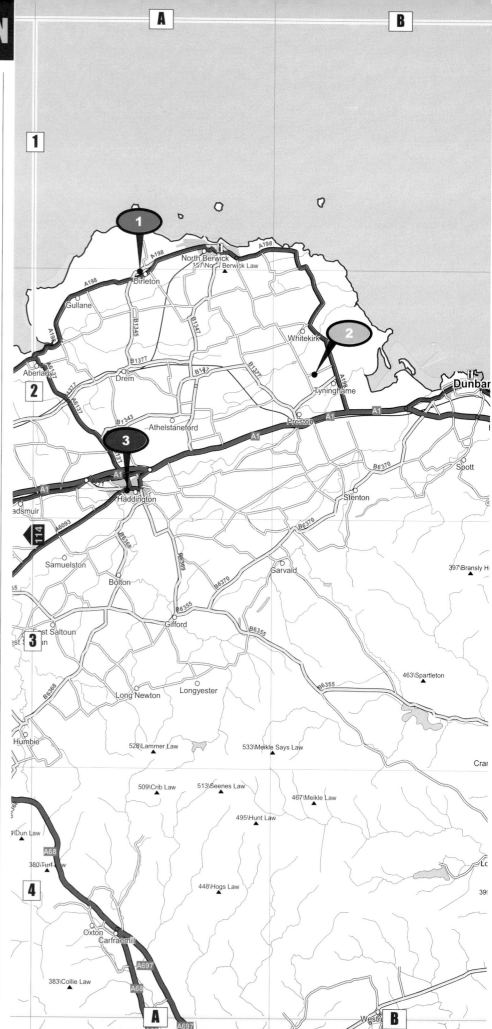

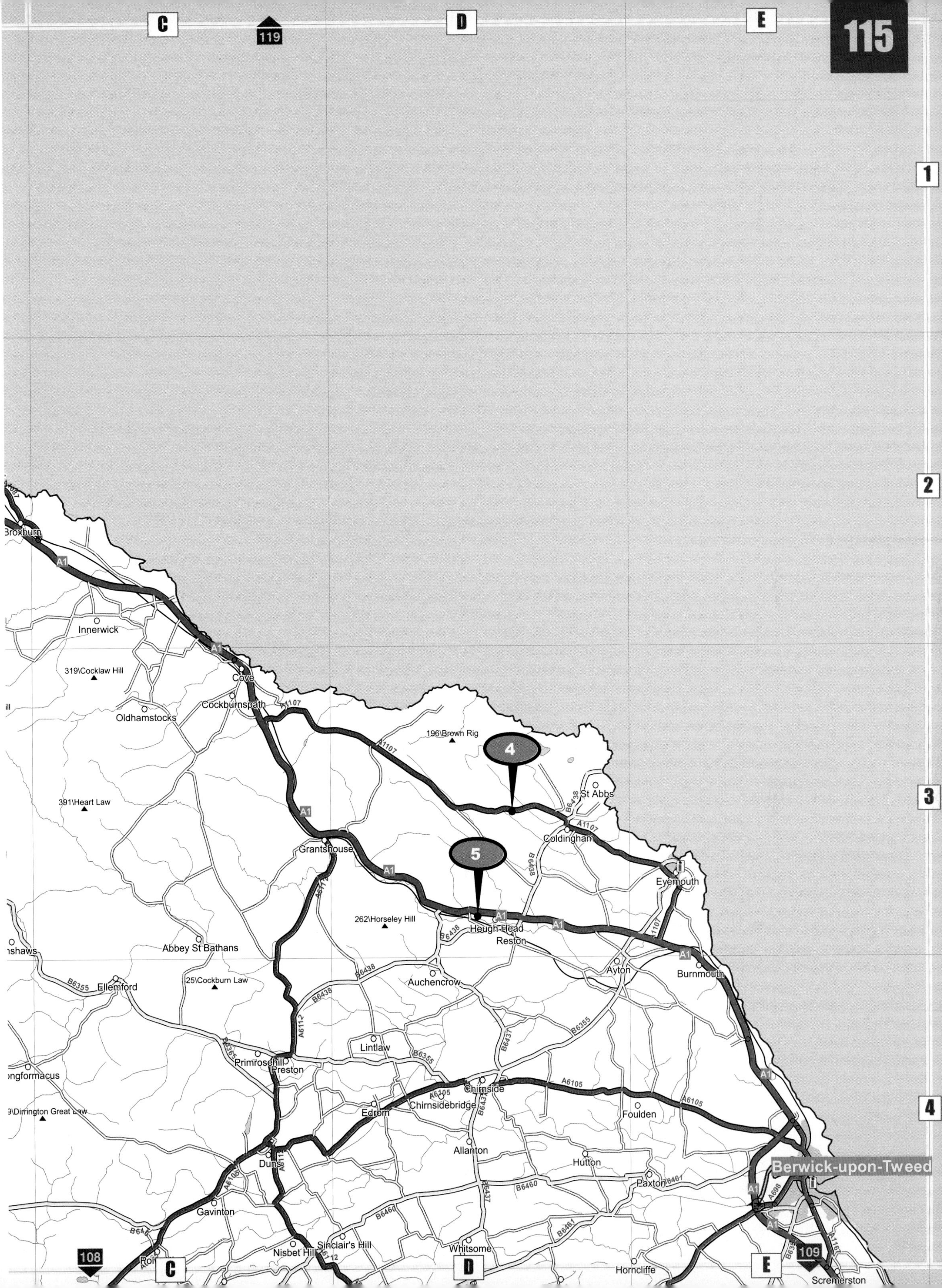

1

2

Broxburn

Innerwick

319\Cocklaw Hill

Cove

Cockburnspath

Oldhamstocks

196\Brown Rig

4

391\Heart Law

St Abbs

3

Grantshouse

Coldingham

5

262\Horseley Hill

Eyemouth

Heugh Head

Reston

Abbey St Bathans

Ayton

Burnmouth

Auchencrow

Ellemford

25\Cockburn Law

Primrosehill

Lintlaw

Preston

Chirnside

4

Dirrington Great Law

Chirnsidebridge

Edrom

Foulden

Allanton

Berwick-upon-Tweed

Duns

Hutton

Paxton

Gavinton

Whitsome

Sinclair's Hill

Nisbet Hill

Horncliffe

Scremerston

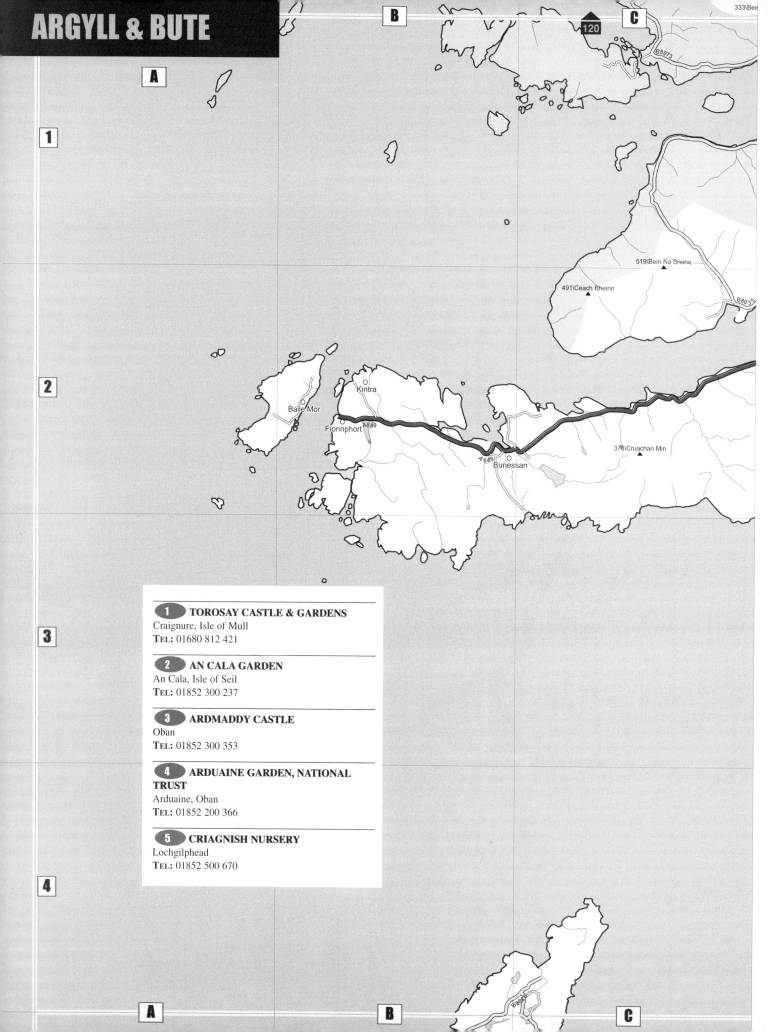

**A**

**B**

**C**

120

1

333\Bein

B8073

519\Bein Na Sreine ▲

491\Ceach Bheinn ▲

B803

2

Kintra ○

Baile Mor

Fionnphort ○   A849

A849   376\Cruachan Min ▲

Bunessan ○

3

**1  TOROSAY CASTLE & GARDENS**
Craignure, Isle of Mull
**TEL:** 01680 812 421

**2  AN CALA GARDEN**
An Cala, Isle of Seil
**TEL:** 01852 300 237

**3  ARDMADDY CASTLE**
Oban
**TEL:** 01852 300 353

**4  ARDUAINE GARDEN, NATIONAL TRUST**
Arduaine, Oban
**TEL:** 01852 200 366

**5  CRIAGNISH NURSERY**
Lochgilphead
**TEL:** 01852 500 670

4

B8085

**A**

**B**

**C**

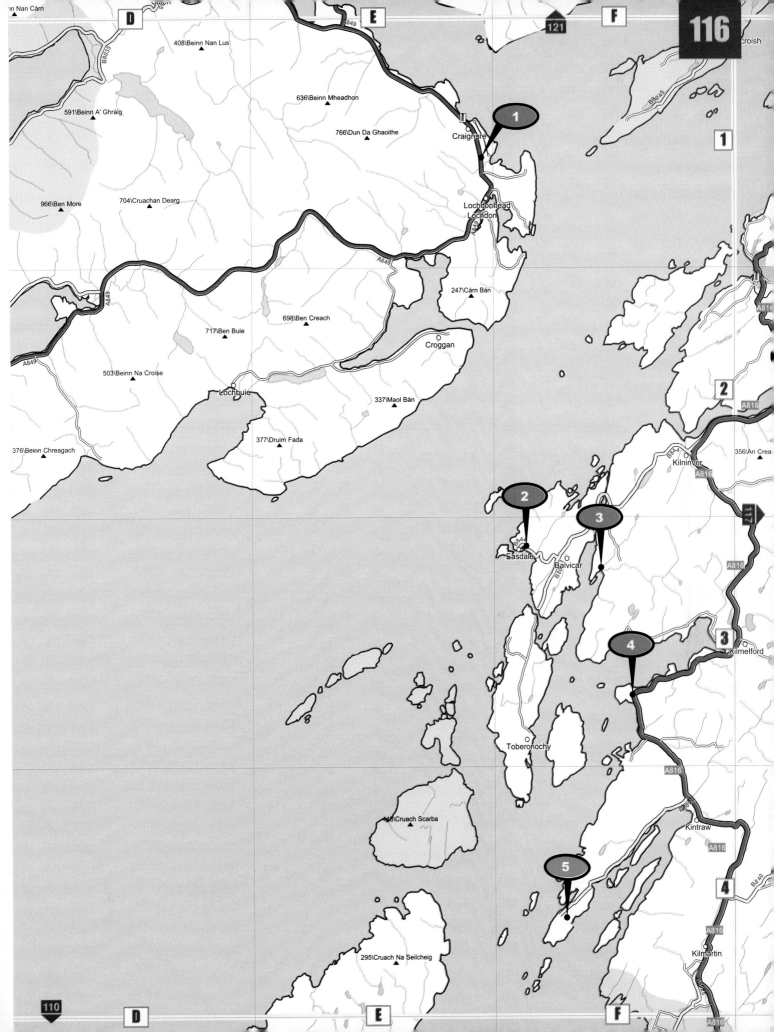

**1 ARDCHATTEN PRIORY GARDEN**
Oban
**TEL:** 01631 750 238

 **2 ACHNACLOICH**
Connel, Oban
**TEL:** 01631 710 221

 **3 BARGUILLEAN ANGUS GARDEN**
Taynuilt
**TEL:** 01866 822 381

 **4 ANGUS GARDEN**
Taynuilt, Oban
**TEL:** 01866 822 254

 **5 ARDANAISEIG HOTEL GARDEN**
Loch Awe, Kilchrenan
**TEL:** 01866 833 333

 **6 TREE SHOP**
Cairndow, Argyll & Bute, PA26 8BH.
**TEL:** 01499 600 263
**EMAIL:** tree.shop@virgin.net
*Plant centre and quality gift shop, specialising in trees, rhododendrons and woodwork.*
**OPEN:** Open daily 9.30-5.
**SPECIALITIES:** Rhododendrons and azaleas, Trees, Conifers, Conservatory plants, Shrubs.
**FACILITIES:** Credit cards, Wheelchair access, Gift tokens, Bookshop, Coffee shop, Plant guarantee, Gift shop, HTA gift tokens, Sell plants.

 **7 ARDKINGLAS WOODLAND GARDEN**
Cairndow, Argyll, PA26 8BH.
**TEL:** 01499 600 261
**EMAIL:** ardkinglas@btinternet.com
**WEB:** www.ardkinglas.com
*Britain's finest collection of conifers including the "Mightiest Conifer in Europe" and the "Tallest Tree in Britain" and a spectacular display of rhododendrons and azaleas.*
**OPEN:** Open daily from dawn-dusk.
**ENTRY COSTS:** £3, Child: Under 16s free.
**SPECIALITIES:** Bluebells, Conifers, Trees Rhododendrons and azaleas.
**FACILITIES:** Coffee shop, Gift shop, Toilets.

 **8 HIGHLAND HEATHERS**
Lochgilphead
**TEL:** 01546 810 253

 **9 CRARAE GARDENS**
Minard, Inveraray
**TEL:** 01546 886 614

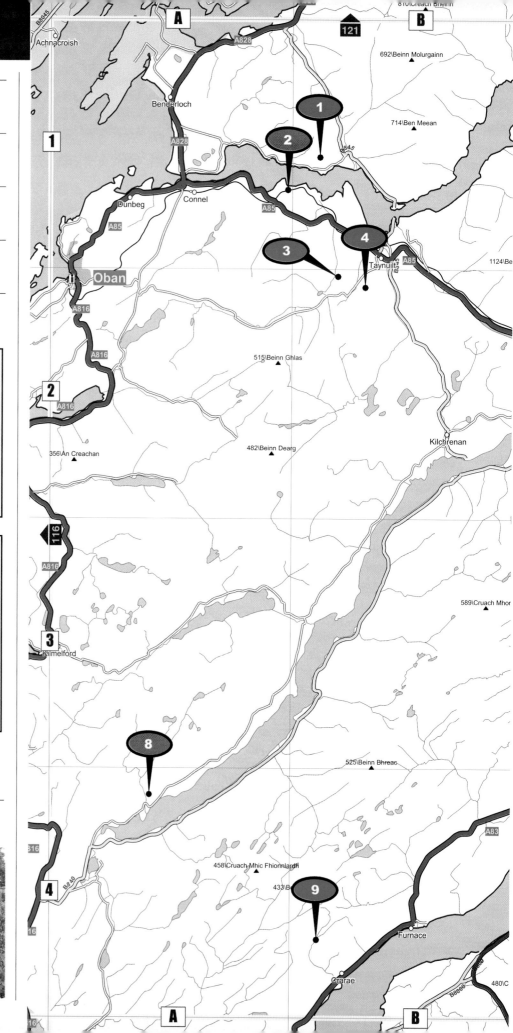

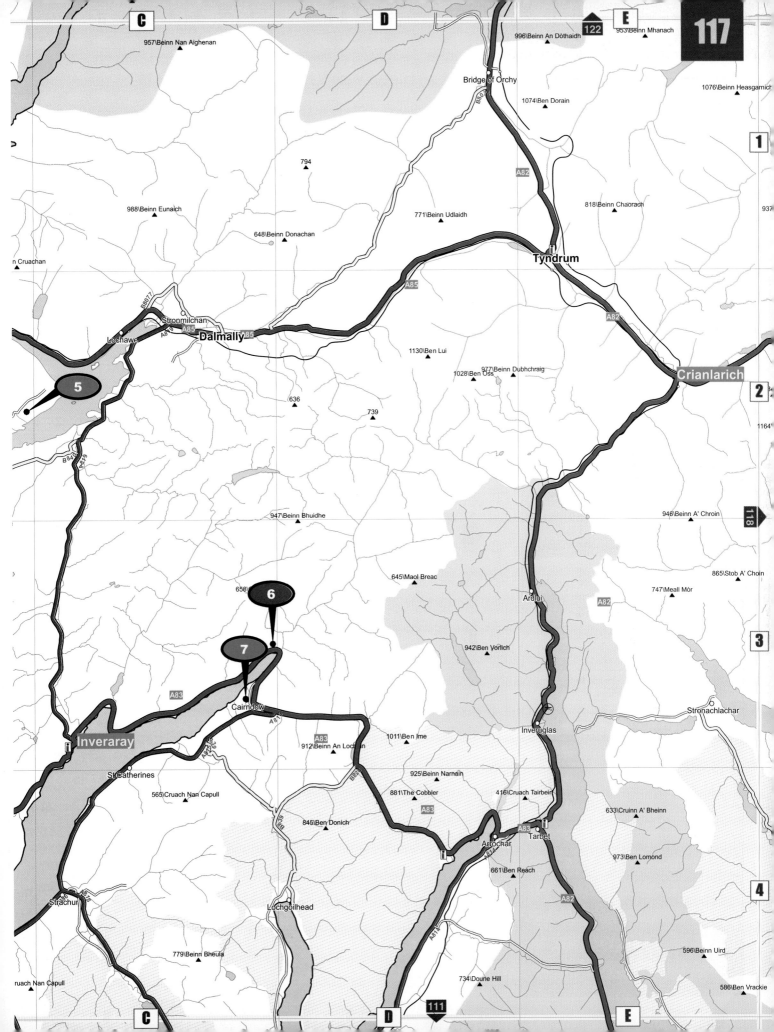

# SCOTLAND

 **WOODLANDS NURSERY**
Comrie, Crieff
TEL: 01764 670 038

 **CRIEFF PLANT CENTRE**
Muthill Road, Crieff
TEL: 01764 652 722

 **DRUMMOND CASTLE GARDENS**
Muthill, Crieff
TEL: 01764 681 257

 **BLAIRHOYLE NURSERY**
Blairhoyle, Port of Menteith, Stirling
TEL: 01877 385 669

 **STOCKBRIDGE NURSERY**
Dunblane
TEL: 01786 821 515

 **CASTLE CAMPBELL, HISTORIC SCOTLAND**
Dollar, Stirling, FK14 7PP.
TEL: 01259 742 408
WEB: www.historic-scotland.net

*Set at the head of Dollar Glen, this spectacularly sited 15th century fortress was the lowland stronghold of the Campbells. Stunning views from the parapet walk.*
**OPEN:** Apr-Sep: 9.30-6.30. Oct-Mar: Mon-Wed & Sat 9.30-4.30, Thu 9.30-12, Sun 2-4.30.
**ENTRY COSTS:** £2.80, Child: £1, OAP £2.
**SPECIALITIES:** Woodland plants, Waterfalls.
**FACILITIES:** Coffee shop, Gift shop.

 **WILSON NURSERY**
Chapelle, Tillicoultry
TEL: 01259 752 867

Rose

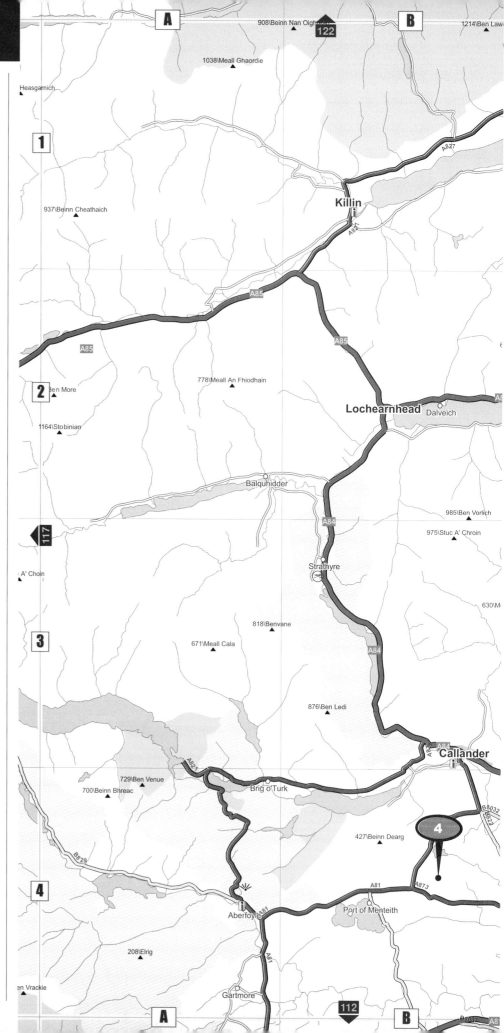

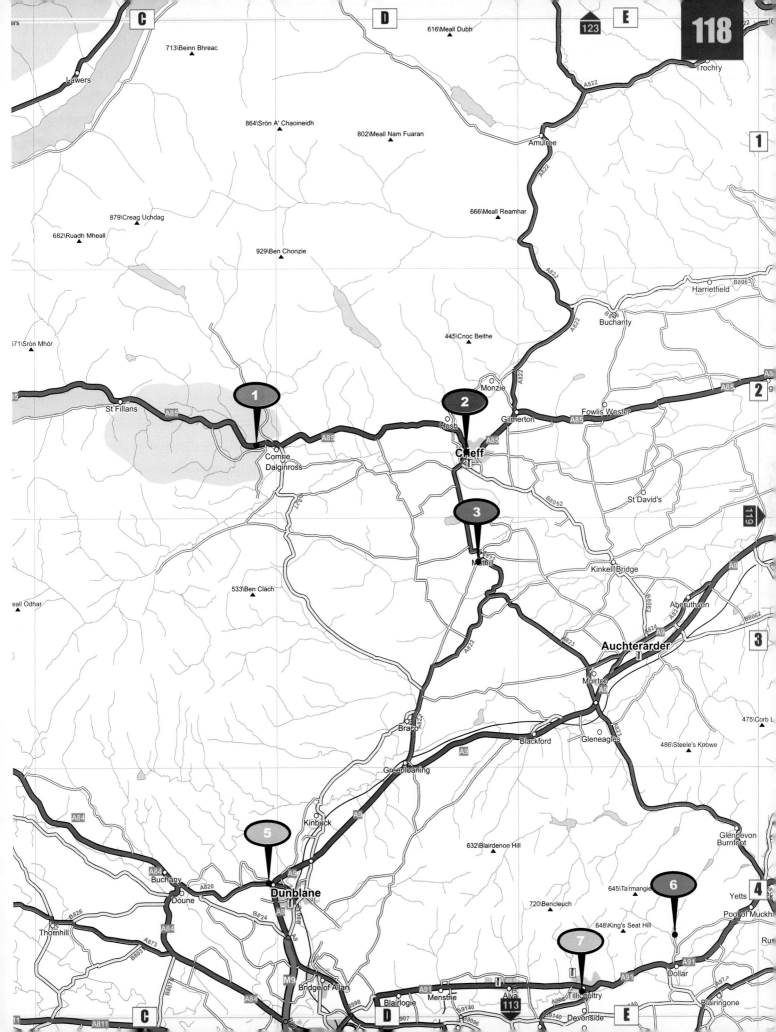

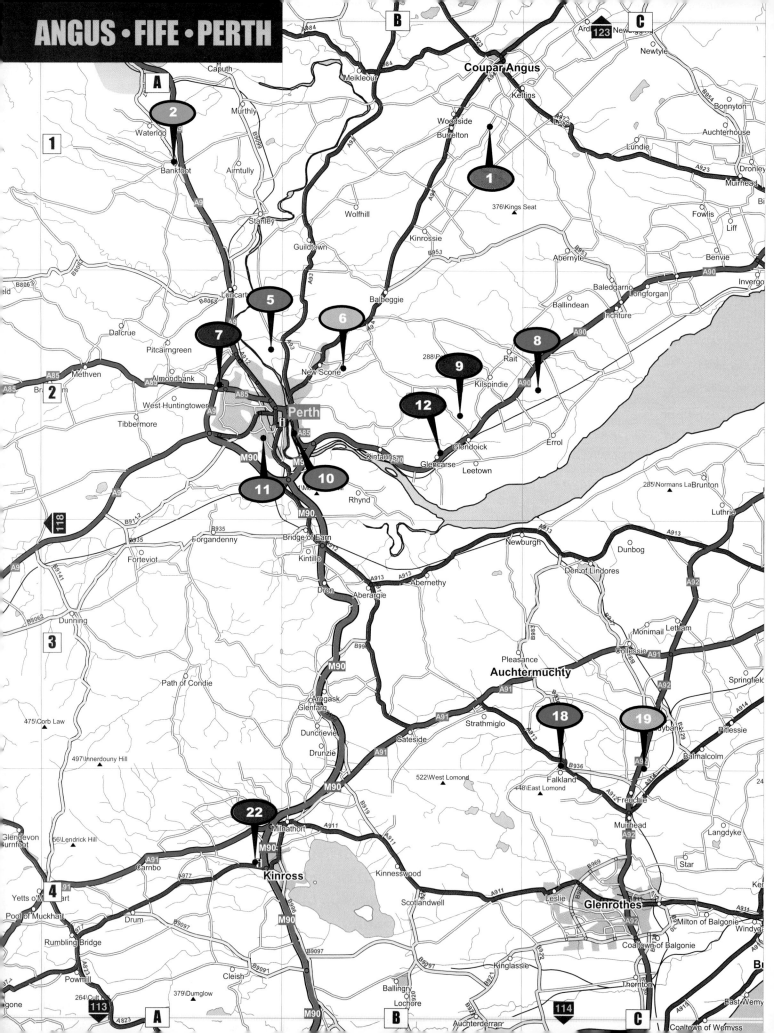

# ANGUS · FIFE · PERTH

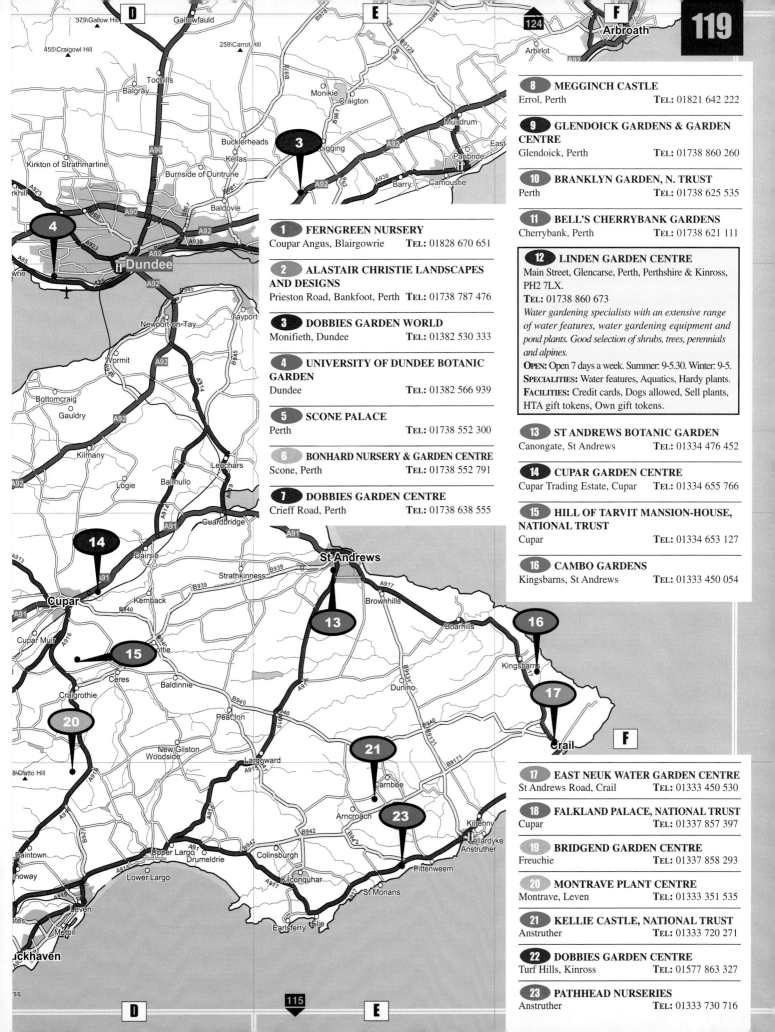

**8  MEGGINCH CASTLE**
Errol, Perth          **Tel:** 01821 642 222

**9  GLENDOICK GARDENS & GARDEN CENTRE**
Glendoick, Perth          **Tel:** 01738 860 260

**10  BRANKLYN GARDEN, N. TRUST**
Perth          **Tel:** 01738 625 535

**11  BELL'S CHERRYBANK GARDENS**
Cherrybank, Perth          **Tel:** 01738 621 111

**12  LINDEN GARDEN CENTRE**
Main Street, Glencarse, Perth, Perthshire & Kinross, PH2 7LX.
**Tel:** 01738 860 673
*Water gardening specialists with an extensive range of water features, water gardening equipment and pond plants. Good selection of shrubs, trees, perennials and alpines.*
**Open:** Open 7 days a week. Summer: 9-5.30. Winter: 9-5.
**Specialities:** Water features, Aquatics, Hardy plants.
**Facilities:** Credit cards, Dogs allowed, Sell plants, HTA gift tokens, Own gift tokens.

**13  ST ANDREWS BOTANIC GARDEN**
Canongate, St Andrews          **Tel:** 01334 476 452

**14  CUPAR GARDEN CENTRE**
Cupar Trading Estate, Cupar          **Tel:** 01334 655 766

**15  HILL OF TARVIT MANSION-HOUSE, NATIONAL TRUST**
Cupar          **Tel:** 01334 653 127

**16  CAMBO GARDENS**
Kingsbarns, St Andrews          **Tel:** 01333 450 054

**1  FERNGREEN NURSERY**
Coupar Angus, Blairgowrie          **Tel:** 01828 670 651

**2  ALASTAIR CHRISTIE LANDSCAPES AND DESIGNS**
Prieston Road, Bankfoot, Perth  **Tel:** 01738 787 476

**3  DOBBIES GARDEN WORLD**
Monifieth, Dundee          **Tel:** 01382 530 333

**4  UNIVERSITY OF DUNDEE BOTANIC GARDEN**
Dundee          **Tel:** 01382 566 939

**5  SCONE PALACE**
Perth          **Tel:** 01738 552 300

**6  BONHARD NURSERY & GARDEN CENTRE**
Scone, Perth          **Tel:** 01738 552 791

**7  DOBBIES GARDEN CENTRE**
Crieff Road, Perth          **Tel:** 01738 638 555

**17  EAST NEUK WATER GARDEN CENTRE**
St Andrews Road, Crail          **Tel:** 01333 450 530

**18  FALKLAND PALACE, NATIONAL TRUST**
Cupar          **Tel:** 01337 857 397

**19  BRIDGEND GARDEN CENTRE**
Freuchie          **Tel:** 01337 858 293

**20  MONTRAVE PLANT CENTRE**
Montrave, Leven          **Tel:** 01333 351 535

**21  KELLIE CASTLE, NATIONAL TRUST**
Anstruther          **Tel:** 01333 720 271

**22  DOBBIES GARDEN CENTRE**
Turf Hills, Kinross          **Tel:** 01577 863 327

**23  PATHHEAD NURSERIES**
Anstruther          **Tel:** 01333 730 716

124
115

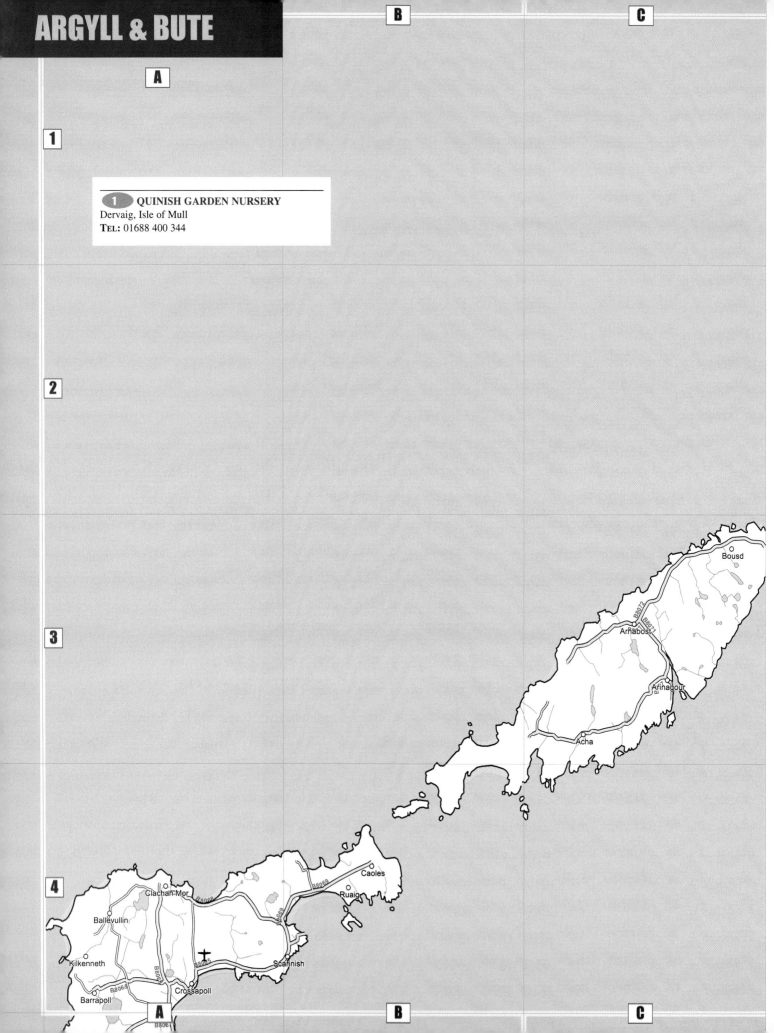

**1** QUINISH GARDEN NURSERY
Dervaig, Isle of Mull
**TEL:** 01688 400 344

Bousd

Arinabost

Arinagour

Acha

Caoles

Clachan-Mor

Ruaig

Ballevullin

Kilkenneth

Scarinish

Barrapoll

Crossapoll

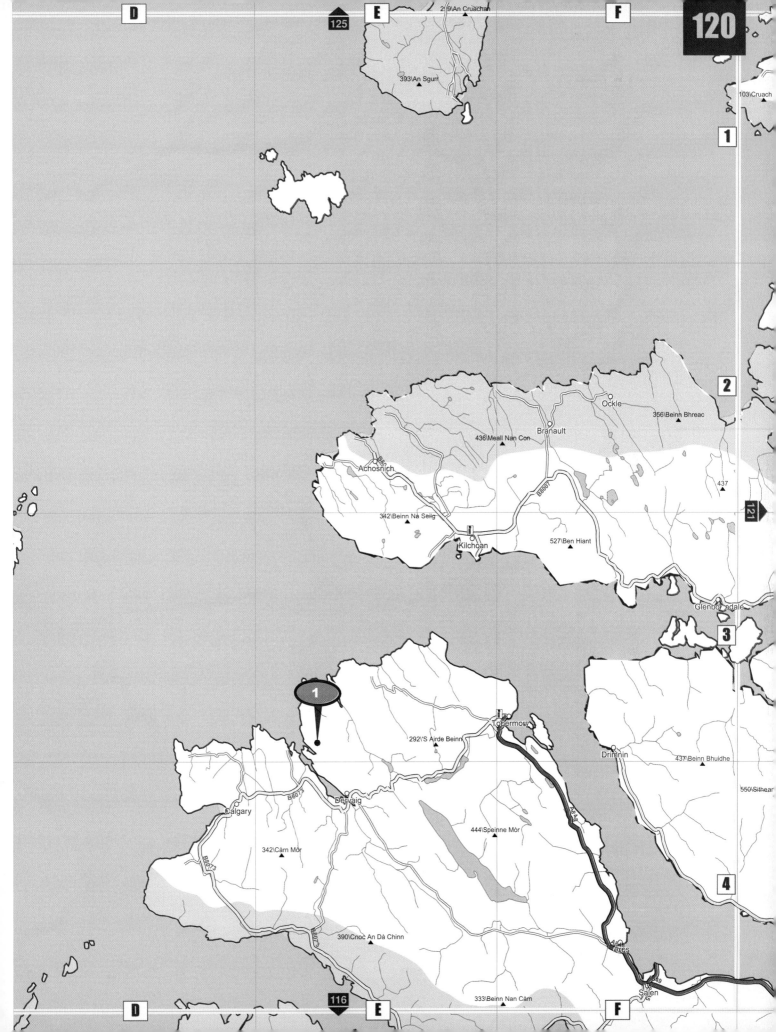

103\Cruach

393\An Sgurr

Ockle

356\Beinn Bhreac

Branault

436\Meall Nan Con

Achosnich

B8007

437

342\Beinn Na Seilg

Kilchoan

527\Ben Hiant

Glenborrodale

1

Tobermory

292\'S Airde Beinn

Drimnin

437\Beinn Bhuidhe

550\Sithean

B8073

Dervaig

Calgary

444\Speinne Mòr

342\Càrn Mòr

B8073

390\Cnoc An Dà Chinn

Aros

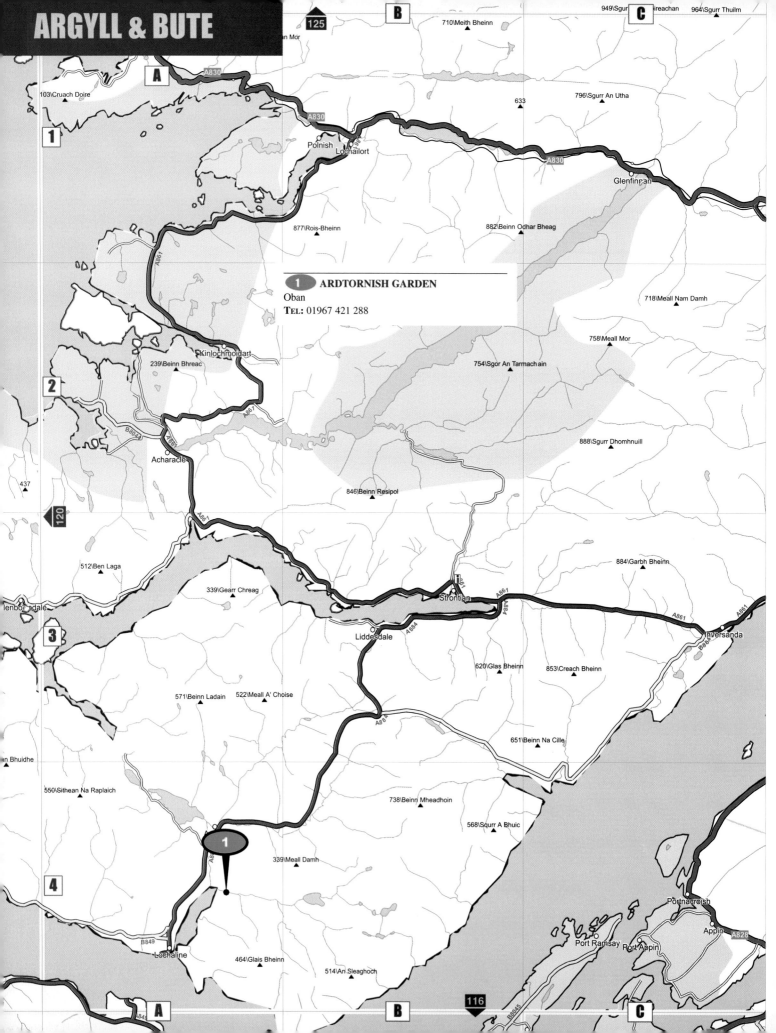

# ARGYLL & BUTE

**1** **ARDTORNISH GARDEN**
Oban
**TEL:** 01967 421 288

103\Cruach Doire

710\Meith Bheinn

949\Sgur ... ireachan

964\Sgurr Thuilm

796\Sgurr An Utha

633

Polnish

Lochailort

Glenfinnan

877\Rois-Bheinn

882\Beinn Odhar Bheag

718\Meall Nam Damh

758\Meall Mor

Kinlochmoidart

239\Beinn Bhreac

754\Sgor An Tarmachain

888\Sgurr Dhomhnuill

Acharacle

846\Beinn Resipol

437

884\Garbh Bheinn

512\Ben Laga

339\Gearr Chreag

Strontian

lenborodale

Liddesdale

Inversanda

571\Beinn Ladain

522\Meall A' Choise

620\Glas Bheinn

853\Creach Bheinn

550\Sithean Na Raplaich

651\Beinn Na Cille

an Bhuidhe

738\Beinn Mheadhoin

568\Squrr A Bhuic

**1**

339\Meall Damh

Portnacroish

Lochaline

Appin

Port Ramsay

Port Appin

464\Glais Bheinn

514\An Sleaghoch

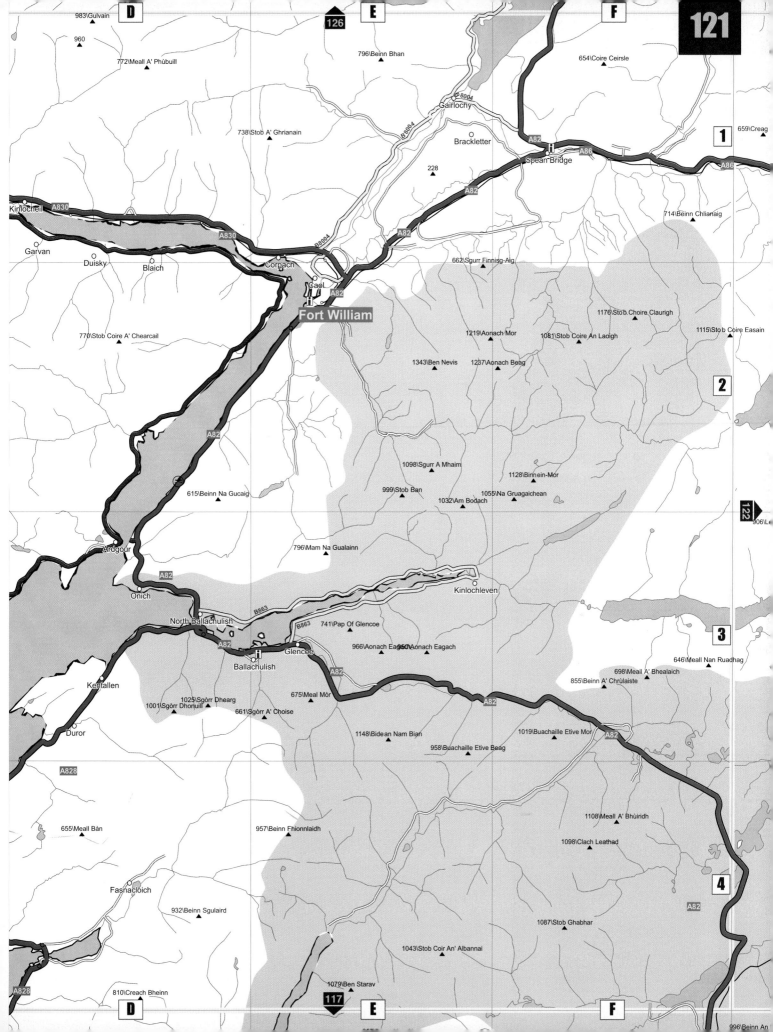

# PERTHSHIRE

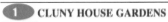

**1** **CLUNY HOUSE GARDENS**
Aberfeldy
**TEL:** 01887 820 795

**2** **BOLFRACKS**
Aberfeldy
**TEL:** 01887 820 207

Euryops

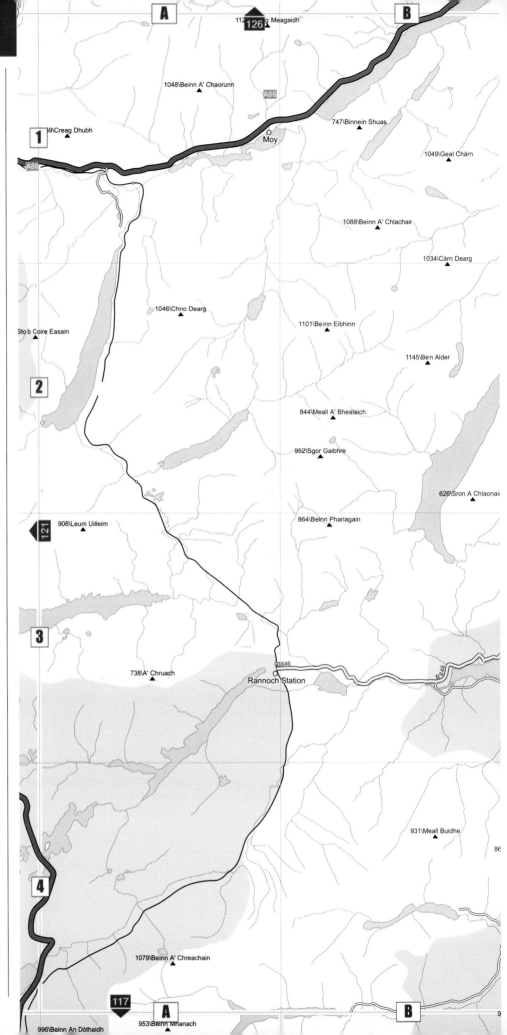

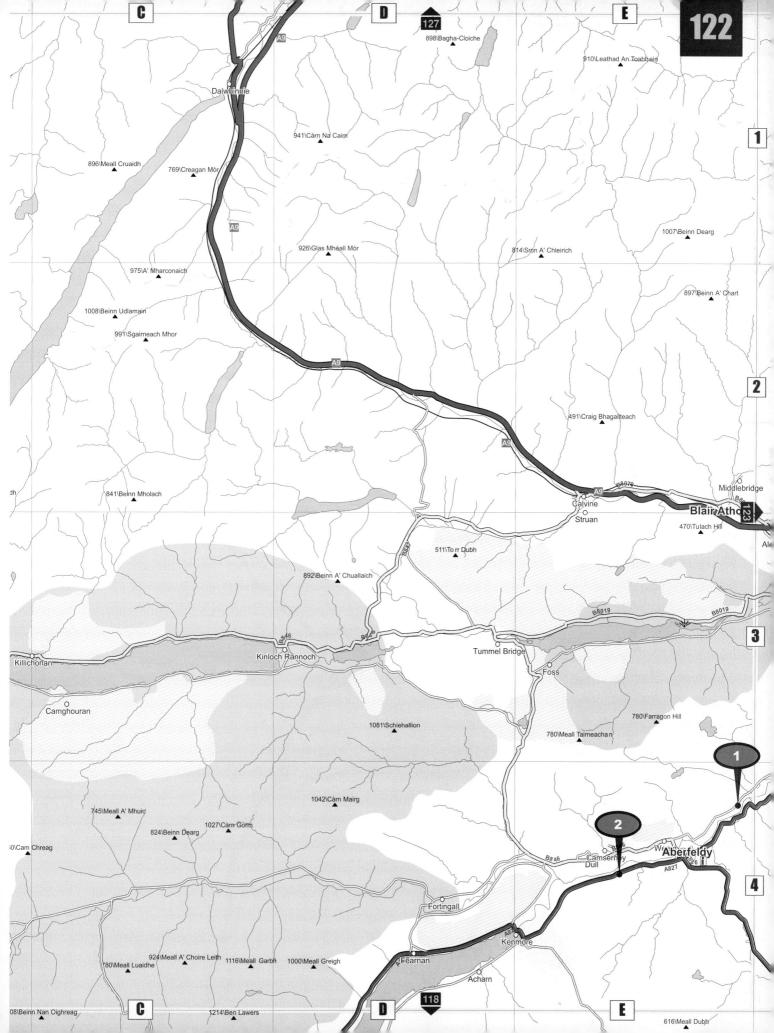

C D 127 E

898\Bagha-Cloiche

910\Leathad An Toabhain

1

941\Càrn Na Caim

896\Meall Cruaidh
769\Creagan Mòr

1007\Beinn Dearg

Dalwhinnie

926\Glas Mhèall Mòr

814\Sron A' Chleirich

975\A' Mharconaich

897\Beinn A' Chart

1008\Beinn Udlamain

991\Sgairneach Mhor

A9

2

491\Craig Bhagailteach

A9

A9
B8079
Middlebridge

841\Beinn Mholach

Calvine
Struan

Blair Atho...
123

470\Tulach Hill

Ale...

511\To rr Dubh

892\Beinn A' Chuallaich

B8019
B8019

3

Killichonan

B-46
B8...
Kinloch Rannoch

Tummel Bridge

Foss

Camghouran

780\Farragon Hill

1081\Schiehallion

780\Meall Tairneacha n

1

1042\Càrn Mairg

2

745\Meall A' Mhuic

824\Beinn Dearg
1027\Càrn Gorm

...0\Cam Chreag

B8 46
Camserney
Dull

We...
Aberfeldy
A82T
i

4

Fortingall

A8...
Kenmore

924\Meall A' Choire Leith
1116\Meall Garbh
1000\Meall Greigh

Fèarnan

Acharn

...08\Beinn Nan Oighreag

C D 118 E

1214\Ben Lawers

616\Meall Dubh

**1 JOSHUA PLUMTREE**
30 Bank Street, Kirriemuir
TEL: 01575 572 030

**2 PATHHEAD NURSERIES**
Forfar Road, Kirriemuir
TEL: 01307 819 007

**3 CHRISTIE'S NURSERY**
Downfield, Main Road, Westmuir
TEL: 01575 572 977

**4 ALEX BUTTER & SON**
Ballinluig, Pitlochry
TEL: 01796 482 614

**5 FERNGREEN GARDEN CENTRE**
Kerriemuir Road, Forfar
TEL: 01307 460 012

**6 BELWOOD TREES**
Meigle
TEL: 01828 640 219

**7 GLAMIS CASTLE**
Glamis, Forfar
TEL: 01307 840 393

**8 SCOTTS GARDEN & PET CENTRE**
29 Reform Street, Blairgowrie
TEL: 01250 874 230

**9 MOYNESS NURSERIES**
Coupar Angus Road, Blairgowrie
TEL: 01250 873 135

# Help us help you

mention the *Gardeners' Atlas* when visiting anywhere on this page.

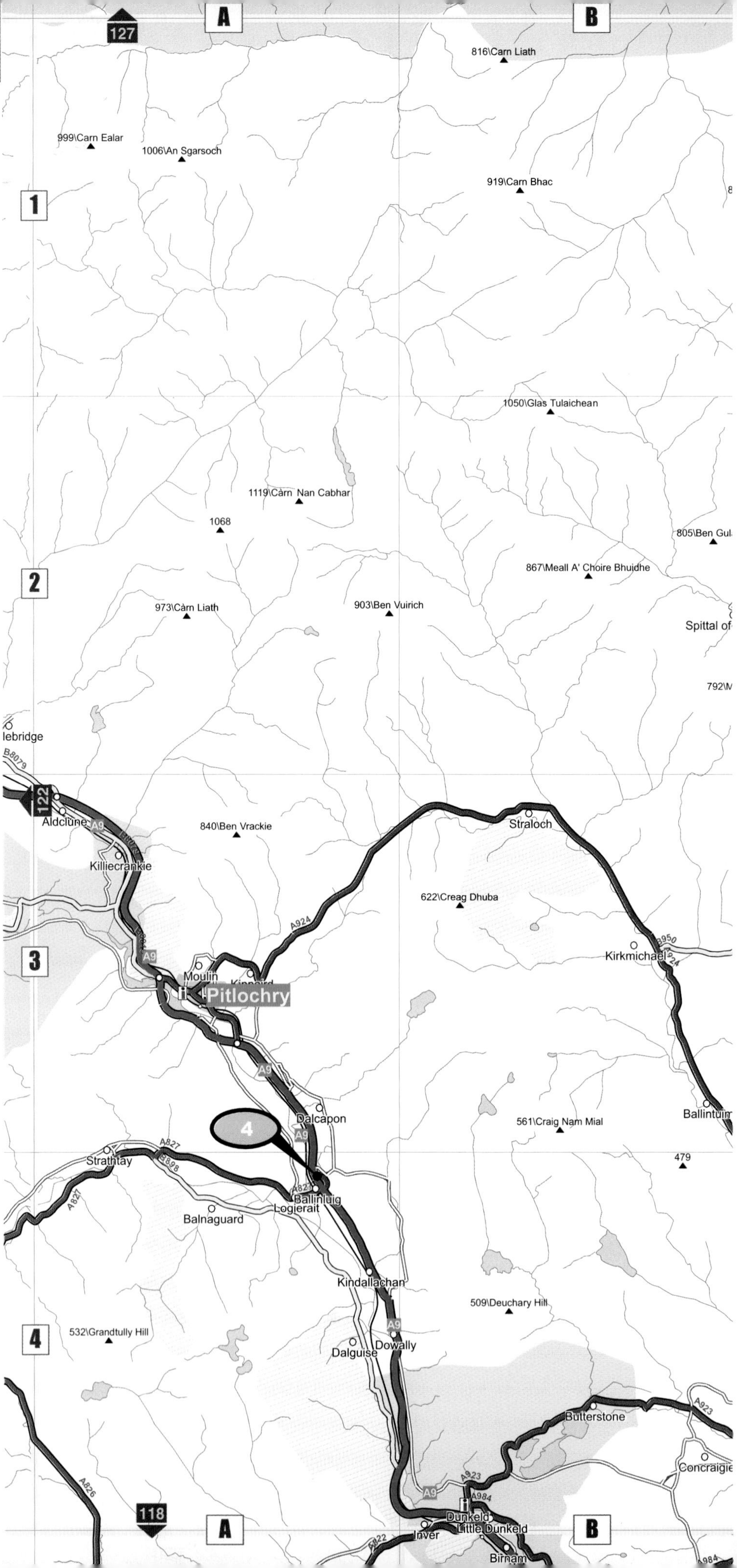

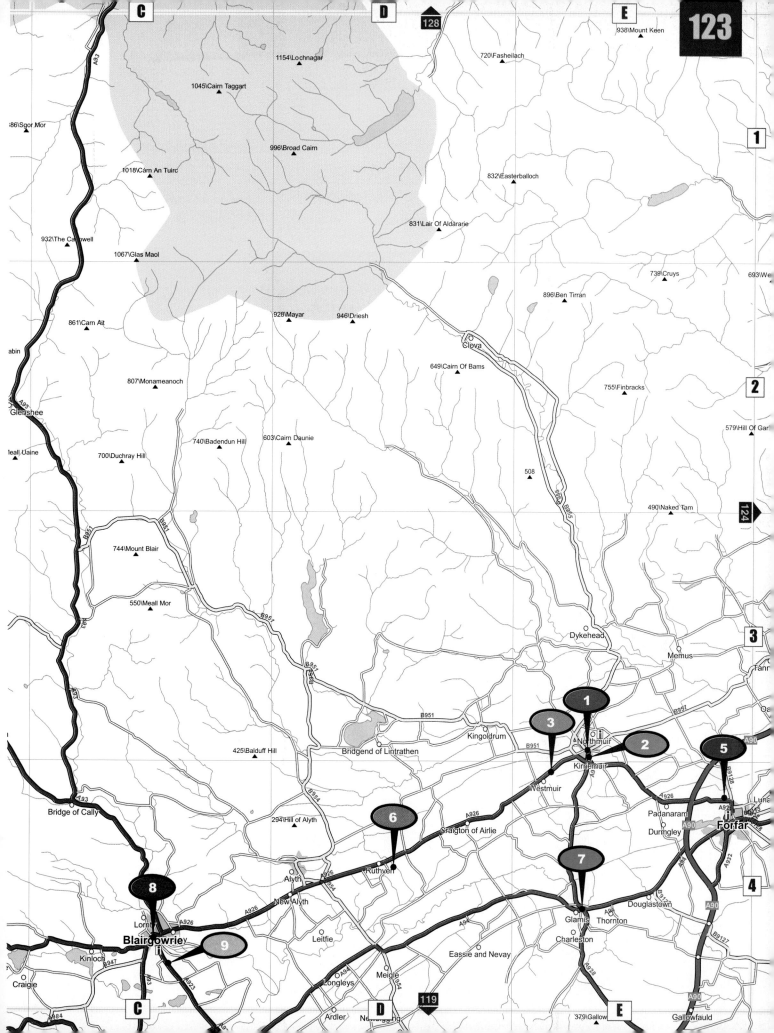

### 1 DUNNOTTAR NURSERIES
Dunnottar Mains, Stonehaven
**TEL:** 01569 763 422

### 2 EDZELL CASTLE, HISTORIC SCOTLAND
Brechin
**TEL:** 01356 648 631

### 3 HOUSE OF DUN, NATIONAL TRUST
Montrose
**TEL:** 01674 810 264

### 4 PATHHEAD NURSERIES
Burnside, Forfar
**TEL:** 01575 572 173

### 5 HOUSE OF PITMUIES
Guthrie, By Forfar, Angus
**TEL:** 01241 828 245

### 6 SILVERWELLS PLANT NURSERY & GARDEN CENTRE
Montrose Road, Arbroath
**TEL:** 01241 875 634

Rose

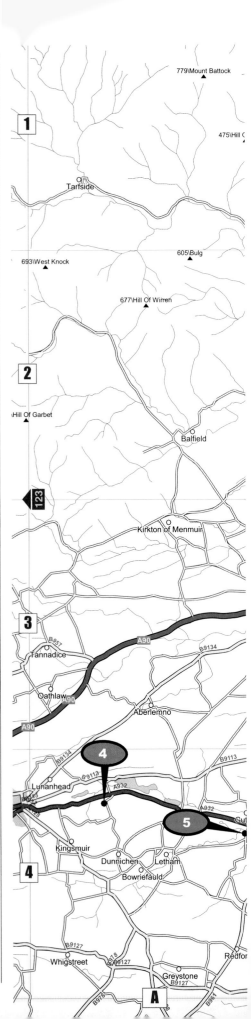

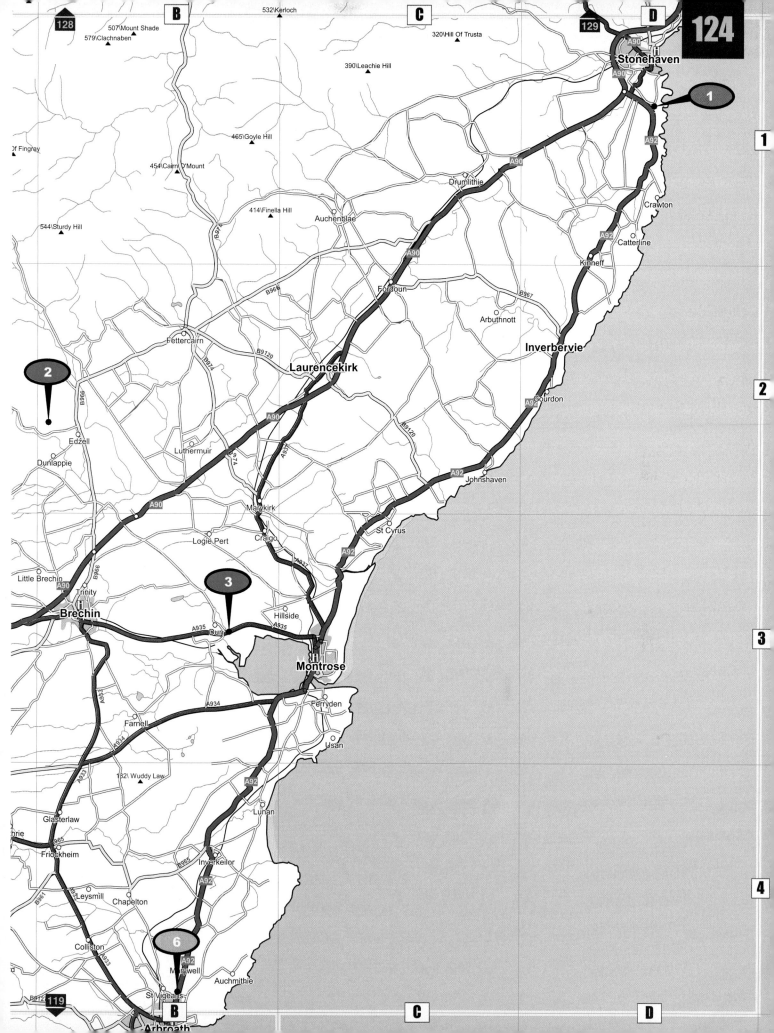

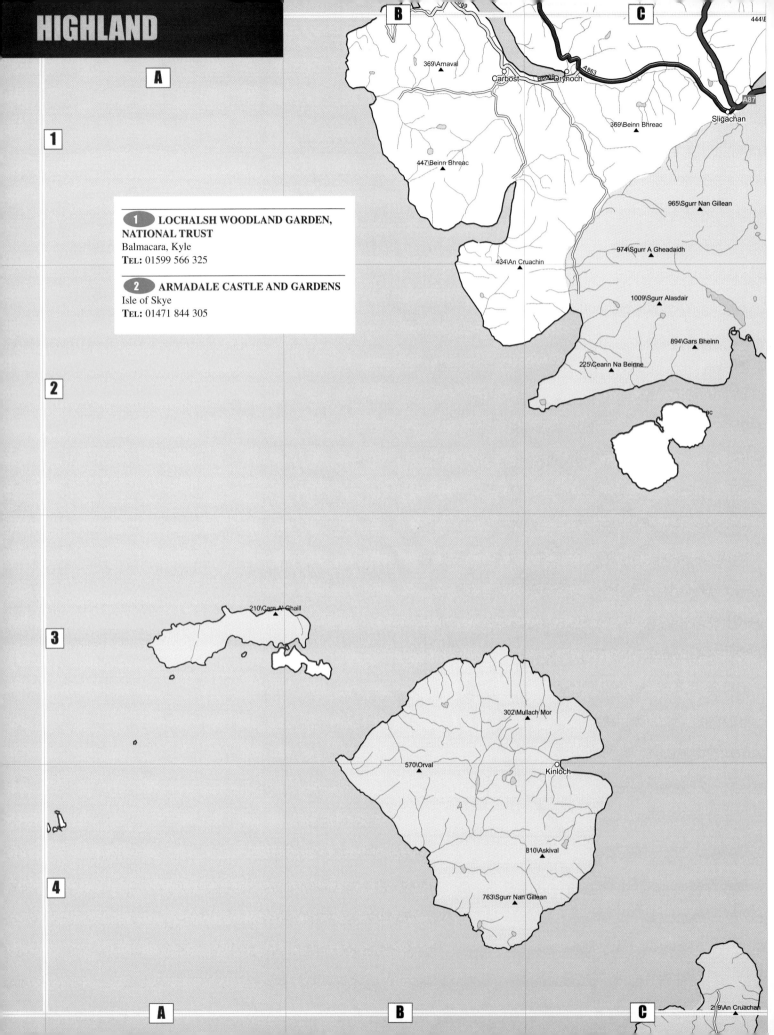

# HIGHLAND

**A**

**B**

**C**

**1**

369\Arnaval

Carbost

Drynoch

A863

369\Beinn Bhreac

Sligachan

A87

447\Beinn Bhreac

965\Sgurr Nan Gillean

974\Sgurr A Gheadaidh

434\An Cruachin

1009\Sgurr Alasdair

894\Gars Bheinn

225\Ceann Na Beinne

**2**

**1** LOCHALSH WOODLAND GARDEN,
NATIONAL TRUST
Balmacara, Kyle
TEL: 01599 566 325

**2** ARMADALE CASTLE AND GARDENS
Isle of Skye
TEL: 01471 844 305

**3**

210\Carn A' Ghaill

302\Mullach Mor

570\Orval

Kinloch

**4**

810\Askival

763\Sgurr Nan Gillean

259\An Cruachan

**A**

**B**

**C**

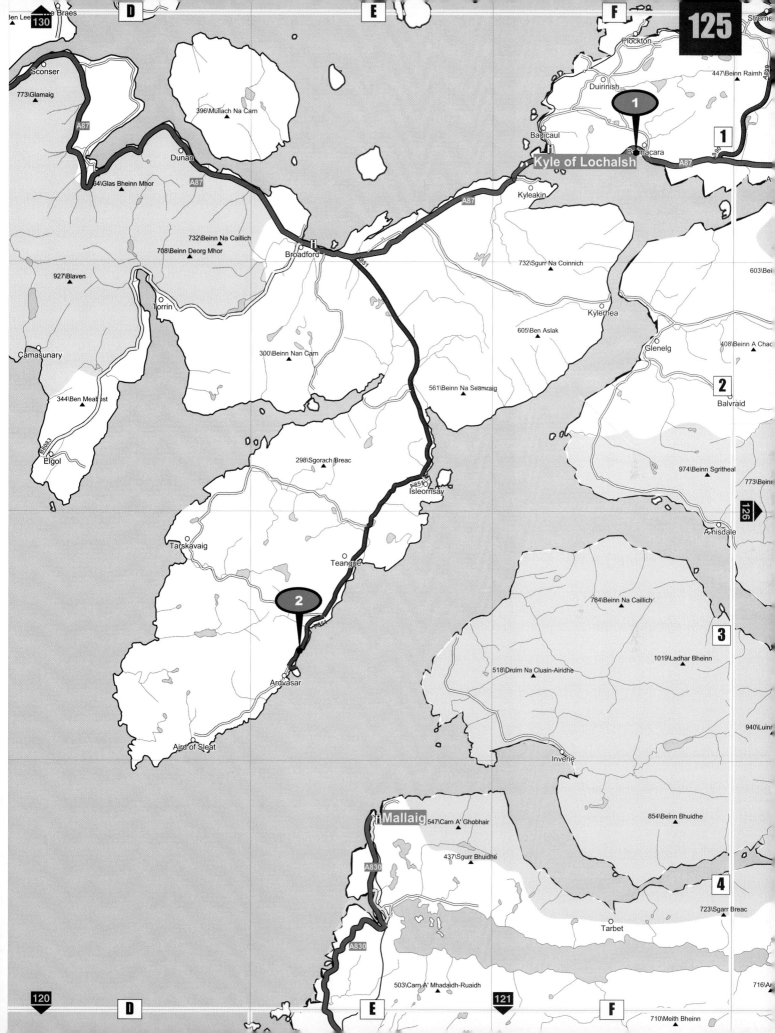

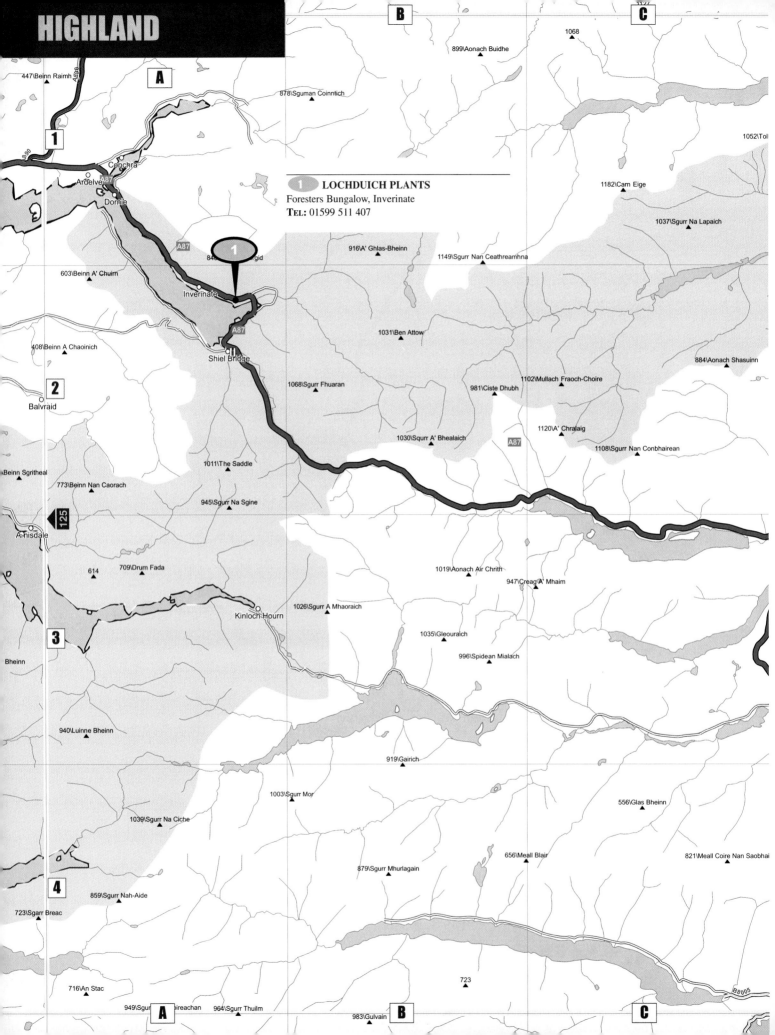

# HIGHLAND

447\Beinn Raimh

**A**

878\Sguman Coinntich

**B**

899\Aonach Buidhe

**C**

1068

1052\Tol

**1**

Conchra

Ardelve

Dornie

**1 LOCHDUICH PLANTS**
Foresters Bungalow, Inverinate
Tel: 01599 511 407

1182\Carn Eige

1037\Sgurr Na Lapaich

A87

849\...rgid

916\A' Ghlas-Bheinn

1149\Sgurr Nan Ceathreamhna

603\Beinn A' Chuirn

Inverinate

1031\Ben Attow

884\Aonach Shasuinn

408\Beinn A Chaoinich

Shiel Bridge

981\Ciste Dhubh

1102\Mullach Fraoch-Choire

**2**

Balvraid

1068\Sgurr Fhuaran

1030\Squrr A' Bhealaich

1120\A' Chralaig

A87

1108\Sgurr Nan Conbhairean

Beinn Sgritheal

773\Beinn Nan Caorach

1011\The Saddle

**125**

945\Sgurr Na Sgine

Arnisdale

614

709\Drum Fada

1019\Aonach Air Chrith

947\Creag A' Mhaim

**3**

Bheinn

1026\Sgurr A Mhaoraich

Kinloch-Hourn

1035\Gleouraich

996\Spidean Mialach

940\Luinne Bheinn

919\Gairich

1003\Sgurr Mor

556\Glas Bheinn

1039\Sgurr Na Ciche

656\Meall Blair

821\Meall Coire Nan Saobhai

879\Sgurr Mhurlagain

**4**

859\Sgurr Nah-Aide

723\Sgarr Breac

723

716\An Stac

**A**

949\Sgur...ireachan

964\Sgurr Thuilm

**B**

983\Gulvain

**C**

B8005

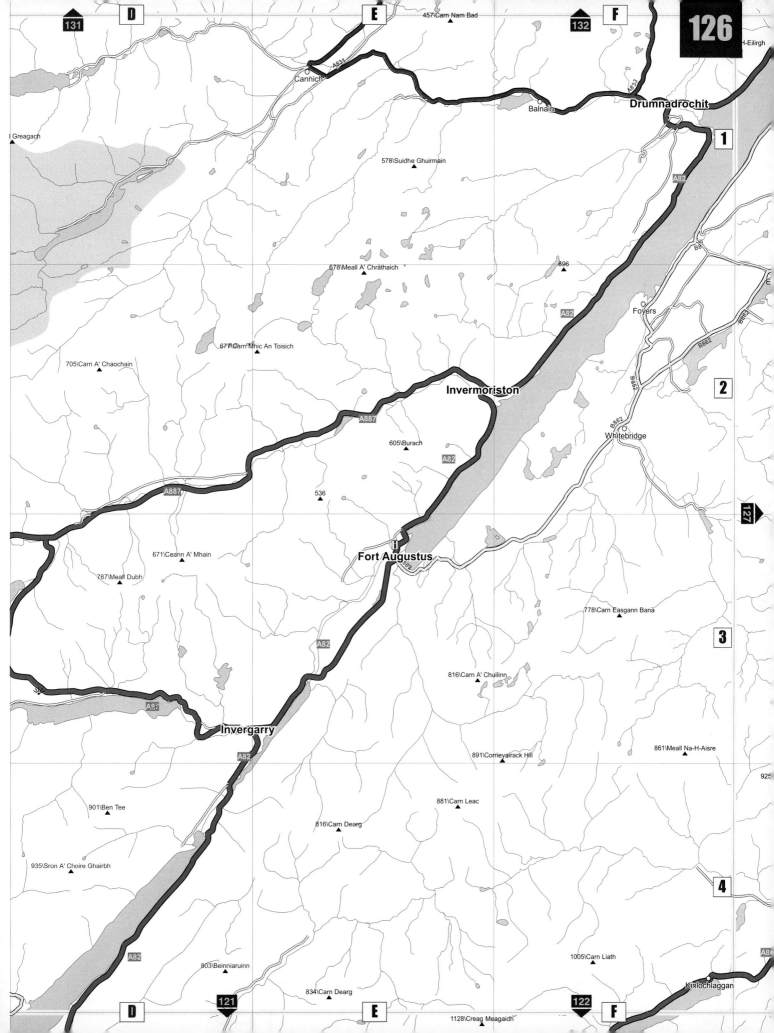

## 1 SPEYSIDE HEATHER CENTRE

Skye of Curr, Dulnain Bridge, Inverness-Shire,
Highland, PH26 3PA.
**TEL:** 01479 851 359
**EMAIL:** enquiries@heathercentre.com
**WEB:** www.heathercentre.com
*Come along and see more heather varieties than you
have ever thought existed at our Heather Centre in
an idyllic Scottish setting in the heart of Strathspey.*
**OPEN:** Open 7 days a week. Summer: Mon-Sat 9-6,
Sun 10-6. Winter: Mon-Sat 9-5, Sun 10-5 or dusk.
**SPECIALITIES:** Heathers.
**FACILITIES:** Gift shop, Sell plants, Restaurant,
Coffee shop, Credit cards, Dogs allowed, Child area,
HTA gift tokens, Own gift tokens, Pushchair friendly,
Wheelchair access, Toilets.

## 2 JACK DRAKES ALPINE NURSERY AND GARDEN

Inshriach, Aviemore
**TEL:** 01540 651 287

Day Lily

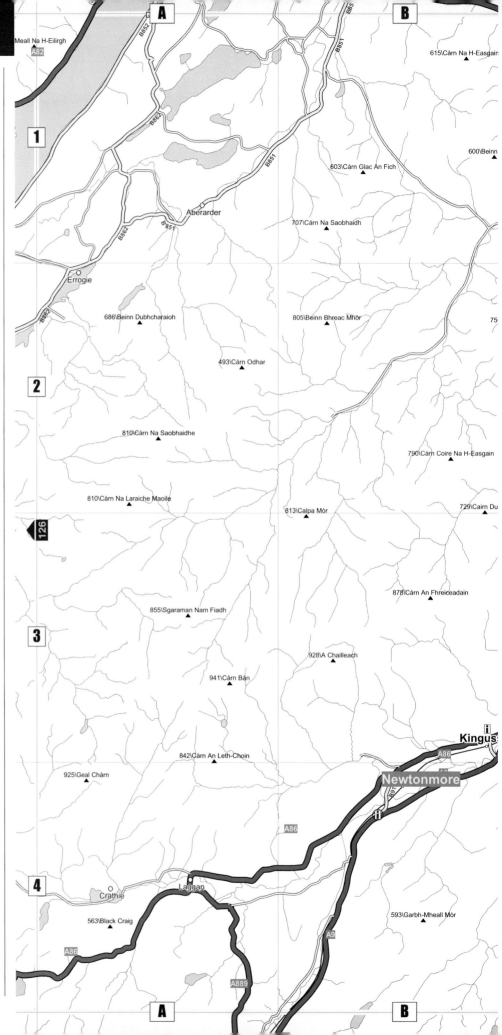

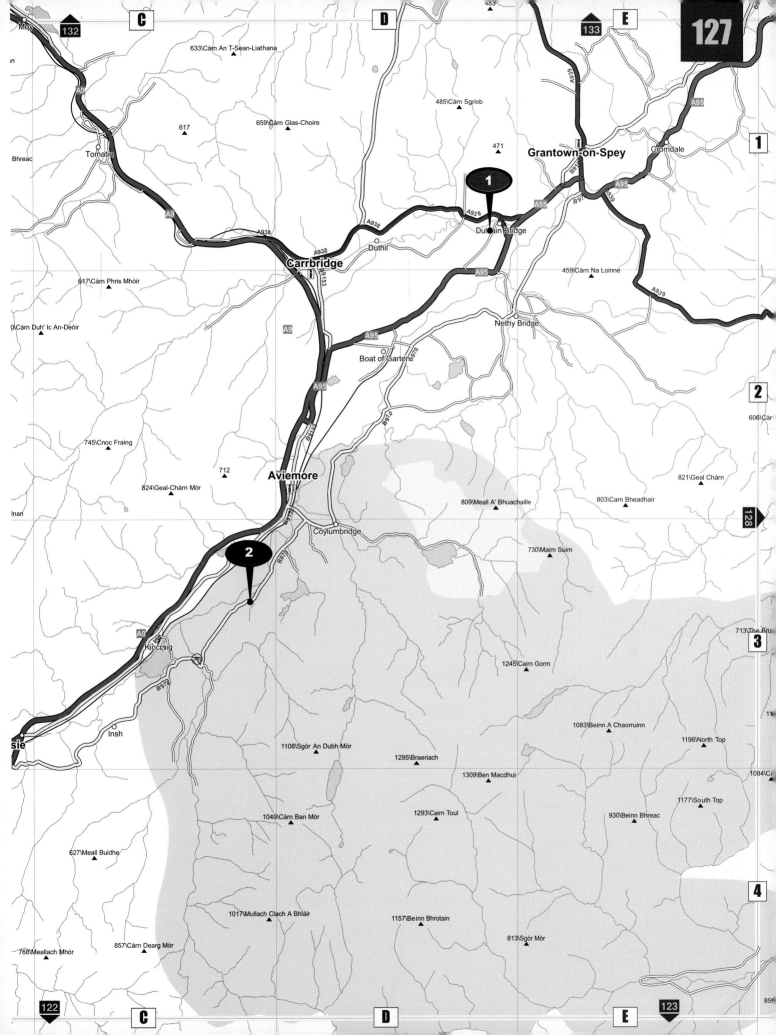

# ABERDEENSHIRE

## 1   LEITH HALL, NATIONAL TRUST
Huntly
**TEL:** 01464 831 216

## 2   BENNACHIE GARDENS & GIFTS
Oyne
**TEL:** 01464 851 489

## 3   MOSSATBURN WATER GARDENS
Mossat, Alford, Aberdeenshire, AB33 8PL.
**TEL:** 01975 571 235
*Large selection of fountains, water features, pumps, liners, medications and chemicals for ponds. UV's, filters and much, much more! All major credit cards accepted.*
**OPEN:** Open 7 days a week. Summer: 9.30-6. Winter: Wed-Mon 10-4. Closed Dec 23-Feb 1.
**SPECIALITIES:** Comprehensive range, Alpines, Aquatics, Gifts, Water features.
**FACILITIES:** Restaurant, Toilets, Credit cards, Gift shop, Sell plants, Own gift tokens.

## 4   KILDRUMMY CASTLE GARDENS
Alford
**TEL:** 01975 571 203

## 5   MONYMUSK WALLED GARDEN
Monymusk, Inverurie
**TEL:** 01467 651 543

## 6   CANDACRAIG GARDENS
Strathdon
**TEL:** 01975 651 226

Iceland Poppy

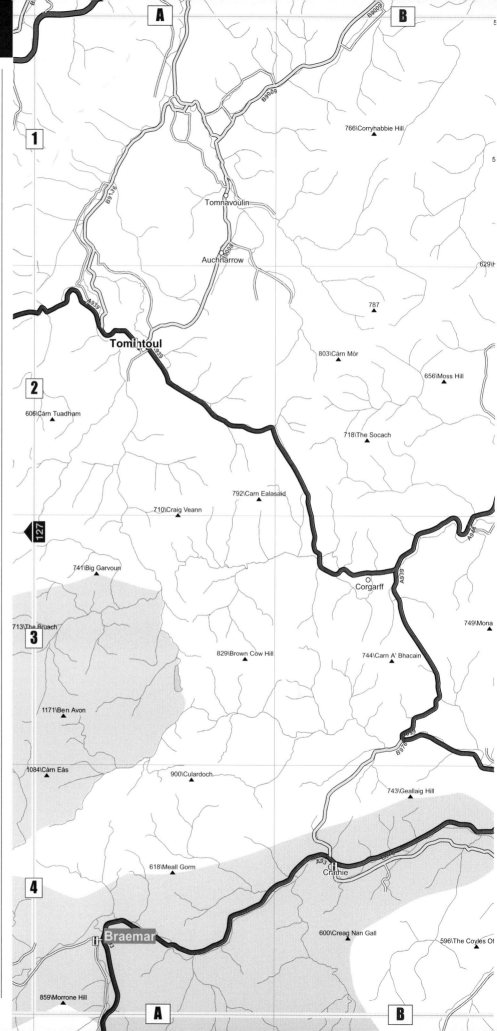

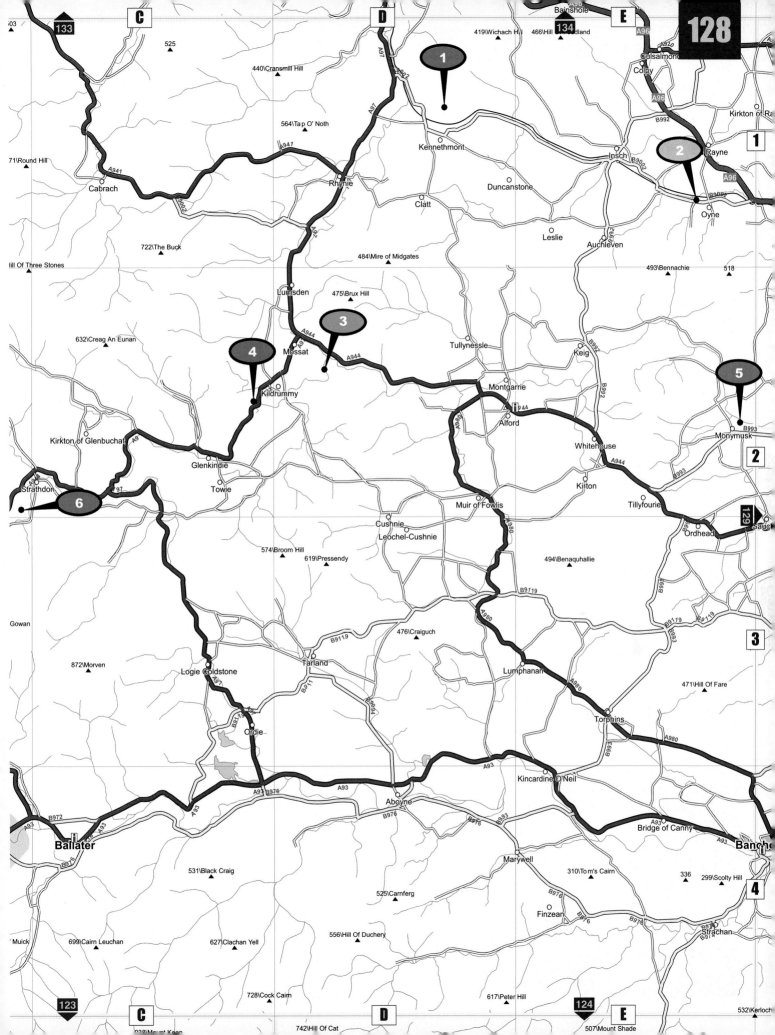

# ABERDEENSHIRE

**1** LOCH-HILLS PLANT CENTRE
Ellon
TEL: 01358 720 694

**2** PITMEDDEN GARDEN, N. TRUST
Ellon
TEL: 01651 842 352

**3** INVERURIE GARDEN & MACHINERY CENTRE
Old Meldrum Road, Inverurie
TEL: 01467 621 402

**4** ORNAMENTAL GRASSES
Kemnay, Inverurie
TEL: 01467 643 544

**5** CASTLE FRASER, NATIONAL TRUST
Inverurie
TEL: 01330 833 463

**6** SEATON PARK
Don Street, Old Aberdeen, Aberdeen
TEL: 01224 522 734

**7** SPRINGHILL NURSERIES
Dunecht, Westhill
TEL: 01330 860 246

**8** WESTBURN PARK
Westburn Road, Aberdeen
TEL: 01224 522 734

**9** LINKS
Beach Esplanade, Aberdeen
TEL: 01224 522 734

**10** COCKERS GARDEN CENTRE
Whitemyres, Lang Stracht, Aberdeen
TEL: 01224 313 261

**11** VICTORIA PARK
Watson Street, Aberdeen
TEL: 01224 522 734

**12** UNION TERRACE GARDENS
Union Terrace, Aberdeen
TEL: 01224 522 734

**13** HAZELHEAD PARK
Hazelhead Avenue, Aberdeen
TEL: 01224 522 734

**14** RUBISLAW TERRACE GARDENS
Albyn Place, Aberdeen
TEL: 01224 522 734

**15** DOBBIES GARDEN CENTRE
Hazledene Road, Aberdeen
TEL: 01224 318 658

**16** JOHNSTON GARDEN
View Field Road, Aberdeen
TEL: 01224 522 734

**17** GORDON HIGHLANDERS MUSEUM
St Luke's Viewfield Road, Aberdeen
TEL: 01224 342 00

**18** DUTHIE PARK WINTER GARDENS
Polmuir Road, Aberdeen
TEL: 01224 522 984

**19** PINEWOOD PARK NURSERIES
Countesswells Road, Aberdeen
TEL: 01224 318 744

**20** FOXLANE GARDEN CENTRE
Aberdeen
TEL: 01224 861 222

**21** W LEIPER
Lochinch Croft, Charleston, Nigg
TEL: 01224 897 338

**22** DRUM CASTLE, NATIONAL TRUST
Banchory
TEL: 01330 811 204

**23** HEATHER CENTRE
Banchory
TEL: 01330 811 234

**24** CRATHES CASTLE GARDEN, N. TRUST
Banchory
TEL: 01330 844 525

**25** DEESIDE HOUSE & GARDEN CENTRE
North Deeside Road, Banchory
TEL: 01330 820 118

Daisy

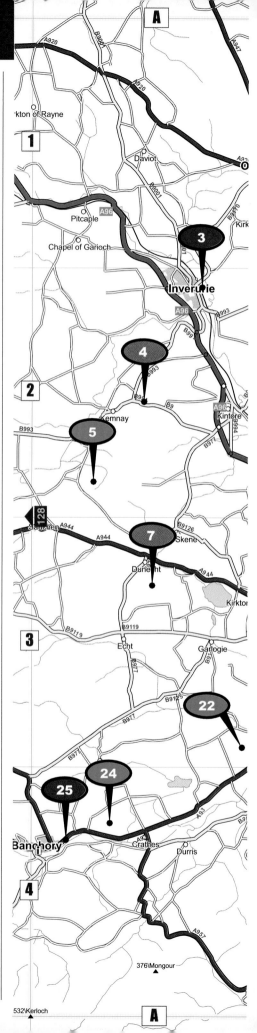

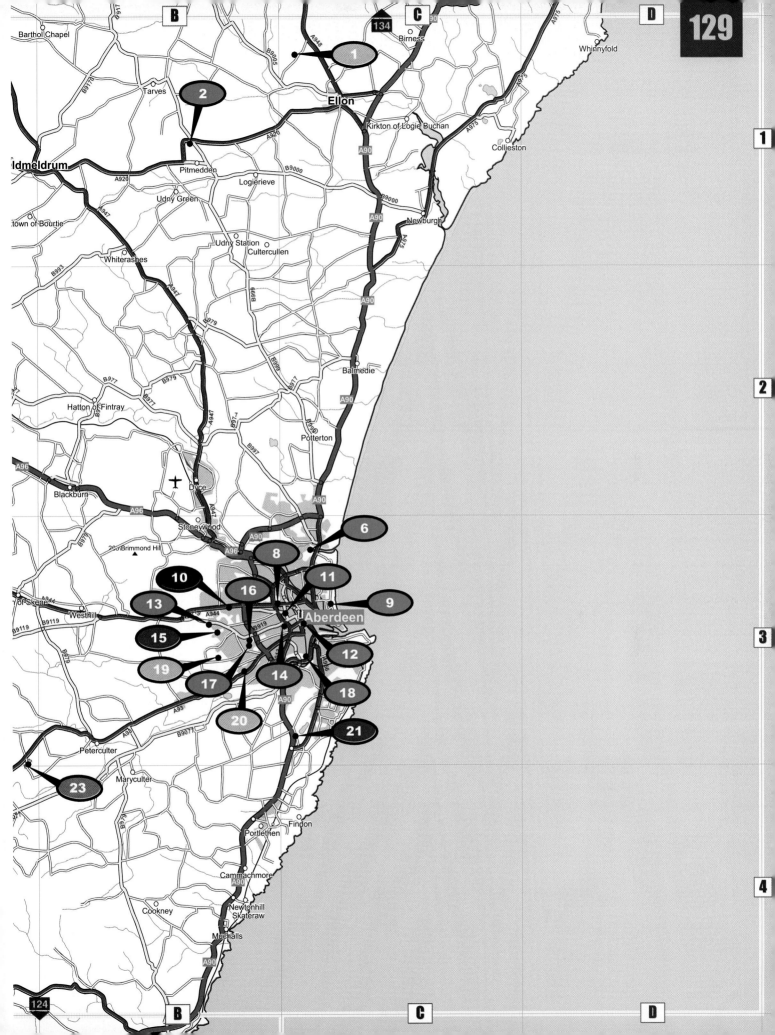

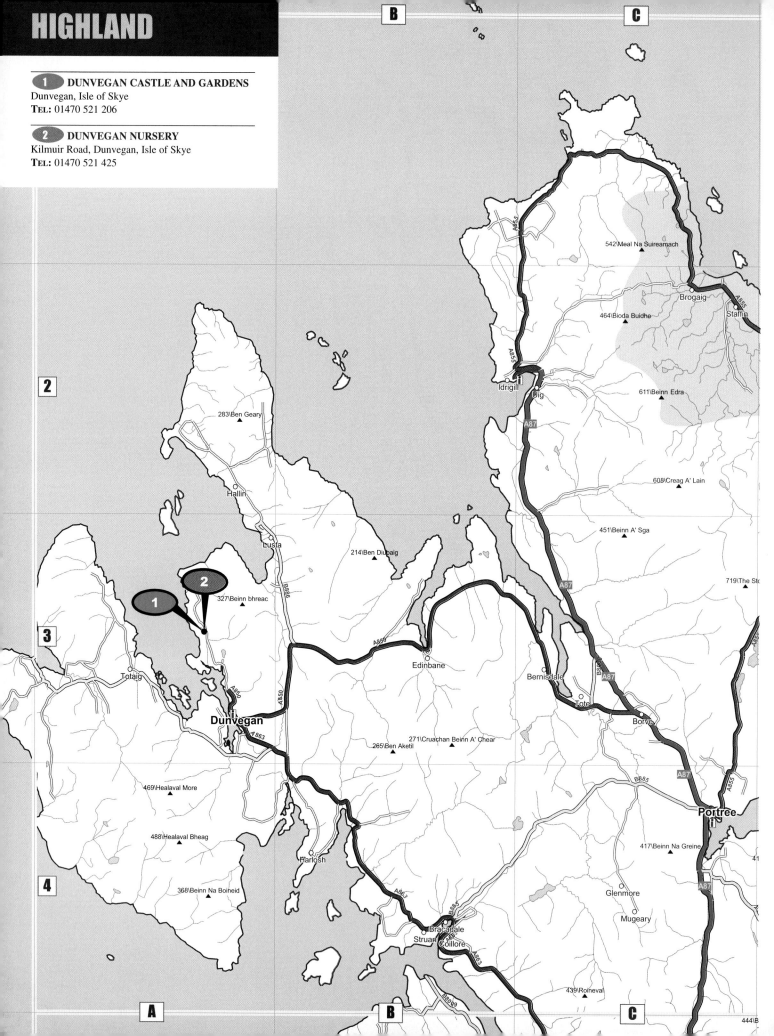

# HIGHLAND

**1** **DUNVEGAN CASTLE AND GARDENS**
Dunvegan, Isle of Skye
TEL: 01470 521 206

**2** **DUNVEGAN NURSERY**
Kilmuir Road, Dunvegan, Isle of Skye
TEL: 01470 521 425

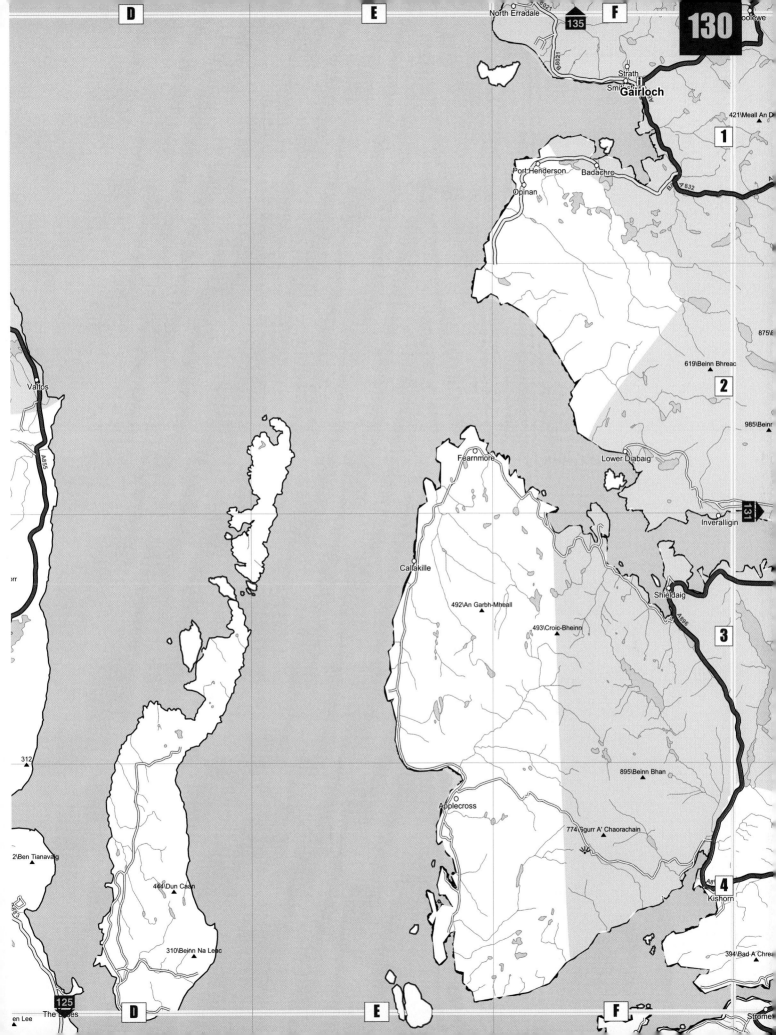

D     E     F

North Erradale

135

B 8021

oolewe

Strath

Smit... ...le

Gairloch

421\Meall An D

1

Port Henderson    Badachro

B... 832

Opinan

875\...

619\Beinn Bhreac

2

985\Beinn

Valtos

A855

Fearnmore

Lower Diabaig

131

Inveralligin

Callakille

312

492\An Garbh-Mheall

493\Croic-Bheinn

Shieldaig

A896

3

895\Beinn Bhan

2\Ben Tianavaig

Applecross

774\Sgurr A' Chaorachain

444\Dun Caan

A8...

4

Kishorn

310\Beinn Na Leac

394\Bad A Chrea

Strome

# HIGHLAND

**1** **ATTADALE GARDENS**
Attadale Estate, Strathcarron, Wester Ross
TEL: 01520 722 217

Nemesia

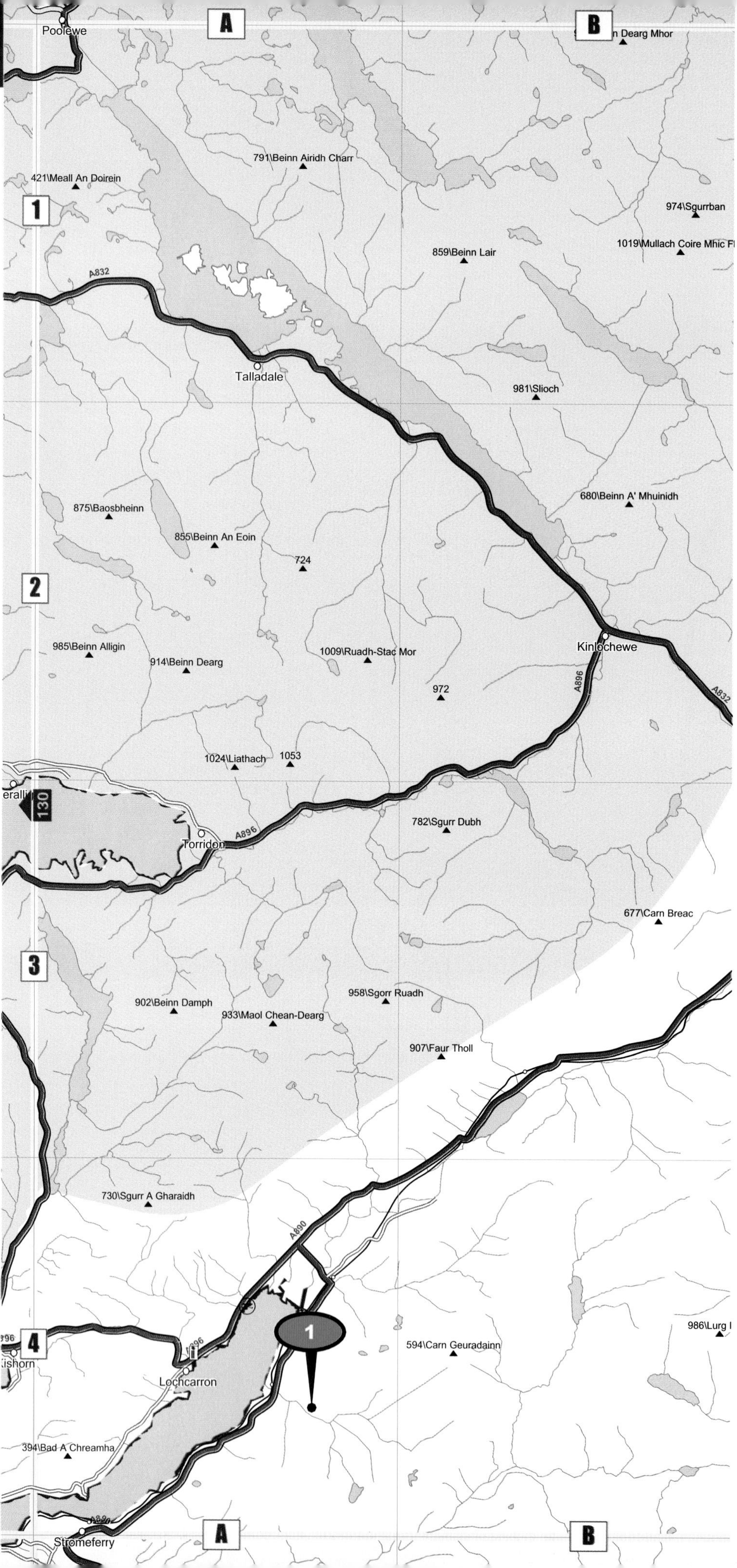

---

**A** **B**

Poolewe

n Dearg Mhor

**1**

791\Beinn Airidh Charr

421\Meall An Doirein

974\Sgurrban

A 832

859\Beinn Lair

1019\Mullach Coire Mhic F

Talladale

981\Slioch

875\Baosbheinn

680\Beinn A' Muinidh

855\Beinn An Eoin

724

**2**

985\Beinn Alligin

Kinlochewe

914\Beinn Dearg

1009\Ruadh-Stac Mor

972

A 896

A 832

1024\Liathach 1053

eralli

130

782\Sgurr Dubh

Torridon

A 896

677\Carn Breac

**3**

902\Beinn Damph

958\Sgorr Ruadh

933\Maol Chean-Dearg

907\Faur Tholl

730\Sgurr A Gharaidh

A 890

986\Lurg

594\Carn Geuradainn

996 **4**

896

**1**

cishorn

Lochcarron

394\Bad A Chreamha

**A** **B**

Stromeferry

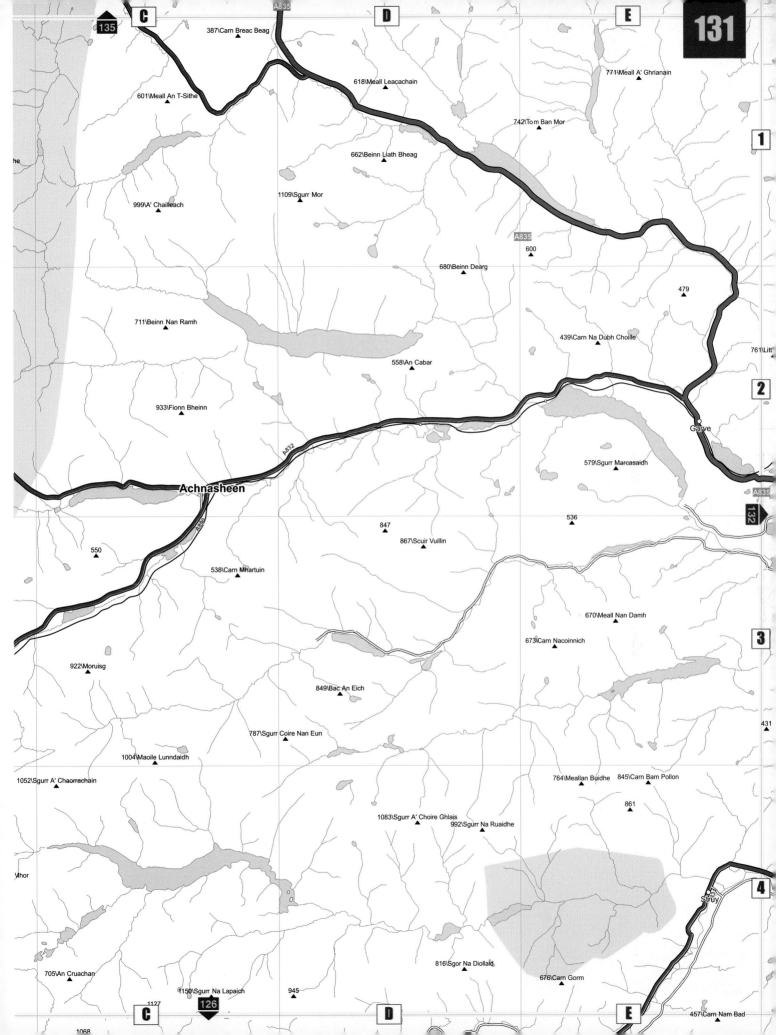

A835

135

387\Carn Breac Beag

601\Meall An T-Sithe

618\Meall Leacachain

771\Meall A' Ghrianain

742\Tom Ban Mor

662\Beinn Liath Bheag

1

1109\Sgurr Mor

999\A' Chailleach

A835

600

680\Beinn Dearg

479

711\Beinn Nan Ramh

439\Carn Na Dubh Choille

761\Litt'

558\An Cabar

2

933\Fionn Bheinn

A832

Garve

579\Sgurr Marcasaidh

Achnasheen

A835

132

847

536

867\Scuir Vuillin

550

538\Carn Mhartuin

670\Meall Nan Damh

673\Carn Nacoinnich

3

431

922\Moruisg

849\Bac An Eich

787\Sgurr Coire Nan Eun

1004\Maoile Lunndaidh

1052\Sgurr A' Chaorrachain

764\Meallan Buidhe    845\Carn Bam Pollon

861

1083\Sgurr A' Choire Ghlais

992\Sgurr Na Ruaidhe

Vhor

Struy

4

705\An Cruachan

816\Sgor Na Diollaid

676\Carn Gorm

1052

1150\Sgurr Na Lapaich

945

1127

126

457\Carn Nam Bad

1068

# HIGHLAND · MORAY

**1** **CAMEONS GARDEN CENTRE**
109 High Street, Invergordon
**TEL:** 01349 854 303

**2** **POYNTZFIELD HERB NURSERY**
Black Isle, Dingwall
**TEL:** 01381 610 352

**3** **DYKE NURSERIES**
Dyke, Forres
**TEL:** 01309 641 362

**4** **BRODIE CASTLE, NATIONAL TRUST**
Forres
**TEL:** 01309 641 371

**5** **CANONBURY NURSERY & GARDEN CENTRE**
Precincts Road, Fortrose
**TEL:** 01381 620 043

**6** **RIVERBANK NURSERY GARDEN CENTRE**
Riverbank Road, Conon Bridge, Dingwall
**TEL:** 01349 861 720

**7** **BROADLEY GARDEN CENTRE**
Cawdor Road, Nairn
**TEL:** 01667 452 955

**8** **CAWDOR CASTLE & GARDENS**
Nairn
**TEL:** 01667 404 615

**9** **GREENS NURSERIES**
New Fleenas Farm, Nairn
**TEL:** 01667 452 760

**10** **HOWDENS GARDEN CENTRE**
51 Telford Street, Inverness
**TEL:** 01463 711 134

**11** **ARDFEARN NURSERY**
Bunchrew, Inverness
**TEL:** 01463 243 250

**12** **DOCHFOUR GARDENS**
Dochfour Estate, Inverness
**TEL:** 01463 861 218

**13** **HIGHLAND LILIUMS**
10 Loaneckheim, Kiltarlity, Beauly
**TEL:** 01463 741 365

**14** **ABRIACHAN GARDENS & NURSERY**
Loch Ness Side, Inverness
**TEL:** 01463 861 232

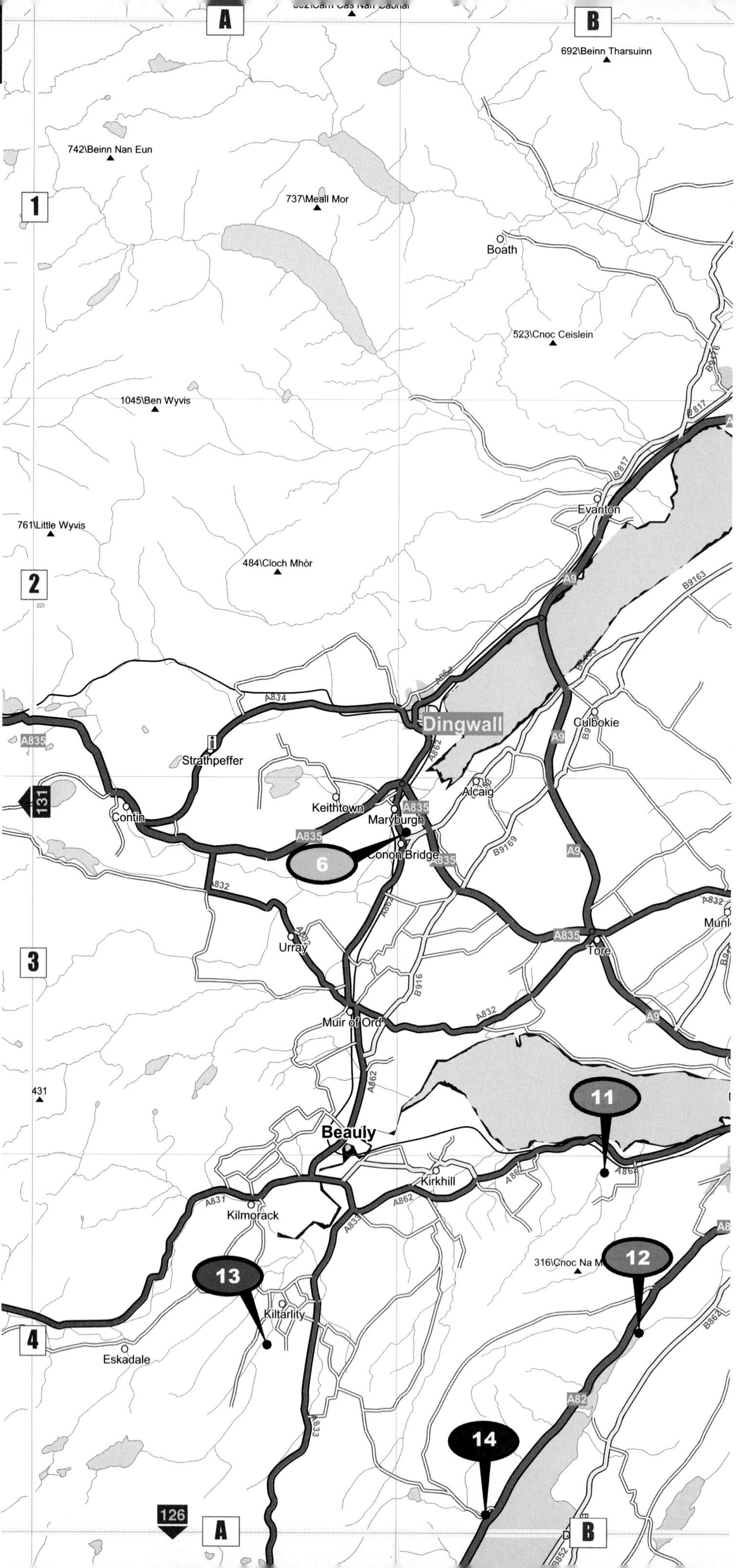

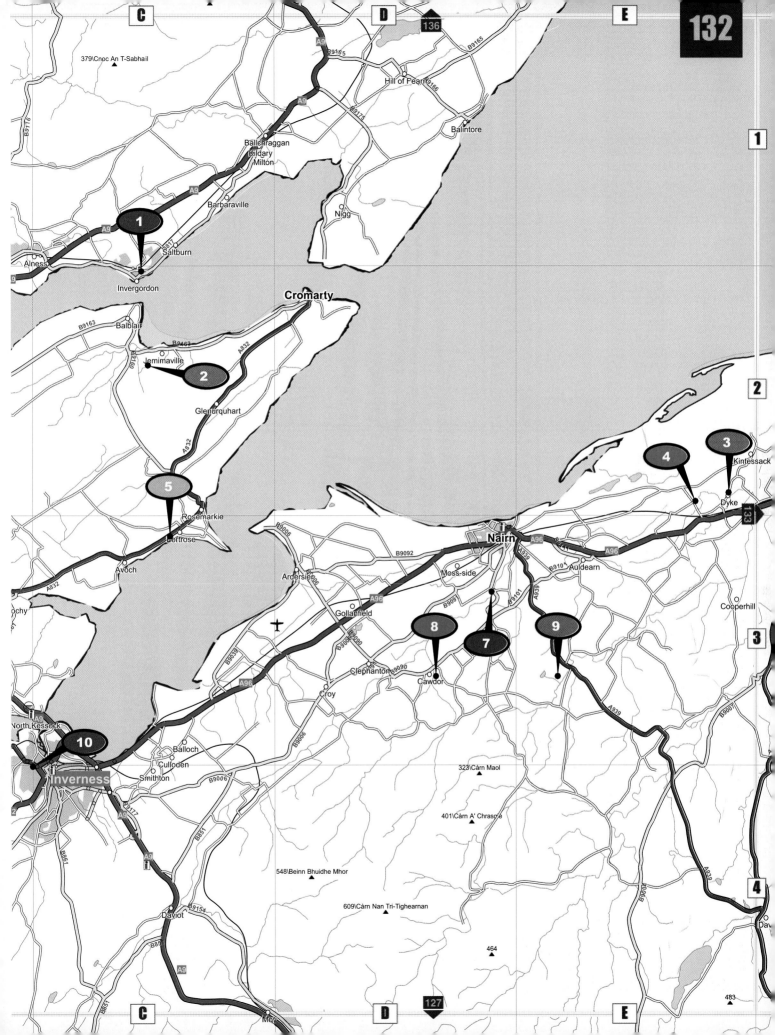

# SCOTLAND

**1** **TOM THUMB'S**
Lossiemouth
**TEL:** 01343 814 333

**2** **CHRISTIES ELITE NURSERIES**
Forres
**TEL:** 01309 672 633

**3** **CHRISTIES (FOCHABERS) LTD**
The Nurseries, Fochabers
**TEL:** 01343 820 362

**4** **GLEN GRANT GARDEN**
Rothes, Aberlour
**TEL:** 01542 783 318

**5** **KING GEORGE V GARDEN CENTRE**
Steven Road, Huntly
**TEL:** 01466 793 908

**6** **BALLINDALLOCH CASTLE**
Grantown-on-Spey
**TEL:** 01807 500 205

Phlox

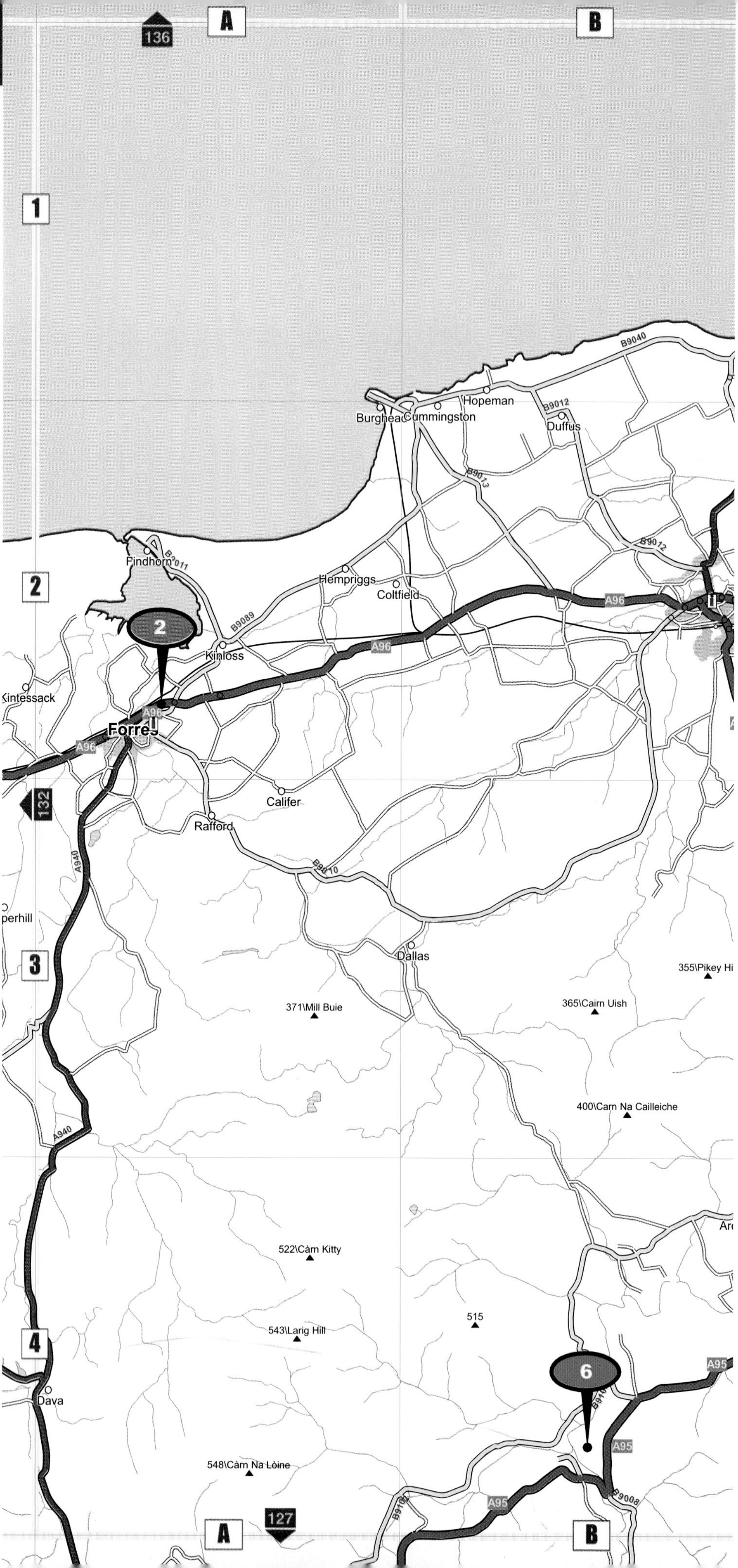

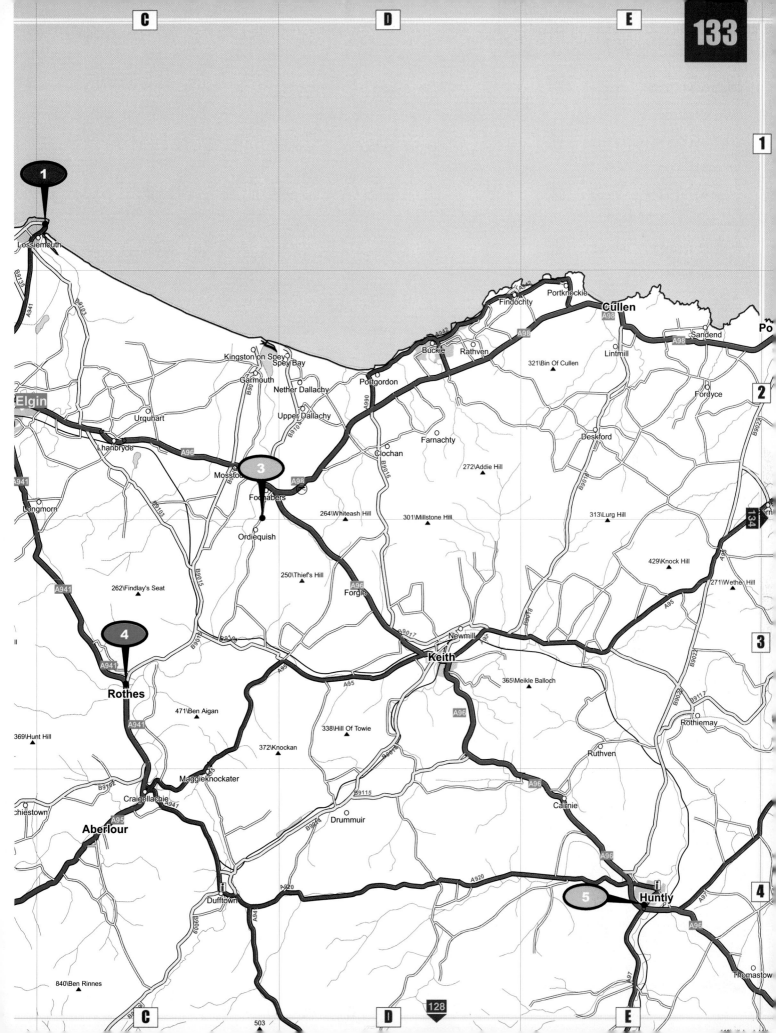

# ABERDEENSHIRE

### 1   C & E LAING
The Nurseries, Turriff
**TEL:** 01888 563 236

### 2   AULTAN NURSERY
Turriff
**TEL:** 01888 544 702

### 3   WHITE LODGE NURSERY
Carnousie, Turriff
**TEL:** 01888 562 924

### 4   SIMPSON & FLORENCE
Millmoss Nurseries, Turriff
**TEL:** 01888 563 511

### 5   FYVIE CASTLE, NATIONAL TRUST
Turriff
**TEL:** 01651 891 266

Tulips

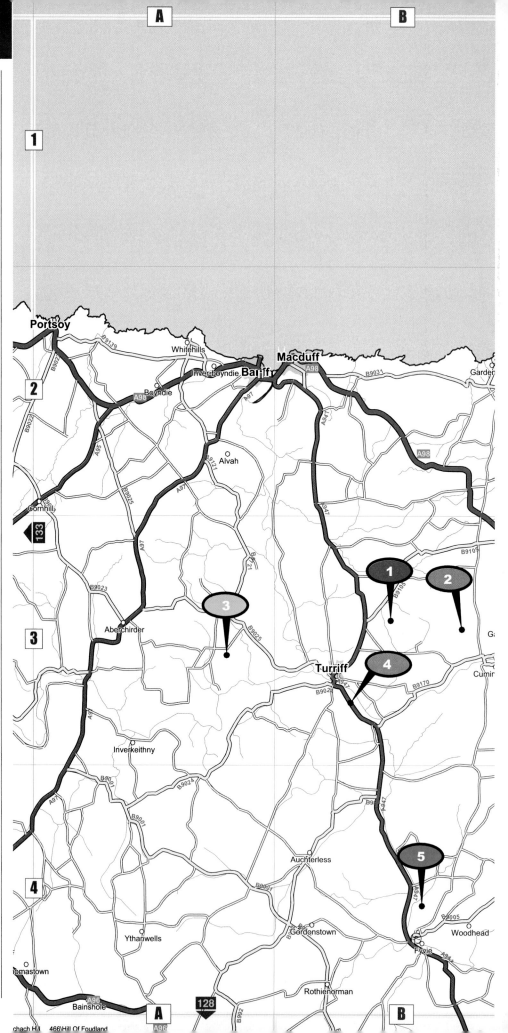

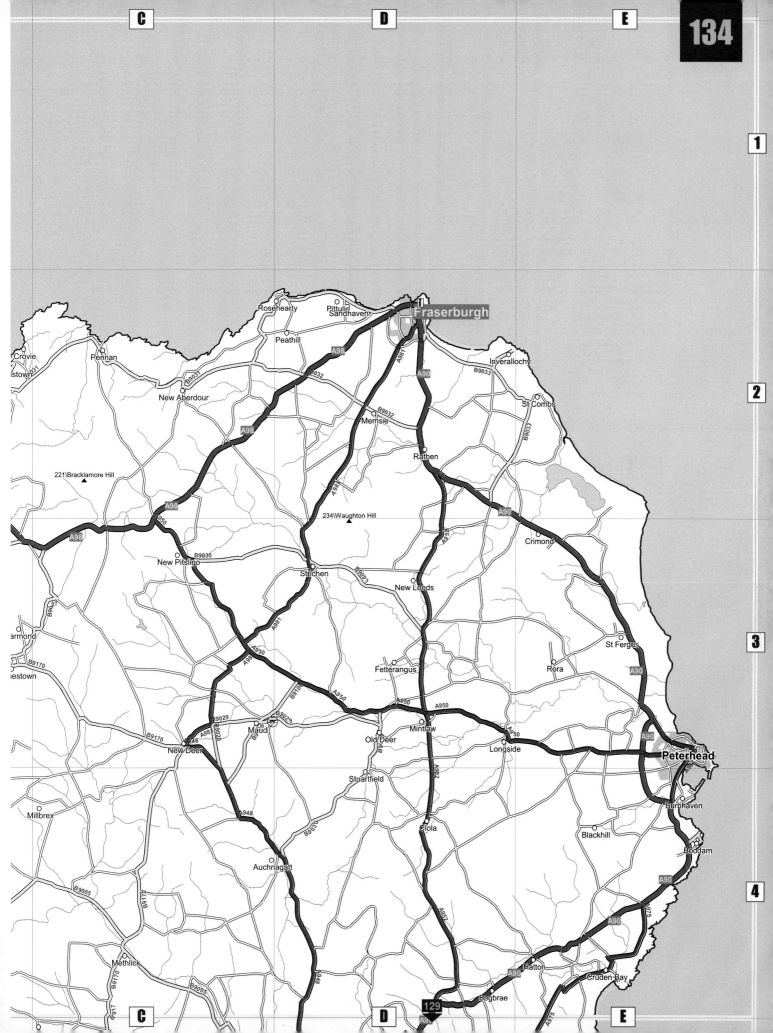

C D E

1

2

3

4

Crovie
Pennan
stown

Rosehearty
Pittulie
Sandhaven
Peathill

Fraserburgh

Inverallochy
B9033
St Combs

New Aberdour
B9031
B9032

Memsie
B9032

Rathen

A98

A981

A90

B9033

221\Bracklamore Hill

A98

A950

234\Waughton Hill

A90

Crimond

New Pitsligo
B9030

Strichen

B9093

New Leeds

A98

A952

armond
B9170
B9170
estown

A981

A950

A98

St Fergus
A90

Fetterangus

Rora

A950

B9170

A950

A950

A950

Mintlaw
A50
Longside
A90
Peterhead
Millbrex
B9029
B9029
Maud
B9028
New Deer
A98
A948
Old Deer
B9030
Stuartfield
A952
Burnhaven
Blackhill
Boddam
Auchnagatt
B9030
Clola
A952
A90
B9005
B9170
A948
A90
A975
Methlick
B9170
A948
B9005
B9917
A948
Hatton
Cruden Bay
Bogbrae
A90
A975

C D E

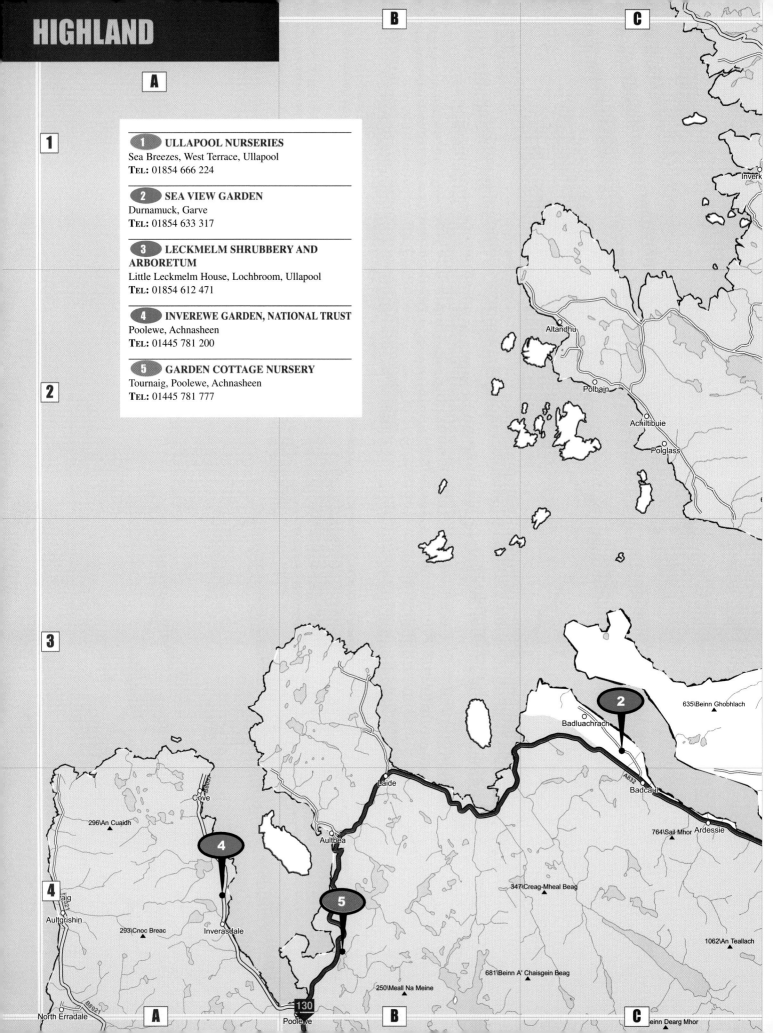

**A**

**B**

**C**

**1** ULLAPOOL NURSERIES
Sea Breezes, West Terrace, Ullapool
TEL: 01854 666 224

**2** SEA VIEW GARDEN
Durnamuck, Garve
TEL: 01854 633 317

**3** LECKMELM SHRUBBERY AND
ARBORETUM
Little Leckmelm House, Lochbroom, Ullapool
TEL: 01854 612 471

**4** INVEREWE GARDEN, NATIONAL TRUST
Poolewe, Achnasheen
TEL: 01445 781 200

**5** GARDEN COTTAGE NURSERY
Tournaig, Poolewe, Achnasheen
TEL: 01445 781 777

Inverk

Altandhu

Polbain

Achiltibuie

Polglass

635\Beinn Ghobhlach

Badluachrach

A832

Badcaul

764\Sail Mhor  Ardessie

Laide

Cove

296\An Cuaidh

Aultbea

347\Creag-Mheal Beag

1062\An Teallach

aig

Aultgrishin

293\Cnoc Breac

Inverasdale

681\Beinn A' Chaisgein Beag

North Erradale

B8021

250\Meall Na Meine

130

Poolewe

einn Dearg Mhor

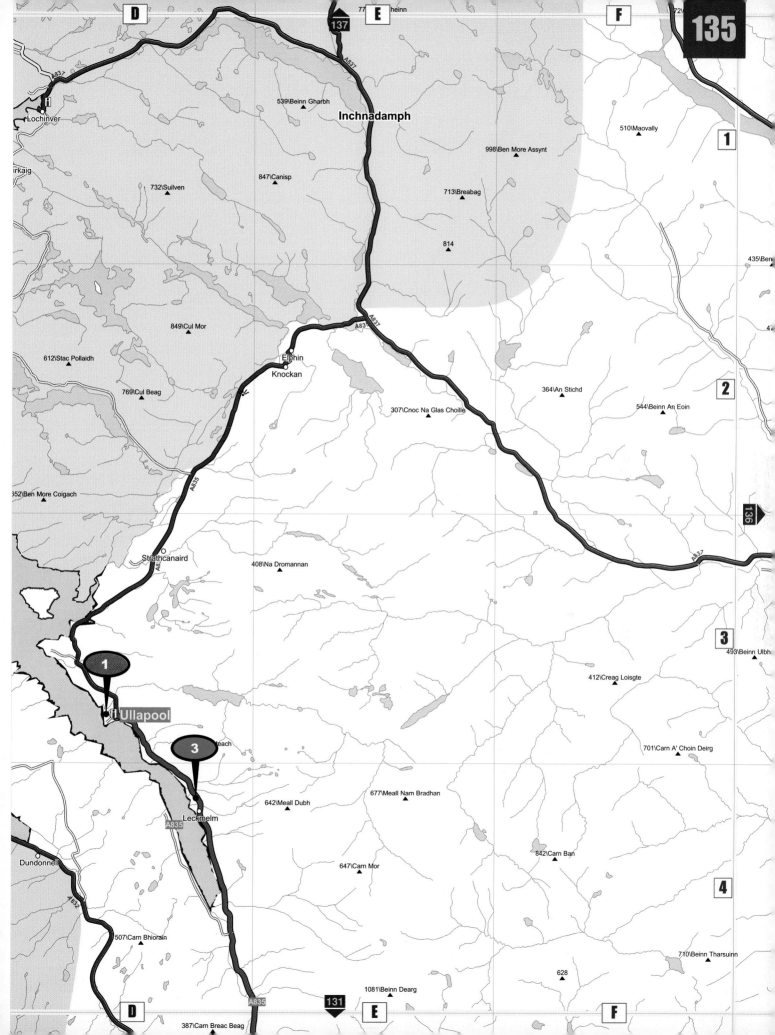

137

77\heinn

539\Beinn Gharbh

**Inchnadamph**

510\Maovally

**1**

998\Ben More Assynt

847\Canisp

732\Suilven

713\Breabag

435\Ben

814

849\Cul Mor

612\Stac Pollaidh

Elphin

Knockan

364\An Stichd

**2**

544\Beinn An Eoin

769\Cul Beag

307\Cnoc Na Glas Choille

652\Ben More Coigach

**136**

Strathcanaird

408\Na Dromannan

**3**

493\Beinn Ulbh

1

412\Creag Loisgte

**Ullapool**

3

701\Carn A' Choin Deirg

each

677\Meall Nam Bradhan

642\Meall Dubh

Leckmelm

842\Carn Ban

Dundonnell

647\Carn Mor

**4**

507\Carn Bhiorain

710\Beinn Tharsuinn

628

1081\Beinn Dearg

387\Carn Breac Beag

# HIGHLAND

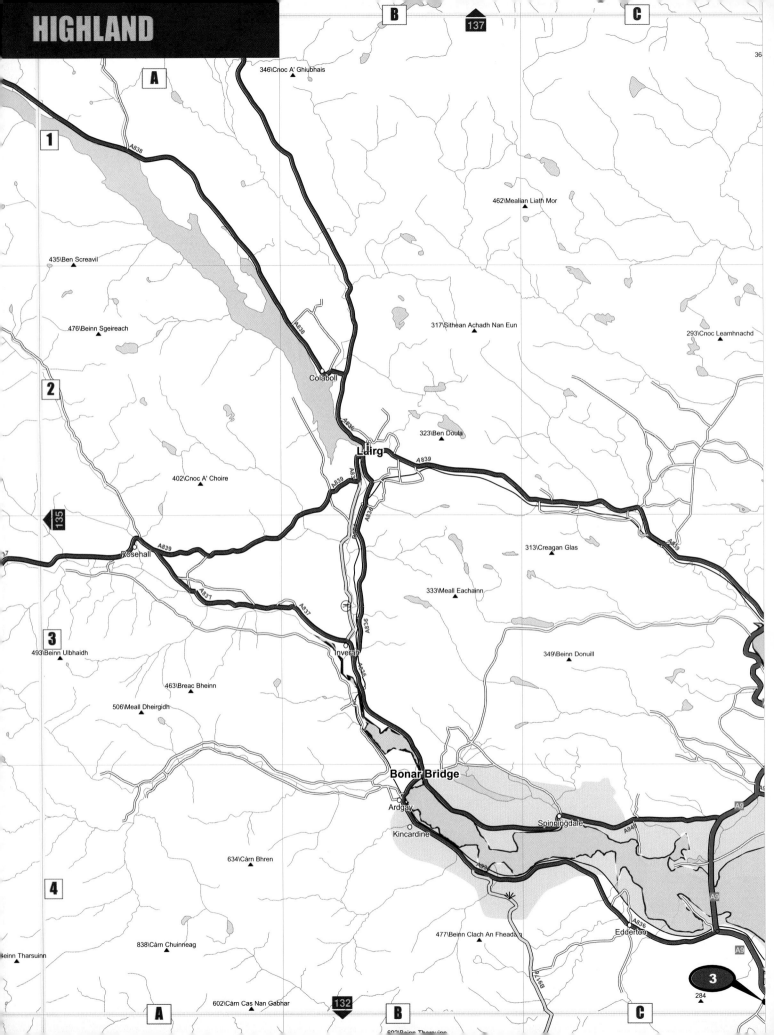

A

B

137

C

346\Cnoc A' Ghiubhais

1

462\Meallan Liath Mor

435\Ben Screavil

476\Beinn Sgeireach

317\Sithean Achadh Nan Eun

293\Cnoc Leamhnachd

Colaboll

2

323\Ben Doula

Lairg

402\Cnoc A' Choire

135

313\Creagan Glas

Rosehall

333\Meall Eachainn

3

493\Beinn Ulbhaidh

349\Beinn Donuill

463\Breac Bheinn

Inveran

506\Meall Dheirgidh

Bonar Bridge

Ardgay

Spinningdale

Kincardine

634\Càrn Bhren

4

838\Càrn Chuinneag

477\Beinn Clach An Fheada

Edderton

Beinn Tharsuinn

602\Càrn Cas Nan Gabhar

132

284

3

A

B

C

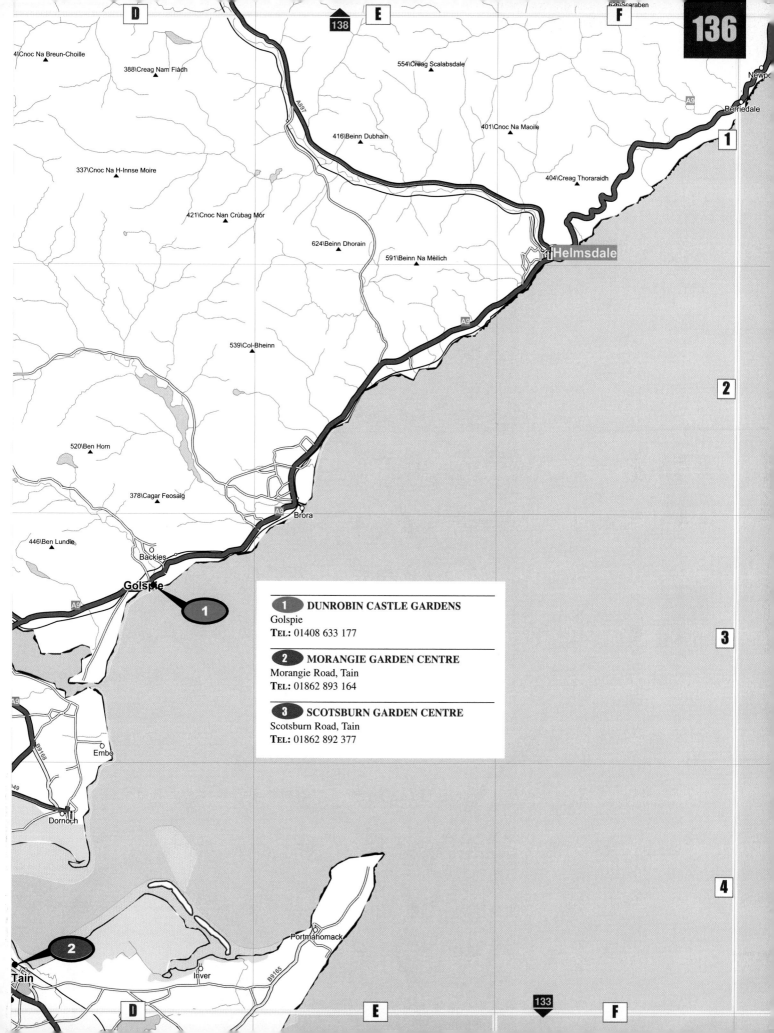

D

E

138

F

626\Scaraben

4\Cnoc Na Breun-Choille

388\Creag Nam Fiàdh

554\Creag Scalabsdale

Newpo

Berriedale

1

416\Beinn Dubhain

401\Cnoc Na Maoile

337\Cnoc Na H-Innse Moire

404\Creag Thoraraidh

421\Cnoc Nan Crùbag Mòr

624\Beinn Dhorain

Helmsdale

591\Beinn Na Mèilich

2

539\Col-Bheinn

A9

520\Ben Horn

378\Cagar Feosaig

A9

Brora

446\Ben Lundie

Backies

Golspie

A9

1

**1** DUNROBIN CASTLE GARDENS
Golspie
**Tel:** 01408 633 177

**2** MORANGIE GARDEN CENTRE
Morangie Road, Tain
**Tel:** 01862 893 164

**3** SCOTSBURN GARDEN CENTRE
Scotsburn Road, Tain
**Tel:** 01862 892 377

3

A9

B9168

Embo

A49

Dornoch

4

Portmahomack

2

Tain

Inver

B9165

D

E

133

F

# HIGHLAND

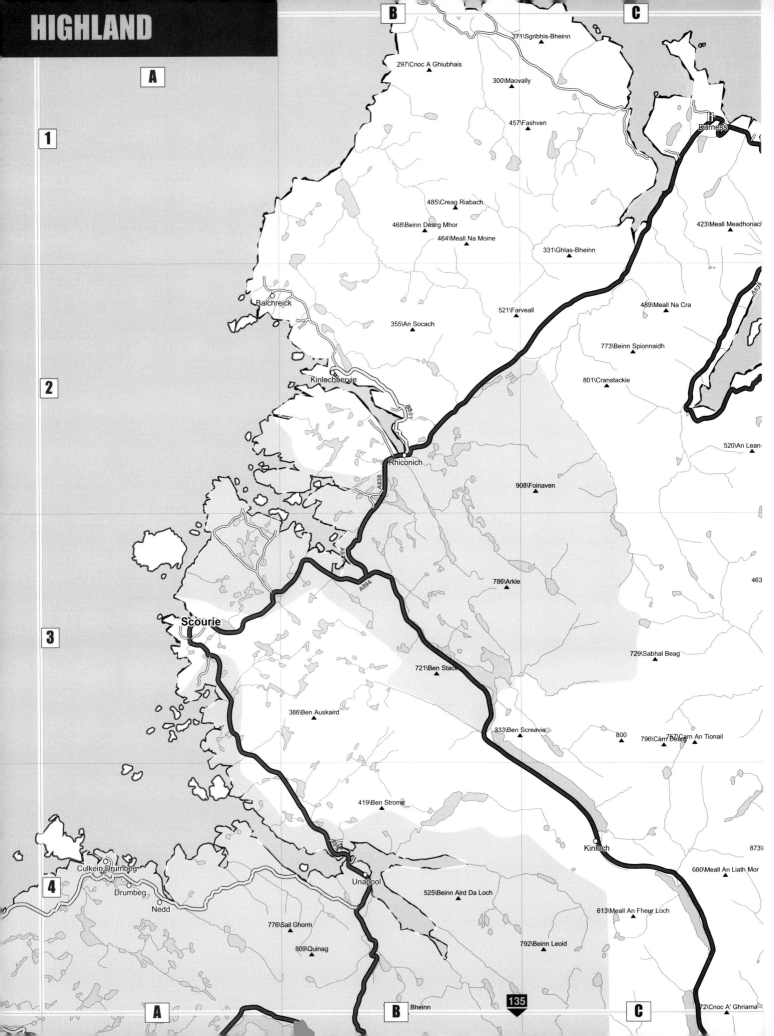

A

B

C

1

371\Sgribhis-Bheinn
297\Cnoc A Ghiubhais
300\Maovally
457\Fashven

Durness

485\Creag Riabach
468\Beinn Dearg Mhor
464\Meall Na Moine
331\Ghlas-Bheinn

423\Meall Meadhonach

Balchreick

521\Farveall

489\Meall Na Cra

355\An Socach

773\Beinn Spionnaidh

801\Cranstackie

2

Kinlochbervie

520\An Lean-

Rhiconich

908\Foinaven

463

786\Arkle

3

Scourie

721\Ben Stack

729\Sabhal Beag

386\Ben Auskaird

333\Ben Screavie

800
796\Carn Beag
757\Carn An Tionail

419\Ben Strome

Kinloch

873\

Culkein Drumbeg

680\Meall An Liath Mor

4

Drumbeg

Unapool

525\Beinn Aird Da Loch

613\Meall An Fheur Loch

Nedd

776\Sail Ghorm

792\Beinn Leod

809\Quinag

A

B

Bheinn

135

C

72\Cnoc A' Ghriama

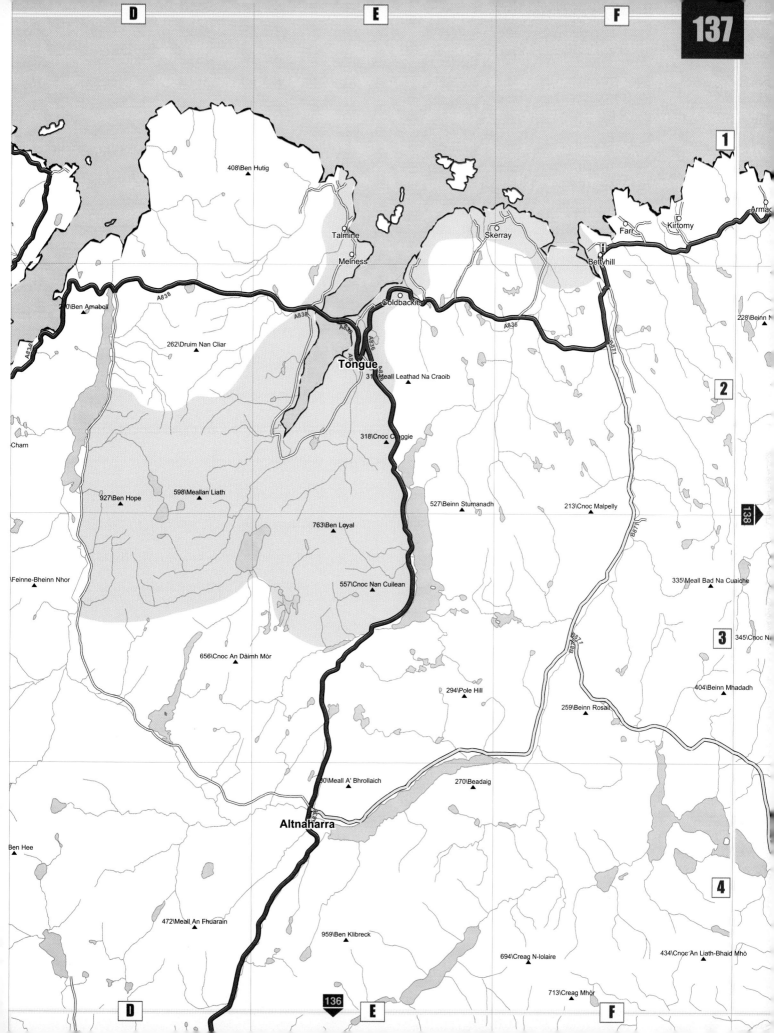

408\Ben Hutig

Talmine

Skerray

Farr

Kirtomy

Armad

Melness

Bettyhill

270\Ben Arnaboll

A838

Coldbackie

A838

A836

228\Beinn N

A838

262\Druim Nan Cliar

A836

B871

Tongue

31\Meall Leathad Na Craoib

Charn

318\Cnoc Craggie

927\Ben Hope

598\Meallan Liath

527\Beinn Stumanadh

213\Cnoc Malpelly

763\Ben Loyal

Feinne-Bheinn Nhor

335\Meall Bad Na Cuaiche

557\Cnoc Nan Cuilean

B871

B871

345\Cnoc N

656\Cnoc An Dàimh Mòr

294\Pole Hill

404\Beinn Mhadadh

259\Beinn Rosail

30\Meall A' Bhrollaich

270\Beadaig

Altnaharra

Ben Hee

472\Meall An Fhuarain

959\Ben Klibreck

694\Creag N-Iolaire

434\Cnoc An Liath-Bhaid Mhò

713\Creag Mhòr

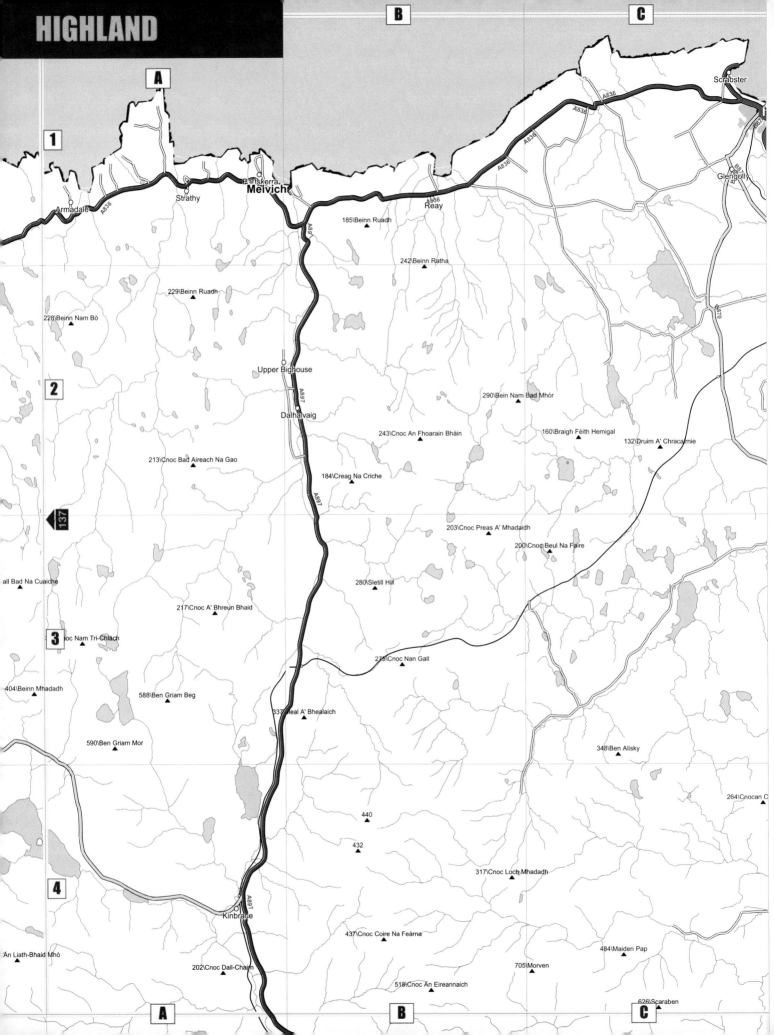

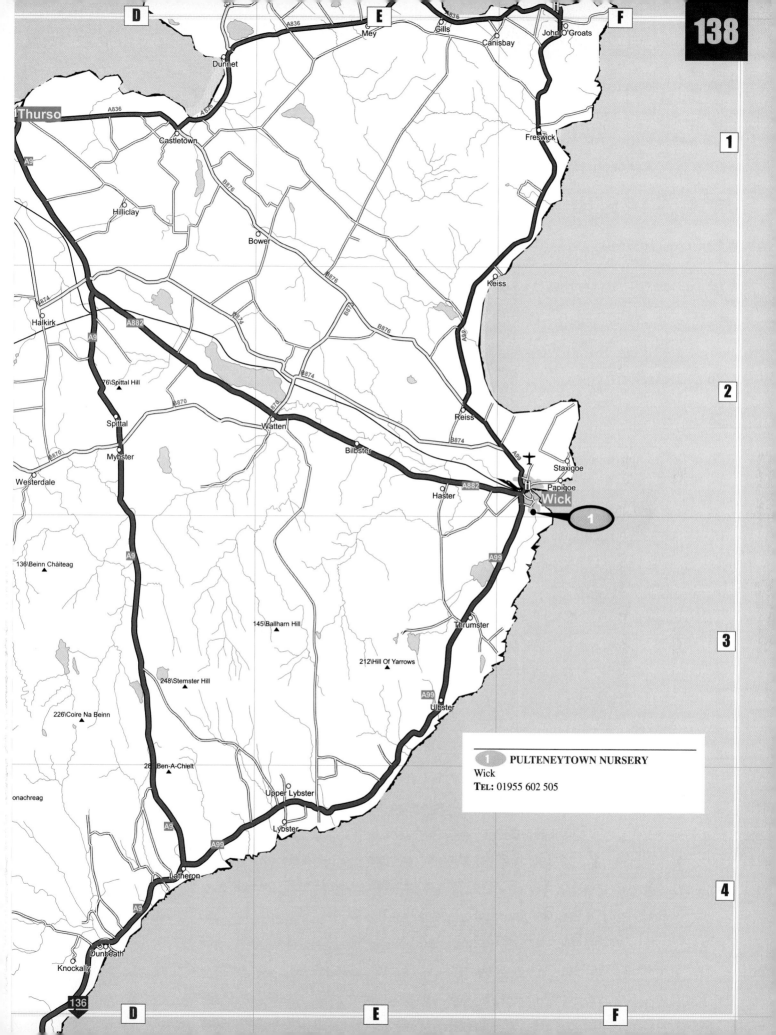

**1** **PULTENEYTOWN NURSERY**
Wick
**Tel:** 01955 602 505

# ISLANDS

**1** **TRESCO ABBEY GARDENS**
Tresco, Isles of Scilly   TEL: 01720 424 105

**2** **WILLOWGLEN GARDEN CENTRE**
Macauley Road, Stornoway   TEL: 01851 705 656

**3** **PLANTIECRUB GROWERS**
Gott   TEL: 01595 840 600

**4** **WELLPARK GARDEN CENTRE**
Mill Street, Kirkwall   TEL: 01856 874 203

**5** **VICTORIA GARDENS**
71 Victoria Street, Kirkwall   TEL: 01856 873 189

**6** **BALLALHEANAGH GARDENS**
Glen Roy, Ionan   TEL: 01624 861 875

**7** **GUERNSEY FREESIA CENTRE**
Box 433, La Route Carre, St Sampson's
TEL: 01481 248 185

**8** **LA SEIGNEURIE**
Sark   TEL: 01481 832 345

**9** **CANDIE GARDENS**
Candie Road, St Peter Port   TEL: 01481 720 904

**10** **GUERNSEY BIRD GARDENS**
La Villiaze, St Andrews   TEL: 01481 236 690

---

**11** **THE ART PARK**
Sausmarez Manor, St Martin, Guernsey, GY4 6SG.
TEL: 01481 235 571
EMAIL: peter@desausmarez.fsnet.co.uk
WEB: www.artparks.co.uk

*The greatest variety of sculptures in the open in Britain. Set in a lush subtropical woodland garden with banana trees, tree ferns, bamboo groves, camellias, lilies, and clematis.*
OPEN: Apr-Dec: 10-5.
ENTRY COSTS: £2.50, Child: £2, OAPs: £2.
SPECIALITIES: Exotic plants, Bamboos, Camellias, Palms, Water features.
FACILITIES: Child area, Coffee shop, Credit cards, Gift shop, Toilets, Wheelchair access, Pushchair friendly.

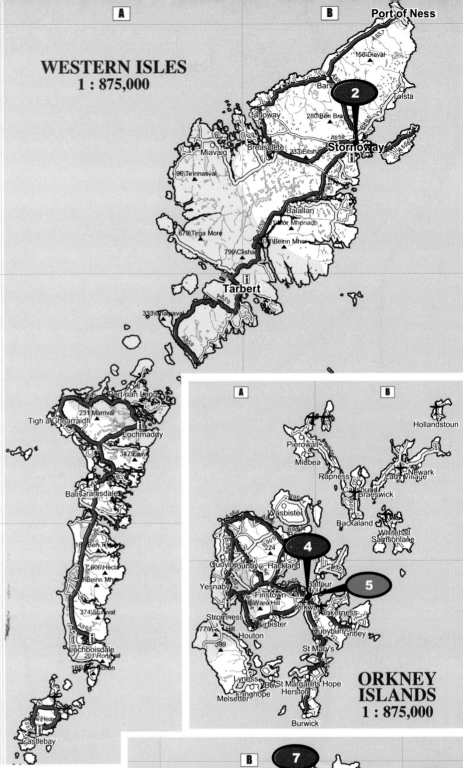

**WESTERN ISLES**
1 : 875,000

**ORKNEY ISLANDS**
1 : 875,000

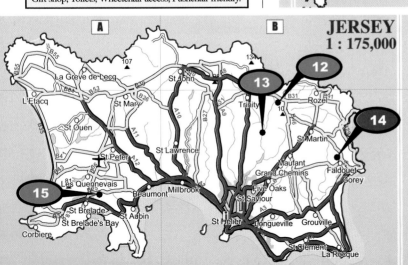

**JERSEY**
1 : 175,000

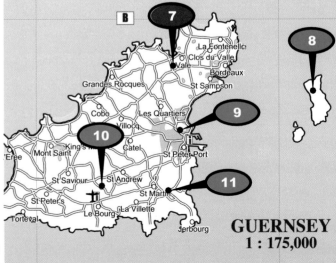

**GUERNSEY**
1 : 175,000

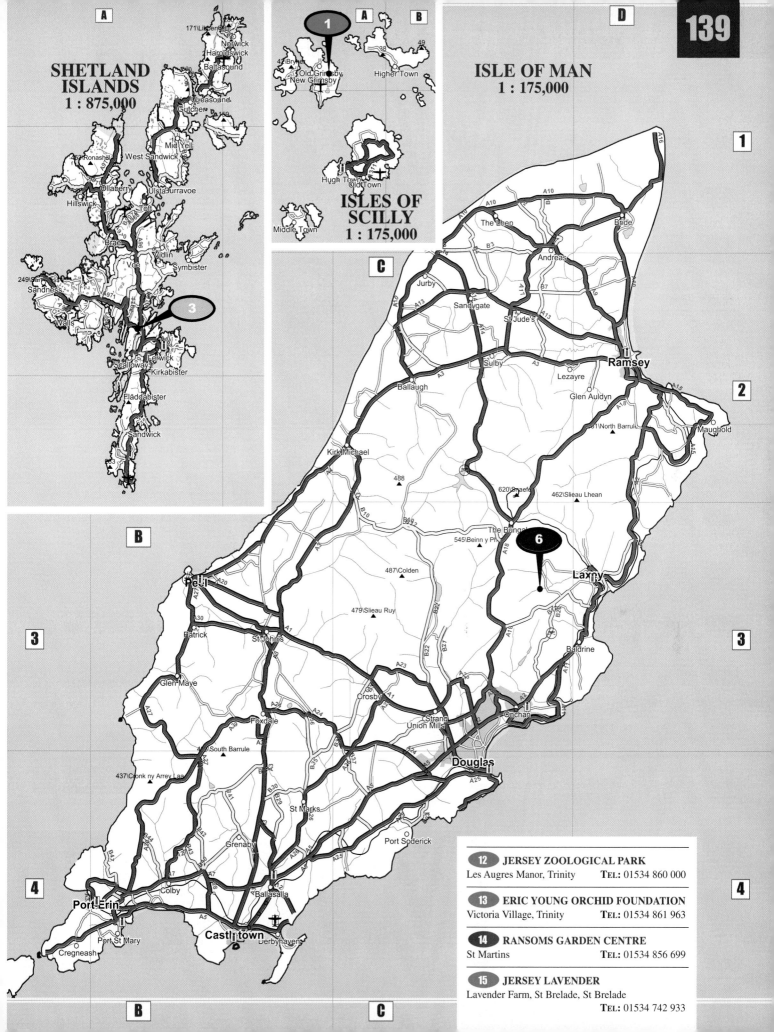

**SHETLAND ISLANDS**
1 : 875,000

Norwick
171\Libberswick
Haroldswick
Baltasound
Uyeasound
Gutcher
462\Ronashill
West Sandwick
Mid Yell
Ollaberry
Ulsta Burravoe
Hillswick
Toft
Brae
Vidlin
Voe
Symbister
249\Sandness
Sandness
Walls
3
Lerwick
Scalloway
Kirkabister
Fladdabister
Sandwick

**A** **B**
1
41\Bryher
Old Grimsby
New Grimsby
Higher Town
49
38

Hugh Town
Old Town

**ISLES OF SCILLY**
1 : 175,000

Middle Town

**ISLE OF MAN**
1 : 175,000

**A** **B** **C** **D**

The Lhen
Bride
A10
A16
A10
Andreas
Jurby
Sandygate
St Jude's
A13
A14
Ramsey
Sulby
A3
Lezayre
Glen Auldyn
Ballaugh
51\North Barrule
Maughold
Kirk Michael
488
620\Snaefell
462\Slieau Lhean
The Bungalow
545\Beinn y Phott
6
Laxey
487\Colden
479\Slieau Ruy
Baldrine
Peel
A20
A27
A30
Patrick
St John's
A1
Crosby
A1
Glen Maye
Foxdale
Strang
Union Mills
Onchan
A27
South Barrule
437\Cronk ny Arrey Laa
St Marks
Douglas
A25
Port Soderick
Grenaby
Colby
Ballasalla
Port Erin
Castletown
Derbyhaven
Cregneash
Port St Mary

| 12 | **JERSEY ZOOLOGICAL PARK** |
|----|----|
| | Les Augres Manor, Trinity   **TEL:** 01534 860 000 |
| 13 | **ERIC YOUNG ORCHID FOUNDATION** |
| | Victoria Village, Trinity   **TEL:** 01534 861 963 |
| 14 | **RANSOMS GARDEN CENTRE** |
| | St Martins   **TEL:** 01534 856 699 |
| 15 | **JERSEY LAVENDER** |
| | Lavender Farm, St Brelade, St Brelade |
| | **TEL:** 01534 742 933 |

1
2
3
4

**A** **B** **C** **D**

**1 BUTTERFIELDS NURSERY**
Harvest Hill, Bourne End
**TEL:** 01628 525 455

**2 MAIDENHEAD AQUATICS CENTRE**
Bourne End Centre, Hedsor Road, Bourne End
**TEL:** 01628 528 882

**3 BOURNE END GARDEN CENTRE**
Hedsor Road, Bourne End
**TEL:** 01628 523 926

**4 CLIVEDEN, NATIONAL TRUST**
Taplow
**TEL:** 01628 605 069

**5 ABBEY ROSE GARDENS**
Nashdom lane, Burnham, Slough
**TEL:** 01628 603 000

**6 WYEVALE GARDEN CENTRE**
Cedar Cottage, Crown Lane, Farnham Royal
**TEL:** 01753 645 627

**7 CHENIES AQUATICS**
Wyevale Garden Centre, Crown Lane, Farnham Royal
**TEL:** 01753 646 989

**8 SLOUGH BOROUGH COUNCIL SPEEDWELL PLANT SALE**
Wexham Nursery, Wexham Road, Slough
**TEL:** 01753 526 408

**9 LANGLEY PARK**
Wexham, Slough
**TEL:** 01753 511 060

**10 WILLIAM WOOD & SON**
The Bishop Centre Shopping Village, Bath Rd, Taplow
**TEL:** 01628 605 454

**11 MOOR GROWERS**
Little Farm Nurseries, North Town Moor, Maidenhead
**TEL:** 01628 634 275

**12 WOOD LANE GARDEN CENTRE**
Wood Lane, Iver
**TEL:** 020 8420 1959

**13 BRAYWICK HEATH NURSERY & GARDEN CENTRE**
41 Braywick Road, Maidenhead
**TEL:** 01628 622 510

**14 J C ALLGROVE**
The Nursery, Middle Green, Slough
**TEL:** 01753 520 155

**15 BLOOMS OF DORNEY**
Dorney Court, Dorney, Windsor
**TEL:** 01628 669 999

**16 DORNEY COURT AND BRESSINGHAM PLANT CENTRE**
Court Lane, Dorney, Windsor
**TEL:** 01628 604 638

**17 BERKSHIRE GARDEN CENTRE**
Sutton Lane, Langley, Slough
**TEL:** 01753 544 368

**18 SQUIRE'S GARDEN CENTRE**
Maidenhead Road, Windsor
**TEL:** 01753 865 076

**19 WYEVALE GARDEN CENTRE**
Dedworth Road, Windsor
**TEL:** 01753 841 791

**20 MOSS END WATER GARDENS**
Moss End Garden Centre, Moss End, Warfield, Bracknell, Berkshire, RG12 6EJ.
**TEL:** 01344 300 520
**WEB:** www.moss-end.co.uk

*Aquatic superstore for every need, indoor and outdoor. Maintenance, installation, landscaping available.*
**OPEN:** Open 7 days a week. Summer: Mon-Sat 9.30-5.30, Sun 10.30-4.30. Winter: Mon-Sat 9.30-5, Sun 10.30-4.30.
**SPECIALITIES:** Water plants.
**FACILITIES:** Toilets, Credit cards, Wheelchair access, Restaurant, Gift tokens, Coffee shop.

**21 WYEVALE GARDEN CENTRE**
42 Wraysbury Road, Wraysbury, Staines
**TEL:** 01784 482 146

**22 VALLEY GARDENS, WINDSOR GREAT PARK**
Access via Wick Road, Englefield Green, Windsor
**TEL:** 01753 860 222

**23 OAK TREE NURSERY**
Brock Hill, Bracknell Road, Warfield
**TEL:** 01344 890 667

**25 H J PEARCEY & SONS**
41 Clarence Street, Egham
**TEL:** 01784 432 805

**26 EGHAM GARDEN CENTRE**
Vicarage Road, Egham
**TEL:** 01784 433 388

**27 MAYFLOWER NURSERIES**
Thorpe Lea Road, Egham
**TEL:** 01784 432 945

**24 SAVILL GARDEN, WINDSOR GREAT PARK**
Access via Wick Lane, Englefield Green, Egham, Surrey.
**TEL:** 01753 847 518
**EMAIL:** savillgarden@crownestate.org.uk
**WEB:** www.savillgarden.co.uk

*Tranquil 35-acre garden within Windsor Great Park. Spectacular spring displays in the woodland; sweepng summer herbaceous borders and formal rose beds; superb autumn leaf colour.*
**OPEN:** Mar-Oct: 10-6. Nov-Feb: 10-4. Closed Christmas & Boxing Day.
**ENTRY COSTS:** £5-£3 Child: £2-£1, OAPs: £4.50-£2.50.
**SPECIALITIES:** Rhododendrons and azaleas, Roses, Camellias, Ferns, Herbaceous plants.
**FACILITIES:** Toilets, Credit cards, Wheelchair access, Restaurant, Coffee shop, Gift shop, Own gift tokens, Sell plants, Pushchair friendly.

**28 PANTILES PLANT & GARDEN CENTRE**
Almners Road, Lyne, Chertsey
**TEL:** 01932 872 195

**29 PLANTA VERA**
Lyne Hill Nursery, Farm Close, Chertsey
**TEL:** 01932 563 011

**30 SUNNINGDALE WATER GARDEN**
London Road, Windlesham
**TEL:** 01344 625 599

**31 HILLIER GARDEN CENTRE**
London Road, Windlesham
**TEL:** 01344 623 166

**32 WYEVALE GARDEN CENTRE**
London Road, Windlesham
**TEL:** 01344 621 411

**33 WORLD OF WATER**
Holloway Hill, Chertsey
**TEL:** 01932 569 690

**34 SQUIRE'S GARDEN CENTRE**
Holloway Hill, Chertsey
**TEL:** 01932 563 727

Paper Bark flower

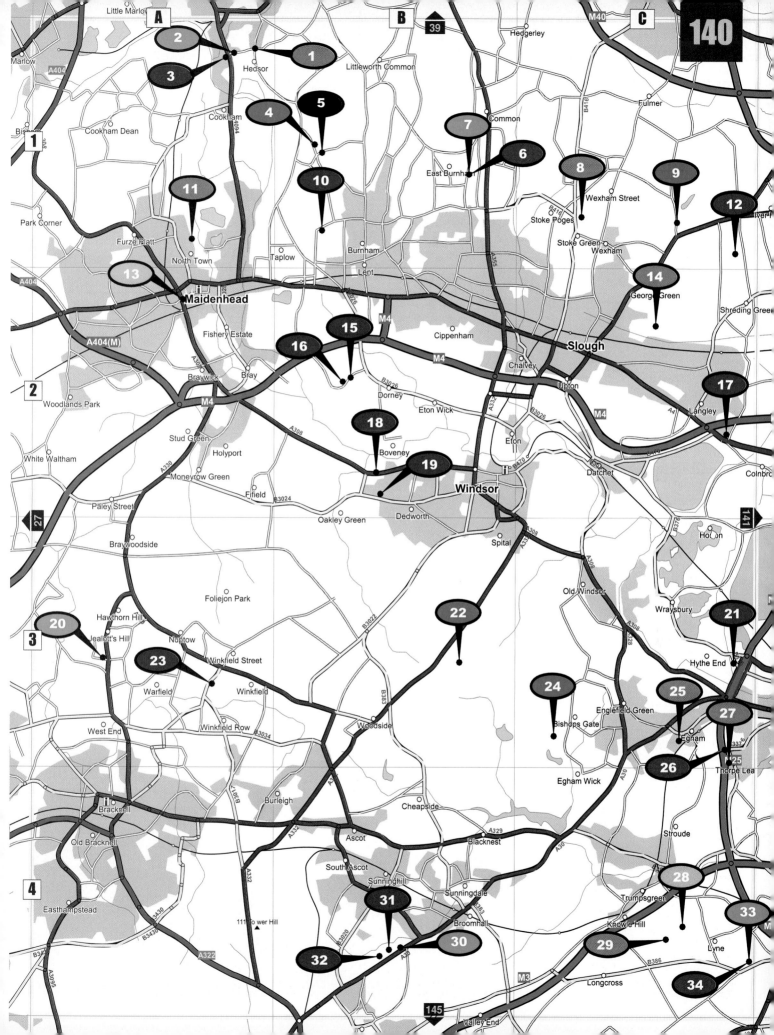

**1  SPRINGBRIDGE NURSERIES**
24-26 Oxford Road, Denham
**TEL:** 01895 835 939

**2  SHANE'S NURSERY**
29 Oxford Road, Denham
**TEL:** 01895 833 289

**3  ALPA GARDEN & AQUATIC CENTRE**
142-144 Swallow Street, Iver
**TEL:** 01753 654 101

**4  WYEVALE GARDEN CENTRE**
Pield Heath Road, Hillingdon
**TEL:** 01895 236 141

**5  JOHN TRAIN PLANTS**
Harmondsworth Road, West Drayton
**TEL:** 020 8759 3010

**6  HEATHROW GARDEN CENTRE**
Sipson Road, Sipson, West Drayton
**TEL:** 020 8897 8893

**7  AIRPORT AQUARIA**
Heathrow Garden Centre, Sipson Rd, West Drayton
**TEL:** 020 8897 2563

**8  WYEVALE GARDEN CENTRE**
Holloway Lane, Harmondsworth, West Drayton
**TEL:** 020 8897 6075

**9  PANNELLS GARDEN CENTRE**
New Heston Road, Heston
**TEL:** 020 8570 4602

**10  WATERLIFE**
Bath Road, Longford, West Drayton
**TEL:** 01753 685 696

**11  VERMEULEN'S GARDEN CENTRE**
Horton Road, Stanwell Moor, Staines
**TEL:** 01784 451 737

**12  LAKESIDE GARDEN CENTRE**
Bedfont Road, Feltham
**TEL:** 020 8844 2261

**13  BULLDOG NURSERIES**
Town Lane, Staines
**TEL:** 01784 254 545

**14  P J'S PALMS & EXOTICS**
41 Salcombe Road, Ashford
**TEL:** 01784 250 181

**15  ADRIAN HALL**
The Garden Centre, Feltham Hill Road, Feltham
**TEL:** 020 8890 5057

**16  NOTCUTTS GARDEN CENTRE**
Staines Road, Laleham, Staines
**TEL:** 01784 460 832

**17  CREEK AQUATIC GARDEN CENTRE**
Walton Road, West Molesey
**TEL:** 020 8941 8758

**18  FUNKEY FISH**
Squire's Garden Centre, Halliford Road, Shepperton
**TEL:** 020 8897 2563

**20  JUNGLE GARDEN & PET CENTRE**
Fordbridge Road, Sunbury on Thames
**TEL:** 01932 772 136

**21  WOBURN HILL NURSERY**
Woburn Hill, Addlestone, Weybridge
**TEL:** 01932 821 066

**22  CHASE ORGANICS**
Riverdene Estate, Molesey Road, Addlesetone
**TEL:** 01932 253 666

Daisy

**19  SQUIRE'S GARDEN CENTRE**

Halliford Road, Upper Halliford, Shepperton,
Middlesex, TW17 8RU.
**TEL:** 01932 784 121
**WEB:** www.squiresgardencentres.co.uk
*Extensive range of quality plants and garden
products, hosts many horticultural shows, situated
adjacent to our  Rose Nurseries. G.C.A. Centre of
Excellence 2001 and 2002.*
**OPEN:** Mon-Sat 9-6 (late nights spring), Sun 10.30-4.30.
**SPECIALITIES:** Bedding plants, Climbers, Shrubs,
Garden & conservatory furniture, Herbaceous plants.
**FACILITIES:** Toilets, Credit cards, Wheelchair access,
Restaurant, Gift tokens, Dogs allowed, Bookshop,
Child area, Farm shop, Coffee shop, Plant guarantee,
Gift shop, HTA gift tokens, Own gift tokens,
Pushchair friendly, Sell plants.

# Root out
## more
## information from
## www.gardenersatlas.co.uk

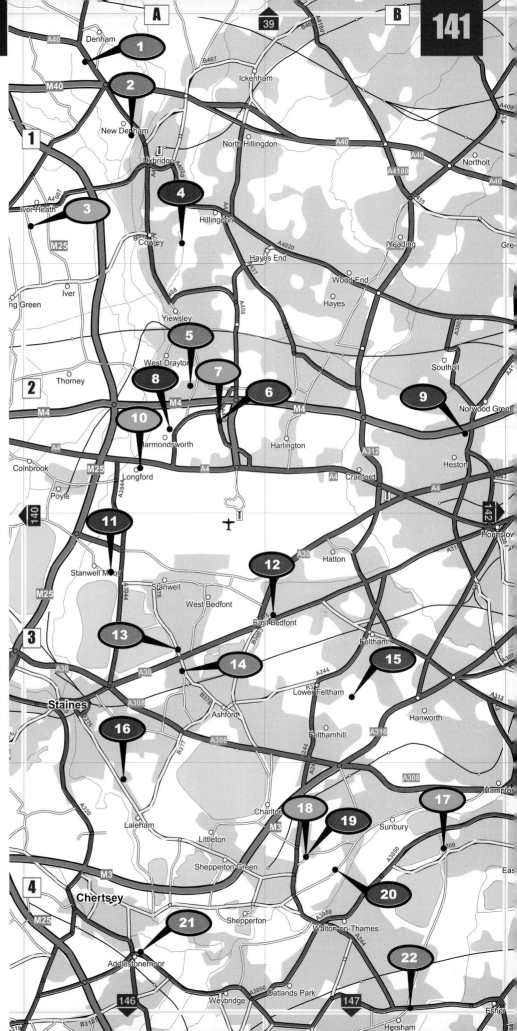

**1** **THE GREENHOUSE**
Birchen Grove, Kingsbury, London
**TEL:** 020 8905 9189

**2** **GRANVILLE GARDEN CENTRE**
170 Granville Road, London
**TEL:** 020 8455 3654

**3** **HAMPSTEAD GARDEN CENTRE**
161-163 Iverson Road, West Hampstead, London
**TEL:** 020 7328 3208

**4** **PENSTEMONS BY COLOUR**
76 Grove Avenue, Hanwell, London
**TEL:** 020 8840 3199

**5** **SPRINGBRIDGE NURSERIES**
2a Gordon Road, Ealing, London
**TEL:** 020 8997 4415

**6** **HOLLAND PARK**
The Stable Yard, Ilchester Place, Kensington
**TEL:** 020 7602 2226

**7** **GINKGO GARDEN CENTRE**
Ravenscourt Park, Ravenscourt Ave, Hammersmith
**TEL:** 020 8563 7112

**8** **WYEVALE GARDEN CENTRE**
Windmill Lane, Osterley
**TEL:** 020 8847 2468

**9** **ROYAL BOTANIC GARDENS, KEW**
Kew, Richmond
**TEL:** 020 8940 1171

**10** **CHISWICK HOUSE, ENGLISH HERITAGE**
Burlington Lane, Chiswick, London
**TEL:** 020 8995 0508

**11** **WYEVALE GARDEN CENTRE**
Syon Park, Brentford
**TEL:** 020 8568 0134

**12** **SYON HOUSE & PARK**
The Estate Office, Brentford
**TEL:** 020 8560 0881

**13** **FULHAM PALACE GARDEN CENTRE**
Bishops Avenue, London
**TEL:** 020 7736 3233

**14** **ADRIAN HALL**
Putney Garden Centre, Dryburgh Road, Putney
**TEL:** 020 8789 9518

**15** **SHEEN GARDEN CENTRE**
181-189 Upper Richmond Road West, East Sheen
**TEL:** 020 8876 3648

**16** **KNELLER GARDEN SUPPLIES**
297 Whitton Dene, Isleworth
**TEL:** 020 8898 7494

**17** **ISABELLA PLANTATION**
Richmond Park, Richmond
**TEL:** 020 8948 3209

**18** **MARBLE HILL HOUSE, ENGLISH HERITAGE**
Richmond Road, Twickenham
**TEL:** 020 8892 5115

**19** **PETERSHAM NURSERIES**
Petersham Road, Petersham, Richmond
**TEL:** 020 8940 5230

**20** **HAM HOUSE, NATIONAL TRUST**
Ham, Richmond
**TEL:** 020 8940 1950

**21** **PALM CENTRE**
Ham Central Nursery, Ham Street, Richmond
**TEL:** 020 8255 6191

**22** **SQUIRE'S GARDEN CENTRE**
Sixth Cross Road, Twickenham, Middlesex, TW2 5PA.
**TEL:** 020 8977 9241
**EMAIL:** admin@squiresgardencentres.co.uk
**WEB:** www.squiresgardencentres.co.uk

*Flagship of the Squire's group. Vast selection of quality plants and garden products. Judged Best Garden Centre in G.C.A. 2001. Shop interior remodelled for Spring 2002.*
**OPEN:** Mon-Sat 9-6 (late nights spring), Sun 10.30-4.30.
**SPECIALITIES:** Bedding plants, Climbers, Garden & conservatory furniture, Comprehensive range, Herbaceous plants.
**FACILITIES:** Toilets, Credit cards, Restaurant, Wheelchair access, Gift tokens, Bookshop, Plant guarantee, Dogs allowed, Gift shop, HTA gift tokens, Own gift tokens, Sell plants, Pushchair friendly.

**23** **MARKS WATER GARDEN**
156 High Street, Teddington
**TEL:** 020 8943 9799

**24** **TEDDINGTON STATION GARDEN CENTRE**
Station Road, Teddington
**TEL:** 020 8943 5222

**25** **CANNIZARO PARK**
West Side Common, Wimbledon Village, London
**TEL:** 020 8946 7349

**26** **COTTENHAM PARK**
Cambridge Road, London
**TEL:** 020 8946 1991

**27** **WATERHOUSE PLANTATION**
Bushy Park, Hampton
**TEL:** 020 8979 1586

**28** **GARDENERS WORLD**
530 Kingston Road, Raynes Park, London
**TEL:** 020 8542 5678

**29** **HAMPTON COURT PALACE & GARDENS**
Hampton Court Palace, East Molesey
**TEL:** 020 8781 9500

**30** **PEACHPRINT**
350 West Barnes Lane, New Malden
**TEL:** 020 8942 0303

**31** **WYEVALE GARDEN CENTRE**
Lower Morden Lane, Morden
**TEL:** 020 8337 7781

**32** **AQUAJOY**
31 Lower Morden Lane, Morden
**TEL:** 020 8337 7373

**33** **J DOBBE & SONS**
Stonecot Nurseries, Stonecot Close, Cheam
**TEL:** 020 8644 9412

**34** **EGMONT WATER GARDEN CENTRE**

132 Tolworth Rise South, Surbiton, Surrey, KT5 9NJ.
**TEL:** 020 8337 9605
**WEB:** www.egmontwatergardens.co.uk
*For your pond, water features, stream, rill or waterfall and for all waterplants and oxygenators, lilies, pumps, liners and fish. We can advise and supply exactly to your needs and quantities.*
**OPEN:** Mar-Sep: open daily. Sep-Feb: open 6 days.
**SPECIALITIES:** Aquatic plants, Unique water features, Terracotta.
**FACILITIES:** Wheelchair access, Pushchair friendly, Credit cards, Bookshop, Gift shop, Own gift tokens, Plant guarantee, Toilets.

California Poppies

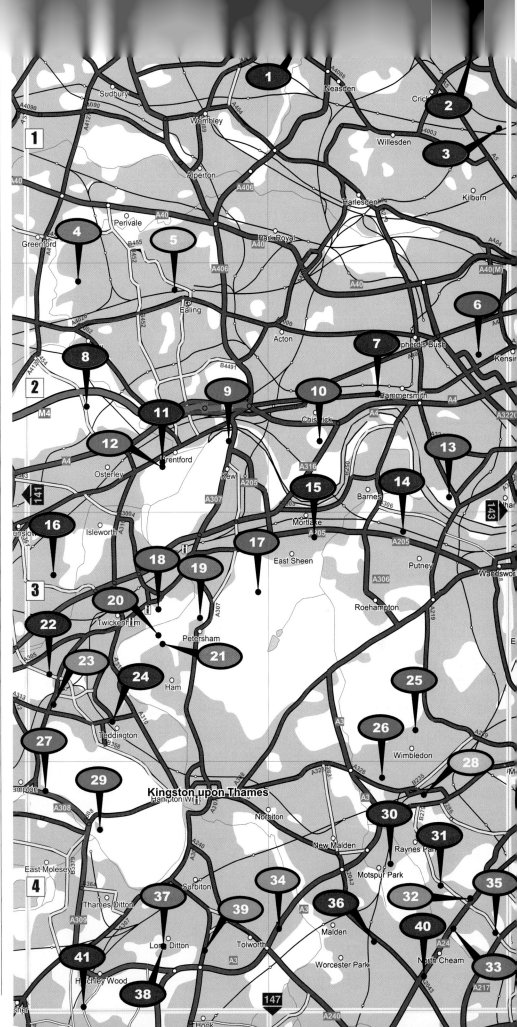

**1 SPRINGFIELD PARK**
Upper Clapton Road, Hackney, London
TEL: 020 8806 1826

**2 GOLDERS HILL PARK**
North End Way, Hampstead, London
TEL: 020 8455 5183

**3 NOEL-BAKER PEACE GARDEN**
Elthorne Park, Hazelville Road, London

**4 HILL GARDEN**
Inverforth Close, North End Way, London
TEL: 020 8455 5183

**5 FENTON HOUSE, NATIONAL TRUST**
Windmill Hill, Hampstead, London
TEL: 020 7435 3471

**6 NORTH ONE GARDEN CENTRE**
25a Englefield Road, Islington, London
TEL: 020 7923 3553

---

**7 CAMDEN GARDEN CENTRE**
2 Barker Drive, St Pancras Way, Camden,
London, Greater London, NW1 0JW.
TEL: 020 7387 7080
EMAIL: info@camdengardencentre.co.uk
WEB: www.camdengardencentre.co.uk
*Exciting range of plants, containers, trellis and
gardening products for gardens, balconies and
window boxes. Delivery service and car park.*
OPEN: Apr-Sep: Mon-Sat 9-5.30, Sun & BH 11-5.
Oct-Mar: Mon-Sat 9-5, Sun 10-4.
SPECIALITIES: Shrubs, Climbers, Bedding plants,
Hardy plants, Herbs, Terracotta pots.
FACILITIES: Credit cards, Wheelchair access, Gift
tokens, Plant guarantee, Bookshop, Child area,
Toilets, Sell plants, Pushchair friendly.

---

**8 CULPEPPER COMMUNITY GARDEN**
1 Cloudesley Road, Islington, London
TEL: 020 7833 3951

**9 LONDON ZOO**
Regent's Park, London
TEL: 020 7722 3333

**10 GEFFRYE MUSEUM HERB GARDEN**
Kingsland Road, London
TEL: 020 7739 9893

**11 MILE END PARK**
Mile End Road, Mile End, London
TEL: 020 7264 4660

**12 REGENT'S PARK & QUEEN MARY`S ROSE GARDEN**
Inner Circle, Regent's Park, London
TEL: 020 7298 2000

**13 CALTHORPE PROJECT**
258-274 Grays Inn Road, Camden, London
TEL: 020 7837 8019

**14 CLIFTON NURSERIES**
5a Clifton Villas, Little Venice, London
TEL: 020 7289 6851

**15 COLVILLE PLACE GARDENS**
Colville Place Gallery, London
TEL: 020 7436 1330

**16 MUSEUM OF LONDON GARDEN**
The Museum of London, London Wall, London
TEL: 020 7600 3699

**17 PHOENIX GARDEN**
21 Stacey Street, London
TEL: 020 7379 3187

**18 DOCKLANDS GARDEN CENTRE**
244-246 Ratcliffe Lane, London
TEL: 020 7790 1146

**19 KENSINGTON GARDENS**
Kensington, London
TEL: 020 7298 2000

**20 KENSINGTON PALACE & GARDENS**
Kensington Palace, London
TEL: 020 7376 2452

**21 ST JAMES'S PARK**
London
TEL: 020 7930 1793

**22 PIRELLI GARDEN**
Victoria & Albert Museum, Cromwell Road, London
TEL: 020 7942 2209

**23 CHELSEA GARDENER**
125 Sydney Street, Chelsea, London
TEL: 020 7352 5656

**24 ROYAL HOSPITAL, RANELAGH GARDENS**
Royal Hospital Road, London
TEL: 020 7730 0161

**25 CHELSEA PHYSIC GARDEN**
66 Royal Hospital Road, Chelsea, London
TEL: 020 7352 5646

**26 PARKSIDE NURSERY**
Denmark Hill, Camberwell, London
TEL: 020 7738 4240

**27 HYDE PARK**
London
TEL: 020 7298 2000

**28 DULWICH GARDEN CENTRE**
20-22 Grove Vale, East Dulwich, London
TEL: 020 8299 1089

**29 CROXTED ROAD GARDEN CENTRE**
Croxted Road, Herne Hill, London
TEL: 020 8674 4366

**30 BROCKWELL PARK GARDENS**
Brockwell Park, Tulse Hill, London
TEL: 020 7926 0105

**31 HORNIMAN GARDENS**
Hornimans Drive, Forest Hill, London
TEL: 020 8699 8924

**32 SHANNON'S**
99-105 Stanstead Road, Forest Hill, London
TEL: 020 8291 1507

Dutch Iris

**33** **PATIO GARDEN CENTRE**
100 Tooting Bec Road, Tooting Bec, London
TEL: 020 8672 2251

**34** **THE ROOKERY**
Streatham Common South, , London
TEL: 020 8671 0994

**35** **THE SECRET GARDEN**
70 Westow Street, Upper Norwood, London
TEL: 020 8771 8200

**36** **MENDIP COTTAGE NURSERY**
43 Copers Cope Road, Beckenham
TEL: 020 8658 6094

**37** **CRYSTAL PALACE PARK**
Crystal Palace Road, London
TEL: 020 8313 4407

**38** **CASTLE NURSERY**
159 Elmers End Road, Beckenham
TEL: 020 8650 2899

**39** **MORDEN HALL GARDEN CENTRE**
Morden Hall Road, Morden
TEL: 020 8646 3002

**40** **MORDEN HALL PARK, NATIONAL TRUST**
Morden Hall Road, Morden
TEL: 020 8648 1845

**41** **WYEVALE GARDEN CENTRE**
Wickham Road, Shirley, Croydon
TEL: 020 8654 3720

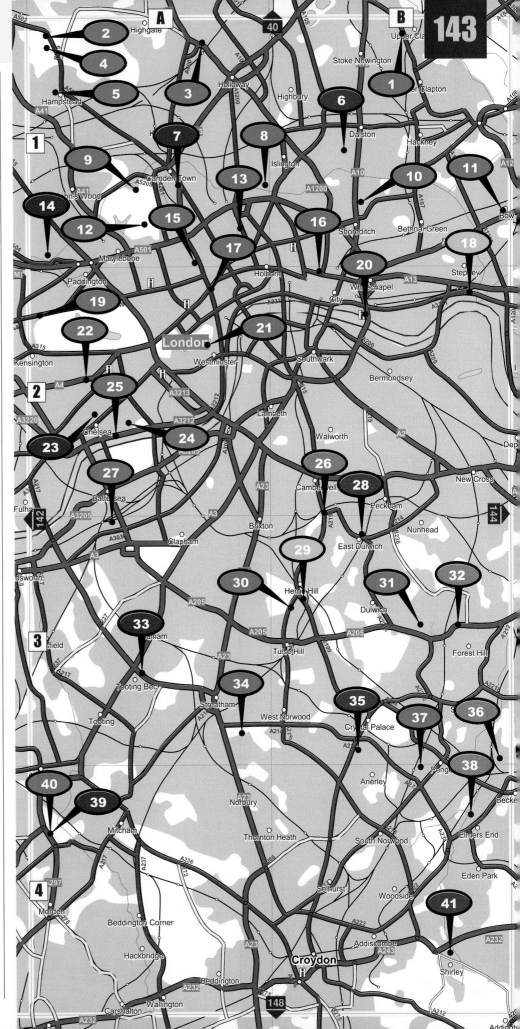

**1  MANOR AQUATICS CENTRE**
653-655 Romford Road, Manor Park, London
**TEL:** 020 8478 4478

**2  FOREST FLOWERS & GARDEN CENTRE**
131 Forest Lane, London
**TEL:** 020 8555 4299

**3  URBAN AQUATICS**
Unit 2, Horizon House, Rainham
**TEL:** 01708 630 811

**4  T CUTLER**
41 Derby Road, Lower Kilburn, London
**TEL:** 01332 881 080

**5  WEST HAM PARK**
Upton Lane, Forest Gate, London
**TEL:** 020 8472 3584

**6  BRIAN LAWLER**
65 The Shopping Hall, Myrtle Road, London
**TEL:** 020 8472 7791

**7  ROYS STORES**
45a Bostall Hill, Abbey Wood, London
**TEL:** 020 8311 5212

**8  ROYS STORES**
191 Sandyhill Road, Woolwich, London
**TEL:** 020 8854 5368

**9  BELVEDERE PET & GARDEN CENTRE**
6 Albert Road, Belvedere
**TEL:** 01322 432 482

**10  THE GREENHOUSE**
18 Royal Hill, Greenwich, London
**TEL:** 020 8305 1772

**11  THOMPSON'S PLANT & GARDEN CENTRE**
Shooters Hill, Welling
**TEL:** 020 8856 2933

**12  CITY GARDENER**
150 Long Lane, Bexleyheath
**TEL:** 020 8303 2838

**13  WESTWOOD NURSERY**
65 Yorkland Avenue, Welling
**TEL:** 020 8301 0886

**14  DANSON PARK**
Bexleyheath
**TEL:** 020 8304 2631

**15  HALL PLACE**
Bourne Road, Bexley
**TEL:** 01322 526 574

**16  ELTHAM PALACE, ENGLISH HERITAGE**
Court Yard, London
**TEL:** 020 8294 2548

**17  BROADVIEW GARDENS**
Mottingham Lane, Tonbridge
**TEL:** 020 8851 8793

**18  PHOEBE'S GARDEN CENTRE**
Penerley Road, Catford, London
**TEL:** 020 8698 4365

**19  STUART'S NURSERIES**
North Cray Road, Sidcup
**TEL:** 020 8300 1933

**20  HEATHSIDE NURSERY**
64 Leyton Cross Road, Dartford
**TEL:** 01322 224 482

**21  ST MARY'S NURSERY**
103 Birchwood Road, Wilmington, Dartford
**TEL:** 01322 667 883

**22  WEATHERLEY FENCING & GARDEN CENTRE**
The Orchard, 135 North Cray Road, Sidcup
**TEL:** 020 8308 1316

**23  THOMPSON'S PLANT & GARDEN CENTRE**
Perry Street, Chislehurst
**TEL:** 020 8300 1025

**24  RUXLEY NURSERIES**
Maidstone Road, Foots Cray, Sidcup
**TEL:** 020 8300 2515

**25  RUXLEY MANOR GARDEN CENTRE LTD**
Maidstone Road, Sidcup, Kent, DA14 5BQ.
**TEL:** 020 8300 0084
**EMAIL:** rmgc@ruxley-manor.co.uk

*A large garden centre selling a comprehensive range of gardening and leisure products, specialising in garden furniture, gifts, house plants, terracotta, stoneware, sundries and Christmas.*
**OPEN:** Open 7 days a week. Summer: Mon-Sat 9-5.30, Sun 10-4. Winter: Mon-Sat 9-5, Sun 10-4. Closed Easter Sun & Christmas-New Year.
**SPECIALITIES:** Garden & conservatory furniture, Gifts, Hardy plants, House plants, Stone ornaments.
**FACILITIES:** Bookshop, Credit cards, Farm shop, Gift shop, HTA gift tokens, Own gift tokens, Plant guarantee, Pushchair friendly, Restaurant, Sell plants, Toilets, Wheelchair access.

**26  HARRINGTON'S NURSERY**
Silver Birches, Highlands Hill, Swanley
**TEL:** 01322 663 239

**27  I H BEALE**
Swanley Village Road, Swanley
**TEL:** 01322 664 041

**28  PRIORY GARDENS**
High Street, Orpington
**TEL:** 020 8464 3333

**29  JUST BAMBOO**
109 Hayes Lane, Bromley
**TEL:** 020 8462 1800

**30  EDEN PARK NURSERIES**
Upper Elmers End Road, Beckenham
**TEL:** 020 8650 2424

**31  KENT CACTI**
35 Rutland Way, Orpington
**TEL:** 01689 836 249

**32  CONNOISSEURS' CACTI**
51 Chelsfield Lane, Orpington
**TEL:** 01689 837 781

**33  BROMLEY MUSEUM & PRIORY GARDENS**
The Priory Church Hill, Orpington
**TEL:** 01689 873 826

**34  MAYFIELD NURSERIES**
Chelsfield Lane, Orpington
**TEL:** 01689 876 602

**35  WORLD OF KOI**
Bencewell Farm, Oakley Road, Bromley
**TEL:** 020 8462 9479

**36  EYNSFORD NURSERY**
Riverside, Eynsford, Dartford
**TEL:** 01322 864 439

**37  KOI WATER BARN**
Lillys Farm, Chelsfield Lane, Chelsfield Village
**TEL:** 01689 878 161

**38  WYEVALE GARDEN CENTRE**
Oakley Road, Keston Mark, Bromley
**TEL:** 01689 859 419

**39  LULLINGSTONE CASTLE**
Lullingstone Park, Eynsford
**TEL:** 01322 862 114

Gladioli

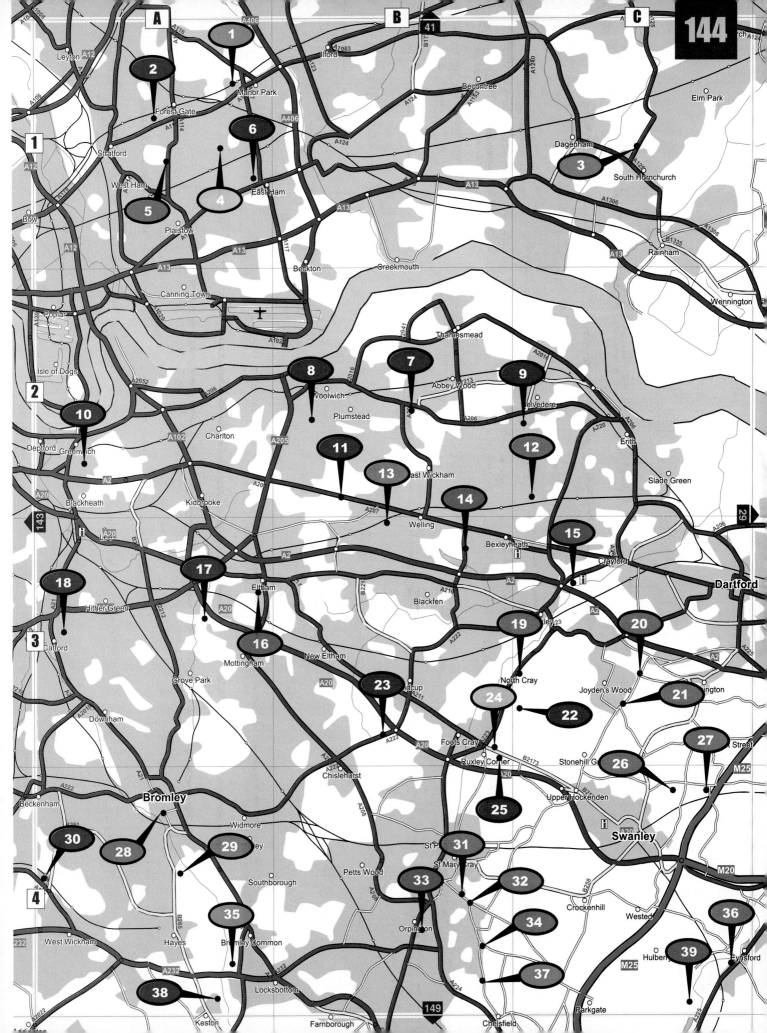

**NOTCUTTS GARDEN CENTRE**
Waterers Nurseries, London Road, Bagshot
**Tel:** 01276 472 288

 **THE PLANT CENTRE**
Bagshot Road, Chobham, Surrey, GU24 8SJ.
**Tel:** 01276 855 408

*A true plant centre with a superb range of top quality plants and knowledgeable staff on hand to advise. Many unusual and specimen plants.*
**Open:** Mon-Sat 8.30-6, Sun 10-4. Closed Christmas & Boxing Day.
**Specialities:** Fruit & fruit trees, Hedging, Trees, Japanese maples, Hostas.

 **LINCLUDEN NURSERY**
Bisley Green, Bisley, Woking
**Tel:** 01483 797 005

 **MERRIST WOOD PLANT CENTRE**
Merrist Wood College, Holly Lane, Worplesdon
**Tel:** 01483 235 122

 **WOODLANDS FARM NURSERY**
The Green, Woodstreet Village, Guildford
**Tel:** 01483 235 536

 **OAKS NURSERY**
Foreman Road, Ash, Aldershot
**Tel:** 01252 285 90

**7 LITTLE BROOK FUCHSIAS**
Ash Green Lane West, Ash Green, Aldershot, Surrey, GU12 6HL.
**Tel:** 01252 329 731
**Email:** carol.gubler@business.ntl.com
**Web:** www.littlebrookfuchsias.co.uk
*Specialist nursery selling all sorts of fuchsias- new and old. Plants vary in size and price according to season. Friendly advice always available*
**Open:** Jan 1-Jul 7: Wed-Sun 9-5.
**Specialities:** Fuchsias.
**Facilities:** Wheelchair access, Pushchair friendly, Sell plants.

 **BADSHOT LEA GARDEN CENTRE**
Badshot Lea Roa, Farnham
**Tel:** 01252 333 666

 **LITTLE ACRES NURSERY**
St Georges Road, Runfold St George, Farnham
**Tel:** 01252 782 942

 **SEALE NURSERIES**
Seale Lane, Seale, Farnham, Surrey, GU10 1LD.
**Tel:** 01252 782 410
**Email:** ga@sealenurseries.demon.co.uk
**Web:** www.sealesuperroses.com

*Family run, est. 1948, extensive selection of home grown hardy plants. Speciality 'Seale Super Roses' uniquely container grown, ensuring unsurpassed quality.*
**Open:** Open daily. Closed Christmas week.
**Specialities:** Roses, Shrubs, Herbaceous plants, Hedging, Pelargoniums.
**Facilities:** Toilets, Credit cards, Wheelchair access, Gift tokens, Dogs allowed, Plant guarantee, HTA gift tokens, Pushchair friendly.

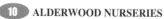 **ALDERWOOD NURSERIES**
Runfold St George, Badshot Lea, Farnham
**Tel:** 01252 782 493

**12 HAZELBANK NURSERY**
Tilford Street, Tilford, Farnham
**Tel:** 01252 782 405

### 13 FRENSHAM GARDEN CENTRE

The Reeds Road, Frensham, Farnham,
Surrey, GU10 3BP.
**TEL:** 01252 792 545
**EMAIL:** info@frensham-gardencentre.co.uk
**WEB:** www.frensham.co.uk

**GA OFFER**

*Picturesque garden centre in mature woodland
setting, offering full range of plants, sundries and
furniture. Incorporating Frensham Coffee shop &
Camping World.*
**OPEN:** Mon-Sat 9-5.30, Sun 10.30-4.30.
**SPECIALITIES:** Shrubs, Furniture, Japanese maples,
Terracotta pots.
**FACILITIES:** Toilets, Credit cards, Wheelchair access,
Bookshop, Dogs allowed, Gift tokens, Child area,
Coffee shop, Plant guarantee, Sell plants, Gift shop,
HTA gift tokens, Restaurant, Pushchair friendly.

### 14 F A SECRETT

Hurst Farm, Milford, Godalming
**TEL:** 01483 520 500

Lush garden

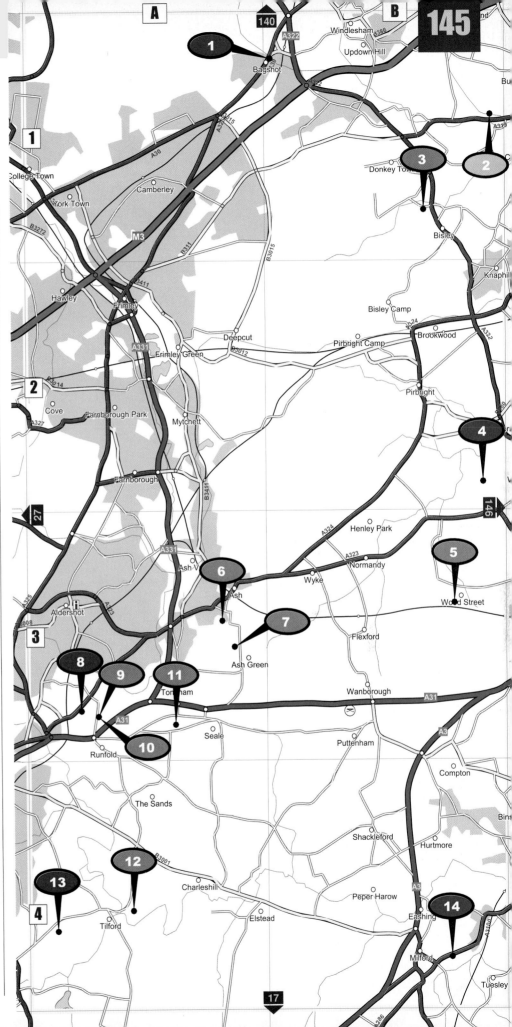

**1** **BOURNE VALLEY GARDEN CENTRE**
Woodham Park Road, Woodham Addlestone
**TEL:** 01932 342 013

**2** **F W CHARLES**
33 The Avenue, Addlestone
**TEL:** 01932 346 600

**3** **RIVERSIDE NURSERIES**
Philpot Lane, Chobham, Woking
**TEL:** 01276 857 687

**4** **MIMBRIDGE GARDEN CENTRE**
Station Road, Chobham, Woking
**TEL:** 01276 858 237

**5** **SQUIRE'S GARDEN CENTRE**
Littlewick Road, Horsell, Woking
**TEL:** 01276 858 446

**6** **BOTANY BARNS**
Knaphill Garden Centre, Barrs Lane, Knaphill
**TEL:** 01483 481 212

**7** **PENTANGLE WATER GARDENS & AQUARIA**
Knaphill Garden Centre, Barrs Lane, Woking
**TEL:** 01483 489 757

**8** **WISLEY GARDEN, ROYAL HORTICULTURAL SOCIETY**
Wisley, Woking, Surrey, GU23 6QB.
**TEL:** 01483 224 234
**WEB:** www.rhs.org.uk
*Whatever the season, RHS Garden Wisley demonstrates British gardening at its best with 240 acres of glorious garden.*
**OPEN:** Mon-Fri, 10-6 (or sunset), Sat-Sun 9-6 (or sunset), RHS members only on Sun. Closed Christmas Day.
**ENTRY COSTS:** £6, Child: £2 Under 6s free.
**SPECIALITIES:** Alpines, Fruit & fruit trees, Herbaceous plants, Rhododendrons and azaleas, Roses.
**FACILITIES:** Toilets, Credit cards, Wheelchair access, Restaurant, Gift tokens, Bookshop, Gift shop, Pushchair friendly.

**9** **TOOBEES EXOTICS**
20 Inglewood, Woking, Surrey, GU21 3HX.
**TEL:** 01483 722 600
**EMAIL:** bbpotter@compuserve.com
**WEB:** www.toobees-exotics.com
*Specialists in South African and Madagascan succulents, plus selections of cacti, palms, cycads, carniverous air plants and other exotics.*
**OPEN:** Apr 18-Sep 29: 10-5.
**SPECIALITIES:** Cacti, Carnivorous plants, Conservatory plants, Exotic plants, Palms.
**FACILITIES:** Credit cards, Wheelchair access, Dogs allowed, Pushchair friendly, Sell plants.

**10** **WYEVALE GARDEN CENTRE**
Egley Road, Mayford, Woking
**TEL:** 01432 276 568

**11** **BRIARWOOD NURSERIES**
Saunders Lane, Mayford, Woking
**TEL:** 01483 763 216

**12** **WOKING NURSERY**
99 Westfield Road, Woking
**TEL:** 01483 725 646

**13** **KAYTIE FISHER NURSERY**
South End Cottage, Long Reach, Ockham
**TEL:** 01483 282 304

**14** **RIPLEY NURSERIES** | **GA OFFER**
Portsmouth Road, Ripley, Woking, Surrey, GU23 6EY.
**TEL:** 01483 225 090
**WEB:** www.ripleynurseries.co.uk

*Ripley Nurseries*

*The nursery is one mile south of Wisley RHS, set in natural surroundings offering an extensive range of ornamental plants and specimens.*
**OPEN:** Open daily. Closed Christmas and New Year's Day.
**SPECIALITIES:** Alpines, Conifers, Shrubs, Trees, Summer & Winter bedding.
**FACILITIES:** Credit cards, Wheelchair access, Dogs allowed, Gift tokens.

**15** **SUTTON GREEN GARDEN NURSERY**
Guildford Road, Sutton Green, Guildford
**TEL:** 01483 232 366

**16** **ELM NURSERY**
Sutton Green Road, Guildford
**TEL:** 01483 761 748

**17** **JUNIPER NURSERIES**
Whitmoor Lane, Sutton Green, Guildford
**TEL:** 01945 420 672

**18** **TANGLEY GARDENS NURSERY**
Pitch Place, Worplesdon Road, Guildford
**TEL:** 01483 232 243

**19** **BLOOMS OF WEST CLANDON**
West Clandon, Guildford
**TEL:** 01483 222 925

**20** **CLANDON PARK, NATIONAL TRUST**
West Clandon, Guildford
**TEL:** 01483 222 482

**21** **GUILDFORD CASTLE GARDENS**
Castle Street, Guildford
**TEL:** 01483 505 050

**22** **COMPTON NURSERY**
Compton, Guildford
**TEL:** 01483 811 387

**23** **LOXHILL NURSERY**
Old Portsmouth Road, Artington, Guildford
**TEL:** 01483 457 979

**25** **HEATH NURSERY**
Heath Lane, Albury Heath, Albury
**TEL:** 01483 203 264

**26** **HIGHBANKS NURSERY**
Birtley Road, Bramley, Guildford
**TEL:** 01483 893 380

**27** **BUSBRIDGE LAKES, WATERFOWL & GARDENS**
Busbridge Lakes, Hambledon Road, Godalming
**TEL:** 01483 421 955

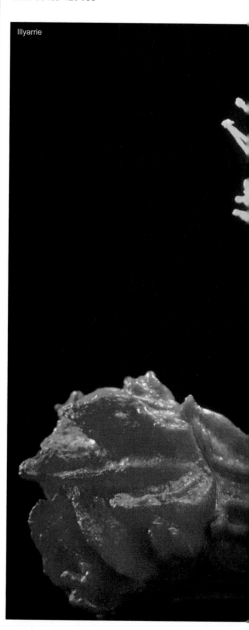
Illyarrie

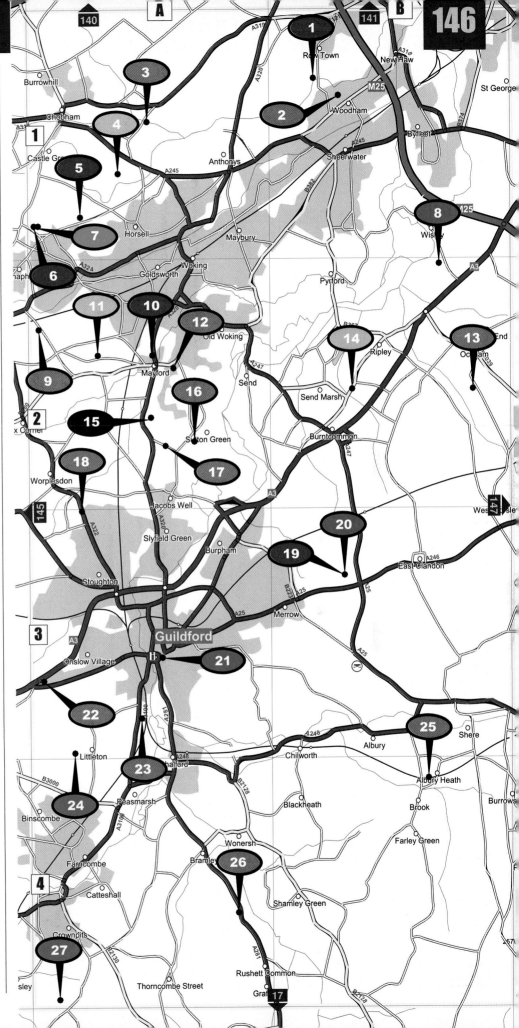

## 24 LOSELEY PARK
Guildford, Surrey, GU3 1HS.
**Tel:** 01483 304 440
**Email:** enquiries@loseley-park.com
**Web:** www.loseley-park.com

*Loseley Walled Garden, based on a Gertrude Jekyll design, includes an award-winning rose garden, flower garden and a glorious moat walk. Set in the grounds of Loseley House.*

**Open:** May 6 -Sep 29: Wed-Sun 11-5.
**Entry costs:** £3, Child: £1.50, OAPs: £2.50.
**Specialities:** Bedding plants, Climbers, Hardy plants, Pot plants, Roses.
**Facilities:** Toilets, Wheelchair access, Coffee shop, Gift shop, Restaurant, Sell plants, Child area.

## 1 GARSONS

Winterdown Road, West End, Esher, Surrey, KT10 8LS.
**TEL:** 01372 460 181
**EMAIL:** mail@garsons.co.uk
**WEB:** www.garsons.co.uk

*Large, modern garden centre with restaurant, PYO farm and farm shop selling local, fresh and specialist foods in traditional farm barns.*
**OPEN:** Open 7 days a week. Summer: Mon-Sat 9-6, Sun 11-5. Winter: Mon-Sat 9-5, Sun 11-5 Sun. Closed Christmas & Boxing Day.
**SPECIALITIES:** Comprehensive range.
**FACILITIES:** Toilets, Credit cards, Wheelchair access, Restaurant, Dogs allowed, Gift tokens, Bookshop, Child area, Coffee shop, Farm shop, Plant guarantee, Gift shop, HTA gift tokens, Pushchair friendly, Sell plants, Own gift tokens.

## 2 SQUIRE'S GARDEN CENTRE

Burwood Road, Hersham, Surrey, KT12 4AR.
**TEL:** 01932 247 579
**WEB:** www.squiresgardencentres.co.uk
*New building and restaurant opened June 2000. G.C.A. Centre of Excellence 2001.*
**OPEN:** Mon-Sat 9-6, Sun 10.30-4.30.
**SPECIALITIES:** Bedding plants, Climbers, Shrubs, Garden & conservatory furniture, Herbaceous plants.
**FACILITIES:** Toilets, Credit cards, Wheelchair access, Restaurant, Gift tokens, Bookshop, Coffee shop, Plant guarantee, HTA gift tokens, Gift shop, Own gift tokens, Sell plants, Dogs allowed, Pushchair friendly.

## 3 CLAREMONT LANDSCAPE GARDEN, NATIONAL TRUST

Portsmouth Road, Esher
**TEL:** 01372 467 806

## 4 JACQUES CANN

Seven Hills Road, Walton on Thames
**TEL:** 01932 844 575

## 5 CHESSINGTON GARDEN CENTRE

Leatherhead Road, Chessington
**TEL:** 01372 725 638

## 6 PAINSHILL LANDSCAPE GARDEN

Painshill Park Trust, Portsmouth Road, Cobham, Surrey, KT11 1JE.
**TEL:** 01932 868 113
**EMAIL:** info@painshill.co.uk
**WEB:** www.painshill.co.uk
*One of Europe's finest 18th century landscape gardens. A Gothic Temple, Chinese Bridge, Crystal Grotto, Turkish Tent, working vineyard. New visitor centre with licensed restaurant and gift shop.*

**OPEN:** Open all year. For opening times and entry costs telephone 01932 864 674.
**SPECIALITIES:** 18th Century landscaped garden.
**FACILITIES:** Toilets, Credit cards, Wheelchair access, Restaurant, Gift shop, Pushchair friendly.

## 7 WILLOUGHBYS NURSERIES

Leatherhead Road, Oxshott
**TEL:** 01372 842 434

## 8 COBHAM PARK NURSERY

Plough Lane, Downside, Cobham, Surrey, KT11 3LT.
**TEL:** 01932 863 933
*All plants are grown in our nursery, so many other plants are also available during the year, including summer bedding.*
**OPEN:** Thu-Tue 10-5. Closed Christmas Day.
**SPECIALITIES:** Comprehensive range.
**FACILITIES:** Pushchair friendly, Sell plants, Dogs allowed, Wheelchair access.

## 9 A J DOBBE AND SONS

Bramley Nurseries, Bramley Way, Ashtead
**TEL:** 01372 273 924

## 11 MARSDEN GARDEN CENTRE

Pleasure Pit Road, Ashtead
**TEL:** 01372 273 891

## 12 FARM LANE NURSERIES

Farm Lane, Ashtead
**TEL:** 01372 274 400

## 10 SEYMOURS GARDEN & LEISURE CENTRE OF STOKE D'ABERNON

Stoke Road, Stoke D'Abernon, Cobham, Surrey, KT11 3PU.
**TEL:** 01932 862 530
**EMAIL:** enquiries@seymours-gardens.com
**WEB:** www.seymours-gardens.com

*Well known centre offering service, value and quality. Plants and equipment, landscape services and materials, garden furniture and excellent restaurant.*
**OPEN:** Mon-Sat 8.30-5.30, Sun 10.30-4.30. Closed Christmas and Easter Sun.
**SPECIALITIES:** Herbaceous plants, Shrubs, Alpines, Garden services, Furniture.
**FACILITIES:** Toilets, Restaurant, Credit cards, Wheelchair access, Gift tokens, Child area, Coffee shop.

## 13 CEDAR NURSERY

Horsley Road, Cobham, Surrey, KT11 3JX.
**TEL:** 01932 862 473
**EMAIL:** info@landscaping.co.uk
**WEB:** www.landscaping.co.uk

*We grow a wide range of trees, shrubs and perennials. We source specimen plants from Europe. Other services and products include plant sourcing and exclusive Impruneta terracotta.*
**OPEN:** Mon-Sat 8.30-5.30.
**SPECIALITIES:** Shrubs, Terracotta pots, Bamboos, Topiary, Box hedges.
**FACILITIES:** Toilets, Credit cards, Dogs allowed, Sell plants.

### 14 LOWER ROAD NURSERY AND PLANT CENTRE

Lower Road, Effingham, Surrey, KT24 5JP.
*Top quality plants at lower prices. Bedding plants, trees and shrubs to large specimens. Pots and sundries. Many plants grown on site. Plant advice available.*
**OPEN:** Open daily 9-5. Closed Christmas & Boxing Day.
**SPECIALITIES:** Comprehensive range, Cyclamen, Fuchsias, Geraniums, Shrubs.
**FACILITIES:** Credit cards, Dogs allowed, HTA gift tokens, Pushchair friendly, Sell plants, Wheelchair access.

### 15 DOBBE'S NURSERIES

Guildford Road, Great Bookham
**TEL:** 01372 454 553

### 16 SQUIRE'S GARDEN CENTRE

Epsom Road, West Horsley, Leatherhead, Surrey, KT24 6AR.
**TEL:** 01483 282 911
**WEB:** www.squiresgardencentres.co.uk
*An extensive garden centre adjacent to our plant nursery for the very freshest stock. G.C.A. Centre of Excellence 2001.*
**OPEN:** Mon-Sat 9- 6, Sun 10.30-4.30.
**SPECIALITIES:** Bedding plants, Climbers, Garden & conservatory furniture, Shrubs, Herbaceous plants.
**FACILITIES:** Toilets, Credit cards, Wheelchair access, Restaurant, Gift tokens, Dogs allowed, Bookshop, Coffee shop, Plant guarantee, Gift shop, HTA gift tokens, Own gift tokens, Sell plants, Pushchair friendly.

### 17 POLESDEN LACEY, NATIONAL TRUST

Great Bookham, Dorking
**TEL:** 01372 452 048

### 18 WYEVALE GARDEN CENTRE

Reigate Road, Dorking
**TEL:** 01306 884 845

### 19 FOLIAGE SCENTED & HERB PLANTS

Walton Poor, Crocknorth Road, Ranmore Common
**TEL:** 01483 282 273

### 20 ZIEGLERS ORNAMENTAL GARDEN STATUORY LTD

Village Street, Newdigate, Dorking
**TEL:** 01306 631 287

Scotch Broom

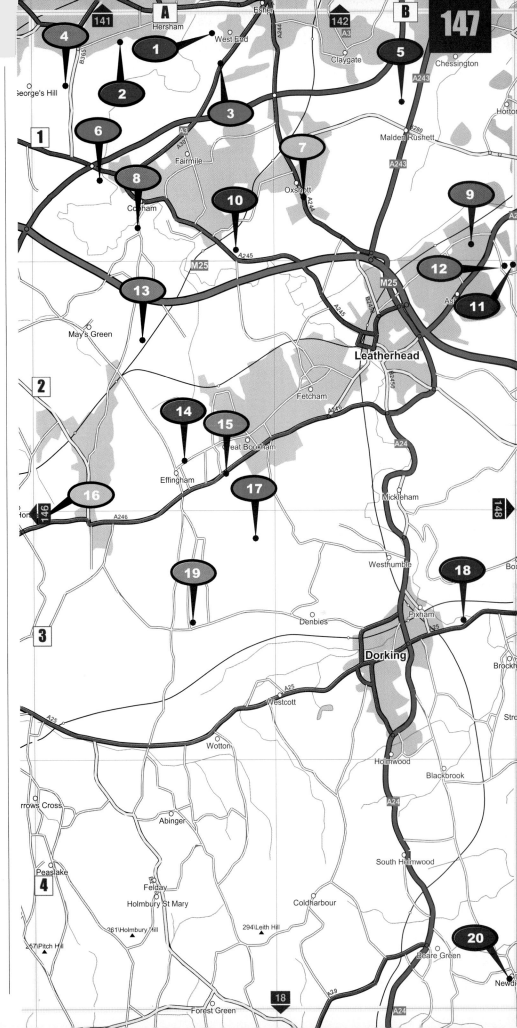

**1 RUSKIN GARDEN CENTRE**
9 Ruskin Road, Carshalton    TEL: 020 8669 8205

**2 WYEVALE GARDEN CENTRE**
Wadden Way, Purley Way, Croydon
TEL: 020 8688 5117

**3 BRIAN HILEY**
Telegraph Track, 25 Little Woodcote Estate, Wallington
TEL: 020 8647 9679

**4 WOODCOTE GREEN NURSERIES**
Woodmansterne Lane, Wallington TEL: 020 8647 6838

**5 BARNES NURSERIES**
46 Woodmansterne Lane, Wallington
TEL: 020 8647 8213

**6 MELBOURNE NURSERY**
43 Woodmansterne Lane, Wallington
TEL: 020 8647 2368

**7 FLITTON'S NURSERY & PLANT CENTRE**
51 Woodmansterne Lane, Wallington
TEL: 020 8647 5615

**8 VERNON GERANIUM NURSERY**
Cuddington Way, Cheam, Sutton   TEL: 020 8393 7616

**9 WONDER NURSERIES**
69 Lower Pillory Downs, Little Woodcote,
Carshalton, Surrey, SM5 4DD.
TEL: 020 8668 3133
EMAIL: wondernurseries@talk21.com

*An old established nursery specialising in fuchsias, geraniums, universal pansies and bedding plants.*
OPEN: Open 7 days a week. Summer: 9-6. Winter: 9-4. Closed Nov-Mar.
SPECIALITIES: Bedding plants, Hanging baskets.
FACILITIES: Pushchair friendly, Sell plants, Toilets, Wheelchair access.

**12 ROCKHAM NURSERY**
139 Reigate Road, Ewell    TEL: 020 8394 2186

**13 CHELSHAM PLACE**
Limpsfield Road, Chelsham    TEL: 01883 622 340

**14 ROSEDENE NURSERY**
Woldingham    TEL: 01883 653 142

**15 MEARE CLOSE NURSERIES**
Tadworth Street, Tadworth    TEL: 01737 812 449

**16 PONDLIFE COMPANY**
5 Wood Lane, Caterham    TEL: 01883 345 806

**10 BEECHCROFT NURSERY**
127 Reigate Road, Ewell, Surrey, KT17 3DE.
TEL: 020 8393 4265

*A nursery growing a very wide range of conifers, alpines, heathers, perennials and winter bedding.*
OPEN: Mon-Sat 10-4. Closed Christmas-New Year week.
SPECIALITIES: Alpines, Conifers, Fuchsias, Hanging baskets, Perennials.
FACILITIES: Wheelchair access, Credit cards, Sell plants, Pushchair friendly, Toilets.

**11 S G CLARKE MARKET GARDEN & NURSERY**
23 Croydon Lane, Banstead, Surrey, SM7 3BE.
TEL: 020 8643 3836
*Bedding plants, shrubs, farm shop with fruit, vegetables and flowers. Christmas trees.*
OPEN: Farm shop; Jun-Dec: 9-5. Nursery stock; Apr-Dec: 9-5.
ENTRY COSTS: Free.
SPECIALITIES: Bedding plants, Shrubs, Vegetables, Christmas trees, Roses.
FACILITIES: Wheelchair access, Farm shop, Sell plants.

**17 RUPERT BOWLBY**
Gatton, Reigate    TEL: 01737 642 221

**18 BUCKLAND NURSERIES**
Buckland, Reigate    TEL: 01737 242 990

**19 SQUIRE'S GARDEN CENTRE HIGH TREES**
Main Road, Buckland, Reigate   TEL: 01737 247 217

**20 WALKERS GARDEN LEISURE**
Anglefield Corner, South Godstone
TEL: 01342 893 109

**21 KNIGHTS GARDEN CENTRE**
Oxted Road, Godstone    TEL: 01883 742 275

**22 IVY MILL NURSERY**
Bletchingley Road, Godstone   TEL: 01883 742 665

**23 NETTLETONS NURSERY**
Ivy Mill Lane, Godstone    TEL: 01883 742 426

**24 HEATHFIELD NURSERIES**
Flanchford Road, Reigate    TEL: 01737 247 641

**25 BLOOMS OF BETCHWORTH**
Station Road, Betchworth    TEL: 01737 842 099

**26 CLAY LANE NURSERY**
The Surrey Fuchsia Centre, 3 Clay Lane, South Nutfield
TEL: 01737 823 307

**27 REIGATE GARDEN CENTRE**
143 Sandcross Lane, South Park, Reigate, Surrey, RH2 8HH.
TEL: 01737 248 188
EMAIL: contact@reigategardencente.fsnet.co.uk
WEB: www.reigategardencente.co.uk
*All types of garden furniture, lawnmowers, garden machinery, sheds, garden buildings, landscape materials, ponds, plants, trees and coffee shop.*

OPEN: Mon-Sat 9-6, Sun 10.30-4.30.
SPECIALITIES: Garden & conservatory furniture, Garden machinery, Garden buildings, Shrubs, Landscape materials.
FACILITIES: Toilets, Credit cards, Wheelchair access, Restaurant, Gift tokens, Dogs allowed, Coffee shop.

**28 WOODHAM NURSERY**
Eastbourne Rd, South Godstone  TEL: 01342 892 331

**29 NUTFIELD NURSERIES**
Crabhill Lane, South Nutfield, Redhill
TEL: 01737 823 277

**30 HILLSIDE HARDY PLANT NURSERY**
109 Horley Road, Earlswood, Redhill
TEL: 01737 765 645

**31 BROOK NURSERY**
Eastbourne Rd, South Godstone  TEL: 01342 893 265

**32 CATERHAM KOI**
Walkers Garden Centre, Anglefield Corner, Godstone
TEL: 01342 893 303

**33 RUSHMORE GARDEN CENTRE**
Walkers Garden Leisure, Eastbourne Rd, South Godstone
TEL: 01342 893 109

**34 SUNNYACRES NURSERY**
18 Reigate Road, Hookwood, Horley
TEL: 01293 785 435

**35 LANGSHOTT MANOR**
Langshott, Gatwick    TEL: 01293 786 680

**36 WILLOW TREE NURSERY**
Newchapel Road, Lingfield    TEL: 01342 834 961

**37 HERONS BONSAI NURSERY**
Wiremill Lane, Newchapel, Lingfield
TEL: 01342 832 657

**38 WATERSIDE AQUATICS & KOI CENTRE**
West Park Road, Copthorne   TEL: 01342 712 332

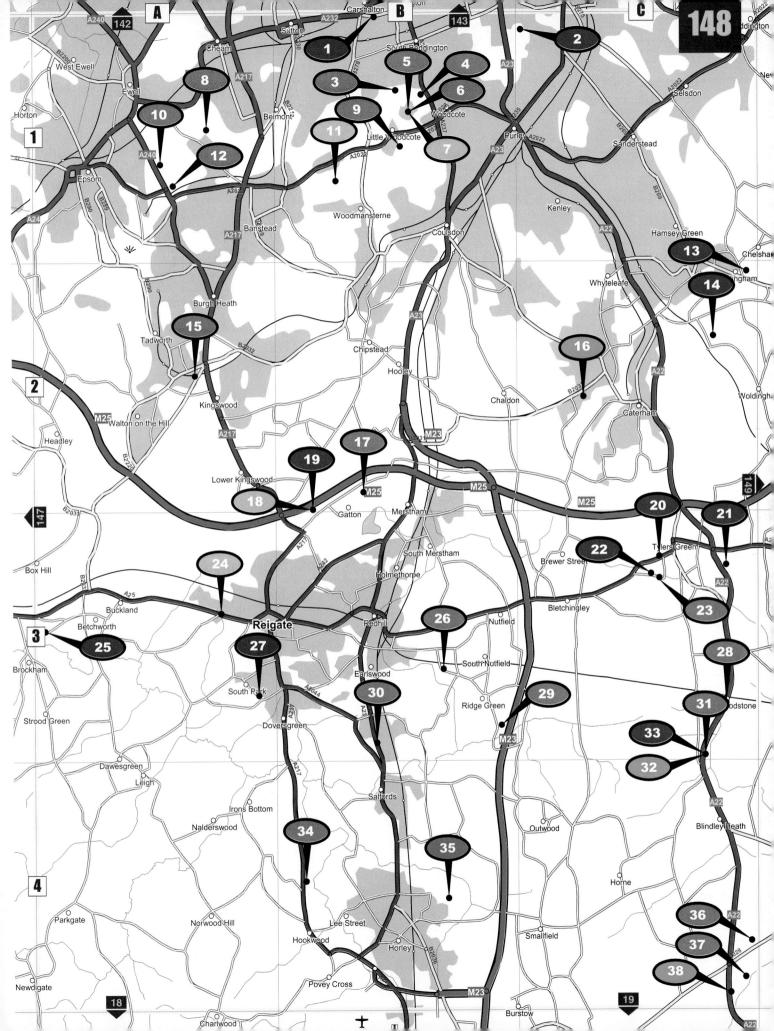

**1** **GLENSIDE GARDEN CENTRE**
Brittenden Parade, High Street, Orpington
TEL: 01689 855 557

**2** **POLHILL GARDEN CENTRE**
London Road, Badgers Mount, Sevenoaks
TEL: 01959 534 212

**3** **THE NURSERY**
Filstone Farm, London Road, Badgers Mount
TEL: 01959 534 362

**4** **COOLING'S NURSERIES**
Rushmore Hill Nurseries, Knockholt, Sevenoaks
TEL: 01959 532 269

**5** **RANDLES HANGING BASKETS**
Randles House, Rushmoor Hill, Knockholt
TEL: 01732 760 050

**6** **DOWN HOUSE**
Luxted Road, Downe
TEL: 01689 859 119

**7** **WYEVALE GARDEN CENTRE**
Main Road, Knockholt, Sevenoaks
TEL: 01959 532 187

**8** **RIVER GARDEN NURSERIES**
Troutbeck, Otford, Sevenoaks
TEL: 01959 525 588

**9** **WESTERHAM HEIGHTS NURSERY**
Main Road, Westerham Hill, Westerham
TEL: 01959 571 545

**10** **SELECT GARDEN & PET CENTRE**
Main Road, Sundridge, Sevenoaks
TEL: 01959 562 400

**11** **SQUERRYES COURT**
Squerryes, Westerham
TEL: 01959 562 345

**12** **EMMETTS GARDEN, NATIONAL TRUST**
Ide Hill, Sevenoaks
TEL: 01732 750 367

**13** **NEWLANDS NURSERY**
Goathurst Common, Ide Hill, Sevenoaks
TEL: 01732 750 591

**14** **CHARTWELL, NATIONAL TRUST**
Westerham
TEL: 01732 866 368 / 01732 868 381

**15** **FRENCH STREET NURSERIES**
Hosey Common Lane, Westerham
TEL: 01959 563 366

**16** **RING LODGE NURSERY**
Main Road, Edenbridge
TEL: 01732 862 930

**17** **HEVER CASTLE & GARDENS**
Edenbridge, Kent, TN8 7NG.
TEL: 01732 865 224
EMAIL: mail@hevercastle.co.uk
WEB: www.hevercastle.co.uk
*13th century castle, childhood home of Anne Boleyn. Award winning gardens. Italian, Tudor, and Rose gardens, Yew and water mazes, 110 metre herbaceous border and a thirty-five acre lake.*
OPEN: Mar-Nov: 11-6.
ENTRY COSTS: £8.20, Child: £4.50, OAPs: £7, Family: £20.90.
SPECIALITIES: Herbaceous plants, Themed gardens, Ornaments, Rhododendrons and azaleas, Roses.
FACILITIES: Toilets, Credit cards, Wheelchair access, Restaurant, Dogs allowed, Bookshop, Child area, Coffee shop, Gift shop, Sell plants.

**18** **CHIDDINGSTONE CASTLE**
Chiddingstone, Edenbridge
TEL: 01892 870 347

**19** **OCCASIONALLY YOURS**
Lingfield Common Road, Lingfield
TEL: 01342 833 937

**20** **STARBOROUGH NURSERY**
Starborough Road, Marsh Green, Edenbridge
TEL: 01732 865 614

**21** **ROGER PLATTS GARDEN DESIGN & NURSERIES**
Stick Hill, Edenbridge, Kent, TN8 5NH.
TEL: 01732 863 318
EMAIL: plattsgdn@aol.com

*Traditional nursery with emphasis on garden design. Interesting range of plants available, including a wide variety of hardy perennials.*
OPEN: Open daily 9-5. Closed Christmas & Boxing Day.
SPECIALITIES: Garden design & landscaping, Perennials, Roses, Shrubs, Trees.
FACILITIES: Wheelchair access, Gift tokens, Credit cards, Dogs allowed, HTA gift tokens, Own gift tokens, Sell plants.

**22** **PENSHURST PLACE & GARDENS**
Penshurst, Tonbridge
TEL: 01892 870 307

Lily Pond

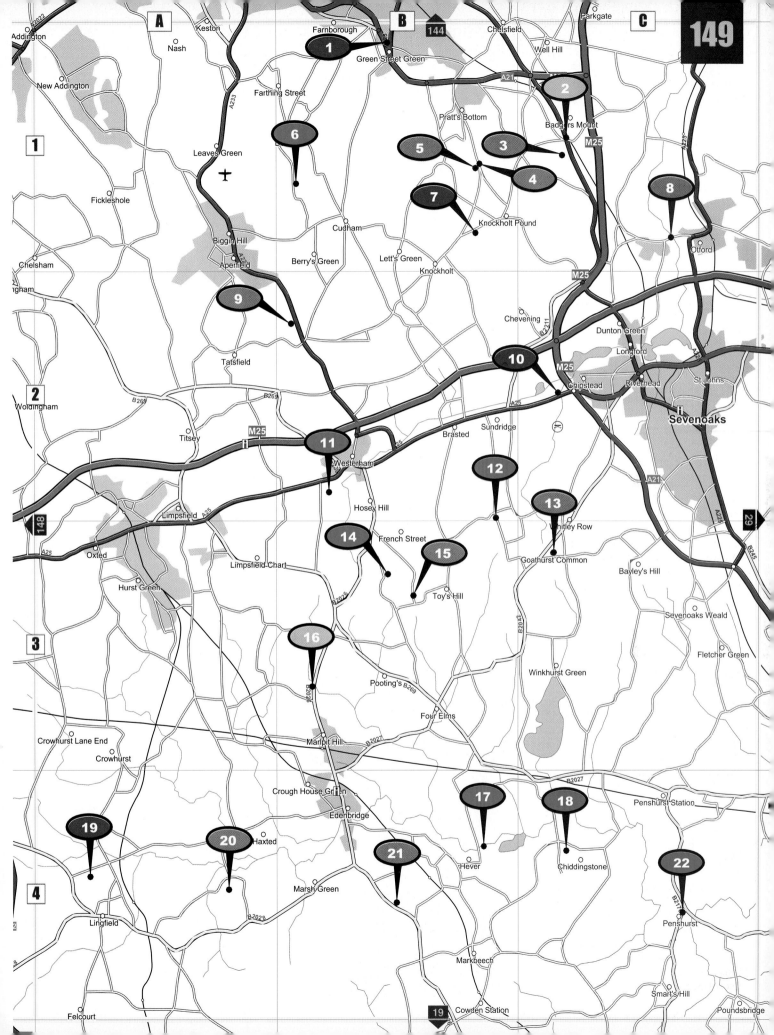

# LARGE GARDEN

B&Q, B&Q Warehouse, Focus, Focus Do It All and Sainsbury's Homebase, are now part of our everyday lives. You can buy garden furniture, plants and pesticides from all of them. They also sell household goods and you can grab a cup of tea or a bite to eat in one of their coffee shops or restaurants. All of these stores are visited by many garden enthusiasts and can be found quite easily in any town or city, therefore our mapping is not essential.
The list below is sorted by town, with their phone numbers, should you need to contact them before visiting.

## B&Q

| | |
|---|---|
| Abingdon | 01235 550 022 |
| Airdrie | 01236 433 357 |
| Alfreton | 01773 540 840 |
| Altrincham | 0161 928 4222 |
| Ashford | 01233 636 931 |
| Aylesbury | 01296 338 753 |
| Aylesford | 01732 870 470 |
| Ayr | 01292 886 644 |
| Banbury | 01295 273 372 |
| Bangor | 01248 370 258 |
| Barnsley | 01226 292 939 |
| Barnstaple | 01271 379 040 |
| Barrow in Furness | 01229 834 023 |
| Basildon | 01268 534 884 |
| Bexhill-on-sea | 01424 730 977 |
| Birmingham | 0121 789 7227 |
| Bishop Auckland | 01388 662 120 |
| Bishopbriggs | 0141 762 4556 |
| Blackburn | 01254 543 28 |
| Blackburn | 01253 798 111 |
| Bognor Regis | 01243 867 111 |
| Bolton | 01204 595 454 |
| Boston | 01205 355 877 |
| Bournemouth | 01202 534 131 |
| Bournemouth | 01202 297 631 |
| Bradford | 01274 688 327 |
| Bradford | 01274 668 309 |
| Braintree | 01376 347 313 |
| Bridge of Don | 01224 822 079 |
| Bridgend | 01656 768 611 |
| Bridgwater | 01278 428 118 |
| Bridlington | 01262 400 061 |
| Brierley Hill | 01384 572 772 |
| Brighton | 01273 679 926 |
| Brislington | 0117 977 9254 |
| Bristol, BS34 5TS | 0117 959 0621 |
| Bristol, BS37 9NN | 0117 951 0722 |
| Bristol, BS37 5PQ | 01454 311 074 |
| Burton upon Trent | 01283 536 957 |
| Bury | 0161 764 8844 |
| Bury St Edmunds | 01284 706 316 |
| Cambridge | 01223 322 639 |
| Cannock | 01543 468 839 |
| Cardiff | 02920 395 936 |
| Carlisle | 01228 548 814 |
| Carmarthen | 01267 238 007 |
| Cheadle Hulme | 0161 485 8807 |
| Chelmsford | 01245 495 678 |
| Cheltenham | 01242 572 525 |
| Chester | 01244 372 773 |
| Chesterfield | 01246 211 957 |
| Chorley | 01257 260 361 |
| Christchurch | 01202 473 536 |
| Clacton-on-sea | 01255 430 022 |
| Colchester | 01206 574 767 |
| Coventry | 024 7660 1600 |
| Coventry | 024 7665 2000 |
| Crawley | 01293 611 651 |
| Crewe | 01270 257 824 |
| crickelwood | 020 8450 1255 |
| Cumbernauld | 01236 724 714 |
| Cwmbran | 01633 877 323 |
| Dagenham | 020 8595 4116 |
| Darlington | 01325 480 812 |
| Dartford | 01322 223 878 |
| Derby, DE2 8ST | 01332 574 818 |
| Derby, DE22 3FA | 01332 203 090 |
| Derby, DE21 7BR | 01332 281 479 |
| Dewsbury | 01924 457 435 |
| Douglas | 01624 677 077 |
| Dover | 01304 240 373 |
| Dundee | 01382 623 175 |
| Dundee | 01382 500 950 |
| Dunfermline | 01383 621 058 |
| East Shotton | 01244 830 497 |
| Eastbourne | 01323 509 466 |
| Eastleigh | 023 8061 1219 |
| Eastwood | 01773 530 290 |
| Edinb'h, EH9 8LD | 0131 554 1464 |
| Edinb'h, EH14 2ER | 0131 455 7637 |
| Edinb'h, N15 4QD | 0131 346 1563 |
| Edinb'h, EH7 4HL | 0131 557 1300 |
| Ellesmere | 0151 357 1414 |
| Exeter | 01392 444 645 |
| Exmouth | 01395 224 116 |
| Falkirk | 01324 636 152 |
| Fareham | 01489 582 855 |
| Galashiels | 01896 754 044 |
| Gateshead | 0191 488 8144 |
| Gillingham | 01634 263 983 |
| Glasgow | 0141 954 1565 |
| Glastonbury | 01458 835 618 |
| Gloucester | 01452 300 744 |
| Gorseinon | 01792 897 337 |
| Grantham | 01476 591 112 |
| Gravesend | 01474 536 534 |
| Greenford | 020 8575 7175 |
| Grimsby | 01472 267 602 |
| Guildford | 01483 304 881 |
| Halifax | 01422 348 421 |
| Harlow | 01279 453 738 |
| Hartlepool | 01429 272 229 |
| Hastings | 01424 441 133 |
| Hayes | 020 8848 1898 |
| Hemel Hempstead | 01442 216 644 |
| Hengoed | 01443 815 888 |
| Hereford | 01432 357 447 |
| High Wycombe | 01494 463 400 |
| Hitchin | 01462 455 253 |
| Hogganfield | 0141 770 8668 |
| Hull | 01482 565 160 |
| Ilford | 020 8554 6653 |
| Inverness | 01463 234 562 |
| Ipswich | 01473 232 823 |
| Irvine | 01294 471 909 |
| Keighley | 01535 611 057 |
| Kettering | 01536 482 431 |
| Killingbeck | 0113 249 4554 |
| Kilmarnock | 01563 570 222 |
| Kirkcaldy | 01592 267 208 |
| Lancaster | 01524 388 366 |
| Leatherhead | 01372 373 793 |
| Leicester | 01455 250 000 |
| Leicester | 0116 288 1360 |
| Leigh | 01942 608 521 |
| Lincoln | 01522 520 515 |
| Liverpool | 0151 254 2044 |
| Liverpool | 0151 523 0111 |
| Llandudno | 01492 878 181 |
| London, E4 8QF | 020 8503 3576 |
| London, SE9 3AN | 020 8850 4411 |
| London, N15 4QD | 020 7252 0657 |
| London, E10 7PQ | 020 8365 1699 |
| Lond'n, SW18 1EW | 020 8558 4817 |
| Lond'n, SE27 9AF | 020 8875 1052 |
| London, W4 5QL | 020 8761 1236 |
| London, N20 OPD | 020 8995 8028 |
| Lond'n, SW19 7JY | 020 8445 3696 |
| London | 020 8879 3322 |
| Loughborough | 01509 236 454 |
| Lowestoft | 01502 561 814 |
| Luton | 01582 728 821 |
| Macclesfield | 01625 616 729 |
| Maidstone | 01622 672 488 |
| Manch'r, M19 1BA | 0161 257 2839 |
| Manch'r, M8 8LN | 0161 832 2901 |
| Manc'r, SK17 7BD | 0161 367 9095 |
| Manch'r, M32 0YP | 0161 865 8435 |
| Manch'r, M27 6AN | 0161 794 8411 |
| Margate | 01843 298 833 |
| Merthyr Tydfil | 01685 723 231 |
| Milton Keynes | 01908 648 511 |
| Mitcham | 020 8685 1551 |
| Motherwell | 01698 269 124 |
| Mount Vernon | 0141 778 8563 |
| Neath | 01639 635 001 |
| Nelson | 01282 698 008 |
| New Haven | 01273 515 818 |
| New Malden | 020 8336 0365 |
| Newbury | 01635 528 515 |
| Newcastle Upon Tyne | 0191 276 6496 |
| Newcastle Upon Tyne | 0191 271 3333 |
| Newport | 01983 821 281 |
| Newport | 01633 213 241 |
| Newton Abbot | 01626 369 177 |
| Northallerton | 01609 773 161 |
| Northampton | 01604 232 926 |
| Northwich | 01606 481 54 |
| Nott'm, NG3 5RW | 0115 926 3456 |
| Nott'm, NG18 2RA | 01623 620 171 |
| Nott'm, NG19 9BG | 01623 651 252 |
| Oldham | 0161 626 7623 |
| Oxford | 01865 749 339 |
| Penrith | 01768 890 777 |
| Penzance | 01736 330 712 |
| Perth | 01738 620 884 |
| Peterborough | 01733 561 206 |
| Plymouth | 01752 346 462 |
| Pontypridd | 01443 480 851 |
| Portsmouth | 023 9269 4751 |
| Preston | 01772 258 232 |
| Reading | 0118 931 2211 |
| Redditch | 01527 550 552 |
| Redruth | 01209 717 281 |
| Renfrew | 0141 885 2040 |
| Rhyl | 01745 338 369 |
| Rochdale | 01706 350 446 |
| Rochester | 01634 712 801 |
| Rotherham | 01709 829 081 |
| Rutherglen | 0141 647 1945 |
| Salisbury | 01722 332 299 |
| Scarborough | 01723 500 477 |
| Selly Oak | 0121 414 1710 |
| Sheffield | 0114 250 7685 |
| Sheffield | 0114 233 6330 |
| Shiremoor | 0191 251 3513 |
| Shoreham-by-Sea | 01273 463 423 |
| Shrewsbury | 01743 448 696 |
| Sidcup | 020 8308 1844 |
| Solihull | 0121 733 1212 |
| South Shields | 0191 456 6218 |
| Southampton | 023 8078 8311 |
| Southampton | 023 8058 4724 |
| Southend-on-Sea | 01702 619 922 |
| Southport | 01704 500 085 |
| St Austell | 01726 730 14 |
| St Helens | 01744 451 594 |
| Stafford | 01785 253 377 |
| Stanmore | 020 8204 8181 |
| Stevenage | 01438 315 722 |
| Stirling | 01786 449 559 |
| Stoke-on-Trent | 01782 205 158 |
| Stoke-on-Trent | 01782 272 770 |
| Stoke-on-Trent | 01782 771 323 |
| Stourbridge | 01384 390 676 |
| Sunderland | 0191 521 1898 |
| Swansea | 01792 580 262 |
| Swansea | 01792 701 702 |
| Swindon | 01793 616 349 |
| Tamworth | 01827 281 888 |
| Taunton | 01823 444 429 |
| Telford | 01952 290 284 |
| Tonbridge | 01732 770 441 |
| Torquay | 01803 213 841 |
| Wakefield | 01924 377 988 |
| Wallsend | 0191 263 3330 |
| Warrington | 01925 571 747 |
| Welwyn Garden City | 01707 371 543 |
| Wembley | 020 8998 9019 |
| West Bromwich | 0121 525 1090 |
| Weymouth | 01305 778 103 |
| Whitstable | 01227 794 663 |
| Widnes | 0151 495 1668 |
| Wigan | 01942 323 030 |
| Wisbech | 01945 463 748 |
| Workington | 01900 685 85 |
| Worksop | 01909 531 127 |
| Worthing | 01903 821 104 |
| Wrexham | 01978 362 777 |
| Yeading | 020 8841 3092 |
| Yeovil | 01935 429 147 |
| York | 01904 693 030 |
| York | 01904 611 000 |

## B&Q Warehouse

| | |
|---|---|
| Aberdeen | 01224 326 262 |
| Ashton under Lyme | 0161 371 0082 |
| Basingstoke | 01256 460 876 |
| Blackpool | 01253 594 234 |
| Bristol | 0117 960 2126 |
| Bury | 0161 763 1012 |
| Canterbury | 01227 760 066 |
| Cardiff | 02920 731 200 |
| Coseley | 01902 408 783 |
| Croydon | 020 8649 9930 |
| Darlington | 01325 480 180 |
| Doncaster | 01302 787 382 |
| Edinburgh | 0131 657 2555 |
| Enfield | 0845 300 2894 |
| Exeter | 01392 413 506 |
| Farnborough | 01252 372 005 |
| Glasgow | 0141 621 2244 |
| Glasgow | 0141 949 1122 |
| Halesowen | 0121 550 9099 |
| Havant | 023 9247 6051 |
| Hedge End | 01489 799 711 |
| Huddersfield | 01484 455 004 |
| Hull | 01482 839 183 |
| Leeds | 0113 276 1761 |
| Leicester | 0116 253 2012 |
| Liverpool | 0151 427 4488 |
| London | 020 8591 7666 |
| Luton | 01582 429 293 |
| Newcastle Upon Tyne | 0191 274 3344 |
| Norwich | 01603 488 422 |
| Nottingham | 0115 986 4818 |
| Oldham | 0161 626 1769 |
| Paisley | 0141 889 9146 |
| Poole | 01202 685 516 |
| Romford | 01708 372 200 |
| Slough | 01753 571 333 |
| Southampton | 023 8074 0877 |
| St Helier | 01534 636 500 |
| St Peter Port | 01481 713 018 |
| Stockport | 0161 429 7117 |
| Stockton on Tees | 01642 670 022 |
| Stratford-upon-Avon | 01789 415 446 |
| Sunderland | 0191 567 1444 |
| Sutton | 020 8643 8933 |
| Wallasey | 0151 346 9698 |
| Washington | 0191 201 5711 |
| Watford | 01923 225 533 |
| Wednesbury | 0121 526 5555 |
| West Thurrock | 01708 680 331 |
| Winwick | 01925 245 522 |
| York | 01904 438 441 |

## Focus

| | |
|---|---|
| Aberdeen | 01224 276 766 |
| Aberystwyth | 01970 627 722 |
| Aldershot | 01252 334 252 |
| Ashford | 01784 256 761 |
| Barnsley | 01226 207 635 |
| Barnstaple | 01271 379 709 |
| Bedford | 01234 217 773 |
| Beverley | 01482 860 612 |
| Bracknell | 01344 862 343 |
| Bradford | 01274 617 028 |
| Bridgwater | 01278 426 530 |
| Bristol | 0117 977 9348 |
| Bristol | 0117 965 3127 |
| Bristol | 0117 960 3849 |
| Bromley | 020 8460 9969 |
| Burton upon Trent | 01283 539 080 |
| Caerphilly | 029 2086 7712 |
| Cambridge | 01223 362 000 |
| Carmarthen | 01267 235 257 |
| Chesham | 01494 778 383 |
| Chester | 01244 346 206 |
| Chippenham | 01249 659 203 |
| Coulby Newham | 01642 576 200 |
| Darlington | 01325 481 414 |
| Daventry | 01327 311 616 |
| Devizes | 01380 730 500 |
| Doncaster | 01302 730 014 |
| Dumfries | 01387 248 623 |
| Edinburgh | 0131 316 4553 |
| Evesham | 01386 446 684 |
| Exeter | 01392 496 633 |
| Fareham | 01329 823 133 |
| Gloucester | 01452 311 811 |
| Goole | 01405 726 600 |
| Gravesend | 01474 564 040 |
| Hanley | 01782 268 999 |
| Harrogate | 01423 524 181 |
| Haverhill | 01440 760 200 |
| Horwich | 01204 664 600 |
| Huntingdon | 01480 434 492 |
| Inverness | 01463 711 644 |
| Ipswich | 01473 610 823 |
| Kendal | 01539 729 977 |
| Kingswinford | 01384 401 951 |
| Llanelli | 01554 771 121 |
| London, E4 9JG | 020 8523 1131 |
| Lond'n, SE18 2BD | 020 8316 6060 |
| Longbridge | 0121 478 1881 |
| Lowestoft | 01502 565 155 |
| Macclesfield | 01625 427 777 |
| Maldon | 01621 840 044 |
| March | 01354 661 561 |
| Merthyr Tydfil | 01685 723 488 |
| Middlesbrough | 01642 440 044 |
| Milton Keynes | 01908 282 330 |
| Netherfield | 0115 940 0830 |
| Newark | 01636 673 111 |
| Newport | 01633 896 236 |
| Northampton | 01604 416 002 |
| Paisley | 0141 848 1331 |
| Paulton | 01761 412 594 |
| Peterborough | 01733 897 877 |
| Peterhead | 01779 474 111 |
| Poole | 01202 733 032 |
| Reading | 0118 945 1566 |
| Redruth | 01209 612 010 |
| Ruislip | 020 8845 2372 |
| Rushden | 01933 418 558 |
| Saltash | 01752 848 069 |
| Sheffield | 0114 275 2756 |
| Sheffield | 0114 251 4050 |
| Skipton | 01756 798 899 |
| Southampton | 01489 789 333 |
| Stoke-on-Trent | 01782 711 880 |
| Stroud | 01453 753 636 |
| Sudbury | 01787 880 101 |
| Taunton | 01823 259 545 |
| Thetford | 01842 751 362 |
| Torquay | 01803 617 317 |
| Trowbridge | 01225 763 944 |
| Tunstall | 01782 839 031 |
| Twickenham | 0208 943 3978 |
| Uddingston | 01698 810 606 |
| Walsall | 01543 377 700 |
| Walsall | 01922 645 590 |
| Warwick | 01926 425 415 |
| West Drayton | 01895 448 261 |
| Wst-Sup-Mare | 01934 412 326 |
| Witney | 01993 778 981 |
| Worksop | 01909 473 444 |
| Yeovil | 01935 422 116 |

## Focus Do It All

| | |
|---|---|
| Aberdare | 01685 884 005 |
| Aberdeen | 01224 782 889 |
| Airdrie | 01236 765 458 |
| Aldridge | 01922 743 565 |
| Alloa | 01259 724 612 |
| Andover | 01264 338 115 |
| Arbroath | 01241 870 600 |
| Ashford | 01233 503 974 |
| Ashington | 01670 852 570 |
| Banbury | 01295 275 642 |
| Bangor | 01248 370 037 |
| Barnsley | 01226 770 627 |
| Bathgate | 01506 632 912 |
| Belper | 01773 880 108 |
| Benfleet | 01268 759 666 |
| Bishop Auckland | 01388 608 918 |
| Bishop's Stortford | 01279 653232 |
| Blackburn | 01254 573 05 |
| Blackpool | 01253 695 936 |
| Blackpool | 01253 408 070 |
| Blantyre | 01698 712 178 |
| Bodmin | 01208 765 00 |
| Bolton | 01204 361414 |
| Borehamwood | 020 8207 5277 |
| Bradford | 01274 725 175 |
| Bromborough | 0151 334 4060 |
| Bromsgrove | 01527 575 540 |
| Bulwell | 01159 757 796 |
| Burnley | 01282 457 511 |
| Burton upon Trent | 01283 516 809 |
| Cannock | 01543 574 467 |
| Canterbury | 01227 780 105 |
| Cardiff, CF14 5EB | 0292 0747 494 |
| Cardiff, CF23 78D | 0292 0498 780 |
| Cardiff, CF11 8LR | 0292 0233 038 |
| Carlisle | 01228 511 171 |
| Chester | 01244 390 700 |
| Chesterfield | 01246 208 551 |
| Clevedon | 01275 340 032 |
| Coalville | 01530 814 663 |
| Cobridge | 01782 287 011 |
| Colchester | 01206 767 700 |
| Consett | 01207 580 606 |
| Corby | 01536 202 555 |
| Cramlington | 01670 717 777 |
| Crewe | 01270 252 522 |
| Crowborough | 01892 665 344 |
| Darlaston | 01922 720 730 |
| Derby | 01332 292 142 |
| Dewsbury | 01924 457 598 |
| Didcot | 01235 811 366 |
| Doncaster | 01302 768 447 |
| Dudley | 01384 242 186 |
| Dunfermline | 01383 623 888 |
| Ebbw Vale | 01495 304 567 |
| Edinburgh | 0131 4482 485 |
| Epsom | 01372 748 890 |
| Flint | 01352 731 515 |
| Folkestone | 01303 277 258 |
| Formby | 01704 878 658 |
| Frome | 01373 467 658 |
| Gainsborough | 01427 811 373 |
| Glenrothes | 01592 770 474 |
| Grantham | 01476 570 666 |
| Great Yarmouth | 01493 442 654 |
| Grimsby | 01472 240 169 |
| Guiseley | 01943 870 059 |
| Halesowen | 0121 550 9980 |
| Halifax | 01422 330 170 |
| Hartlepool | 01429 233 633 |
| Hereford | 01432 355 535 |
| Hertford | 01992 501 808 |
| Hinckley | 01455 251 089 |
| Ilkeston | 01159 443 990 |

# CENTRE GROUPS

| | |
|---|---|
| Kettering | 01536 410 144 |
| Kettering | 01536 412 447 |
| Kidderminster | 01562 748 402 |
| Kilmarnock | 01563 573 721 |
| King's Lynn | 01553 691 169 |
| Leicester | 01858 461 481 |
| Lichfield | 01543 416 121 |
| Lincoln | 01522 567 007 |
| Littlehampton | 01903 723 229 |
| Liverp'l, L24 9WA | 0151 486 5455 |
| Liverp'l, L4 9XU | 0151 256 7418 |
| London | 020 8208 4588 |
| Loughborough | 01509 236 414 |
| Macclesfield | 01625 426 610 |
| Malvern | 01684 577 911 |
| Manchester | 0161 688 6227 |
| Middleton | 0161 721 4421 |
| Morecombe | 01524 350 23 |
| Newcastle Upon Tyne | 0191 213 1633 |
| Newport | 01633 222 268 |
| Nottingham | 01602 700 588 |
| Nuneaton | 024 763 44560 |
| Oldham | 0161 628 5819 |
| Paignton | 01803 528 810 |
| Paisley | 0141 848 9164 |
| Pembroke Dock | 01646 687 246 |
| Penrith | 01768 890 840 |
| Peterborough | 01733 320 910 |
| Plymouth | 01752 337 223 |
| Plympton | 01752 337 223 |
| Pontefract | 01977 602 323 |
| Pontypridd | 01443 843 536 |
| Port Talbot | 01639 822 295 |
| Rochdale | 01706 524 010 |
| Rotherham | 01709 780 228 |
| Rugby | 01788 541 245 |
| Rustington | 01903 787 779 |
| Scunthorpe | 01724 849 883 |
| Selby | 01757 210 153 |
| Shipley | 01274 592 866 |
| Shrewsbury | 01743 367 222 |
| South Shields | 0191 454 6160 |
| St Albans | 01727 836 668 |
| Stafford | 01785 223 363 |
| Stamford | 01780 482 131 |
| Stirchley | 0121 459 8908 |
| Stockport | 0161 477 3961 |
| Stoke-on-Trent | 01782 287 011 |
| Stoke-on-Trent | 01782 744 045 |
| Straiton | 0131 448 2485 |
| Sunderland | 0191 567 0717 |
| Swansea | 01792 793 318 |
| Swindon | 01793 423 241 |
| Tamworth | 01827 652 13 |
| Taplow | 01628 666 434 |
| Tavistock | 01822 616 438 |
| Telford | 01952 291 023 |
| Truro | 01872 241 935 |
| Tunbridge Wells | 01892 510 225 |
| Walsall | 01922 720 730 |
| Walton le Dale | 01772 203 320 |
| Warwick | 01926 401 434 |
| Washington | 0191 419 1558 |
| Whitehaven | 01946 690 710 |
| Widnes | 0151 495 2050 |
| Wigan | 01942 824 848 |
| Winnersh | 0118 9770 184 |
| Winsford | 01606 862 983 |
| Wolverhampton | 01902 717 387 |
| Yeovil | 01935 432 100 |
| York | 01904 692 799 |

### Sainsbury's Homebase

| | |
|---|---|
| Abingdon | 01235 521 004 |
| Accrington | 01254 872 767 |
| Andover | 01264 337 796 |
| Ashford | 01233 503 051 |
| Aylesbury | 01296 394 495 |
| Aylesford | 01622 715 071 |
| Ayr | 01292 610 063 |
| Barnstaple | 01271 323 087 |
| Barrow in Furness | 01229 813 303 |
| Basildon | 01268 534 921 |
| Basildon | 01268 550 656 |
| Basingstoke | 01256 355 658 |
| Bath | 01225 339 225 |
| Bedford | 01234 340 014 |
| Bedworth | 024 7664 3231 |
| Berwick upon Tweed | 01289 330 939 |
| Bicester | 01869 320 265 |
| Biggleswade | 01767 312 870 |
| Bir'ham, B14 7SN | 0121 443 3513 |
| Bir'ham, B29 6SJ | 0121 414 1144 |
| Bishop's Stortford | 01279 657 627 |
| Blackpool | 01253 341 274 |
| Bolton | 01204 364 825 |
| Boston | 01205 357 337 |
| Bracknell | 01344 483 868 |
| Bradford | 01274 614 712 |
| Bridge of Don | 01224 703 884 |
| Bridgend | 01656 648 548 |
| Bristol | 0117 923 6459 |
| Bristol | 0117 960 6622 |
| Broadheath | 0161 929 7262 |
| Broadstairs | 01843 866 116 |
| Bromborough | 0151 334 0555 |
| Camberley | 01276 685 408 |
| Cambridge | 01223 360 888 |
| Cannock | 01543 468 174 |
| Canterbury | 01227 456 881 |
| Cardiff, CF3 7AN | 02920 486 604 |
| Cardiff, CF5 4UG | 02920 599 900 |
| Carlisle | 01228 541 700 |
| Chaddesden Sidings | 01332 280 680 |
| Chatham | 01634 200 200 |
| Cheltenham | 01242 261 807 |
| Chester | 01244 378 881 |
| Chesterfield | 01246 230 538 |
| Chichester | 01243 532 221 |
| Chippenham | 01249 444 748 |
| Christchurch | 01202 487 890 |
| Clacton-on-sea | 01255 221 115 |
| Colchester | 01206 866 644 |
| Colchester | 01206 563 297 |
| Coventry | 024 7671 6271 |
| Coventry | 024 7660 2120 |
| Crawley | 01293 534 040 |
| Crayford | 01322 556 658 |
| Croydon | 020 8667 1088 |
| Croydon | 020 8689 5503 |
| Cwmbran | 01633 872 637 |
| Dagenham | 020 8517 0838 |
| Darlington | 01325 359 426 |
| Dartford | 01322 277 126 |
| Daybrook | 0115 967 9713 |
| Derby | 01332 291 102 |
| Doncaster | 01302 325 806 |
| Dover | 01304 826 537 |
| Droitwich | 01905 795 553 |
| Dumbarton | 01389 734 071 |
| Dumfries | 01387 257 188 |
| Dundee | 01382 828 681 |
| Dunfermline | 01383 620 920 |
| Dunstable | 01582 472 028 |
| East Dereham | 01362 691 022 |
| East Grinstead | 01342 302 087 |
| East Kilbride | 01355 245 330 |
| Eastbourne | 01323 431 012 |
| Eastleigh | 023 80629 729 |
| Edinb'h, EH4 2LN | 0131 315 3530 |
| Edinb'h, EH11 4DG | 0131 442 2633 |
| Edinb'h, EH8 9RD | 0131 668 3663 |
| Edin'h, EH20 9PW | 0131 448 2125 |
| Elgin | 01343 548 641 |
| Enfield | 020 8366 1490 |
| Epsom | 020 8393 5085 |
| Exeter | 01392 216 099 |
| Falkirk | 01324 624 953 |
| Fareham | 01329 822 595 |
| Farnborough | 01329 822 595 |
| Farnham | 01252 717 180 |
| Felixstowe | 01394 670 192 |
| Feltham | 020 8893 8361 |
| Folkestone | 01303 243 566 |
| Gateshead | 0191 482 0077 |
| Glasgow, G64 2TS | 0141 772 9899 |
| Glasgow, G62 6JP | 0141 956 6575 |
| Glasg'w, G43 1BH | 0141 649 2120 |
| Glenrothes | 01592 630 544 |
| Gloucester | 01452 507 589 |
| Godalming | 01483 414 609 |
| Great Yarmouth | 01493 652 137 |
| Greenock | 01475 783 132 |
| Grimsby | 01472 355 966 |
| Guildford | 01483 538 735 |
| Hamilton | 01698 426 336 |
| Harlow | 01279 451 144 |
| Harlow | 01279 431 885 |
| Harrow | 020 8424 2130 |
| Hatfield | 01707 269 025 |
| Havant | 023 9249 2739 |
| Hayes | 020 8561 2450 |
| Hemel Hempstead | 01442 258 490 |
| Hemel Hempstead | 01442 212 596 |
| Hereford | 01432 278 906 |
| Herne Bay | 01227 740 221 |
| Hessle | 01482 506 055 |
| High Wycombe | 01494 465 016 |
| High Wycombe | 01628 810 333 |
| Horsham | 01403 217 653 |
| Hove | 01273 729 637 |
| Huddersfield | 01484 451 693 |
| Huntingdon | 01480 411 327 |
| Ilford | 020 8503 8284 |
| Inverness | 01463 240 898 |
| Ipswich | 01473 241 687 |
| Ipswich | 01473 719 155 |
| Irvine | 01294 277 912 |
| Isleworth | 020 8847 3687 |
| King's Lynn | 01553 769 179 |
| Kirkcaldy | 01592 641 561 |
| Leamington Spa | 01926 330 161 |
| Leeds | 0113 393 0296 |
| Leeds | 0113 235 0442 |
| Leicester | 0116 254 3155 |
| Leighton Buzzard | 01525 852 800 |
| Lincoln | 01522 539 096 |
| Liverpool | 0151 521 8692 |
| Liverpool | 0151 254 1049 |
| Livingston | 01506 414 666 |
| Llandudno | 01492 860 278 |
| Lond'n, SW11 5HY | 020 7228 7666 |
| London, SE6 3NU | 020 8697 8511 |
| London, E4 8TB | 020 8531 8129 |
| London, NW3 6LU | 020 7435 3457 |
| L'ndon, SE10 0QJ | 020 8858 3826 |
| London, N4 1DT | 020 8800 6673 |
| L'ndon, NW9 6SS | 020 8200 7500 |
| L'ndon, W14 8PU | 020 7603 6397 |
| London, SE3 9PP | 020 8856 9122 |
| L'ndon, SW19 3XD | 020 8543 0026 |
| London, NW7 2ET | 020 8203 9312 |
| London, N11 1QJ | 020 8361 1235 |
| London, N12 0DA | 020 8343 9790 |
| L'ndon, SE20 8RB | 020 8778 0950 |
| L'ndon, SW16 6UJ | 020 8679 8284 |
| London, E17 4EE | 020 8527 4355 |
| L'ndon, SW18 1EW | 020 8875 1426 |
| L'ndon, NW10 2JH | 020 8451 5666 |
| London, SW19 8UG | 020 8944 1044 |
| Loughborough | 01509 237 622 |
| Luton | 01582 491 165 |
| Maidstone | 01622 761 542 |
| Manchester | 0161 872 4074 |
| Milton Keynes | 01908 609 069 |
| New Malden | 020 8336 0202 |
| New Malden | 020 8336 0202 |
| Newbury | 01635 529 102 |
| Newcastle Under Lyme | 01782 711 277 |
| Newcastle Under Lyme | 01782 617 755 |
| Newport | 01633 816 682 |
| Newton Abbot | 01626 331 959 |
| Northampton | 01604 407 830 |
| Northampton | 01604 755 217 |
| Norwich | 01603 628 731 |
| Norwich | 01603 789 573 |
| Nott'ham, NG7 1GY | 0115 941 3800 |
| Nott'ham, NG7 5QJ | 0115 948 4595 |
| Oldham | 0161 628 7009 |
| Orpington | 01689 890 470 |
| Oxford | 01865 728 952 |
| Oxford | 01865 749 660 |
| Perth | 01738 442 011 |
| Peterborough | 01733 558 286 |
| Pity Me | 01913 832 455 |
| Plymouth | 01752 222 877 |
| Poole | 01202 762 133 |
| Portlethen | 01224 782 233 |
| Portsmouth | 023 926 91217 |
| Portsmouth | 0239 2200 197 |
| Preston | 01772 252 580 |
| Preston | 01772 720 828 |
| Rayleigh | 01268 745 555 |
| Reading | 01189 323 110 |
| Reading | 01189 571 331 |
| Redditch | 01527 637 88 |
| Reigate | 01737 247 661 |
| Richmond | 020 8392 9979 |
| Rochdale | 01706 860 656 |
| Rochford | 01702 549 525 |
| Romford | 01708 730 131 |
| Rotherham | 01709 780 400 |
| Rugby | 01788 551 967 |
| Salisbury | 01722 422 050 |
| Scunthorpe | 01724 848 396 |
| Sevenoaks | 01732 455 928 |
| Sheffield | 0114 255 4634 |
| Sheffield | 0114 261 9150 |
| Shoreham By Sea | 01273 871 403 |
| Shrewsbury | 01743 464 016 |
| Sleaford | 01529 414 475 |
| Slough | 01753 511 120 |
| Solihull | 0121 733 8690 |
| South Ruislip | 020 8841 6730 |
| Southampton | 01489 789 709 |
| Southampton | 023 80510 024 |
| Southport | 01704 500 490 |
| St Albans | 01727 855 487 |
| St Austell | 01726 763 73 |
| Staines | 01784 463 593 |
| Stevenage | 01438 740 256 |
| Stockport | 0161 480 8984 |
| Stockton on Tees | 01642 678 822 |
| Stratford Upon Avon | 01789 414 885 |
| Sutton Coldfield | 0121 313 1343 |
| Sutton Coldfield | 0121 354 7893 |
| Sutton In Ashfield | 01623 441 777 |
| Swansea | 01792 473 240 |
| Swindon | 01793 420 092 |
| Swindon | 01793 828 130 |
| Tamworth | 01827 282 191 |
| Taunton | 01823 444 345 |
| Telford | 01952 261 800 |
| Tiverton | 01884 258 693 |
| Tonbridge | 01732 771 288 |
| Truro | 01872 263 905 |
| Tunbridge Wells | 01892 511 775 |
| Tunbridge Wells | 01892 546 566 |
| Upton | 0151 604 1277 |
| Wakefield | 01924 367 367 |
| Waltham Cross | 01992 629 276 |
| Walton on Thames | 01932 254 429 |
| Warley | 0121 544 9088 |
| Warrington | 01925 231 088 |
| Washington | 0191 415 5722 |
| Watford | 01923 247 565 |
| Wellingborough | 01933 441 212 |
| Wstn-Spr-Mare | 01934 515 817 |
| Wigan | 01942 230 345 |
| Winchester | 01962 840 054 |
| Wishaw | 01698 359 191 |
| Woking | 01483 799 525 |
| Worcester | 01905 763 021 |
| Worcester | 01905 755 551 |
| Worcester | 01905 429 426 |
| Yealdon | 0113 239 1313 |
| York | 01904 690 997 |
| York | 01904 643 803 |

# ASSOCIATIONS, CLUBS, SOCIETIES & CHARITIES

We have gathered the website addresses of a number of groups, societies and charities in the gardening world. It is by no means a comprehensive list, but we hope to with your help. If you know of any gardening association, club, society or charity that would be of interest to others please contact us on 01603 633 808 and we will include them in the next edition of the **Gardeners' Atlas** and on **www.gardenersatlas.co.uk.**

| | |
|---|---|
| African Violet Society of America | www.avsaorg.org.co.uk |
| Alpine Society | www.alpinegaradensociety.org |
| American Bamboo Society | www.bamboo.org/abs |
| American Rose Society | www.ars.org |
| Bonsai Club International | www.bonsai-bci.com |
| British Association of Landscape Industries | www.bali.co.uk |
| British Fuchsias Society | www.the bfs.co.uk |
| Council for National Parks | www.cnp.org.uk |
| English Heritage | www.englishheritage.org.uk |
| English Nature | www.english-nature.org.uk |
| Eric Young Orchid Foundation | www.ericyoungorchidfoundation.co.uk |
| FOE | www.foe.co.uk |
| Foresters | www.foresters.org/rsfs |
| Garden Post | www.gardeners-grbs.org.uk |
| Gordon Highlanders Garden & Museum | www.gordonhighlanders.co.uk |
| Historic Houses Association | www.historic-houses-assn.org |
| Ilkley Gardeners | www.ilkleygardeners.org.uk |
| Institute of Horticulture | www.horticulture.demon.co.uk |
| Jungle Garden & Pet Centre | www.cla.org.uk |
| MAFF | www.maff.gov.uk |
| National Council for the Conservation of Plants & Gardens | www.nccpg.org.uk |
| National Tree Club of the Arboricultural Association | www.trees.org.uk |
| National Trust | www.nationaltrust.org.uk |
| National Trust for Scotland | www.nts.org.uk |
| Old Lawnsmowers Club | www.artizan.demon.co.uk/olc |
| Plantlife | www.plantlife.org.uk |
| Red Cross | www.redcross.org.uk/opengardens |
| Royal Horticultural Society | www.rhs.org.uk |
| Royal National Rose Society | www.roses.co.uk/harkness/rnrs.htm |
| The Cottage Gardener | www.alfresco.demon.co.uk/cgs |
| Thrive | www.carryongardening.org.uk |
| Tidy Britain | www.tidybritain.org.uk |

# PRODUCTS

This is a brand new section to the **Gardeners' Atlas.** We thought it would be useful to include a guide to companies that offer Garden Products and Services in England, Scotland and Wales. This is not a comprehensive list but we have tried to include as many providers of different products and services as we could find. If we have missed anyone out then please contact us on 01603 633 808 or visit www.gardenersatlas.co.uk

Companies are sorted alphabetically by category, and we have included their telephone number for you to contact them. If you decide to speak to an outlet we have listed do not forget to mention where you got their details from!

## Help us help you

mention the *Gardeners' Atlas* when visiting anywhere on this page.

### AQUATICS, WATER, IRRIGATION & POND
| | |
|---|---|
| Butyl Products Ltd | 01277 653 281 |
| Featureworld | 01773 712 551 |
| Fosstone | 01904 750 910 |
| Fountain Timber Products | 01283 223 399 |
| Jayhawk International Ltd | 08707 300 111 |
| Norman Garden Products | 01243 539 185 |
| Oakland Plastics | 01675 466 321 |
| Oase (UK) Ltd | 01264 333 225 |
| Precise Irrigation uk ltd | 01235 763 760 |
| S L Pearcy | 01823 251 690 |
| Stone & Waterscapes | 01983 867 249 |
| Tetra | 023 8062 500 |
| The Fountains Company | 01623 753 861 |
| Water Garden Specialist | 01943 872 658 |
| Waterstone Fountains | 01934 820 967 |

### ARBORICULTURE
| | |
|---|---|
| Original Butterfly Man | 01490 430 300 |

### AWNINGS
| | |
|---|---|
| Premier Blinds & Awnings Ltd | 01372 377 112 |

### BARBECUES & ACCESSORIES
| | |
|---|---|
| Outback | 01622 671 771 |
| Sunshine Barbecues | 01865 884 433 |

### CASH & CARRY
| | |
|---|---|
| F J Jackson & Son Ltd | 01404 422 28 |

### CLOTHING
| | |
|---|---|
| Stay Safeguard | 0121 551 9534 |

### COMPREHENSIVE RANGE
| | |
|---|---|
| Golden Larch | 01202 892 121 |
| Over the Garden Wall | 01653 698 880 |
| PBI Home and Garden Ltd | 020 8344 6800 |
| Robinsons of Falgrave | 01723 360 752 |

### CONSERVATORIES
| | |
|---|---|
| Amdega | 0800 591 523 |
| B A C Conservatories | 0800 666 444 |
| Bartholemew Conservatories | 01428 658 771 |
| Camelot Conservatories | 0800 592 897 |
| Coldseal Conservatories | 0800 221 155 |
| Landsdowne Conservatories | 01494 432 223 |
| Marston & langinger limited | 0207 881 5717 |
| Portland Conservatories | 0800 269 126 |

### DESIGN & LANDSCAPING
| | |
|---|---|
| Bradstone Home & Garden Landscaping | 01335 372 222 |
| Dandaf Design Ltd | 01943 463 621 |
| G D C Ltd | 01493 488 228 |
| Gwent Landscapes | 01633 413 269 |
| Mike Armstrong | 0191 250 1129 |
| Petre Wood & Garden Products | 01254 246 161 |
| Rain-Tech | 020 8342 8444 |
| Topiary by Design | 01377 271 000 |

### FENCING
| | |
|---|---|
| All Types Fencing Specialists Ltd | 01268 545 192 |
| Foxhall Fencing | 01449 674 925 |
| Frontier Fencing and Decking Ltd. | 01948 861 000 |
| Metpost | 02920 777 877 |

### FURNITURE
| | |
|---|---|
| A1 Patios | 01656 720 428 |
| Abbotts Grove Garden Furniture Ltd | 01386 831 805 |
| Acotn Woodcraft | 01769 560 108 |
| Anchor Fast Products Ltd | 0115 922 7821 |
| Andromeda's Garden | 01225 317 924 |
| Anglesey Wood Products | 01248 421 086 |
| Anglian Garden Furniture | 01763 852 839 |
| B D Leisure | 01827 261 621 |
| B L W Engineering | 01285 861 191 |
| Blue Ridge Furniture Company | 01522 791 051 |
| Broadland Garden Furniture | 01603 754 995 |
| Bulbeck Foundry | 01638 743 153 |
| Cane & Garden Furniture Supplies | 01472 268 188 |
| Cathedral Garden Furniture | 0191 517 1700 |
| Chatsworth Carpenters | 01246 582 394 |
| Classic Country Furniture | 01454 299 466 |
| Classic Garden Furniture | 01695 732 315 |
| Countryside Furniture | 01933 279 243 |
| Country Affairs | 01202 671 123 |
| Countrystyle | 01255 830 140 |
| Cumbrian Rustic of Coniston | 01539 441 395 |

| | |
|---|---|
| Damar Leisure Ltd | 01268 761 716 |
| Dave's Garden Ornaments | 01268 792 415 |
| David Sharp Studios | 01773 606 066 |
| Dawson Teak Benches | 01274 545 347 |
| Derek Fox & Sons (Timber) Ltd | 01772 784 626 |
| Elegant Ltd | 01255 850 750 |
| Elite Garden Furniture | 01204 597 929 |
| Forecast Furniture Ltd | 020 7722 8698 |
| Fred Chaffin | 01909 501 327 |
| Freebird Leisure | 01271 860 025 |
| Garden Artefacts | 01628 628 494 |
| Garden Furniture Co | 01923 818 111 |
| Garden Leisure (UK) | 01562 745 656 |
| Garden Leisure Furniture Ltd | 01299 251 883 |
| Gardencare | 01709 373 158 |
| Geln Rustic Handmade Garden Furniture | 01379 650 918 |
| Genesis | 01473 723 888 |
| George Barker & Sons | 01539 531 236 |
| Goodwood Garden Furniture | 01702 291 911 |
| Harbo (UK) Ltd/Regatta Furniture | 01245 477 747 |
| The Garden Shop | 01249 656 467 |
| Henlog | 01752 843 675 |
| Hillcrest Leisure Products | 01902 755 615 |
| Holloways | 01886 884 665 |
| Home & Garden Furnishings | 01298 74 330 |
| Indian Ocean Trading Co | 01244 537 906 |
| Iveson Furniture | 01285 850 333 |
| J & P Garden Products | 01594 829 007 |
| J Allen Supplies | 01924 422 564 |
| J B Scott Ltd | 01505 850 368 |
| Jacqueline Edge | 020 7229 1172 |
| Judith Barnett | 01492 533 390 |
| Just Popples | 01543 419 740 |
| Kestrel Garden Furniture | 0121 449 5333 |
| King Cole Forge | 01473 824 120 |
| Kootensaw Dovecotes | 01548 821 415 |
| Leamill Wood Products | 01626 879 696 |
| Leisure & Furniture Garden Design | 01782 564 500 |
| Leisure Form 2000 Ltd | 01885 482 000 |
| Leisure Furniture Ltd | 020 8518 1234 |
| Leisure Grow | 01462 451 700 |
| Leisure Plan | 01279 816 001 |
| Lilo Leisure Products Ltd | 01902 730 888 |
| Link Stake Ltd | 01327 260 329 |
| Lytham Garden Furniture | 01253 795 544 |
| Meadow Designs Ltd | 01584 856 562 |
| Mexican Hammocks | 020 8880 1090 |
| Millington Woodcraft | 0161 486 9540 |
| N Meade | 01823 254 555 |
| Neptune Classics | 01793 881 144 |
| New Dawn Furniture | 01243 375 535 |
| Newbridge House | 01275 331 080 |
| P J Brdigman & Co Ltd | 020 8804 7474 |
| Patio Pets | 01202 665 746 |
| Peter Smith Garden Furniture | 01274 664 000 |
| Practical Pine | 01492 878 658 |
| Prima Pots | 01892 824 474 |
| Provincial Garden Furniture | 01773 541 888 |
| Quality Garden Furniture | 01564 777 416 |
| R F Bellis | 0161 998 5767 |
| Roman Stone | 01934 744 713 |
| Royal Arrow | 020 7938 2000 |
| Rustacraft | 01522 721 014 |
| Rustic Garden Furniture | 01257 475 160 |
| Sense West Crafts | 0121 544 4544 |
| Sid Paver & Sons Joinery Service | 01636 816 188 |
| Smallburgh Crafts | 01692 536 547 |
| Southern Rustics | 01258 454 609 |
| Staithe Steel Crafts | 01692 598 899 |
| Stangwrach Garden Furniture | 01558 668 287 |
| Steadfast Timber Products | 01282 414 193 |
| Stonebow Leisure | 01529 455 666 |
| Sunset Garden Seating | 01455 612 401 |
| Swan Hattersley Ltd | 01952 680 288 |
| Swift Garden Furniture | 01525 852 508 |
| Teak Company | 01858 468 308 |
| Teak House | 01749 813 050 |
| Teak Tiger | 01787 312 612 |
| Teak Tiger Trading Co | 01787 880 900 |
| Teesdale Garden Crafts | 01833 631 772 |
| The Garden Outlet | 01924 827 065 |
| Three Seasons | 01708 723 426 |
| Timber Garden Supplies | 01782 837 364 |
| Tor Stone | 01458 834 320 |
| Trebark Garden Furniture | 01726 833 382 |
| Trevis Smith Ltd | 01384 569 581 |
| Uppingtons Timber Products | 0117 908 0030 |

| | |
|---|---|
| Walkham Teak Garden Furniture | 01822 852 252 |
| Whelans | 01795 663 879 |
| Whitehill Ltd | 01775 840 925 |
| Wold Woodworking | 01430 872 828 |
| Wood & Garden Furniture | 01752 368 780 |
| Wood Themes | 01202 828 162 |

### GARDEN CARE
| | |
|---|---|
| Banks Home & Garden Supplies | 01704 220 907 |
| Coopers | 01751 472 248 |
| Cuprinol Ltd | 01753 877 930 |
| F Strickland & Sons | 01424 423 348 |
| Garden and Pet Supplies | 023 9281 1822 |
| Gem Gardening | 01254 356 660 |
| Henchman | 01635 299 847 |
| Procter Bros Ltd | 0113 243 0531 |
| Roebuck-Eyot Ltd | 01388 772 233 |
| Rowlan (Turf Growers) Ltd | 01959 533 071 |
| Samsons | 01562 825 201 |

### GARDEN SUPPLIES
| | |
|---|---|
| Bee & Jay Garden Supplies | 01322 664 827 |
| Blunts Rustic Supplies | 0116 253 9735 |
| C C Hadfield | 01625 423 259 |
| Dorest Garden Supplies | 01202 871 432 |
| Harts Garden Supplies Ltd | 01258 472 788 |
| Hayes Fuels | 01268 545 781 |
| ISS Aquaturf | 01725 513 880 |
| Prospect Garden Products | 01752 561 179 |
| Roman Way Garden Supplies | 01908 542 427 |
| Sanders Garden Supplies | 01223 350 091 |
| Trident Water Garden Products Ltd | 0247 666 9021 |
| Turf & Tmber | 01382 202 111 |

### GATES & RAILINGS
| | |
|---|---|
| A & G Chapman | 01548 856 264 |
| A1 Ironwork | 01502 516 862 |
| A6 Gates | 01204 701 690 |
| Abbey Fencong & Gates | 024 7651 1159 |
| Acanthus Designs | 01225 334 913 |
| Ackton Hall Forge | 01977 600 318 |
| Alfab | 0191 371 2932 |
| Anchor to Needle Fabrications Ltd | 0141 248 1616 |
| Andros Engineering | 01983 565 566 |
| Anglia Advanced Automation | 01767 691 910 |
| APS Jig & Tool Company | 01582 672 250 |
| Arc Metal Craft | 01752 558 249 |
| Argon Arc Welding Services | 020 8368 2593 |
| Autogate Systems | 0113 239 4444 |
| Automation & Security | 0191 4280 788 |
| Automation Gate Services | 0115 986 7922 |
| B E Jones | 01889 270 709 |
| B F Elton | 01934 750 433 |
| B Rourke & Co Ltd | 01282 422 841 |
| BFT Northern | 01670 737 645 |
| Boss Automation Ltd | 0161 4066 191 |
| Bronzewood Partnership | 01263 577 820 |
| Burbage Ironcraft Ltd | 01455 251 656 |
| C J Jeneson | 01202 820 688 |
| Cannock Gates | 01543 462 500 |
| Classic Gate Systems | 01327 844 522 |
| Classic Gates & Rails | 01347 810 425 |
| Country Gates | 0161 449 7607 |
| Countryside Gates | 01636 679 983 |
| Craftsman Gates | 01977 604 225 |
| Creatove Ironwork (Ludlow) | 01584 872 104 |
| Cruddas Ironcraft Ltd | 01384 569 307 |
| Curley Metalworks | 01934 852 922 |
| D & D Ironcraft | 01388 746 887 |
| D M Young | 01506 811 088 |
| Danks Engineering | 01422 839 617 |
| Davyweld | 01723 864 893 |
| Decorative Metal Work | 01924 823 711 |
| Drovers Forge | 01207 506 234 |
| East Riding Gates | 01405 763 371 |
| Electric Gate & Barrier UK Co Ltd | 01274 732 333 |
| Fleetwood Gates & Railings | 01253 876 825 |
| Flintlock Forge | 01255 820 929 |
| Flow Line | 01296 651 770 |
| Freegate Metal Products Co Ltd | 01535 632 723 |
| G D Turner Engineering | 01332 340 584 |
| G F G | 01472 290 233 |
| Gallacher Blacksmiths | 0141 336 5149 |
| Gate Expectations | 0161 7661 502 |
| Geoff Buck | 01904 704 480 |
| Great Victorian Railing Co Ltd | 01784 250 500 |
| H Pointer | 01865 391 454 |
| The Metal Shop | 0113 279 0279 |
| Himanet | 01623 420 646 |

# & SERVICES

| | |
|---|---|
| Holt Bros (Horwich) Ltd | 01204 697 393 |
| Ironworld | 01325 488 095 |
| J & J Gates | 0161 865 6589 |
| J D M Metal Craft | 01259 724 278 |
| J Oddy & Sons | 01277 352 388 |
| J W Lowry | 01440 712 895 |
| Just Gates Ltd | 01994 241 010 |
| Kenneth (AGRIC) Rees Ltd | 029 2075 2623 |
| Kingsway Electrical | 01908 263 624 |
| Lomondcrest Ltd | 01389 877 477 |
| London Gates & Grilles | 020 8519 8088 |
| Metal Art Products | 0121 447 7651 |
| Metal Gates & Railings | 0121 426 5610 |
| Michael Roberts S F W C B | 01285 821 244 |
| Mike Gaze Gates | 01379 650 918 |
| Mountainstone Forge | 01524 401 292 |
| Newton Gates & Welding | 01942 238 057 |
| Noble Gates | 01785 714 148 |
| Northern Creative Metal Art | 01924 466 770 |
| Ornamental Engineering | 01773 533 393 |
| P J Webster | 01924 452 720 |
| P W A Enterprises | 01246 431 115 |
| Panos Gates & Railings | 0161 301 4551 |
| Parsons Brothers | 0121 588 4871 |
| R & N D Hissitt | 01485 535 825 |
| Railing Renovations | 020 8993 0253 |
| Remote Control Installations | 01584 890 908 |
| Rowley Engineering Co Ltd | 01785 223 831 |
| Sabeka Timber Products | 01244 390 921 |
| Savage Gate Automation | 01268 698 182 |
| Scotty's Gates | 0117 977 8865 |
| Stately Gates | 01332 881 299 |
| Suffolk Gate Co | 01284 388 399 |
| Tarporley Gates | 01829 781 444 |
| Thameside Gates & Railings | 01784 464 655 |
| The Gate Makers | 01296 630 798 |
| The Gate Place | 01704 224 365 |
| The Gate Shop | 0161 749 8944 |
| Thomas Fabrications | 01925 652 770 |
| Town & Country Gates | 01255 224 007 |
| Trew Gates & Co | 01286 660 418 |
| Trident Gates & Railings | 01298 849 51 |
| Tudor Forge | 01702 348 049 |
| Two Gates Garden Market | 01384 567 582 |
| Ursa Security Gates | 01355 901 686 |
| Walter Spencer | 0131 334 0688 |
| Willforge | 01752 779 399 |
| Windsor Gates | 01695 578 033 |
| Wyber Automatic Gates & Doors | 01993 844 200 |
| Yarcombe Woodland Products Ltd | 01460 762 38 |

## GIFTS & ACCESSORIES

| | |
|---|---|
| Aswood Garden Services & Crafts | 023 9259 9778 |
| Eccleshall Garden Supplies & Stone Co | 0114 236 6691 |
| English Garden Wares | 01243 543 804 |
| F. W. Myhill & Son Ltd | 01953 602 172 |
| Fiddichside Flower Tubbs | 01466 702 212 |
| Garden Art | 01488 681 881 |
| Garden Bits Dovecotes Manufacturers | 01704 880 047 |
| Garden Crafts Ltd | 0115 951 9595 |
| I K Supplies | 0118 979 2142 |
| Rural Supplies (Dalry) Ltd | 01644 430 291 |
| Spanish Rings | 020 8224 9381 |
| Suffolk Garden Craft | 01394 278 673 |
| Suncoast UK | 01539 729 964 |
| T D Bright Garden Crafts | 01938 580 401 |
| Telford Garden Supplies | 01952 248 955 |

## GREENHOUSES

| | |
|---|---|
| Alitex Limited | 01420 828 60 |
| Alton greenhouses | 0800 269 850 |
| Hartley Greenhouses | 01457 873 244 |
| New Century Glazing | 01262 608 831 |
| Trimetals Ltd(Eden Greenhouses) | 01258 459 441 |

## HYDROPONICS

| | |
|---|---|
| Addloes Lighting & Hydrophonics | 01202 432 212 |
| All Grow Hydrophonics | 0121 384 4111 |
| Applewoods Hydroponica | 07941 214 785 |
| Aquaculture Hydroponics | 0114 273 8228 |
| Britelight Hydrophonics | 020 8656 1481 |
| Glassgrow, the Hydroponic Co | 0141 552 7522 |
| Green Finger Hydrophonics | 020 8397 6125 |
| Harvest Hydrophonics & Lighting Sysytems | 01452 720 166 |
| Holland Hydrophonics | 0161 832 7009 |
| Hydro Culture | 01226 285 487 |

## LIGHTING

| | |
|---|---|
| Jati Teak Trading Company | 01780 765 999 |
| Wagner Spraytech (UK )Ltd | 01295 265 353 |

## MACHINERY

| | |
|---|---|
| A & S E Hayton Garden Machine Centre | 016973 203 55 |
| A Thompson | 01262 674 273 |
| Abba Hire | 01244 531 986 |
| AL-KO Britain Ltd | 01926 466 666 |
| Allen Power Equipment Ltd | 01235 515 400 |
| Ambleside Forest & Garden Machinery Centre | 01539 433 683 |
| Atco-Qualcast bosch group | 01449 742 000 |
| Black & Decker | 01753 511 234 |
| Castor Engineering Garden Machinery | 01803 856 691 |
| Countax Ltd | 01844 278 800 |
| E P Barrus ltd | 01869 363 636 |
| Friendly Robotics | 01844 261 653 |
| G C Carle & Son | 01224 722 445 |
| Gardena UK Ltd | 0191 217 3608 |
| Gloucester Garden Machinery Centre | 01472 268 188 |
| Hayter Limited | 01279 723 444 |
| Helston Garden Equipment | 01326 574 339 |
| Hemming and Wood Ltd | 01543 256 711 |
| Howit & Mowit Growing IT | 01380 848 118 |
| Husqvarna Forest & Garden UK | 01453 820 310 |
| J B Mowers | 0151 420 8881 |
| John Deer Ltd | 01949 860 491 |
| Kutters | 01904 791 736 |
| Makita (UK) Ltd | 01908 211 678 |
| Market Drayton Mowing Machine Centre | 01630 657 707 |
| Nuneaton Horticultural | 024 7638 5479 |
| O H E Garden Machinery Centre Ltd | 01305 853 450 |
| Peterborough Garden Machinery | 01733 268 168 |
| Powercut | 01267 235 625 |
| Riley's Electrical Ltd | 0121 559 1807 |
| Stihl Ltd | 01276 202 02 |
| Temedale Garden Machinery Centre | 01584 876 936 |
| Textron Golf Turf and Speciality Products | 01473 270 000 |
| Toro Wheel Horse UK | 01202 209 209 |
| Weymouth Mower Centre | 01305 835 907 |
| Wolf Garden | 01495 306 600 |

## MAIL ORDER

| | |
|---|---|
| Claire Austin Hardy Plants | 01902 376 333 |
| Sutton Consumer Products | 01803 696 300 |

## ORNAMENTAL

| | |
|---|---|
| A J Thomas | 01646 681 575 |
| Acorn Garden Ornaments | 0191 427 9012 |
| Ann Brewster | 01502 724 618 |
| Architectural Heritage | 01386 584 414 |
| Aston Garden Ornaments | 01923 263 809 |
| Braestone | 01466 751 277 |
| Brinkhill Pottery | 01507 480 702 |
| Callaghan Stoneware | 01933 275 501 |
| Carew Patio Products | 01646 651 116 |
| Chatsworth Stonecraft | 01335 346 311 |
| Chilstone | 01892 740 866 |
| Conarts Garden Moulds | 01777 870 521 |
| Country Charm Ltd | 01536 408 166 |
| Country Collection Sundials | 01746 861 330 |
| Cranborne Stone | 01258 472 685 |
| Creative Gardens | 01777 248 649 |
| Crislyn Collection | 0191 424 1155 |
| Dave's Woodcrafts | 01606 784 270 |
| David Harber Sundials | 01491 577 074 |
| Design Castings | 01388 819 722 |
| Devonshire Statuary Ltd | 01395 233 288 |
| Ecocrafts | 01455 273 024 |
| Four Seasons Garden Ornaments | 01455 844 991 |
| Garden Crafts | 01580 292 070 |
| Garden Ornaments Direct | 01895 443 591 |
| Garden Supplies Department | 01623 863 439 |
| Garstone | 01626 775 925 |
| Goodwin's Garden Ornaments | 01372 377 112 |
| Granite Connections ltd | 01773 533 090 |
| Griffin Stone | 01206 240 318 |
| H Bray | 01299 266 301 |
| H Crowther Ltd | 020 8994 2326 |
| Hollywood Stne | 0121 474 4283 |
| Ilford Stonecraft | 020 8478 5866 |
| Ironart Ltd | 01225 311 273 |
| Italia Classic Statues | 0121 454 5559 |
| J & P Cartwright | 02476 385 279 |
| J F B Ornamental Ironwork | 01384 573 823 |
| Juro Antiques | 01866 821 261 |
| Kingfisher Concrete Products | 01773 533 553 |
| KM J Stonecraft | 01283 512 368 |
| Lawmans Ornamental Stoneware | 020 8760 0082 |
| Life-Like Garden Ornaments | 01209 313 233 |
| M R Wilson | 01328 829 359 |
| Marshalls | 01422 306 000 |
| Melmar Stone | 01777 248 992 |
| Neils Crafts | 01386 861 661 |
| Ornament Express | 0121 706 9481 |
| Ornate Fountain & Statue Ltd | 01623 429 126 |
| Ornate Garden Ornaments | 01254 234 769 |
| Owl Wood | 01631 570 088 |
| Oxford Stone & Marble Craft | 01865 778 568 |
| Peachstone | 020 8950 9488 |
| Penarth Garden Ornaments | 029 2071 2777 |
| Powell Garden Ornaments | 01902 324 672 |
| Pretty pipes & walls | 020 8684 4061 |
| Priory Garden Ornaments | 01827 895 548 |
| R & V Garden Ornaments | 01432 277 790 |
| Redwood Stone Ltd | 01749 677 777 |
| Selby Stone | 01430 861 717 |
| Somerset Stone | 01278 699 099 |
| Southdown Stone | 01522 519 168 |
| Sprite Alloys Ltd | 0121 557 1628 |
| Stafford Stone Ltd | 024 763 20352 |
| Stancombe Stone Ltd | 01285 821 839 |
| Stonecraft | 01908 566 797 |
| Stonecraft 2000 | 01983 884 715 |
| Stonecraft Garden Ornaments | 01564 785 411 |
| Tarka Garden Art | 01271 866 726 |
| Three Bees Garden Ornaments | 01432 351 861 |
| Touchstone Objet D'art Ltd | 01458 273 740 |
| Tre-Beirdd Farm | 01352 700 322 |
| V Coccia | 01225 339 265 |
| Vulcns Forge | 01244 571 009 |
| Westone Garden Ornaments | 01736 756 192 |
| Willowstone (Distraker) Ltd | 01452 830 774 |
| Woodlands Ornamentals Ltd | 01623 622 122 |
| World of Terracotta | 01903 877 196 |
| Wrought Art | 01332 340 563 |

## OUTBUILDINGS & DECKING

| | |
|---|---|
| A & T Fabrications Ltd | 01924 266 635 |
| A C Timber Buildings | 01959 562 049 |
| A L S Bamptons Fabrications | 01702 613 838 |
| A M Fabrications | 0115 929 9600 |
| Ace Sheds | 01733 206 707 |
| Agriframes Ltd | 01342 328 644 |
| Archidecks | 01548 830 022 |
| B S Joinery Services | 01467 625 300 |
| Bluebell Conservatory & Greenhouse Show Centre | 01642 300 819 |
| Board Walk | 020 8392 2662 |
| Bourne Buildings | 01252 718 481 |
| BSW Timber Plc | 01397 772 455 |
| Champion | 020 8949 1621 |
| Dandf from Pascoe (UK) Ltd | 01977 704 796 |
| Derwdeck from Qualcraft | 01544 350 671 |
| Forest Fencing Plc | 01886 812 451 |
| Glasshouses | 020 7607 6071 |
| Gwyn Jones | 01269 832 535 |
| Hillhout Ltd | 01502 718 091 |
| J & K Garden Sheds | 0191 496 0643 |
| Keybrick Ltd | 01299 406 016 |
| Larch-Lap Ltd | 01299 251 725 |
| Leisure Deck limited | 01582 563 080 |
| Lindsay Teak (PAC COnsultants) | 01737 822 562 |
| M R G Woodworking | 01935 475 547 |
| Merit Garden Products | 01359 27 1363 |
| Merseyside Shed Centre | 0151 922 5282 |
| New Line Sheds | 0118 971 2245 |
| Outdoor Deck Company | 020 8876 8464 |
| Rainham Sheds | 01708 557 819 |
| Ridgmont Rustics Ltd | 01633 680 818 |
| Robinson Greenhouses | 01295 770 717 |
| Robinson's Garden Buildings | 01436 679 191 |
| S F G Holdings | 01530 245 345 |
| Sheds & Fencing Centre | 0151 922 9405 |
| Sheds Direct | 01397 703 222 |
| Stuart Garden Architecture | 01984 667 458 |
| Suttons Timber Sheds | 01253 822 075 |
| The Garden Buildings Centre | 01743 874 220 |
| The Shed Centre | 01324 622 590 |
| The Shed Shop | 029 2047 1171 |
| Ultra from Interval Systems Ltd | 01483 727 888 |
| Vale Garden Houses Ltd | 01476 564 433 |
| W R Archer | 01423 527 505 |
| Wallgrove Fabrications | 01948 662 908 |

## PAVING & PATIOS

| | |
|---|---|
| Inverness Patio Centre | 01463 714 493 |
| Merlin Garden Supplies | 01637 879 100 |
| Patio & Garden | 01756 792 526 |
| Patio and Garden Products | 01856 877 170 |
| Patio Centre | 01752 788 001 |
| Patio Centre | 01489 579 119 |
| Paving Systems uk | 0800 838 084 |
| Taylors Patio Centre | 01761 463 303 |
| The Patio | 01476 579 421 |

## POTS & CONTAINERS

| | |
|---|---|
| Clevedon Pottery & Patio Centre | 01275 876 449 |
| Dulwich Village Pottery | 020 7978 8310 |
| Get Direct(Vectre Terracotta) | 01522 866 300 |
| Half Price Pots Shop | 020 8341 2716 |
| Pembridge Terracotta | 01544 388 696 |
| Plenti-Full-Pots | 01280 850 479 |
| Potmania | 01603 401 144 |
| Pots Direct | 01603 625 180 |
| Potstop | 020 8804 4466 |
| Potteries Garden Stoneware | 01782 335 400 |
| Shribs & Tubs Ltd | 020 8559 8595 |
| Snap Dragon Ltd | 020 8463 0503 |
| The Fyba Pot Company Limited | 01977 677 676 |
| The Pot People | 01458 840 652 |
| The Potting Shed | 01625 585 819 |
| Wadham Trading Co | 01451 830 308 |
| Whichford Pottery | 01608 684 416 |
| Willowmere Pottery | 01733 844 110 |
| World of Pots (Peterborough) | 01733 558 787 |

## SEEDS

| | |
|---|---|
| Chiltern Seeds | 01229 581 137 |
| Mr Fothergill's Seeds Ltd | 01638 751 161 |
| Nicky's Nursery | 01843 601 897 |

## SWIMMING POOLS & SPAS

| | |
|---|---|
| Canadian Spa Company | 01293 522 266 |
| Hotspring | 01245 265 036 |
| Pool Cover | 01823 288 515 |
| Solardome Industries ltd | 023 8076 8751 |

## TOOLS & EQUIPMENT

| | |
|---|---|
| Brunwell Garden Machinery | 01834 871 480 |
| Cheltenham Garden Machinery | 01242 238 342 |
| D K Tools Ltd | 01895 435 556 |
| Darlac Products | 01753 547 790 |
| Devon Garden Machinery | 01803 872 124 |
| Draper Tools Ltd | 0238 0266 355 |
| Garden Tools & Engineering | 01362 694 990 |
| Green Jem | 01777 710 107 |
| Green-tech | 01423 324 342 |
| Hozelock Cyprio | 01844 292 002 |
| J C Powerco Ltd | 01977 612 319 |
| James Gray & Son Ltd | 0131 225 7381 |
| Langley Home & Garden | 01923 264 982 |
| N J E Briers Ltd | 01747 841 401 |
| Neill Tools (Spear & Jacksons Plc) | 0114 281 4242 |
| Neill Tools (Spear & Jacksons Plc) | 0114 281 4242 |
| Rouse Power Equipment | 01263 733 655 |
| Rowena Garden Equipment | 01248 750 477 |
| Stanley Europe | 0114 276 8888 |
| Stonebank | 01285 720 737 |
| Taskers Garden Equipment | 01255 815 048 |
| The Truggery | 01323 832 314 |

## TREATMENT & GARDEN CARE

| | |
|---|---|
| Algon Ltd | 01257 262 620 |
| City Irrigation Ltd | 020 8462 4221 |
| D M Boyer Garden Supplies | 01344 882 532 |
| Doff Portland Ltd. | 0845 0500 131 |
| Earth Core | 01285 740 529 |
| Garden Care Supplies Ltd | 020 8337 9922 |
| MOO POO | 01743 790 459 |
| Pinnacle Concept | 01209 821 613 |
| Scotts Co UK Ltd | 01483 410 210 |
| Vertigrow | 01904 400 092 |

# GARDENERS' ATLAS

Sourcing: We originally contacted more than 5,000 companies sourced from the Yellow Pages Business Database and sent every outlet an entry form and map to identify their precise location. We mailed reminders and duplicate entry forms but there were a few outlets whose completed forms were not returned by the deadline. Where companies did not manage to respond in time, we took informed decisions based upon the company name, source information and postcode, and included them where appropriate.

Locations are mapped using GeoConcept software; the post code provides coordinates which gives accuracy to the nearest 100 metres.

Each outlet has been contacted and given the opportunity to be listed in one of four ways; *a basic listing, a standard listing (box and text), a premier listing (box, text and picture) or a diamond listing (box, text, picture and diamond logo).* The latter three listings are paid entries.

For further information please contact the **Gardeners' Atlas** on 01603 633 808 or email info@gardenersatlas.co.uk.

# HAVE WE MISSED ANYONE?

To ensure the **Gardeners' Atlas** is as up to date and accurate as possible we would like to hear about anywhere we have missed.

Please complete the form below and send it to:

**Gardeners' Atlas,
St Faiths House, Mountergate,
Norwich, Norfolk NR1 1PY
Or email: info@gardenersatlas.co.uk
Or fax us on: 01603 632 808
Or visit: www.gardenersatlas.co.uk**

NAME OF LOCATION _____

Garden ☐  Garden centre ☐  Nursery ☐  Water garden specialist ☐

Other (please specify) _____

ADDRESS _____
_____

TOWN _____

COUNTY _____ POSTCODE _____

TELEPHONE NUMBER (if known) _____

Please tick this box if you are the manager or owner of the outlet ☐

MR/MRS/MISS  NAME _____

ADDRESS _____
_____

TOWN _____

COUNTY _____ POSTCODE _____

EMAIL _____

WEBSITE _____

# INDEX
## BY OUTLET NAME

Buc-Cou • OUTLET NAME XXi


| OUTLET NAME | MAP NUMBER |
|---|---|
| Buckland Abbey, Yelverton | 4-12 |
| Buckland Nurseries, Reigate | 148-18 |
| Buckland Plants, Kirkcudbright | 96-2 |
| Bucknell Nurseries, Bucknell | 46-2 |
| Bulldog Nurseries, Staines | 141-13 |
| Bumbles Nursery, Cranbrook | 21-2 |
| Bungalow Nurseries, Rugby | 49-11 |
| Burford Garden Company, Burford | 37-17 |
| Burford House Gardens, Tenbury Wells | 47-14 |
| Burghley House, Stamford | 61-13 |
| Burleydam Garden Centre, Ellesmere Port | 78-48 |
| Burnby Hall Gardens, Pocklington | 89-9 |
| Burncoose Garden & Nurseries, Redruth | 2-13 |
| Burncross Nurseries, Sheffield | 81-16 |
| Burnham Garden Centre, Burnham-on-sea | 23-41 |
| Burniston Nurseries, Scarborough | 94-3 |
| Burnside Garden Centre, Blackpool | 85-8 |
| Burrington Coombe Garden Centre, Bristol | 23-37 |
| Burrow Farm Gardens, Axminster | 11-42 |
| Burston Rose & Garden Centre, St Albans | 39-34 |
| Burstow Nurseries, Horley | 18-2 |
| Burton Agnes Hall Gardens, Driffield | 90-1 |
| Burton Constable Hall Gardens, Leyburn | 93-10 |
| Burton Nurseries & Garden Centre, Neston | 77-31 |
| Burtonwood Nurseries, Poulton le Fylde | 85-10 |
| Bury Bank Plant Centre, Bury Bank | 69-33 |
| Bury Lane Farm Shop & Nursery, Royston | 52-24 |
| Busbridge Lakes, Waterfowl & Gardens, Godalming | 146-27 |
| Buscot Park, Faringdon | 37-25 |
| Bush Green Cottage Nursery, Boughton in Furness | 91-17 |
| Bush School Cash & Carry Nursery, Pembroke | 32-13 |
| Busheyfields Nursery, Herne Bay | 31-10 |
| Bushukan Bonsai, Hockley | 42-29 |
| Busy Bee Plant Centre, Ryde | 8-8 |
| Butterfields Nursery, Bourne End | 140-1 |
| Bybrook Barn Garden Centre, Ashford | 30-46 |
| By-Pass Nurseries, Capel St Mary | 53-28 |
| Byrkley Park, Burton upon Trent | 59-4 |
| C & D Garden & Pet Centre, Liverpool | 78-30 |
| C & E Laing, Turriff | 134-1 |
| C & K Jones, Tarvin | 68-9 |
| C E Stonehouse, Burton upon Trent | 59-5 |
| C Gregory Roses, Weston | 62-6 |
| C J Skilton Aquarist, Sandon | 42-22 |
| C S Lockyer (Fuchsias), Bristol | 24-6 |
| C W Warwick, Northampton | 50-29 |
| Cabbages & Kings, Uckfield | 19-33 |
| Cadbury Garden & Leisure, Congresbury | 23-28 |
| Caddicks Clematis Nursery, Warrington | 79-35 |
| Cae Hir, Lampeter | 44-4 |
| Caerphilly Garden Centre & Coffee Shop, Cardiff | 23-1 |
| Calderstone Park, Liverpool | 78-43 |
| California Gardens, Howden | 89-15 |
| Calke Abbey, Ticknall | 59-7 |
| Callwood Nursery, Belper | 70-17 |
| Cally Gardens Nursery, Castle Douglas | 95-1 |
| Calthorpe Project, London | 143-13 |
| Calver Sough Nurseries, Hope Valley | 81-36 |
| Cambo Gardens, St Andrews | 119-16 |
| Camborne Garden Centre, Camborne | 1-4 |
| Cambridge Garden Plants, Horningsea | 52-11 |
| Cambridge University Botanic Garden, Cambridge | 52-15 |
| Camden Garden Centre, Camden | 143-7 |
| Camelia Botnar Garden & Craft Centre, Horsham | 18-10 |
| Cameons Garden Centre, Invergordon | 132-1 |
| Camford Nurseries, Taunton | 10-1 |
| Canal Turn Nurseries, Retford | 83-25 |
| Candacraig Gardens, Strathdon | 128-6 |
| Candie Gardens, St Peter Port | 139-9 |
| Canford Park Garden Centre, Wimborne | 13-36 |
| Cannington College Heritage Gardens, Bridgwater | 11-1 |
| Cannizaro Park, London | 142-25 |
| Cannon Hall Country Park, Barnsley | 81-9 |
| Cannon Hall Garden Centre, Barnsley | 81-8 |
| Cannon Hill Park, Birmingham | 58-43 |
| Canonbury Nursery & Garden Centre, Fortrose | 132-5 |
| Canons Ashby House, Daventry | 49-28 |
| Cantilever Garden Centre, Warrington | 79-32 |
| Capel Manor, Enfield | 40-38 |
| Capital Gardens Ltd Highgate Garden Centre, London | 40-60 |
| Capital Gardens Ltd Temple Fortune Garden Centre, London | 40-59 |
| Capital Gardens Ltd Woods of Berkhamsted, Berkhamsted | 39-26 |
| Cardwell Nursery Garden Centre, Inverclyde | 111-10 |
| Carlton Garden Centre, Llay | 67-7 |
| Carlton Nurseries & Landscape Gardeners, Bingley | 87-14 |
| Carnfield Hall Garden & Craft Centre, Alfreton | 71-17 |
| Carnon Downs Garden Centre, Truro | 2-11 |
| Carpenders Park Nursery, Watford | 39-55 |
| Carpenter's Nursery, St Albans | 39-22 |
| Carr Bank Garden Centre, Milnthorpe | 91-23 |
| Carr Farm Garden Centre, Hoylake | 77-13 |
| Carr Gate Nurseries, Wakefield | 88-42 |
| Carwinion Gardens , Falmouth | 2-19 |
| Casablanca Nurseries, Hartfield | 19-16 |
| Cash Hardware Stores, Swansea | 33-18 |
| Cassillis Nursery, Maybole | 106-11 |
| Casssington Nurseries, Witney | 37-19 |

| OUTLET NAME | MAP NUMBER |
|---|---|
| Castle Acre Priory, Castle Acre | 63-4 |
| Castle Ashby Gardens, Northampton | 50-25 |
| Castle Bromwich Hall Gardens, Birmingham | 58-36 |
| Castle Campbell, Historic Scotland, Dollar | 118-6 |
| Castle Douglas Garden Centre, Kirkcudbright | 101-7 |
| Castle Drogo, Exeter | 5-5 |
| Castle Fraser, Inverurie | 129-5 |
| Castle Gardens Plant Centre, Sherborne | 12-16 |
| Castle Howard, York | 94-14 |
| Castle Kennedy Gardens, Stranraer | 100-5 |
| Castle Nurseries, Swadlincote | 59-16 |
| Castle Nursery, Beckenham | 143-38 |
| Catchfrench Manor Gardens, Saltash | 4-16 |
| Caterham Koi, Godstone | 148-32 |
| Causeway Nursery, Ormskirk | 78-6 |
| Cawdor Castle & Gardens, Nairn | 132-8 |
| Cedar Nurseries, Northampton | 50-10 |
| Cedar Nurseries, Romsey | 14-9 |
| Cedar Nursery, Chichester | 16-33 |
| Cedar Nursery, Cobham | 147-13 |
| Cefn Onn Park, Cardiff | 23-7 |
| Cefn Vaenor Nurseries, Aberystwyth | 55-3 |
| Celyn Vale Eucalyptus Nurseries, Corwen | 67-13 |
| Chalcroft Nurseries and Garden Centre, Bognor Regis | 17-47 |
| Chalk Farm Nursery, Near Swaffham | 63-8 |
| Chamney Garden Centre, Leicester | 60-35 |
| Chanctonbury Nurseries, Pulborough | 18-32 |
| Chandlers Cross Garden Centre, Rickmansworth | 39-45 |
| Chandlers Farm Nursery, Reading | 27-28 |
| Chandlers Garden Centre, Newcastle Upon Tyne | 104-12 |
| Chapel End Nursery, Dunmow | 41-4 |
| Chapel Farm House Nursery, Beaworthy | 9-18 |
| Chapel Garden Centre, Skegness | 74-1 |
| Chapelfield Nursery, London | 40-46 |
| Chapman's Nurseries, Swadlincote | 59-15 |
| Chard Garden Centre, Chard | 11-35 |
| Charlecote Fruit & Flowers, Warwick | 48-30 |
| Charlecote Park, Warwick | 48-29 |
| Charles F Ellis, Stanston | 48-57 |
| Charleston, Lewes | 19-47 |
| Charlesworth Nursery & Garden Centre, Glossop | 80-15 |
| Charlie Brown's Garden Centre, Leicester | 60-41 |
| Charlton Park Garden Centre, Wantage | 37-31 |
| Charnock Farm Garden Centre, Preston | 85-33 |
| Charter House Nursery, Dumfries | 101-1 |
| Chartwell, Westerham | 149-14 |
| Chase Organics, Addlesetone | 141-22 |
| Chatelherault Garden Centre, Hamilton | 112-28 |
| Chatsworth Garden Centre, Matlock | 70-3 |
| Chatsworth, Bakewell | 70-2 |
| Chelsea Gardener, Enfield | 40-34 |
| Chelsea Gardener, London | 143-23 |
| Chelsea Physic Garden, London | 143-25 |
| Chelsham Place, Chelsham | 148-13 |
| Chelston Nurseries, Wellington | 11-22 |
| Cheltenham Pot & Plant Centre, Cheltenham | 36-20 |
| Chenies Aquatics, Farnham Royal | 140-7 |
| Chenies Aquatics, Rickmansworth | 39-47 |
| Chennels Gate Gardens & Nursery, Eardisley | 46-14 |
| Cherry Hill Nurseries, Middlesborough | 99-15 |
| Cherry Tree Lodge Nursery, Preston | 85-17 |
| Cherry Tree Nursery, Bournemouth | 13-37 |
| Cheshire Herbs, Tarporley | 68-10 |
| Cheshire Waterlife, Northwich | 68-5 |
| Cheslyn House, Watford | 39-43 |
| Chessington Garden Centre, Chessington | 147-5 |
| Chester Road Nursery, Tarporley | 68-8 |
| Chester Zoo, Chester | 68-7 |
| Chesterfield Aquatics, Chesterfield | 71-6 |
| Cheviot View Nurseries, Newcastle Upon Tyne | 104-25 |
| Chew Valley Trees, Bristol | 23-30 |
| Chiddingstone Castle, Edenbridge | 149-18 |
| Chigwell Nursery, Chigwell | 41-26 |
| Chillingham Castle, Chillingham | 109-8 |
| Chiltern Aquatics, Harlington | 39-3 |
| China Maroc Bonsai, Colchester | 43-22 |
| Chipchase Castle Nursery, Hexham | 103-3 |
| Chirk Castle, Wrexham | 67-14 |
| Chiswick House, London | 142-10 |
| Cho Kee, Upminster | 41-34 |
| Chobham Nurseries, Chobham | 27-33 |
| Choice Landscapes Priory Farm Nursery, Wisbech | 62-17 |
| Choice Plants, Romsey | 14-8 |
| Choice Plants, Spilsby | 73-9 |
| Chris Ling Garden Scene, Ipswich | 54-33 |
| Chris Pattinson, Pendock | 36-1 |
| Christies Elite Nurseries, Forres | 133-2 |
| Christie's Nursery, Westmuir | 123-3 |
| Christies, Fochabers | 133-3 |
| Chubbs Nursery, Lewes | 19-38 |
| Chubb's Nursery, Poole | 7-14 |
| Church Hill Cottage Gardens and Nursery, Ashford | 30-42 |
| Churchfield Farm, Pulborough | 18-28 |
| Churchtown Nursery, Truro | 2-14 |
| Cicely's Cottage Plants, Skelmersdale | 78-16 |
| Cider Press Plant Centre, Totnes | 5-32 |
| Cilwern Plants, Llandeilo | 33-1 |

| OUTLET NAME | MAP NUMBER |
|---|---|
| Cinders Lane Nursery, Yapton | 17-44 |
| Citrus Centre, Pulborough | 17-17 |
| City Gardener, Bexleyheath | 144-12 |
| Clacton Garden Centre, Clacton-on-Sea | 43-26 |
| Clandon Park, Guildford | 146-20 |
| Claptons Conservatory & Garden Centre, Grantham | 72-29 |
| Clare College Fellows' Garden, Cambridge | 52-14 |
| Claremont Aquatic Nurseries, Preston | 85-32 |
| Claremont Landscape Garden, Esher | 147-3 |
| Claremont Nursery, Hintlesham | 53-24 |
| Clarenount Nurseries, Maldon | 42-20 |
| Claverton Manor, Bath | 24-26 |
| Clay Lane Nursery, South Nutfield | 148-26 |
| Claycliffe Garden Centre, Barnsley | 81-11 |
| Clayhill Nurseries, Lewes | 19-42 |
| Clays Garden Centre , Washington | 104-30 |
| Cleeve Nursery, Bristol | 23-27 |
| Cleggs Nurseries, Stalmine | 85-5 |
| Cleveland Garden Centre, Manchester | 80-10 |
| Cley Nurseries, Cley | 75-1 |
| Clifton Nurseries, London | 143-14 |
| Clifton Place Garden Centre, Dalbeattie | 101-9 |
| Clipston Nursery, Market Harborough | 60-50 |
| Cliveden, Taplow | 140-4 |
| Cluny House Gardens, Aberfeldy | 122-1 |
| Clyde Valley Garden Centre, Larkhall | 113-26 |
| Clyne Gardens, Swansea | 33-16 |
| Coach House Garden Centre, Hook | 27-43 |
| Cobham Park Nursery, Cobham | 147-8 |
| Cockers Garden Centre, Aberdeen | 129-10 |
| Cockington Nursery, Callington | 4-10 |
| Codsall and Wergs Garden Centre, Wolverhampton | 57-24 |
| Coinros Nursery, Coleford | 35-11 |
| Colby Woodland Garden, Narberth | 32-7 |
| Cold Harbour Nursery, Poole | 7-4 |
| Coldharbour Nurseries, Weymouth | 6-14 |
| Coldharbour Nursery, Hailsham | 20-33 |
| Coleford Garden Centre, Coleford | 35-9 |
| Coleton Fishacre House & Garden, Dartmouth | 5-40 |
| Colin's Nurseries & Garden Centre, Southport | 78-5 |
| Collinwood Nurseries, Macclesfield | 80-38 |
| Collinwood Nurseries, Nottingham | 71-33 |
| Collyer's Nurseries, Derby | 71-46 |
| Colne Valley Garden Centre, Huddersfield | 81-3 |
| Colville Place Gardens, London | 143-15 |
| Compton Acres Garden, Poole | 7-16 |
| Compton Lane Nurseries, Moreton in Marsh | 37-5 |
| Compton Nursery, Guildford | 146-22 |
| Congham Hall Herb Garden, King's Lynn | 63-1 |
| Congleton Garden Centre, Congleton | 69-10 |
| Conifer Nursery, Great Missenden | 39-42 |
| Conifox Nurseries, Kirkliston | 114-9 |
| Coniger Nurseries, Eastleigh | 15-15 |
| Conkers Garden Centre, Basingstoke | 27-46 |
| Connoisseurs' Cacti, Orpington | 144-32 |
| Contented Gardener, Bardney | 73-7 |
| Conwy Valley Nurseries, Conwy | 76-10 |
| Cookoo Box Nursery, Maidstone | 30-36 |
| Cooks Garden Centre, Stourport on Severn | 47-12 |
| Cooks Ridgeway Nurseries, Sheffield | 82-29 |
| Cooling's Nurseries, Sevenoaks | 149-4 |
| Coombe Country Park, Coventry | 49-1 |
| Coombland Gardens Nursery, Billingshurst | 18-21 |
| Coopers Croft Nurseries, Hailsham | 20-29 |
| Coppins Plant Centre, Ferndown | 13-32 |
| Coppull Moor Lane Nurseries, Chorley | 78-8 |
| Copton Ash Specialist Nursery, Faversham | 30-26 |
| Corley Nursery & Corley Koi Aquatics, Coventry | 59-37 |
| Cornell's Garden Centre, Stanford le Hope | 29-4 |
| Corner Shop Garden Centre, Ebbw Vale | 34-7 |
| Cornish Garden Centre, Truro | 2-15 |
| Corsham Court, Corsham | 25-13 |
| Cotehele, Saltash | 4-11 |
| Coton Manor Gardens, Northampton | 50-7 |
| Cotswold Garden Centre & Farmshop, Stow-on-the-Wold | 37-10 |
| Cotswold Garden Flowers, Evesham | 48-50 |
| Cotswold Hardy Plants, Taunton | 22-21 |
| Cottage Farm Nurseries, Bedford | 51-14 |
| Cottage Garden Centre, Newbury | 26-21 |
| Cottage Garden Nurseries, West-Cliff-On-Sea | 42-50 |
| Cottage Garden Nursery, Barnet | 40-49 |
| Cottage Garden Nursery, Eighton Banks | 104-28 |
| Cottage Garden Plants, Newbury | 26-13 |
| Cottage Garden, Staplehurst | 30-50 |
| Cottage Herbary, Tenbury Wells | 47-13 |
| Cottage Nurseries, Alford | 84-22 |
| Cottage Nursery, Larkhall | 112-30 |
| Cottage Rose Gardens, Stretton | 57-13 |
| Cottenham Park, London | 142-26 |
| Cottesbrooke Hall & Gardens, Northampton | 50-6 |
| Coughton Court, Alcester | 48-25 |
| Country Cabin, Stoke-on-Trent | 69-26 |
| Country Fayre, Ferring | 18-51 |
| Country Flowers Wildflower Nursery, Romney Marsh | 21-20 |
| Country Garden Plant Centre, Shrewsbury | 56-3 |
| Country Homes and Gardens, Reading | 27-14 |
| Country Homes and Gardens, Royston | 52-21 |

| OUTLET NAME | MAP NUMBER |
|---|---|
| Howards of Horsham, Horsham | 18-17 |
| Howdens Garden Centre, Inverness | 132-10 |
| Howick Hall & Gardens, Alnwick | 109-10 |
| Hughenden Manor, High Wycombe | 39-50 |
| Hull Farm Nursery, Colchester | 43-7 |
| Hunneyhill Aquatics, Newport | 8-10 |
| Hunters Chase Garden Centre, Brentwood | 41-21 |
| Hunters Croft Nursery, Axminster | 11-44 |
| Huntershill Garden & Gift Centre, Bishopbriggs | 112-10 |
| Huntington Garden & Leisure, Huntingdon | 51-2 |
| Huntroyde Nurseries, Padiham | 86-15 |
| Hunts Court, Dursley | 36-42 |
| Hurrans Garden Centre, Banbury | 49-36 |
| Hurrans Garden Centre, Cowbridge | 22-11 |
| Hurrans Garden Centre, Gloucester | 36-17 |
| Hurrans Garden Centre, Leamington Spa | 49-22 |
| Hurrans Garden Centre, Leigh Sinton | 47-30 |
| Hurrans Garden Centre, Newport | 35-22 |
| Hurrans Garden Centre, West Hagley | 47-2 |
| Hurrans Nursery, London | 40-52 |
| Hutton Garden Centre, Brentwood | 41-20 |
| Hutton Garden Centre, Weston-Super-Mare | 23-36 |
| Hutton-in-the-Forest, Penrith | 97-6 |
| Huttons Nurseries, Loxley | 81-21 |
| Hyde Hall, The Royal Horticultural Society, Chelmsford | 42-26 |
| Hyde Park, London | 143-27 |
| Hydon Nurseries, Godalming | 17-2 |
| Hydroponics Centre, Coventry | 59-39 |
| Hyrons Trees, Rickmansworth | 39-41 |
| I H Beale, Swanley | 144-27 |
| Ickleton Garden Centre & Aquatics, Saffron Walden | 52-23 |
| Ickworth Park & Garden, Horringer | 53-15 |
| Iden Croft Herbs, Staplehurst | 30-47 |
| Ightham Mote, Sevenoaks | 29-29 |
| Ightham Plant Centre, Ightham | 29-21 |
| Ilam park, Ashbourne | 70-15 |
| Ilkley Moor Garden Centre, Ilkley | 87-5 |
| Imberhorne Lane Nursery, East Grinstead | 19-9 |
| Ingatestone Garden Centre, Ingatestone | 41-16 |
| Inveresk Lodge, Musselburgh | 114-11 |
| Inverewe Garden, Achnasheen | 135-4 |
| Inverurie Garden & Machinery Centre, Inverurie | 129-3 |
| Ipswich Road Garden Centre, Norwich | 64-16 |
| Irton Garden Centre, Scarborough | 94-6 |
| Irvines of Pollokshields, Glasgow | 112-16 |
| Isabella Plantation, Richmond | 142-17 |
| Ise Garden Centre, Kettering | 50-3 |
| Island Garden Nursery, Weymouth | 6-10 |
| Ivor Thompson Nurseries, Nottingham | 72-30 |
| Ivy Mill Nursery, Godstone | 148-22 |
| J & D Marston, Nafferton | 89-2 |
| J B McIntosh, Bonnybridge | 113-13 |
| J B Turner, Wimborne | 13-19 |
| J C Allgrove , Slough | 140-14 |
| J C Gardens, Trowbridge | 25-26 |
| J Deen & Sons, Cardiff Gate | 23-4 |
| J Dobbe & Sons, Cheam | 142-33 |
| J H Park, Kendal | 91-13 |
| J P Foss, Barnsley | 82-5 |
| Jack Drakes Alpine Nursery and Garden, Aviemore | 127-2 |
| Jack's Patch Garden Centre, Teignmouth | 5-17 |
| Jacksons Garden Centre, Stoke-on-Trent | 69-14 |
| Jacksons Nurseries & Garden Centre, Rhyl | 77-21 |
| Jackson's Nurseries, Tamworth | 59-22 |
| Jacques Armand, Stanmore | 39-56 |
| Jacques Cann, Walton on Thames | 147-4 |
| James Coles & Sons, Leicester | 60-25 |
| James Lamprey & Sons, Pontefract | 82-1 |
| James Smith Nurseries, Matlock | 70-8 |
| James Whitaker & Sons, Prescot | 78-29 |
| Jane Lane Nurseries, Preston | 85-13 |
| Japanese Garden & Bonsai Nursery, Newquay | 3-6 |
| Jardinerie , Cardiff | 23-5 |
| Jardinerie , Cheltenham | 36-11 |
| Jardinerie , Gloucester | 36-30 |
| Jardinerie , High Wycombe | 38-27 |
| Jardinerie , Solihull | 48-1 |
| Jardinerie , Swindon | 25-7 |
| Jarrett Nursery, Bristol | 24-14 |
| Jedburgh Abbey, Historic Scotland, Jedburgh | 108-12 |
| Jennikings Garden Centre, Chigwell | 41-25 |
| Jephson Gardens, Leamington Spa | 49-21 |
| Jersey lavender, St Brelade | 139-15 |
| Jersey Zoological Park, Trinity | 139-12 |
| Jesmond Dene Park, Newcastle Upon Tyne | 104-17 |
| Jewels Garden Centre, Springfield | 42-15 |
| Jobs Cottage Nurseries, Southampton | 15-21 |
| John Clayfield, Clunton | 46-1 |
| John Dawber Garden, Lincoln | 73-2 |
| John James Gardening, Worcester Park | 142-36 |
| John Smith & Son, Coalville | 60-23 |
| John Train Plants, West Drayton | 141-5 |
| Johnson Hall Nurseries, Stafford | 69-35 |
| Johnsons Garden Centre, Boston | 73-20 |
| Johnsons Nursery, Whitstable | 31-8 |
| Johnston Garden, Aberdeen | 129-16 |
| Joshua Plumtree, Kirriemuir | 123-1 |

| OUTLET NAME | MAP NUMBER |
|---|---|
| Jubilee Garden Centre, Sandown | 8-20 |
| Jungle Garden & Pet Centre, Sunbury on Thames | 141-20 |
| Juniper Garden Centre, Tydd | 62-15 |
| Juniper Nurseries, Guildford | 146-17 |
| Jura House Walled Garden, Isle of Jura | 110-1 |
| Just Bamboo , Bromley | 144-29 |
| Just Plants, Kenilworth | 49-13 |
| Just Roses, Rye | 21-24 |
| K Cross & Son, Moreton | 77-10 |
| Kailzie Gardens, Peebles | 108-2 |
| Kaminski Home & Garden Centre, Tavistock | 4-8 |
| Kathleen Muncaster Fuschias, Gainsborough | 83-20 |
| Kayes Garden Nursery, Rearsby | 60-9 |
| Kaytie Fisher Nursery, Ockham | 146-13 |
| Kedleston Hall, Derby | 70-22 |
| Kellie Castle, Anstruther | 119-21 |
| Kelly's Nursery, Chichester | 16-42 |
| Kelways Nursery and Plant Centre , Langport | 11-10 |
| Kenchester Water Gardens, Hereford | 46-22 |
| Kennilworth Nurseries, Retford | 83-29 |
| Kensington Gardens, London | 143-19 |
| Kensington Palace & Gardens, London | 143-20 |
| Kent Cacti, Orpington | 144-31 |
| Kent Street Nurseries, Battle | 21-32 |
| Kenwick Farmhouse Nursery, Louth | 84-15 |
| Kenwith Nursery, Great Torrington | 9-15 |
| Kenwood House, London | 40-61 |
| Kenyon Lane Nurseries, Warrington | 79-14 |
| Kerry Hill Nurseries, Stoke-on-Trent | 69-20 |
| Kershaw's Garden Centre, Brighouse | 87-26 |
| Kershaws Nurseries, Askrigg | 92-2 |
| Kersney Abbey and Russell Gardens, Dover | 31-35 |
| Kerswell Garden Centre, Torquay | 5-27 |
| Keydell Nurseries, Waterlooville | 16-20 |
| Kibworth Garden Centre, Leicester | 60-37 |
| Kildrummy Castle Gardens, Alford | 128-4 |
| Killerton House, Exeter | 10-16 |
| Kiln Nurseries, Stanmore | 39-54 |
| King Easton , London | 40-50 |
| King George V Garden Centre, Huntly | 133-5 |
| King John's Lodge, Etchingham | 20-16 |
| Kingfisher Nurseries & Garden Centre, Hertford | 40-24 |
| Kingfisher Nurseries, Bromsgrove | 48-14 |
| Kinglea Plant Centre, Waltham Abbey | 40-22 |
| Kings Toll Nursery, Tonbridge | 20-2 |
| Kingsbury Garden Centre, Tamworth | 59-29 |
| Kingsfield Conservation Nursery, Chard | 11-36 |
| Kingsfold Nursery Plant Centre, Horsham | 18-7 |
| Kingsgate & Kenver Nurseries, Broadstairs | 31-2 |
| Kingston Lacy, Wimborne Minster | 13-22 |
| Kingston Maurward Gardens, Dorchester | 7-15 |
| Kingswood Nurseries, Walsall | 58-10 |
| Kinross Nurseries, Yarm | 93-3 |
| Kirby Hall, Corby | 61-25 |
| Kirkcaldy Garden Centre, Kirkcaldy | 114-1 |
| Kirkley Hall College Gardens, Ponteland | 104-8 |
| Kiwi Nurseries, Wigan | 78-12 |
| Klondyke Garden Centre, Edinburgh | 114-17 |
| Klondyke Garden Centre, Falkirk | 113-12 |
| Klondyke Garden Centre, Glasgow | 112-4 |
| Klondyke Garden Centre, Kelso | 109-6 |
| Klondyke Garden Centre, Livingston | 113-22 |
| Klondyke Garden Centre, Stirling | 113-3 |
| Knabb Hall Nurseries, Matlock | 70-7 |
| Knebworth House and Country Park, Knebworth | 40-6 |
| Kneller Garden Supplies, Isleworth | 142-16 |
| Knights Garden Centre, Godstone | 148-21 |
| Knightshayes Court, Tiverton | 10-6 |
| Knoll Gardens & Nursery, Wimborne | 13-27 |
| Knot Garden Nursery, Wood Dalling | 75-18 |
| Knowler Nursery, Gillingham | 30-9 |
| Knypersley Hall Garden Centre, Stoke-on-Trent | 69-16 |
| Koi Shop Aquatic Centre, Three Legged Cross | 13-16 |
| Koi Water Barn, Chelsfield Village | 144-37 |
| K's Nursery and Garden Centre, Chester | 68-2 |
| Kyre Park Gardens, Tenbury Wells | 47-22 |
| L S Mummery Nurseries, Southend-on-Sea | 43-28 |
| L Swann Nursery, Woodbridge | 54-26 |
| L W Plants, Harpenden | 39-13 |
| La Seigneurie, Sark | 139-8 |
| Lacock Abbey, Chippenham | 25-17 |
| Ladd's Garden Village, Reading | 27-9 |
| Lady Green Nurseries & Garden Centre, Formby | 77-5 |
| Lady Helen Nurseries, Lochgelly | 114-2 |
| Ladybird Nurseries, Saxmundham | 54-18 |
| Ladyridge Garden Centre, Cheadle | 80-23 |
| Lakeside Garden Centre, Colne | 86-7 |
| Lakeside Garden Centre, Feltham | 141-12 |
| Lakeside Garden Centre, Tadley | 26-18 |
| Lakeside Garden Centre, Warminster | 25-34 |
| Lakeside Plant Centre and Fuchsia Fantasy, Cleethorpes | 84-3 |
| Lamberlea Pond & Garden Centre, Egremont | 91-1 |
| Lambley Aquatics, Lambley | 71-27 |
| Lamport Hall Gardens, Northampton | 50-4 |
| Lancasters Nursery, Henfield | 18-33 |
| Landford Trees, Salisbury | 14-17 |
| Landlife Wildflowers, Liverpool | 78-32 |

| OUTLET NAME | MAP NUMBER |
|---|---|
| Lane End Nursery, Warrington | 79-37 |
| Lane Nurseries, Newcastle Upon Tyne | 104-9 |
| Lanes Garden Centre, Draycott | 71-44 |
| Langford Nurseries & Garden Centre, Biggleswade | 51-17 |
| Langlands Nurseries & Garden Centre, York | 89-11 |
| Langley Boxwood Nursery, Liss | 16-9 |
| Langley Park, Slough | 140-9 |
| Langshott Manor, Gatwick | 148-35 |
| Langthorns Plantery, Dunmow | 41-7 |
| Lanhydrock, Bodmin | 3-8 |
| Lanscape Centre, Hull | 90-5 |
| Larch Cottage Nurseries, Penrith | 97-10 |
| Larmer Tree Gardens, Salisbury | 13-9 |
| Lashlake Nurseries, Thame | 38-19 |
| Laurel Farm Garden Centre, Ipswich | 54-29 |
| Laurel Farm Herbs, Saxmundham | 54-9 |
| Laurels Nursery, Benenden | 21-18 |
| Laurels Plant Centre, Reading | 27-24 |
| Laurence Hobbs Orchids, Crawley Down | 19-5 |
| Lavenham Guildhall of Corpus Christi, Sudbury | 53-19 |
| Law's Nurseries, Maryport | 96-4 |
| Layham Garden Centre, Canterbury | 31-20 |
| Laylocks Nurseries, Worcester | 47-28 |
| Leabrook Nurseries, Rossendale | 86-26 |
| Lealans Nurseries & Garden Centre, Pattingham | 57-28 |
| Leamside Nurseries, Houghton Le Spring | 98-9 |
| Lechlade Garden Centre, Lechlade | 37-22 |
| Leckmelm Shrubbery and Arboretum, Ullapool | 135-3 |
| Ledbury's Secret Garden Centre, Ledbury | 47-40 |
| Leeds Castle, Maidstone | 30-34 |
| Lee's Nursery, Ashford | 21-3 |
| Leigh Garden & Timber Supplies, Leigh on Sea | 30-2 |
| Leighton Buzzard Garden Centre, Leighton Buzzard | 39-7 |
| Leiston Garden Centre, Leiston | 54-12 |
| Leith Hall, Huntly | 128-1 |
| Leonardslee Gardens, Horsham | 18-19 |
| Lesley Marshall, King's Lynn | 62-13 |
| Levens Hall, Kendal | 91-19 |
| Lewden Garden Centre, Melksham | 25-19 |
| Lewes Castle and Barbican House Museum, Lewes | 19-45 |
| Leydene Gardens Nursery, Fareham | 15-35 |
| Lillies Nursery & Caravan Park, Bognor Regis | 17-34 |
| Lilliesleaf Nursery, Lillisleaf | 108-9 |
| Lily Vale Nurseries, Nottingham | 72-20 |
| Lime Cross Nursery, Hailsham | 20-28 |
| Linclon Green Clematis Nursery, Market Rasen | 83-18 |
| Lincluden Nursery, Woking | 145-3 |
| Lincoln Cathedral, Lincoln | 73-4 |
| Lincolnfield Nurseries, North Thoresby | 84-11 |
| Linden Garden Centre, Perth | 119-12 |
| Lindhill Nursery, Wakefield | 88-44 |
| Lindisfarne Castle, Berwick upon Tweed | 109-1 |
| Lingen Nursery & Gardens, Bucknell | 46-3 |
| Links, Aberdeen | 129-9 |
| Linn Botanic Gardens & Nursery, Helensburgh | 111-7 |
| Liss Pet & Aquatic Centre, Liss | 16-12 |
| Litlington Nursery, Litlington | 19-53 |
| Little Acres Nursery, Farnham | 145-9 |
| Little Brook Fuchsias, Aldershot | 145-7 |
| Little Creek Nursery, Weston-Super-Mare | 23-35 |
| Little Garden Centre, West Bromwich | 58-34 |
| Little Heath Farm Nursery, Berkhamsted | 39-25 |
| Little Heath Garden Centre, Bromsgrove | 48-17 |
| Little Hermitage, Ventnor | 8-24 |
| Little Moreton Hall, Congleton | 69-12 |
| Little Oak Bonsai, Sidlesham | 16-37 |
| Little Rhyndaston Nurseries, Haverfordwest | 32-2 |
| Little Treasures, Horsedowns | 1-9 |
| Littlebanks Nursery, Ringwood | 13-18 |
| Littleton Monocot Nursery, Somerton | 12-7 |
| Living Rainforest, Newbury | 26-5 |
| Living World, Leeds | 87-16 |
| Llanarth Garden Centre, Llanarth | 44-1 |
| Llandovery Pet & Garden Centre, Llandovery | 45-5 |
| Lloyd Wath Garden Centre, Rotherham | 82-14 |
| Lloyds Nurseries, Ormskirk | 78-14 |
| Lochalsh Woodland Garden, Kyle | 125-1 |
| Lochduich Plants, Invernate | 126-1 |
| Lochend Nursery, Glasgow | 112-13 |
| Loch-Hills Plant Centre, Ellon | 129-1 |
| Locko Nurseries, Derby | 71-40 |
| Lodge Farm Nurseries, Swainsthorpe | 64-20 |
| Lodge Hill Nursery, Wickham | 15-27 |
| Lodge Nature Reserve, RSPB, Sandy | 51-13 |
| Lodge Nursery, Hastings | 21-33 |
| Logan Botanic Garden, Stranraer | 95-3 |
| Lomax Nurseries, Cheadle | 80-22 |
| Londesboro Nurseries & Garden Centre, Hutton Cranswick | 89-6 |
| London Zoo, London | 143-9 |
| Long Cross Victorian Gardens, Port Isaac | 3-2 |
| Longacre Nurseries, Hythe | 21-13 |
| Longacre Nursery, Faversham | 30-31 |
| Longcombe Nursery & Garden Centre, Totnes | 5-35 |
| Longdendale Nursery, High Peak | 81-32 |
| Longfields Nursery, Cottenham | 52-9 |
| Longframlington Centre for Plants, Morpeth | 104-2 |
| Longleat, Warminster | 24-42 |

| OUTLET NAME | MAP NUMBER |
|---|---|
| Longridge Nurseries, Market Harborough | 61-26 |
| Longstock Park Nursery, Stockbridge | 14-1 |
| Lorna Cross Nursery, Matlock | 70-10 |
| Loseley Park, Guildford | 146-24 |
| Lost Gardens of Heligan, St Austell | 2-5 |
| Loughborough Road Nurseries, Loughborough | 60-6 |
| Louth Garden Centre, Louth | 84-14 |
| Louvain Organic Nurseries, Peacehaven | 19-51 |
| Lower Icknield Farm Nurseries, Aylesbury | 38-15 |
| Lower Road Nursery and Plant Centre, Effingham | 147-14 |
| Lower Severalls Garden & Nursery, Crewkerne | 11-33 |
| Lower Spring Nursery, Shrewsbury | 56-16 |
| Lowertrees Nursery, Angmering | 17-43 |
| Loxhill Nursery, Guildford | 146-23 |
| Loxwood Conifer Nurseries, Loxwood | 17-12 |
| Lullingstone Castle, Eynsford | 144-39 |
| Lumby Garden Centre, South Milford | 88-36 |
| Luscar Nursery, Dunfermline | 113-4 |
| Lushington Garden Centre, Wootton Bridge | 8-4 |
| Luxton Garden Centre, Exmouth | 6-11 |
| Lydford Alpine Nursery, Okehampton | 4-3 |
| Lydiate Barn Nurseries, Liverpool | 78-18 |
| Lydney Garden & Aquatic Centre, Lydney | 35-13 |
| Lyme Park, Stockport | 80-32 |
| Lymefield Garden Nursery, Hyde | 80-16 |
| Lymington Plant Centre, Lymington | 14-37 |
| Lynash Nurseries, Merriott | 11-29 |
| Lyndene Nurseries, Preston | 85-38 |
| Lyndhurst Garden Centre, Skegness | 74-3 |
| Lyndhurst Nurseries, Ormesby | 99-11 |
| Lynford Arboretum, Thetford | 63-15 |
| Lynwood Garden Centre, Newport | 8-5 |
| Lyonshall Nurseries and Garden Centre, Kington | 46-12 |
| M & M Plants, Umberleigh | 9-13 |
| M B R Green, Ibstock | 60-15 |
| M E Brown & Sons, York | 88-6 |
| M G M Nurseries, Kingsbridge | 5-41 |
| M G M Garden & Leisure , Kilmarnock | 106-6 |
| M G W Plants, Wakefield | 88-39 |
| M Gould, South Walsham | 65-9 |
| Macclesfield Garden Centre, Macclesfield | 69-2 |
| MacFarlanes Nursery & Garden Centre, Folkestone | 31-38 |
| Macgregors Plants for Shade, Romsey | 14-5 |
| MacKnade Garden Centre, Faversham | 30-24 |
| Macpennys Nurseries, Christchurch | 14-31 |
| Macplants, Pencaitland | 114-15 |
| Madresfield Nursery & Garden Centre, Malvern | 47-33 |
| Madrona Nursery, Ashford | 30-48 |
| Magill's Nurseries, Wirral | 77-9 |
| Magpies, Thetford | 63-14 |
| Maidenhead Aquatics Centre, Bourne End | 140-2 |
| Makhams Nurseries, Grimsby | 84-7 |
| Malleny Garden, Edinburgh | 114-19 |
| Mallet Court Nursery, Taunton | 11-20 |
| Mandy's Plants and Garden Centre, Alford | 84-23 |
| Mannington Gardens, Norwich | 75-14 |
| Manor Aquatics Centre, London | 144-1 |
| Manor Gardens, Basildon | 42-49 |
| Manor Gardens, Rotherham | 82-19 |
| Manor Nurseries, Saffron Walden | 52-31 |
| Manor Nursery, Angmering | 17-40 |
| Manor Nursery, Barnham | 17-33 |
| Manor Nursery, Chichester | 17-46 |
| Manor Road Nurseries, North Shields | 104-14 |
| Manorowen Walled Garden, Fishguard | 44-14 |
| Mansfield Nurseries, Leigh on Sea | 42-47 |
| Mansfield Nurseries, Weston-Super-Mare | 23-32 |
| Marble Hill House, Twickenham | 142-18 |
| Marbury Hall Nurseries, Northwich | 79-51 |
| Marcham Plants, Abingdon | 37-24 |
| Marden Cottage Nursery, Kneesworth | 52-25 |
| Maristow Nursery Gardens, Plymouth | 4-14 |
| Markeaton Garden Centre & Nursery, Derby | 70-24 |
| Markham Grange Nursery, Doncaster | 82-6 |
| Marks Hall Arboretum, Colchester | 42-6 |
| Marks Water Garden, Teddington | 142-23 |
| Marle Place Gardens, Tonbridge | 20-3 |
| Marlows DIY & Garden Centre, Bury St Edmunds | 53-8 |
| Marsden Garden Centre, Ashtead | 147-11 |
| Marshall's Malmaison, Tetbury | 36-43 |
| Marshbroad Moor Nursery, Ottery St Mary | 6-2 |
| Marshments Garden Centre, Burton upon Trent | 59-3 |
| Martin Nest Nurseries, Gainsborough | 83-21 |
| Martins Nurseries, Bury St Edmunds | 53-18 |
| Martins Nursery, Sandwich | 31-24 |
| Marwood Hill Gardens, Barnstaple | 9-2 |
| Marwood House Nursery, Sibsey | 73-19 |
| Mary Arden's House, Stratford-upon-Avon | 48-28 |
| Mary's Acre, Llanfairpwllgwyngyll | 66-5 |
| Master's Garden, Warwick | 49-24 |
| Matlock Garden Water Life & Pet Centre, Matlock | 70-9 |
| Maudlin Nursery, Chichester | 17-28 |
| Maurice Rowe, Boston | 73-18 |
| Mayfield Garden Centre, Doncaster | 83-3 |
| Mayfield Nurseries, Orpington | 144-34 |
| Mayfield Nursery, Billingshurst | 18-23 |
| Mayflower Nurseries, Egham | 140-27 |

| OUTLET NAME | MAP NUMBER |
|---|---|
| Mayflower Nursery & Garden Centre, Chelmsford | 43-27 |
| Maypole Pet & Garden Centre, Witham | 42-13 |
| May's Garden Centre, Newmarket | 52-8 |
| Mayshade Garden Centre, Dalkeith | 114-20 |
| McBean's Orchids, Lewes | 19-41 |
| McGrath Nurseries, Maulden | 51-18 |
| McGreal's Nursery, Wirral | 77-11 |
| Mead Nursery, Westbury | 25-31 |
| Meadgate Farm Nurseries, Bath | 24-33 |
| Meadow Cottage Plants, Ivybridge | 4-18 |
| Meadow Farm Nursery, Hayling Island | 16-34 |
| Meadow Grange Nursery, Whitstable | 30-18 |
| Meadowmill Garden Centre & Nursery, Tranent | 114-10 |
| Meadows Nursery, Frome | 24-38 |
| Meare Close Nurseries , Tadworth | 148-15 |
| Medina Garden Centre, Wootton | 8-7 |
| Medina Nurseries, Southampton | 15-37 |
| Megginch Castle, Perth | 119-8 |
| Melbicks Garden & Leisure , Birmingham | 59-36 |
| Melbourne Hall Gardens, Melbourne | 60-2 |
| Melbourne Nursery, Wallington | 148-6 |
| Melford Hall, Sudbury | 53-23 |
| Mellerstain House, Gordon | 108-1 |
| Mendip Cottage Nursery, Beckenham | 143-36 |
| Mendle Nursery, Scunthorpe | 83-7 |
| Merchant Adventurers' Hall & Garden, York | 88-19 |
| Merebrook Water Plants, Worcester | 47-36 |
| Meresborough Nursery, Gillingham | 30-16 |
| Merlin Garden Supplies, Newquay | 3-10 |
| Merriments Gardens & Nursery, Hurst Green | 20-17 |
| Merrist Wood Plant Centre, Worplesdon | 145-4 |
| Merryfield Nurseries, Canterbury | 31-17 |
| Merton Nurseries, Bicton | 56-5 |
| Meudon Hotel & Gardens, Falmouth | 2-20 |
| Meynell Langley Gardens, Ashbourne | 70-23 |
| Michelham Priory, Hailsham | 20-38 |
| Mickfield Watergarden Centre, Stowmarket | 54-14 |
| Middle Farm Nurseries, Hornsea | 90-2 |
| Midlandscapes Building & Garden Centre, Wolverhampton | 57-26 |
| Midway Nurseries, Llandrindod Wells | 45-2 |
| Midway Nurseries, Lowestoft | 65-18 |
| Mildene Nursery, Telford | 57-4 |
| Mile End Park, London | 143-11 |
| Mill Cottage Plants, Wookey | 23-42 |
| Mill Dene, Moreton in Marsh | 48-59 |
| Mill End Nursery, Buntingford | 40-1 |
| Mill Garden Centre, Bathgate | 113-19 |
| Mill Hill Plants, East Stoke | 72-17 |
| Mill Lane Nurseries, Evesham | 48-43 |
| Mill Lane Nurseries, Pershore | 47-32 |
| Mill Race Nursery, Colchester | 43-9 |
| Mill View Nursery, Oxford | 38-17 |
| Millais Nurseries, Farnham | 17-5 |
| Millbrook Garden Company, Crowborough | 19-25 |
| Millbrook Garden Company, Gravesend | 29-10 |
| Millbrook Nursery & Garden Centre, Monmouth | 35-8 |
| Millfield Nurseries, Retford | 83-26 |
| Millgate House, Richmond | 93-6 |
| Millingtons Garden Centre, Newport | 57-6 |
| Mill's Farm Plants & Gardens, Stowmarket | 53-9 |
| Mills Nurseries, Dorchester | 7-21 |
| Millstone Garden Centre, Grimsby | 84-8 |
| Millwater Gardens, Romsey | 14-13 |
| Millyard Nurseries, West Malling | 29-20 |
| Milton Ernest Garden Centre, Bedford | 51-7 |
| Milton Garden Plants, Gillingham | 12-9 |
| Milton Nurseries, Wigan | 78-17 |
| Mimbridge Garden Centre, Woking | 146-4 |
| Minshull's Nursery, Crewe | 68-16 |
| Minterne Gardens, Dorchester | 12-23 |
| Miserden Nursery, Stroud | 36-33 |
| Moat Road Nursery, King's Lynn | 62-12 |
| Moffat Garden Centre, Moffat | 107-5 |
| Mompesson House, Salisbury | 13-6 |
| Monkton Elm Garden & Pet Centre, Taunton | 11-9 |
| Montacute House, Yeovil | 12-15 |
| Monteviot House Gardens, Jedburgh | 108-11 |
| Montrave Plant Centre, Leven | 119-20 |
| Monymusk Walled Garden, Inverurie | 128-5 |
| Moor Farm Nursery, Whitland | 32-4 |
| Moor Growers, Maidenhead | 140-11 |
| Moor Monkton Nurseries, York | 88-8 |
| Moordown Garden Centre, Bournemouth | 7-1 |
| Moores Nurseries, Nottingham | 72-33 |
| Moore's Nursery , Leicester | 60-38 |
| Moores Pet & Garden Stores, Bristol | 23-10 |
| Moorland Cottage Plants, Crymych | 44-16 |
| Moorland Nurseries & Garden Centre, Knaresborough | 88-12 |
| Moorlands, Crowborough | 19-18 |
| Morangie Garden Centre, Tain | 136-2 |
| Morden Hall Garden Centre, Morden | 143-39 |
| Morden Hall Park, Morden | 143-40 |
| Morehall Nurseries, Sheffield | 81-15 |
| Moreton Park Garden Centre, Wrexham | 67-15 |
| Morley Nurseries, Southend-on-Sea | 43-30 |
| Morley Nursery, Wilmslow | 80-33 |
| Morton Hall Gardens, Retford | 83-27 |

| OUTLET NAME | MAP NUMBER |
|---|---|
| Morton Manor, Sandown | 8-13 |
| Moseley Old Hall, Wolverhampton | 58-18 |
| Moss Bridge Garden Centre, Rochdale | 80-1 |
| Moss End Water Gardens, Warfield | 140-20 |
| Moss Farm Conifers, Halifax | 87-18 |
| Mossatburn Water Gardens, Alford | 128-3 |
| Mottisfont Abbey & Garden, Romsey | 14-3 |
| Moulton Nurseries, Acle | 65-13 |
| Mount Edgcumbe House & Gardens, Torpoint | 4-24 |
| Mount Ephraim Gardens, Faversham | 30-27 |
| Mount Folly Nurseries, Wickham | 15-31 |
| Mount Grace Priory, Northallerton | 93-7 |
| Mount Pleasant Nursery, Berkeley | 35-16 |
| Mount Stuart Gardens, Isle of Bute | 111-13 |
| Mousehold Garden Centre, Norwich | 65-11 |
| Moyness Nurseries, Blairgowrie | 123-9 |
| Moyses Nurseries, Mayfield | 20-18 |
| Mozart House Nursery Garden, Wigston | 60-30 |
| Mrs Jane Sadler, Billingshurst | 17-13 |
| Mud Island Nurseries, Fareham | 15-30 |
| Mulu Nurseries, Tenbury Wells | 47-16 |
| Muncaster Castle, Gardens & Owl Centre, Ravenglass | 91-9 |
| Munsborough Nurseries, Rotherham | 82-20 |
| Murrells Nursery, Pulborough | 17-16 |
| Museum of London Garden, London | 143-16 |
| Museum of Welsh Life, Cardiff | 22-9 |
| Myddelton House Gardens, Enfield | 40-42 |
| Myrtle Nursery, Manaccan | 2-24 |
| Mythic Garden , Newton Abbot | 5-9 |
| N F & M C Kempster, Braintree | 42-1 |
| N J Scott Farm Shop & Nursery, Ipswich | 54-25 |
| Naked Cross Nurseries, Wimborne | 13-39 |
| Nanney's Bridge Nursery, Nantwich | 68-15 |
| Narey's Garden Centre, Stowmarket | 53-16 |
| Narkurs Nursery, Torpoint | 4-19 |
| Nash's House & New Place, Stratford-upon-Avon | 48-35 |
| National Botanic Gardens of Wales, Llanarthne | 33-5 |
| National Collection of Passiflora, Clevedon | 23-26 |
| National Forest Plant Centre, Swadlincote | 59-17 |
| Natural Surroundings, Holt | 75-5 |
| Naturescape Wildflower Farm, Langar | 72-31 |
| Necton Garden Centre, Swaffham | 63-11 |
| Ned Yates Garden Centre, Wilmslow | 80-36 |
| Nelsons Farm Shop & Nursery, Ormskirk | 78-7 |
| Ness Botanic Gardens, South Wirral | 77-28 |
| Nethercott Nurseries, Wedmore | 23-40 |
| Nettletons Nursery, Godstone | 148-23 |
| New Horizons Garden Centre, Morpeth | 104-4 |
| New Inn Lane Nurseries, Evesham | 48-41 |
| New Inn Nurseries, Boncath | 44-12 |
| New Leaf Plant Centre, Sheffield | 81-34 |
| New Road Nurseries, Hailsham | 20-30 |
| New Widnes Home & Garden Centre, Widnes | 78-38 |
| Newbank Garden Centre, Radcliffe | 80-6 |
| Newbridge Nurseries, Horsham | 18-9 |
| Newby Hall and Gardens, Ripon | 93-22 |
| Newchurch Nurseries, Newchurch | 8-19 |
| Newcroft Nurseries, Manchester | 79-18 |
| Newhailes Estate, Musselburgh | 114-13 |
| Newhailes Nursery, Musselburgh | 114-12 |
| Newhall Nurseries, Hockley | 42-31 |
| Newingreen Nurseries, Hythe | 21-10 |
| Newington Nurseries, Wallingford | 38-25 |
| Newlake Gardens, Crawley | 18-3 |
| Newland Nurseries, Tamworth | 59-31 |
| Newlands Nursery, Sevenoaks | 149-13 |
| Newquay Garden Centre, Newquay | 3-12 |
| Newstead Abbey Park, Ravenshead | 71-20 |
| Newton Hill Alpines, Wakefield | 88-43 |
| Newton Nurseries, Preston | 85-25 |
| Nicky's Nursery, Broadstairs | 31-5 |
| Nicky's Rock Garden Nursery, Honiton | 11-39 |
| Nidus Garden Centre, Dereham | 63-9 |
| Nimmerdor Nurseries, Spalding | 62-9 |
| Nine Acres Nurseries, Stockton on Tees | 98-17 |
| Nishikigoi Centre, Hawkhurst | 20-15 |
| Noel Clay Garden Centre, Awsworth | 71-30 |
| Noel-Baker Peace Garden, London | 143-3 |
| Nomads Fuchsias & Pelargonium Specialists, Cheltenham | 36-3 |
| Norburns Plant Centre, Grimsby | 84-9 |
| Norden Alpines, Goole | 89-16 |
| Norden Farm Shop & Mini Garden Centre, Wareham | 7-24 |
| Norfolk Herbs, Dereham | 63-3 |
| Norfolk Lavender, King's Lynn | 74-6 |
| Normanby Hall Victorian Walled Gardens, Scunthorpe | 83-1 |
| Normandale Nurseries, Loxley | 81-22 |
| North Cheam Garden Centre, Sutton | 142-40 |
| North One Garden Centre, London | 143-6 |
| North Perrott Garden Centre, Crewkerne | 12-20 |
| North Street Garden Centre, Romford | 41-33 |
| North Street Garden Centre, Taunton | 10-3 |
| North Wales Water Gardens, Rhyl | 77-29 |
| North Walsham Garden Centre & Garden Machinery, North Walsham | 75-16 |
| Northern Garden Supplies, Worksop | 82-33 |
| Northfield Nurseries, London | 40-44 |
| Northfield Nursery, Lymington | 7-2 |

Nor-Por • OUTLET NAME XXVii


| OUTLET NAME | MAP NUMBER |
|---|---|
| Northway Nurseries, Liverpool | 78-19 |
| Northwick Garden Centre, Canvey Island | 29-3 |
| Northwood Garden Centre, Newcastle under Lyme | 69-23 |
| Norton Green Garden Centre, Bath | 24-36 |
| Norton Nursery & Garden Centre, Bristol | 24-22 |
| Norton Priory Museum and Gardens, Runcorn | 78-41 |
| Norwell Nurseries, Newark | 72-8 |
| Nostell Priory, Wakefield | 82-2 |
| Notcutts Garden Centre, Ardleigh | 43-6 |
| Notcutts Garden Centre, Bagshot | 145-1 |
| Notcutts Garden Centre, Cranleigh | 17-4 |
| Notcutts Garden Centre, Maidstone | 30-30 |
| Notcutts Garden Centre, Near Marlow | 38-32 |
| Notcutts Garden Centre, Norwich | 64-14 |
| Notcutts Garden Centre, Oxford | 38-23 |
| Notcutts Garden Centre, Peterborough | 61-22 |
| Notcutts Garden Centre, Solihull | 48-6 |
| Notcutts Garden Centre, St Albans | 39-27 |
| Notcutts Garden Centre, Staines | 141-16 |
| Notcutts Garden Centre, Tunbridge Wells | 20-1 |
| Notcutts Garden Centre, Woodbridge | 54-28 |
| Nunnington Hall, York | 94-10 |
| Nurdens Garden Centre, Malmesbury | 36-46 |
| Nurseries Direct, Mauchline | 106-9 |
| Nurseries, Consett | 98-4 |
| Nursery of Miniatures, Honiton | 11-40 |
| Nutfield Nurseries, Redhill | 148-29 |
| Nutlin Nursery, Uckfield | 19-26 |
| Nymans Garden, Haywards Heath | 18-15 |
| Oak Cottage Walled Herb Garden, Harmer Hill | 56-7 |
| Oak Dene Nurseries, Barnsley | 81-6 |
| Oak Farm Nursery, Coventry | 49-2 |
| Oak Nurseries, Preston | 85-14 |
| Oak Tree Farm Nurseries, Chester | 68-6 |
| Oak Tree Nursery, Selby | 89-14 |
| Oak Tree Nursery, Warfield | 140-23 |
| Oakabank Gardens, Carlisle | 102-3 |
| Oakdale Rose & Garden Centre, Coventry | 49-4 |
| Oakdean Nursery, Horsham | 18-16 |
| Oakdene Alpine Nursery, Heathfield | 20-20 |
| Oaken Nurseries, Wolverhampton | 57-21 |
| Oakfield Nurseries, Chester | 78-40 |
| Oakfield Nursery, Doncaster | 83-2 |
| Oakhurst Garden Centre, Cockermouth | 96-5 |
| Oakhurst Nursery, Crowborough | 19-20 |
| Oakington Garden Centre, Cambridge | 52-10 |
| Oaklands Nurseries, Sittingbourne | 30-13 |
| Oakleigh Nurseries , Alresford | 16-8 |
| Oakridge Nursery, Sawbridgeworth | 41-8 |
| Oaks Garden Centre, Wimborne | 13-33 |
| Oaks Nurseries, Nuneaton | 59-32 |
| Oaks Nursery, Aldershot | 145-6 |
| Oakview Nurseries, Colchester | 43-5 |
| Oasis, Brading | 8-12 |
| Oasis, South Benfleet | 30-1 |
| Oast Farm, Uckfield | 19-32 |
| Occasionally Yours, Lingfield | 149-19 |
| Ockendens Gdn, Littlehampton | 17-45 |
| Ockley Court Farm, Dorking | 18-1 |
| Odiham Waterlily Collection, Hook | 27-49 |
| Oilwell Nursery, Tibshelf | 71-12 |
| Okell's Nurseries, Tarporley | 68-13 |
| Olands Garden and Plant Centre, Ripon | 93-21 |
| Olantigh Garden Nurseries, Ashford | 30-43 |
| Olbarr Nurseries, Lichfield | 58-5 |
| Old Barn Nurseries, Horsham | 18-26 |
| Old Church House, Wantage | 37-32 |
| Old Court Nurseries, Malvern | 47-37 |
| Old Edlington Nurseries, Doncaster | 82-17 |
| Old Hall Nurseries, Neston | 77-36 |
| Old Hall Nursery, Leek | 70-14 |
| Old Mill Garden Centre, Wetherby | 88-23 |
| Old Mill Herbary, Bodmin | 3-3 |
| Old Mill House Garden Nursery, Witham | 42-10 |
| Old Orchard Nursery, Burwash | 20-21 |
| Old Railway Line Nursery, Brecon | 46-24 |
| Old Vicarage Garden Centre, Frodsham | 68-1 |
| Old Vicarage Nursery, Leominster | 46-5 |
| Old Walled Garden, Hadlow | 29-31 |
| Old Wardour Castle, Salisbury | 13-8 |
| Old Withy Garden Nursery, Helston | 1-20 |
| Oldbury Nurseries, Ashford | 21-4 |
| Ollerton Nursery and Plant Centre, Knutsford | 79-49 |
| One House Nursery, Macclesfield | 80-40 |
| Orange Tree, Lichfield | 58-6 |
| Orchard House Nursery, Harrogate | 88-1 |
| Orchard Nurseries, Canterbury | 31-30 |
| Orchard Nurseries, Grantham | 72-23 |
| Orchard Nurseries, Threeholes | 62-28 |
| Orchard Nurseries, York | 89-5 |
| Orchard Nursery Garden Centre, Retford | 83-31 |
| Orchard Nursery, East Grinstead | 19-3 |
| Orchard View Nurseries, Broadway | 48-56 |
| Orchardleigh Nurseries, Southampton | 15-19 |
| Orchid Aswers, Chichester | 16-43 |
| Orchid Paradise, Newton Abbot | 5-16 |
| Ormesby Hall, Middlesbrough | 99-9 |

| OUTLET NAME | MAP NUMBER |
|---|---|
| Ormiston & Renwick, Melrose | 108-8 |
| Ornamental Conifers, King's Lynn | 62-10 |
| Ornamental Grasses, Inverurie | 129-4 |
| Ornamental Tree Nursery, Kingsland | 46-10 |
| Osborne House, East Cowes | 8-1 |
| Oscroft Nurseries, Doncaster | 82-9 |
| Oscroft's Dahlias, Solihull | 48-15 |
| Otley Hall, Ipswich | 54-22 |
| Otter Nurseries & Garden Centre , Torquay | 5-29 |
| Otter Nurseries Garden Centre, Ottery St Mary | 10-18 |
| Otter Nurseries Of Plymouth, Plymouth | 4-26 |
| Overbecks Museum & Garden, Salcombe | 8-27 |
| Overstrand Cottage Garden Centre, Cromer | 75-7 |
| Owermoigne Nurseries, Dorchester | 7-23 |
| Owl House Gardens, Tunbridge Wells | 20-7 |
| Oxburgh Hall & Garden, Swaffham | 63-12 |
| Oxford Botanic Gardens, Oxford | 38-14 |
| P & A Plant Supplies, Norwich | 65-2 |
| P F Stubbs, Shrewsbury | 56-1 |
| P J's Palms & Exotics, Ashford | 141-14 |
| P Perella, Littlehampton | 17-32 |
| P Verheul, Pulborough | 17-19 |
| P W & H E Bradley, Sheffield | 82-27 |
| P W Plants, Kenninghall | 64-27 |
| P Whelan, Cowbridge | 22-12 |
| Pacific Nurseries, Walsall | 58-24 |
| Packwood House, Solihull | 48-18 |
| Paddock Farm Nurseries, Darlington | 93-5 |
| Padlock Croft, Cambridge | 52-18 |
| Paignton Zoo and Botanical Gardens, Paignton | 5-34 |
| Painshill Landscape Garden, Cobham | 147-6 |
| Painswick Rococo Garden, Painswick | 36-32 |
| Palm Centre, Richmond | 142-21 |
| Palm Farm, Ulceby | 90-7 |
| Palmer Nurseries, Pudsey | 87-13 |
| Palmers Garden Centre, Leicester | 60-29 |
| Pannells Garden Centre, Heston | 141-9 |
| Pantiles Plant & Garden Centre, Chertsey | 140-28 |
| Paradise Centre, Bures | 53-30 |
| Paradise Garden, Pulborough | 18-39 |
| Paradise Park, Newhaven | 19-52 |
| Paradise Park, St Ives | 1-7 |
| Parham Bungalow Plants, Devizes | 25-28 |
| Parham Elizabethan House and Gardens, Pulborough | 17-20 |
| Park Green Nurseries, Stowmarket | 54-10 |
| Park House Nurseries, Liversedge | 87-25 |
| Park Nurseries, Knaresborough | 88-5 |
| Park Place Farm nursery, Wickham | 15-29 |
| Parkers Garden & Aquatic Centre, Bristol | 24-2 |
| Parker's Garden Centre, Manchester | 80-13 |
| Parkers Mottram St Andrew Garden Centre, Macclesfield | 80-34 |
| Parkgate Nurseries, Neston | 77-24 |
| Parkhall Nurseries & Garden Centre, Huntingdon | 52-1 |
| Parks Perennials, Bournemouth | 7-7 |
| Parkside Nurseries, Wisbech | 62-20 |
| Parkside Nursery, London | 143-26 |
| Parkside Rose Nursery, Knutsford | 79-52 |
| Parkwall Garden Centre, Caldicot | 35-18 |
| Parnwell Plants, Peterborough | 61-17 |
| Parrotts Corner Nursery, Doncaster | 83-15 |
| Parwoods Nursery, Northallerton | 93-8 |
| Pashley Manor Gardens, Wadhurst | 20-14 |
| Pathhead Nurseries, Anstruther | 119-23 |
| Pathhead Nurseries, Forfar | 124-4 |
| Pathhead Nurseries, Kirriemuir | 123-2 |
| Patio Garden Centre, London | 143-33 |
| Patio Planting by Hazel, Lincoln | 73-1 |
| Paul Bromfield Aquatics, Hitchin | 39-6 |
| Pauls Koi & Pond Supplies, Darlington | 98-19 |
| Paultons Nursery and Plant Centre, Southampton | 14-22 |
| Pavilion Garden Centre, Wolverhampton | 57-30 |
| Pavilion Gardens, Buxton | 81-39 |
| Peachprint, New Malden | 142-30 |
| Pear Tree Cottage Plants, Shepton Mallet | 12-1 |
| Pearson Garden Supplies, Loxley | 81-20 |
| Pebbly Hill Farm Nursery, Chipping Norton | 37-9 |
| Peckover House & Garden, Wisbech | 62-18 |
| Peco Gardens, Seaton | 6-7 |
| Pembroke Farm Nursery, Ely | 52-2 |
| Pembroke Garden Centre, Pembroke Dock | 32-12 |
| Pencarrow, Bodmin | 3-5 |
| Pencoed College Garden Centre, Bridgend | 22-4 |
| Pendle Heritage Centre, Nelson | 86-10 |
| Pengethley Nursery & Garden Centre, Harewood End | 35-3 |
| Penhow Nurseries, Penhow | 35-19 |
| Penlan Perennials, Llandysul | 44-7 |
| Penlan-Uchaf Farm Gardens, Fishguard | 44-13 |
| Pennells Garden centre, Grimsby | 84-5 |
| Pennells Garden Centre, Lincoln | 72-6 |
| Penpergwm Plants, Abergavenny | 34-8 |
| Penrallt Farm Nursery, Cardigan | 44-6 |
| Penrhyn Castle, Bangor | 76-12 |
| Penshurst Place & Gardens, Tonbridge | 149-22 |
| Penstemons by Colour, London | 142-4 |
| Pensthorpe Waterfowl park, Fakenham | 74-10 |
| Pentangle Water Gardens & Aquaria, Woking | 146-7 |
| Pentewan Valley Nursery, St Austell | 2-4 |

| OUTLET NAME | MAP NUMBER |
|---|---|
| Pentraeth Nurseries, Pentraeth | 76-6 |
| Penwood Nurseries, Newbury | 26-19 |
| People's Park, Grimsby | 84-4 |
| Percevall Hall Gardens, Skipton | 87-2 |
| Percy Thrower's Gardening & Leisure, Shrewsbury | 56-8 |
| Perennial Nursery, Haverfordwest | 32-1 |
| Perhill Nurseries, Great Witley | 47-19 |
| Perryhill Nurseries, Hartfield | 19-6 |
| Perry's Plants, Whitby | 94-1 |
| Perrywood Nurseries, Tiptree | 42-9 |
| Pet and Garden Centre, Welwyn Garden City | 40-13 |
| Peter Barratt's Garden Centre, Newcastle Upon Tyne | 104-13 |
| Peter Barratt's Garden Centre, Stockton on Tees | 99-10 |
| Peter Beale's Roses, Attleborough | 64-24 |
| Peter Mardon, Dorchester | 6-5 |
| Peter Plants, Leicester | 60-39 |
| Peter Trenear Nurseries, Hook | 27-36 |
| Petersfield Physic Garden, Petersfield | 16-13 |
| Petersham Nurseries, Richmond | 142-19 |
| Peto Garden, Bradford on Avon | 24-32 |
| Pets & Gardens, Sutton Coldfield | 58-30 |
| Petworth House and Park, Petworth | 17-15 |
| Peveril Clematis Nursery, Exeter | 5-12 |
| Philipshill Garden Centre, Glasgow | 112-25 |
| Phillimore Garden Centre, Royston | 52-22 |
| Phoebe's Garden Centre, London | 144-18 |
| Phoenix Garden, London | 143-17 |
| Pickard's Magnolia Gardens, Canterbury | 31-19 |
| Picton Castle, Haverfordwest | 32-5 |
| Picton Garden and the Old Court Nurseries, Malvern | 47-35 |
| Pikes Oak Farm Nurseries, Keyworth | 71-41 |
| Pilgrim House Herbs, Maidstone | 30-33 |
| Pimbo Nurseries & Garden Centre, Skelmersdale | 78-21 |
| Pine Lodge Garden & Nursery, St Austell | 3-15 |
| Pine Tree Nursery, Devizes | 25-20 |
| Pinecove Nurseries, Tenterden | 21-17 |
| Pinegrove Plant Nursery, Dunfermline | 113-6 |
| Pines Garden, Dover | 31-34 |
| Pinewood Garden Centre, Preston | 85-2 |
| Pinewood Park Nurseries, Aberdeen | 129-19 |
| Pioneer Nursery, Letchworth | 40-4 |
| Pirelli Garden, London | 143-22 |
| Pitmedden Garden, Ellon | 129-2 |
| Plant Emporium, Blackpool | 85-22 |
| Plant Nursery, Northampton | 50-15 |
| Plant Place Garden Centre, Thornton-Cleveleys | 85-9 |
| Plant Place, Cambridge | 52-7 |
| Plant World Gardens & Nursery, Newton Abbot | 5-24 |
| Planta Exotica, Banbury | 49-39 |
| Planta Vera, Chertsey | 140-29 |
| Plantarama Garden Centre, Middlesbrough | 99-14 |
| Plantasia, Bicester | 38-6 |
| Plantasia, Gaerwen | 66-1 |
| Plantation Garden, Norwich | 64-12 |
| Plantbase, Tonbridge | 20-4 |
| Planters Garden Centre, Freasley | 59-27 |
| Plantiecrub Growers , Gott | 139-3 |
| Plantland Garden Centre, Lincoln | 72-3 |
| Plantome Nurseries & Garden Centre, Wickford | 42-28 |
| Plants Direct, Watford | 39-44 |
| Plants 'n' Gardens, Crawley | 19-12 |
| Plants of Special Interest Nursery, Rotherham | 82-21 |
| Plantsman Nursery, Okehampton | 5-7 |
| Plantsman, Northampton | 50-8 |
| Plantsman's Preference, Diss | 64-29 |
| Plantwise Nurseries, Lynton | 22-16 |
| Plantworld Nursery, Gillingham | 12-10 |
| Plantworld, Temple Normanton | 71-7 |
| Plas Brondanw Gardens, Panrhyndeudreath | 66-10 |
| Plas Newydd, Anglesey | 66-4 |
| Plas Tan-Y-Bwlch, Maentwrog | 66-11 |
| Plas yn Rhiw, Pwllheli | 66-14 |
| Plassey Plants, Wrexham | 68-22 |
| Platation Garden Centre, Harrow | 39-62 |
| Plaxtol Nurseries, Sevenoaks | 29-28 |
| Pleasant View Garden Centre, Maidstone | 30-37 |
| Pleasant View Nursery and Garden, Newton Abbot | 5-19 |
| Plough Farm Nurseries, Newport | 57-5 |
| Plowmans Garden Nursery & Plant Centre, Ferndown | 13-30 |
| Plymouth Garden Centre, Plymouth | 4-17 |
| Pococks Roses, Romsey | 14-11 |
| Podington Garden Centre, Wellingborough | 50-22 |
| Poets Cottage Shrub Nursery, Whitby | 94-2 |
| Polesden Lacey, Dorking | 147-17 |
| Polhill Garden Centre, Sevenoaks | 149-2 |
| Pond Services, West Calder | 113-24 |
| Pondlife Company, Caterham | 148-16 |
| Pondlife, Colchester | 43-15 |
| Pontarddulais Garden Centre, Swansea | 33-6 |
| Poplar Nurseries, Bath | 24-19 |
| Poplar Nurseries, Colchester | 43-16 |
| Poplar Tree Garden Centre, Durham | 98-12 |
| Poplars Nursery Garden Centre, Dunstable | 39-4 |
| Poplett of Peacehaven, Peacehaven | 19-54 |
| Pops Plants, Fordingbridge | 14-25 |
| Port Lympne Wild Animal Park, Hythe | 21-12 |
| Port Sunlight Garden Centre, Wirral | 77-19 |

# GAZETTEER


| PLACE | PAGE | GRID |
|---|---|---|
| Abbas Combe, Som | 12 | C2 |
| Abberley, Worc | 47 | B2 |
| Abberton, Essex | 43 | A2 |
| Abberton, Worc | 48 | A3 |
| Abbess Roding, Essex | 41 | B2 |
| Abbey Dore, Heref | 35 | A1 |
| Abbey Green, Staff | 69 | C2 |
| Abbey St Bathans, Bord | 115 | C3 |
| Abbey Town, Cumb | 96 | E1 |
| Abbey Village, Lanc | 86 | A4 |
| Abbey Wood, G Lon | 144 | B2 |
| Abbeystead, Lanc | 85 | C1 |
| Abbots Bickington, Devon | 9 | C3 |
| Abbots Bromley, Staff | 58 | B1 |
| Abbots Leigh, Som | 23 | D2 |
| Abbots Ripton, Camb | 51 | C1 |
| Abbot's Salford, Warw | 48 | B3 |
| Abbotsham, Devon | 9 | C2 |
| Abbotskerswell, Devon | 5 | B3 |
| Abbotsley, Camb | 51 | C3 |
| Abbott Street, Dors | 13 | A4 |
| Abbotts Ann, Hamp | 26 | A4 |
| Abdon, Shrop | 56 | D4 |
| Aber, Gwyn | 76 | D4 |
| Aberaeron, Cered | 44 | F2 |
| Aberangell, Gwyn | 55 | C2 |
| Aberarder, High | 127 | A1 |
| Aberargie, Perth | 119 | B3 |
| Aberarth, Cered | 44 | F2 |
| Abercarn, Caer | 34 | D4 |
| Abercastle, Pemb | 32 | C1 |
| Abercegir, Powys | 55 | C3 |
| Aberchirder, Aber | 134 | A3 |
| Abercraf, Powys | 34 | A2 |
| Abercregan, Neath | 34 | A4 |
| Abercwmboi, Rhond | 34 | C3 |
| Abercych, Pemb | 44 | D4 |
| Abercynon, Rhond | 34 | C4 |
| Aberdare, Rhond | 34 | C3 |
| Aberdaron, Gwyn | 66 | A4 |
| Aberdeen, Aber | 129 | C3 |
| Aberdour, Fife | 114 | A1 |
| Aberdulais, Neath | 34 | A3 |
| Aberdyfi, Gwyn | 55 | A3 |
| Aberedw, Powys | 45 | E3 |
| Abereiddy, Pemb | 32 | B1 |
| Abererch, Gwyn | 66 | C4 |
| Aberfan, Merth | 34 | C3 |
| Aberfeldy, Perth | 122 | E4 |
| Aberffraw, Angle | 66 | C1 |
| Aberford, W York | 88 | B3 |
| Aberfoyle, Stirl | 118 | A4 |
| Abergavenny, Monm | 34 | E2 |
| Abergele, Ab & Col | 77 | A4 |
| Abergorlech, Carm | 33 | C1 |
| Abergwesyn, Powys | 45 | C3 |
| Abergwili, Carm | 33 | B2 |
| Abergwynfi, Neath | 34 | B4 |
| Abergynolwyn, Gwyn | 55 | B2 |
| Aberkenfig, Brid | 22 | E1 |
| Aberlady, E Loth | 115 | A2 |
| Aberlemno, Angus | 124 | A3 |
| Aberllefenni, Gwyn | 55 | B2 |
| Aberllynfi, Powys | 46 | A4 |
| Aberlour, Moray | 133 | C4 |
| Abermule, Powys | 56 | A3 |
| Abernant, Carm | 33 | A1 |
| Abernethy, Perth | 119 | B3 |
| Abernyte, Perth | 119 | C1 |
| Aberporth, Cered | 44 | D3 |
| Abersoch, Gwyn | 66 | C4 |
| Abersychan, Torf | 34 | E3 |
| Aberthin, Glam | 22 | F2 |
| Abertillery, Gwent | 34 | D3 |
| Abertridwr, Caer | 34 | D4 |
| Abertridwr, Powys | 55 | E1 |
| Aberuthven, Perth | 118 | E3 |
| Aberystwyth, Cered | 55 | A4 |
| Abingdon, Oxon | 37 | D4 |
| Abinger, Surr | 147 | A4 |
| Abington, S Lan | 107 | C3 |
| Abington Pigotts, Camb | 51 | C4 |
| Ablington, Glouc | 37 | A3 |
| Abney, Derby | 81 | B4 |
| Aboyne, Aber | 128 | D4 |
| Abram, G Man | 79 | A2 |
| Abridge, Essex | 41 | A4 |
| Abson, Glouc | 24 | B2 |
| Abthorpe, Nhants | 50 | A3 |
| Aby, Linc | 84 | C4 |
| Acaster Selby, N York | 88 | C3 |
| Accrington, Lanc | 86 | B4 |
| Acha, Argyll | 120 | C3 |
| Acharacle, High | 121 | A2 |
| Acharn, High | 121 | A4 |
| Acharn, Perth | 122 | D4 |
| Achiltibuie, High | 135 | C2 |
| Achnacroish, Argyll | 117 | A1 |
| Achnamara, Argyll | 110 | F1 |
| Achnasheen, High | 131 | C2 |
| Achosnich, High | 120 | E2 |
| Achurch, Nhants | 61 | C4 |
| Acklam, N York | 89 | B1 |
| Acklington, Nthumb | 104 | B1 |
| Ackton, W York | 88 | B4 |
| Ackworth Moor Top, W York | 82 | A1 |
| Acle, Norf | 65 | B2 |
| Acol, Kent | 31 | B2 |
| Acomb, Nthumb | 103 | D4 |
| Aconbury, Heref | 35 | B1 |
| Acton, Chesh | 68 | C2 |

| PLACE | PAGE | GRID |
|---|---|---|
| Acton, Staff | 69 | B3 |
| Acton, Suff | 53 | C4 |
| Acton, G Lon | 142 | B2 |
| Acton Beauchamp, Heref | 47 | A3 |
| Acton Bridge, Chesh | 79 | A4 |
| Acton Burnell, Shrop | 56 | D3 |
| Acton Green, Heref | 47 | B3 |
| Acton Round, Shrop | 57 | A3 |
| Acton Trussell, Staff | 58 | A1 |
| Acton Turville, Glouc | 24 | B1 |
| Adbaston, Staff | 69 | A4 |
| Adber, Dors | 12 | B2 |
| Adbolton, Notts | 71 | B3 |
| Adderbury, Oxon | 49 | B4 |
| Adderley, Shrop | 68 | C3 |
| Addingham, W York | 87 | A2 |
| Addington, Bucks | 38 | C1 |
| Addington, Kent | 29 | A3 |
| Addington, G Lon | 148 | C1 |
| Addiscombe, G Lon | 143 | B4 |
| Addlestonemoor, Surr | 141 | A4 |
| Addlethorpe, Linc | 74 | B1 |
| Adfa, Powys | 55 | E3 |
| Adforton, Heref | 46 | C1 |
| Adisham, Kent | 31 | A3 |
| Adlestrop, Glouc | 37 | B1 |
| Adlingfleet, E R of Y | 89 | B4 |
| Adlington, Lanc | 79 | A1 |
| Admaston, Shrop | 57 | A2 |
| Admaston, Staff | 58 | B1 |
| Admington, Warw | 48 | C3 |
| Adscombe, Som | 11 | A1 |
| Adstock, Bucks | 38 | C1 |
| Adversane, W Suss | 17 | B2 |
| Adwick Le Street, S York | 82 | B1 |
| Adwick upon Dearne, S York | 82 | A2 |
| Ae, D & G | 101 | D2 |
| Affpuddle, Dors | 7 | A1 |
| Afon-wen, Flint | 67 | D1 |
| Agglethorpe, N York | 92 | E3 |
| Aike, E R of Y | 89 | D2 |
| Aiketgate, Cumb | 97 | B1 |
| Aikton, Cumb | 96 | F1 |
| Ailey, Heref | 46 | B3 |
| Ailsworth, Camb | 61 | D3 |
| Ainderby Quernhow, N York | 93 | B3 |
| Aingers Green, Essex | 43 | B2 |
| Ainstable, Cumb | 97 | B1 |
| Ainthorpe, N York | 94 | A1 |
| Aird, D & G | 100 | B4 |
| Aird of Sleat, High | 125 | D3 |
| Airdrie, N Lan | 112 | C3 |
| Airmyn, E R of Y | 89 | A4 |
| Airntully, Perth | 119 | A1 |
| Airth, Falkirk | 113 | B1 |
| Airton, N York | 86 | C1 |
| Aisby, Linc | 83 | C3 |
| Aisby, Linc | 73 | A3 |
| Aish, Devon | 5 | A3 |
| Aish, Devon | 5 | B4 |
| Aisholt, Som | 11 | A1 |
| Aiskew, N York | 93 | A2 |
| Aislaby, Durham | 99 | A4 |
| Aislaby, N York | 94 | B3 |
| Aisthorpe, Linc | 83 | C4 |
| Akeld, Nthumb | 109 | C2 |
| Akeley, Bucks | 50 | A4 |
| Akenham, Suff | 54 | A3 |
| Albaston, Corn | 4 | B3 |
| Alberbury, Shrop | 56 | C2 |
| Albourne, W Suss | 18 | B3 |
| Albrighton, Shrop | 56 | D1 |
| Albrighton, Shrop | 57 | B2 |
| Alburgh, Norf | 65 | A4 |
| Albury, Herts | 41 | A1 |
| Albury, Surr | 146 | B3 |
| Albury Heath, Surr | 146 | B4 |
| Alcaig, High | 132 | B2 |
| Alcaston, Shrop | 56 | C4 |
| Alcester, Warw | 48 | B2 |
| Alciston, E Sus | 19 | B4 |
| Alconbury, Camb | 51 | B1 |
| Alconbury Weston, Camb | 51 | B1 |
| Aldborough, Norf | 75 | B4 |
| Aldbourne, Wilts | 25 | D1 |
| Aldbrough, E R of Y | 90 | B3 |
| Aldbrough St John, N York | 98 | C4 |
| Aldbury, Herts | 39 | A2 |
| Aldcliffe, Lanc | 85 | C1 |
| Aldclune, Perth | 123 | A3 |
| Aldeburgh, Suff | 54 | C2 |
| Aldeby, Norf | 65 | B3 |
| Aldenham, Herts | 39 | C4 |
| Alderbury, Wilts | 14 | A2 |
| Alderford, Norf | 64 | B1 |
| Alderholt, Dors | 13 | B3 |
| Alderley, Glouc | 36 | A4 |
| Alderley Edge, Chesh | 80 | A4 |
| Aldermaston, Berks | 26 | C2 |
| Alderminster, Warw | 48 | C3 |
| Aldershot, Hamp | 145 | A3 |
| Alderton, Glouc | 36 | C1 |
| Alderton, Nhants | 50 | B3 |
| Alderton, Suff | 54 | B4 |
| Alderton, Wilts | 25 | A1 |
| Alderwasley, Derby | 70 | C2 |
| Aldfield, N York | 93 | A4 |
| Aldford, Chesh | 68 | A2 |
| Aldham, Essex | 43 | A1 |

| PLACE | PAGE | GRID |
|---|---|---|
| Aldham, Suff | 53 | D3 |
| Aldingbourne, W Suss | 17 | A4 |
| Aldingham, Cumb | 91 | D4 |
| Aldington, Kent | 21 | C1 |
| Aldington, Worc | 48 | B4 |
| Aldreth, Camb | 52 | B1 |
| Aldridge, W Mids | 58 | B3 |
| Aldringham, Suff | 54 | C2 |
| Aldsworth, Glouc | 37 | A3 |
| Aldwark, Derby | 70 | B2 |
| Aldwark, N York | 88 | B1 |
| Aldwincle, Nhants | 61 | C4 |
| Alexandria, Dumb | 111 | E2 |
| Aley, Som | 11 | A1 |
| Alfold, Surr | 17 | B1 |
| Alfold Crossways, Surr | 17 | B1 |
| Alford, Aber | 128 | D2 |
| Alford, Linc | 84 | D4 |
| Alford, Som | 12 | B1 |
| Alfreton, Derby | 71 | A2 |
| Alfrick, Worc | 47 | B3 |
| Alfrick Pound, Worc | 47 | B3 |
| Alfriston, E Sus | 19 | B4 |
| Algarkirk, Linc | 73 | C4 |
| Alhampton, Som | 12 | B1 |
| Alkborough, Linc | 89 | C4 |
| Alkham, Kent | 31 | B4 |
| Alkmonton, Derby | 70 | B3 |
| All Cannings, Wilts | 25 | C3 |
| All Saints South Elmham, Suff | 65 | A4 |
| All Stretton, Shrop | 56 | C3 |
| Allaleigh, Devon | 5 | B4 |
| Allanbank, N Lan | 113 | A4 |
| Allanton, Bord | 115 | D4 |
| Allanton, N Lan | 113 | A4 |
| Allen End, Warw | 59 | A3 |
| Allendale, Nthumb | 97 | E1 |
| Allenheads, Nthumb | 97 | E2 |
| Allen's Green, Herts | 41 | A2 |
| Allensmore, Heref | 46 | D4 |
| Aller, Devon | 10 | A2 |
| Aller, Som | 11 | C2 |
| Allerby, Cumb | 96 | D2 |
| Allercombe, Devon | 6 | A1 |
| Allerford, Som | 22 | E4 |
| Allerston, N York | 94 | C3 |
| Allerthorpe, E R of Y | 89 | B2 |
| Allesley, W Mids | 59 | B4 |
| Allexton, Leics | 61 | A3 |
| Allgreave, Chesh | 69 | C1 |
| Allhallows, Kent | 30 | A1 |
| Allington, Linc | 72 | C3 |
| Allington, Wilts | 25 | A2 |
| Allington, Wilts | 25 | C3 |
| Allington, Wilts | 14 | A1 |
| Allithwaite, Cumb | 91 | E3 |
| Alloa, Clack | 113 | A1 |
| Allonby, Cumb | 96 | D2 |
| Alloway, S Ayr | 106 | D3 |
| Allowenshay, Som | 11 | C3 |
| Alltmawr, Powys | 45 | E3 |
| Alltwalis, Carm | 33 | B1 |
| Alltwen, Neath | 33 | D3 |
| Alltyblaca, Cered | 44 | F3 |
| Allweston, Dors | 12 | B3 |
| Almeley, Heref | 46 | B3 |
| Almeley Wooton, Heref | 46 | B3 |
| Almer, Dors | 12 | D4 |
| Almholme, S York | 82 | B1 |
| Almington, Staff | 69 | A4 |
| Almondbank, Perth | 119 | A2 |
| Almondsbury, Glouc | 24 | A1 |
| Alne, N York | 93 | C4 |
| Alness, High | 132 | C1 |
| Alnham, Nthumb | 109 | C4 |
| Alnmouth, Nthumb | 109 | E4 |
| Alnwick, Nthumb | 109 | E4 |
| Alperton, G Lon | 142 | A1 |
| Alphamstone, Essex | 53 | B4 |
| Alpheton, Suff | 53 | B3 |
| Alport, Derby | 70 | B1 |
| Alpraham, Chesh | 68 | C2 |
| Alresford, Essex | 43 | B2 |
| Alrewas, Staff | 59 | A1 |
| Alsager, Chesh | 69 | A2 |
| Alsop en le Dale, Derby | 70 | B2 |
| Alston, Devon | 11 | B4 |
| Alston, Cumb | 97 | D1 |
| Alstone, Glouc | 36 | C1 |
| Alstonefield, Staff | 70 | A2 |
| Alswear, Devon | 10 | A2 |
| Altandhu, High | 135 | C2 |
| Altarnun, Corn | 4 | A2 |
| Althorne, Essex | 43 | A4 |
| Althorpe, Linc | 83 | B1 |
| Altnaharra, High | 137 | E4 |
| Alton, Derby | 70 | C1 |
| Alton, Staff | 70 | A3 |
| Alton, Hamp | 16 | A1 |
| Alton Barnes, Wilts | 25 | C3 |
| Alton Pancras, Dors | 12 | C4 |
| Altrincham, G Man | 79 | B3 |
| Alva, Clack | 118 | D4 |
| Alvah, Aber | 134 | A2 |
| Alvanley, Chesh | 78 | B4 |
| Alvecote, Warw | 59 | A2 |
| Alvediston, Wilts | 13 | A2 |
| Alveley, Shrop | 57 | B4 |
| Alverdiscott, Devon | 9 | D2 |
| Alverton, Notts | 72 | B3 |

| PLACE | PAGE | GRID |
|---|---|---|
| Alvescot, Oxon | 37 | B3 |
| Alveston, Glouc | 35 | C4 |
| Alveston, Warw | 48 | C3 |
| Alvingham, Linc | 84 | C3 |
| Alvington, Glouc | 35 | C3 |
| Alwinton, Nthumb | 109 | B4 |
| Alyth, Perth | 123 | D4 |
| Ambergate, Derby | 70 | C2 |
| Amberley, W Suss | 17 | B3 |
| Amble, Nthumb | 109 | E4 |
| Ambleside, Cumb | 91 | E1 |
| Ambleston, Pemb | 32 | D1 |
| Ambrosden, Oxon | 38 | A2 |
| Amcotts, Linc | 83 | C1 |
| Amersham, Bucks | 39 | A4 |
| Amesbury, Wilts | 25 | C4 |
| Amisfield Town, D & G | 101 | D2 |
| Amlwch, Angle | 76 | C3 |
| Ammanford, Carm | 33 | C2 |
| Ampfield, Hamp | 15 | A2 |
| Ampleforth, N York | 93 | D3 |
| Ampney St Mary, Glouc | 37 | A3 |
| Ampney St Peter, Glouc | 37 | A3 |
| Amport, Hamp | 26 | A4 |
| Ampthill, Beds | 51 | A4 |
| Ampton, Suff | 53 | B1 |
| Amroth, Pemb | 32 | E3 |
| Amulree, Perth | 118 | E1 |
| Amwell, Herts | 39 | C2 |
| Ancaster, Linc | 73 | A3 |
| Anchor, Shrop | 56 | A4 |
| Ancroft, Nthumb | 109 | C1 |
| Ancrum, Bord | 108 | D3 |
| Anderby, Linc | 84 | D4 |
| Andover, Hamp | 26 | A4 |
| Andoversford, Glouc | 36 | C2 |
| Andreas, I o M | 139 | C1 |
| Anerley, G Lon | 143 | B4 |
| Angarrack, Corn | 1 | C1 |
| Angelbank, Shrop | 46 | D1 |
| Angersleigh, Som | 11 | A2 |
| Angle, Pemb | 32 | C3 |
| Angram, N York | 88 | C2 |
| Anmer, Norf | 74 | C4 |
| Anmore, Hamp | 16 | A3 |
| Anna Valley, Hamp | 26 | A4 |
| Annan, D & G | 102 | A4 |
| Annbank, S Ayr | 106 | D3 |
| Annfield Plain, Durham | 98 | C1 |
| Ansford, Som | 12 | B1 |
| Ansley, Warw | 59 | B3 |
| Anslow, Staff | 59 | A1 |
| Anslow Gate, Staff | 59 | A1 |
| Anstey, Herts | 40 | B1 |
| Anstey, Leics | 60 | B2 |
| Anstruther, Fife | 119 | E4 |
| Ansty, W Suss | 18 | B2 |
| Ansty, Warw | 60 | A4 |
| Ansty, Wilts | 13 | A2 |
| Anthonys, Surr | 146 | A1 |
| Anthorn, Cumb | 102 | A4 |
| Antingham, Norf | 75 | C4 |
| Anton's Gowt, Linc | 73 | C3 |
| Antony, Corn | 4 | B4 |
| Antrobus, Chesh | 79 | A4 |
| Anwick, Linc | 73 | B2 |
| Aperfield, G Lon | 149 | A1 |
| Apethorpe, Nhants | 61 | C3 |
| Apley, Linc | 84 | A4 |
| Apperknowle, Derby | 81 | C4 |
| Apperley, Glouc | 36 | B1 |
| Appin, Argyll | 121 | C4 |
| Appleby, Linc | 83 | C1 |
| Appleby Magna, Leics | 59 | B2 |
| Appleby-in-Westmorland, Cumb | 97 | C4 |
| Applecross, High | 130 | E4 |
| Appledore, Devon | 9 | D1 |
| Appledore, Kent | 21 | B2 |
| Appleford, Oxon | 38 | A4 |
| Appleshaw, Hamp | 26 | A4 |
| Appleton, Oxon | 37 | D3 |
| Appleton Roebuck, N York | 88 | C2 |
| Appleton Thorn, Chesh | 79 | A3 |
| Appleton Wiske, N York | 93 | C1 |
| Appleton-le-Moors, N York | 94 | A2 |
| Appleton-le-Street, N York | 94 | B4 |
| Appletreewick, N York | 87 | A1 |
| Appley, Som | 10 | D2 |
| Appley Bridge, Lanc | 78 | B1 |
| Apse Heath, I of W | 8 | B2 |
| Apsley End, Beds | 39 | C1 |
| Arbirlot, Angus | 119 | F1 |
| Arbroath, Angus | 119 | F1 |
| Arbuthnott, Aber | 124 | C2 |
| Archdeacon Newton, Durham | 98 | C4 |
| Archiestown, Moray | 133 | B4 |
| Arclid Green, Chesh | 69 | A1 |
| Ardbeg, Argyll | 105 | B1 |
| Ardeley, Herts | 40 | A1 |
| Ardelve, High | 126 | A1 |
| Arden, Argyll | 111 | E1 |
| Ardens Grafton, Warw | 48 | B3 |
| Ardentinny, Argyll | 111 | C1 |
| Ardersier, High | 132 | D3 |
| Ardessie, High | 135 | C4 |
| Ardgay, High | 136 | B4 |
| Ardgour, High | 121 | D3 |
| Ardingly, W Suss | 19 | A1 |
| Ardington, Oxon | 37 | D4 |

| PLACE | PAGE | GRID |
|---|---|---|
| Ardleigh, Essex | 43 | B1 |
| Ardleigh Heath, Essex | 43 | B1 |
| Ardler, Perth | 123 | D4 |
| Ardley, Oxon | 38 | A1 |
| Ardlui, Argyll | 117 | E3 |
| Ardminish, Argyll | 105 | D1 |
| Ardnadam, Argyll | 111 | C2 |
| Ardrishaig, Argyll | 111 | A1 |
| Ardrossan, N Ayr | 106 | C1 |
| Ardsley East, W York | 88 | A4 |
| Ardvasar, High | 125 | E3 |
| Ardwell, D & G | 95 | B1 |
| Arford, Hamp | 16 | B1 |
| Argoed, Caer | 34 | D3 |
| Arinagour, Argyll | 120 | C3 |
| Arisaig, High | 121 | A1 |
| Arkendale, N York | 88 | B1 |
| Arkesden, Essex | 52 | B4 |
| Arkholme, Lanc | 92 | A4 |
| Arkley, G Lon | 40 | A4 |
| Arksey, S York | 82 | B1 |
| Arlecdon, Cumb | 96 | D4 |
| Arlesey, Beds | 51 | B4 |
| Arley, Chesh | 79 | A4 |
| Arley, Warw | 59 | B4 |
| Arlingham, Glouc | 36 | A2 |
| Arlington, Devon | 9 | E1 |
| Arlington, E Sus | 19 | B3 |
| Armadale, High | 138 | A1 |
| Armadale, W Loth | 113 | B3 |
| Armaside, Cumb | 96 | E3 |
| Armathwaite, Cumb | 97 | B1 |
| Arminghall, Norf | 65 | A2 |
| Armitage, Staff | 58 | B1 |
| Armston, Nhants | 61 | C4 |
| Armthorpe, S York | 83 | A2 |
| Arnabost, Argyll | 120 | C3 |
| Arncliffe, N York | 92 | D4 |
| Arncroach, Fife | 119 | E4 |
| Arne, Dors | 7 | C1 |
| Arnesby, Leics | 60 | B3 |
| Arngask, Perth | 119 | B3 |
| Arnisdale, High | 125 | F3 |
| Arnold, E R of Y | 90 | A3 |
| Arnprior, Stirl | 112 | B1 |
| Arnside, Cumb | 91 | E3 |
| Aros, Argyll | 120 | F4 |
| Arrad Foot, Cumb | 91 | D3 |
| Arram, E R of Y | 89 | D2 |
| Arrathorne, N York | 93 | A2 |
| Arreton, I of W | 8 | B1 |
| Arrington, Camb | 52 | A3 |
| Arrochar, Argyll | 117 | D4 |
| Arrow, Warw | 48 | B2 |
| Arscott, Shrop | 56 | C2 |
| Arthington, W York | 87 | B2 |
| Arthingworth, Nhants | 61 | A4 |
| Arundel, W Suss | 17 | B3 |
| Asby, Cumb | 96 | D4 |
| Ascog, Argyll | 111 | C3 |
| Ascot, Berks | 140 | B4 |
| Ascott-under-Wychwood, Oxon | 37 | C2 |
| Asenby, N York | 93 | C4 |
| Asfordby, Leics | 60 | C1 |
| Asfordby Hill, Leics | 60 | C1 |
| Asgarby, Linc | 73 | B3 |
| Asgarby, Linc | 73 | D1 |
| Ash, Kent | 31 | B3 |
| Ash, Som | 12 | A2 |
| Ash, Surr | 145 | A3 |
| Ash Green, Surr | 145 | A3 |
| Ash Magna, Shrop | 68 | B3 |
| Ash Mill, Devon | 10 | B2 |
| Ash Parva, Shrop | 68 | B3 |
| Ash Priors, Som | 11 | A2 |
| Ash Thomas, Devon | 10 | D3 |
| Ash Vale, Surr | 145 | A3 |
| Ashampstead, Berks | 26 | C1 |
| Ashampstead Green, Berks | 26 | C1 |
| Ashbocking, Suff | 54 | A3 |
| Ashbocking Green, Suff | 54 | A3 |
| Ashbourne, Derby | 70 | B3 |
| Ashbrittle, Som | 10 | D2 |
| Ashburton, Devon | 5 | A3 |
| Ashbury, Devon | 9 | D4 |
| Ashbury, Oxon | 25 | D1 |
| Ashby by Partney, Linc | 74 | A1 |
| Ashby cum Fenby, Linc | 84 | B2 |
| Ashby de la Launde, Linc | 73 | A2 |
| Ashby Folville, Leics | 60 | C2 |
| Ashby Parva, Leics | 60 | B4 |
| Ashby Puerorum, Linc | 73 | D1 |
| Ashby St Ledgers, Nhants | 49 | C2 |
| Ashby St Mary, Norf | 65 | A3 |
| Ashby-de-la-Zouch, Leics | 59 | B1 |
| Ashchurch, Glouc | 36 | C1 |
| Ashcombe, Devon | 5 | C2 |
| Ashcott, Som | 11 | C1 |
| Ashdon, Essex | 52 | C4 |
| Ashe, Hamp | 26 | C4 |
| Asheldham, Essex | 43 | A3 |
| Ashen, Essex | 53 | A4 |
| Ashendon, Bucks | 38 | B2 |
| Asheridge, Bucks | 39 | A3 |
| Ashfield, Suff | 54 | A2 |
| Ashfield Green, Suff | 54 | B1 |
| Ashford, Devon | 9 | D1 |
| Ashford, Devon | 8 | A1 |
| Ashford, Kent | 30 | C4 |
| Ashford, Surr | 141 | A3 |

| PLACE | PAGE | GRID |
|---|---|---|
| Ashford Bowdler, Shrop | 46 | D1 |
| Ashford Carbonel, Shrop | 46 | D1 |
| Ashford Hill, Hamp | 26 | C3 |
| Ashford in the Water, Derby | 70 | B1 |
| Ashill, Devon | 10 | D3 |
| Ashill, Norf | 63 | B2 |
| Ashill, Som | 11 | B3 |
| Ashingdon, Essex | 42 | B4 |
| Ashington, Som | 12 | A2 |
| Ashington, Nthumb | 104 | B2 |
| Ashkirk, Bord | 108 | C3 |
| Ashleworth, Glouc | 36 | A1 |
| Ashleworth Quay, Glouc | 36 | B1 |
| Ashley, Camb | 53 | A2 |
| Ashley, Chesh | 79 | B3 |
| Ashley, Glouc | 36 | C4 |
| Ashley, Hamp | 14 | B1 |
| Ashley, Kent | 31 | B4 |
| Ashley, Nhants | 61 | A4 |
| Ashley, Staff | 69 | A4 |
| Ashley, Wilts | 25 | A2 |
| Ashley Green, Bucks | 39 | B3 |
| Ashmansworth, Hamp | 26 | B3 |
| Ashmansworthy, Devon | 9 | C3 |
| Ashmore, Dors | 12 | D3 |
| Ashorne, Warw | 49 | A2 |
| Ashover, Derby | 70 | C1 |
| Ashow, Warw | 49 | A1 |
| Ashperton, Heref | 47 | A4 |
| Ashprington, Devon | 5 | B4 |
| Ashreigney, Devon | 9 | E3 |
| Ashtead, Surr | 147 | B2 |
| Ashton, Chesh | 68 | B1 |
| Ashton, Corn | 1 | C2 |
| Ashton, Devon | 5 | B1 |
| Ashton, Heref | 46 | D2 |
| Ashton, Nhants | 50 | B3 |
| Ashton, Nhants | 61 | C4 |
| Ashton Common, Wilts | 25 | A3 |
| Ashton Keynes, Wilts | 37 | A4 |
| Ashton under Hill, Worc | 48 | A4 |
| Ashton-in-Makerfield, G Man | 78 | B2 |
| Ashton-under-Lyne, G Man | 80 | B2 |
| Ashurst, Hamp | 14 | B3 |
| Ashurst, Kent | 19 | B1 |
| Ashurst, W Suss | 18 | A3 |
| Ashurstwood, W Suss | 19 | A1 |
| Ashwater, Devon | 9 | C4 |
| Ashwell, Herts | 51 | C4 |
| Ashwell, Rut | 61 | B2 |
| Ashwellthorpe, Norf | 64 | B3 |
| Ashwick, Som | 24 | A4 |
| Ashwicken, Norf | 63 | A1 |
| Askam in Furness, Cumb | 91 | C3 |
| Askern, S York | 82 | B1 |
| Askerswell, Dors | 6 | E1 |
| Askett, Bucks | 38 | C3 |
| Askham, Cumb | 97 | B3 |
| Askham, Notts | 83 | B4 |
| Askham Bryan, N York | 88 | C2 |
| Askham Richard, N York | 88 | C2 |
| Askrigg, N York | 92 | D2 |
| Askwith, N York | 87 | B2 |
| Aslackby, Linc | 73 | B4 |
| Aslockton, Notts | 72 | B3 |
| Aspatria, Cumb | 96 | E2 |
| Aspenden, Herts | 40 | B1 |
| Aspley Guise, Beds | 50 | C4 |
| Aspley Heath, Beds | 50 | C4 |
| Aspull, G Man | 79 | A1 |
| Asselby, E R of Y | 89 | A4 |
| Assington, Suff | 53 | C4 |
| Assington Green, Suff | 53 | A3 |
| Astbury, Chesh | 69 | B1 |
| Astcote, Nhants | 50 | A3 |
| Asterley, Shrop | 56 | C2 |
| Asterton, Shrop | 56 | C4 |
| Asthall, Oxon | 37 | C2 |
| Asthall Leigh, Oxon | 37 | C2 |
| Astley, G Man | 79 | B2 |
| Astley, Shrop | 56 | D1 |
| Astley, Warw | 59 | B4 |
| Astley, Worc | 47 | B2 |
| Aston, Berks | 27 | B1 |
| Aston, Chesh | 78 | B4 |
| Aston, Chesh | 68 | C3 |
| Aston, Derby | 81 | B3 |
| Aston, Heref | 46 | C1 |
| Aston, Herts | 40 | A1 |
| Aston, Oxon | 37 | C3 |
| Aston, S York | 82 | A3 |
| Aston, Shrop | 68 | B4 |
| Aston, Shrop | 57 | A2 |
| Aston, Shrop | 57 | B3 |
| Aston, Staff | 69 | A3 |
| Aston, Staff | 57 | C1 |
| Aston, Staff | 69 | B4 |
| Aston Abbotts, Bucks | 38 | C2 |
| Aston Botterell, Shrop | 57 | A4 |
| Aston Cantlow, Warw | 48 | B2 |
| Aston Crews, Heref | 35 | C1 |
| Aston End, Herts | 40 | A1 |
| Aston le Walls, Nhants | 49 | B3 |
| Aston Magna, Glouc | 48 | C4 |
| Aston Munslow, Shrop | 56 | D4 |
| Aston on Clun, Shrop | 56 | C4 |
| Aston Pigott, Shrop | 56 | B2 |
| Aston Rogers, Shrop | 56 | B2 |
| Aston Somerville, Worc | 48 | B4 |
| Aston Subedge, Glouc | 48 | B4 |

| PLACE | PAGE | GRID |
|---|---|---|
| Aston Tirrold, Oxon | 26 | C1 |
| Aston Upthorpe, Oxon | 26 | C1 |
| Aston-upon-Trent, Derby | 71 | A4 |
| Astwick, Beds | 51 | C4 |
| Astwood, Bucks | 50 | C3 |
| Astwood, Worc | 48 | A2 |
| Astwood Bank, Worc | 48 | A2 |
| Aswarby, Linc | 73 | A3 |
| Aswardby, Linc | 73 | D1 |
| Atch Lench, Worc | 48 | A3 |
| Atcham, Shrop | 56 | D2 |
| Athelhampton, Dors | 7 | A1 |
| Athelington, Suff | 54 | A1 |
| Athelney, Som | 11 | B2 |
| Athelstaneford, E Loth | 115 | A2 |
| Atherington, Devon | 9 | E2 |
| Atherstone on Stour, Warw | 48 | C3 |
| Atherton, G Man | 79 | A2 |
| Atlow, Derby | 70 | B3 |
| Atterby, Linc | 83 | D3 |
| Atterton, Leics | 59 | B3 |
| Attleborough, Norf | 64 | A3 |
| Attlebridge, Norf | 64 | B1 |
| Atwick, E R of Y | 90 | A2 |
| Atworth, Wilts | 25 | A2 |
| Aubourn, Linc | 72 | C1 |
| Auchenblae, Aber | 124 | C1 |
| Auchenbowie, Stirl | 113 | A1 |
| Auchencairn, D & G | 96 | B1 |
| Auchencrow, Bord | 115 | D4 |
| Auchendinny, M Loth | 114 | B3 |
| Auchengray, S Lan | 113 | B4 |
| Auchenmalg, D & G | 95 | C1 |
| Auchinleck, E Ayr | 106 | F3 |
| Auchinloch, N Lan | 112 | C3 |
| Auchinstarry, N Lan | 112 | C2 |
| Auchleven, Aber | 128 | E1 |
| Auchlochan, S Lan | 107 | B2 |
| Auchmillan, E Ayr | 106 | E2 |
| Auchmithie, Angus | 124 | B4 |
| Auchnagatt, Aber | 134 | C4 |
| Auchnarrow, Moray | 128 | A1 |
| Auchterarder, Perth | 118 | E3 |
| Auchterderran, Fife | 119 | B4 |
| Auchterhouse, Angus | 119 | C1 |
| Auchterless, Aber | 134 | B4 |
| Auchtermuchty, Fife | 119 | C3 |
| Auchtertool, Fife | 114 | A1 |
| Auckley, S York | 83 | A2 |
| Audlem, Chesh | 68 | C3 |
| Audley, Staff | 69 | A2 |
| Audley End, Essex | 52 | B4 |
| Audley End, Suff | 53 | B3 |
| Aughertree, Cumb | 96 | F2 |
| Aughton, E R of Y | 89 | A3 |
| Aughton, Lanc | 78 | A2 |
| Aughton, Lanc | 91 | F4 |
| Aughton, S York | 82 | A3 |
| Auldearn, High | 132 | E3 |
| Aulden, Heref | 46 | C3 |
| Auldgirth, D & G | 101 | D2 |
| Ault Hucknall, Derby | 71 | A1 |
| Aultbea, High | 135 | B4 |
| Aultgrishin, High | 135 | A4 |
| Aunsby, Linc | 73 | A3 |
| Aust, Glouc | 35 | B4 |
| Austerfield, S York | 83 | A3 |
| Austrey, Warw | 59 | B2 |
| Austwick, N York | 92 | B4 |
| Authorpe, Linc | 84 | C4 |
| Avebury, Wilts | 25 | C2 |
| Aveley, Essex | 29 | A1 |
| Avening, Glouc | 36 | B4 |
| Averham, Notts | 72 | B2 |
| Aveton Gifford, Devon | 8 | A1 |
| Aviemore, High | 127 | D2 |
| Avington, Berks | 26 | A2 |
| Avoch, High | 132 | C3 |
| Avon, Hamp | 13 | B4 |
| Avon Dassett, Warw | 49 | B3 |
| Avonbridge, Falkirk | 113 | B2 |
| Avonmouth, Bristol | 23 | D1 |
| Avonwick, Devon | 5 | A4 |
| Awliscombe, Devon | 11 | A4 |
| Awre, Glouc | 36 | A3 |
| Awsworth, Notts | 71 | A3 |
| Axbridge, Som | 23 | C3 |
| Axford, Hamp | 26 | C4 |
| Axford, Wilts | 25 | D2 |
| Axminster, Devon | 11 | B4 |
| Axmouth, Devon | 6 | C1 |
| Aycliffe, Durham | 98 | D3 |
| Aydon, Nthumb | 103 | D4 |
| Aylburton, Glouc | 35 | C3 |
| Aylesbeare, Devon | 6 | A1 |
| Aylesbury, Bucks | 38 | C2 |
| Aylesby, Linc | 84 | B1 |
| Aylesford, Kent | 29 | B3 |
| Aylmerton, Norf | 75 | B3 |
| Aylsham, Norf | 75 | B4 |
| Aylton, Heref | 47 | A4 |
| Aylworth, Glouc | 37 | A2 |
| Aymestrey, Heref | 46 | C2 |
| Aynho, Nhants | 38 | A1 |
| Ayot St Lawrence, Herts | 39 | C2 |
| Ayr, S Ayr | 106 | D3 |
| Aysgarth, N York | 92 | D2 |
| Ayshford, Devon | 10 | D3 |
| Ayside, Cumb | 91 | E3 |
| Ayston, Rut | 61 | B3 |
| Aythorpe Roding, Essex | 41 | B2 |
| Ayton, Bord | 115 | D3 |
| Azerley, N York | 93 | A4 |
| Babbs Green, Herts | 40 | B2 |
| Babcary, Som | 12 | A2 |
| Babington, Som | 24 | B4 |
| Babraham, Camb | 52 | B3 |
| Babworth, Notts | 83 | A4 |
| Backaland, Ork | 139 | B1 |
| Backford, Chesh | 68 | A1 |
| Backies, High | 136 | D3 |
| Backwell, Som | 23 | D2 |
| Baconsthorpe, Norf | 75 | B4 |
| Bacton, Heref | 35 | A1 |
| Bacton, Norf | 75 | C4 |
| Bacton, Suff | 53 | D2 |
| Bacup, Lanc | 86 | C4 |
| Badachro, High | 130 | F1 |
| Badbury, Wilts | 25 | D1 |
| Badby, Nhants | 49 | C2 |
| Badcaul, High | 135 | C4 |
| Baddesley Clinton, Warw | 48 | C1 |
| Baddesley Ensor, Warw | 59 | A3 |
| Badger, Shrop | 57 | B3 |
| Badgers Mount, Kent | 149 | C1 |
| Badgeworth, Glouc | 36 | B2 |
| Badgworth, Som | 23 | C4 |
| Badicaul, High | 125 | F1 |
| Badingham, Suff | 54 | B2 |
| Badlesmere, Kent | 30 | C3 |
| Badluachrach, High | 135 | C3 |
| Badsey, Worc | 48 | B4 |
| Badsworth, W York | 82 | A1 |
| Badwell Ash, Suff | 53 | C1 |
| Bagber, Dors | 12 | C3 |
| Bagby, N York | 93 | C3 |
| Bagillt, Flint | 77 | C4 |
| Baginton, Warw | 49 | A1 |
| Baglan, Neath | 33 | D4 |
| Bagley, Shrop | 68 | A4 |
| Bagmore, Hamp | 27 | A4 |
| Bagnall, Staff | 69 | C2 |
| Bagot, Shrop | 47 | A1 |
| Bagshot, Surr | 145 | B1 |
| Bagstone, Glouc | 24 | A1 |
| Bagworth, Leics | 60 | A2 |
| Bagwy Llydiart, Heref | 35 | A1 |
| Baile Mor, Argyll | 116 | B2 |
| Bainbridge, N York | 92 | D2 |
| Bainshole, Aber | 134 | A4 |
| Bainton, Camb | 61 | D2 |
| Bainton, E R of Y | 89 | C2 |
| Baintown, Fife | 119 | D4 |
| Bakewell, Derby | 70 | B1 |
| Bala, Gwyn | 67 | B4 |
| Balallan, W Isles | 139 | B2 |
| Balbeggie, Perth | 119 | B2 |
| Balblair, High | 132 | C2 |
| Balchreick, High | 137 | A2 |
| Balcombe, W Suss | 18 | B1 |
| Baldersby, N York | 93 | B3 |
| Baldersby St James, N York | 93 | B3 |
| Balderstone, Lanc | 86 | A3 |
| Baldinnie, Fife | 119 | D3 |
| Baldock, Herts | 51 | C4 |
| Baldovie, Dund | 119 | D1 |
| Baldrine, I o M | 139 | D3 |
| Baldslow, E Sus | 21 | A3 |
| Bale, Norf | 75 | A4 |
| Baledgarno, Perth | 119 | C2 |
| Balerno, Edin | 114 | A3 |
| Balfield, Angus | 124 | A2 |
| Balfour, Ork | 139 | B2 |
| Balfron, Stirl | 112 | B1 |
| Balgonar, Fife | 113 | C1 |
| Balgracie, D & G | 100 | A4 |
| Balgray, Angus | 119 | D1 |
| Balham, G Lon | 143 | A3 |
| Balintore, High | 132 | D1 |
| Balivanich, W Isles | 139 | A3 |
| Balk, N York | 93 | C3 |
| Balkholme, E R of Y | 89 | B4 |
| Ballachulish, High | 121 | E3 |
| Ballantrae, S Ayr | 100 | B2 |
| Ballasalla, I o M | 139 | B4 |
| Ballater, Aber | 128 | C4 |
| Ballaugh, I o M | 139 | C2 |
| Ballchraggan, High | 132 | C1 |
| Ballevullin, Argyll | 120 | A4 |
| Ballidon, Derby | 70 | B2 |
| Ballindean, Perth | 119 | C2 |
| Ballinger Common, Bucks | 39 | A3 |
| Ballingham, Heref | 35 | B1 |
| Ballingry, Fife | 119 | B4 |
| Ballinluig, Perth | 123 | A4 |
| Ballintuim, Perth | 123 | B3 |
| Balloch, High | 132 | C3 |
| Ballochroy, Argyll | 110 | E4 |
| Balls Cross, W Suss | 17 | B2 |
| Ballygrant, Argyll | 110 | C3 |
| Balmacara, High | 125 | F1 |
| Balmaclellan, D & G | 101 | A3 |
| Balmaha, Stirl | 111 | E1 |
| Balmalcolm, Fife | 119 | C3 |
| Balmedie, Aber | 129 | C2 |
| Balmore, E Dunb | 112 | B2 |
| Balmullo, Fife | 119 | D2 |
| Balnaguard, Perth | 123 | A4 |
| Balnain, High | 126 | F1 |
| Balquhidder, Stirl | 118 | A2 |
| Balsall Common, W Mids | 48 | C1 |
| Balscote, Oxon | 49 | B4 |
| Balsham, Camb | 52 | C3 |
| Baltasound, Shet | 139 | B1 |
| Baltersan, D & G | 100 | D4 |
| Baltonsborough, Som | 12 | A1 |
| Balvicar, Argyll | 116 | F3 |
| Balvraid, High | 125 | F2 |
| Bamber Bridge, Lanc | 85 | C4 |
| Bamber's Green, Essex | 41 | B1 |
| Bamburgh, Nthumb | 109 | E2 |
| Bamford, Derby | 81 | B4 |
| Bampton, Cumb | 97 | B4 |
| Bampton, Oxon | 37 | C3 |
| Bampton, Devon | 10 | C2 |
| Banbury, Oxon | 49 | B4 |
| Bancffosfelem, Carm | 33 | B2 |
| Banchory, Aber | 129 | A4 |
| Bancycapel, Carm | 33 | B2 |
| Bancyfelin, Carm | 33 | A2 |
| Banff, Aber | 134 | A2 |
| Bangor, Gwyn | 66 | E1 |
| Bangor-is-y-coed, Wrex | 68 | A3 |
| Banham, Norf | 64 | A4 |
| Bank, Hamp | 14 | B3 |
| Bankend, D & G | 101 | E4 |
| Bankfoot, Perth | 119 | A1 |
| Bankglen, E Ayr | 106 | F4 |
| Banks, Lanc | 85 | B4 |
| Banningham, Norf | 75 | B4 |
| Bannister Green, Essex | 42 | A2 |
| Banstead, Surr | 148 | A1 |
| Banton, N Lan | 112 | C2 |
| Banwell, Som | 23 | C3 |
| Bapchild, Kent | 30 | B3 |
| Bapton, Wilts | 13 | A1 |
| Bar Hill, Camb | 52 | A2 |
| Barbaraville, High | 132 | C1 |
| Barbon, Cumb | 92 | A3 |
| Barbrook, Devon | 22 | C4 |
| Barby, Nhants | 49 | C1 |
| Barcheston, Warw | 48 | C4 |
| Barcombe, E Sus | 19 | A3 |
| Barcombe Cross, E Sus | 19 | A3 |
| Barden, N York | 92 | E2 |
| Bardfield Saling, Essex | 42 | A1 |
| Bardney, Linc | 73 | B1 |
| Bardon, Leics | 60 | A2 |
| Bardowie, E Dunb | 112 | B2 |
| Bardsea, Cumb | 91 | D4 |
| Bardsey, W York | 88 | A2 |
| Bardwell, Suff | 53 | C1 |
| Barewood, Heref | 46 | C3 |
| Barford, Norf | 64 | A2 |
| Barford, Warw | 48 | C2 |
| Barford St John, Oxon | 37 | D1 |
| Barford St Martin, Wilts | 13 | B1 |
| Barford St Michael, Oxon | 37 | D1 |
| Barfrestone, Kent | 31 | B4 |
| Bargoed, Caer | 34 | D3 |
| Barham, Camb | 51 | B1 |
| Barham, Kent | 31 | A4 |
| Barham, Suff | 54 | A3 |
| Barholm, Linc | 61 | D2 |
| Barkby, Leics | 60 | C2 |
| Barkby Thorpe, Leics | 60 | C2 |
| Barkestone-le-Vale, Leics | 72 | B4 |
| Barkham, Berks | 27 | B2 |
| Barking, Suff | 53 | D3 |
| Barking Tye, Suff | 53 | D3 |
| Barkisland, W York | 87 | A4 |
| Barkston, Linc | 72 | C3 |
| Barkston Ash, N York | 88 | B3 |
| Barkway, Herts | 52 | A4 |
| Barlaston, Staff | 69 | B3 |
| Barlavington, W Suss | 17 | B3 |
| Barlborough, Derby | 82 | A4 |
| Barlestone, Leics | 60 | A2 |
| Barley, Herts | 52 | A4 |
| Barley, Lanc | 86 | C3 |
| Barleythorpe, Rut | 61 | A2 |
| Barling, Essex | 43 | A4 |
| Barlings, Linc | 83 | D4 |
| Barlow, Derby | 81 | C4 |
| Barlow, N York | 89 | A4 |
| Barlow, T & W | 104 | A4 |
| Barmby Moor, E R of Y | 89 | B2 |
| Barmby on the Marsh, E R of Y | 89 | A4 |
| Barmouth, Gwyn | 55 | A1 |
| Barmpton, Durham | 98 | D4 |
| Barmston, E R of Y | 90 | A1 |
| Barnack, Camb | 61 | C2 |
| Barnard Castle, Durham | 98 | B4 |
| Barnard Gate, Oxon | 37 | D2 |
| Barnardiston, Suff | 53 | A3 |
| Barnburgh, S York | 82 | A2 |
| Barnby, Suff | 65 | A4 |
| Barnby Dun, S York | 82 | B1 |
| Barnby in the Willows, Notts | 72 | C2 |
| Barnby Moor, Notts | 83 | A3 |
| Barnes, G Lon | 142 | B2 |
| Barnet, G Lon | 140 | A4 |
| Barnetby le Wold, Linc | 83 | D1 |
| Barney, Norf | 74 | E4 |
| Barnham, Suff | 53 | B1 |
| Barnham, W Suss | 17 | A4 |
| Barnham Broom, Norf | 64 | A2 |
| Barningham, Durham | 92 | E1 |
| Barningham, Suff | 53 | C1 |
| Barnoldby le Beck, Linc | 84 | B2 |
| Barns Green, W Suss | 18 | A2 |
| Barnsley, Glouc | 37 | A3 |
| Barnsley, S York | 81 | C2 |
| Barnstaple, Devon | 9 | E1 |
| Barnston, Essex | 41 | B2 |
| Barnston, Mers | 77 | D4 |
| Barnstone, Notts | 72 | A4 |
| Barnt Green, Worc | 48 | A1 |
| Barnton, Chesh | 79 | A4 |
| Barnwell All Saints, Nhants | 61 | C4 |
| Barnwell St Andrew, Nhants | 61 | C4 |
| Barr, S Ayr | 100 | C1 |
| Barrapoll, Argyll | 120 | A4 |
| Barrasford, Nthumb | 103 | C3 |
| Barrhead, E Renf | 112 | A4 |
| Barrhill, S Ayr | 100 | C2 |
| Barrington, Camb | 52 | A3 |
| Barrington, Som | 11 | C2 |
| Barripper, Corn | 1 | D1 |
| Barrmill, N Ayr | 111 | E4 |
| Barrow, Glouc | 36 | B1 |
| Barrow, Lanc | 86 | B3 |
| Barrow, Rut | 61 | B1 |
| Barrow, Som | 12 | C1 |
| Barrow, Suff | 53 | A2 |
| Barrow Burn, Nthumb | 109 | B4 |
| Barrow Gurney, Som | 23 | D2 |
| Barrow Haven, Linc | 89 | D4 |
| Barrow upon Soar, Leics | 60 | B1 |
| Barrowby, Linc | 72 | C4 |
| Barrowden, Rut | 61 | B3 |
| Barrowford, Lanc | 86 | C3 |
| Barrow-in-Furness, Cumb | 91 | C4 |
| Barrow-upon-Humber, Linc | 89 | D4 |
| Barry, Angus | 119 | E1 |
| Barry, Glam | 23 | A2 |
| Barsby, Leics | 60 | C2 |
| Barsham, Suff | 65 | B4 |
| Barston, W Mids | 48 | C1 |
| Bartestree, Heref | 46 | D4 |
| Barthol Chapel, Aber | 129 | B1 |
| Bartholomew Green, Essex | 42 | A2 |
| Barthomley, Chesh | 69 | A2 |
| Bartley, Hamp | 14 | B3 |
| Bartlow, Essex | 52 | C4 |
| Barton, Camb | 52 | A3 |
| Barton, Chesh | 68 | A2 |
| Barton, Glouc | 37 | A1 |
| Barton, Lanc | 78 | A1 |
| Barton, Lanc | 85 | C3 |
| Barton, N York | 93 | A1 |
| Barton Bendish, Norf | 63 | A2 |
| Barton Hartshorn, Bucks | 38 | B1 |
| Barton in Fabis, Notts | 71 | B4 |
| Barton in the Beans, Leics | 60 | A2 |
| Barton Mills, Suff | 53 | A1 |
| Barton Seagrave, Nhants | 50 | C1 |
| Barton St David, Som | 12 | A1 |
| Barton Stacey, Hamp | 26 | B4 |
| Barton Town, Devon | 10 | A1 |
| Barton Waterside, Linc | 89 | D4 |
| Barton-le-Clay, Beds | 39 | C1 |
| Barton-le-Street, N York | 94 | A4 |
| Barton-le-Willows, N York | 89 | A1 |
| Barton-on-the-Heath, Warw | 37 | B1 |
| Barton-upon-Humber, Linc | 89 | D4 |
| Barvas, W Isles | 139 | B2 |
| Barway, Camb | 52 | C1 |
| Barwell, Leics | 60 | A3 |
| Barwick, Devon | 9 | E3 |
| Barwick, Som | 12 | A3 |
| Barwick in Elmet, W York | 88 | B3 |
| Baschurch, Shrop | 56 | C1 |
| Bascote, Warw | 49 | B2 |
| Bashall Eaves, Lanc | 86 | A2 |
| Basildon, Berks | 26 | C1 |
| Basildon, Essex | 42 | A4 |
| Basingstoke, Hamp | 27 | A4 |
| Baslow, Derby | 81 | B4 |
| Bason Bridge, Som | 23 | B4 |
| Bassenthwaite, Cumb | 96 | E3 |
| Bassingbourn, Camb | 52 | A4 |
| Bassingham, Linc | 72 | C2 |
| Bassingthorpe, Linc | 73 | A4 |
| Bassus Green, Herts | 40 | A1 |
| Baston, Linc | 61 | D2 |
| Bastwick, Norf | 65 | B1 |
| Batchworth, Herts | 39 | B4 |
| Batcombe, Dors | 12 | B4 |
| Batcombe, Som | 12 | B1 |
| Bath, Som | 24 | B2 |
| Bathampton, Som | 24 | B2 |
| Bathealton, Som | 10 | D2 |
| Batheaston, Som | 24 | B2 |
| Bathford, Som | 24 | B2 |
| Bathgate, W Loth | 113 | B3 |
| Bathley, Notts | 72 | B2 |
| Bathpool, Corn | 4 | A2 |
| Bathway, Som | 24 | A4 |
| Batley, W York | 87 | B4 |
| Batsford, Glouc | 48 | C4 |
| Battersby, N York | 93 | D1 |
| Battersea, G Lon | 143 | A2 |
| Battisford Tye, Suff | 53 | D3 |
| Battle, E Sus | 20 | B3 |
| Battle, Powys | 34 | C1 |
| Battlesbridge, Essex | 42 | B4 |
| Battleton, Som | 10 | C2 |
| Baughton, Worc | 47 | C4 |
| Baughurst, Hamp | 26 | C3 |
| Baulking, Oxon | 37 | C4 |
| Baumber, Linc | 84 | B4 |
| Baunton, Glouc | 36 | C3 |
| Baverstock, Wilts | 13 | A1 |
| Bawburgh, Norf | 64 | B2 |
| Bawdeswell, Norf | 64 | A1 |
| Bawdrip, Som | 11 | B1 |
| Bawdsey, Suff | 54 | B4 |
| Bawtry, S York | 83 | A3 |
| Baxterley, Warw | 59 | B3 |
| Baycliff, Cumb | 91 | D4 |
| Baydon, Wilts | 26 | A1 |
| Bayford, Herts | 40 | A3 |
| Bayford, Som | 12 | C2 |
| Bayford's Hill, Kent | 149 | C3 |
| Baylham, Suff | 53 | D3 |
| Bayston Hill, Shrop | 56 | D2 |
| Bayton, Worc | 47 | A1 |
| Bayworth, Oxon | 37 | D3 |
| Beachampton, Bucks | 50 | B4 |
| Beachamwell, Norf | 63 | A2 |
| Beacon, Devon | 11 | A4 |
| Beacon's Bottom, Bucks | 38 | C4 |
| Beaconsfield, Bucks | 39 | A4 |
| Beadlam, N York | 94 | A3 |
| Beadlow, Beds | 51 | B4 |
| Beadnell, Nthumb | 109 | E2 |
| Beaford, Devon | 9 | E3 |
| Beal, N York | 88 | C4 |
| Beal, Nthumb | 109 | D1 |
| Bealsmill, Corn | 4 | B2 |
| Beaminster, Dors | 12 | A4 |
| Beamish, Durham | 98 | C1 |
| Beamsley, N York | 87 | A2 |
| Beanacre, Wilts | 25 | A2 |
| Beanley, Nthumb | 109 | D3 |
| Beardon, Devon | 4 | C1 |
| Beare, Devon | 10 | C4 |
| Beare Green, Surr | 147 | B4 |
| Bearley, Warw | 48 | C2 |
| Bearpark, Durham | 98 | C2 |
| Bearsden, Dumb | 112 | A3 |
| Bearsted, Kent | 30 | A3 |
| Bearstone, Shrop | 69 | A3 |
| Beattock, D & G | 101 | E1 |
| Beauchamp Roding, Essex | 41 | B3 |
| Beaufort, Gwent | 34 | D2 |
| Beaulieu, Hamp | 14 | B4 |
| Beauly, High | 132 | A3 |
| Beaumaris, Angle | 76 | D4 |
| Beaumont, Cumb | 102 | B4 |
| Beaumont, Essex | 43 | C1 |
| Beaumont, Jers | 139 | A2 |
| Beausale, Warw | 48 | C1 |
| Beaworthy, Devon | 9 | D4 |
| Bebington, Mers | 77 | D4 |
| Beccles, Suff | 65 | B4 |
| Becconsall, Lanc | 85 | B4 |
| Beck Row, Suff | 53 | A1 |
| Beck Side, Cumb | 91 | D3 |
| Beckbury, Shrop | 57 | B3 |
| Beckenham, G Lon | 144 | A4 |
| Beckering, Linc | 84 | A4 |
| Beckermet, Cumb | 91 | B1 |
| Beckfoot, Cumb | 96 | D1 |
| Beckford, Worc | 48 | A4 |
| Beckhampton, Wilts | 25 | C2 |
| Beckingham, Linc | 72 | C2 |
| Beckingham, Notts | 83 | B3 |
| Beckington, Som | 24 | B4 |
| Beckley, E Sus | 21 | A2 |
| Beckley, Oxon | 38 | A2 |
| Beckton, G Lon | 144 | B1 |
| Beckwithshaw, N York | 87 | B1 |
| Becontree, G Lon | 144 | B1 |
| Bedale, N York | 93 | A2 |
| Bedchester, Dors | 12 | D3 |
| Beddingham, E Sus | 19 | B3 |
| Beddington, G Lon | 143 | A4 |
| Beddington Corner, G Lon | 143 | A4 |
| Bedfield, Suff | 54 | A2 |
| Bedford, Beds | 51 | A3 |
| Bedham, W Suss | 17 | B2 |
| Bedingfield, Suff | 54 | A1 |
| Bedingfield Street, Suff | 54 | A2 |
| Bedlam, N York | 87 | B1 |
| Bedlam Lane, Kent | 30 | A4 |
| Bedlington, Nthumb | 104 | B2 |
| Bedlinog, Merth | 34 | C3 |
| Bedmond, Herts | 39 | C3 |
| Bednall, Staff | 58 | A1 |
| Bedrule, Bord | 108 | D3 |
| Bedstone, Shrop | 46 | C1 |
| Bedwas, Caer | 34 | D4 |
| Bedwellty, Caer | 34 | D3 |
| Bedworth, Warw | 59 | B4 |
| Beeby, Leics | 60 | C2 |
| Beech, Hamp | 16 | A1 |
| Beech, Staff | 69 | B3 |
| Beechingstoke, Wilts | 25 | C3 |
| Beedon, Berks | 26 | B1 |
| Beedon Hill, Berks | 26 | B1 |
| Beeford, E R of Y | 90 | A1 |
| Beeley, Derby | 70 | B1 |
| Beelsby, Linc | 84 | B2 |
| Beenham, Berks | 26 | C2 |
| Beer, Devon | 6 | B1 |
| Beer, Som | 11 | C1 |
| Beesands, Devon | 8 | B1 |
| Beesby, Linc | 84 | D4 |
| Beeson, Devon | 8 | B1 |
| Beeston, Beds | 51 | B3 |
| Beeston, Chesh | 68 | B2 |
| Beeston, Norf | 63 | C1 |
| Beeston, Notts | 71 | B4 |
| Beeston Regis, Norf | 75 | B3 |
| Beeswing, D & G | 101 | D3 |
| Beetham, Cumb | 91 | F3 |
| Beetham, Som | 11 | B3 |
| Beetley, Norf | 63 | C1 |
| Begbroke, Oxon | 37 | D2 |
| Begelly, Pemb | 32 | E3 |
| Beguildy, Powys | 46 | A1 |
| Beighton, Norf | 65 | B2 |
| Beighton Hill, Derby | 70 | C2 |
| Beith, N Ayr | 111 | E4 |
| Belaugh, Norf | 65 | A1 |
| Belbroughton, Worc | 47 | C1 |
| Belchalwell, Dors | 12 | C3 |
| Belchalwell Street, Dors | 12 | C3 |
| Belchamp Otten, Essex | 53 | B4 |
| Belchamp St Paul, Essex | 53 | B4 |
| Belchamp Walter, Essex | 53 | B4 |
| Belchford, Linc | 84 | B4 |
| Belford, Nthumb | 109 | D2 |
| Bell Busk, N York | 86 | C1 |
| Bell End, Worc | 48 | A1 |
| Bell o' th' Hill, Chesh | 68 | B3 |
| Belleau, Linc | 84 | C4 |
| Bellerby, N York | 92 | E2 |
| Bellingdon, Bucks | 39 | A3 |
| Bellingham, Nthumb | 103 | C2 |
| Bellochantuy, Argyll | 105 | D2 |
| Bellows Cross, Dors | 13 | B3 |
| Bells Yew Green, E Sus | 20 | A1 |
| Bellshill, N Lan | 112 | C4 |
| Bellside, N Lan | 113 | A4 |
| Belluton, Som | 24 | A3 |
| Belmont, Lanc | 79 | A1 |
| Belmont, G Lon | 148 | B1 |
| Belper, Derby | 70 | C3 |
| Belper Lane End, Derby | 70 | C2 |
| Belsay, Nthumb | 104 | A3 |
| Belses, Bord | 108 | C3 |
| Belsford, Devon | 5 | A4 |
| Belsize, Herts | 39 | B3 |
| Belstead, Suff | 54 | A4 |
| Belstone, Devon | 4 | D1 |
| Beltingham, Nthumb | 103 | B4 |
| Beltoft, Linc | 83 | B2 |
| Belton, Leics | 60 | A1 |
| Belton, Linc | 83 | B1 |
| Belton, Linc | 72 | C3 |
| Belton, Norf | 65 | C3 |
| Belton, Rut | 61 | A3 |
| Belvedere, G Lon | 144 | C2 |
| Belvoir, Leics | 72 | B4 |
| Bembridge, I of W | 8 | C1 |
| Bempton, E R of Y | 94 | E4 |
| Benacre, Suff | 65 | C4 |
| Benderloch, Argyll | 117 | A1 |
| Benenden, Kent | 21 | A1 |
| Benhall Street, Suff | 54 | C2 |
| Beningbrough, N York | 88 | C1 |
| Benington, Herts | 40 | A1 |
| Benington, Linc | 73 | D3 |
| Benllech, Angle | 76 | C4 |
| Benniworth, Linc | 84 | B4 |
| Benson, Oxon | 38 | B4 |
| Bentley, E R of Y | 89 | D3 |
| Bentley, Hamp | 27 | B4 |
| Bentley, Suff | 53 | D4 |
| Benton, Devon | 10 | A1 |
| Bentpath, D & G | 102 | B2 |
| Bentwichen, Devon | 10 | A1 |
| Bentworth, Hamp | 16 | A1 |
| Benvie, Angus | 119 | C1 |
| Benville, Dors | 12 | A4 |
| Benwick, Camb | 62 | B4 |
| Beoley, Worc | 48 | B1 |
| Bepton, W Suss | 17 | A2 |
| Berden, Essex | 41 | A1 |
| Bere Alston, Devon | 4 | C3 |
| Bere Ferrers, Devon | 4 | C3 |
| Bere Regis, Dors | 7 | B1 |
| Berea, Pemb | 32 | B1 |
| Bergh Apton, Norf | 65 | A3 |
| Berinsfield, Oxon | 38 | A4 |
| Berkeley, Glouc | 35 | C3 |
| Berkhamsted, Herts | 39 | B3 |
| Berkley, Som | 24 | B4 |
| Berkswell, W Mids | 48 | C1 |
| Bermondsey, G Lon | 143 | B2 |
| Bernisdale, High | 130 | C3 |
| Berrick Prior, Oxon | 38 | B4 |
| Berrick Salome, Oxon | 38 | B4 |
| Berrier, Cumb | 97 | A3 |
| Berriew, Powys | 56 | A3 |
| Berrington, Shrop | 56 | D2 |
| Berrington, Worc | 46 | D2 |
| Berrow, Som | 23 | B4 |
| Berrynarbor, Devon | 22 | B4 |
| Berry's Green, G Lon | 149 | B1 |
| Bersham, Wrex | 67 | E3 |
| Berwick, E Sus | 19 | B4 |
| Berwick Bassett, Wilts | 25 | C2 |
| Berwick Hill, Nthumb | 104 | B3 |
| Berwick St James, Wilts | 13 | B1 |
| Berwick St John, Wilts | 13 | A2 |
| Berwick-upon-Tweed, Nthumb | 115 | E4 |
| Bescaby, Leics | 72 | B4 |
| Besford, Worc | 47 | C4 |
| Bessacarr, S York | 82 | B2 |
| Bessingby, E R of Y | 94 | E4 |
| Bessingham, Norf | 75 | B4 |
| Besthorpe, Norf | 64 | A3 |
| Besthorpe, Notts | 72 | B1 |
| Beswick, E R of Y | 89 | D2 |
| Betchworth, Surr | 148 | A3 |
| Bethel, Gwyn | 66 | D1 |
| Bethel, Angle | 66 | C1 |
| Bethersden, Kent | 21 | B1 |
| Bethesda, Gwyn | 66 | E1 |
| Bethesda, Pemb | 32 | E2 |
| Bethlehem, Carm | 33 | D1 |
| Bethnal Green, G Lon | 143 | B1 |
| Betley, Staff | 69 | A3 |
| Betteshanger, Kent | 31 | B4 |
| Bettiscombe, Dors | 11 | C4 |
| Bettisfield, Wrex | 68 | A4 |
| Bettws, Newport | 34 | E4 |
| Bettws Bledrws, Cered | 45 | A3 |
| Bettws Cedewain, Powys | 56 | A3 |
| Bettws Evan, Cered | 44 | D3 |
| Bettws-Newydd, Monm | 35 | A3 |
| Bettyhill, High | 137 | F1 |
| Betws, Brid | 22 | E1 |
| Betws Gwerfil Goch, Denb | 67 | C3 |
| Betws-y-coed, Ab & Col | 67 | A2 |
| Betws-yn-Rhos, Ab & Col | 77 | A4 |
| Beulah, Cered | 44 | D3 |
| Beulah, Powys | 45 | D3 |
| Bevercotes, Notts | 83 | A4 |
| Beverley, E R of Y | 89 | D3 |
| Beverstone, Glouc | 36 | B4 |
| Bewcastle, Cumb | 102 | D3 |
| Bewdley, Worc | 47 | B1 |
| Bewerley, N York | 92 | E4 |
| Bewholme, E R of Y | 90 | A2 |
| Bexhill, E Sus | 20 | B3 |
| Bexley, G Lon | 144 | C3 |
| Bexleyheath, G Lon | 144 | B3 |
| Beyton, Suff | 53 | C2 |
| Bibury, Glouc | 37 | A3 |
| Bicester, Oxon | 38 | A1 |
| Bickenhill, W Mids | 59 | A4 |
| Bicker, Linc | 73 | C3 |
| Bickerstaffe, Lanc | 78 | A2 |
| Bickerton, N York | 88 | B2 |
| Bickford, Staff | 57 | C2 |
| Bickington, Devon | 5 | B2 |
| Bickleigh, Devon | 10 | C3 |
| Bickleigh, Devon | 4 | C3 |
| Bickley, N York | 94 | C2 |
| Bickley, G Lon | 144 | A4 |
| Bickley Moss, Chesh | 68 | B3 |
| Bicknacre, Essex | 42 | B3 |
| Bicknoller, Som | 10 | D1 |
| Bicknor, Kent | 30 | A3 |
| Bicton, Shrop | 56 | C1 |
| Bicton, Shrop | 56 | B4 |
| Biddenden, Kent | 21 | A1 |
| Biddenham, Beds | 51 | A3 |
| Biddestone, Wilts | 25 | A2 |
| Biddisham, Som | 23 | C3 |
| Biddlesden, Bucks | 50 | A4 |
| Biddulph, Staff | 69 | B2 |
| Biddulph Moor, Staff | 69 | B2 |
| Bideford, Devon | 9 | D2 |
| Bidford-on-Avon, Warw | 48 | B3 |
| Bielby, E R of Y | 89 | B2 |
| Bierley, I of W | 8 | B2 |
| Bierton, Bucks | 38 | C2 |
| Bigbury, Devon | 8 | A1 |
| Bigbury-on-Sea, Devon | 8 | B1 |
| Bigby, Linc | 83 | D1 |
| Biggar, S Lan | 107 | D1 |
| Biggin, Derby | 70 | B3 |
| Biggin, Derby | 70 | A2 |
| Biggin, N York | 88 | C3 |
| Biggin Hill, G Lon | 149 | A1 |
| Biggleswade, Beds | 51 | B4 |
| Bighton, Hamp | 15 | B1 |
| Biglands, Cumb | 96 | F1 |
| Bignor, W Suss | 17 | B3 |
| Bigrigg, Cumb | 96 | C4 |
| Bilbrook, Som | 10 | D1 |
| Bilbrough, N York | 88 | C2 |

| PLACE | PAGE | GRID |
|---|---|---|
| Bilbster, High | 138 | E2 |
| Bildershaw, Durham | 98 | C3 |
| Bildeston, Suff | 53 | C3 |
| Billericay, Essex | 42 | A4 |
| Billesley, Warw | 48 | B3 |
| Billingborough, Linc | 73 | B4 |
| Billinge, Mers | 78 | B2 |
| Billingford, Norf | 64 | A1 |
| Billingford, Norf | 54 | A1 |
| Billingham, Durham | 99 | A3 |
| Billinghay, Linc | 73 | B2 |
| Billingley, S York | 82 | A2 |
| Billingshurst, W Suss | 18 | A2 |
| Billingsley, Shrop | 57 | B4 |
| Billington, Beds | 39 | A1 |
| Billington, Lanc | 86 | B3 |
| Billockby, Norf | 65 | B2 |
| Billy Row, Durham | 98 | C2 |
| Bilsborrow, Lanc | 85 | C3 |
| Bilsby, Linc | 84 | D4 |
| Bilsham, W Suss | 17 | B4 |
| Bilsington, Kent | 21 | C1 |
| Bilsthorpe, Notts | 72 | A1 |
| Bilton, N York | 88 | B2 |
| Bilton, Warw | 49 | B1 |
| Binbrook, Linc | 84 | B3 |
| Binfield Heath, Oxon | 27 | B1 |
| Bingham, Notts | 72 | A3 |
| Bingham's Melcombe, Dors | 12 | C4 |
| Bingley, W York | 87 | A3 |
| Binham, Norf | 74 | E3 |
| Binley, Hamp | 26 | B3 |
| Binscombe, Surr | 146 | A4 |
| Binstead, Hamp | 16 | B1 |
| Binton, Warw | 48 | B3 |
| Bintree, Norf | 64 | A1 |
| Birch, Essex | 43 | A2 |
| Birch Cross, Staff | 70 | A4 |
| Birch Green, Essex | 43 | A2 |
| Birch Green, Worc | 47 | C3 |
| Birch Vale, Derby | 80 | B3 |
| Birch Wood, Som | 11 | B3 |
| Bircham Newton, Norf | 74 | C4 |
| Birchanger, Essex | 41 | A1 |
| Bircher, Heref | 46 | D2 |
| Birchgrove, E Sus | 19 | A1 |
| Birchgrove, Swan | 33 | D4 |
| Birchley Heath, Warw | 59 | B3 |
| Birchover, Derby | 70 | B1 |
| Bircotes, Notts | 83 | A3 |
| Birdbrook, Essex | 53 | A4 |
| Birdforth, N York | 93 | C4 |
| Birdham, W Suss | 16 | B4 |
| Birdingbury, Warw | 49 | B1 |
| Birdlip, Glouc | 36 | B2 |
| Birds Edge, W York | 81 | B1 |
| Birds Green, Essex | 41 | A3 |
| Birdsall, N York | 94 | B4 |
| Birdsgreen, Shrop | 57 | B4 |
| Birdsmoorgate, Dors | 11 | C4 |
| Birgham, Bord | 109 | A1 |
| Birkby, N York | 93 | B1 |
| Birkenhead, Mers | 77 | D3 |
| Birkenshaw, W York | 87 | B4 |
| Birkhill, Angus | 119 | D1 |
| Birkin, N York | 88 | C4 |
| Birley, Heref | 46 | C3 |
| Birling, Kent | 29 | B3 |
| Birlingham, Worc | 48 | A4 |
| Birmingham, W Mids | 58 | B4 |
| Birnam, Perth | 119 | A1 |
| Birness, Aber | 129 | C1 |
| Birstall, Leics | 60 | B2 |
| Birstwith, N York | 87 | B4 |
| Birtley, Heref | 46 | C1 |
| Birtley, Nthumb | 103 | C3 |
| Birtley, T & W | 98 | C1 |
| Birts Street, Worc | 47 | B4 |
| Biscathorpe, Linc | 84 | B3 |
| Bish Mill, Devon | 10 | A2 |
| Bisham, Berks | 27 | B1 |
| Bishampton, Worc | 48 | A3 |
| Bishop Auckland, Durham | 98 | D3 |
| Bishop Burton, E R of Y | 89 | D3 |
| Bishop Middleham, Durham | 98 | A4 |
| Bishop Monkton, N York | 93 | B4 |
| Bishop Norton, Linc | 83 | D3 |
| Bishop Sutton, Som | 24 | A3 |
| Bishop Thornton, N York | 87 | B1 |
| Bishop Wilton, E R of Y | 89 | B1 |
| Bishopbridge, Linc | 83 | D3 |
| Bishops Cannings, Wilts | 25 | B3 |
| Bishop's Castle, Shrop | 56 | B4 |
| Bishop's Caundle, Dors | 12 | C3 |
| Bishop's Cleeve, Glouc | 36 | C1 |
| Bishop's Frome, Heref | 47 | A3 |
| Bishops Gate, Surr | 140 | C3 |
| Bishop's Green, Essex | 41 | B2 |
| Bishop's Itchington, Warw | 49 | C2 |
| Bishops Lydeard, Som | 11 | A2 |
| Bishop's Norton, Glouc | 36 | B1 |
| Bishop's Nympton, Devon | 10 | A2 |
| Bishop's Offley, Staff | 69 | A4 |
| Bishop's Stortford, Herts | 41 | A2 |
| Bishop's Sutton, Hamp | 15 | B1 |
| Bishop's Tachbrook, Warw | 49 | A2 |
| Bishop's Waltham, Hamp | 15 | B3 |
| Bishop's Wood, Staff | 57 | C2 |
| Bishopsbourne, Kent | 31 | A4 |
| Bishopsteignton, Devon | 5 | C4 |
| Bishopston, Swan | 33 | C4 |
| Bishopstone, Bucks | 38 | C3 |
| Bishopstone, E Sus | 19 | B4 |
| Bishopstone, Heref | 46 | C4 |
| Bishopstone, Wilts | 13 | B2 |
| Bishopstone, Wilts | 25 | D1 |
| Bishopstrow, Wilts | 25 | A4 |
| Bishopswood, Som | 11 | B3 |
| Bishopthorpe, N York | 88 | C2 |
| Bishopton, Durham | 98 | D4 |
| Bishopton, Renf | 112 | A3 |
| Bishton, Newport | 23 | C1 |
| Bishton, Staff | 58 | A1 |
| Bisley, Glouc | 36 | B3 |
| Bisley, Surr | 145 | B1 |
| Bisley Camp, Surr | 145 | B2 |
| Bissoe, Corn | 2 | A1 |
| Bisterne, Hamp | 13 | B4 |
| Bitchfield, Linc | 73 | A4 |
| Bittadon, Devon | 22 | B4 |
| Bittaford, Devon | 5 | A4 |
| Bitterley, Shrop | 46 | D1 |
| Bitteswell, Leics | 60 | B4 |
| Bitton, Glouc | 24 | A2 |
| Blaby, Leics | 60 | B3 |
| Black Bourton, Oxon | 37 | C3 |
| Black Callerton, T & W | 104 | B3 |
| Black Dog, Devon | 10 | B3 |
| Black Notley, Essex | 42 | A4 |
| Black Torrington, Devon | 9 | D4 |
| Blackawton, Devon | 5 | B4 |
| Blackborough, Devon | 10 | D3 |
| Blackborough End, Norf | 63 | A1 |
| Blackbrook, Derby | 70 | C3 |
| Blackbrook, Staff | 69 | A3 |
| Blackbrook, Surr | 147 | B4 |
| Blackburn, Aber | 129 | B2 |
| Blackburn, W Loth | 113 | B3 |
| Blackburn, Lanc | 86 | A4 |
| Blackdown, Dors | 11 | C4 |
| Blacker Hill, S York | 81 | C2 |
| Blackfen, G Lon | 144 | B3 |
| Blackfield, Hamp | 15 | A4 |
| Blackford, Perth | 118 | E3 |
| Blackford, Som | 23 | C4 |
| Blackfordby, Leics | 59 | B1 |
| Blackhall Colliery, Durham | 99 | A2 |
| Blackheath, Suff | 54 | C1 |
| Blackheath, Surr | 146 | B4 |
| Blackheath, G Lon | 144 | A2 |
| Blackhill, Aber | 134 | E4 |
| Blackland, Som | 10 | B1 |
| Blackmill, Brid | 22 | E1 |
| Blackmoor, Hamp | 16 | B1 |
| Blackmoor, Som | 23 | D3 |
| Blackmoorfoot, W York | 81 | A1 |
| Blackmore, Essex | 41 | B3 |
| Blackmore End, Essex | 42 | A1 |
| Blackness, Falkirk | 113 | C2 |
| Blacknest, Berks | 140 | B4 |
| Blacknest, Hamp | 27 | B4 |
| Blacko, Lanc | 86 | C2 |
| Blackpool, Devon | 8 | B1 |
| Blackpool, Lanc | 85 | A3 |
| Blackridge, W Loth | 113 | B3 |
| Blackrod, G Man | 79 | A1 |
| Blackshaw Head, W York | 86 | D4 |
| Blacksnape, Lanc | 86 | B4 |
| Blackstone, W Suss | 18 | B3 |
| Blackthorn, Oxon | 38 | B2 |
| Blackthorpe, Suff | 53 | C2 |
| Blackwall, Derby | 70 | B2 |
| Blackwater, Corn | 2 | A1 |
| Blackwater, Norf | 11 | B3 |
| Blackwaterfoot, N Ayr | 105 | F2 |
| Blackwell, Cumb | 97 | A1 |
| Blackwell, Derby | 70 | A1 |
| Blackwell, Derby | 71 | A2 |
| Blackwell, Warw | 48 | C4 |
| Blackwell, Worc | 48 | A1 |
| Blackwood, Caer | 34 | D4 |
| Blackwood, S Lan | 107 | B1 |
| Bladnoch, D & G | 95 | D1 |
| Bladon, Oxon | 37 | D2 |
| Blaenannerch, Cered | 44 | D3 |
| Blaenau Ffestiniog, Gwyn | 66 | F3 |
| Blaenavon, Torf | 34 | E3 |
| Blaenffos, Pemb | 44 | C4 |
| Blaengarw, Brid | 34 | B4 |
| Blaengwrach, Neath | 34 | A3 |
| Blaengwynfi, Neath | 34 | B4 |
| Blaenpennal, Cered | 45 | A2 |
| Blaenplwyf, Cered | 45 | A1 |
| Blaenporth, Cered | 44 | D3 |
| Blaenwaun, Carm | 32 | F1 |
| Blaen-y-Coed, Carm | 33 | A1 |
| Blaen-y-cwm, Gwent | 34 | D2 |
| Blaen-y-cwm, Rhond | 34 | B4 |
| Blagdon, Som | 23 | D3 |
| Blagdon Hill, Som | 11 | A3 |
| Blaich, High | 121 | D1 |
| Blaina, Gwent | 34 | D3 |
| Blair Atholl, Perth | 122 | E2 |
| Blairgowrie, Perth | 123 | C4 |
| Blairingone, Perth | 118 | E4 |
| Blairlogie, Stirl | 118 | D4 |
| Blairmore, Argyll | 111 | C2 |
| Blaisdon, Glouc | 36 | A2 |
| Blakedown, Worc | 47 | C1 |
| Blakemere, Heref | 46 | C4 |
| Blakeney, Glouc | 35 | C3 |
| Blakeney, Norf | 75 | A3 |
| Blakenhall, Chesh | 69 | A3 |
| Blakesley, Nhants | 50 | A3 |
| Blanchland, Nthumb | 98 | A1 |
| Bland Hill, N York | 87 | B1 |
| Blandford Forum, Dors | 12 | D4 |
| Blandford St Mary, Dors | 12 | D4 |
| Blanefield, Stirl | 112 | B2 |
| Blankney, Linc | 73 | A2 |
| Blantyre, S Lan | 112 | C4 |
| Blaston, Leics | 61 | A3 |
| Blatherwycke, Nhants | 61 | C3 |
| Blawith, Cumb | 91 | D2 |
| Blaxhall, Suff | 54 | C2 |
| Blaxton, S York | 83 | A3 |
| Blaydon, T & W | 104 | B4 |
| Bleadon, Som | 23 | B3 |
| Blean, Kent | 31 | A3 |
| Bleasby, Notts | 72 | A2 |
| Bleasdale, Lanc | 85 | C2 |
| Bleddfa, Powys | 46 | A1 |
| Bledington, Glouc | 37 | B1 |
| Bledlow, Bucks | 38 | C3 |
| Blencarn, Cumb | 97 | C3 |
| Blencogo, Cumb | 96 | E1 |
| Blendworth, Hamp | 16 | A3 |
| Blennerhasset, Cumb | 96 | E2 |
| Bletchingdon, Oxon | 38 | A2 |
| Bletchingley, Surr | 148 | C3 |
| Bletchley, Bucks | 39 | A1 |
| Bletchley, Shrop | 68 | C4 |
| Bletherston, Pemb | 32 | D2 |
| Bletsoe, Beds | 51 | A2 |
| Blewbury, Oxon | 26 | C1 |
| Blickling, Norf | 75 | B4 |
| Blidworth, Notts | 71 | B2 |
| Blidworth Bottoms, Notts | 71 | B2 |
| Blindcrake, Cumb | 96 | E2 |
| Blindley Heath, Surr | 148 | C4 |
| Blisland, Corn | 3 | E2 |
| Bliss Gate, Worc | 47 | B1 |
| Blissford, Hamp | 14 | A3 |
| Blisworth, Nhants | 50 | A3 |
| Blithbury, Staff | 58 | B1 |
| Blo Norton, Norf | 53 | D1 |
| Blockley, Glouc | 48 | C4 |
| Blofield, Norf | 65 | A2 |
| Blore, Staff | 69 | A4 |
| Blore, Staff | 70 | A4 |
| Bloxham, Oxon | 49 | B4 |
| Bloxholm, Linc | 73 | A2 |
| Bloxworth, Dors | 7 | B1 |
| Blubberhouses, N York | 87 | B1 |
| Blue Anchor, Som | 22 | F4 |
| Blue Bell Hill, Kent | 29 | B3 |
| Blundeston, Suff | 65 | C3 |
| Blunham, Beds | 51 | B3 |
| Blunsdon St Andrew, Wilts | 37 | A4 |
| Bluntington, Worc | 47 | C1 |
| Bluntisham, Camb | 52 | A1 |
| Blyborough, Linc | 83 | C3 |
| Blyford, Suff | 54 | C1 |
| Blymhill, Staff | 57 | B2 |
| Blyth, Notts | 83 | A3 |
| Blyth, Nthumb | 104 | C2 |
| Blyth Bridge, Bord | 107 | E1 |
| Blythburgh, Suff | 54 | C1 |
| Blyton, Linc | 83 | C3 |
| Boarhills, Fife | 119 | D2 |
| Boarhunt, Hamp | 15 | B3 |
| Boarstall, Bucks | 38 | B2 |
| Boat of Garten, High | 127 | D2 |
| Bobbing, Kent | 30 | A2 |
| Bobbington, Staff | 57 | B3 |
| Boddam, Aber | 134 | E4 |
| Boddington, Glouc | 36 | B1 |
| Bodedern, Angle | 76 | B4 |
| Bodelwyddan, Denb | 77 | B3 |
| Bodenham, Heref | 46 | D3 |
| Bodenham, Wilts | 14 | A2 |
| Bodenham Moor, Heref | 46 | D3 |
| Bodewryd, Angle | 76 | B3 |
| Bodfari, Denb | 67 | C1 |
| Bodffordd, Angle | 76 | C4 |
| Bodfuan, Gwyn | 66 | C3 |
| Bodham, Norf | 75 | B3 |
| Bodicote, Oxon | 49 | B4 |
| Bodinnick, Corn | 3 | E4 |
| Bodmin, Corn | 3 | E3 |
| Bodsham Green, Kent | 30 | C4 |
| Bogbrae, Aber | 134 | E4 |
| Bognor Regis, W Suss | 17 | A4 |
| Bogue, D & G | 101 | C2 |
| Bohortha, Corn | 2 | B2 |
| Bolam, Durham | 98 | C3 |
| Bolberry, Devon | 8 | A1 |
| Boldre, Hamp | 14 | B4 |
| Boldron, Durham | 98 | A4 |
| Bole, Notts | 83 | B3 |
| Bolehill, Derby | 70 | C2 |
| Bolham, Devon | 10 | C3 |
| Bolham Water, Devon | 11 | A3 |
| Bolingey, Corn | 3 | C3 |
| Bollington, Chesh | 80 | B4 |
| Bolney, W Suss | 18 | B3 |
| Bolnhurst, Beds | 51 | B2 |
| Bolsover, Derby | 71 | A1 |
| Bolsterstone, S York | 81 | B2 |
| Boltby, N York | 93 | C3 |
| Bolton, Cumb | 97 | C3 |
| Bolton, E Loth | 115 | A3 |
| Bolton, E R of Y | 89 | B1 |
| Bolton, Nthumb | 109 | D4 |
| Bolton, G Man | 79 | B1 |
| Bolton Abbey, N York | 87 | A1 |
| Bolton le Sands, Lanc | 91 | F4 |
| Bolton Low Houses, Cumb | 96 | F2 |
| Bolton Percy, N York | 88 | C2 |
| Boltonfellend, Cumb | 102 | D3 |
| Boltongate, Cumb | 96 | F2 |
| Bolventor, Corn | 3 | E2 |
| Bonar Bridge, High | 136 | B4 |
| Bonby, Linc | 83 | D1 |
| Boncath, Pemb | 44 | C4 |
| Bonchester Bridge, Bord | 108 | D2 |
| Bondleigh, Devon | 9 | E4 |
| Bonds, Lanc | 85 | C2 |
| Bo'ness, Falkirk | 113 | B2 |
| Boningale, Shrop | 57 | B3 |
| Bonkle, N Lan | 113 | A4 |
| Bonnington, Kent | 21 | C1 |
| Bonnyrigg, M Loth | 114 | B3 |
| Bonnyton, Angus | 119 | C1 |
| Bonsall, Derby | 70 | C2 |
| Bont-Dolgadfan, Powys | 55 | C3 |
| Bontnewydd, Cered | 45 | A2 |
| Bontnewydd, Gwyn | 66 | D2 |
| Bontuchel, Denb | 67 | C2 |
| Bonvilston, Glam | 22 | F2 |
| Boode, Devon | 9 | D1 |
| Boohay, Devon | 5 | B4 |
| Booley, Shrop | 56 | D1 |
| Boosbeck, N York | 99 | C4 |
| Boose's Green, Essex | 42 | B1 |
| Boot, Cumb | 91 | C1 |
| Booth, E R of Y | 89 | A4 |
| Boothby Graffoe, Linc | 73 | A2 |
| Boothby Pagnell, Linc | 73 | A4 |
| Boothstown, G Man | 79 | B2 |
| Bootle, Cumb | 91 | B2 |
| Bootle, Mers | 77 | D2 |
| Boraston, Shrop | 47 | A1 |
| Bordeaux, Guer | 139 | B2 |
| Borden, Kent | 30 | A3 |
| Bordon, Hamp | 16 | B1 |
| Boreham, Essex | 42 | A3 |
| Boreham, Wilts | 25 | A4 |
| Boreham Street, E Sus | 20 | B3 |
| Borehamwood, Herts | 39 | C4 |
| Boreland, D & G | 102 | A2 |
| Borgue, D & G | 95 | F1 |
| Borley, Essex | 53 | B4 |
| Borness, D & G | 95 | F1 |
| Borough Green, Kent | 29 | B3 |
| Boroughbridge, N York | 93 | C4 |
| Borrowash, Derby | 71 | A4 |
| Borrowby, N York | 93 | C2 |
| Borrowstoun, Falkirk | 113 | B2 |
| Borth, Cered | 55 | A4 |
| Borth-y-Gest, Gwyn | 66 | C4 |
| Borve, High | 130 | C3 |
| Borwick, Lanc | 91 | F4 |
| Bosbury, Heref | 47 | A3 |
| Boscastle, Corn | 3 | C1 |
| Boscombe, Wilts | 14 | A1 |
| Bosham, W Suss | 16 | B4 |
| Bosherston, Pemb | 32 | D4 |
| Bosley, Chesh | 69 | B1 |
| Bossall, N York | 89 | A1 |
| Bossiney, Corn | 3 | D1 |
| Bossingham, Kent | 31 | A4 |
| Bossington, Som | 22 | E4 |
| Bostock Green, Chesh | 68 | C1 |
| Boston, Linc | 73 | D3 |
| Boston Spa, W York | 88 | B2 |
| Boswinger, Corn | 2 | C1 |
| Botany Bay, G Lon | 40 | A3 |
| Botesdale, Suff | 53 | D1 |
| Bothal, Nthumb | 104 | B2 |
| Bothampstead, Berks | 26 | C1 |
| Bothamsall, Notts | 83 | A4 |
| Bothel, Cumb | 96 | E2 |
| Bothwell, S Lan | 112 | C4 |
| Botley, Bucks | 39 | B3 |
| Botley, Hamp | 15 | B3 |
| Botolph Claydon, Bucks | 38 | B1 |
| Botolphs, W Suss | 18 | A3 |
| Bottesford, Leics | 72 | B3 |
| Bottisham, Camb | 52 | C2 |
| Bottomcraig, Fife | 119 | D2 |
| Bottoms, W York | 86 | D4 |
| Botusfleming, Corn | 4 | B3 |
| Botwnnog, Gwyn | 66 | B4 |
| Boughton, Nhants | 50 | B2 |
| Boughton, Norf | 63 | A3 |
| Boughton, Notts | 72 | A1 |
| Boughton Aluph, Kent | 30 | C4 |
| Boughton Lees, Kent | 30 | C4 |
| Boughton Street, Kent | 30 | C3 |
| Bouldon, Shrop | 56 | D4 |
| Boulmer, Nthumb | 109 | E4 |
| Bourn, Camb | 52 | A3 |
| Bourne, Linc | 61 | C1 |
| Bourne End, Beds | 50 | C4 |
| Bourne End, Herts | 39 | B3 |
| Bournemouth, Dors | 7 | D1 |
| Bournheath, Worc | 48 | A1 |
| Bourton, Dors | 12 | C1 |
| Bourton, Oxon | 25 | D1 |
| Bourton, Shrop | 57 | A3 |
| Bourton, Wilts | 25 | B2 |
| Bourton-on-the-Water, Glouc | 37 | B2 |
| Bousd, Argyll | 120 | C3 |
| Bouth, Cumb | 91 | D3 |
| Boveney, Bucks | 140 | B2 |
| Boveridge, Dors | 13 | B3 |
| Bovingdon, Herts | 39 | B3 |
| Bow, Devon | 10 | A4 |
| Bow, G Lon | 143 | B1 |
| Bow, Ork | 139 | A2 |
| Bow Brickhill, Bucks | 50 | C4 |
| Bow Street, Cered | 55 | A4 |
| Bowburn, Durham | 98 | D2 |
| Bowcombe, I of W | 8 | A1 |
| Bowd, Devon | 6 | A1 |
| Bowden, Bord | 108 | C2 |
| Bowden Hill, Wilts | 25 | B2 |
| Bowdon, G Man | 79 | B3 |
| Bower, High | 138 | E1 |
| Bowerchalke, Wilts | 13 | A2 |
| Bower's Row, W York | 88 | B4 |
| Bowershall, Fife | 113 | C1 |
| Bowes, Durham | 98 | A4 |
| Bowgreave, Lanc | 85 | C2 |
| Bowley, Heref | 46 | D3 |
| Bowlhead Green, Surr | 17 | A1 |
| Bowling, Dumb | 112 | A2 |
| Bowmanstead, Cumb | 91 | D2 |
| Bowmore, Argyll | 110 | B4 |
| Bowness-on-Solway, Cumb | 102 | A4 |
| Bowriefauld, Angus | 124 | A4 |
| Bowsden, Nthumb | 109 | C1 |
| Box, Wilts | 25 | A2 |
| Box Hill, Surr | 148 | A3 |
| Boxford, Berks | 26 | B2 |
| Boxford, Suff | 53 | C4 |
| Boxgrove, W Suss | 17 | A3 |
| Boxted, Essex | 43 | A1 |
| Boxted, Suff | 53 | B3 |
| Boxted Cross, Essex | 43 | A1 |
| Boxted Heath, Essex | 43 | A1 |
| Boxworth, Camb | 52 | A2 |
| Boyden Gate, Kent | 31 | A2 |
| Boyndie, Aber | 134 | A2 |
| Boynton, E R of Y | 94 | B4 |
| Boyton, Corn | 4 | B1 |
| Boyton, Suff | 54 | C3 |
| Boyton, Wilts | 13 | A1 |
| Boyton Cross, Essex | 41 | B3 |
| Boyton End, Suff | 53 | C2 |
| Bozeat, Nhants | 50 | C2 |
| Brabourne, Kent | 30 | C4 |
| Brabourne Lees, Kent | 21 | C1 |
| Bracadale, High | 130 | B4 |
| Braceborough, Linc | 61 | C2 |
| Bracebridge Heath, Linc | 73 | A1 |
| Braceby, Linc | 73 | A4 |
| Bracewell, Lanc | 86 | C2 |
| Brackenfield, Derby | 70 | C2 |
| Brackletter, High | 121 | D1 |
| Brackley, Nhants | 49 | C4 |
| Bracknell, Berks | 140 | A4 |
| Braco, Perth | 118 | D3 |
| Bracon Ash, Norf | 64 | B3 |
| Bradbourne, Derby | 70 | B2 |
| Bradbury, Durham | 98 | D3 |
| Bradden, Nhants | 50 | A3 |
| Bradenstoke, Wilts | 25 | B1 |
| Bradfield, Berks | 26 | C2 |
| Bradfield, Devon | 10 | D3 |
| Bradfield, Essex | 43 | C1 |
| Bradfield, Norf | 75 | C4 |
| Bradfield, S York | 81 | B3 |
| Bradfield Combust, Suff | 53 | C2 |
| Bradfield Green, Chesh | 68 | C2 |
| Bradfield Heath, Essex | 43 | C1 |
| Bradfield St Clare, Suff | 53 | C2 |
| Bradfield St George, Suff | 53 | C2 |
| Bradford, Devon | 9 | C3 |
| Bradford, W York | 87 | B3 |
| Bradford Abbas, Dors | 12 | B3 |
| Bradford Leigh, Wilts | 25 | A3 |
| Bradford Peverell, Dors | 6 | F1 |
| Bradford-on-Avon, Wilts | 25 | A3 |
| Bradley, Derby | 70 | B3 |
| Bradley, Hamp | 27 | A4 |
| Bradley, Linc | 84 | B2 |
| Bradley, Staff | 57 | C1 |
| Bradley, Worc | 48 | A2 |
| Bradley in the Moors, Staff | 70 | A3 |
| Bradmore, Notts | 71 | B4 |
| Bradninch, Devon | 10 | C4 |
| Bradnop, Staff | 69 | C2 |
| Bradpole, Dors | 6 | E1 |
| Bradshaw, W York | 87 | A4 |
| Bradstone, Devon | 4 | B2 |
| Bradwall Green, Chesh | 69 | A1 |
| Bradwell, Derby | 81 | B4 |
| Bradwell, Essex | 42 | B1 |
| Bradwell Waterside, Essex | 43 | A3 |
| Bradwell-on-Sea, Essex | 43 | A3 |
| Bradworthy, Devon | 9 | C3 |
| Brae, Shet | 139 | A2 |
| Braegrum, Perth | 119 | A2 |
| Braehead, S Lan | 113 | B4 |
| Braemar, Aber | 128 | A4 |
| Braeswick, Ork | 139 | B1 |
| Brafferton, Durham | 98 | D4 |
| Brafferton, N York | 93 | C4 |
| Bragbury End, Herts | 40 | A2 |
| Braidwood, S Lan | 107 | B1 |
| Brailsford, Derby | 70 | B3 |
| Braintree, Essex | 42 | A1 |
| Braiseworth, Suff | 54 | A1 |
| Braishfield, Hamp | 14 | B2 |
| Braithwaite, Cumb | 96 | E3 |
| Bramcote, Warw | 60 | A4 |
| Bramdean, Hamp | 15 | B2 |
| Bramerton, Norf | 65 | A2 |
| Bramfield, Herts | 40 | A2 |
| Bramfield, Suff | 54 | C1 |
| Bramford, Suff | 54 | A3 |
| Bramhall, G Man | 80 | A3 |
| Bramham, W York | 88 | B2 |
| Bramhope, W York | 87 | B2 |
| Bramley, Hamp | 27 | A3 |
| Bramley, S York | 82 | A3 |
| Bramley, Surr | 146 | A4 |
| Bramling, Kent | 31 | A3 |
| Brampford Speke, Devon | 10 | C4 |
| Brampton, Camb | 51 | C1 |
| Brampton, Cumb | 97 | C3 |
| Brampton, Linc | 83 | B4 |
| Brampton, S York | 82 | A2 |
| Brampton, Suff | 65 | C4 |
| Brampton, Cumb | 102 | D4 |
| Brampton Abbotts, Heref | 35 | C1 |
| Brampton Ash, Nhants | 61 | A4 |
| Bramshall, Staff | 70 | A4 |
| Bramshaw, Hamp | 14 | A3 |
| Bramshott, Hamp | 16 | B1 |
| Bramwell, Som | 11 | C2 |
| Bran End, Essex | 41 | B1 |
| Branault, High | 120 | F2 |
| Brancaster, Norf | 74 | C3 |
| Brancaster Staithe, Norf | 74 | D3 |
| Brancepeth, Durham | 98 | C2 |
| Brandesburton, E R of Y | 90 | A2 |
| Brandeston, Suff | 54 | B2 |
| Brandiston, Norf | 64 | B1 |
| Brandon, Durham | 98 | C2 |
| Brandon, Linc | 72 | C3 |
| Brandon, Suff | 63 | B4 |
| Brandon, Warw | 49 | B1 |
| Brandon Parva, Norf | 64 | A2 |
| Brandsby, N York | 93 | D4 |
| Brandy Wharf, Linc | 83 | D2 |
| Bransbury, Hamp | 26 | B4 |
| Bransby, Linc | 83 | C4 |
| Branscombe, Devon | 6 | B1 |
| Bransford, Worc | 47 | B3 |
| Bransgore, Hamp | 14 | A4 |
| Bransley, Shrop | 47 | A1 |
| Branston, Leics | 72 | B3 |
| Branston, Linc | 73 | A1 |
| Branston, Staff | 59 | A1 |
| Branston Booths, Linc | 73 | A1 |
| Brant Broughton, Linc | 72 | C2 |
| Brantham, Suff | 53 | D4 |
| Branthwaite, Cumb | 96 | D3 |
| Branthwaite, Cumb | 96 | F2 |
| Brantingham, E R of Y | 89 | C4 |
| Branton, S York | 82 | B2 |
| Branton, Nthumb | 109 | D3 |
| Branton Green, N York | 88 | B1 |
| Branxton, Nthumb | 109 | C1 |
| Brassington, Derby | 70 | B2 |
| Brasted, Kent | 149 | C4 |
| Bratoft, Linc | 74 | A1 |
| Brattleby, Linc | 83 | C4 |
| Bratton, Wilts | 25 | A4 |
| Bratton Clovelly, Devon | 4 | C1 |
| Bratton Fleming, Devon | 9 | E1 |
| Bratton Seymour, Som | 12 | B1 |
| Braughing, Herts | 40 | B1 |
| Braunston, Nhants | 49 | C2 |
| Braunston, Rut | 61 | A2 |
| Braunton, Devon | 9 | D1 |
| Brawby, N York | 94 | B3 |
| Bray, Berks | 140 | A2 |
| Bray Shop, Corn | 4 | B2 |
| Braybrooke, Nhants | 61 | A4 |
| Brayford, Devon | 10 | A1 |
| Braythorn, N York | 87 | B2 |
| Brayton, N York | 88 | C3 |
| Braywick, Berks | 140 | A2 |
| Braywoodside, Berks | 140 | A3 |
| Breachwood Green, Herts | 39 | C3 |
| Breadsall, Derby | 70 | C3 |
| Breadstone, Glouc | 36 | A3 |
| Breage, Corn | 1 | D2 |
| Breamore, Hamp | 14 | A3 |
| Brean, Som | 23 | B3 |
| Brearton, N York | 88 | A1 |
| Breasclete, W Isles | 139 | B2 |
| Breaston, Derby | 71 | A4 |
| Brechfa, Carm | 33 | B1 |
| Brechin, Angus | 124 | B3 |
| Breckles, Norf | 63 | C3 |
| Brecon, Powys | 34 | C1 |
| Brede, E Sus | 21 | A2 |
| Bredenbury, Heref | 47 | A3 |
| Bredfield, Suff | 54 | B3 |
| Bredgar, Kent | 30 | A3 |
| Bredon, Worc | 47 | C4 |
| Bredon's Norton, Worc | 48 | A4 |
| Bredwardine, Heref | 46 | B4 |
| Breighton, E R of Y | 89 | A3 |
| Breinton, Heref | 46 | D4 |
| Bremhill, Wilts | 25 | B2 |
| Brendon, Devon | 22 | C4 |
| Brenfield, Argyll | 111 | A2 |
| Brent Eleigh, Suff | 53 | C3 |
| Brent Knoll, Som | 23 | B4 |
| Brent Mill, Devon | 5 | A4 |
| Brent Pelham, Herts | 41 | A1 |
| Brentford, G Lon | 142 | A2 |
| Brentingby, Leics | 61 | A1 |
| Brentwood, Essex | 41 | B4 |
| Brenzett, Kent | 21 | B2 |
| Brereton Green, Chesh | 69 | A1 |
| Bressingham, Norf | 64 | A4 |
| Bretby, Derby | 59 | B1 |
| Bretford, Warw | 49 | B1 |
| Bretforton, Worc | 48 | B4 |
| Bretherton, Lanc | 85 | C4 |
| Brettenham, Norf | 63 | C4 |
| Brettenham, Suff | 53 | C3 |
| Bretton, Flint | 68 | A1 |
| Brewer Street, Surr | 148 | C3 |
| Brewood, Staff | 57 | C2 |
| Briantspuddle, Dors | 7 | B1 |
| Brickendon, Herts | 40 | B3 |
| Bricklehampton, Worc | 48 | A4 |
| Bride, I o M | 139 | D1 |
| Bridekirk, Cumb | 96 | D3 |
| Bridestowe, Devon | 4 | C1 |
| Bridford, Devon | 5 | B1 |
| Bridge, Corn | 1 | D1 |
| Bridge, Kent | 31 | A3 |
| Bridge End, Surr | 146 | B2 |
| Bridge Hewick, N York | 93 | B4 |
| Bridge of Allan, Stirl | 118 | D4 |
| Bridge of Cally, Perth | 123 | C4 |
| Bridge of Canny, Aber | 128 | E4 |
| Bridge of Dee, D & G | 101 | B4 |
| Bridge of Earn, Perth | 119 | B3 |
| Bridge of Orchy, Argyll | 117 | D1 |
| Bridge of Weir, Renf | 111 | E3 |
| Bridge Sollers, Heref | 46 | C4 |
| Bridge Street, Suff | 53 | B3 |
| Bridgehampton, Som | 12 | A2 |
| Bridgend, Argyll | 110 | B3 |
| Bridgend, W Loth | 113 | C2 |
| Bridgend, Brid | 22 | E1 |
| Bridgend of Lintrathen, Angus | 123 | D3 |
| Bridgerule, Devon | 9 | B4 |
| Bridgetown, Som | 10 | C1 |
| Bridgham, Norf | 63 | C4 |
| Bridgnorth, Shrop | 57 | B3 |
| Bridgwater, Som | 11 | B1 |
| Bridlington, E R of Y | 94 | E4 |
| Bridport, Dors | 6 | E1 |
| Bridstow, Heref | 35 | C1 |
| Brierfield, Lanc | 86 | C3 |
| Brierley, Glouc | 35 | C2 |
| Brierley, S York | 82 | A1 |
| Brig o'Turk, Stirl | 118 | A4 |
| Brigg, Linc | 83 | D1 |
| Briggate, Norf | 75 | C4 |
| Briggswath, N York | 94 | C1 |
| Brigham, Cumb | 96 | D3 |
| Brigham, E R of Y | 89 | D1 |
| Brighouse, W York | 87 | A4 |
| Brighstone, I of W | 8 | A2 |
| Brighthampton, Oxon | 37 | C3 |
| Brightgate, Derby | 70 | E4 |
| Brightley, Devon | 9 | E4 |
| Brightling, E Sus | 20 | B2 |
| Brightlingsea, Essex | 43 | B2 |
| Brighton, E Sus | 19 | A4 |
| Brightons, Falkirk | 113 | B2 |
| Brightwalton, Berks | 26 | B1 |
| Brightwell, Suff | 54 | B4 |
| Brightwell Baldwin, Oxon | 38 | B4 |
| Brightwell Upperton, Oxon | 38 | B4 |
| Brightwell-cum-Sotwell, Oxon | 38 | A4 |
| Brignall, Durham | 98 | B4 |
| Brigsley, Linc | 84 | B3 |
| Brigsteer, Cumb | 91 | F2 |
| Brigstock, Nhants | 61 | C4 |
| Brill, Bucks | 38 | B2 |
| Brilley, Heref | 46 | B3 |
| Brimfield, Shrop | 46 | D2 |
| Brimfield Cross, Shrop | 46 | D2 |
| Brimington, Derby | 82 | A4 |
| Brimley, Devon | 5 | B1 |
| Brimpsfield, Glouc | 36 | C2 |

| PLACE | PAGE | GRID |
|---|---|---|
| Brimpton, Berks | 26 | C2 |
| Brimscombe, Glouc | 36 | B3 |
| Brimstage, Mers | 77 | D4 |
| Brind, E R of Y | 89 | B3 |
| Brindle, Lanc | 86 | A4 |
| Brineton, Staff | 57 | B2 |
| Brington, Camb | 51 | B1 |
| Briningham, Norf | 75 | A4 |
| Brinkhill, Linc | 84 | C4 |
| Brinkley, Camb | 52 | C3 |
| Brinklow, Warw | 49 | B1 |
| Brinkworth, Wilts | 25 | B1 |
| Brinscall, Lanc | 86 | A4 |
| Brinsley, Notts | 71 | A3 |
| Brinton, Norf | 75 | A4 |
| Brinyan, Ork | 139 | A1 |
| Brisley, Norf | 63 | C1 |
| Brissenden Green, Kent | 21 | B1 |
| Bristol, Bristol | 24 | A2 |
| Briston, Norf | 75 | A4 |
| Britford, Wilts | 14 | A2 |
| Brithdir, Caer | 34 | D3 |
| Brithdir, Gwyn | 55 | B1 |
| British Legion Village, Kent | 29 | B3 |
| Briton Ferry, Neath | 33 | D4 |
| Britwell Salome, Oxon | 38 | B4 |
| Brixham, Devon | 5 | C4 |
| Brixton, Devon | 4 | D4 |
| Brixton, G Lon | 143 | A2 |
| Brixton Deverill, Wilts | 12 | D1 |
| Brixworth, Nhants | 50 | B1 |
| Brize Norton, Oxon | 37 | C3 |
| Broad Alley, Worc | 47 | C2 |
| Broad Blunsdon, Wilts | 37 | A4 |
| Broad Campden, Glouc | 48 | C4 |
| Broad Carr, W York | 87 | A4 |
| Broad Chalke, Wilts | 13 | A2 |
| Broad Green, Essex | 42 | B1 |
| Broad Green, Suff | 53 | B2 |
| Broad Green, Worc | 47 | B3 |
| Broad Haven, Pemb | 32 | C2 |
| Broad Hinton, Wilts | 25 | C1 |
| Broad Laying, Hamp | 26 | B3 |
| Broad Marston, Worc | 48 | B3 |
| Broad Oak, E Sus | 21 | A2 |
| Broad Oak, E Sus | 20 | A2 |
| Broad Oak, Heref | 35 | B2 |
| Broad Street, E Sus | 21 | A3 |
| Broad Street, Kent | 30 | A3 |
| Broad Town, Wilts | 25 | C1 |
| Broadbottom, G Man | 80 | B3 |
| Broadbridge, W Suss | 16 | B4 |
| Broadclyst, Devon | 10 | C4 |
| Broadford, High | 125 | E1 |
| Broadford Bridge, W Suss | 18 | A2 |
| Broadhembury, Devon | 10 | D4 |
| Broadhempston, Devon | 5 | B3 |
| Broadland Row, E Sus | 21 | A2 |
| Broadmayne, Dors | 7 | A1 |
| Broadmoor, Pemb | 32 | E3 |
| Broadoak, Dors | 11 | C4 |
| Broad's Green, Essex | 42 | A2 |
| Broadstone, Shrop | 56 | D4 |
| Broadwas, Worc | 47 | B3 |
| Broadway, Pemb | 32 | C2 |
| Broadway, Som | 11 | B3 |
| Broadway, Worc | 48 | B4 |
| Broadwell, Glouc | 37 | B1 |
| Broadwell, Oxon | 37 | B3 |
| Broadwell, Warw | 49 | B2 |
| Broadwindsor, Dors | 11 | C4 |
| Broadwood Kelly, Devon | 9 | E4 |
| Broadwoodwidger, Devon | 4 | B1 |
| Brockamin, Worc | 47 | B3 |
| Brockbridge, Hamp | 15 | B2 |
| Brockhall, Nhants | 50 | A2 |
| Brockham, Surr | 147 | B3 |
| Brockhampton, Glouc | 36 | C1 |
| Brockhampton, Heref | 35 | C1 |
| Brockholes, W York | 81 | A1 |
| Brocklesby, Linc | 84 | A1 |
| Brockley, Som | 23 | D2 |
| Brockley, Suff | 53 | B1 |
| Brockley Green, Suff | 53 | A3 |
| Brockley Green, Suff | 53 | B3 |
| Brockton, Shrop | 56 | B2 |
| Brockton, Shrop | 56 | B4 |
| Brockton, Shrop | 56 | D3 |
| Brockton, Staff | 69 | B4 |
| Brockweir, Glouc | 35 | B3 |
| Brockworth, Glouc | 36 | B2 |
| Brocton, Staff | 58 | A1 |
| Brodick, N Ayr | 106 | A2 |
| Brodsworth, S York | 82 | B1 |
| Brogaig, High | 130 | C2 |
| Brokenborough, Wilts | 36 | B4 |
| Brokerswood, Wilts | 25 | A4 |
| Brome, Suff | 54 | A1 |
| Brome Street, Suff | 54 | A1 |
| Bromeswell, Suff | 54 | B3 |
| Bromfield, Cumb | 96 | E1 |
| Bromfield, Shrop | 46 | D1 |
| Bromham, Beds | 51 | A3 |
| Bromham, Wilts | 25 | B2 |
| Bromley, Shrop | 57 | B3 |
| Bromley, G Lon | 144 | A4 |
| Bromley Common, G Lon | 144 | A4 |
| Brompton, N York | 93 | B2 |
| Brompton, N York | 94 | C3 |
| Brompton Ralph, Som | 10 | D1 |
| Brompton Regis, Som | 10 | C1 |
| Brompton-on-Swale, N York | 93 | A1 |
| Bromsberrow, Glouc | 47 | B4 |
| Bromsberrow Heath, Glouc | 36 | A1 |
| Bromsgrove, Worc | 48 | A1 |
| Bromyard, Heref | 47 | A3 |
| Bronant, Cered | 45 | A2 |
| Brongest, Cered | 44 | E3 |
| Bronington, Wrex | 68 | B3 |
| Bronllys, Powys | 46 | A4 |
| Bronwydd, Carm | 33 | A1 |
| Bronygarth, Shrop | 67 | E4 |
| Brook, Surr | 146 | B4 |
| Brook, Hamp | 14 | A3 |
| Brook, Hamp | 14 | B2 |
| Brook, Kent | 30 | C4 |
| Brook Hill, Hamp | 14 | A3 |
| Brook Street, Essex | 41 | B4 |
| Brook Street, Kent | 21 | B1 |
| Brooke, Norf | 65 | A3 |
| Brooke, Rut | 61 | A2 |
| Brookhouse Green, Chesh | 69 | B1 |
| Brookhouses, Derby | 80 | B3 |
| Brookland, Kent | 21 | B2 |
| Brookmans Park, Herts | 40 | A3 |
| Brookthorpe, Glouc | 36 | B2 |
| Brookwood, Surr | 145 | B2 |
| Broom, Beds | 51 | B4 |
| Broom, Warw | 48 | B3 |
| Broom Hill, S York | 82 | A2 |
| Broom Hill, Worc | 47 | C1 |
| Broome, Norf | 65 | A3 |
| Broome, Shrop | 56 | C4 |
| Broome, Worc | 47 | C1 |
| Broomedge, Chesh | 79 | B3 |
| Broomfield, Som | 11 | A1 |
| Broomfleet, E R of Y | 89 | C4 |
| Broomhall, Surr | 140 | B4 |
| Broomhaugh, Nthumb | 103 | D4 |
| Broomhill, Nthumb | 104 | B1 |
| Brora, High | 136 | E2 |
| Broseley, Shrop | 57 | A3 |
| Brotherlee, Durham | 97 | E2 |
| Brotherton, N York | 88 | B4 |
| Brotton, N York | 99 | C4 |
| Brough, E R of Y | 89 | C4 |
| Brough, Notts | 72 | B2 |
| Brough, Cumb | 97 | D4 |
| Brough Sowerby, Cumb | 97 | D4 |
| Broughton, Bord | 107 | D2 |
| Broughton, Bucks | 50 | C4 |
| Broughton, Camb | 51 | C1 |
| Broughton, Flint | 67 | E1 |
| Broughton, Hamp | 14 | B1 |
| Broughton, Lanc | 85 | C3 |
| Broughton, Linc | 83 | C1 |
| Broughton, N York | 86 | D2 |
| Broughton, N York | 94 | B4 |
| Broughton, Nhants | 50 | B1 |
| Broughton, Oxon | 49 | B4 |
| Broughton, Staff | 69 | A4 |
| Broughton, Glam | 22 | E2 |
| Broughton Astley, Leics | 60 | B3 |
| Broughton Green, Worc | 48 | A2 |
| Broughton Hackett, Worc | 47 | C3 |
| Broughton Mills, Cumb | 91 | C2 |
| Broughton Poggs, Oxon | 37 | B3 |
| Broughton-in-Furness, Cumb | 91 | C3 |
| Brown Candover, Hamp | 15 | B1 |
| Brown Edge, Staff | 69 | B2 |
| Brownhills, Fife | 119 | E3 |
| Brownhills, W Mids | 58 | B2 |
| Browninghill Green, Hamp | 26 | C3 |
| Brownsham, Devon | 9 | B2 |
| Brownston, Devon | 5 | A4 |
| Broxa, N York | 94 | C2 |
| Broxburn, E Loth | 115 | B2 |
| Broxburn, W Loth | 113 | C2 |
| Broxted, Essex | 41 | B1 |
| Broxwood, Heref | 46 | C3 |
| Bruichladdich, Argyll | 110 | A3 |
| Bruisyard, Suff | 54 | B2 |
| Bruisyard Street, Suff | 54 | B2 |
| Brund, Staff | 70 | A1 |
| Brundall, Norf | 65 | A2 |
| Brundish, Suff | 54 | B1 |
| Brundish Street, Suff | 54 | B1 |
| Brunthwaite, W York | 87 | A2 |
| Bruntingthorpe, Leics | 60 | B4 |
| Brunton, Fife | 119 | C2 |
| Brunton, Nthumb | 109 | E3 |
| Brunton, Wilts | 25 | D3 |
| Brushford, Som | 10 | C2 |
| Brushford Barton, Devon | 10 | A3 |
| Bruton, Som | 12 | B1 |
| Bryanston, Dors | 12 | D3 |
| Brydekirk, D & G | 102 | A3 |
| Bryn, Neath | 34 | A4 |
| Bryn Gates, G Man | 79 | A2 |
| Bryn Saith Marchog, Denb | 67 | C2 |
| Brynaman, Carm | 33 | D2 |
| Brynberian, Pemb | 44 | C4 |
| Bryncir, Gwyn | 66 | D3 |
| Bryn-coch, Neath | 33 | D3 |
| Bryncroes, Gwyn | 66 | B4 |
| Bryncrug, Gwyn | 55 | A2 |
| Bryneglwys, Denb | 67 | D3 |
| Brynford, Flint | 77 | C4 |
| Bryngwran, Angle | 76 | B4 |
| Bryngwyn, Monm | 35 | A3 |
| Bryngwyn, Powys | 46 | A3 |
| Bryn-Henllan, Pemb | 44 | B4 |
| Brynhoffnant, Cered | 44 | E3 |
| Brynmawr, Gwent | 34 | D2 |
| Bryn-mawr, Gwyn | 66 | B4 |
| Brynmenyn, Brid | 22 | E1 |
| Brynna, Rhond | 22 | E1 |
| Brynsadler, Rhond | 22 | F1 |
| Brynsiencyn, Angle | 66 | D1 |
| Bubbenhall, Warw | 49 | A1 |
| Bubwith, E R of Y | 89 | A3 |
| Buchanty, Perth | 118 | E2 |
| Buchany, Stirl | 118 | C4 |
| Buchlyvie, Stirl | 112 | B1 |
| Buckabank, Cumb | 97 | A1 |
| Buckden, Camb | 51 | B2 |
| Buckden, N York | 92 | D3 |
| Buckenham, Norf | 65 | B2 |
| Buckerell, Devon | 11 | A4 |
| Buckfast, Devon | 5 | A3 |
| Buckfastleigh, Devon | 5 | A3 |
| Buckhaven, Fife | 119 | D4 |
| Buckholt, Monm | 35 | B2 |
| Buckhorn Weston, Dors | 12 | C2 |
| Buckie, Moray | 133 | D2 |
| Buckingham, Bucks | 50 | A4 |
| Buckland, Bucks | 39 | A2 |
| Buckland, Devon | 8 | A1 |
| Buckland, Glouc | 48 | B4 |
| Buckland, Herts | 52 | A4 |
| Buckland, Oxon | 37 | C4 |
| Buckland, Surr | 148 | A3 |
| Buckland Brewer, Devon | 9 | C2 |
| Buckland Dinham, Som | 24 | B4 |
| Buckland Filleigh, Devon | 9 | D3 |
| Buckland in the Moor, Devon | 5 | A2 |
| Buckland Monachorum, Devon | 4 | C3 |
| Buckland Newton, Dors | 12 | B4 |
| Buckland Ripers, Dors | 6 | F2 |
| Buckland St Mary, Som | 11 | B3 |
| Buckland-Tout-Saints, Devon | 8 | A1 |
| Bucklebury, Berks | 26 | C2 |
| Bucklerheads, Angus | 119 | D1 |
| Bucklers Hard, Hamp | 15 | A4 |
| Bucklesham, Suff | 54 | B4 |
| Buckley, Flint | 67 | E1 |
| Buckminster, Leics | 61 | B1 |
| Bucknall, Linc | 73 | B1 |
| Bucknell, Oxon | 38 | A1 |
| Bucknell, Shrop | 46 | C1 |
| Buck's Cross, Devon | 9 | C2 |
| Bucks Green, W Suss | 18 | A1 |
| Buck's Mills, Devon | 9 | C2 |
| Buckton, E R of Y | 94 | E4 |
| Buckton, Nthumb | 109 | D1 |
| Buckworth, Camb | 51 | B1 |
| Budbrooke, Warw | 48 | C2 |
| Budby, Notts | 71 | B1 |
| Budd's Titson, Corn | 9 | B4 |
| Bude, Corn | 9 | B4 |
| Budge's Shop, Corn | 4 | B4 |
| Budleigh Salterton, Devon | 6 | A2 |
| Budock Water, Corn | 2 | A2 |
| Buerton, Chesh | 68 | C3 |
| Bugbrooke, Nhants | 50 | A2 |
| Bugle, Corn | 3 | D4 |
| Bugthorpe, E R of Y | 89 | B1 |
| Buildwas, Shrop | 57 | A2 |
| Builth Wells, Powys | 45 | E3 |
| Bulbridge, Wilts | 13 | B1 |
| Bulford, Wilts | 25 | D4 |
| Bulkeley, Chesh | 68 | B2 |
| Bulkington, Warw | 60 | A4 |
| Bulkington, Wilts | 25 | B3 |
| Bulkworthy, Devon | 9 | C3 |
| Bullington, Hamp | 26 | B4 |
| Bullington, Linc | 84 | A4 |
| Bulmer, Essex | 53 | B4 |
| Bulmer, N York | 94 | A4 |
| Bulmer Tye, Essex | 53 | B4 |
| Bulphan, Essex | 29 | A1 |
| Bulwick, Nhants | 61 | B3 |
| Bumble's Green, Essex | 40 | B3 |
| Bunbury, Chesh | 68 | B2 |
| Bunessan, Argyll | 116 | B2 |
| Bungay, Suff | 65 | A4 |
| Bunnahabhainn, Argyll | 110 | C2 |
| Bunny, Notts | 71 | B4 |
| Buntingford, Herts | 40 | B1 |
| Bunwell, Norf | 64 | B3 |
| Bunwell Street, Norf | 64 | A3 |
| Burchett's Green, Berks | 27 | B1 |
| Burcombe, Wilts | 13 | B1 |
| Burcott, Bucks | 39 | A1 |
| Bures, Essex | 53 | C4 |
| Burford, Oxon | 37 | B2 |
| Burford, Shrop | 47 | A1 |
| Burgess Hill, W Suss | 19 | A2 |
| Burgh by Sands, Cumb | 102 | B4 |
| Burgh Castle, Norf | 65 | C2 |
| Burgh Heath, Surr | 148 | A2 |
| Burgh le Marsh, Linc | 74 | A1 |
| Burgh next Aylsham, Norf | 64 | B1 |
| Burgh on Bain, Linc | 84 | B3 |
| Burgh St Margaret, Norf | 65 | B2 |
| Burgh St Peter, Norf | 65 | B3 |
| Burghclere, Hamp | 26 | B3 |
| Burghead, Moray | 133 | A1 |
| Burghfield, Berks | 27 | A2 |
| Burghfield Common, Berks | 27 | A2 |
| Burghill, Heref | 46 | D4 |
| Burghwallis, S York | 82 | B1 |
| Burham, Kent | 29 | B3 |
| Buriton, Hamp | 16 | B2 |
| Burland, Chesh | 68 | C2 |
| Burlawn, Corn | 3 | D3 |
| Burleigh, Glouc | 36 | B3 |
| Burleigh, Berks | 140 | B4 |
| Burlescombe, Devon | 10 | D3 |
| Burley, Hamp | 14 | A4 |
| Burley, Rut | 61 | B2 |
| Burley Gate, Heref | 47 | A3 |
| Burley in Wharfedale, W York | 87 | B2 |
| Burley Street, Hamp | 14 | A4 |
| Burley Wood Head, W York | 87 | A2 |
| Burleydam, Chesh | 68 | C3 |
| Burlingham Green, Norf | 65 | B2 |
| Burlton, Shrop | 68 | A4 |
| Burmarsh, Kent | 21 | C1 |
| Burmington, Warw | 48 | C4 |
| Burn, N York | 88 | C4 |
| Burnaston, Derby | 70 | C4 |
| Burnby, E R of Y | 89 | B2 |
| Burneside, Cumb | 91 | F2 |
| Burneston, N York | 93 | B3 |
| Burnett, Som | 24 | A2 |
| Burnfoot, Bord | 108 | B4 |
| Burnfoot, D & G | 102 | B2 |
| Burnfoot, Perth | 118 | E4 |
| Burnham, Bucks | 140 | B1 |
| Burnham Green, Herts | 40 | A2 |
| Burnham Market, Norf | 74 | D3 |
| Burnham Norton, Norf | 74 | D3 |
| Burnham Overy, Norf | 74 | D3 |
| Burnham Overy Staithe, Norf | 74 | D3 |
| Burnham Thorpe, Norf | 74 | D3 |
| Burnham-on-Crouch, Essex | 43 | A4 |
| Burnham-on-Sea, Som | 23 | B4 |
| Burnhaven, Aber | 134 | E4 |
| Burnhead, D & G | 101 | C1 |
| Burnhill Green, Staff | 57 | B3 |
| Burnhope, Durham | 98 | C1 |
| Burnhouse, N Ayr | 111 | E4 |
| Burniston, N York | 94 | D2 |
| Burnley, Lanc | 86 | C3 |
| Burnmoor, Durham | 98 | D1 |
| Burnmouth, Bord | 115 | E4 |
| Burnopfield, Durham | 104 | B4 |
| Burnsall, N York | 86 | D1 |
| Burnside of Duntrune, Angus | 119 | D1 |
| Burnt Yates, N York | 87 | B1 |
| Burntcommon, Surr | 146 | B2 |
| Burntisland, Fife | 114 | B1 |
| Burntwood, Staff | 58 | B2 |
| Burnworthy, Som | 11 | A3 |
| Burpham, W Suss | 17 | B3 |
| Burpham, Surr | 146 | A3 |
| Burradon, Nthumb | 109 | C4 |
| Burravoe, Shet | 139 | A2 |
| Burrells, Cumb | 97 | C4 |
| Burrelton, Perth | 119 | B1 |
| Burridge, Hamp | 15 | B3 |
| Burrill, N York | 93 | A3 |
| Burrington, Devon | 9 | E3 |
| Burrington, Heref | 46 | C1 |
| Burrington, Som | 23 | D3 |
| Burrough on the Hill, Leics | 61 | A2 |
| Burrow, Lanc | 92 | A4 |
| Burrow, Som | 22 | E4 |
| Burrow Bridge, Som | 11 | C1 |
| Burrowhill, Surr | 146 | A1 |
| Burrows Cross, Surr | 147 | A4 |
| Burry Port, Carm | 33 | B3 |
| Burrygreen, Swan | 33 | B4 |
| Burscough, Lanc | 78 | A1 |
| Burscough Bridge, Lanc | 78 | A1 |
| Bursea, E R of Y | 89 | B3 |
| Bursledon, Hamp | 15 | A3 |
| Burstall, Suff | 53 | D4 |
| Burstock, Dors | 11 | C4 |
| Burston, Norf | 64 | B4 |
| Burstow, Surr | 148 | B4 |
| Burstwick, E R of Y | 90 | B4 |
| Burtersett, N York | 92 | C2 |
| Burtholme, Cumb | 102 | D4 |
| Burthorpe Green, Suff | 53 | A2 |
| Burtoft, Linc | 73 | C4 |
| Burton, Chesh | 77 | D4 |
| Burton, Chesh | 68 | B1 |
| Burton, Dors | 7 | E1 |
| Burton, Linc | 83 | C4 |
| Burton, Pemb | 32 | D3 |
| Burton, Som | 23 | A4 |
| Burton, Wilts | 25 | A1 |
| Burton Agnes, E R of Y | 90 | A1 |
| Burton Coggles, Linc | 61 | C1 |
| Burton End, Essex | 41 | A1 |
| Burton Fleming, E R of Y | 94 | E4 |
| Burton Hastings, Warw | 60 | A4 |
| Burton in Lonsdale, N York | 92 | A4 |
| Burton Joyce, Notts | 72 | A3 |
| Burton Latimer, Nhants | 50 | C1 |
| Burton Lazars, Leics | 61 | A1 |
| Burton Leonard, N York | 88 | A1 |
| Burton on the Wolds, Leics | 60 | B1 |
| Burton Overy, Leics | 60 | C3 |
| Burton Pedwardine, Linc | 73 | B3 |
| Burton Pidsea, E R of Y | 90 | B3 |
| Burton Salmon, N York | 88 | B4 |
| Burton upon Stather, Linc | 83 | C1 |
| Burton upon Trent, Staff | 59 | A1 |
| Burton-in-Kendal, Cumb | 91 | F3 |
| Burton's Green, Essex | 42 | B1 |
| Burtonwood, Chesh | 78 | B3 |
| Burwardsley, Chesh | 68 | B2 |
| Burwarton, Shrop | 57 | A4 |
| Burwash Common, E Sus | 20 | A2 |
| Burwell, Camb | 52 | C2 |
| Burwell, Linc | 84 | C4 |
| Burwen, Angle | 76 | B3 |
| Burwick, Ork | 139 | A4 |
| Bury, Camb | 62 | A4 |
| Bury, Som | 10 | C2 |
| Bury, W Suss | 17 | B3 |
| Bury, G Man | 79 | B1 |
| Bury Green, Herts | 41 | A2 |
| Bury St Edmunds, Suff | 53 | B2 |
| Burythorpe, N York | 94 | B4 |
| Buscot, Oxon | 37 | B4 |
| Bush Bank, Heref | 46 | C3 |
| Bushey, Herts | 39 | C4 |
| Bushley, Worc | 47 | C4 |
| Bushton, Wilts | 25 | C1 |
| Bussex, Som | 11 | C1 |
| Butcher's Pasture, Essex | 41 | B1 |
| Butcombe, Som | 23 | D3 |
| Butleigh, Som | 12 | A1 |
| Butleigh Wootton, Som | 12 | A1 |
| Butlers Marston, Warw | 49 | A3 |
| Butley, Suff | 54 | C3 |
| Buttercrambe, N York | 89 | A1 |
| Butterleigh, Devon | 10 | C3 |
| Buttermere, Cumb | 96 | E4 |
| Butterstone, Perth | 123 | B4 |
| Butterton, Staff | 69 | B3 |
| Butterton, Staff | 70 | A2 |
| Butterwick, Linc | 73 | D3 |
| Butterwick, N York | 94 | A3 |
| Butterwick, N York | 94 | D4 |
| Buttington, Powys | 56 | B2 |
| Buttonoak, Shrop | 47 | B1 |
| Buxted, E Sus | 19 | B2 |
| Buxton, Norf | 64 | B1 |
| Buxton, Derby | 81 | A4 |
| Buxton Heath, Norf | 64 | B1 |
| Bwlch, Powys | 34 | D1 |
| Bwlchgwyn, Wrex | 67 | E2 |
| Bwlchllan, Cered | 45 | A2 |
| Bwlch-y-cibau, Powys | 56 | A1 |
| Bwlch-y-ffridd, Powys | 55 | E3 |
| Bwlch-y-groes, Pemb | 44 | D4 |
| Bwlch-y-sarnau, Powys | 45 | E1 |
| Byers Green, Durham | 98 | C3 |
| Byfield, Nhants | 49 | C3 |
| Byfleet, Surr | 146 | B1 |
| Byford, Heref | 46 | C4 |
| Bylchau, Ab & Col | 67 | B1 |
| Byley, Chesh | 69 | A1 |
| Byrness, Nthumb | 103 | B1 |
| Bythorn, Camb | 51 | A1 |
| Byton, Heref | 46 | C2 |
| Byworth, W Suss | 17 | B2 |
| Cabourne, Linc | 84 | A2 |
| Cabrach, Moray | 128 | C1 |
| Cabus, Lanc | 85 | C2 |
| Cadbury, Devon | 10 | C4 |
| Cadder, E Dunb | 112 | B3 |
| Caddington, Beds | 39 | B2 |
| Cade Street, E Sus | 20 | A2 |
| Cadeby, Leics | 60 | A3 |
| Cadeby, S York | 82 | B2 |
| Cadeleigh, Devon | 10 | C3 |
| Cadgwith, Corn | 1 | D3 |
| Cadley, Wilts | 25 | D2 |
| Cadley, Wilts | 25 | D3 |
| Cadmore End, Bucks | 38 | C4 |
| Cadney, Linc | 83 | D2 |
| Caeathro, Gwyn | 66 | D1 |
| Caenby, Linc | 83 | D3 |
| Caeo, Carm | 45 | B4 |
| Caer Farchell, Pemb | 32 | B1 |
| Caerau, Brid | 34 | A4 |
| Caergeiliog, Angle | 76 | B4 |
| Caergwrle, Flint | 67 | E2 |
| Caerleon, Newport | 34 | E4 |
| Caernarfon, Gwyn | 66 | D1 |
| Caerphilly, Caer | 23 | A1 |
| Caersws, Powys | 55 | E3 |
| Caerwedros, Cered | 44 | E3 |
| Caerwent, Monm | 35 | B4 |
| Caerwys, Flint | 77 | C4 |
| Cairndow, Argyll | 117 | C3 |
| Cairneyhill, Fife | 113 | C1 |
| Cairngarroch, D & G | 95 | A1 |
| Cairnie, Aber | 133 | E4 |
| Cairnryan, D & G | 100 | A3 |
| Caister-on-Sea, Norf | 65 | C2 |
| Caistor, Linc | 84 | A2 |
| Caistor St Edmund, Norf | 64 | B2 |
| Calbourne, I of W | 8 | A1 |
| Calcot, Flint | 77 | C4 |
| Calcot, Glouc | 37 | A3 |
| Caldbeck, Cumb | 96 | F2 |
| Caldecote, Camb | 61 | D4 |
| Caldecote, Camb | 52 | A3 |
| Caldecote, Herts | 51 | C4 |
| Caldecote Highfields, Camb | 52 | A2 |
| Caldecott, Nhants | 51 | A1 |
| Caldecott, Rut | 61 | B3 |
| Calder Bridge, Cumb | 91 | B1 |
| Calder Grove, W York | 81 | C1 |
| Calder Vale, Lanc | 85 | C2 |
| Caldercruix, N Lan | 113 | A3 |
| Caldicot, Monm | 35 | B4 |
| Caldwell, N York | 98 | C4 |
| Calfsound, Ork | 139 | B1 |
| Calgary, Argyll | 120 | D4 |
| Califer, Moray | 133 | A3 |
| California, Falkirk | 113 | B2 |
| California, Norf | 65 | C1 |
| Calke, Derby | 59 | B1 |
| Callakille, High | 130 | E3 |
| Callander, Stirl | 118 | B3 |
| Callestick, Corn | 3 | B4 |
| Callington, Corn | 4 | B3 |
| Callow, Heref | 46 | D4 |
| Callow End, Worc | 47 | C3 |
| Callow Hill, Wilts | 25 | B1 |
| Calmsden, Glouc | 37 | A3 |
| Calne, Wilts | 25 | B2 |
| Calshot, Hamp | 15 | A4 |
| Calstock, Corn | 4 | C3 |
| Calstone Wellington, Wilts | 25 | B2 |
| Calthorpe Street, Norf | 65 | B1 |
| Calthwaite, Cumb | 97 | B2 |
| Calton, Staff | 70 | A2 |
| Calveley, Chesh | 68 | C2 |
| Calver, Derby | 81 | B4 |
| Calverhall, Shrop | 68 | C4 |
| Calverleigh, Devon | 10 | C3 |
| Calverton, Bucks | 50 | B4 |
| Calverton, Notts | 71 | B2 |
| Calvine, Perth | 122 | E2 |
| Calvo, Cumb | 96 | E1 |
| Cam, Glouc | 36 | A3 |
| Camasunary, High | 125 | D2 |
| Camber, E Sus | 21 | B2 |
| Camberley, Surr | 145 | A1 |
| Camberwell, G Lon | 143 | B2 |
| Camblesforth, N York | 89 | A4 |
| Cambo, Nthumb | 103 | D2 |
| Camborne, Corn | 1 | D1 |
| Cambridge, Camb | 52 | B2 |
| Cambus, Clack | 113 | A1 |
| Cambusbarron, Stirl | 113 | A1 |
| Cambuslang, S Lan | 112 | B4 |
| Camden Town, G Lon | 143 | A1 |
| Camelford, Corn | 3 | E1 |
| Camer's Green, Worc | 47 | B4 |
| Camerton, Cumb | 96 | D3 |
| Camerton, Som | 24 | A3 |
| Camghouran, Perth | 122 | C3 |
| Cammachmore, Aber | 129 | B4 |
| Cammeringham, Linc | 83 | C4 |
| Campbeltown, Argyll | 105 | D3 |
| Campsall, S York | 82 | B1 |
| Campsea Ash, Suff | 54 | B3 |
| Campton, Beds | 51 | B4 |
| Camptown, Bord | 108 | D4 |
| Camrose, Pemb | 32 | C2 |
| Camserney, Perth | 122 | E4 |
| Canada, Hamp | 14 | B3 |
| Candlesby, Linc | 74 | A1 |
| Cane End, Oxon | 27 | A1 |
| Canewdon, Essex | 43 | A4 |
| Canford Magna, Dors | 13 | A4 |
| Canisbay, High | 138 | E1 |
| Cann, Dors | 12 | D2 |
| Cannich, High | 126 | E1 |
| Canning Town, G Lon | 144 | A2 |
| Cannington, Som | 11 | B1 |
| Cannock, Staff | 58 | A2 |
| Cannon Bridge, Heref | 46 | C4 |
| Canon Frome, Heref | 47 | A4 |
| Canon Pyon, Heref | 46 | C3 |
| Canonbie, D & G | 102 | C3 |
| Canons Ashby, Nhants | 49 | C3 |
| Canonstown, Corn | 1 | C2 |
| Canterbury, Kent | 31 | A3 |
| Cantley, Norf | 65 | B2 |
| Cantley, S York | 83 | A2 |
| Cantsfield, Lanc | 92 | A4 |
| Canvey Island, Essex | 30 | A1 |
| Canwick, Linc | 73 | A1 |
| Canworthy Water, Corn | 4 | A1 |
| Caol, High | 121 | E2 |
| Caoles, Argyll | 120 | B4 |
| Capel, Kent | 29 | A4 |
| Capel, Surr | 18 | A1 |
| Capel Bangor, Cered | 55 | A4 |
| Capel Coch, Angle | 76 | C4 |
| Capel Curig, Ab & Col | 66 | F2 |
| Capel Dewi, Carm | 33 | B2 |
| Capel Dewi, Cered | 44 | F4 |
| Capel Garmon, Ab & Col | 67 | A2 |
| Capel Gwynfe, Carm | 33 | D1 |
| Capel Hendre, Carm | 33 | C2 |
| Capel Iwan, Carm | 44 | D4 |
| Capel le Ferne, Kent | 21 | E1 |
| Capel Mawr, Angle | 66 | C1 |
| Capel Seion, Cered | 45 | A1 |
| Capel St Andrew, Suff | 54 | C3 |
| Capel St Mary, Suff | 53 | D4 |
| Capel-Dewi, Cered | 55 | A4 |
| Capelulo, Ab & Col | 76 | E4 |
| Capenhurst, Chesh | 78 | A4 |
| Capheaton, Nthumb | 103 | D2 |
| Capton, Devon | 5 | B4 |
| Capton, Som | 10 | D1 |
| Caputh, Perth | 119 | A1 |
| Car Colston, Notts | 72 | A3 |
| Carbost, High | 125 | B1 |
| Carbrooke, Norf | 63 | C3 |
| Carcroft, S York | 82 | B1 |
| Cardenden, Fife | 114 | A1 |
| Cardiff, Cardiff | 23 | A1 |
| Cardigan, Cered | 44 | C3 |
| Cardington, Beds | 51 | B3 |
| Cardington, Shrop | 56 | D3 |
| Cardinham, Corn | 3 | E3 |
| Cardross, Argyll | 111 | E2 |
| Cardurnock, Cumb | 102 | A4 |
| Careby, Linc | 61 | C1 |
| Carew, Pemb | 32 | D3 |
| Carew Newton, Pemb | 32 | D3 |
| Carey, Heref | 35 | B1 |
| Carfraemill, Bord | 115 | A4 |
| Cargate Green, Norf | 65 | B2 |
| Cargo, Cumb | 102 | C4 |
| Cargreen, Corn | 4 | C3 |
| Carham, Nthumb | 109 | A1 |
| Carhampton, Som | 22 | F4 |
| Carharrack, Corn | 1 | D1 |
| Cark, Cumb | 91 | E3 |
| Carkeel, Corn | 4 | B3 |
| Carlbury, Durham | 98 | C4 |
| Carlby, Linc | 61 | C2 |
| Carlcroft, Nthumb | 109 | B4 |
| Carleton, N York | 86 | D2 |
| Carleton Forehoe, Norf | 64 | A2 |
| Carleton Rode, Norf | 64 | A3 |
| Carlingcott, Som | 24 | B3 |
| Carlisle, Cumb | 97 | A1 |
| Carlops, Bord | 114 | A4 |
| Carloway, W Isles | 139 | B2 |
| Carlton, Beds | 50 | C3 |
| Carlton, Camb | 52 | C3 |
| Carlton, Durham | 99 | A4 |
| Carlton, Leics | 60 | A2 |
| Carlton, N York | 92 | E3 |
| Carlton, N York | 93 | D3 |
| Carlton, N York | 89 | A4 |
| Carlton, S York | 81 | C1 |
| Carlton, Suff | 54 | C2 |
| Carlton, W York | 88 | A4 |
| Carlton Colville, Suff | 65 | C4 |
| Carlton Curlieu, Leics | 60 | C3 |
| Carlton Green, Camb | 52 | C3 |
| Carlton Husthwaite, N York | 93 | C3 |
| Carlton in Lindrick, Notts | 82 | B3 |
| Carlton Miniott, N York | 93 | C3 |
| Carlton Scroop, Linc | 72 | C3 |
| Carlton-in-Cleveland, N York | 93 | D1 |
| Carlton-le-Moorland, Linc | 72 | C2 |
| Carlton-on-Trent, Notts | 72 | B1 |
| Carluke, S Lan | 113 | A4 |
| Carmarthen, Carm | 33 | A2 |
| Carmel, Carm | 33 | C2 |
| Carmel, Gwyn | 66 | D2 |
| Carmunnock, Glas | 112 | B4 |
| Carn Brea, Corn | 1 | D1 |
| Carnaby, E R of Y | 94 | E4 |
| Carnbee, Fife | 119 | E4 |
| Carnbo, Perth | 119 | A4 |
| Carnforth, Lanc | 91 | F4 |
| Carnhell Green, Corn | 1 | C1 |
| Carnkie, Corn | 1 | D2 |
| Carno, Powys | 55 | D3 |
| Carnon Downs, Corn | 2 | A1 |
| Carnoustie, Angus | 119 | E1 |
| Carnwath, S Lan | 107 | C1 |
| Carol Green, W Mids | 48 | C1 |
| Carperby, N York | 92 | D2 |
| Carr Gate, W York | 88 | A4 |
| Carr Shield, Nthumb | 97 | D1 |
| Carradale, Argyll | 105 | E1 |
| Carrbridge, High | 127 | D1 |
| Carreglefn, Angle | 76 | B3 |
| Carrhouse, Linc | 83 | B2 |
| Carrick, Argyll | 111 | A1 |
| Carrick Castle, Argyll | 111 | D1 |
| Carriden, Falkirk | 113 | C2 |
| Carrington, G Man | 79 | B3 |
| Carrington, M Loth | 114 | B4 |

| PLACE | PAGE | GRID |
|---|---|---|
| Cold Hanworth, Linc | 83 | D4 |
| Cold Higham, Nhants | 50 | A3 |
| Cold Kirby, N York | 93 | D3 |
| Cold Norton, Essex | 42 | B3 |
| Cold Overton, Leics | 61 | A2 |
| Coldbackie, High | 137 | E2 |
| Colden, W York | 86 | D4 |
| Coldharbour, Surr | 147 | B4 |
| Coldingham, Bord | 115 | D3 |
| Coldmeece, Staff | 69 | B4 |
| Coldred, Kent | 31 | B4 |
| Coldstream, Bord | 109 | B1 |
| Coldwaltham, W Suss | 17 | B3 |
| Coldwell, Heref | 46 | C4 |
| Cole, Som | 12 | B1 |
| Colebatch, Shrop | 56 | B4 |
| Colebrook, Devon | 10 | D4 |
| Colebrooke, Devon | 10 | A4 |
| Coleby, Linc | 89 | C4 |
| Coleby, Linc | 73 | A2 |
| Coleford, Devon | 10 | A4 |
| Coleford, Glouc | 35 | B2 |
| Coleford, Som | 24 | A4 |
| Coleford Water, Som | 10 | D1 |
| Coleman's Hatch, E Sus | 19 | B1 |
| Colemere, Shrop | 68 | A4 |
| Colemore, Hamp | 16 | A1 |
| Colerne, Wilts | 25 | A2 |
| Colesbourne, Glouc | 36 | C2 |
| Coleshill, Bucks | 39 | A4 |
| Coleshill, Oxon | 37 | B4 |
| Coleshill, Warw | 59 | A4 |
| Coley, Som | 24 | A3 |
| Colgate, W Suss | 18 | B1 |
| Colinsburgh, Fife | 119 | E4 |
| Colintraive, Argyll | 111 | B2 |
| Colkirk, Norf | 74 | E4 |
| Collaton St Mary, Devon | 5 | B4 |
| College Town, Berks | 145 | A1 |
| Collessie, Fife | 119 | C3 |
| Collier Street, Kent | 29 | B4 |
| Collier's End, Herts | 40 | B2 |
| Collieston, Aber | 129 | C1 |
| Collin, D & G | 101 | E3 |
| Collingbourne Ducis, Wilts | 25 | D3 |
| Collingbourne Kingston, Wilts | 25 | D3 |
| Collingham, Notts | 72 | B1 |
| Collingham, W York | 88 | B2 |
| Collington, Heref | 47 | A2 |
| Collingtree, Nhants | 50 | B3 |
| Collins Green, Chesh | 78 | B3 |
| Colliston, Angus | 124 | B4 |
| Colliton, Devon | 10 | D4 |
| Collyweston, Nhants | 61 | C2 |
| Colmonell, S Ayr | 100 | B2 |
| Colmworth, Beds | 51 | B2 |
| Coln Rogers, Glouc | 37 | A3 |
| Coln St Aldwyns, Glouc | 37 | A3 |
| Colnbrook, Berks | 141 | A2 |
| Colne, Camb | 52 | A1 |
| Colne, Lanc | 86 | C3 |
| Colne Engaine, Essex | 42 | B1 |
| Colney, Norf | 64 | B2 |
| Colney Heath, Herts | 40 | A3 |
| Colpy, Aber | 128 | E1 |
| Colston Bassett, Notts | 72 | A4 |
| Coltfield, Moray | 133 | A2 |
| Coltishall, Norf | 65 | A1 |
| Colton, Cumb | 91 | D3 |
| Colton, N York | 88 | C2 |
| Colton, Norf | 64 | A2 |
| Colton, Staff | 58 | B1 |
| Colt's Hill, Kent | 29 | A4 |
| Colva, Powys | 46 | A3 |
| Colvend, D & G | 96 | B1 |
| Colwall, Heref | 47 | B4 |
| Colwell, Nthumb | 103 | D3 |
| Colwich, Staff | 58 | A1 |
| Colwinston, Glam | 22 | E2 |
| Colworth, W Suss | 17 | A4 |
| Colwyn Bay, Ab & Col | 76 | F4 |
| Colyford, Devon | 6 | C1 |
| Colyton, Devon | 6 | C1 |
| Combe, Berks | 26 | A3 |
| Combe, Heref | 46 | B2 |
| Combe, Oxon | 37 | D2 |
| Combe Down, Som | 24 | B3 |
| Combe Fishacre, Devon | 5 | B3 |
| Combe Florey, Som | 11 | A1 |
| Combe Hay, Som | 24 | B3 |
| Combe Martin, Devon | 22 | B4 |
| Combe St Nicholas, Som | 11 | B3 |
| Comberbach, Chesh | 79 | A4 |
| Comberford, Staff | 59 | A2 |
| Comberton, Camb | 52 | A3 |
| Comberton, Heref | 46 | D2 |
| Combrook, Warw | 49 | A3 |
| Combs, Derby | 81 | A4 |
| Combs, Suff | 53 | D3 |
| Combwich, Som | 23 | B4 |
| Commercial, Pemb | 32 | E2 |
| Commins Coch, Powys | 55 | C2 |
| Common Moor, Corn | 4 | A3 |
| Commondale, N York | 94 | A1 |
| Compstall, G Man | 80 | B3 |
| Compton, Berks | 26 | C1 |
| Compton, Devon | 5 | B3 |
| Compton, Staff | 57 | C4 |
| Compton, Surr | 145 | B4 |
| Compton, W Suss | 16 | B3 |
| Compton, Wilts | 25 | C4 |
| Compton Abbas, Dors | 12 | D2 |
| Compton Abdale, Glouc | 37 | A2 |
| Compton Bassett, Wilts | 25 | B2 |
| Compton Beauchamp, Oxon | 26 | A1 |
| Compton Bishop, Som | 23 | C3 |
| Compton Chamberlayne, Wilts | 13 | A1 |
| Compton Dando, Som | 24 | A2 |
| Compton Dundon, Som | 12 | A1 |
| Compton Durville, Som | 11 | C3 |
| Compton Greenfield, Glouc | 23 | D1 |
| Compton Martin, Som | 23 | D3 |

| PLACE | PAGE | GRID |
|---|---|---|
| Compton Pauncefoot, Som | 12 | B2 |
| Compton Valence, Dors | 6 | F1 |
| Comrie, Fife | 113 | C1 |
| Comrie, Perth | 118 | D2 |
| Conchra, High | 126 | A1 |
| Concraigie, Perth | 123 | B4 |
| Conderton, Worc | 48 | A4 |
| Condicote, Glouc | 37 | A1 |
| Condover, Shrop | 56 | D2 |
| Coney Weston, Suff | 53 | C1 |
| Coneysthorpe, N York | 94 | A4 |
| Congerstone, Leics | 59 | B2 |
| Congham, Norf | 63 | A1 |
| Congleton, Chesh | 69 | B1 |
| Congresbury, Som | 23 | C3 |
| Conington, Camb | 61 | D4 |
| Conington, Camb | 52 | A2 |
| Conisbrough, S York | 82 | B2 |
| Conisholme, Linc | 84 | C2 |
| Coniston, Cumb | 91 | D2 |
| Coniston, E R of Y | 90 | A3 |
| Coniston Cold, N York | 86 | C1 |
| Conistone, N York | 92 | D4 |
| Connah's Quay, Flint | 67 | E1 |
| Connel, Argyll | 117 | A1 |
| Connor Downs, Corn | 1 | C1 |
| Conon Bridge, High | 132 | B3 |
| Cononley, N York | 86 | D2 |
| Consall, Staff | 69 | C3 |
| Consett, Durham | 98 | B1 |
| Constable Burton, N York | 93 | A2 |
| Constantine, Corn | 1 | D2 |
| Contin, High | 132 | A3 |
| Conwy, Ab & Col | 76 | F4 |
| Conyer's Green, Suff | 53 | B2 |
| Cookbury, Devon | 9 | C4 |
| Cookham, Berks | 140 | A1 |
| Cookham Dean, Berks | 140 | A1 |
| Cookhill, Worc | 48 | B2 |
| Cookley, Suff | 54 | B1 |
| Cookley, Worc | 57 | C4 |
| Cookley Green, Oxon | 38 | B4 |
| Cookney, Aber | 129 | B4 |
| Cooks Green, Suff | 53 | C3 |
| Cook's Green, Essex | 43 | C2 |
| Cooksmill Green, Essex | 41 | B3 |
| Coolham, W Suss | 18 | A2 |
| Cooling, Kent | 29 | B1 |
| Coombe, Glouc | 36 | A4 |
| Coombe, Hamp | 16 | A2 |
| Coombe Bissett, Wilts | 13 | B2 |
| Coombe Cellars, Devon | 5 | C2 |
| Coombe End, Som | 10 | D1 |
| Coombe Hill, Glouc | 36 | B1 |
| Coombe Keynes, Dors | 7 | B1 |
| Cooperhill, Moray | 132 | E3 |
| Coopersale Common, Essex | 41 | A3 |
| Cop Street, Kent | 31 | B3 |
| Copdock, Suff | 53 | D4 |
| Copford Green, Essex | 43 | A1 |
| Copgrove, N York | 88 | A1 |
| Cople, Beds | 51 | B3 |
| Copley, Durham | 98 | B3 |
| Copmanthorpe, N York | 88 | C2 |
| Copmere End, Staff | 69 | A4 |
| Copp, Lanc | 85 | B3 |
| Coppathorne, Corn | 9 | B4 |
| Coppenhall, Staff | 57 | C1 |
| Coppingford, Camb | 61 | D4 |
| Copplestone, Devon | 10 | B4 |
| Coppull, Lanc | 78 | B1 |
| Copsale, W Suss | 18 | A2 |
| Copster Green, Lanc | 86 | A3 |
| Copston Magna, Warw | 60 | A4 |
| Copt Hewick, N York | 93 | B4 |
| Copt Oak, Leics | 60 | A2 |
| Copthorne, Surr | 19 | A1 |
| Corbiere, Jers | 139 | A2 |
| Corbridge, Nthumb | 103 | D4 |
| Corby, Nhants | 61 | B4 |
| Corby Glen, Linc | 61 | C1 |
| Coreley, Shrop | 47 | A1 |
| Corfe, Som | 11 | A2 |
| Corfe Castle, Dors | 7 | C2 |
| Corfton, Shrop | 56 | D4 |
| Corgarff, Aber | 128 | B3 |
| Corhampton, Hamp | 15 | B2 |
| Corley, Warw | 59 | B4 |
| Corley Ash, Warw | 59 | B4 |
| Cornard Tye, Suff | 53 | C4 |
| Cornforth, Durham | 98 | D2 |
| Cornhill, Aber | 134 | A2 |
| Cornholme, W York | 86 | C4 |
| Cornsay, Durham | 98 | B2 |
| Cornsay Colliery, Durham | 98 | C2 |
| Corntown, Glam | 22 | E1 |
| Cornwell, Oxon | 37 | B1 |
| Cornwood, Devon | 4 | D4 |
| Cornworthy, Devon | 5 | B4 |
| Corpach, High | 121 | E1 |
| Corpusty, Norf | 75 | A4 |
| Corrie, D & G | 102 | A2 |
| Corrie, N Ayr | 106 | A1 |
| Corringham, Essex | 29 | B1 |
| Corringham, Linc | 83 | C3 |
| Corris, Gwyn | 55 | B2 |
| Corris Uchaf, Gwyn | 55 | B2 |
| Corscombe, Devon | 9 | E4 |
| Corscombe, Dors | 12 | A4 |
| Corse Lawn, Glouc | 36 | B1 |
| Corsham, Wilts | 25 | A2 |
| Corsley, Wilts | 25 | A4 |
| Corsley Heath, Wilts | 25 | A4 |
| Corsock, D & G | 101 | B3 |
| Corston, Som | 24 | B2 |
| Corston, Wilts | 25 | A1 |
| Corton, Wilts | 13 | A1 |
| Corton Denham, Som | 12 | B2 |
| Corwen, Denb | 67 | C3 |
| Coryton, Devon | 4 | C1 |
| Coryton, Essex | 29 | B1 |
| Cosby, Leics | 60 | B3 |
| Cosgrove, Nhants | 50 | B4 |
| Cosheston, Pemb | 32 | D3 |

| PLACE | PAGE | GRID |
|---|---|---|
| Cossall, Notts | 71 | A3 |
| Cossington, Leics | 60 | B2 |
| Cossington, Som | 11 | C1 |
| Costessey, Norf | 64 | B2 |
| Costock, Notts | 71 | B4 |
| Coston, Leics | 61 | A1 |
| Coston, Norf | 64 | A2 |
| Cote, Oxon | 37 | C3 |
| Cotebrook, Chesh | 68 | B1 |
| Cotehill, Cumb | 97 | B1 |
| Cotes, Leics | 60 | B1 |
| Cotesbach, Leics | 60 | B4 |
| Cotgrave, Notts | 72 | A4 |
| Cotham, Notts | 72 | B3 |
| Cotherstone, Durham | 98 | A4 |
| Cothill, Oxon | 37 | D3 |
| Cotleigh, Devon | 11 | A4 |
| Coton, Camb | 52 | A2 |
| Coton, Nhants | 50 | A1 |
| Coton, Staff | 57 | C1 |
| Coton in the Elms, Derby | 59 | A1 |
| Cott, Devon | 5 | B3 |
| Cottam, Lanc | 85 | C3 |
| Cottam, Notts | 83 | B4 |
| Cottenham, Camb | 52 | B2 |
| Cottered, Herts | 40 | B1 |
| Cotterstock, Nhants | 61 | C4 |
| Cottesbrooke, Nhants | 50 | A1 |
| Cottesmore, Rut | 61 | B2 |
| Cottingham, E R of Y | 89 | D3 |
| Cottisford, Oxon | 38 | A1 |
| Cotton, Suff | 53 | D2 |
| Cotts, Devon | 4 | C3 |
| Coughton, Warw | 48 | B2 |
| Coulport, Argyll | 111 | D1 |
| Coulsdon, Surr | 148 | B1 |
| Coulston, Wilts | 25 | B3 |
| Coulter, S Lan | 107 | D2 |
| Coulton, N York | 94 | A4 |
| Cound, Shrop | 56 | D2 |
| Coundon, Durham | 98 | C3 |
| Countersett, N York | 92 | C2 |
| Countesthorpe, Leics | 60 | B3 |
| Countisbury, Devon | 22 | C4 |
| Coupar Angus, Perth | 119 | B1 |
| Coupland, Nthumb | 109 | C2 |
| Courance, D & G | 101 | E2 |
| Court Henry, Carm | 33 | C1 |
| Courteenhall, Nhants | 50 | B3 |
| Courtsend, Essex | 43 | B4 |
| Courtway, Som | 11 | A1 |
| Cousland, M Loth | 114 | C3 |
| Cove, Argyll | 111 | D2 |
| Cove, Bord | 115 | C3 |
| Cove, Devon | 10 | C2 |
| Cove, High | 135 | A4 |
| Cove, Hamp | 145 | A2 |
| Covehithe, Suff | 65 | C4 |
| Coven, Staff | 57 | C2 |
| Coveney, Camb | 62 | C4 |
| Covenham St Bartholomew, Linc | 84 | C3 |
| Covenham St Mary, Linc | 84 | C3 |
| Coventry, W Mids | 49 | A1 |
| Coverack, Corn | 2 | A3 |
| Coverack Bridges, Corn | 1 | D2 |
| Coverham, N York | 92 | E3 |
| Covington, Camb | 51 | A1 |
| Cow Honeybourne, Worc | 48 | B4 |
| Cowbit, Linc | 62 | A1 |
| Cowbridge, Glam | 22 | E2 |
| Cowden, Kent | 19 | B1 |
| Cowden Station, Kent | 149 | B4 |
| Cowdenbeath, Fife | 114 | A1 |
| Cowes, I of W | 15 | A4 |
| Cowesby, N York | 93 | C2 |
| Cowfold, W Suss | 18 | B2 |
| Cowhill, Glouc | 35 | C4 |
| Cowie, Stirl | 113 | A1 |
| Cowley, Devon | 10 | C4 |
| Cowley, Glouc | 36 | C2 |
| Cowley, G Lon | 141 | A1 |
| Cowling, N York | 93 | A3 |
| Cowlinge, Suff | 53 | A3 |
| Cowshill, Durham | 97 | E2 |
| Cowslip Green, Som | 23 | D3 |
| Cowthorpe, N York | 88 | B2 |
| Coxbank, Chesh | 68 | C3 |
| Coxbench, Derby | 70 | C3 |
| Coxford, Norf | 74 | D4 |
| Coxhoe, Durham | 98 | D2 |
| Coxley, Som | 23 | D4 |
| Coxley Wick, Som | 23 | D4 |
| Coxtie Green, Essex | 41 | B4 |
| Coxwold, N York | 93 | D3 |
| Coychurch, Brid | 22 | E1 |
| Coylton, S Ayr | 106 | D3 |
| Coylumbridge, High | 127 | D3 |
| Coytrahen, Brid | 22 | E1 |
| Crabtree, W Suss | 18 | B2 |
| Crackenthorpe, Cumb | 97 | C4 |
| Crackington Haven, Corn | 9 | A4 |
| Crackleybank, Shrop | 57 | B2 |
| Cracoe, N York | 86 | D1 |
| Craddock, Devon | 10 | D3 |
| Cradley, Heref | 47 | B3 |
| Cradoc, Powys | 34 | C1 |
| Crafthole, Corn | 4 | B4 |
| Crafton, Bucks | 39 | A2 |
| Cragg Vale, W York | 86 | D4 |
| Craghead, Durham | 98 | C1 |
| Crai, Powys | 34 | B1 |
| Craig Llangiwg, Neath | 33 | D3 |
| Craigbank, E Ayr | 106 | F4 |
| Craigellachie, Moray | 133 | C4 |
| Craighouse, Argyll | 110 | D3 |
| Craigie, Perth | 123 | B4 |
| Craigie, S Ayr | 106 | E2 |
| Craignure, Argyll | 116 | E1 |
| Craigo, Angus | 124 | B3 |
| Craigrothie, Fife | 119 | D3 |
| Craigton, Angus | 119 | E1 |
| Craigton of Airlie, Angus | 123 | D4 |
| Crail, Fife | 119 | F3 |
| Crailing, Bord | 108 | D3 |
| Craiselound, Linc | 83 | B2 |

| PLACE | PAGE | GRID |
|---|---|---|
| Crakehall, N York | 93 | A2 |
| Crambe, N York | 94 | A4 |
| Cramlington, Nthumb | 104 | B3 |
| Cranage, Chesh | 69 | A1 |
| Cranberry, Staff | 69 | B4 |
| Cranborne, Dors | 13 | B3 |
| Cranbrook, Kent | 21 | A1 |
| Cranfield, Beds | 50 | C4 |
| Cranford, G Lon | 141 | B2 |
| Cranford St Andrew, Nhants | 50 | C1 |
| Cranford St John, Nhants | 50 | C1 |
| Cranham, Glouc | 36 | B2 |
| Crank, Mers | 78 | B2 |
| Cranleigh, Surr | 17 | B1 |
| Cranmore, Som | 24 | A4 |
| Cranoe, Leics | 61 | A3 |
| Cransford, Suff | 54 | B2 |
| Cranshaws, Bord | 115 | B3 |
| Crantock, Corn | 3 | B4 |
| Cranwell, Linc | 73 | A2 |
| Cranwich, Norf | 63 | B3 |
| Cranworth, Norf | 63 | C2 |
| Crarae, Argyll | 117 | B4 |
| Craswall, Heref | 46 | B4 |
| Cratfield, Suff | 54 | B1 |
| Crathes, Aber | 129 | A4 |
| Crathie, Aber | 128 | B4 |
| Crathie, High | 127 | A4 |
| Craven Arms, Shrop | 56 | C4 |
| Crawford, S Lan | 107 | C3 |
| Crawfordjohn, S Lan | 107 | B3 |
| Crawick, D & G | 107 | B4 |
| Crawley, Hamp | 15 | A1 |
| Crawley, Oxon | 37 | C2 |
| Crawley, W Suss | 18 | B1 |
| Crawshawbooth, Lanc | 86 | C4 |
| Crawton, Aber | 124 | D1 |
| Cray, N York | 92 | D3 |
| Crayford, G Lon | 144 | C3 |
| Crayke, N York | 93 | D4 |
| Crays Hill, Essex | 42 | A4 |
| Craze Lowman, Devon | 10 | C3 |
| Creacombe, Devon | 10 | B2 |
| Creaton, Nhants | 50 | A1 |
| Credenhill, Heref | 46 | C4 |
| Crediton, Devon | 10 | B4 |
| Creekmouth, G Lon | 144 | B1 |
| Creeting St Mary, Suff | 53 | D2 |
| Creeton, Linc | 61 | C1 |
| Creetown, D & G | 100 | E4 |
| Cregneash, I o M | 139 | A4 |
| Creigiau, Cardiff | 22 | F1 |
| Cremyll, Corn | 4 | C4 |
| Cressage, Shrop | 57 | A2 |
| Cressbrook, Derby | 81 | B4 |
| Cresselly, Pemb | 32 | D3 |
| Cresswell, Nthumb | 104 | C1 |
| Cresswell, Pemb | 32 | D3 |
| Cresswell, Staff | 69 | C3 |
| Creswell, Derby | 82 | B4 |
| Cretingham, Suff | 54 | A2 |
| Crew Green, Powys | 56 | B1 |
| Crewe, Chesh | 68 | A2 |
| Crewe, Chesh | 69 | A2 |
| Crewe Green, Chesh | 69 | A2 |
| Crewkerne, Som | 11 | C3 |
| Crianlarich, Stirl | 117 | E2 |
| Cribyn, Cered | 44 | F3 |
| Criccieth, Gwyn | 66 | D3 |
| Crick, Nhants | 49 | C1 |
| Crickadarn, Powys | 45 | E4 |
| Crickhowell, Powys | 34 | D2 |
| Cricklade, Wilts | 37 | A4 |
| Cricklewood, G Lon | 142 | B1 |
| Cridling Stubbs, N York | 88 | C4 |
| Crieff, Perth | 118 | D2 |
| Criggion, Powys | 56 | B1 |
| Crigglestone, W York | 81 | C1 |
| Crimond, Aber | 134 | E3 |
| Crimplesham, Norf | 62 | D2 |
| Crinan, Argyll | 110 | F1 |
| Cringleford, Norf | 64 | B2 |
| Crinow, Pemb | 32 | E2 |
| Crockenhill, Kent | 144 | C4 |
| Crockernwell, Devon | 5 | A1 |
| Crockerton, Wilts | 25 | A4 |
| Crocketford, D & G | 101 | C3 |
| Croeserw, Neath | 34 | A4 |
| Croes-goch, Pemb | 32 | B1 |
| Croes-lan, Cered | 44 | E4 |
| Croesor, Gwyn | 66 | E3 |
| Croesyceiliog, Carm | 33 | A2 |
| Croft, Chesh | 79 | A3 |
| Croft, Leics | 60 | B3 |
| Croft, Linc | 74 | A1 |
| Croftamie, Stirl | 112 | A1 |
| Crofton, W York | 81 | C1 |
| Crofty, Swan | 33 | B4 |
| Croggan, Argyll | 116 | E2 |
| Croglin, Cumb | 97 | B1 |
| Cromarty, High | 132 | D2 |
| Cromdale, High | 127 | E1 |
| Cromer, Herts | 40 | A1 |
| Cromer, Norf | 75 | B3 |
| Cromford, Derby | 70 | C2 |
| Cromhall, Glouc | 36 | A4 |
| Cromwell, Notts | 72 | B1 |
| Cronberry, E Ayr | 106 | F3 |
| Crondall, Hamp | 27 | B4 |
| Cronton, Mers | 78 | B3 |
| Crook, Cumb | 91 | F2 |
| Crook, Durham | 98 | C2 |
| Crooked Holme, Cumb | 102 | D4 |
| Crookham, Berks | 26 | C2 |
| Crookham, Nthumb | 109 | B1 |
| Crookham Village, Hamp | 27 | B4 |
| Cropredy, Oxon | 49 | B3 |
| Cropston, Leics | 60 | B2 |
| Cropthorne, Worc | 48 | A3 |
| Cropton, N York | 94 | B2 |
| Cropwell Bishop, Notts | 72 | A4 |
| Crosby, Cumb | 96 | D2 |
| Crosby, Mers | 77 | D2 |
| Crosby, I o M | 139 | C3 |
| Crosby Garret, Cumb | 92 | B1 |

| PLACE | PAGE | GRID |
|---|---|---|
| Crosby Ravensworth, Cumb | 97 | C4 |
| Croscombe, Som | 24 | A4 |
| Cross, Som | 23 | C3 |
| Cross Ash, Monm | 35 | A2 |
| Cross Green, Suff | 53 | B3 |
| Cross Green, Suff | 53 | C3 |
| Cross Hands, Carm | 33 | C2 |
| Cross Houses, Shrop | 56 | D2 |
| Cross in Hand, E Sus | 20 | A2 |
| Cross Inn, Cered | 44 | E2 |
| Cross Keys, Argyll | 111 | E1 |
| Cross Lane Head, Shrop | 57 | B3 |
| Cross o' th' hands, Derby | 70 | C3 |
| Crossaig, Argyll | 110 | F4 |
| Crossapoll, Argyll | 120 | A4 |
| Cross-at-Hand, Kent | 30 | A4 |
| Crosscanonby, Cumb | 96 | D2 |
| Crossford, Fife | 113 | C1 |
| Crossford, S Lan | 107 | B1 |
| Crossgatehall, E Loth | 114 | C3 |
| Crossgill, Lanc | 85 | C1 |
| Crosshands, E Ayr | 106 | E2 |
| Crosshill, S Ayr | 106 | D4 |
| Crosskeys, Caer | 34 | D4 |
| Crosslands, Cumb | 91 | D2 |
| Crosslee, Renf | 111 | E3 |
| Crossmichael, D & G | 101 | B4 |
| Crosswell, Pemb | 44 | C4 |
| Crosthwaite, Cumb | 91 | E2 |
| Croston, Lanc | 85 | C4 |
| Crostwick, Norf | 65 | A1 |
| Crouch Hill, Dors | 12 | C3 |
| Croucheston, Wilts | 13 | B2 |
| Crough House Green, Kent | 149 | B4 |
| Croughton, Nhants | 38 | A1 |
| Crovie, Aber | 134 | B2 |
| Crow Edge, S York | 81 | B2 |
| Crow Hill, Heref | 35 | C1 |
| Crowan, Corn | 1 | D2 |
| Crowborough, E Sus | 19 | B1 |
| Crowcombe, Som | 11 | A1 |
| Crowdecote, Derby | 70 | A1 |
| Crowell, Oxon | 38 | C3 |
| Crowfield, Suff | 54 | A2 |
| Crowhurst, E Sus | 20 | B3 |
| Crowhurst, Surr | 149 | A3 |
| Crowhurst Lane End, Surr | 149 | A3 |
| Crowland, Linc | 62 | A2 |
| Crowland, Suff | 53 | D1 |
| Crowlas, Corn | 1 | C2 |
| Crowle, Linc | 83 | B1 |
| Crowle, Worc | 47 | C3 |
| Crowle Green, Worc | 47 | C3 |
| Crown Corner, Suff | 54 | B1 |
| Crownpits, Surr | 146 | A4 |
| Crownthorpe, Norf | 64 | A2 |
| Crows-an-Wra, Corn | 1 | B2 |
| Crowthorne, Berks | 27 | B3 |
| Crowton, Chesh | 78 | B4 |
| Croxdale, Durham | 98 | C2 |
| Croxden, Staff | 70 | A3 |
| Croxton, Camb | 51 | C2 |
| Croxton, Linc | 84 | A1 |
| Croxton, Norf | 74 | E4 |
| Croxton, Norf | 63 | B4 |
| Croxton Kerrial, Leics | 72 | B4 |
| Croy, High | 132 | D3 |
| Croy, N Lan | 112 | C2 |
| Croyde, Devon | 9 | D1 |
| Croydon, Camb | 52 | A3 |
| Croydon, G Lon | 143 | B4 |
| Cruckmeole, Shrop | 56 | C2 |
| Cruckton, Shrop | 56 | C2 |
| Cruden Bay, Aber | 134 | E4 |
| Crudgington, Shrop | 57 | A1 |
| Crudwell, Wilts | 36 | C4 |
| Crug-y-byddar, Powys | 56 | A4 |
| Crumlin, Caer | 34 | D4 |
| Crumplehorn, Corn | 4 | A4 |
| Crundale, Kent | 30 | C4 |
| Crunwear, Pemb | 32 | E2 |
| Crux Easton, Hamp | 26 | B3 |
| Crwbin, Carm | 33 | B2 |
| Cryers Hill, Bucks | 39 | A4 |
| Crymmych, Pemb | 44 | C4 |
| Crynant, Neath | 34 | A3 |
| Crystal Palace, G Lon | 143 | B3 |
| Cubert, Corn | 3 | B4 |
| Cublington, Bucks | 38 | C1 |
| Cublington, Heref | 46 | C4 |
| Cuckfield, W Suss | 18 | B2 |
| Cucklington, Som | 12 | C2 |
| Cuckney, Notts | 71 | B1 |
| Cuddesdon, Oxon | 38 | A3 |
| Cuddington, Bucks | 38 | C2 |
| Cuddington, Chesh | 68 | C1 |
| Cuddington Heath, Chesh | 68 | B3 |
| Cudham, G Lon | 149 | B1 |
| Cudworth, S York | 81 | C1 |
| Cudworth, Som | 11 | C3 |
| Cuffley, Herts | 40 | A3 |
| Culbokie, High | 132 | B2 |
| Culcheth, Chesh | 79 | A3 |
| Culford, Suff | 53 | B1 |
| Culgaith, Cumb | 97 | C3 |
| Culham, Oxon | 38 | A4 |
| Culkein Drumbeg, High | 137 | A4 |
| Culkerton, Glouc | 36 | C4 |
| Cullen, Moray | 133 | E2 |
| Cullingworth, W York | 87 | A3 |
| Culloden, High | 132 | C3 |
| Cullompton, Devon | 10 | D3 |
| Culm Davy, Devon | 11 | A3 |
| Culmington, Shrop | 56 | D4 |
| Culmstock, Devon | 10 | D3 |
| Culross, Fife | 113 | B1 |
| Culroy, S Ayr | 106 | D4 |
| Culsalmond, Aber | 128 | E1 |
| Cultercullen, Aber | 129 | B1 |
| Culverstone Green, Kent | 29 | A3 |
| Culverthorpe, Linc | 73 | A3 |
| Culworth, Nhants | 49 | C3 |
| Cumbernauld, N Lan | 112 | C2 |
| Cumberworth, Linc | 84 | D4 |

| PLACE | PAGE | GRID |
|---|---|---|
| Cuminestown, Aber | 134 | B3 |
| Cummertrees, D & G | 102 | A4 |
| Cummingston, Moray | 133 | B1 |
| Cumnock, E Ayr | 106 | F3 |
| Cumnor, Oxon | 37 | D3 |
| Cumrew, Cumb | 97 | B1 |
| Cumwhinton, Cumb | 97 | A1 |
| Cumwhitton, Cumb | 97 | B1 |
| Cundall, N York | 93 | C4 |
| Cupar, Fife | 119 | D3 |
| Cupar Muir, Fife | 119 | D3 |
| Curbar, Derby | 81 | B4 |
| Curbridge, Hamp | 15 | B3 |
| Curbridge, Oxon | 37 | C3 |
| Curdridge, Hamp | 15 | B3 |
| Curdworth, Warw | 59 | A3 |
| Curland, Som | 11 | B3 |
| Curridge, Berks | 26 | B2 |
| Currie, Edin | 114 | A3 |
| Curry Mallet, Som | 11 | B2 |
| Curry Rivel, Som | 11 | C2 |
| Curtisden Green, Kent | 20 | B1 |
| Curtisknowle, Devon | 5 | A4 |
| Cury, Corn | 1 | D3 |
| Cushnie, Aber | 128 | D2 |
| Cusop, Heref | 46 | B4 |
| Cutcombe, Som | 10 | C1 |
| Cutsdean, Glouc | 37 | A1 |
| Cutthorpe, Derby | 81 | C4 |
| Cuxton, Kent | 29 | B2 |
| Cuxwold, Linc | 84 | A2 |
| Cwm, Denb | 77 | B4 |
| Cwm Crawnon, Powys | 34 | D2 |
| Cwm Morgan, Carm | 44 | D4 |
| Cwmafan, Neath | 34 | A4 |
| Cwmaman, Rhond | 34 | C3 |
| Cwmbach, Carm | 32 | F1 |
| Cwmbach, Powys | 46 | A4 |
| Cwmbach, Rhond | 34 | C3 |
| Cwmbach Llechrhyd, Powys | 45 | E3 |
| Cwmbran, Torf | 34 | E4 |
| Cwmcarn, Caer | 34 | D4 |
| Cwmcarvan, Monm | 35 | B3 |
| Cwm-cou, Cered | 44 | D4 |
| Cwmdare, Rhond | 34 | B3 |
| Cwmdu, Powys | 34 | D1 |
| Cwmduad, Carm | 33 | A1 |
| Cwmfelin, Brid | 34 | A4 |
| Cwmfelin, Merth | 34 | C3 |
| Cwmfelin Boeth, Carm | 32 | E2 |
| Cwmfelinfach, Caer | 34 | D4 |
| Cwmffrwd, Carm | 33 | A2 |
| Cwmgiedd, Powys | 34 | A2 |
| Cwmgorse, Carm | 33 | D3 |
| Cwmhiraeth, Carm | 44 | E4 |
| Cwm-Llinau, Powys | 55 | C2 |
| Cwmllynfell, Neath | 33 | D2 |
| Cwmpengraig, Carm | 44 | E4 |
| Cwmsychbant, Cered | 44 | F3 |
| Cwmtillery, Gwent | 34 | D3 |
| Cwm-y-glo, Carm | 33 | C2 |
| Cwm-y-glo, Gwyn | 66 | E1 |
| Cwmystwyth, Cered | 45 | C1 |
| Cwrt-newydd, Cered | 44 | F3 |
| Cylibebyll, Neath | 33 | D3 |
| Cymer, Neath | 34 | A4 |
| Cynghordy, Carm | 45 | C4 |
| Cynonville, Neath | 34 | A4 |
| Cynwyd, Denb | 67 | C3 |
| Cynwyl Elfed, Carm | 33 | A1 |
| Dacre, Cumb | 97 | A3 |
| Dacre, N York | 87 | B1 |
| Daddry Shield, Durham | 97 | E2 |
| Dadford, Bucks | 50 | A4 |
| Dadlington, Leics | 60 | A3 |
| Dagenham, G Lon | 144 | C1 |
| Daglingworth, Glouc | 36 | C3 |
| Dagnall, Bucks | 39 | B2 |
| Dailly, S Ayr | 100 | C1 |
| Dainton, Devon | 5 | B3 |
| Dairsie, Fife | 119 | D3 |
| Dalbeattie, D & G | 101 | C4 |
| Dalby, N York | 94 | A4 |
| Dalcapon, Perth | 123 | A3 |
| Dalcrue, Perth | 119 | A2 |
| Dalditch, Devon | 6 | A1 |
| Dale, Derby | 71 | A3 |
| Dale, Pemb | 32 | B3 |
| Dalgety Bay, Fife | 114 | A2 |
| Dalginross, Perth | 118 | D2 |
| Dalguise, Perth | 123 | A4 |
| Dalhalvaig, High | 138 | B2 |
| Dalham, Suff | 53 | A2 |
| Dalkeith, M Loth | 114 | B3 |
| Dallas, Moray | 133 | B3 |
| Dallinghoo, Suff | 54 | B3 |
| Dallington, E Sus | 20 | A2 |
| Dalmally, Argyll | 117 | C2 |
| Dalmellington, E Ayr | 106 | E4 |
| Dalmeny, Edin | 114 | A2 |
| Dalry, N Ayr | 111 | D4 |
| Dalrymple, E Ayr | 106 | D4 |
| Dalserf, S Lan | 113 | A4 |
| Dalston, Cumb | 97 | A1 |
| Dalston, G Lon | 143 | B1 |
| Dalswinton, D & G | 101 | D2 |
| Dalton, D & G | 101 | E3 |
| Dalton, N York | 92 | E1 |
| Dalton, N York | 93 | C3 |
| Dalton, Nthumb | 104 | A3 |
| Dalton Piercy, Durham | 99 | A3 |
| Dalton-in-Furness, Cumb | 91 | C4 |
| Dalton-le-Dale, Durham | 99 | A1 |
| Dalton-on-Tees, N York | 93 | B1 |
| Dalveich, Stirl | 118 | B2 |
| Dalwhinnie, High | 122 | C1 |
| Damerham, Hamp | 13 | B3 |
| Damgate, Norf | 65 | B2 |
| Danbury, Essex | 42 | B3 |
| Danby, N York | 94 | A1 |
| Danby Wiske, N York | 93 | B2 |
| Dane Street, Kent | 30 | C3 |
| Danebridge, Chesh | 69 | C1 |
| Danehill, E Sus | 19 | A2 |
| Daresbury, Chesh | 78 | B4 |

| PLACE | PAGE | GRID |
|---|---|---|
| Darfield, S York | 82 | A2 |
| Dargate, Kent | 30 | C3 |
| Darite, Corn | 4 | A3 |
| Darley, N York | 87 | B1 |
| Darley Bridge, Derby | 70 | B1 |
| Darley Dale, Derby | 70 | B1 |
| Darley Green, W Mids | 48 | C1 |
| Darleyhall, Herts | 39 | C1 |
| Darlingscott, Warw | 48 | C4 |
| Darlington, Durham | 98 | D4 |
| Darowen, Powys | 55 | C3 |
| Darracott, Devon | 9 | B3 |
| Darracott, Devon | 9 | D1 |
| Darras Hall, Nthumb | 104 | A3 |
| Darrington, W York | 88 | B4 |
| Darsham, Suff | 54 | C1 |
| Darshill, Som | 24 | A4 |
| Dartford, Kent | 144 | C3 |
| Dartington, Devon | 5 | B3 |
| Dartmouth, Devon | 5 | B4 |
| Darvel, E Ayr | 106 | F2 |
| Darwen, Lanc | 86 | A4 |
| Datchet, Berks | 140 | C2 |
| Datchworth, Herts | 40 | A2 |
| Dauntsey, Wilts | 25 | B1 |
| Dauntsey Green, Wilts | 25 | B1 |
| Dava, High | 133 | A4 |
| Davenham, Chesh | 68 | C1 |
| Daventry, Nhants | 49 | C2 |
| Davidstow, Corn | 3 | E1 |
| Davington, D & G | 102 | B1 |
| Daviot, Aber | 129 | A1 |
| Daviot, High | 132 | C4 |
| Dawesgreen, Surr | 148 | A3 |
| Dawlish, Devon | 5 | C2 |
| Dawlish Warren, Devon | 5 | C2 |
| Dawn, Ab & Col | 76 | F4 |
| Daylesford, Glouc | 37 | B1 |
| Deal, Kent | 31 | C4 |
| Dean, Cumb | 96 | D3 |
| Dean, Devon | 22 | C4 |
| Dean, Devon | 5 | A3 |
| Dean, Hamp | 15 | A1 |
| Dean, Hamp | 15 | B2 |
| Dean, Oxon | 37 | C1 |
| Dean Bottom, Kent | 29 | A2 |
| Dean Prior, Devon | 5 | A3 |
| Deanburnhaugh, Bord | 108 | B4 |
| Deancombe, Devon | 5 | A3 |
| Deane, Hamp | 26 | C4 |
| Deanhead, W York | 81 | A1 |
| Deanland, Dors | 13 | A2 |
| Deanraw, Nthumb | 103 | C4 |
| Deanscales, Cumb | 96 | D3 |
| Deanshanger, Nhants | 50 | B4 |
| Dearham, Cumb | 96 | D2 |
| Debach, Suff | 54 | B3 |
| Debden, Essex | 41 | B1 |
| Debenham, Suff | 54 | A2 |
| Deblin's Green, Worc | 47 | C3 |
| Deddington, Oxon | 37 | D1 |
| Dedham, Essex | 43 | B1 |
| Dedworth, Berks | 140 | B2 |
| Deene, Nhants | 61 | B3 |
| Deenethorpe, Nhants | 61 | B3 |
| Deepcut, Surr | 145 | A2 |
| Deeping St Nicholas, Linc | 62 | A1 |
| Deerhurst, Glouc | 36 | B1 |
| Defford, Worc | 47 | C4 |
| Defynnog, Powys | 34 | B1 |
| Deganwy, Ab & Col | 76 | F4 |
| Deighton, N York | 93 | B1 |
| Deighton, N York | 89 | A2 |
| Deiniolen, Gwyn | 66 | E1 |
| Delabole, Corn | 3 | D1 |
| Delamere, Chesh | 68 | B1 |
| Dell Quay, W Suss | 16 | B4 |
| Dembleby, Linc | 73 | A3 |
| Den of Lindores, Fife | 119 | C3 |
| Denaby, S York | 82 | A2 |
| Denbies, Surr | 147 | B3 |
| Denbigh, Denb | 67 | C1 |
| Denbury, Devon | 5 | B3 |
| Denby, Derby | 71 | A3 |
| Denby Dale, W York | 81 | B1 |
| Denchworth, Oxon | 37 | C4 |
| Denford, Nhants | 51 | A1 |
| Dengie, Essex | 43 | A3 |
| Denham, Bucks | 141 | A1 |
| Denham, Suff | 53 | A2 |
| Denham, Suff | 54 | A1 |
| Denham Green, Bucks | 39 | B4 |
| Denholm, Bord | 108 | C3 |
| Denholme, W York | 87 | A3 |
| Denmead, Hamp | 16 | A3 |
| Dennington, Suff | 54 | B2 |
| Denny, Falkirk | 113 | A2 |
| Dennyloanhead, Falkirk | 113 | A2 |
| Densole, Kent | 31 | A4 |
| Denston, Suff | 53 | A3 |
| Denstone, Staff | 70 | A3 |
| Denstroude, Kent | 30 | C3 |
| Dent, Cumb | 92 | B3 |
| Denton, Camb | 61 | D4 |
| Denton, G Man | 80 | A3 |
| Denton, Kent | 31 | A4 |
| Denton, Linc | 72 | C4 |
| Denton, N York | 87 | A2 |
| Denton, Nhants | 50 | B2 |
| Denton, Norf | 65 | A4 |
| Denver, Norf | 62 | D3 |
| Denwick, Nthumb | 109 | E4 |
| Deopham, Norf | 64 | A3 |
| Deopham Green, Norf | 64 | A3 |
| Deptford, Wilts | 13 | A1 |
| Deptford, G Lon | 144 | A2 |
| Derby, Derby | 70 | C4 |
| Derbyhaven, I o M | 139 | B4 |
| Dereham, Norf | 63 | C2 |
| Deri, Caer | 34 | D3 |
| Derringstone, Kent | 31 | A4 |
| Derrington, Staff | 57 | C1 |
| Derry Hill, Wilts | 25 | B2 |
| Dersingham, Norf | 74 | C4 |
| Dervaig, Argyll | 120 | E4 |
| Derwen, Denb | 67 | C2 |

| PLACE | PAGE | GRID |
|---|---|---|
| Derwenlas, Powys | 55 | B3 |
| Desborough, Nhants | 61 | A4 |
| Desford, Leics | 60 | A2 |
| Deskford, Moray | 133 | E2 |
| Detling, Kent | 30 | A3 |
| Devauden, Monm | 35 | B4 |
| Devizes, Wilts | 25 | B3 |
| Devonside, Clack | 118 | E4 |
| Devoran, Corn | 2 | A1 |
| Dewlish, Dors | 12 | C4 |
| Dewsbury, W York | 87 | B4 |
| Deytheur, Powys | 56 | B1 |
| Dial Post, W Suss | 18 | A2 |
| Dibden, Hamp | 15 | A3 |
| Dickleburgh, Norf | 64 | B4 |
| Didbrook, Glouc | 37 | A1 |
| Didcot, Oxon | 38 | A4 |
| Diddington, Camb | 51 | B2 |
| Diddlebury, Shrop | 56 | D4 |
| Didling, W Suss | 16 | B2 |
| Didmarton, Glouc | 25 | A1 |
| Digby, Linc | 73 | A2 |
| Diggle, G Man | 80 | B1 |
| Dihewyd, Cered | 44 | F3 |
| Dilham, Norf | 65 | A1 |
| Dilhorne, Staff | 69 | C3 |
| Dillington, Camb | 51 | B2 |
| Dilston, Nthumb | 103 | D4 |
| Dilton, Wilts | 25 | A4 |
| Dilton Marsh, Wilts | 25 | A4 |
| Dilwyn, Heref | 46 | C3 |
| Dinas, Gwyn | 66 | B4 |
| Dinas, Pemb | 44 | B4 |
| Dinas-Mawddwy, Gwyn | 55 | C1 |
| Dinder, Som | 23 | D4 |
| Dinedor, Heref | 46 | D4 |
| Dingestow, Monm | 35 | A3 |
| Dingley, Nhants | 61 | A4 |
| Dingwall, High | 132 | B2 |
| Dinnington, S York | 82 | B3 |
| Dinnington, Som | 11 | C3 |
| Dinnington, T & W | 104 | B3 |
| Dinorwic, Gwyn | 66 | E1 |
| Dinton, Bucks | 38 | C2 |
| Dinton, Wilts | 13 | A1 |
| Dinworthy, Devon | 9 | B3 |
| Dippertown, Devon | 4 | C1 |
| Diptford, Devon | 5 | A4 |
| Dipton, Durham | 98 | C1 |
| Dirleton, E Loth | 115 | A2 |
| Dirt Pot, Nthumb | 97 | E1 |
| Diseworth, Leics | 60 | A1 |
| Dishforth, N York | 93 | B4 |
| Disley, Chesh | 80 | B3 |
| Diss, Norf | 64 | A4 |
| Distington, Cumb | 96 | D3 |
| Ditchburn, Nthumb | 109 | D3 |
| Ditcheat, Som | 12 | B1 |
| Ditchingham, Norf | 65 | A4 |
| Ditchling, E Sus | 19 | A3 |
| Ditteridge, Wilts | 25 | A2 |
| Dittisham, Devon | 5 | B4 |
| Ditton, Kent | 29 | B3 |
| Ditton Green, Camb | 52 | C2 |
| Ditton Priors, Shrop | 57 | A4 |
| Dixton, Glouc | 36 | C1 |
| Dixton, Monm | 35 | B2 |
| Dobcross, G Man | 80 | B2 |
| Dobwalls, Corn | 4 | A3 |
| Doccombe, Devon | 5 | B1 |
| Docker, Lanc | 91 | F4 |
| Docking, Norf | 74 | C4 |
| Docklow, Heref | 46 | D2 |
| Dockray, Cumb | 97 | A4 |
| Doddinghurst, Essex | 41 | B3 |
| Doddington, Camb | 62 | B4 |
| Doddington, Kent | 30 | B3 |
| Doddington, Linc | 72 | C1 |
| Doddington, Nthumb | 109 | C2 |
| Doddiscombsleigh, Devon | 5 | B1 |
| Dodd's Green, Chesh | 68 | C3 |
| Dodford, Nhants | 49 | C2 |
| Dodford, Worc | 48 | A1 |
| Dodington, Glouc | 24 | B1 |
| Dodington, Som | 11 | A1 |
| Dodleston, Chesh | 68 | A1 |
| Dod's Leigh, Staff | 69 | C4 |
| Dodworth, S York | 81 | C2 |
| Dog Village, Devon | 10 | C4 |
| Dogdyke, Linc | 73 | C2 |
| Dogmersfield, Hamp | 27 | B3 |
| Dolanog, Powys | 55 | E2 |
| Dolbenmaen, Gwyn | 66 | D3 |
| Dolfach, Powys | 55 | D3 |
| Dolfor, Powys | 55 | E4 |
| Dolgarrog, Ab & Col | 66 | F1 |
| Dolgellau, Gwyn | 55 | B1 |
| Dollar, Clack | 118 | E4 |
| Dolphin, Flint | 77 | C4 |
| Dolphinholme, Lanc | 85 | C1 |
| Dolphinton, S Lan | 107 | D1 |
| Dolton, Devon | 9 | E3 |
| Dolwen, Ab & Col | 76 | F4 |
| Dolwyddelan, Ab & Col | 66 | F2 |
| Domgay, Powys | 56 | B1 |
| Doncaster, S York | 82 | B2 |
| Donhead St Andrew, Wilts | 12 | D2 |
| Donhead St Mary, Wilts | 12 | D2 |
| Doniford, Som | 22 | F4 |
| Donington, Linc | 73 | C4 |
| Donington on Bain, Linc | 84 | B4 |
| Donisthorpe, Leics | 59 | B2 |
| Donkey Town, Surr | 145 | B1 |
| Donnington, Glouc | 37 | B1 |
| Donnington, Shrop | 56 | D2 |
| Donyatt, Som | 11 | B3 |
| Dorchester, Oxon | 38 | A4 |
| Dorchester, Dors | 6 | F1 |
| Dordon, Warw | 59 | A3 |
| Dores, High | 132 | B4 |
| Dorking, Surr | 147 | B3 |
| Dormington, Heref | 47 | A4 |
| Dormston, Worc | 48 | A2 |
| Dorney, Bucks | 140 | B2 |
| Dornie, High | 126 | A1 |
| Dornoch, High | 136 | D4 |

| PLACE | PAGE | GRID |
|---|---|---|
| Dornock, D & G | 102 | A4 |
| Dorridge, W Mids | 48 | C1 |
| Dorrington, Linc | 73 | A2 |
| Dorrington, Shrop | 56 | D2 |
| Dorrington, Shrop | 69 | A3 |
| Dorsington, Warw | 48 | B3 |
| Dorstone, Heref | 46 | B4 |
| Dorton, Bucks | 38 | B2 |
| Douglas, S Lan | 107 | B2 |
| Douglas, I o M | 139 | C4 |
| Douglas Water, S Lan | 107 | B2 |
| Douglastown, Angus | 123 | E4 |
| Doulting, Som | 24 | A4 |
| Dounby, Ork | 139 | A1 |
| Doune, Stirl | 118 | C4 |
| Dousland, Devon | 4 | C3 |
| Dove Holes, Derby | 81 | A4 |
| Dovenby, Cumb | 96 | D3 |
| Dover, Kent | 31 | B4 |
| Doverdale, Worc | 47 | C2 |
| Doveridge, Derby | 70 | A4 |
| Doversgreen, Surr | 148 | B3 |
| Dowally, Perth | 123 | A4 |
| Dowdeswell, Glouc | 36 | C2 |
| Dowland, Devon | 9 | E3 |
| Down Ampney, Glouc | 37 | A4 |
| Down Hatherley, Glouc | 36 | B1 |
| Down St Mary, Devon | 10 | A4 |
| Down Thomas, Devon | 4 | C4 |
| Downderry, Corn | 4 | B4 |
| Downe, G Lon | 149 | B1 |
| Downend, Glouc | 36 | B4 |
| Downgate, Corn | 4 | A3 |
| Downgate, Corn | 4 | B2 |
| Downham, Camb | 62 | C4 |
| Downham, Essex | 42 | A4 |
| Downham, Lanc | 86 | B2 |
| Downham, G Lon | 144 | A3 |
| Downham Market, Norf | 62 | D2 |
| Downhead, Som | 12 | A2 |
| Downhead, Som | 24 | A4 |
| Downholme, N York | 92 | E2 |
| Downside, Surr | 147 | A2 |
| Downton, Hamp | 7 | E1 |
| Downton, Wilts | 14 | A2 |
| Downton on the Rock, Heref | 46 | C1 |
| Dowsby, Linc | 73 | B4 |
| Doynton, Glouc | 24 | B2 |
| Draethen, Caer | 23 | A1 |
| Draffan, S Lan | 107 | B1 |
| Drakeholes, Notts | 83 | A3 |
| Drakemyre, N Ayr | 111 | D4 |
| Drakes Broughton, Worc | 48 | A3 |
| Draughton, N York | 86 | D2 |
| Draughton, Nhants | 50 | B1 |
| Drax, N York | 89 | A4 |
| Draycote, Warw | 49 | B1 |
| Draycott, Glouc | 48 | C4 |
| Draycott, Som | 23 | D4 |
| Draycott in the Clay, Staff | 70 | A4 |
| Draycott in the Moors, Staff | 69 | C3 |
| Drayton, Leics | 61 | A3 |
| Drayton, Norf | 64 | B2 |
| Drayton, Oxon | 49 | B4 |
| Drayton, Oxon | 37 | D4 |
| Drayton, Som | 11 | C2 |
| Drayton, Worc | 47 | C1 |
| Drayton Bassett, Staff | 59 | A3 |
| Drayton Beauchamp, Bucks | 39 | A2 |
| Drayton Parslow, Bucks | 38 | C1 |
| Dreen Hill, Pemb | 32 | C2 |
| Drefach, Carm | 44 | E4 |
| Drefach, Carm | 33 | B2 |
| Drefach, Cered | 44 | F3 |
| Drellingore, Kent | 21 | E1 |
| Drem, E Loth | 115 | A2 |
| Drewsteignton, Devon | 5 | A1 |
| Driby, Linc | 84 | C4 |
| Driffield, Glouc | 37 | A3 |
| Driffield, E R of Y | 89 | D1 |
| Drift, Corn | 1 | B2 |
| Drigg, Cumb | 91 | B1 |
| Drighlington, W York | 87 | B4 |
| Drimnin, High | 120 | F3 |
| Drimpton, Dors | 11 | C4 |
| Drinkstone, Suff | 53 | C2 |
| Drinkstone Green, Suff | 53 | C2 |
| Drointon, Staff | 69 | C4 |
| Droitwich, Worc | 47 | C2 |
| Dron, Perth | 119 | B3 |
| Dronfield, Derby | 81 | C4 |
| Drongan, E Ayr | 106 | E3 |
| Dronley, Angus | 119 | C1 |
| Droop, Dors | 12 | C3 |
| Droxford, Hamp | 15 | B2 |
| Droylsden, G Man | 80 | A2 |
| Druid, Denb | 67 | C3 |
| Druidston, Pemb | 32 | C2 |
| Drum, Perth | 119 | A4 |
| Drumbeg, High | 137 | A4 |
| Drumburgh, Cumb | 102 | B4 |
| Drumburn, D & G | 96 | B1 |
| Drumclog, S Lan | 106 | F1 |
| Drumeldrie, Fife | 119 | D4 |
| Drumelzier, Bord | 107 | E2 |
| Drumleaning, Cumb | 96 | F1 |
| Drumlithie, Aber | 124 | C1 |
| Drummuir, Moray | 133 | D4 |
| Drumnadrochit, High | 126 | F1 |
| Drunzie, Perth | 119 | B3 |
| Dry Doddington, Linc | 72 | C3 |
| Dry Drayton, Camb | 52 | A2 |
| Drybeck, Cumb | 97 | C4 |
| Drybridge, N Ayr | 106 | D2 |
| Drybrook, Glouc | 35 | C2 |
| Dryburgh, Bord | 108 | D2 |
| Drym, Corn | 1 | D2 |
| Drymen, Stirl | 112 | A1 |
| Drynoch, High | 125 | D1 |
| Dryton, Shrop | 57 | A2 |
| Ducklington, Oxon | 37 | C3 |
| Duddington, Nhants | 61 | C3 |
| Duddlestone, Som | 11 | B2 |
| Duddlewick, Shrop | 57 | A4 |

| PLACE | PAGE | GRID |
|---|---|---|
| Duddo, Nthumb | 109 | C1 |
| Duddon, Chesh | 68 | B1 |
| Dudleston, Shrop | 67 | E3 |
| Dudley, T & W | 104 | B3 |
| Dudley, W Mids | 58 | A4 |
| Duffield, Derby | 70 | C3 |
| Duffryn, Neath | 34 | A4 |
| Dufftown, Moray | 133 | C4 |
| Duffus, Moray | 133 | B2 |
| Dufton, Cumb | 97 | C3 |
| Duggleby, N York | 94 | C4 |
| Duirinish, High | 125 | F1 |
| Duisky, High | 121 | D1 |
| Duke Street, Suff | 53 | D4 |
| Dukinfield, G Man | 80 | B2 |
| Dulcote, Som | 23 | D4 |
| Dulford, Devon | 10 | D4 |
| Dull, Perth | 122 | E4 |
| Dullingham, Camb | 52 | C2 |
| Dulnain Bridge, High | 127 | D1 |
| Duloe, Corn | 4 | A4 |
| Dulverton, Som | 10 | C2 |
| Dulwich, G Lon | 143 | B3 |
| Dumbarton, Dumb | 111 | E2 |
| Dumbleton, Glouc | 48 | A4 |
| Dumfries, D & G | 101 | D3 |
| Dummer, Hamp | 26 | C4 |
| Dun, Angus | 124 | B3 |
| Dunan, Argyll | 111 | C3 |
| Dunan, High | 125 | D1 |
| Dunbar, E Loth | 115 | B2 |
| Dunbeath, High | 138 | D4 |
| Dunbeg, Argyll | 117 | A1 |
| Dunblane, Stirl | 118 | D4 |
| Dunbog, Fife | 119 | C3 |
| Duncanstone, Aber | 128 | D1 |
| Dunchideock, Devon | 5 | B1 |
| Dunchurch, Warw | 49 | B1 |
| Duncow, D & G | 101 | D2 |
| Duncrievie, Perth | 119 | B3 |
| Duncton, W Suss | 17 | A3 |
| Dundee, Dund | 119 | D1 |
| Dundon, Som | 12 | A1 |
| Dundonald, S Ayr | 106 | D2 |
| Dundonnell, High | 135 | D4 |
| Dundraw, Cumb | 96 | E1 |
| Dundrennan, D & G | 96 | A1 |
| Dundry, Som | 23 | D2 |
| Dunecht, Aber | 129 | A3 |
| Dunfermline, Fife | 113 | C1 |
| Dunfield, Glouc | 37 | A4 |
| Dunham, Notts | 83 | B4 |
| Dunham Town, G Man | 79 | B3 |
| Dunham-on-the-Hill, Chesh | 78 | B4 |
| Dunhampton, Worc | 47 | C2 |
| Dunholme, Linc | 83 | D4 |
| Dunino, Fife | 119 | E3 |
| Dunipace, Falkirk | 113 | A2 |
| Dunkeld, Perth | 123 | B4 |
| Dunkerton, Som | 24 | B3 |
| Dunkeswell, Devon | 11 | A3 |
| Dunkeswick, N York | 88 | A2 |
| Dunkirk, Glouc | 24 | B1 |
| Dunkirk, Kent | 30 | C3 |
| Dunlappie, Angus | 124 | B2 |
| Dunley, Worc | 47 | B1 |
| Dunmore, Falkirk | 113 | B1 |
| Dunnet, High | 138 | D1 |
| Dunnichen, Angus | 124 | A4 |
| Dunning, Perth | 119 | A3 |
| Dunnington, E R of Y | 90 | A2 |
| Dunnington, N York | 89 | A2 |
| Dunnockshaw, Lanc | 86 | C4 |
| Dunoon, Argyll | 111 | C2 |
| Dunragit, D & G | 100 | B4 |
| Duns, Bord | 115 | C4 |
| Duns Tew, Oxon | 37 | D1 |
| Dunsby, Linc | 73 | B4 |
| Dunscore, D & G | 101 | C2 |
| Dunsdale, N York | 99 | B4 |
| Dunsden Green, Oxon | 27 | B1 |
| Dunsdon, Devon | 9 | B3 |
| Dunsfold, Surr | 17 | B1 |
| Dunsford, Devon | 5 | B1 |
| Dunshalt, Fife | 119 | C3 |
| Dunsley, N York | 99 | E4 |
| Dunsmore, Bucks | 39 | A3 |
| Dunsop Bridge, Lanc | 86 | A2 |
| Dunstable, Beds | 39 | B2 |
| Dunstall, Staff | 59 | A1 |
| Dunstan, Nthumb | 109 | E3 |
| Dunster, Som | 22 | E4 |
| Dunston, Linc | 73 | A1 |
| Dunston, Norf | 64 | B3 |
| Dunston, Staff | 58 | A1 |
| Dunstone, Devon | 4 | D4 |
| Dunstone, Devon | 5 | A2 |
| Dunswell, E R of Y | 89 | D3 |
| Dunsyre, S Lan | 107 | D1 |
| Dunterton, Devon | 4 | B2 |
| Duntisbourne Abbots, Glouc | 36 | C3 |
| Duntisbourne Rouse, Glouc | 36 | C3 |
| Duntish, Dors | 12 | B4 |
| Duntocher, Dumb | 112 | A2 |
| Dunton, Bucks | 38 | C1 |
| Dunton, Norf | 74 | D4 |
| Dunton Bassett, Leics | 60 | B4 |
| Dunton Green, Kent | 149 | C2 |
| Dunure, S Ayr | 106 | C3 |
| Dunvant, Swan | 33 | C4 |
| Dunvegan, High | 130 | A3 |
| Dunwich, Suff | 54 | D1 |
| Durgan, Corn | 2 | A2 |
| Durham, Durham | 98 | D2 |
| Durisdeer, D & G | 107 | C4 |
| Durleigh, Som | 11 | B1 |
| Durley, Hamp | 15 | B3 |
| Durley, Wilts | 25 | D3 |
| Durlock, Kent | 31 | B3 |
| Durmgley, Angus | 123 | E4 |
| Durness, High | 137 | C1 |
| Duror, High | 121 | D3 |
| Durrington, Wilts | 25 | C4 |
| Durris, Aber | 129 | A4 |

| PLACE | PAGE | GRID |
|---|---|---|
| Dursley, Glouc | 36 | A4 |
| Dursley Cross, Glouc | 36 | A2 |
| Durston, Som | 11 | B2 |
| Durweston, Dors | 12 | D3 |
| Duthil, High | 127 | D1 |
| Dutton, Chesh | 78 | B4 |
| Duxford, Camb | 52 | B3 |
| Duxford, Oxon | 37 | C3 |
| Dwygyfylchi, Ab & Col | 76 | E4 |
| Dwyran, Angle | 66 | D1 |
| Dyce, Aber | 129 | B2 |
| Dyffryn Ardudwy, Gwyn | 55 | A1 |
| Dyke, Linc | 61 | D1 |
| Dyke, Moray | 132 | E2 |
| Dykehead, Angus | 123 | E3 |
| Dymchurch, Kent | 21 | C1 |
| Dymock, Glouc | 36 | A1 |
| Dyrham, Glouc | 24 | B2 |
| Dyserth, Denb | 77 | B4 |
| Eagland Hill, Lanc | 85 | B2 |
| Eagle, Linc | 72 | C1 |
| Eaglesfield, Cumb | 96 | D3 |
| Eaglesfield, D & G | 102 | A3 |
| Eaglesham, E Renf | 112 | B4 |
| Eakring, Notts | 72 | A1 |
| Ealand, Linc | 83 | B1 |
| Ealing, G Lon | 142 | A2 |
| Eals, Nthumb | 97 | C1 |
| Eamont Bridge, Cumb | 97 | B3 |
| Earby, Lanc | 86 | C2 |
| Eardington, Shrop | 57 | B4 |
| Eardisland, Heref | 46 | C2 |
| Eardisley, Heref | 46 | B3 |
| Eardiston, Shrop | 56 | C1 |
| Eardiston, Worc | 47 | B1 |
| Earith, Camb | 52 | A1 |
| Earl Soham, Suff | 54 | A2 |
| Earl Sterndale, Derby | 70 | A1 |
| Earley, Berks | 27 | B2 |
| Earls Barton, Nhants | 50 | C2 |
| Earls Colne, Essex | 42 | B1 |
| Earls Common, Worc | 48 | A2 |
| Earl's Croome, Worc | 47 | C4 |
| Earlsferry, Fife | 119 | E4 |
| Earlsfield, G Lon | 143 | A3 |
| Earlston, Bord | 108 | C1 |
| Earlswood, Surr | 148 | B3 |
| Earlswood, W Mids | 48 | B1 |
| Earnley, W Suss | 16 | B4 |
| Earsdon, Nthumb | 104 | B1 |
| Earsham, Norf | 65 | A4 |
| Eartham, W Suss | 17 | A3 |
| Easby, N York | 93 | D1 |
| Easdale, Argyll | 116 | F3 |
| Easebourne, W Suss | 17 | A2 |
| Easenhall, Warw | 49 | B1 |
| Eashing, Surr | 145 | B4 |
| Easington, Bucks | 38 | B3 |
| Easington, Durham | 99 | A2 |
| Easington, E R of Y | 90 | C4 |
| Easington, N York | 99 | D4 |
| Easington Colliery, Durham | 99 | A2 |
| Easingwold, N York | 93 | D4 |
| Eassie and Nevay, Angus | 123 | D4 |
| East Aberthaw, Glam | 22 | F2 |
| East Allington, Devon | 8 | A1 |
| East Anstey, Devon | 10 | B2 |
| East Ashey, I of W | 8 | B1 |
| East Ayton, N York | 94 | D3 |
| East Barkwith, Linc | 84 | A4 |
| East Barming, Kent | 29 | B3 |
| East Beckham, Norf | 75 | B3 |
| East Bedfont, G Lon | 141 | B3 |
| East Bergholt, Suff | 53 | D4 |
| East Bilney, Norf | 63 | C1 |
| East Boldon, T & W | 104 | C4 |
| East Boldre, Hamp | 14 | B4 |
| East Brent, Som | 23 | B4 |
| East Bridgford, Notts | 72 | A3 |
| East Buckland, Devon | 10 | A1 |
| East Budleigh, Devon | 6 | A1 |
| East Burnham, Bucks | 140 | B1 |
| East Butterwick, Linc | 83 | B2 |
| East Calder, W Loth | 113 | C3 |
| East Carleton, Norf | 64 | B3 |
| East Carlton, Nhants | 61 | A4 |
| East Chiltington, E Sus | 19 | A3 |
| East Chisenbury, Wilts | 25 | C4 |
| East Clandon, Surr | 146 | B3 |
| East Coker, Som | 12 | A3 |
| East Compton, Som | 24 | A4 |
| East Cottingwith, E R of Y | 89 | A2 |
| East Cowes, I of W | 15 | A4 |
| East Cowick, E R of Y | 89 | A4 |
| East Cowton, N York | 93 | B1 |
| East Cranmore, Som | 24 | A4 |
| East Creech, Dors | 7 | C2 |
| East Dean, E Sus | 20 | A4 |
| East Dean, Glouc | 35 | C2 |
| East Dean, Hamp | 14 | A2 |
| East Dean, W Suss | 17 | A3 |
| East Down, Devon | 22 | B4 |
| East Drayton, Notts | 83 | B4 |
| East Dulwich, G Lon | 143 | B3 |
| East End, Kent | 21 | A1 |
| East End, Oxon | 37 | D2 |
| East Everleigh, Wilts | 25 | D3 |
| East Farleigh, Kent | 29 | B3 |
| East Farndon, Nhants | 60 | C4 |
| East Ferry, Linc | 83 | B2 |
| East Garston, Berks | 26 | A1 |
| East Goscote, Leics | 60 | C2 |
| East Grafton, Wilts | 25 | D3 |
| East Grimstead, Wilts | 14 | A2 |
| East Grinstead, W Suss | 19 | A1 |
| East Guldeford, E Sus | 21 | B2 |
| East Haddon, Nhants | 50 | A2 |
| East Hagbourne, Oxon | 38 | A4 |
| East Halton, Linc | 90 | A4 |
| East Ham, G Lon | 144 | A1 |
| East Hanney, Oxon | 37 | D4 |
| East Hanningfield, Essex | 42 | A3 |
| East Hardwick, W York | 88 | B4 |
| East Harling, Norf | 63 | C4 |
| East Harlsey, N York | 93 | C1 |

| PLACE | PAGE | GRID |
|---|---|---|
| East Harptree, Som | 23 | D3 |
| East Harting, W Suss | 16 | B2 |
| East Hatch, Wilts | 13 | A2 |
| East Hatley, Camb | 51 | C3 |
| East Haven, Angus | 119 | F1 |
| East Heckington, Linc | 73 | B3 |
| East Hedleyhope, Durham | 98 | B2 |
| East Hendred, Oxon | 37 | D4 |
| East Heslerton, N York | 94 | C3 |
| East Hewish, Som | 23 | C2 |
| East Hoathly, E Sus | 19 | B3 |
| East Holme, Dors | 7 | B1 |
| East Horrington, Som | 24 | A4 |
| East Huntspill, Som | 23 | B4 |
| East Ilsley, Berks | 26 | B1 |
| East Keal, Linc | 73 | D1 |
| East Kennett, Wilts | 25 | C2 |
| East Keswick, W York | 88 | A2 |
| East Kilbride, S Lan | 112 | B4 |
| East Kirkby, Linc | 73 | D1 |
| East Knighton, Dors | 7 | B1 |
| East Knoyle, Wilts | 12 | D1 |
| East Kyloe, Nthumb | 109 | D1 |
| East Lambrook, Som | 11 | C2 |
| East Langdon, Kent | 31 | B4 |
| East Lavington, W Suss | 17 | A3 |
| East Layton, N York | 93 | A1 |
| East Leake, Notts | 71 | B4 |
| East Lockinge, Oxon | 37 | D4 |
| East Lound, Linc | 83 | B2 |
| East Lulworth, Dors | 7 | B2 |
| East Lutton, N York | 94 | C4 |
| East Marden, W Suss | 16 | B3 |
| East Markham, Notts | 83 | B4 |
| East Marton, N York | 86 | C2 |
| East Meon, Hamp | 16 | A2 |
| East Mersea, Essex | 43 | B2 |
| East Molesey, Surr | 142 | A4 |
| East Morden, Dors | 7 | B1 |
| East Morton, W York | 87 | A2 |
| East Ness, N York | 94 | A3 |
| East Norton, Leics | 61 | A3 |
| East Orchard, Dors | 12 | D3 |
| East Peckham, Kent | 29 | B4 |
| East Pennard, Som | 12 | B1 |
| East Portlemouth, Devon | 8 | A1 |
| East Prawle, Devon | 8 | B2 |
| East Preston, W Suss | 17 | B4 |
| East Pulham, Dors | 12 | C3 |
| East Putford, Devon | 9 | C3 |
| East Quantoxhead, Som | 23 | A4 |
| East Rainton, T & W | 98 | D1 |
| East Ravendale, Linc | 84 | B2 |
| East Raynham, Norf | 63 | B1 |
| East Rigton, W York | 88 | A2 |
| East Rudham, Norf | 74 | D4 |
| East Runton, Norf | 75 | B3 |
| East Ruston, Norf | 75 | C4 |
| East Saltoun, E Loth | 115 | A3 |
| East Sheen, G Lon | 142 | B3 |
| East Shefford, Berks | 26 | A2 |
| East Stockwith, Linc | 83 | B3 |
| East Stoke, Dors | 7 | B1 |
| East Stour, Dors | 12 | C2 |
| East Stowford, Devon | 9 | E2 |
| East Stratton, Hamp | 15 | B1 |
| East Studdal, Kent | 31 | B4 |
| East Taphouse, Corn | 3 | E3 |
| East Thirston, Nthumb | 104 | B1 |
| East Tilbury, Essex | 29 | B1 |
| East Tisted, Hamp | 16 | A1 |
| East Torrington, Linc | 84 | A4 |
| East Tuddenham, Norf | 64 | A2 |
| East Tytherley, Hamp | 14 | B2 |
| East Tytherton, Wilts | 25 | B2 |
| East Village, Devon | 10 | B4 |
| East Wall, Shrop | 56 | D3 |
| East Walton, Norf | 63 | A1 |
| East Week, Devon | 5 | A1 |
| East Wellow, Hamp | 14 | B2 |
| East Wemyss, Fife | 119 | C4 |
| East Wickham, G Lon | 144 | B2 |
| East Williamston, Pemb | 32 | E3 |
| East Winch, Norf | 63 | A1 |
| East Winterslow, Wilts | 14 | A1 |
| East Wittering, W Suss | 16 | B4 |
| East Woodburn, Nthumb | 103 | C2 |
| East Woodhay, Hamp | 26 | B3 |
| East Worldham, Hamp | 16 | B1 |
| East Wretham, Norf | 63 | C4 |
| East Youlstone, Devon | 9 | B3 |
| Eastbourne, E Sus | 20 | A4 |
| Eastbridge, Suff | 54 | C2 |
| Eastburn, W York | 86 | D2 |
| Eastbury, Berks | 26 | A1 |
| Eastby, N York | 86 | D1 |
| Eastchurch, Kent | 30 | B2 |
| Eastcombe, Glouc | 36 | B3 |
| Eastcote, Nhants | 50 | A3 |
| Eastcote, W Mids | 48 | C1 |
| Eastcott, Wilts | 25 | B3 |
| Eastcourt, Wilts | 36 | C4 |
| Eastcourt, Wilts | 25 | D3 |
| Eastend, Essex | 43 | A4 |
| Easter Compton, Glouc | 23 | D1 |
| Easterton, Wilts | 25 | B3 |
| Eastfield, N Lan | 113 | B3 |
| Eastfield, N York | 94 | D3 |
| Eastgate, Durham | 98 | A2 |
| Eastgate, Norf | 64 | B1 |
| Easthampstead, Berks | 140 | A4 |
| Easthampton, Heref | 46 | C2 |
| Easthope, Shrop | 56 | D3 |
| Easthorpe, Essex | 43 | A2 |
| Eastington, Devon | 10 | A3 |
| Eastington, Glouc | 37 | A2 |
| Eastington, Glouc | 36 | A3 |
| Eastleach Martin, Glouc | 37 | B3 |
| Eastleach Turville, Glouc | 37 | B3 |
| Eastleigh, Devon | 9 | D2 |
| Eastleigh, Hamp | 15 | A2 |
| Eastling, Kent | 30 | B3 |
| Eastnor, Heref | 47 | B4 |
| Eastoft, Linc | 83 | B1 |
| Easton, Camb | 51 | B1 |
| Easton, Cumb | 102 | B4 |

| PLACE | PAGE | GRID |
|---|---|---|
| Easton, Devon | 5 | A1 |
| Easton, Dors | 6 | F3 |
| Easton, Hamp | 15 | B1 |
| Easton, Linc | 72 | C4 |
| Easton, Norf | 64 | B2 |
| Easton, Som | 23 | D4 |
| Easton, Suff | 54 | B2 |
| Easton, Wilts | 25 | A2 |
| Easton Grey, Wilts | 36 | B4 |
| Easton Maudit, Nhants | 50 | C2 |
| Easton on the Hill, Nhants | 61 | C2 |
| Easton Royal, Wilts | 25 | D3 |
| Eastrea, Camb | 62 | A3 |
| Eastriggs, D & G | 102 | B4 |
| Eastrington, E R of Y | 89 | B4 |
| Eastry, Kent | 31 | B3 |
| Eastville, Linc | 73 | D2 |
| Eastwell, Leics | 72 | B4 |
| Eastwick, Herts | 41 | A2 |
| Eastwood, Notts | 71 | A3 |
| Eastwood, W York | 86 | D4 |
| Eathorpe, Warw | 49 | B1 |
| Eaton, Chesh | 68 | B1 |
| Eaton, Chesh | 69 | B1 |
| Eaton, Leics | 72 | B4 |
| Eaton, Notts | 83 | A4 |
| Eaton, Oxon | 37 | D3 |
| Eaton, Shrop | 56 | D4 |
| Eaton Bray, Beds | 39 | B2 |
| Eaton Green, Beds | 39 | B2 |
| Eaton Hastings, Oxon | 37 | B4 |
| Eaton Mascott, Shrop | 56 | D2 |
| Eaton Socon, Camb | 51 | B2 |
| Eaton upon Tern, Shrop | 57 | A1 |
| Ebberston, N York | 94 | C3 |
| Ebbesborne Wake, Wilts | 13 | A2 |
| Ebbw Vale, Gwent | 34 | D3 |
| Ebchester, Durham | 98 | B1 |
| Ebford, Devon | 5 | C1 |
| Ebnal, Chesh | 68 | B3 |
| Ebrington, Glouc | 48 | C4 |
| Ebsworthy Town, Devon | 4 | C1 |
| Ecchinswell, Hamp | 26 | B3 |
| Ecclefechan, D & G | 102 | A3 |
| Eccles, Bord | 109 | A1 |
| Eccles, G Man | 79 | B2 |
| Eccles, Kent | 29 | B3 |
| Eccleshall, Staff | 69 | B4 |
| Ecclesmachan, W Loth | 113 | C2 |
| Eccleston, Chesh | 68 | A1 |
| Eccleston, Lanc | 78 | B1 |
| Echt, Aber | 129 | A3 |
| Eckford, Bord | 109 | A3 |
| Eckington, Derby | 82 | A4 |
| Eckington, Worc | 47 | C4 |
| Ecton, Nhants | 50 | B2 |
| Edale, Derby | 81 | A3 |
| Edburton, W Suss | 18 | B3 |
| Edderton, High | 136 | C4 |
| Eddleston, Bord | 108 | A1 |
| Eden Park, G Lon | 143 | B4 |
| Edenbridge, Kent | 149 | B4 |
| Edenfield, Lanc | 86 | B4 |
| Edenhall, Cumb | 97 | B3 |
| Edenham, Linc | 61 | C1 |
| Edensor, Derby | 70 | B1 |
| Edenthorpe, S York | 83 | A2 |
| Edern, Gwyn | 66 | B3 |
| Edgcott, Bucks | 38 | B1 |
| Edgcott, Som | 10 | B1 |
| Edge, Glouc | 36 | B3 |
| Edge, Shrop | 56 | C2 |
| Edgefield, Norf | 75 | A4 |
| Edgefield Green, Norf | 75 | A4 |
| Edgeworth, Glouc | 36 | C3 |
| Edgmond, Shrop | 57 | B1 |
| Edgton, Shrop | 56 | C4 |
| Edgworth, Lanc | 79 | B1 |
| Edinbane, High | 130 | B3 |
| Edinburgh, Edin | 114 | B2 |
| Edingale, Staff | 59 | A2 |
| Edingley, Notts | 72 | A2 |
| Edingthorpe, Norf | 75 | C4 |
| Edingthorpe Green, Norf | 75 | C4 |
| Edington, Nthumb | 104 | A2 |
| Edington, Som | 11 | C1 |
| Edington, Wilts | 25 | A3 |
| Edington Burtle, Som | 23 | C4 |
| Edingworth, Som | 23 | C3 |
| Edith Weston, Rut | 61 | B2 |
| Edithmead, Som | 23 | B4 |
| Edlesborough, Bucks | 39 | B2 |
| Edlingham, Nthumb | 109 | D4 |
| Edlington, Linc | 73 | C1 |
| Edmondsham, Dors | 13 | B3 |
| Edmondsley, Durham | 98 | C1 |
| Edmondthorpe, Leics | 61 | B1 |
| Edmundbyers, Durham | 98 | A1 |
| Ednam, Bord | 109 | A2 |
| Edrom, Bord | 115 | D4 |
| Edstaston, Shrop | 68 | B4 |
| Edstone, Warw | 48 | C2 |
| Edwinstowe, Notts | 72 | A1 |
| Edworth, Beds | 51 | C4 |
| Edwyn Ralph, Heref | 47 | A2 |
| Edzell, Angus | 124 | B2 |
| Efail Isaf, Rhond | 22 | F1 |
| Efail-fach, Neath | 34 | A4 |
| Efailnewydd, Gwyn | 66 | C4 |
| Efailwen, Carm | 32 | E1 |
| Efenechtyd, Denb | 67 | C2 |
| Effingham, Surr | 147 | A2 |
| Efford, Devon | 10 | C4 |
| Egerton, G Man | 79 | B1 |
| Egerton, Kent | 30 | B4 |
| Eggesford, Devon | 10 | A3 |
| Eggington, Beds | 39 | A1 |
| Egginton, Derby | 70 | B4 |
| Eggleston, Durham | 98 | A3 |
| Egham, Surr | 140 | C3 |
| Egham Wick, Surr | 140 | C4 |
| Egleton, Rut | 61 | B2 |
| Eglingham, Nthumb | 109 | D3 |
| Egloshayle, Corn | 3 | D2 |
| Egloskerry, Corn | 4 | A1 |
| Eglwys Cross, Wrex | 68 | B3 |

| PLACE | PAGE | GRID |
|---|---|---|
| Eglwysbach, Ab & Col | 67 | A1 |
| Eglwyswrw, Pemb | 44 | C4 |
| Egmanton, Notts | 72 | A1 |
| Egremont, Cumb | 91 | B1 |
| Egton, N York | 94 | B1 |
| Egton Bridge, N York | 94 | B1 |
| Eight Ash Green, Essex | 43 | A1 |
| Elan Village, Powys | 45 | D2 |
| Elberton, Glouc | 35 | C4 |
| Elcombe, Wilts | 25 | C1 |
| Eldersfield, Worc | 36 | A1 |
| Elderslie, Renf | 112 | A3 |
| Eldon, Durham | 98 | C3 |
| Elford, Staff | 59 | A2 |
| Elgin, Moray | 133 | B2 |
| Elgol, High | 125 | D2 |
| Elham, Kent | 31 | A4 |
| Elie, Fife | 119 | E4 |
| Elim, Angle | 76 | B3 |
| Eling, Hamp | 14 | B3 |
| Elkesley, Notts | 83 | A4 |
| Elkstone, Glouc | 36 | C2 |
| Elland, W York | 87 | A4 |
| Ellary, Argyll | 110 | F2 |
| Ellastone, Staff | 70 | A3 |
| Ellel, Lanc | 85 | C1 |
| Ellemford, Bord | 115 | C4 |
| Ellenhall, Staff | 69 | B4 |
| Ellen's Green, Surr | 18 | A1 |
| Ellerbeck, N York | 93 | C2 |
| Ellerby, N York | 99 | D4 |
| Ellerdine Heath, Shrop | 57 | A1 |
| Ellerker, E R of Y | 89 | C4 |
| Ellerton, E R of Y | 89 | A3 |
| Ellerton, N York | 93 | A2 |
| Ellesborough, Bucks | 38 | C3 |
| Ellesmere, Shrop | 68 | A4 |
| Ellesmere Port, Chesh | 78 | A4 |
| Ellingham, Norf | 65 | B3 |
| Ellingham, Nthumb | 109 | E3 |
| Ellingstring, N York | 93 | A3 |
| Ellington, Camb | 51 | B1 |
| Ellington, Nthumb | 104 | C1 |
| Ellington Thorpe, Camb | 51 | B1 |
| Elliots Green, Som | 24 | B4 |
| Ellisfield, Hamp | 27 | A4 |
| Ellistown, Leics | 60 | A2 |
| Ellon, Aber | 129 | C1 |
| Ellonby, Cumb | 97 | A2 |
| Elloughton, E R of Y | 89 | C4 |
| Ellwood, Glouc | 35 | C3 |
| Elm, Camb | 62 | C2 |
| Elm Park, G Lon | 144 | C1 |
| Elmbridge, Worc | 47 | C2 |
| Elmdon, Essex | 52 | B4 |
| Elmdon, W Mids | 59 | A4 |
| Elmers End, G Lon | 143 | B4 |
| Elmhurst, Staff | 58 | B2 |
| Elmley Castle, Worc | 48 | A4 |
| Elmley Lovett, Worc | 47 | C1 |
| Elmore, Glouc | 36 | A2 |
| Elmore Back, Glouc | 36 | A2 |
| Elmsett, Suff | 53 | D3 |
| Elmstead Market, Essex | 43 | B1 |
| Elmstone, Kent | 31 | B3 |
| Elmstone Hardwicke, Glouc | 36 | B1 |
| Elmswell, E R of Y | 89 | D1 |
| Elmswell, Suff | 53 | C2 |
| Elmton, Derby | 82 | A4 |
| Elphin, High | 135 | E2 |
| Elphinstone, E Loth | 114 | C3 |
| Elrig, D & G | 95 | D1 |
| Elrington, Nthumb | 103 | C4 |
| Elsdon, Nthumb | 103 | D1 |
| Elsenham, Essex | 41 | A1 |
| Elsfield, Oxon | 38 | A3 |
| Elsham, Linc | 83 | D1 |
| Elsing, Norf | 64 | A1 |
| Elslack, N York | 86 | D2 |
| Elsrickle, S Lan | 107 | D1 |
| Elstead, Surr | 145 | A4 |
| Elsted, W Suss | 16 | B2 |
| Elsthorpe, Linc | 61 | C1 |
| Elston, Notts | 72 | B3 |
| Elstone, Devon | 10 | A3 |
| Elstow, Beds | 51 | A3 |
| Elstree, Herts | 39 | C4 |
| Elstronwick, E R of Y | 90 | B3 |
| Elswick, Lanc | 85 | B3 |
| Elsworth, Camb | 52 | A2 |
| Elterwater, Cumb | 91 | D1 |
| Eltham, G Lon | 144 | A3 |
| Eltisley, Camb | 51 | C2 |
| Elton, Camb | 61 | D3 |
| Elton, Chesh | 78 | A4 |
| Elton, Derby | 70 | B1 |
| Elton, Durham | 99 | A4 |
| Elton, Heref | 46 | C1 |
| Elton, Notts | 72 | B3 |
| Eltringham, Nthumb | 104 | A4 |
| Elvanfoot, S Lan | 107 | C3 |
| Elvaston, Derby | 71 | A4 |
| Elveden, Suff | 63 | B4 |
| Elvington, Kent | 31 | B4 |
| Elvington, N York | 89 | A2 |
| Elwick, Durham | 99 | A3 |
| Elworth, Chesh | 69 | A1 |
| Elworthy, Som | 10 | D1 |
| Ely, Camb | 62 | C4 |
| Emberton, Bucks | 50 | C3 |
| Embleton, Nthumb | 109 | E3 |
| Embo, High | 136 | D3 |
| Emborough, Som | 24 | A4 |
| Embsay, N York | 86 | D1 |
| Emley, W York | 81 | B1 |
| Emmington, Oxon | 38 | C3 |
| Emneth, Norf | 62 | C2 |
| Emneth Hungate, Norf | 62 | C2 |
| Empingham, Rut | 61 | B2 |
| Empshott, Hamp | 16 | B1 |
| Emsworth, Hamp | 16 | B4 |
| Enborne Row, Hamp | 26 | B3 |
| Endmoor, Cumb | 91 | F3 |
| Endon, Staff | 69 | C2 |
| Enfield, G Lon | 40 | B4 |

| PLACE | PAGE | GRID |
|---|---|---|
| Enford, Wilts | 25 | C4 |
| Engine Common, Glouc | 24 | B1 |
| Englefield, Berks | 27 | A2 |
| Englefield Green, Surr | 140 | C3 |
| Englesea-brook, Chesh | 69 | A2 |
| English Bicknor, Glouc | 35 | C2 |
| English Frankton, Shrop | 68 | A4 |
| Englishcombe, Som | 24 | B3 |
| Enmore, Som | 11 | B1 |
| Ennerdale Bridge, Cumb | 96 | D4 |
| Ensdon, Shrop | 56 | C1 |
| Ensis, Devon | 9 | E2 |
| Enstone, Oxon | 37 | C1 |
| Enville, Staff | 57 | C4 |
| Epney, Glouc | 36 | A2 |
| Epperstone, Notts | 72 | A3 |
| Epping, Essex | 41 | A3 |
| Epping Green, Essex | 41 | A3 |
| Epping Upland, Essex | 41 | A3 |
| Eppleby, N York | 98 | C4 |
| Epsom, Surr | 148 | A1 |
| Epwell, Oxon | 49 | A4 |
| Epworth, Linc | 83 | B2 |
| Erbistock, Wrex | 68 | A3 |
| Eridge Green, E Sus | 20 | A1 |
| Eriswell, Suff | 53 | A1 |
| Erith, G Lon | 144 | C2 |
| Erlestoke, Wilts | 25 | B3 |
| Ermington, Devon | 4 | D4 |
| Erpingham, Norf | 75 | B4 |
| Errogie, High | 127 | A2 |
| Errol, Perth | 119 | C2 |
| Erskine, Renf | 112 | A3 |
| Erwarton, Suff | 54 | A4 |
| Erwood, Powys | 45 | E4 |
| Eryholme, N York | 93 | B1 |
| Eryrys, Denb | 67 | D2 |
| Escomb, Durham | 98 | C3 |
| Escrick, N York | 89 | A2 |
| Esgairgeiliog, Powys | 55 | B2 |
| Esh, Durham | 98 | C2 |
| Esh Winning, Durham | 98 | C2 |
| Esher, Surr | 141 | B4 |
| Eshott, Nthumb | 104 | B1 |
| Eskadale, High | 132 | A4 |
| Eskdale Green, Cumb | 91 | C1 |
| Eskdalemuir, D & G | 102 | B1 |
| Esprick, Lanc | 85 | B3 |
| Essendine, Rut | 61 | C2 |
| Essendon, Herts | 40 | A3 |
| Essington, Staff | 58 | A2 |
| Eston, N York | 99 | B4 |
| Etal, Nthumb | 109 | C1 |
| Etchilhampton, Wilts | 25 | C3 |
| Etchingham, E Sus | 20 | B2 |
| Etchinghill, Kent | 21 | D1 |
| Eton, Berks | 140 | B2 |
| Eton Wick, Bucks | 140 | B2 |
| Ettersgill, Durham | 97 | E3 |
| Ettington, Warw | 48 | C3 |
| Etton, Camb | 61 | D2 |
| Etton, E R of Y | 89 | D2 |
| Ettrick, Bord | 108 | A4 |
| Ettrickbridge, Bord | 108 | B3 |
| Etwall, Derby | 70 | B4 |
| Euston, Suff | 53 | C1 |
| Euxton, Lanc | 85 | C4 |
| Evanton, High | 132 | B2 |
| Evedon, Linc | 73 | B3 |
| Evenjobb, Powys | 46 | B2 |
| Evenley, Nhants | 49 | C4 |
| Evenlode, Glouc | 37 | B1 |
| Evercreech, Som | 12 | B1 |
| Everingham, E R of Y | 89 | B2 |
| Everleigh, Wilts | 25 | D3 |
| Eversholt, Beds | 39 | B1 |
| Evershot, Dors | 12 | A4 |
| Eversley, Hamp | 27 | B3 |
| Eversley Cross, Hamp | 27 | B3 |
| Everthorpe, E R of Y | 89 | C3 |
| Everton, Beds | 51 | C3 |
| Everton, Notts | 83 | A3 |
| Evertown, D & G | 102 | C3 |
| Evesbatch, Heref | 47 | A3 |
| Evesham, Worc | 48 | A4 |
| Ewden Village, S York | 81 | C2 |
| Ewell, Surr | 148 | A1 |
| Ewelme, Oxon | 38 | B4 |
| Ewen, Glouc | 36 | C4 |
| Ewenny, Glam | 22 | E1 |
| Ewerby, Linc | 73 | B3 |
| Ewesley, Nthumb | 104 | A1 |
| Ewhurst, Surr | 18 | A1 |
| Ewhurst Green, Surr | 18 | A1 |
| Ewloe, Flint | 67 | E1 |
| Eworthy, Devon | 9 | D4 |
| Ewshot, Hamp | 27 | B4 |
| Ewyas Harold, Heref | 35 | A1 |
| Exbourne, Devon | 9 | E4 |
| Exbury, Hamp | 15 | A4 |
| Exebridge, Som | 10 | C2 |
| Exelby, N York | 93 | B3 |
| Exeter, Devon | 5 | C1 |
| Exford, Som | 10 | B1 |
| Exfordsgreen, Shrop | 56 | C2 |
| Exhall, Warw | 48 | B3 |
| Exhall, Warw | 59 | B4 |
| Exlade Street, Oxon | 27 | A1 |
| Exminster, Devon | 5 | C1 |
| Exmouth, Devon | 5 | C2 |
| Exning, Suff | 52 | C2 |
| Exton, Devon | 5 | C1 |
| Exton, Hamp | 15 | B2 |
| Exton, Rut | 61 | B2 |
| Exton, Som | 10 | C1 |
| Eyam, Derby | 81 | B4 |
| Eydon, Nhants | 49 | C3 |
| Eye, Camb | 62 | A3 |
| Eye, Heref | 46 | D2 |
| Eye, Suff | 54 | A1 |
| Eyemouth, Bord | 115 | E3 |
| Eyeworth, Beds | 51 | C3 |
| Eyhorne Street, Kent | 30 | A3 |
| Eyke, Suff | 54 | B3 |
| Eynsford, Kent | 144 | C4 |
| Eynsham, Oxon | 37 | D3 |

| PLACE | PAGE | GRID |
|---|---|---|
| Eype, Dors | 6 | D1 |
| Eythorne, Kent | 31 | B4 |
| Eyton, Heref | 46 | D2 |
| Eyton, Shrop | 56 | C2 |
| Eyton, Shrop | 56 | C1 |
| Eyton, Shrop | 56 | C4 |
| Eyton on Severn, Shrop | 57 | A2 |
| Eyton upon the Weald Moors, Shrop | 57 | A1 |
| Faccombe, Hamp | 26 | B3 |
| Faceby, N York | 93 | C1 |
| Fachwen, Powys | 55 | E1 |
| Fadmoor, N York | 94 | A2 |
| Failand, Som | 23 | D2 |
| Failsworth, G Man | 80 | A2 |
| Fair Oak Green, Hamp | 27 | A3 |
| Fairbourne, Gwyn | 55 | A2 |
| Fairburn, N York | 88 | B4 |
| Fairfield, Worc | 48 | A1 |
| Fairford, Glouc | 37 | A3 |
| Fairgirth, D & G | 96 | B1 |
| Fairlie, N Ayr | 111 | D4 |
| Fairlight, E Sus | 21 | A3 |
| Fairmile, Surr | 147 | A1 |
| Fairmile, Devon | 10 | D4 |
| Fairnilee, Bord | 108 | B2 |
| Fairoak, Staff | 69 | A4 |
| Fairseat, Kent | 29 | A3 |
| Fairstead, Essex | 42 | A2 |
| Fairwarp, E Sus | 19 | B2 |
| Fairy Cross, Devon | 9 | C2 |
| Fakenham, Norf | 74 | E4 |
| Fakenham Magna, Suff | 53 | C1 |
| Fala, M Loth | 114 | C3 |
| Fala Dam, M Loth | 114 | C3 |
| Faldingworth, Linc | 83 | D3 |
| Faldouet, Jers | 139 | B2 |
| Falfield, Glouc | 35 | C4 |
| Falkenham, Suff | 54 | B4 |
| Falkirk, Falkirk | 113 | A2 |
| Falkland, Fife | 119 | C3 |
| Fallin, Stirl | 113 | A1 |
| Falloden, Nthumb | 109 | E3 |
| Fallowfield, Nthumb | 103 | D4 |
| Falmer, E Sus | 19 | A3 |
| Falmouth, Corn | 2 | A2 |
| Falstone, Nthumb | 103 | B2 |
| Fancott, Beds | 39 | B1 |
| Fangdale Beck, N York | 93 | D2 |
| Fangfoss, E R of Y | 89 | B1 |
| Far End, Cumb | 91 | D2 |
| Far Green, Glouc | 36 | A3 |
| Far Sawrey, Cumb | 91 | E2 |
| Far Thorpe, Linc | 84 | B4 |
| Farcet, Camb | 62 | A3 |
| Fareham, Hamp | 15 | B4 |
| Farewell, Staff | 58 | B2 |
| Faringdon, Oxon | 37 | C4 |
| Farington, Lanc | 85 | C4 |
| Farlam, Cumb | 102 | D4 |
| Farleigh Hungerford, Som | 24 | B3 |
| Farleigh Wallop, Hamp | 27 | A4 |
| Farlesthorpe, Linc | 84 | D4 |
| Farleton, Cumb | 91 | F3 |
| Farley, Staff | 70 | A3 |
| Farley, Wilts | 14 | A2 |
| Farley Green, Suff | 53 | A3 |
| Farley Green, Surr | 146 | B4 |
| Farley Hill, Berks | 27 | B2 |
| Farleys End, Glouc | 36 | A2 |
| Farlington, N York | 93 | D4 |
| Farlow, Shrop | 57 | A4 |
| Farmborough, Som | 24 | A3 |
| Farmcote, Glouc | 37 | A1 |
| Farmers, Carm | 45 | A4 |
| Farmington, Glouc | 37 | A2 |
| Farmoor, Oxon | 37 | D3 |
| Farnachty, Moray | 133 | D2 |
| Farnborough, Berks | 26 | B1 |
| Farnborough, Hamp | 145 | A2 |
| Farnborough, Warw | 49 | B3 |
| Farnborough, G Lon | 144 | B4 |
| Farnborough Park, Hamp | 145 | A2 |
| Farncombe, Surr | 146 | A4 |
| Farndish, Beds | 50 | C2 |
| Farndon, Chesh | 68 | A2 |
| Farndon, Notts | 72 | B2 |
| Farnell, Angus | 124 | B3 |
| Farnham, Essex | 41 | A1 |
| Farnham, N York | 88 | A1 |
| Farnham, Suff | 54 | C2 |
| Farnham, Surr | 27 | B4 |
| Farnham Common, Bucks | 140 | B1 |
| Farnley, N York | 87 | B2 |
| Farnley Tyas, W York | 81 | B1 |
| Farnsfield, Notts | 72 | A2 |
| Farnworth, G Man | 79 | B2 |
| Farr, High | 137 | F1 |
| Farringdon, Devon | 6 | A1 |
| Farrington Gurney, Som | 24 | A3 |
| Farthing Street, G Lon | 149 | B1 |
| Farthinghoe, Nhants | 49 | C4 |
| Farthingstone, Nhants | 49 | C3 |
| Fasnacloich, Argyll | 121 | D4 |
| Fauldhouse, W Loth | 113 | B4 |
| Faulkbourne, Essex | 42 | B2 |
| Faulkland, Som | 24 | B3 |
| Fauls, Shrop | 68 | C4 |
| Faversham, Kent | 30 | C3 |
| Fawdington, N York | 93 | C4 |
| Fawdon, Nthumb | 109 | C3 |
| Fawkham Green, Kent | 29 | A3 |
| Fawler, Oxon | 37 | C2 |
| Fawley, Berks | 26 | B1 |
| Fawley, Bucks | 27 | B1 |
| Fawley, Hamp | 15 | A4 |
| Faxfleet, E R of Y | 89 | C4 |
| Faygate, W Suss | 18 | B1 |
| Fazeley, Staff | 59 | A3 |
| Fearby, N York | 93 | A3 |
| Fearnan, Perth | 122 | D4 |
| Fearnmore, High | 130 | E2 |
| Featherstone, Staff | 58 | A2 |
| Featherstone, W York | 88 | B4 |
| Feckenham, Worc | 48 | A2 |
| Feering, Essex | 42 | B2 |

| PLACE | PAGE | GRID |
|---|---|---|
| Feetham, N York | 92 | D2 |
| Felbrigg, Norf | 75 | B3 |
| Felcourt, Surr | 149 | A4 |
| Felday, Surr | 147 | A4 |
| Felin gwm Isaf, Carm | 33 | B1 |
| Felin gwm Uchaf, Carm | 33 | B1 |
| Felindre, Carm | 33 | C2 |
| Felindre, Carm | 44 | E4 |
| Felindre, Powys | 56 | A4 |
| Felindre, Swan | 33 | C3 |
| Felindre Farchog, Pemb | 44 | C4 |
| Felixkirk, N York | 93 | C3 |
| Felixstowe, Suff | 54 | B4 |
| Felixstowe Ferry, Suff | 54 | B4 |
| Felling, T & W | 104 | C4 |
| Felmersham, Beds | 51 | A2 |
| Felmingham, Norf | 75 | C4 |
| Felsham, Suff | 53 | C2 |
| Felsted, Essex | 42 | A2 |
| Feltham, G Lon | 141 | B3 |
| Felthamhill, Surr | 141 | B3 |
| Felthorpe, Norf | 64 | B1 |
| Felton, Heref | 46 | D3 |
| Felton, Nthumb | 104 | B1 |
| Felton Butler, Shrop | 56 | C1 |
| Feltwell, Norf | 63 | A4 |
| Fen Ditton, Camb | 52 | B2 |
| Fen Drayton, Camb | 52 | A1 |
| Fen Street, Norf | 63 | C3 |
| Fence, Lanc | 86 | C3 |
| Fence, S York | 82 | A3 |
| Fencote, N York | 93 | B2 |
| Fendike Corner, Linc | 74 | A2 |
| Feniscowles, Lanc | 86 | A4 |
| Feniton, Devon | 10 | D4 |
| Fenny Bentley, Derby | 70 | B2 |
| Fenny Bridges, Devon | 10 | D4 |
| Fenny Compton, Warw | 49 | B3 |
| Fenny Drayton, Leics | 59 | B3 |
| Fenstanton, Camb | 52 | A1 |
| Fenstead End, Suff | 53 | B3 |
| Fenton, Camb | 52 | A1 |
| Fenton, Cumb | 97 | B1 |
| Fenton, Linc | 83 | B4 |
| Fenton, Linc | 72 | C2 |
| Fenton, Notts | 83 | B4 |
| Fenton, Nthumb | 109 | C2 |
| Fenwick, E Ayr | 106 | E1 |
| Fenwick, Nthumb | 109 | D1 |
| Fenwick, Nthumb | 104 | A3 |
| Fenwick, S York | 82 | B1 |
| Feock, Corn | 2 | A1 |
| Ferndale, Rhond | 34 | B4 |
| Fernham, Oxon | 37 | C4 |
| Fernhill Heath, Worc | 47 | C2 |
| Fernhurst, W Suss | 17 | A2 |
| Fernilee, Derby | 80 | B4 |
| Ferrensby, N York | 88 | A1 |
| Ferring, W Suss | 18 | A4 |
| Ferryden, Angus | 124 | C3 |
| Ferryhill, Durham | 98 | D3 |
| Ferryside, Carm | 33 | A3 |
| Fersfield, Norf | 64 | A4 |
| Fetcham, Surr | 147 | B2 |
| Fetterangus, Aber | 134 | D3 |
| Fettercairn, Aber | 124 | B2 |
| Fewston, N York | 87 | B1 |
| Ffair Rhos, Cered | 45 | B2 |
| Ffairfach, Carm | 33 | C2 |
| Ffestiniog, Gwyn | 66 | F3 |
| Fforest, Carm | 33 | C3 |
| Ffostrasol, Cered | 44 | E3 |
| Ffrith, Flint | 67 | E2 |
| Ffynnongroew, Flint | 77 | C4 |
| Fickleshole, G Lon | 149 | A1 |
| Fiddington, Glouc | 36 | B1 |
| Fiddington, Som | 11 | A1 |
| Fiddleford, Dors | 12 | C3 |
| Fiddlers Green, Corn | 3 | B4 |
| Field, Staff | 69 | C4 |
| Field Broughton, Cumb | 91 | E3 |
| Field Dalling, Norf | 75 | A3 |
| Fifehead Neville, Dors | 12 | C3 |
| Fifehead St Quinton, Dors | 12 | C3 |
| Fifield, Berks | 140 | A2 |
| Fifield, Oxon | 37 | B2 |
| Figheldean, Wilts | 25 | C4 |
| Filby, Norf | 65 | B2 |
| Filey, N York | 94 | E3 |
| Filgrave, Bucks | 50 | C3 |
| Filkins, Oxon | 37 | B3 |
| Filleigh, Devon | 10 | A2 |
| Filleigh, Devon | 10 | A3 |
| Fillingham, Linc | 83 | C3 |
| Fimber, E R of Y | 89 | C1 |
| Fincham, Norf | 63 | A2 |
| Finchdean, Hamp | 16 | B3 |
| Finchingfield, Essex | 42 | A1 |
| Findern, Derby | 70 | C4 |
| Findhorn, Moray | 133 | A2 |
| Findochty, Moray | 133 | D2 |
| Findon, Aber | 129 | C4 |
| Finedon, Nhants | 50 | C1 |
| Fingal Street, Suff | 54 | A1 |
| Finghall, N York | 93 | A2 |
| Fingringhoe, Essex | 43 | B2 |
| Finmere, Oxon | 38 | B1 |
| Finningham, Suff | 53 | D1 |
| Finningley, S York | 83 | A2 |
| Finstall, Worc | 48 | A1 |
| Finsthwaite, Cumb | 91 | E2 |
| Finstock, Oxon | 37 | C2 |
| Finstown, Ork | 139 | A2 |
| Fintry, Stirl | 112 | B1 |
| Finzean, Aber | 128 | E4 |
| Fionnphort, Argyll | 116 | B2 |
| Fir Tree, Durham | 98 | B2 |
| Firbank, Cumb | 92 | A2 |
| Firbeck, S York | 82 | B3 |
| Firby, N York | 93 | A3 |
| Firby, N York | 94 | B4 |
| Firsby, Linc | 74 | A1 |
| Fishbourne, I of W | 8 | B1 |
| Fishburn, Durham | 98 | D3 |
| Fishcross, Clack | 113 | B1 |
| Fisherton, S Ayr | 106 | C3 |

| PLACE | PAGE | GRID |
|---|---|---|
| Fisherton de la Mere, Wilts | 13 | A1 |
| Fishery Estate, Berks | 140 | A2 |
| Fishguard, Pemb | 44 | A4 |
| Fishlake, S York | 83 | A1 |
| Fishtoft, Linc | 73 | D3 |
| Fishtoft Drove, Linc | 73 | D3 |
| Fiskerton, Linc | 73 | A1 |
| Fiskerton, Notts | 72 | B2 |
| Fittleton, Wilts | 25 | C4 |
| Fittleworth, W Suss | 17 | B2 |
| Fitz, Shrop | 56 | C1 |
| Fitzhead, Som | 11 | A2 |
| Fitzwilliam, W York | 82 | A1 |
| Five Ashes, E Sus | 20 | A2 |
| Five Bells, Som | 22 | F4 |
| Five Oak Green, Kent | 29 | A4 |
| Five Oaks, Jers | 139 | B2 |
| Fivehead, Som | 11 | C2 |
| Fladbury, Worc | 48 | A3 |
| Fladdabister, Shet | 139 | A3 |
| Flagg, Derby | 70 | A1 |
| Flamborough, E R of Y | 94 | F4 |
| Flamstead, Herts | 39 | B2 |
| Flansham, W Suss | 17 | A4 |
| Flasby, N York | 86 | D1 |
| Flash, Staff | 69 | C1 |
| Flaunden, Herts | 39 | B3 |
| Flawith, N York | 93 | C4 |
| Flax Bourton, Som | 23 | D2 |
| Flaxby, N York | 88 | B1 |
| Flaxley, Glouc | 35 | C2 |
| Flaxpool, Som | 11 | A1 |
| Flaxton, N York | 89 | A1 |
| Fleckney, Leics | 60 | C3 |
| Flecknoe, Warw | 49 | C2 |
| Fledborough, Notts | 72 | B1 |
| Fleet, Hamp | 27 | B3 |
| Fleet, Linc | 62 | B1 |
| Fleet Hargate, Linc | 62 | B1 |
| Fleetwood, Lanc | 85 | A2 |
| Flemingston, Glam | 22 | F2 |
| Flempton, Suff | 53 | B1 |
| Fletcher Green, Kent | 149 | C3 |
| Fletchertown, Cumb | 96 | E2 |
| Fletching, E Sus | 19 | A2 |
| Flexford, Surr | 145 | B3 |
| Flimby, Cumb | 96 | D3 |
| Flimwell, E Sus | 20 | B1 |
| Flint, Flint | 77 | D4 |
| Flintham, Notts | 72 | B3 |
| Flinton, E R of Y | 90 | B3 |
| Flitcham, Norf | 74 | C4 |
| Flitton, Beds | 51 | A4 |
| Flitwick, Beds | 51 | A4 |
| Flixborough, Linc | 83 | C1 |
| Flixton, N York | 94 | D3 |
| Flixton, Suff | 65 | A4 |
| Flockton, W York | 81 | B1 |
| Flockton Green, W York | 81 | B1 |
| Flookburgh, Cumb | 91 | E4 |
| Flordon, Norf | 64 | B3 |
| Flore, Nhants | 50 | A2 |
| Flowton, Suff | 53 | D3 |
| Flushing, Corn | 2 | A2 |
| Fluxton, Devon | 6 | A1 |
| Flyford Flavell, Worc | 48 | A3 |
| Fobbing, Essex | 29 | B1 |
| Fochabers, Moray | 133 | C2 |
| Fockerby, Linc | 89 | B4 |
| Foddington, Som | 12 | A1 |
| Foel, Powys | 55 | D2 |
| Foggathorpe, E R of Y | 89 | B3 |
| Fogo, Bord | 109 | A1 |
| Fole, Staff | 69 | C4 |
| Foliejon Park, Berks | 140 | A3 |
| Folke, Dors | 12 | B3 |
| Folkestone, Kent | 21 | D1 |
| Folkingham, Linc | 73 | A4 |
| Folkington, E Sus | 20 | A4 |
| Folksworth, Camb | 61 | D4 |
| Folkton, N York | 94 | D3 |
| Follifoot, N York | 88 | A2 |
| Folly Gate, Devon | 9 | E4 |
| Fonthill Bishop, Wilts | 13 | A1 |
| Fonthill Gifford, Wilts | 12 | D1 |
| Fontmell Magna, Dors | 12 | D3 |
| Fontwell, W Suss | 17 | A3 |
| Foolow, Derby | 81 | B4 |
| Foots Cray, G Lon | 144 | B3 |
| Forcett, N York | 98 | C4 |
| Ford, Bucks | 38 | C3 |
| Ford, Derby | 82 | A4 |
| Ford, Devon | 9 | C2 |
| Ford, Devon | 8 | B1 |
| Ford, Glouc | 37 | A1 |
| Ford, Nthumb | 109 | C2 |
| Ford, Som | 10 | D2 |
| Ford, Staff | 70 | A2 |
| Ford, W Suss | 17 | B4 |
| Ford, Wilts | 25 | A2 |
| Ford End, Essex | 42 | A2 |
| Ford Street, Som | 11 | A2 |
| Fordcombe, Kent | 19 | B1 |
| Fordell, Fife | 114 | A1 |
| Forden, Powys | 56 | A3 |
| Forder Green, Devon | 5 | B3 |
| Fordham, Camb | 52 | C1 |
| Fordham, Essex | 43 | A1 |
| Fordham, Norf | 62 | D3 |
| Fordingbridge, Hamp | 13 | B3 |
| Fordon, E R of Y | 94 | D4 |
| Fordoun, Aber | 124 | C2 |
| Fordstreet, Essex | 43 | A1 |
| Fordyce, Aber | 133 | E2 |
| Foremark, Derby | 70 | C4 |
| Forest Becks, Lanc | 86 | B2 |
| Forest Chapel, Chesh | 69 | C1 |
| Forest Gate, G Lon | 144 | A1 |
| Forest Green, Surr | 147 | A4 |
| Forest Hill, Oxon | 38 | A3 |
| Forest Hill, G Lon | 143 | B3 |
| Forest Mill, Clack | 113 | B1 |
| Forest Row, E Sus | 19 | A1 |
| Forestside, W Suss | 16 | B3 |
| Forfar, Angus | 123 | E4 |

| PLACE | PAGE | GRID |
|---|---|---|
| Forgandenny, Perth | 119 | A3 |
| Forgie, Moray | 133 | D3 |
| Formby, Mers | 77 | D1 |
| Forncett End, Norf | 64 | B3 |
| Forncett St Mary, Norf | 64 | B3 |
| Forncett St Peter, Norf | 64 | B3 |
| Fornham All Saints, Suff | 53 | B2 |
| Fornham St Martin, Suff | 53 | B2 |
| Forres, Moray | 133 | A2 |
| Forsbrook, Staff | 69 | C3 |
| Fort Augustus, High | 126 | E3 |
| Fort William, High | 121 | E2 |
| Forteviot, Perth | 119 | A3 |
| Forth, S Lan | 113 | B4 |
| Forthampton, Glouc | 36 | B1 |
| Fortingall, Perth | 122 | D4 |
| Forton, Hamp | 26 | B4 |
| Forton, Lanc | 85 | C2 |
| Forton, Shrop | 56 | C1 |
| Forton, Som | 11 | B3 |
| Forton, Staff | 57 | B1 |
| Fortrose, High | 132 | C3 |
| Fortuneswell, Dors | 6 | F2 |
| Fosbury, Wilts | 26 | A3 |
| Foscot, Oxon | 37 | B2 |
| Fosdyke, Linc | 73 | D4 |
| Foss, Perth | 122 | E3 |
| Fossebridge, Glouc | 37 | A2 |
| Foston, Derby | 70 | B4 |
| Foston, Leics | 60 | B3 |
| Foston, Linc | 72 | C3 |
| Foston, N York | 94 | A4 |
| Foston on the Wolds, E R of Y | 90 | A1 |
| Fotheringhay, Nhants | 61 | C3 |
| Foul End, Warw | 59 | A3 |
| Foulden, Bord | 115 | E4 |
| Foulridge, Lanc | 86 | C2 |
| Foulsham, Norf | 64 | A1 |
| Fountainhall, Bord | 108 | B1 |
| Four Ashes, Suff | 53 | C1 |
| Four Crosses, Powys | 56 | B1 |
| Four Elms, Kent | 149 | B3 |
| Four Forks, Som | 11 | A1 |
| Four Gotes, Camb | 62 | C1 |
| Four Lanes, Corn | 1 | D1 |
| Four Marks, Hamp | 16 | A1 |
| Four Mile Bridge, Angle | 76 | A4 |
| Four Oaks, W Mids | 59 | A4 |
| Four Roads, Carm | 33 | B3 |
| Four Throws, Kent | 21 | A1 |
| Fovant, Wilts | 13 | A2 |
| Fowey, Corn | 3 | E4 |
| Fowlhall, Kent | 29 | B4 |
| Fowlis, Angus | 119 | C1 |
| Fowlis Wester, Perth | 118 | E2 |
| Fowlmere, Camb | 52 | A3 |
| Fownhope, Heref | 47 | A4 |
| Fox Corner, Surr | 145 | B2 |
| Foxcote, Som | 24 | B3 |
| Foxdale, I o M | 139 | B3 |
| Foxearth, Essex | 53 | B4 |
| Foxfield, Cumb | 91 | C3 |
| Foxhole, Corn | 3 | D4 |
| Foxholes, N York | 94 | D4 |
| Foxley, Norf | 64 | A1 |
| Foxt, Staff | 69 | C3 |
| Foxton, Camb | 52 | A3 |
| Foxton, Leics | 60 | C4 |
| Foxton, N York | 93 | C2 |
| Foxwood, Shrop | 47 | A1 |
| Foy, Heref | 35 | C1 |
| Foyers, High | 126 | F2 |
| Fraddon, Corn | 3 | C4 |
| Fradley, Staff | 59 | A2 |
| Fradswell, Staff | 69 | C4 |
| Fraisthorpe, E R of Y | 90 | A1 |
| Framfield, E Sus | 19 | B2 |
| Framingham Earl, Norf | 65 | A3 |
| Framingham Pigot, Norf | 65 | A2 |
| Framlingham, Suff | 54 | B2 |
| Frampton, Dors | 12 | B4 |
| Frampton, Linc | 73 | D3 |
| Frampton Mansell, Glouc | 36 | B3 |
| Frampton on Severn, Glouc | 36 | A3 |
| Framsden, Suff | 54 | A2 |
| Frances Green, Lanc | 86 | A3 |
| Frankby, Mers | 77 | D3 |
| Frankley, Worc | 58 | A4 |
| Frankton, Warw | 49 | B1 |
| Frant, E Sus | 20 | A1 |
| Fraserburgh, Aber | 134 | D2 |
| Frating, Essex | 43 | B1 |
| Frating Green, Essex | 43 | B1 |
| Freathy, Corn | 4 | B4 |
| Freckenham, Suff | 53 | A1 |
| Freckleton, Lanc | 85 | B4 |
| Freeby, Leics | 61 | A1 |
| Freefolk, Hamp | 26 | B4 |
| Freeland, Oxon | 37 | D2 |
| Freethorpe Common, Norf | 65 | B2 |
| Freiston, Linc | 73 | D3 |
| Fremington, Devon | 9 | D1 |
| Fremington, N York | 92 | E2 |
| French Street, Kent | 149 | B3 |
| Freshford, Som | 24 | B3 |
| Freshwater, I of W | 7 | F1 |
| Fressingfield, Suff | 54 | B1 |
| Freswick, High | 138 | F1 |
| Fretherne, Glouc | 36 | A3 |
| Frettenham, Norf | 65 | A1 |
| Freuchie, Fife | 119 | C4 |
| Freystrop, Pemb | 32 | C2 |
| Friday Bridge, Camb | 62 | C2 |
| Fridaythorpe, E R of Y | 89 | C1 |
| Friesthorpe, Linc | 83 | D4 |
| Frieston, Linc | 72 | C3 |
| Frieth, Bucks | 38 | C4 |
| Frilford, Oxon | 37 | D4 |
| Frilsham, Berks | 26 | C2 |
| Frimley, Surr | 145 | A2 |
| Frimley Green, Surr | 145 | A2 |
| Fring, Norf | 74 | C4 |
| Fringford, Oxon | 38 | A1 |
| Frinsted, Kent | 30 | B3 |
| Frinton-on-Sea, Essex | 43 | C2 |
| Friockheim, Angus | 124 | B4 |
| Frisby on the Wreake, Leics | 60 | C1 |
| Friskney, Linc | 74 | A2 |
| Friston, E Sus | 20 | A4 |
| Friston, Suff | 54 | C2 |
| Fritchley, Derby | 70 | C2 |
| Fritham, Hamp | 14 | A3 |
| Frithelstock, Devon | 9 | D2 |
| Frithelstock Stone, Devon | 9 | D2 |
| Frithville, Linc | 73 | D2 |
| Frittenden, Kent | 21 | A1 |
| Frittiscombe, Devon | 8 | B1 |
| Fritton, Norf | 65 | B3 |
| Fritton, Norf | 64 | B3 |
| Fritwell, Oxon | 38 | A1 |
| Frizington, Cumb | 96 | D4 |
| Frocester, Glouc | 36 | A3 |
| Frodesley, Shrop | 56 | D3 |
| Frodsham, Chesh | 78 | B4 |
| Frog End, Camb | 52 | A3 |
| Frog Pool, Worc | 47 | B2 |
| Froggatt, Derby | 81 | B4 |
| Froghall, Staff | 69 | C3 |
| Frogmore, Devon | 8 | B1 |
| Frognall, Linc | 61 | D2 |
| Frogwell, Corn | 4 | B3 |
| Frolesworth, Leics | 60 | B4 |
| Frome, Som | 24 | B4 |
| Frome St Quintin, Dors | 12 | B4 |
| Fromes Hill, Heref | 47 | A3 |
| Fron Isaf, Wrex | 67 | E3 |
| Froncysyllte, Denb | 67 | E3 |
| Fron-goch, Gwyn | 67 | B3 |
| Frosterley, Durham | 98 | A2 |
| Froxfield, Wilts | 26 | A2 |
| Froxfield Green, Hamp | 16 | A2 |
| Fulbeck, Linc | 72 | C2 |
| Fulbourn, Camb | 52 | B3 |
| Fulbrook, Oxon | 37 | B2 |
| Fulford, Som | 11 | A2 |
| Fulford, Staff | 69 | C3 |
| Fulham, G Lon | 142 | B2 |
| Fulking, W Suss | 18 | B3 |
| Full Sutton, E R of Y | 89 | B1 |
| Fuller Street, Essex | 42 | A2 |
| Fulletby, Linc | 84 | B4 |
| Fullready, Warw | 49 | A3 |
| Fulmer, Bucks | 140 | C1 |
| Fulnetby, Linc | 84 | A4 |
| Fulstow, Linc | 84 | C2 |
| Fulwell, Oxon | 37 | C1 |
| Fundenhall, Norf | 64 | B3 |
| Furley, Devon | 11 | B4 |
| Furnace, Argyll | 117 | B4 |
| Furness Vale, Derby | 80 | B4 |
| Furneux Pelham, Herts | 41 | A1 |
| Furze Platt, Berks | 140 | A1 |
| Furzley, Hamp | 14 | B3 |
| Fyfield, Essex | 41 | B3 |
| Fyfield, Hamp | 26 | A4 |
| Fyfield, Oxon | 37 | D4 |
| Fyfield, Wilts | 25 | C2 |
| Fyfield, Wilts | 25 | D3 |
| Fylingthorpe, N York | 94 | C1 |
| Fyning, W Suss | 16 | B2 |
| Fyvie, Aber | 134 | B4 |
| Gaddesby, Leics | 60 | C2 |
| Gaddesden Row, Herts | 39 | B2 |
| Gaer, Powys | 34 | D2 |
| Gaer-llwyd, Monm | 35 | A4 |
| Gaerwen, Angle | 66 | D1 |
| Gailes, N Ayr | 106 | D2 |
| Gailey, Staff | 57 | C2 |
| Gainford, Durham | 98 | C4 |
| Gainsborough, Linc | 83 | B3 |
| Gainsford End, Essex | 53 | A4 |
| Gairloch, High | 130 | F1 |
| Gairlochy, High | 121 | E1 |
| Gaitsgill, Cumb | 97 | A1 |
| Galashiels, Bord | 108 | C2 |
| Galgate, Lanc | 85 | C1 |
| Galhampton, Som | 12 | B1 |
| Gallowfauld, Angus | 123 | E4 |
| Galmpton, Devon | 8 | A1 |
| Galphay, N York | 93 | A4 |
| Galston, E Ayr | 106 | E2 |
| Gamblesby, Cumb | 97 | C2 |
| Gamlingay, Camb | 51 | C3 |
| Gamston, Notts | 83 | A4 |
| Ganllwyd, Gwyn | 55 | B1 |
| Ganstead, E R of Y | 90 | A3 |
| Ganthorpe, N York | 94 | A4 |
| Ganton, N York | 94 | D3 |
| Garboldisham, Norf | 63 | C4 |
| Gardeners Green, Berks | 27 | B2 |
| Gardenstown, Aber | 134 | B2 |
| Gare Hill, Wilts | 12 | C1 |
| Garelochhead, Argyll | 111 | D1 |
| Garford, Oxon | 37 | D4 |
| Garforth, W York | 88 | B3 |
| Gargrave, N York | 86 | D1 |
| Gargunnock, Stirl | 112 | C1 |
| Garlic Street, Norf | 64 | B4 |
| Garlieston, D & G | 95 | E1 |
| Garlinge Green, Kent | 30 | C3 |
| Garlogie, Aber | 129 | A3 |
| Garmond, Aber | 134 | B3 |
| Garmouth, Moray | 133 | C2 |
| Garmston, Shrop | 57 | A2 |
| Garn-Dolbenmaen, Gwyn | 66 | D3 |
| Garras, Corn | 1 | D3 |
| Garrigill, Cumb | 97 | D2 |
| Garrochtrie, D & G | 95 | B2 |
| Garsdale Head, Cumb | 92 | B2 |
| Garsdon, Wilts | 36 | C4 |
| Garshall Green, Staff | 69 | C4 |
| Garsington, Oxon | 38 | A3 |
| Garstang, Lanc | 85 | C2 |
| Garth, Denb | 67 | E3 |
| Garth, Powys | 45 | D3 |
| Garth Penrhyncoch, Cered | 55 | A4 |
| Garth Row, Cumb | 91 | F2 |
| Garthmyl, Powys | 56 | A3 |
| Garthorpe, Leics | 61 | A1 |
| Gartmore, Stirl | 118 | A4 |
| Gartness, N Lan | 113 | A3 |
| Gartness, Stirl | 112 | A1 |
| Gartocharn, Dumb | 112 | A1 |
| Garton, E R of Y | 90 | B3 |
| Garton-on-the-Wolds, E R of Y | 89 | D1 |
| Garvald, E Loth | 115 | B3 |
| Garvan, High | 121 | D1 |
| Garve, High | 131 | E2 |
| Garvestone, Norf | 64 | A2 |
| Garway, Heref | 35 | A1 |
| Gasper, Wilts | 12 | C1 |
| Gastard, Wilts | 25 | A2 |
| Gasthorpe, Norf | 63 | C4 |
| Gaston Green, Essex | 41 | A2 |
| Gatcombe, I of W | 8 | A1 |
| Gate Helmsley, N York | 89 | A1 |
| Gateforth, N York | 88 | C4 |
| Gatehouse, Nthumb | 103 | B2 |
| Gatehouse of Fleet, D & G | 95 | F1 |
| Gateley, Norf | 63 | C1 |
| Gatenby, N York | 93 | B2 |
| Gateshead, T & W | 104 | B4 |
| Gateside, E Renf | 112 | A4 |
| Gateside, Fife | 119 | B3 |
| Gatley, G Man | 80 | A3 |
| Gatton, Surr | 148 | B2 |
| Gaulby, Leics | 60 | C3 |
| Gauldry, Fife | 119 | D2 |
| Gautby, Linc | 84 | A4 |
| Gavinton, Bord | 115 | C4 |
| Gawcott, Bucks | 38 | B1 |
| Gawsworth, Chesh | 69 | B1 |
| Gawthrop, Cumb | 92 | A3 |
| Gawthwaite, Cumb | 91 | D3 |
| Gaydon, Warw | 49 | A3 |
| Gayhurst, Bucks | 50 | B3 |
| Gayle, N York | 92 | C2 |
| Gayles, N York | 92 | E1 |
| Gayton, Nhants | 50 | A3 |
| Gayton, Norf | 63 | A1 |
| Gayton, Staff | 69 | C4 |
| Gayton le Marsh, Linc | 84 | C3 |
| Gayton Thorpe, Norf | 63 | A1 |
| Gazeley, Suff | 53 | A2 |
| Gedding, Suff | 53 | C2 |
| Geddinge, Kent | 31 | B4 |
| Geddington, Nhants | 61 | B4 |
| Gedney, Linc | 62 | B1 |
| Gedney Broadgate, Linc | 62 | B1 |
| Gedney Drove End, Linc | 74 | A4 |
| Gedney Dyke, Linc | 73 | D4 |
| Gedney Hill, Linc | 62 | B2 |
| Geeston, Rut | 61 | C2 |
| Geldeston, Norf | 65 | B3 |
| Gelli Gynan, Denb | 67 | D2 |
| Gellifor, Denb | 67 | D1 |
| Gelligaer, Caer | 34 | D4 |
| Gellilydan, Gwyn | 66 | F3 |
| Gellywen, Carm | 32 | F1 |
| Gelston, D & G | 101 | C4 |
| Gelston, Linc | 72 | C3 |
| Gembling, E R of Y | 90 | A1 |
| Gentleshaw, Staff | 58 | B2 |
| George Green, Bucks | 140 | C2 |
| George Nympton, Devon | 10 | A2 |
| Georgeham, Devon | 9 | D1 |
| Germansweek, Devon | 4 | C1 |
| Gerrards Cross, Bucks | 39 | B4 |
| Gerrick, N York | 99 | C4 |
| Gestingthorpe, Essex | 53 | B4 |
| Geuffordd, Powys | 56 | A2 |
| Gifford, E Loth | 115 | A3 |
| Giggleswick, N York | 86 | B1 |
| Gilcrux, Cumb | 96 | D2 |
| Gildersome, W York | 87 | B4 |
| Gildingwells, S York | 82 | B3 |
| Gileston, Glam | 22 | F2 |
| Gilfach Goch, Brid | 34 | B4 |
| Gilfachrheda, Cered | 44 | E2 |
| Gilgarran, Cumb | 96 | D3 |
| Gillamoor, N York | 94 | A2 |
| Gilling East, N York | 93 | D3 |
| Gilling West, N York | 93 | A1 |
| Gillingham, Dors | 12 | C2 |
| Gillingham, Norf | 65 | B3 |
| Gillingham, Kent | 30 | A2 |
| Gilmerton, Perth | 118 | D2 |
| Gilmonby, Durham | 98 | A4 |
| Gilmorton, Leics | 60 | B4 |
| Gilsland, Cumb | 103 | A4 |
| Gilwern, Monm | 34 | E2 |
| Gimingham, Norf | 75 | C4 |
| Gipping, Suff | 53 | D2 |
| Gipsey Bridge, Linc | 73 | C2 |
| Girsby, N York | 93 | B1 |
| Girton, Camb | 52 | A2 |
| Girton, Notts | 72 | B1 |
| Girvan, S Ayr | 100 | B1 |
| Gisburn, Lanc | 86 | C2 |
| Gisleham, Suff | 65 | C4 |
| Gislingham, Suff | 53 | D1 |
| Gissing, Norf | 64 | B4 |
| Gittisham, Devon | 11 | A4 |
| Gladestry, Powys | 46 | A3 |
| Gladsmuir, E Loth | 114 | C2 |
| Glais, Swan | 33 | D3 |
| Glaisdale, N York | 94 | B1 |
| Glamis, Angus | 123 | E4 |
| Glanaman, Carm | 33 | D2 |
| Glandford, Norf | 75 | A3 |
| Glandwr, Pemb | 32 | E1 |
| Glandyfi, Cered | 55 | B3 |
| Glanton, Nthumb | 109 | D4 |
| Glanvilles Wootton, Dors | 12 | B3 |
| Glan-y-don, Flint | 77 | C4 |
| Glapthorn, Nhants | 61 | C4 |
| Glasbury, Powys | 46 | A4 |
| Glascwm, Powys | 46 | A3 |
| Glasfryn, Ab & Col | 67 | B2 |
| Glasgow, Glas | 112 | B3 |
| Glasinfryn, Gwyn | 66 | E1 |
| Glasserton, D & G | 95 | D2 |
| Glassford, S Lan | 107 | A1 |
| Glasshouse, Glouc | 36 | A2 |
| Glasshouses, N York | 93 | A4 |
| Glasson, Cumb | 102 | B4 |
| Glasson, Lanc | 85 | B1 |
| Glassonby, Cumb | 97 | B2 |
| Glasterlaw, Angus | 124 | B4 |
| Glaston, Rut | 61 | B3 |
| Glastonbury, Som | 12 | A1 |
| Glatton, Camb | 61 | D4 |
| Glazebrook, Chesh | 79 | B3 |
| Glazebury, Chesh | 79 | A2 |
| Glazeley, Shrop | 57 | B4 |
| Gleaston, Cumb | 91 | D4 |
| Gledrid, Shrop | 67 | E4 |
| Glemsford, Suff | 53 | B3 |
| Glen Auldyn, I o M | 139 | D2 |
| Glen Maye, I o M | 139 | B3 |
| Glenbarr, Argyll | 105 | D2 |
| Glenboig, N Lan | 112 | C3 |
| Glenborrodale, High | 120 | F3 |
| Glenbuck, E Ayr | 107 | A2 |
| Glencaple, D & G | 101 | D3 |
| Glencarse, Perth | 119 | B2 |
| Glencoe, High | 121 | E3 |
| Glencraig, Fife | 114 | A1 |
| Glendaruel, Argyll | 111 | B2 |
| Glendevon, Perth | 118 | E4 |
| Glendoick, Perth | 119 | B2 |
| Gleneagles, Perth | 118 | E3 |
| Glenelg, High | 125 | F2 |
| Glenfarg, Perth | 119 | B3 |
| Glenfinnan, High | 121 | C1 |
| Glengolly, High | 138 | C1 |
| Glenholm, Bord | 107 | D2 |
| Glenkindie, Aber | 128 | C2 |
| Glenluce, D & G | 100 | C4 |
| Glenmavis, N Lan | 112 | C3 |
| Glenmore, High | 130 | C4 |
| Glenridding, Cumb | 97 | A4 |
| Glenrothes, Fife | 119 | C4 |
| Glentham, Linc | 83 | D3 |
| Glentrool Village, D & G | 100 | D3 |
| Glentworth, Linc | 83 | C3 |
| Glenurquhart, High | 132 | C2 |
| Glenwhilly, D & G | 100 | B3 |
| Glewstone, Heref | 35 | B2 |
| Glinton, Camb | 61 | D2 |
| Glooston, Leics | 61 | A3 |
| Glossop, Derby | 80 | B3 |
| Gloucester, Glouc | 36 | B2 |
| Glusburn, N York | 86 | D2 |
| Gluvian, Corn | 3 | C3 |
| Glyn Ceiriog, Wrex | 67 | D3 |
| Glynarthen, Cered | 44 | E3 |
| Glyncorrwg, Neath | 34 | A3 |
| Glynde, E Sus | 19 | B3 |
| Glyndyfrdwy, Denb | 67 | D3 |
| Glyn-Neath, Neath | 34 | A3 |
| Glyntawe, Powys | 34 | A2 |
| Glynteg, Carm | 44 | E4 |
| Gnosall, Staff | 57 | C1 |
| Goadby, Leics | 61 | A3 |
| Goadby Marwood, Leics | 72 | B4 |
| Goatacre, Wilts | 25 | B1 |
| Goathill, Dors | 12 | B3 |
| Goathland, N York | 94 | B1 |
| Goathurst, Som | 11 | B1 |
| Goathurst Common, Kent | 149 | C3 |
| Gobowen, Shrop | 67 | E4 |
| Goddard's Green, Kent | 21 | A1 |
| Godmanchester, Camb | 51 | C1 |
| Godmanstone, Dors | 12 | B4 |
| Godney, Som | 23 | D4 |
| Godolphin Cross, Corn | 1 | C2 |
| Godre'r-graig, Neath | 33 | D3 |
| Godshill, I of W | 8 | B2 |
| Goetre, Monm | 34 | E3 |
| Goff's Oak, Herts | 40 | B3 |
| Gofilon, Monm | 34 | E2 |
| Goginan, Cered | 55 | B4 |
| Golan, Gwyn | 66 | D3 |
| Golant, Corn | 3 | E4 |
| Golberdon, Corn | 4 | B3 |
| Golborne, G Man | 79 | A2 |
| Goldcliff, Newport | 23 | C1 |
| Golden Green, Kent | 29 | A4 |
| Golden Pot, Hamp | 27 | A4 |
| Goldhanger, Essex | 43 | A3 |
| Goldsborough, N York | 99 | D4 |
| Goldsborough, N York | 88 | A1 |
| Goldsithney, Corn | 1 | C2 |
| Goldsworth, Surr | 146 | A2 |
| Goldthorpe, S York | 82 | A2 |
| Goldworthy, Devon | 9 | C2 |
| Gollanfield, High | 132 | D3 |
| Golspie, High | 136 | D3 |
| Gomeldon, Wilts | 14 | A1 |
| Gonalston, Notts | 72 | A3 |
| Good Easter, Essex | 41 | B2 |
| Gooderstone, Norf | 63 | A3 |
| Goodleigh, Devon | 9 | E1 |
| Goodmanham, E R of Y | 89 | C2 |
| Goodnestone, Kent | 30 | C3 |
| Goodnestone, Kent | 31 | B3 |
| Goodrich, Heref | 35 | B2 |
| Goodshaw Fold, Lanc | 86 | B4 |
| Goodworth Clatford, Hamp | 26 | A4 |
| Goole, E R of Y | 89 | B4 |
| Goom's Hill, Worc | 48 | A3 |
| Goonbell, Corn | 3 | A4 |
| Goonhavern, Corn | 3 | B4 |
| Goonvrea, Corn | 3 | A4 |
| Goose Green, Essex | 43 | C1 |
| Goose Green, Essex | 43 | C1 |
| Goose Green, Glouc | 24 | A2 |
| Goosey, Oxon | 37 | C4 |
| Goosnargh, Lanc | 85 | C3 |
| Goostrey, Chesh | 69 | A1 |
| Gordon, Bord | 108 | D1 |
| Gordonstown, Aber | 134 | B4 |
| Gorebridge, M Loth | 114 | B3 |
| Gores, Wilts | 25 | C3 |
| Gorey, Jers | 139 | B2 |
| Goring, Oxon | 26 | C1 |
| Gorran, Corn | 2 | C1 |
| Gorran Haven, Corn | 2 | C1 |
| Gorsedd, Flint | 77 | C4 |
| Gorseinon, Swan | 33 | C4 |
| Gorsgoch, Cered | 44 | F3 |
| Gorslas, Carm | 33 | C2 |
| Gorsley, Glouc | 35 | C1 |
| Gorstello, Chesh | 68 | A1 |
| Gorsty Hill, Staff | 70 | A4 |
| Gosbeck, Suff | 54 | A3 |
| Gosberton, Linc | 73 | C4 |
| Gosfield, Essex | 42 | B1 |
| Gosforth, Cumb | 91 | B1 |
| Gosforth, T & W | 104 | B4 |
| Gospel End, Staff | 57 | C3 |
| Gosport, Hamp | 15 | B4 |
| Gossington, Glouc | 36 | A3 |
| Gotham, Notts | 71 | B4 |
| Gotherington, Glouc | 36 | C1 |
| Gotton, Som | 11 | B2 |
| Goudhurst, Kent | 20 | B1 |
| Goulceby, Linc | 84 | B4 |
| Gourdon, Aber | 124 | D2 |
| Gourock, Inv | 111 | D2 |
| Goveton, Devon | 8 | A1 |
| Gowdall, E R of Y | 89 | A4 |
| Gowerton, Swan | 33 | C4 |
| Gowkhall, Fife | 113 | C1 |
| Goxhill, E R of Y | 90 | A2 |
| Goxhill, Linc | 90 | A4 |
| Graffham, W Suss | 17 | A3 |
| Grafham, Camb | 51 | B1 |
| Grafham, Surr | 146 | A4 |
| Grafton, N York | 88 | B1 |
| Grafton, Oxon | 37 | B3 |
| Grafton, Shrop | 56 | C1 |
| Grafton, Worc | 48 | A4 |
| Grafton Flyford, Worc | 48 | A3 |
| Grafton Regis, Nhants | 50 | B3 |
| Grafton Underwood, Nhants | 61 | B4 |
| Graig, Ab & Col | 67 | A1 |
| Graig-fechan, Denb | 67 | D2 |
| Grain, Kent | 30 | A1 |
| Grainsby, Linc | 84 | B2 |
| Grainthorpe, Linc | 84 | C2 |
| Grampound Road, Corn | 3 | C4 |
| Gramsdale, W Isles | 139 | A3 |
| Granborough, Bucks | 38 | C1 |
| Granby, Notts | 72 | B4 |
| Grand Chemins, Jers | 139 | B2 |
| Grandborough, Warw | 49 | B2 |
| Grandes Rocques, Guer | 139 | B2 |
| Grange, Cumb | 96 | F4 |
| Grange Moor, W York | 81 | B1 |
| Grange Villa, Durham | 98 | C1 |
| Grangemouth, Falkirk | 113 | B2 |
| Grange-over-Sands, Cumb | 91 | E3 |
| Gransmoor, E R of Y | 90 | A1 |
| Granston, Pemb | 44 | A4 |
| Grantchester, Camb | 52 | B3 |
| Grantham, Linc | 72 | C4 |
| Grantown-on-Spey, High | 127 | E1 |
| Grantshouse, Bord | 115 | C3 |
| Grasby, Linc | 84 | A2 |
| Grasmere, Cumb | 91 | D1 |
| Grasscroft, G Man | 80 | B2 |
| Grassington, N York | 86 | D1 |
| Grassmoor, Derby | 71 | A1 |
| Grassthorpe, Notts | 72 | B1 |
| Grateley, Hamp | 26 | A4 |
| Graveley, Camb | 51 | C2 |
| Graveley, Herts | 40 | A1 |
| Graveney, Kent | 30 | C3 |
| Gravesend, Kent | 29 | A2 |
| Grayingham, Linc | 83 | C2 |
| Grayrigg, Cumb | 91 | F2 |
| Grays, Essex | 29 | A1 |
| Grayshott, Hamp | 17 | A1 |
| Grayswood, Surr | 17 | A1 |
| Grazeley, Berks | 27 | A2 |
| Greasbrough, S York | 82 | A2 |
| Greasley, Notts | 71 | A3 |
| Great Addington, Nhants | 50 | C1 |
| Great Alne, Warw | 48 | B2 |
| Great Altcar, Lanc | 77 | D2 |
| Great Amwell, Herts | 40 | B2 |
| Great Asby, Cumb | 97 | C4 |
| Great Ayton, N York | 99 | B4 |
| Great Badminton, Glouc | 24 | B1 |
| Great Bardfield, Essex | 42 | A1 |
| Great Barford, Beds | 51 | B3 |
| Great Barrington, Glouc | 37 | B2 |
| Great Barrow, Chesh | 68 | B1 |
| Great Barton, Suff | 53 | C2 |
| Great Barugh, N York | 94 | B3 |
| Great Bavington, Nthumb | 103 | D2 |
| Great Bealings, Suff | 54 | A3 |
| Great Bedwyn, Wilts | 25 | D2 |
| Great Bentley, Essex | 43 | B2 |
| Great Bircham, Norf | 74 | C4 |
| Great Blakenham, Suff | 53 | D3 |
| Great Blencow, Cumb | 97 | A3 |
| Great Bolas, Shrop | 57 | A1 |
| Great Bookham, Surr | 147 | A2 |
| Great Bosullow, Corn | 1 | B2 |
| Great Bourton, Oxon | 49 | B3 |
| Great Bowden, Leics | 61 | A4 |
| Great Bradley, Suff | 53 | A3 |
| Great Braxted, Essex | 42 | B2 |
| Great Bricett, Suff | 53 | D3 |
| Great Brickhill, Bucks | 39 | A1 |
| Great Bridgeford, Staff | 69 | B4 |
| Great Brington, Nhants | 50 | A2 |
| Great Bromley, Essex | 43 | B1 |
| Great Broughton, Cumb | 96 | D3 |
| Great Budworth, Chesh | 79 | A4 |
| Great Burdon, Durham | 98 | D4 |
| Great Busby, N York | 93 | D1 |
| Great Carlton, Linc | 84 | C3 |
| Great Casterton, Rut | 61 | C2 |
| Great Chart, Kent | 30 | B4 |
| Great Chatfield, Wilts | 25 | A3 |
| Great Chatwell, Staff | 57 | B1 |
| Great Chesterford, Essex | 52 | B4 |
| Great Cheverell, Wilts | 25 | B3 |
| Great Chishill, Camb | 52 | A4 |
| Great Clifton, Cumb | 96 | D3 |
| Great Cowden, E R of Y | 90 | B2 |
| Great Coxwell, Oxon | 37 | B4 |
| Great Cransley, Nhants | 50 | B1 |
| Great Cressingham, Norf | 63 | B3 |
| Great Crosthwaite, Cumb | 96 | F3 |
| Great Cubley, Derby | 70 | B3 |
| Great Dalby, Leics | 61 | A2 |
| Great Dunham, Norf | 63 | B1 |
| Great Dunmow, Essex | 41 | B1 |
| Great Durnford, Wilts | 13 | B1 |
| Great Easton, Essex | 41 | B1 |
| Great Easton, Leics | 61 | A3 |
| Great Eccleston, Lanc | 85 | B3 |
| Great Ellingham, Norf | 64 | A3 |
| Great Elm, Som | 24 | B4 |
| Great Englebourne, Devon | 5 | B4 |
| Great Everdon, Nhants | 49 | C2 |
| Great Eversden, Camb | 52 | A3 |
| Great Finborough, Suff | 53 | D2 |
| Great Fransham, Norf | 63 | C2 |
| Great Gaddesden, Herts | 39 | B2 |
| Great Gidding, Camb | 61 | D4 |
| Great Givendale, E R of Y | 89 | B1 |
| Great Glemham, Suff | 54 | B2 |
| Great Glen, Leics | 60 | C3 |
| Great Gonerby, Linc | 72 | C3 |
| Great Gransden, Camb | 51 | C3 |
| Great Green, Camb | 51 | C4 |
| Great Green, Suff | 53 | C2 |
| Great Habton, N York | 94 | B3 |
| Great Hale, Linc | 73 | B3 |
| Great Hallingbury, Essex | 41 | A2 |
| Great Harrowden, Nhants | 50 | C1 |
| Great Harwood, Lanc | 86 | B3 |
| Great Haseley, Oxon | 38 | B3 |
| Great Hatfield, E R of Y | 90 | A2 |
| Great Haywood, Staff | 58 | A1 |
| Great Heck, N York | 88 | C4 |
| Great Henny, Essex | 53 | B4 |
| Great Hinton, Wilts | 25 | A3 |
| Great Hockham, Norf | 63 | C3 |
| Great Holland, Essex | 43 | C2 |
| Great Horkesley, Essex | 43 | A1 |
| Great Hormead, Herts | 40 | B1 |
| Great Horwood, Bucks | 38 | C1 |
| Great Houghton, Nhants | 50 | B2 |
| Great Houghton, S York | 82 | A2 |
| Great Hucklow, Derby | 81 | B4 |
| Great Kelk, E R of Y | 90 | A1 |
| Great Kimble, Bucks | 38 | C3 |
| Great Kingshill, Bucks | 39 | A4 |
| Great Langdale, Cumb | 91 | D1 |
| Great Langton, N York | 93 | B2 |
| Great Leighs, Essex | 42 | A2 |
| Great Limber, Linc | 84 | A1 |
| Great Linford, Bucks | 50 | B4 |
| Great Livermere, Suff | 53 | B1 |
| Great Lumley, Durham | 98 | D1 |
| Great Malvern, Worc | 47 | B3 |
| Great Maplestead, Essex | 53 | B4 |
| Great Massingham, Norf | 63 | B1 |
| Great Milton, Oxon | 38 | B3 |
| Great Missenden, Bucks | 39 | A3 |
| Great Mongeham, Kent | 31 | B4 |
| Great Moulton, Norf | 64 | B4 |
| Great Musgrave, Cumb | 97 | D4 |
| Great Ness, Shrop | 56 | C1 |
| Great Oak, Monm | 35 | A3 |
| Great Oakley, Essex | 43 | C1 |
| Great Offley, Herts | 39 | C1 |
| Great Ormside, Cumb | 97 | D4 |
| Great Orton, Cumb | 96 | F1 |
| Great Ouseburn, N York | 88 | B1 |
| Great Oxendon, Nhants | 60 | C4 |
| Great Paxton, Camb | 51 | C2 |
| Great Plumpton, Lanc | 85 | B3 |
| Great Plumstead, Norf | 65 | A2 |
| Great Ponton, Linc | 72 | C4 |
| Great Preston, W York | 88 | B4 |
| Great Raveley, Camb | 62 | A4 |
| Great Rissington, Glouc | 37 | B2 |
| Great Rollright, Oxon | 37 | C1 |
| Great Ryburgh, Norf | 74 | E4 |
| Great Ryle, Nthumb | 109 | C4 |
| Great Ryton, Shrop | 56 | D2 |
| Great Saling, Essex | 42 | A1 |
| Great Salkeld, Cumb | 97 | B2 |
| Great Sampford, Essex | 52 | C4 |
| Great Saughall, Chesh | 68 | A1 |
| Great Shefford, Berks | 26 | A2 |
| Great Shelford, Camb | 52 | B3 |
| Great Smeaton, N York | 93 | B1 |
| Great Snoring, Norf | 74 | E4 |
| Great Somerford, Wilts | 25 | B1 |
| Great Soudley, Shrop | 69 | A4 |
| Great Stainton, Durham | 98 | D4 |
| Great Stambridge, Essex | 43 | A4 |
| Great Steeping, Linc | 74 | A1 |
| Great Strickland, Cumb | 97 | B3 |
| Great Stukeley, Camb | 51 | C1 |
| Great Sturton, Linc | 84 | B4 |
| Great Swinburne, Nthumb | 103 | D3 |
| Great Tew, Oxon | 37 | D1 |
| Great Tey, Essex | 43 | A1 |
| Great Torrington, Devon | 9 | D2 |
| Great Tosson, Nthumb | 103 | D1 |
| Great Totham, Essex | 42 | B2 |
| Great Totham, Essex | 42 | B2 |
| Great Urswick, Cumb | 91 | D4 |
| Great Wakering, Essex | 43 | A4 |
| Great Waldingfield, Suff | 53 | C4 |
| Great Walsingham, Norf | 74 | E4 |
| Great Waltham, Essex | 42 | A2 |
| Great Warley, Essex | 41 | B4 |
| Great Washbourne, Glouc | 48 | A4 |
| Great Wenham, Suff | 53 | D4 |
| Great Whittington, Nthumb | 103 | D3 |
| Great Wigborough, Essex | 43 | A2 |
| Great Wilbraham, Camb | 52 | C2 |
| Great Wishford, Wilts | 13 | B1 |
| Great Witcombe, Glouc | 36 | B2 |
| Great Wolford, Warw | 48 | C4 |
| Great Wratting, Suff | 53 | A3 |
| Great Wymondley, Herts | 40 | A1 |
| Great Wyrley, Staff | 58 | A2 |
| Great Yarmouth, Norf | 65 | C2 |

| PLACE | PAGE | GRID |
|---|---|---|
| Great Yeldham, Essex | 53 | A4 |
| Greatford, Linc | 61 | D2 |
| Greatgate, Staff | 70 | A3 |
| Greatham, Durham | 99 | A3 |
| Greatham, Hamp | 16 | B1 |
| Greatham, W Suss | 17 | B3 |
| Greatworth, Nhants | 49 | C4 |
| Green End, Herts | 40 | B1 |
| Green End, Herts | 40 | B1 |
| Green End, Warw | 59 | A4 |
| Green Hammerton, N York | 88 | B1 |
| Green Ore, Som | 23 | D4 |
| Green Quarter, Cumb | 91 | E1 |
| Green Street, Herts | 41 | A2 |
| Green Street, Worc | 47 | C3 |
| Green Street Green, Kent | 29 | A2 |
| Green Street Green, G Lon | 149 | B1 |
| Green Tye, Herts | 41 | A2 |
| Greenfield, Beds | 51 | A4 |
| Greenfield, Flint | 77 | C4 |
| Greenfield, G Man | 80 | B2 |
| Greenford, G Lon | 142 | A1 |
| Greengairs, N Lan | 113 | A3 |
| Greenhalgh, Lanc | 85 | B3 |
| Greenham, Som | 10 | D2 |
| Greenhaugh, Nthumb | 103 | B2 |
| Greenhill, D & G | 101 | E3 |
| Greenholm, E Ayr | 106 | F2 |
| Greenhow Hill, N York | 87 | A1 |
| Greenlaw, Bord | 109 | A1 |
| Greenlea, D & G | 101 | E3 |
| Greenloaning, Perth | 118 | D3 |
| Greenock, Inv | 111 | D2 |
| Greenodd, Cumb | 91 | D3 |
| Greens Norton, Nhants | 50 | A3 |
| Greenside, T & W | 104 | A4 |
| Greenstead Green, Essex | 42 | B1 |
| Greenway, Som | 11 | B2 |
| Greenwich, G Lon | 144 | A2 |
| Greet, Glouc | 36 | C1 |
| Greete, Shrop | 46 | D1 |
| Greetham, Linc | 73 | C1 |
| Greetham, Rut | 61 | B2 |
| Greetland, W York | 87 | A4 |
| Greinton, Som | 11 | C1 |
| Grenaby, I o M | 139 | B4 |
| Grendon, Nhants | 50 | C2 |
| Grendon Underwood, Bucks | 38 | B2 |
| Gresford, Wrex | 67 | E2 |
| Gresham, Norf | 75 | B3 |
| Gressenhall, Norf | 63 | C1 |
| Gressenhall Green, Norf | 63 | C1 |
| Gressingham, Lanc | 91 | F4 |
| Greta Bridge, Durham | 98 | B4 |
| Gretna, D & G | 102 | B4 |
| Gretna Green, D & G | 102 | B4 |
| Gretton, Nhants | 61 | B3 |
| Grewelthorpe, N York | 93 | A3 |
| Greys Green, Oxon | 27 | A1 |
| Greysouthen, Cumb | 96 | D3 |
| Greystoke, Cumb | 97 | A3 |
| Greystone, Angus | 124 | A4 |
| Greywell, Hamp | 27 | A4 |
| Griff, Warw | 59 | B4 |
| Grimeford Village, Lanc | 79 | A1 |
| Grimethorpe, S York | 82 | A1 |
| Grimley, Worc | 47 | C2 |
| Grimoldby, Linc | 84 | C3 |
| Grimpo, Shrop | 68 | A4 |
| Grimsargh, Lanc | 86 | A3 |
| Grimsby, Linc | 84 | B1 |
| Grimscott, Corn | 9 | B3 |
| Grimsthorpe, Linc | 61 | C1 |
| Grimston, Leics | 60 | C1 |
| Grimston, Norf | 63 | A1 |
| Grimstone, Dors | 6 | F1 |
| Grimstone End, Suff | 53 | C1 |
| Grindale, E R of Y | 94 | E4 |
| Grindleford, Derby | 81 | B4 |
| Grindleton, Lanc | 86 | B2 |
| Grindley Brook, Shrop | 68 | B3 |
| Grindlow, Derby | 81 | B4 |
| Grindon, Staff | 70 | A2 |
| Gringley on the Hill, Notts | 83 | B3 |
| Grinsdale, Cumb | 102 | C4 |
| Grinshill, Shrop | 56 | D1 |
| Grinton, N York | 92 | E2 |
| Gristhorpe, N York | 94 | E3 |
| Griston, Norf | 63 | C3 |
| Gritley, Ork | 139 | B2 |
| Grittenham, Wilts | 25 | B1 |
| Grittleton, Wilts | 25 | A1 |
| Grizebeck, Cumb | 91 | D3 |
| Grizedale, Cumb | 91 | D2 |
| Groby, Leics | 60 | B2 |
| Groes, Ab & Col | 67 | C1 |
| Groes-faen, Rhond | 22 | F1 |
| Groesffordd Marli, Denb | 77 | A4 |
| Groes-Wen, Caer | 23 | A1 |
| Gronant, Flint | 77 | B4 |
| Groombridge, E Sus | 19 | B1 |
| Grosmont, Monm | 35 | A1 |
| Grosmont, N York | 94 | B1 |
| Groton, Suff | 53 | C4 |
| Grouville, Jers | 139 | B2 |
| Grove, Notts | 83 | B4 |
| Grove, Oxon | 37 | D4 |
| Grove Park, G Lon | 144 | A3 |
| Grovesend, Swan | 33 | C3 |
| Grundisburgh, Suff | 54 | A3 |
| Guardbridge, Fife | 119 | D2 |
| Guarlford, Worc | 47 | B3 |
| Guestling Green, E Sus | 21 | A3 |
| Guestwick, Norf | 75 | A4 |
| Guide, Lanc | 86 | B4 |
| Guilden Morden, Camb | 51 | C4 |
| Guilden Sutton, Chesh | 68 | A1 |
| Guildford, Surr | 146 | A3 |
| Guildtown, Perth | 119 | B1 |
| Guilsborough, Nhants | 50 | A1 |
| Guilsfield, Powys | 56 | A2 |
| Guisborough, N York | 99 | B4 |
| Guiseley, W York | 87 | B2 |
| Guist, Norf | 63 | C1 |
| Guiting Power, Glouc | 37 | A1 |
| Gullane, E Loth | 115 | A2 |
| Gulworthy, Devon | 4 | C2 |
| Gumfreston, Pemb | 32 | E3 |
| Gumley, Leics | 60 | C4 |
| Gun Hill, E Sus | 20 | A3 |
| Gunby, Linc | 61 | B1 |
| Gunby, Linc | 74 | A1 |
| Gundleton, Hamp | 15 | B1 |
| Gunn, Devon | 9 | E1 |
| Gunnerside, N York | 92 | D2 |
| Gunnerton, Nthumb | 103 | C3 |
| Gunness, Linc | 83 | B1 |
| Gunnislake, Corn | 4 | C3 |
| Gunthorpe, Norf | 75 | A4 |
| Gunthorpe, Notts | 72 | A3 |
| Gunwalloe, Corn | 1 | D3 |
| Gurnard, I of W | 15 | A4 |
| Gurney Slade, Som | 24 | A4 |
| Gurnos, Powys | 34 | A3 |
| Gussage All Saints, Dors | 13 | A3 |
| Gussage St Andrew, Dors | 13 | A3 |
| Gussage St Michael, Dors | 13 | A3 |
| Gutcher, Shet | 139 | A1 |
| Guthrie, Angus | 124 | A4 |
| Guyhirn, Camb | 62 | B2 |
| Guyzance, Nthumb | 109 | E4 |
| Gwaenysgor, Flint | 77 | B4 |
| Gwalchmai, Angle | 76 | B4 |
| Gwaun-Cae-Gurwen, Carm | 33 | D2 |
| Gweek, Corn | 1 | D2 |
| Gwenddwr, Powys | 45 | E4 |
| Gwennap, Corn | 2 | A1 |
| Gwernaffield, Flint | 67 | D1 |
| Gwernesney, Monm | 35 | A3 |
| Gwernogle, Carm | 44 | F4 |
| Gwernymynydd, Flint | 67 | D1 |
| Gwespyr, Flint | 77 | B4 |
| Gwithian, Corn | 1 | C1 |
| Gwyddelwern, Denb | 67 | C3 |
| Gwyddgrug, Carm | 44 | F4 |
| Gwytherin, Ab & Col | 67 | A1 |
| Habberley, Shrop | 56 | C2 |
| Habertoft, Linc | 74 | A1 |
| Habrough, Linc | 84 | A1 |
| Hacconby, Linc | 61 | D1 |
| Haceby, Linc | 73 | A4 |
| Hacheston, Suff | 54 | B2 |
| Hackbridge, G Lon | 143 | A4 |
| Hackford, Norf | 64 | A3 |
| Hackforth, N York | 93 | A2 |
| Hackland, Ork | 139 | A1 |
| Hackleton, Nhants | 50 | B3 |
| Hackness, N York | 94 | D2 |
| Hackney, G Lon | 143 | B1 |
| Hackthorn, Linc | 83 | D4 |
| Hackthorpe, Cumb | 97 | B3 |
| Haddenham, Bucks | 38 | C3 |
| Haddenham, Camb | 52 | B1 |
| Haddington, E Loth | 115 | A2 |
| Haddington, Linc | 72 | C1 |
| Haddiscoe, Norf | 65 | B3 |
| Haddon, Camb | 61 | D3 |
| Hadfield, Derby | 80 | B2 |
| Hadleigh, Suff | 53 | D4 |
| Hadley, Worc | 47 | C2 |
| Hadley End, Staff | 58 | B1 |
| Hadlow, Kent | 29 | A4 |
| Hadnall, Shrop | 56 | D1 |
| Hadstock, Essex | 52 | C4 |
| Hadzor, Worc | 47 | C2 |
| Hafodunos, Ab & Col | 67 | A1 |
| Haggerston, Nthumb | 109 | C1 |
| Haggs, Falkirk | 113 | A2 |
| Hagley, Heref | 46 | D4 |
| Hagley, Worc | 57 | C4 |
| Hagworthingham, Linc | 73 | D1 |
| Hail Weston, Camb | 51 | B2 |
| Haile, Cumb | 91 | B1 |
| Hailey, Oxon | 37 | C2 |
| Hainford, Norf | 64 | B1 |
| Hainton, Linc | 84 | A3 |
| Haisthorpe, E R of Y | 94 | E4 |
| Halam, Notts | 72 | A2 |
| Halberton, Devon | 10 | D3 |
| Hale, Chesh | 78 | B4 |
| Hale, Cumb | 91 | F3 |
| Hale, G Man | 79 | B3 |
| Hale, Hamp | 14 | A2 |
| Hale Street, Kent | 29 | B4 |
| Hales, Norf | 65 | B3 |
| Hales, Staff | 69 | A4 |
| Halesowen, W Mids | 58 | A4 |
| Halesworth, Suff | 54 | C1 |
| Halewood, Mers | 78 | A3 |
| Halford, Devon | 5 | B2 |
| Halford, Warw | 48 | C3 |
| Halfpenny Green, Shrop | 57 | C3 |
| Halfway House, Shrop | 56 | B2 |
| Halifax, W York | 87 | A4 |
| Halkirk, High | 138 | D2 |
| Halkyn, Flint | 67 | D1 |
| Hall Dunnerdale, Cumb | 91 | C2 |
| Halland, E Sus | 19 | B3 |
| Hallaton, Leics | 61 | A3 |
| Hallatrow, Som | 24 | A3 |
| Hallbankgate, Cumb | 103 | A4 |
| Hallen, Glouc | 23 | D1 |
| Hallgarth, Durham | 98 | D2 |
| Hallin, High | 130 | A2 |
| Halling, Kent | 29 | B3 |
| Hallington, Linc | 84 | B3 |
| Hallington, Nthumb | 103 | D3 |
| Halloughton, Notts | 72 | A2 |
| Hall's Green, Herts | 40 | A1 |
| Hallsands, Devon | 8 | B1 |
| Hallmore, Glouc | 36 | A3 |
| Halnaker, W Suss | 17 | A3 |
| Halsall, Lanc | 78 | A1 |
| Halse, Nhants | 49 | C4 |
| Halse, Som | 11 | A2 |
| Halsetown, Corn | 1 | C1 |
| Halsham, E R of Y | 90 | B4 |
| Halstead, Leics | 61 | A2 |
| Halstead, Essex | 42 | B1 |
| Halstock, Dors | 12 | A3 |
| Halsway, Som | 11 | A1 |
| Haltham, Linc | 73 | C1 |
| Halton, Bucks | 39 | A3 |
| Halton, Lanc | 91 | F4 |
| Halton, Nthumb | 103 | D4 |
| Halton, Wrex | 67 | E3 |
| Halton East, N York | 86 | D1 |
| Halton Gill, N York | 92 | C3 |
| Halton Holegate, Linc | 73 | D1 |
| Halton Lea Gate, Nthumb | 103 | A4 |
| Halton Shields, Nthumb | 103 | D3 |
| Halton West, N York | 86 | C1 |
| Haltwhistle, Nthumb | 103 | B4 |
| Halvergate, Norf | 65 | B2 |
| Halwell, Devon | 5 | B4 |
| Halwill, Devon | 9 | D4 |
| Halwill Junction, Devon | 9 | D4 |
| Ham, Glouc | 35 | C4 |
| Ham, Kent | 31 | B3 |
| Ham, Som | 11 | B2 |
| Ham, Wilts | 26 | A3 |
| Ham, G Lon | 142 | A3 |
| Ham Green, Worc | 48 | A2 |
| Hambleden, Bucks | 27 | B1 |
| Hambledon, Hamp | 16 | A3 |
| Hambledon, Surr | 17 | A1 |
| Hamble-le-Rice, Hamp | 15 | A3 |
| Hambleton, Lanc | 85 | B2 |
| Hambleton, N York | 88 | C3 |
| Hambridge, Som | 11 | C2 |
| Hameringham, Linc | 73 | C1 |
| Hamerton, Camb | 51 | B1 |
| Hamilton, S Lan | 112 | C4 |
| Hamlet, Dors | 12 | B3 |
| Hammersmith, G Lon | 142 | B2 |
| Hammerwich, Staff | 58 | B2 |
| Hammoon, Dors | 12 | D3 |
| Hampden Row, Bucks | 39 | A3 |
| Hampnett, Glouc | 37 | A2 |
| Hampole, S York | 82 | B1 |
| Hampreston, Dors | 13 | B4 |
| Hampstead, G Lon | 143 | A1 |
| Hampstead Norrey's, Berks | 26 | C1 |
| Hampsthwaite, N York | 87 | B1 |
| Hampton, Wilts | 37 | B4 |
| Hampton, G Lon | 141 | B4 |
| Hampton Bishop, Heref | 46 | D4 |
| Hampton Heath, Chesh | 68 | B2 |
| Hampton in Arden, W Mids | 59 | A4 |
| Hampton Lucy, Warw | 48 | C2 |
| Hampton on the Hill, Warw | 48 | C2 |
| Hampton Poyle, Oxon | 37 | D2 |
| Hampton Wick, G Lon | 142 | A4 |
| Hamptworth, Wilts | 14 | A2 |
| Hamsey, E Sus | 19 | A3 |
| Hamsey Green, Surr | 148 | C1 |
| Hamstall Ridware, Staff | 58 | B1 |
| Hamsterley, Durham | 98 | B1 |
| Hamsterley, Durham | 98 | B3 |
| Hanbury, Staff | 70 | B4 |
| Hanbury, Worc | 48 | A2 |
| Hanchurch, Staff | 69 | B3 |
| Handley, Chesh | 68 | B2 |
| Handley, Derby | 70 | C1 |
| Hanging Houghton, Nhants | 50 | B1 |
| Hanging Langford, Wilts | 13 | A1 |
| Hankelow, Chesh | 68 | C3 |
| Hankerton, Wilts | 36 | C4 |
| Hanley Castle, Worc | 47 | C4 |
| Hanley Child, Worc | 47 | A2 |
| Hanley Swan, Worc | 47 | B4 |
| Hanley William, Worc | 47 | A2 |
| Hanlith, N York | 86 | C1 |
| Hanmer, Wrex | 68 | A3 |
| Hannington, Hamp | 26 | C3 |
| Hannington, Nhants | 50 | B1 |
| Hannington, Wilts | 37 | B4 |
| Hannington Wick, Wilts | 37 | B4 |
| Hanslope, Bucks | 50 | B3 |
| Hanthorpe, Linc | 61 | D1 |
| Hanwell, Oxon | 49 | B4 |
| Hanwell, G Lon | 142 | A2 |
| Hanworth, Norf | 75 | B4 |
| Hanworth, G Lon | 141 | B3 |
| Happisburgh, Norf | 75 | D4 |
| Happisburgh Common, Norf | 75 | D4 |
| Hapsford, Chesh | 78 | B4 |
| Hapton, Lanc | 86 | B3 |
| Hapton, Norf | 64 | B3 |
| Harberton, Devon | 5 | B4 |
| Harbertonford, Devon | 5 | B4 |
| Harborough Magna, Warw | 49 | B1 |
| Harbottle, Nthumb | 109 | C4 |
| Harbourneford, Devon | 5 | A3 |
| Harbury, Warw | 49 | A2 |
| Harby, Leics | 72 | B4 |
| Harby, Notts | 72 | C1 |
| Harcombe, Devon | 5 | C2 |
| Harcombe Bottom, Devon | 11 | B4 |
| Harden, W York | 87 | A3 |
| Hardgate, D & G | 101 | C4 |
| Hardham, W Suss | 17 | B3 |
| Hardingham, Norf | 64 | A2 |
| Hardingstone, Nhants | 50 | B2 |
| Hardington, Som | 24 | B4 |
| Hardington Mandeville, Som | 12 | A3 |
| Hardington Marsh, Som | 12 | A3 |
| Hardington Moor, Som | 12 | A3 |
| Hardisworthy, Devon | 9 | B2 |
| Hardley, Hamp | 15 | A4 |
| Hardley Street, Norf | 65 | B3 |
| Hardraw, N York | 92 | C2 |
| Hardstoft, Derby | 71 | A1 |
| Hardway, Som | 12 | C1 |
| Hardwick, Bucks | 38 | C2 |
| Hardwick, Camb | 52 | A2 |
| Hardwick, Nhants | 50 | B1 |
| Hardwick, Norf | 64 | B4 |
| Hardwick, Oxon | 37 | C3 |
| Hardwick, Oxon | 38 | A1 |
| Hardwicke, Glouc | 36 | A2 |
| Hardwicke, Glouc | 36 | B1 |
| Hardy's Green, Essex | 43 | A2 |
| Hare Croft, W York | 87 | A3 |
| Hare Green, Essex | 43 | B1 |
| Hare Hatch, Berks | 27 | B1 |
| Hare Street, Herts | 40 | B1 |
| Hareby, Linc | 73 | D1 |
| Harefield, G Lon | 39 | B4 |
| Harehill, Derby | 70 | B4 |
| Harescombe, Glouc | 36 | B3 |
| Haresfield, Glouc | 36 | A2 |
| Harewood, W York | 88 | A2 |
| Harewood End, Heref | 35 | B1 |
| Hargrave, Chesh | 68 | B1 |
| Hargrave, Nhants | 51 | A1 |
| Harkstead, Suff | 54 | A4 |
| Harlaston, Staff | 59 | A2 |
| Harlaxton, Linc | 72 | C4 |
| Harlech, Gwyn | 66 | E4 |
| Harlesden, G Lon | 142 | B1 |
| Harlesthorpe, Derby | 82 | A4 |
| Harleston, Devon | 8 | B1 |
| Harleston, Norf | 65 | A4 |
| Harleston, Suff | 53 | D2 |
| Harlestone, Nhants | 50 | A2 |
| Harley, S York | 81 | C2 |
| Harlington, Beds | 39 | B1 |
| Harlington, S York | 82 | A2 |
| Harlington, G Lon | 141 | B2 |
| Harlosh, High | 130 | B4 |
| Harlow, Essex | 41 | A2 |
| Harlow Hill, Nthumb | 104 | A4 |
| Harlthorpe, E R of Y | 89 | B3 |
| Harlton, Camb | 52 | A3 |
| Harlyn Bay, Corn | 3 | C2 |
| Harman's Cross, Dors | 7 | C2 |
| Harmby, N York | 92 | E2 |
| Harmer Hill, Shrop | 56 | D1 |
| Harmondsworth, G Lon | 141 | A2 |
| Harmston, Linc | 73 | A1 |
| Harnage, Shrop | 56 | D2 |
| Harnhill, Glouc | 37 | A3 |
| Haroldston West, Pemb | 32 | C2 |
| Haroldswick, Shet | 139 | B1 |
| Harome, N York | 94 | A3 |
| Harpenden, Herts | 39 | C2 |
| Harpford, Devon | 6 | A1 |
| Harpham, E R of Y | 90 | A1 |
| Harpley, Norf | 63 | B1 |
| Harpley, Worc | 47 | A2 |
| Harpole, Nhants | 50 | A2 |
| Harpswell, Linc | 83 | C3 |
| Harracott, Devon | 9 | E2 |
| Harrietfield, Perth | 118 | E2 |
| Harrietsham, Kent | 30 | A4 |
| Harrington, Linc | 73 | D1 |
| Harringworth, Nhants | 61 | B3 |
| Harrogate, N York | 88 | A1 |
| Harrold, Beds | 50 | C2 |
| Harrow, G Lon | 39 | C4 |
| Harrow on the Hill, G Lon | 142 | A1 |
| Harrowbarrow, Corn | 4 | B3 |
| Harston, Camb | 52 | A3 |
| Harston, Leics | 72 | B4 |
| Harswell, E R of Y | 89 | B3 |
| Hart, Durham | 99 | A2 |
| Hartburn, Nthumb | 104 | A2 |
| Hartest, Suff | 53 | B3 |
| Hartfield, E Sus | 19 | B1 |
| Hartford End, Essex | 42 | A2 |
| Hartfordbridge, Hamp | 27 | B3 |
| Hartforth, N York | 93 | A1 |
| Harthill, Chesh | 68 | B2 |
| Harthill, N Lan | 113 | B3 |
| Harthill, S York | 82 | A4 |
| Hartington, Derby | 70 | A2 |
| Hartland, Devon | 9 | B2 |
| Hartlebury, Worc | 47 | C1 |
| Hartlepool, Durham | 99 | A3 |
| Hartley, Cumb | 92 | B1 |
| Hartley, Kent | 29 | A2 |
| Hartley, Kent | 20 | B1 |
| Hartley Wintney, Hamp | 27 | B3 |
| Hartlip, Kent | 30 | A2 |
| Harton, N York | 89 | A1 |
| Hartpury, Glouc | 36 | A1 |
| Hartshead, W York | 87 | B4 |
| Hartshill, Warw | 59 | B3 |
| Hartshorne, Derby | 59 | B1 |
| Hartside, Nthumb | 109 | C3 |
| Hartwell, Nhants | 50 | B3 |
| Hartwith, N York | 87 | B1 |
| Harvel, Kent | 29 | A3 |
| Harvington, Worc | 48 | B3 |
| Harwell, Notts | 83 | A3 |
| Harwell, Oxon | 37 | D4 |
| Harwich, Essex | 43 | D1 |
| Harwood Dale, N York | 94 | C2 |
| Harworth, Notts | 82 | B3 |
| Hascombe, Surr | 17 | B1 |
| Haselbeach, Nhants | 50 | A1 |
| Haselbury Plucknett, Som | 12 | A3 |
| Haseley, Warw | 48 | C2 |
| Haselor, Warw | 48 | B2 |
| Hasfield, Glouc | 36 | B1 |
| Haskayne, Lanc | 78 | A1 |
| Hasketon, Suff | 54 | B3 |
| Haslemere, Surr | 17 | A1 |
| Haslingden, Lanc | 86 | B4 |
| Haslingfield, Camb | 52 | A3 |
| Haslington, Chesh | 69 | A2 |
| Hassingham, Norf | 65 | B2 |
| Hassop, Derby | 81 | B4 |
| Haster, High | 138 | E2 |
| Hastingleigh, Kent | 30 | C4 |
| Hastings, E Sus | 21 | A3 |
| Hastingwood, Essex | 41 | A3 |
| Hastoe, Herts | 39 | A3 |
| Haswell, Durham | 98 | D2 |
| Haswell Plough, Durham | 98 | D2 |
| Hatch Beauchamp, Som | 11 | B2 |
| Hatcliffe, Linc | 84 | B2 |
| Hatfield, Heref | 47 | A2 |
| Hatfield, S York | 83 | A1 |
| Hatfield, Herts | 40 | A3 |
| Hatfield Broad Oak, Essex | 41 | B2 |
| Hatfield Heath, Essex | 41 | A2 |
| Hatfield Peverel, Essex | 42 | B2 |
| Hatfield Woodhouse, S York | 83 | A1 |
| Hatford, Oxon | 37 | C4 |
| Hatherden, Hamp | 26 | A4 |
| Hatherleigh, Devon | 9 | E4 |
| Hathern, Leics | 60 | A1 |
| Hatherop, Glouc | 37 | A3 |
| Hathersage, Derby | 81 | B4 |
| Hathersage Booths, Derby | 81 | B4 |
| Hatherton, Chesh | 68 | C3 |
| Hatherton, Staff | 58 | A2 |
| Hatley St George, Camb | 51 | C3 |
| Hatt, Corn | 4 | B3 |
| Hattersley, G Man | 80 | B3 |
| Hatton, Aber | 134 | E4 |
| Hatton, Chesh | 79 | A4 |
| Hatton, Derby | 70 | B4 |
| Hatton, Linc | 84 | A4 |
| Hatton, Shrop | 56 | D4 |
| Hatton, Warw | 48 | C2 |
| Hatton, G Lon | 141 | B3 |
| Hatton of Fintray, Aber | 129 | B2 |
| Haugh, E Ayr | 106 | E3 |
| Haugh of Urr, D & G | 101 | C4 |
| Haugham, Linc | 84 | C4 |
| Haughley, Suff | 53 | D2 |
| Haughley Green, Suff | 53 | D2 |
| Haughton, Shrop | 68 | A4 |
| Haughton, Shrop | 57 | B2 |
| Haughton, Staff | 57 | C1 |
| Haughton Moss, Chesh | 68 | B2 |
| Haultwick, Herts | 40 | B1 |
| Hauxley, Nthumb | 104 | C1 |
| Hauxton, Camb | 52 | B3 |
| Havant, Hamp | 16 | A4 |
| Havenstreet, I of W | 8 | B1 |
| Havercroft, W York | 82 | A1 |
| Haverfordwest, Pemb | 32 | C2 |
| Haverhill, Suff | 53 | A3 |
| Haverigg, Cumb | 91 | C3 |
| Haversham, Bucks | 50 | B4 |
| Haverthwaite, Cumb | 91 | D3 |
| Havyat, Som | 23 | D3 |
| Hawarden, Flint | 67 | E1 |
| Hawbush Green, Essex | 42 | B2 |
| Hawen, Cered | 44 | E3 |
| Hawes, N York | 92 | C2 |
| Hawick, Bord | 108 | C4 |
| Hawkchurch, Devon | 11 | B4 |
| Hawkedon, Suff | 53 | B3 |
| Hawkesbury, Glouc | 24 | B1 |
| Hawkley, Hamp | 16 | B2 |
| Hawkridge, Som | 10 | B1 |
| Hawkshead, Cumb | 91 | E2 |
| Hawkshead Hill, Cumb | 91 | D2 |
| Hawkspur Green, Essex | 41 | B1 |
| Hawkstone, Shrop | 68 | C4 |
| Hawkswick, N York | 92 | D4 |
| Hawksworth, Notts | 72 | B3 |
| Hawksworth, W York | 87 | B2 |
| Hawkwell, Essex | 42 | B4 |
| Hawley, Hamp | 145 | A2 |
| Hawling, Glouc | 37 | A1 |
| Hawnby, N York | 93 | D2 |
| Haworth, W York | 86 | D3 |
| Hawstead, Suff | 53 | B2 |
| Hawthorn, Durham | 99 | A1 |
| Hawthorn Hill, Berks | 140 | A3 |
| Hawton, Notts | 72 | B2 |
| Haxby, N York | 88 | C1 |
| Haxey, Linc | 83 | B2 |
| Haxted, Surr | 149 | A4 |
| Hay Green, Norf | 62 | C1 |
| Hay Street, Herts | 40 | B1 |
| Haydock, Mers | 78 | B2 |
| Haydon, Dors | 12 | B3 |
| Haydon Bridge, Nthumb | 103 | C4 |
| Hayes, G Lon | 144 | A4 |
| Hayes, G Lon | 141 | B2 |
| Hayes End, G Lon | 141 | B1 |
| Hayfield, Derby | 80 | B3 |
| Hayle, Corn | 1 | C1 |
| Hayne, Devon | 10 | C3 |
| Hayne, Devon | 5 | A1 |
| Hay-on-Wye, Powys | 46 | A4 |
| Hayscastle, Pemb | 32 | C1 |
| Hayscastle Cross, Pemb | 32 | C1 |
| Hayton, Cumb | 96 | D2 |
| Hayton, Cumb | 102 | D4 |
| Hayton, E R of Y | 89 | B2 |
| Hayton, Notts | 83 | A3 |
| Haytor Vale, Devon | 5 | A2 |
| Haytown, Devon | 9 | C3 |
| Haywards Heath, W Suss | 19 | A2 |
| Haywood, S York | 82 | B1 |
| Hazel Grove, G Man | 80 | A3 |
| Hazelbank, S Lan | 107 | B1 |
| Hazeleigh, Essex | 42 | B3 |
| Hazelwood, Derby | 70 | C3 |
| Hazlerigg, T & W | 104 | B3 |
| Hazleton, Glouc | 37 | A2 |
| Heacham, Norf | 74 | C4 |
| Headcorn, Kent | 30 | A4 |
| Headlam, Durham | 98 | C4 |
| Headlesscross, N Lan | 113 | B4 |
| Headley, Hamp | 26 | C3 |
| Headley, Hamp | 16 | B1 |
| Headley, Surr | 148 | A2 |
| Headon, Notts | 83 | B4 |
| Heads, S Lan | 107 | A1 |
| Heads Nook, Cumb | 97 | B1 |
| Heage, Derby | 70 | C2 |
| Healaugh, N York | 92 | D2 |
| Healaugh, N York | 88 | B2 |
| Heale, Som | 11 | B2 |
| Heale, Som | 11 | C2 |
| Healey, N York | 93 | A3 |
| Healeyfield, Durham | 98 | B1 |
| Healing, Linc | 84 | B1 |
| Heanor, Derby | 71 | A3 |
| Heapham, Linc | 83 | C3 |
| Heasley Mill, Devon | 10 | A1 |
| Heath, Derby | 71 | A1 |
| Heath, W York | 88 | A4 |
| Heath and Reach, Beds | 39 | A1 |
| Heath Green, Worc | 48 | B1 |
| Heath Hill, Shrop | 57 | B2 |
| Heathcote, Derby | 70 | A2 |
| Heather, Leics | 60 | A2 |
| Heathfield, E Sus | 20 | A2 |
| Heathfield, Som | 11 | A2 |
| Heathton, Shrop | 57 | C3 |
| Heatley, Chesh | 79 | B3 |
| Heatley, Staff | 70 | A4 |
| Heaton, Staff | 69 | C1 |
| Heaton's Bridge, Lanc | 78 | A1 |
| Heaverham, Kent | 29 | A3 |
| Hebburn, T & W | 104 | C4 |
| Hebden, N York | 86 | D1 |
| Hebden Bridge, W York | 86 | D4 |
| Hebing End, Herts | 40 | A1 |
| Hebron, Carm | 32 | E1 |
| Hebron, Nthumb | 104 | B2 |
| Heckfield, Hamp | 27 | A3 |
| Heckfield Green, Suff | 54 | A1 |
| Heckfordbridge, Essex | 43 | A2 |
| Heckington, Linc | 73 | B3 |
| Heckmondwike, W York | 87 | B4 |
| Heddington, Wilts | 25 | B2 |
| Hedenham, Norf | 65 | A3 |
| Hedge End, Hamp | 15 | A3 |
| Hedgerley, Bucks | 140 | C1 |
| Hedley on the Hill, Nthumb | 104 | A4 |
| Hednesford, Staff | 58 | A2 |
| Hedon, E R of Y | 90 | A4 |
| Hedsor, Bucks | 140 | A1 |
| Heighington, Durham | 98 | C3 |
| Heighington, Linc | 73 | A1 |
| Heightington, Worc | 47 | B1 |
| Heiton, Bord | 109 | A2 |
| Hele, Devon | 10 | C4 |
| Hele, Som | 11 | A2 |
| Helensburgh, Argyll | 111 | D2 |
| Helford, Corn | 2 | A2 |
| Helford Passage, Corn | 2 | A2 |
| Helhoughton, Norf | 74 | D4 |
| Helland, Corn | 3 | D3 |
| Hellescott, Corn | 4 | A1 |
| Hellesdon, Norf | 64 | B2 |
| Hellidon, Nhants | 49 | C2 |
| Hellifield, N York | 86 | C1 |
| Helm, Nthumb | 104 | B1 |
| Helmdon, Nhants | 49 | C4 |
| Helme, W York | 81 | A1 |
| Helmingham, Suff | 54 | A2 |
| Helmsdale, High | 136 | F1 |
| Helmshore, Lanc | 86 | B4 |
| Helmsley, N York | 93 | D3 |
| Helperby, N York | 93 | C4 |
| Helperthorpe, N York | 94 | C4 |
| Helpringham, Linc | 73 | B3 |
| Helpston, Camb | 61 | D2 |
| Helsby, Chesh | 78 | B4 |
| Helston, Corn | 1 | D2 |
| Helstone, Corn | 3 | E2 |
| Helton, Cumb | 97 | B4 |
| Hemblington, Norf | 65 | A2 |
| Hemel Hempstead, Herts | 39 | B3 |
| Hemerdon, Devon | 4 | D4 |
| Hemingbrough, N York | 89 | A3 |
| Hemingby, Linc | 84 | B4 |
| Hemingford Abbots, Camb | 51 | C1 |
| Hemingford Grey, Camb | 51 | C1 |
| Hemingstone, Suff | 54 | A3 |
| Hemington, Nhants | 61 | D4 |
| Hemington, Som | 24 | B3 |
| Hemley, Suff | 54 | B4 |
| Hempnall, Norf | 65 | A3 |
| Hempriggs, Moray | 133 | A2 |
| Hempstead, Essex | 52 | C4 |
| Hempstead, Norf | 75 | A4 |
| Hempton, Norf | 74 | E4 |
| Hempton, Oxon | 37 | D1 |
| Hemsby, Norf | 65 | C1 |
| Hemswell, Linc | 83 | C3 |
| Hemsworth, W York | 82 | A1 |
| Hemyock, Devon | 11 | A3 |
| Hendy, Carm | 33 | C3 |
| Hengoed, Caer | 34 | D4 |
| Hengoed, Powys | 46 | A3 |
| Hengrave, Suff | 53 | B1 |
| Henham, Essex | 41 | B1 |
| Henhurst, Kent | 29 | B2 |
| Heniarth, Powys | 56 | A2 |
| Henlade, Som | 11 | B2 |
| Henley, Dors | 12 | B4 |
| Henley, Som | 11 | C1 |
| Henley, Suff | 54 | A3 |
| Henley, W Suss | 17 | A2 |
| Henley Park, Surr | 145 | B3 |
| Henley-in-Arden, Warw | 48 | B2 |
| Henley-on-Thames, Oxon | 27 | B1 |
| Henley's Down, E Sus | 20 | B3 |
| Henllan, Cered | 44 | E4 |
| Henllan, Denb | 67 | C1 |
| Henllys, Torf | 34 | E4 |
| Henlow, Beds | 51 | B4 |
| Hennock, Devon | 5 | B2 |
| Henny Street, Essex | 53 | B4 |
| Henryd, Ab & Col | 76 | E4 |
| Henry's Moat (Castell Hendre), Pemb | 32 | D1 |
| Hensall, N York | 88 | C4 |
| Henshaw, Nthumb | 103 | B4 |
| Henstead, Suff | 65 | C4 |
| Henton, Oxon | 38 | C3 |
| Henton, Som | 23 | D4 |
| Henwood, Corn | 4 | A2 |
| Heol-y-Cyw, Brid | 22 | E1 |
| Hepple, Nthumb | 103 | D1 |
| Hepscott, Nthumb | 104 | B2 |
| Heptonstall, W York | 86 | D4 |
| Hepworth, Suff | 53 | C1 |
| Hepworth, W York | 81 | B2 |
| Herbrandston, Pemb | 32 | C3 |
| Hereford, Heref | 46 | D4 |
| Hermitage, Dors | 12 | B3 |
| Hermon, Pemb | 32 | F1 |
| Herne Hill, G Lon | 143 | B3 |
| Herne Pound, Kent | 29 | B3 |
| Herner, Devon | 9 | E2 |
| Herodsfoot, Corn | 4 | A3 |

| PLACE | PAGE | GRID |
|---|---|---|
| Herriard, Hamp | 27 | A4 |
| Herringfleet, Suff | 65 | C3 |
| Herringswell, Suff | 53 | A1 |
| Herrington, T & W | 98 | D1 |
| Hersden, Kent | 31 | A3 |
| Hersham, Surr | 147 | A1 |
| Herston, Ork | 139 | A2 |
| Hertford, Herts | 40 | B2 |
| Hertford Heath, Herts | 40 | B2 |
| Hertingfordbury, Herts | 40 | A2 |
| Hesket Newmarket, Cumb | 96 | F2 |
| Hesketh Bank, Lanc | 85 | B4 |
| Hesketh Lane, Lanc | 86 | A3 |
| Hessay, N York | 88 | C1 |
| Hessett, Suff | 53 | C2 |
| Hessle, E R of Y | 89 | D4 |
| Heston, G Lon | 141 | B2 |
| Heswall, Mers | 77 | D4 |
| Hethe, Oxon | 38 | A1 |
| Hethersett, Norf | 64 | B2 |
| Hethersgill, Cumb | 102 | D4 |
| Hethpool, Nthumb | 109 | B2 |
| Hetton, N York | 86 | D1 |
| Heugh, Nthumb | 104 | A3 |
| Heugh Head, Bord | 115 | D3 |
| Heveningham, Suff | 54 | B1 |
| Hever, Kent | 149 | B4 |
| Heversham, Cumb | 91 | F3 |
| Hevingham, Norf | 64 | B1 |
| Hewas Water, Corn | 3 | D4 |
| Hewelsfield, Glouc | 35 | B3 |
| Hewish, Som | 23 | C3 |
| Hewish, Som | 11 | C3 |
| Hewood, Dors | 11 | C4 |
| Hexham, Nthumb | 103 | D4 |
| Hexton, Herts | 39 | C1 |
| Hexworthy, Corn | 4 | B2 |
| Hexworthy, Devon | 5 | A2 |
| Heybridge, Essex | 41 | B4 |
| Heybrook Bay, Devon | 4 | C4 |
| Heydon, Camb | 52 | B4 |
| Heydon, Norf | 75 | A4 |
| Heydour, Linc | 73 | A3 |
| Heysham, Lanc | 85 | B1 |
| Heyshott, W Suss | 17 | A3 |
| Heytesbury, Wilts | 25 | A4 |
| Heythrop, Oxon | 37 | C1 |
| Heywood, G Man | 80 | A1 |
| Heywood, Wilts | 25 | A3 |
| Hibaldstow, Linc | 83 | D2 |
| Hickleton, S York | 82 | A2 |
| Hickling, Norf | 65 | B1 |
| Hickling, Notts | 72 | A4 |
| Hickling Green, Norf | 65 | B1 |
| Hickstead, W Suss | 18 | B2 |
| Hidcote Boyce, Glouc | 48 | C4 |
| High Ackworth, W York | 82 | A1 |
| High Bankhill, Cumb | 97 | B2 |
| High Beach, Essex | 40 | B4 |
| High Bickington, Devon | 9 | E2 |
| High Biggins, Cumb | 92 | A3 |
| High Bray, Devon | 10 | A1 |
| High Catton, E R of Y | 89 | A1 |
| High Coniscliffe, Durham | 98 | C4 |
| High Crosby, Cumb | 102 | C4 |
| High Cross, Hamp | 16 | A2 |
| High Cross, Herts | 40 | B2 |
| High Easter, Essex | 41 | B2 |
| High Ellington, N York | 93 | A3 |
| High Ercall, Shrop | 57 | A1 |
| High Etherley, Durham | 98 | C3 |
| High Garrett, Essex | 42 | B1 |
| High Grantley, N York | 93 | A4 |
| High Green, Norf | 64 | B2 |
| High Green, Norf | 64 | B4 |
| High Green, Worc | 47 | C3 |
| High Halden, Kent | 21 | B1 |
| High Halstow, Kent | 30 | A2 |
| High Ham, Som | 11 | C1 |
| High Hatton, Shrop | 57 | A1 |
| High Hawsker, N York | 94 | C1 |
| High Hesket, Cumb | 97 | B2 |
| High Hoyland, S York | 81 | B1 |
| High Hutton, N York | 94 | B4 |
| High Ireby, Cumb | 96 | E2 |
| High Kilburn, N York | 93 | D3 |
| High Lands, Durham | 98 | B3 |
| High Lane, G Man | 80 | B3 |
| High Legh, Chesh | 79 | B3 |
| High Leven, N York | 99 | A4 |
| High Littleton, Som | 24 | A3 |
| High Lorton, Cumb | 96 | E3 |
| High Marnham, Notts | 72 | B1 |
| High Melton, S York | 82 | B2 |
| High Mickley, Nthumb | 104 | A4 |
| High Newton, Cumb | 91 | E3 |
| High Nibthwaite, Cumb | 91 | D2 |
| High Offley, Staff | 69 | A4 |
| High Ongar, Essex | 41 | B3 |
| High Onn, Staff | 57 | C1 |
| High Roding, Essex | 41 | B2 |
| High Spen, T & W | 104 | A4 |
| High Street, Corn | 3 | D4 |
| High Street, Suff | 54 | C3 |
| High Toynton, Linc | 73 | C1 |
| High Trewhitt, Nthumb | 109 | C4 |
| High Urpeth, Durham | 98 | C1 |
| High Valleyfield, Fife | 113 | B1 |
| High Wray, Cumb | 91 | E1 |
| High Wych, Herts | 41 | A2 |
| High Wycombe, Bucks | 39 | A4 |
| Higham, Derby | 71 | A2 |
| Higham, Kent | 29 | B2 |
| Higham, Lanc | 86 | B3 |
| Higham, S York | 81 | C1 |
| Higham, Suff | 53 | A2 |
| Higham, Suff | 53 | D4 |
| Higham Ferrers, Nhants | 50 | C2 |
| Higham on the Hill, Leics | 59 | B3 |
| Highampton, Devon | 9 | D4 |
| Highbridge, Som | 23 | B4 |
| Highbrook, W Suss | 19 | A1 |
| Highburton, W York | 81 | B1 |
| Highbury, Som | 24 | A4 |
| Highbury, G Lon | 143 | B1 |
| Highclere, Hamp | 26 | B3 |

| PLACE | PAGE | GRID |
|---|---|---|
| Higher Ansty, Dors | 12 | C4 |
| Higher Bartle, Lanc | 85 | C3 |
| Higher Combe, Som | 10 | C1 |
| Higher Gabwell, Devon | 5 | C3 |
| Higher Kinnerton, Flint | 67 | E1 |
| Higher Town, Scilly | 139 | B1 |
| Higher Walton, Chesh | 79 | A3 |
| Higher Walton, Lanc | 85 | C4 |
| Higher Wambrook, Som | 11 | B3 |
| Higher Waterston, Dors | 12 | C4 |
| Higher Wheelton, Lanc | 86 | A4 |
| Higher Whitley, Chesh | 79 | A4 |
| Higher Wych, Chesh | 68 | B3 |
| Highfield, T & W | 104 | A4 |
| Highgate, G Lon | 143 | A1 |
| Highlane, Derby | 82 | A4 |
| Highleadon, Glouc | 36 | A1 |
| Highleigh, W Suss | 16 | B4 |
| Highley, Shrop | 57 | B4 |
| Highmoor, Oxon | 27 | A1 |
| Highnam, Glouc | 36 | A2 |
| Highnam Green, Glouc | 36 | A2 |
| Highsted, Kent | 30 | B3 |
| Highstreet, Kent | 30 | C3 |
| Highstreet Green, Surr | 17 | B1 |
| Hightae, D & G | 101 | E3 |
| Hightown, Mers | 77 | D2 |
| Hightown Green, Suff | 53 | C3 |
| Highworth, Wilts | 37 | B4 |
| Hildenborough, Kent | 29 | A4 |
| Hildersham, Camb | 52 | C3 |
| Hilderstone, Staff | 69 | C4 |
| Hilfield, Dors | 12 | B4 |
| Hilgay, Norf | 62 | D3 |
| Hill, Glouc | 35 | C4 |
| Hill, Warw | 49 | B2 |
| Hill Brow, W Suss | 16 | B2 |
| Hill Chorlton, Staff | 69 | A3 |
| Hill Common, Som | 11 | A2 |
| Hill Dyke, Linc | 73 | D3 |
| Hill End, Glouc | 47 | C4 |
| Hill Green, Kent | 30 | A3 |
| Hill of Fearn, High | 132 | D1 |
| Hill Ridware, Staff | 58 | B1 |
| Hill Side, W York | 81 | B1 |
| Hill Top, W York | 81 | C1 |
| Hillam, N York | 88 | C4 |
| Hillbutts, Dors | 13 | A4 |
| Hillcliffane, Derby | 70 | C3 |
| Hillcott, Wilts | 25 | C3 |
| Hillend, Fife | 114 | A2 |
| Hillesden, Bucks | 38 | B1 |
| Hillesley, Glouc | 36 | A4 |
| Hillfarrance, Som | 11 | A2 |
| Hilliclay, High | 138 | D1 |
| Hillingdon, G Lon | 141 | A1 |
| Hillington, Norf | 63 | A1 |
| Hills Town, Derby | 71 | A1 |
| Hillside, Angus | 124 | C3 |
| Hillstreet, Hamp | 14 | B3 |
| Hillswick, Shet | 139 | A2 |
| Hilltown, Devon | 4 | C2 |
| Hilmarton, Wilts | 25 | B2 |
| Hilperton, Wilts | 25 | A3 |
| Hilston, E R of Y | 90 | B3 |
| Hilton, Camb | 51 | C2 |
| Hilton, Cumb | 97 | D4 |
| Hilton, Derby | 70 | B4 |
| Hilton, Durham | 98 | C4 |
| Hilton, N York | 99 | A4 |
| Hilton, Shrop | 57 | B3 |
| Himbleton, Worc | 48 | A2 |
| Himley, Staff | 57 | C4 |
| Hincaster, Cumb | 91 | F3 |
| Hinchley Wood, Surr | 142 | A4 |
| Hinckley, Leics | 60 | A3 |
| Hinderclay, Suff | 53 | D1 |
| Hinderwell, N York | 99 | D4 |
| Hindhead, Surr | 17 | A1 |
| Hindley, G Man | 79 | A2 |
| Hindlip, Worc | 47 | C2 |
| Hindolveston, Norf | 75 | A4 |
| Hindon, Wilts | 12 | D1 |
| Hindringham, Norf | 74 | E4 |
| Hingham, Norf | 64 | A3 |
| Hinstock, Shrop | 57 | A1 |
| Hintlesham, Suff | 53 | D4 |
| Hinton, Glouc | 24 | B1 |
| Hinton, Heref | 46 | B4 |
| Hinton, Shrop | 56 | C2 |
| Hinton Blewett, Som | 23 | E4 |
| Hinton Charterhouse, Som | 24 | B3 |
| Hinton Martell, Dors | 13 | A4 |
| Hinton on the Green, Worc | 48 | A4 |
| Hinton Parva, Wilts | 25 | D1 |
| Hinton St George, Som | 11 | C3 |
| Hinton Waldrist, Oxon | 37 | C3 |
| Hints, Staff | 58 | B3 |
| Hinwick, Beds | 50 | C2 |
| Hinxton, Camb | 52 | B4 |
| Hinxworth, Herts | 51 | C4 |
| Hipperholme, W York | 87 | A4 |
| Hipswell, N York | 93 | A2 |
| Hirn, Aber | 129 | A3 |
| Hirnant, Powys | 55 | E1 |
| Hirst Courtney, N York | 88 | C4 |
| Hirwaun, Rhond | 34 | B3 |
| Hiscott, Devon | 9 | E2 |
| Histon, Camb | 52 | B2 |
| Hitcham, Suff | 53 | C3 |
| Hitcham Causeway, Suff | 53 | C3 |
| Hitchin, Herts | 39 | C1 |
| Hither Green, G Lon | 144 | A3 |
| Hittisleigh, Devon | 10 | A4 |
| Hive, E R of Y | 89 | B3 |
| Hixon, Staff | 58 | A1 |
| Hoaden, Kent | 31 | B3 |
| Hoarwithy, Heref | 35 | B1 |
| Hoath, Kent | 31 | A3 |
| Hobarris, Shrop | 46 | B1 |
| Hobson, Durham | 98 | C1 |
| Hoby, Leics | 60 | C1 |
| Hockering, Norf | 64 | A2 |
| Hockerton, Notts | 72 | A2 |
| Hockley, Essex | 42 | B4 |
| Hockley Heath, W Mids | 48 | B1 |

| PLACE | PAGE | GRID |
|---|---|---|
| Hockliffe, Beds | 39 | B1 |
| Hockwold cum Wilton, Norf | 63 | A4 |
| Hockworthy, Devon | 10 | D2 |
| Hoddesdon, Herts | 40 | B3 |
| Hoddlesden, Lanc | 86 | B4 |
| Hoddom Mains, D & G | 102 | A3 |
| Hodgeston, Pemb | 32 | D3 |
| Hodnet, Shrop | 68 | C4 |
| Hodsall Street, Kent | 29 | A3 |
| Hodsock, Notts | 82 | B3 |
| Hodson, Wilts | 25 | D1 |
| Hodthorpe, Derby | 82 | B4 |
| Hoe, Norf | 63 | C1 |
| Hogben's Hill, Kent | 30 | C3 |
| Hoggeston, Bucks | 38 | C1 |
| Hoggrill's End, Warw | 59 | A3 |
| Hoghton, Lanc | 86 | A4 |
| Hognaston, Derby | 70 | B2 |
| Hogsthorpe, Linc | 74 | A1 |
| Holbeach, Linc | 62 | B1 |
| Holbeach Drove, Linc | 62 | B2 |
| Holbeach Hurn, Linc | 73 | D4 |
| Holbeach St Johns, Linc | 62 | B1 |
| Holbeach St Mark's, Linc | 73 | D4 |
| Holbeach St Matthew, Linc | 73 | D4 |
| Holbeck, Notts | 82 | B4 |
| Holberrow Green, Worc | 48 | A2 |
| Holbeton, Devon | 4 | D4 |
| Holborn, G Lon | 143 | A1 |
| Holbrook, Derby | 70 | C3 |
| Holbrook, Suff | 54 | A4 |
| Holbury, Hamp | 15 | A4 |
| Holcombe, Devon | 5 | C2 |
| Holcombe, Som | 24 | A4 |
| Holcombe Rogus, Devon | 10 | D2 |
| Holcot, Nhants | 50 | B1 |
| Holden, Lanc | 86 | B2 |
| Holdenby, Nhants | 50 | A2 |
| Holdgate, Shrop | 56 | D4 |
| Holdingham, Linc | 73 | A3 |
| Holditch, Dors | 11 | B4 |
| Hole, Devon | 9 | C4 |
| Holford, Som | 23 | A4 |
| Holker, Cumb | 91 | E3 |
| Holkham, Norf | 74 | E3 |
| Hollacombe, Devon | 9 | C4 |
| Holland Fen, Linc | 73 | C2 |
| Hollandstoun, Ork | 139 | B1 |
| Hollesley, Suff | 54 | C4 |
| Hollingdon, Bucks | 39 | A1 |
| Hollington, Derby | 70 | B3 |
| Hollington, Staff | 70 | A3 |
| Hollins Green, Chesh | 79 | B3 |
| Hollinsclough, Staff | 70 | A1 |
| Hollocombe, Devon | 9 | E3 |
| Holloway, Derby | 70 | C2 |
| Holloway, G Lon | 143 | A1 |
| Hollowell, Nhants | 50 | A1 |
| Holly Green, Worc | 47 | C4 |
| Hollybush, Caer | 34 | D3 |
| Hollybush, E Ayr | 106 | D3 |
| Hollybush, Heref | 47 | B4 |
| Hollym, E R of Y | 90 | C4 |
| Holmbridge, W York | 81 | A2 |
| Holmbury St Mary, Surr | 147 | A4 |
| Holme, Camb | 61 | D4 |
| Holme, Cumb | 91 | F3 |
| Holme, N York | 93 | B3 |
| Holme, Notts | 72 | B2 |
| Holme, W York | 81 | A2 |
| Holme Chapel, Lanc | 86 | C4 |
| Holme Green, N York | 88 | C2 |
| Holme Hale, Norf | 63 | B2 |
| Holme Lacy, Heref | 46 | D4 |
| Holme Marsh, Heref | 46 | B3 |
| Holme next the Sea, Norf | 74 | C3 |
| Holme on the Wolds, E R of Y | 89 | C2 |
| Holme Pierrepont, Notts | 72 | A3 |
| Holme St Cuthbert, Cumb | 96 | D1 |
| Holmes Chapel, Chesh | 69 | A1 |
| Holmesfield, Derby | 81 | C4 |
| Holmeswood, Lanc | 78 | A1 |
| Holmethorpe, Surr | 148 | B3 |
| Holmewood, Derby | 71 | A1 |
| Holmpton, E R of Y | 90 | C4 |
| Holmrook, Cumb | 91 | B1 |
| Holmwood, Surr | 147 | B3 |
| Holne, Devon | 5 | A3 |
| Holnest, Dors | 12 | B3 |
| Holnicote, Som | 22 | E4 |
| Holsworthy, Devon | 9 | C4 |
| Holsworthy Beacon, Devon | 9 | C3 |
| Holt, Dors | 13 | A4 |
| Holt, Wilts | 25 | A3 |
| Holt, Worc | 47 | C2 |
| Holt, Wrex | 68 | A2 |
| Holt, Norf | 75 | A3 |
| Holt End, Worc | 48 | B1 |
| Holt Heath, Worc | 47 | C2 |
| Holtby, N York | 89 | A1 |
| Holton, Som | 12 | B2 |
| Holton, Suff | 54 | C1 |
| Holton cum Beckering, Linc | 84 | A4 |
| Holton le Clay, Linc | 84 | B2 |
| Holton le Moor, Linc | 83 | D2 |
| Holton St Mary, Suff | 53 | D4 |
| Holwell, Dors | 12 | C3 |
| Holwell, Herts | 39 | C1 |
| Holwell, Leics | 60 | C1 |
| Holwell, Oxon | 37 | B3 |
| Holwick, Durham | 97 | E3 |
| Holy Island, Nthumb | 109 | D1 |
| Holybourne, Hamp | 16 | A1 |
| Holyhead, Angle | 76 | A4 |
| Holymoorside, Derby | 70 | C1 |
| Holyport, Berks | 140 | A2 |
| Holystone, Nthumb | 103 | D1 |
| Holytown, N Lan | 112 | C4 |
| Holywell, Camb | 52 | A1 |
| Holywell, Corn | 3 | B4 |
| Holywell, Dors | 12 | B4 |
| Holywell, Flint | 77 | C4 |
| Holywell Lake, Som | 10 | D2 |
| Holywell Row, Suff | 53 | A1 |

| PLACE | PAGE | GRID |
|---|---|---|
| Holywood, D & G | 101 | D2 |
| Homer, Shrop | 57 | A3 |
| Homer Green, Mers | 77 | D2 |
| Homersfield, Suff | 65 | A4 |
| Homington, Wilts | 13 | B2 |
| Honey Tye, Suff | 53 | C4 |
| Honeybourne, Worc | 48 | B4 |
| Honeychurch, Devon | 9 | E4 |
| Honeystreet, Wilts | 25 | C3 |
| Honiley, Warw | 48 | C1 |
| Honing, Norf | 75 | C4 |
| Honingham, Norf | 64 | A2 |
| Honington, Linc | 72 | C3 |
| Honington, Suff | 53 | C1 |
| Honington, Warw | 48 | C4 |
| Honiton, Devon | 11 | A4 |
| Honley, W York | 81 | A1 |
| Hoo, Kent | 30 | A2 |
| Hoo Green, Chesh | 79 | B4 |
| Hooe, E Sus | 20 | B3 |
| Hook, Hamp | 27 | A3 |
| Hook, Kent | 29 | A2 |
| Hook, Pemb | 32 | D2 |
| Hook, Wilts | 25 | C1 |
| Hook, G Lon | 147 | B1 |
| Hook Norton, Oxon | 37 | C1 |
| Hooke, Dors | 12 | A4 |
| Hookway, Devon | 10 | B4 |
| Hookwood, Surr | 148 | B4 |
| Hooley, Surr | 148 | B2 |
| Hooton Levitt, S York | 82 | B3 |
| Hooton Pagnell, S York | 82 | A1 |
| Hooton Roberts, S York | 82 | A2 |
| Hope, Derby | 81 | B4 |
| Hope, Devon | 8 | A1 |
| Hope, Flint | 67 | E2 |
| Hope, Shrop | 47 | A1 |
| Hope, Staff | 70 | A2 |
| Hope Bowdler, Shrop | 56 | D3 |
| Hope End Green, Essex | 41 | B2 |
| Hope Mansell, Heref | 35 | C2 |
| Hope under Dinmore, Heref | 46 | D3 |
| Hopeman, Moray | 133 | B1 |
| Hopesay, Shrop | 56 | C4 |
| Hopperton, N York | 88 | B1 |
| Hopstone, Shrop | 57 | B3 |
| Hopton, Staff | 58 | A1 |
| Hopton, Suff | 53 | C1 |
| Hopton Cangeford, Shrop | 56 | D4 |
| Hopton Castle, Shrop | 46 | C1 |
| Hopton on Sea, Norf | 65 | C3 |
| Hopton Wafers, Shrop | 47 | A1 |
| Hoptonheath, Shrop | 46 | C1 |
| Hopwas, Staff | 59 | A2 |
| Hopwood, Worc | 48 | A1 |
| Horam, E Sus | 20 | A3 |
| Horbling, Linc | 73 | B4 |
| Hordley, Shrop | 68 | A4 |
| Horham, Suff | 54 | A1 |
| Horkesley Heath, Essex | 43 | A1 |
| Horkstow, Linc | 83 | D1 |
| Horley, Oxon | 49 | B4 |
| Horley, Surr | 148 | B4 |
| Hornblotton Green, Som | 12 | B1 |
| Hornby, Lanc | 92 | A4 |
| Hornby, N York | 93 | B1 |
| Hornby, N York | 93 | A2 |
| Horncastle, Linc | 73 | C1 |
| Hornchurch, G Lon | 144 | C1 |
| Horncliffe, Nthumb | 115 | E4 |
| Horndean, Bord | 109 | B1 |
| Horndean, Hamp | 16 | A3 |
| Horndon, Devon | 4 | C2 |
| Horndon on the Hill, Essex | 29 | B1 |
| Horne, Surr | 148 | C4 |
| Horner, Som | 22 | E4 |
| Horning, Norf | 65 | A1 |
| Horninghold, Leics | 61 | A3 |
| Horningsea, Camb | 52 | B2 |
| Horningsham, Wilts | 12 | D1 |
| Horningtoft, Norf | 63 | C1 |
| Horns Cross, Devon | 9 | C2 |
| Hornsea, E R of Y | 90 | B2 |
| Hornton, Oxon | 49 | B3 |
| Horrabridge, Devon | 4 | C3 |
| Horridge, Devon | 5 | A2 |
| Horringer, Suff | 53 | B2 |
| Horrocksford, Lanc | 86 | B2 |
| Horsebridge, Devon | 4 | B2 |
| Horsebridge, Hamp | 14 | B1 |
| Horsebridge, Shrop | 56 | C2 |
| Horseheath, Camb | 52 | C3 |
| Horsehouse, N York | 92 | D3 |
| Horsell, Surr | 146 | A1 |
| Horseman's Green, Wrex | 68 | A3 |
| Horsey, Norf | 65 | B1 |
| Horsey, Som | 11 | B1 |
| Horsford, Norf | 64 | B1 |
| Horsham, Worc | 47 | B2 |
| Horsham, W Suss | 18 | A1 |
| Horsham St Faith, Norf | 64 | B1 |
| Horsington, Linc | 73 | B1 |
| Horsington, Som | 12 | C2 |
| Horsley, Derby | 70 | C3 |
| Horsley, Glouc | 36 | B4 |
| Horsley, Nthumb | 103 | C1 |
| Horsley, Nthumb | 104 | A4 |
| Horsley Woodhouse, Derby | 71 | A3 |
| Horsmonden, Kent | 20 | B1 |
| Horspath, Oxon | 38 | A3 |
| Horstead, Norf | 65 | A1 |
| Horsted Keynes, W Suss | 19 | A2 |
| Horton, Berks | 140 | C3 |
| Horton, Bucks | 39 | A2 |
| Horton, Dors | 13 | A3 |
| Horton, Glouc | 24 | B1 |
| Horton, Lanc | 86 | C2 |
| Horton, Nhants | 50 | B3 |
| Horton, Shrop | 57 | A1 |
| Horton, Som | 11 | B3 |
| Horton, Staff | 69 | C2 |
| Horton, Swan | 22 | A1 |
| Horton, Wilts | 25 | C3 |
| Horton, G Lon | 147 | B1 |

| PLACE | PAGE | GRID |
|---|---|---|
| Horton Green, Chesh | 68 | A2 |
| Horton in Ribblesdale, N York | 92 | B4 |
| Horton Kirby, Kent | 29 | A2 |
| Horton-cum-Studley, Oxon | 38 | A2 |
| Horwich, G Man | 79 | A1 |
| Horwood, Devon | 9 | D2 |
| Hose, Leics | 72 | A4 |
| Hosey Hill, Kent | 149 | B2 |
| Hosh, Perth | 118 | D2 |
| Hotham, E R of Y | 89 | C3 |
| Hothfield, Kent | 30 | B4 |
| Hoton, Leics | 60 | B1 |
| Hott, Nthumb | 103 | B2 |
| Hough, Chesh | 69 | A2 |
| Hougham, Linc | 72 | C3 |
| Hough-on-the-Hill, Linc | 72 | C3 |
| Houghton, Camb | 51 | C1 |
| Houghton, Hamp | 14 | B1 |
| Houghton, Pemb | 32 | D3 |
| Houghton, W Suss | 17 | B3 |
| Houghton Conquest, Beds | 51 | A4 |
| Houghton Green, E Sus | 21 | B2 |
| Houghton le Spring, T & W | 98 | D1 |
| Houghton on the Hill, Leics | 60 | C2 |
| Houghton St Giles, Norf | 74 | E4 |
| Hound Green, Hamp | 27 | A3 |
| Houndslow, Bord | 108 | D1 |
| Hounslow, G Lon | 141 | B3 |
| Hounslow Green, Essex | 41 | B2 |
| Houses Hill, W York | 81 | B1 |
| Houston, Renf | 111 | E3 |
| Houton, Ork | 139 | A2 |
| Hove, E Sus | 18 | B4 |
| Hoveringham, Notts | 72 | A3 |
| Hoveton, Norf | 65 | A1 |
| Hovingham, N York | 94 | A4 |
| How Caple, Heref | 35 | C1 |
| How Mill, Cumb | 97 | B1 |
| Howden, E R of Y | 89 | B4 |
| Howden-le-Wear, Durham | 98 | C3 |
| Howe, N York | 93 | B3 |
| Howe, Norf | 65 | A3 |
| Howe Green, Essex | 42 | A3 |
| Howe Street, Essex | 42 | A2 |
| Howe Street, Essex | 53 | A4 |
| Howegreen, Essex | 42 | B3 |
| Howell, Linc | 73 | B3 |
| Howey, Powys | 45 | E2 |
| Howgate, M Loth | 114 | B4 |
| Howick, Nthumb | 109 | E3 |
| Howle, Shrop | 57 | B1 |
| Howle, Durham | 98 | B3 |
| Howle Hill, Heref | 35 | C2 |
| Howlett End, Essex | 52 | C4 |
| Howley, Som | 11 | B3 |
| Hownam, Bord | 109 | A3 |
| Howsham, Linc | 83 | D2 |
| Howsham, N York | 89 | A1 |
| Howtel, Nthumb | 109 | B2 |
| Howwood, Renf | 111 | E4 |
| Hoxne, Suff | 54 | A1 |
| Hoylake, Mers | 77 | C3 |
| Hoyland Nether, S York | 81 | C2 |
| Hoyland Swaine, S York | 81 | B2 |
| Huby, N York | 87 | B2 |
| Huby, N York | 93 | D4 |
| Hucking, Kent | 30 | A3 |
| Hucknall, Notts | 71 | B2 |
| Huddersfield, W York | 81 | A1 |
| Huddington, Worc | 48 | A2 |
| Hudswell, N York | 92 | E1 |
| Huggate, E R of Y | 89 | C1 |
| Hugh Town, Scilly | 139 | A2 |
| Hughley, Shrop | 56 | D3 |
| Huish, Devon | 9 | D3 |
| Huish, Wilts | 25 | C3 |
| Hulberry, Kent | 144 | C4 |
| Hulcott, Bucks | 39 | A2 |
| Hull, E R of Y | 90 | A4 |
| Hulland, Derby | 70 | B3 |
| Hullavington, Wilts | 25 | A1 |
| Hullbridge, Essex | 42 | B4 |
| Hulme, Staff | 69 | C3 |
| Hulme End, Staff | 70 | A2 |
| Hulme Walfield, Chesh | 69 | B1 |
| Hulver Street, Suff | 65 | B4 |
| Hulverstone, I of W | 8 | A1 |
| Humberston, Linc | 84 | B2 |
| Humbie, E Loth | 114 | C3 |
| Humbleton, E R of Y | 90 | B3 |
| Humby, Linc | 73 | A4 |
| Hume, Bord | 109 | A1 |
| Humshaugh, Nthumb | 103 | C3 |
| Huncote, Leics | 60 | B3 |
| Hunderthwaite, Durham | 98 | A4 |
| Hundleby, Linc | 73 | D1 |
| Hundleton, Pemb | 32 | C3 |
| Hundon, Suff | 53 | A3 |
| Hundred End, Lanc | 85 | B4 |
| Hundred House, Powys | 45 | E3 |
| Hungarton, Leics | 60 | C2 |
| Hungerford, Som | 10 | D1 |
| Hungerford, Berks | 26 | A2 |
| Hungerford Newtown, Berks | 26 | A2 |
| Hungerstone, Heref | 46 | C4 |
| Hunmanby, N York | 94 | E3 |
| Hunningham, Warw | 49 | A2 |
| Hunsdon, Herts | 40 | B2 |
| Hunsingore, N York | 88 | B1 |
| Hunsonby, Cumb | 97 | C2 |
| Hunstanton, Norf | 74 | C3 |
| Hunstanworth, Durham | 98 | A1 |
| Hunston, Suff | 53 | C1 |
| Hunston, W Suss | 17 | A4 |
| Hunstrete, Som | 24 | A3 |
| Hunsworth, W York | 87 | B4 |
| Hunterston, Chesh | 69 | A3 |
| Huntham, Som | 11 | B2 |
| Huntingdon, Camb | 51 | C1 |
| Huntingfield, Suff | 54 | B1 |
| Huntington, Chesh | 68 | A1 |
| Huntington, Heref | 46 | B3 |

| PLACE | PAGE | GRID |
|---|---|---|
| Huntington, Staff | 58 | A2 |
| Huntley, Glouc | 36 | A2 |
| Huntly, Aber | 133 | E4 |
| Hunton, Hamp | 15 | A1 |
| Hunton, Kent | 29 | B4 |
| Hunton, N York | 93 | A2 |
| Huntscott, Som | 22 | E4 |
| Huntsham, Devon | 10 | C2 |
| Huntshaw, Devon | 9 | D2 |
| Huntspill, Som | 23 | B4 |
| Huntstile, Som | 11 | B1 |
| Huntworth, Som | 11 | B1 |
| Hunwick, Durham | 98 | C3 |
| Hunworth, Norf | 75 | A4 |
| Hurdcott, Wilts | 14 | A1 |
| Hurley, Warw | 59 | A3 |
| Hurley Common, Warw | 59 | A3 |
| Hurlford, E Ayr | 106 | E2 |
| Hurn, Dors | 13 | B4 |
| Hursley, Hamp | 15 | A2 |
| Hurst, Berks | 27 | B2 |
| Hurst Green, E Sus | 20 | B2 |
| Hurst Green, Lanc | 86 | A3 |
| Hurst Green, Surr | 149 | A3 |
| Hurstbourne Priors, Hamp | 26 | B4 |
| Hurstbourne Tarrant, Hamp | 26 | A3 |
| Hurstley, Heref | 46 | C3 |
| Hurstpierpoint, W Suss | 18 | B3 |
| Hurstwood, Lanc | 86 | C3 |
| Hurtmore, Surr | 145 | B4 |
| Hurworth Place, Durham | 93 | B1 |
| Hurworth-on-Tees, Durham | 93 | B1 |
| Husthwaite, N York | 93 | D4 |
| Huttoft, Linc | 84 | D4 |
| Hutton, Bord | 115 | D4 |
| Hutton, E R of Y | 89 | D1 |
| Hutton, Lanc | 85 | C4 |
| Hutton, Som | 23 | C3 |
| Hutton Bonville, N York | 93 | B1 |
| Hutton Buscel, N York | 94 | D3 |
| Hutton Conyers, N York | 93 | B4 |
| Hutton Cranswick, E R of Y | 89 | D2 |
| Hutton End, Cumb | 97 | A2 |
| Hutton Henry, Durham | 99 | A2 |
| Hutton Lowcross, N York | 99 | B4 |
| Hutton Magna, Durham | 98 | B4 |
| Hutton Roof, Cumb | 97 | A2 |
| Hutton Roof, Cumb | 91 | F3 |
| Hutton Rudby, N York | 93 | C1 |
| Hutton Sessay, N York | 93 | C4 |
| Hutton Wandesley, N York | 88 | C2 |
| Hutton-le-Hole, N York | 94 | A2 |
| Huxley, Chesh | 68 | B1 |
| Hycemoor, Cumb | 91 | B2 |
| Hyde, G Man | 80 | B3 |
| Hyde Heath, Bucks | 39 | A3 |
| Hyde Lea, Staff | 57 | C1 |
| Hyssington, Powys | 56 | B3 |
| Hythe, Hamp | 15 | A3 |
| Hythe, Kent | 21 | D1 |
| Hythe End, Berks | 140 | C3 |
| Ibberton, Dors | 12 | C3 |
| Ible, Derby | 70 | B2 |
| Ibsley, Hamp | 13 | B3 |
| Ibstock, Leics | 60 | A2 |
| Ibstone, Bucks | 38 | C4 |
| Ibthorpe, Hamp | 26 | A3 |
| Iburndale, N York | 94 | C1 |
| Ibworth, Hamp | 26 | C3 |
| Ickburgh, Norf | 63 | B3 |
| Ickenham, G Lon | 141 | A1 |
| Ickford, Bucks | 38 | B3 |
| Ickham, Kent | 31 | A3 |
| Ickleford, Herts | 39 | C1 |
| Ickleton, Camb | 52 | B4 |
| Icklingham, Suff | 53 | A1 |
| Ickornshaw, N York | 86 | D2 |
| Ickwell Green, Beds | 51 | B3 |
| Icomb, Glouc | 37 | B1 |
| Idbury, Oxon | 37 | B2 |
| Iddesleigh, Devon | 9 | E3 |
| Ide, Devon | 5 | C1 |
| Ideford, Devon | 5 | C2 |
| Iden, E Sus | 21 | B2 |
| Iden Green, Kent | 20 | B1 |
| Idless, Corn | 2 | A1 |
| Idlicote, Warw | 49 | A4 |
| Idmiston, Wilts | 14 | A1 |
| Idridgehay, Derby | 70 | C3 |
| Idrigill, High | 130 | B2 |
| Idstone, Oxon | 25 | D1 |
| Iford, E Sus | 19 | A3 |
| Ifton, Monm | 35 | B4 |
| Ightfield, Shrop | 68 | C3 |
| Ightham, Kent | 29 | A3 |
| Iken, Suff | 54 | C3 |
| Ilam, Staff | 70 | A2 |
| Ilchester, Som | 12 | A2 |
| Ilderton, Nthumb | 109 | C3 |
| Ilford, Som | 11 | C3 |
| Ilford, G Lon | 144 | B1 |
| Ilfracombe, Devon | 22 | A4 |
| Ilkeston, Derby | 71 | A3 |
| Ilketshall St Andrew, Suff | 65 | B4 |
| Ilketshall St Margaret, Suff | 65 | A4 |
| Ilkley, W York | 87 | A2 |
| Illand, Corn | 4 | A2 |
| Illey, W Mids | 58 | A4 |
| Illogan, Corn | 1 | D1 |
| Illston on the Hill, Leics | 60 | C3 |
| Ilmer, Bucks | 38 | C3 |
| Ilmington, Warw | 48 | C4 |
| Ilminster, Som | 11 | C3 |
| Ilsington, Devon | 5 | B2 |
| Ilston, Swan | 33 | C4 |
| Ilton, N York | 93 | A3 |
| Ilton, Som | 11 | C3 |
| Immingham, Linc | 84 | A1 |
| Immingham Dock, Linc | 84 | A1 |
| Ince, Chesh | 78 | A4 |
| Ince Blundell, Mers | 77 | D2 |
| Ince-in-Makerfield, G Man | 79 | A2 |
| Inchnadamph, High | 135 | E1 |
| Inchture, Perth | 119 | C2 |
| Indian Queens, Corn | 3 | C4 |

| PLACE | PAGE | GRID |
|---|---|---|
| Ingatestone, Essex | 41 | B3 |
| Ingbirchworth, S York | 81 | B2 |
| Ingestre, Staff | 58 | A1 |
| Ingham, Linc | 83 | C4 |
| Ingham, Norf | 75 | D4 |
| Ingham, Suff | 53 | B1 |
| Ingham Corner, Norf | 75 | D4 |
| Ingleby, Derby | 70 | C4 |
| Ingleby Arncliffe, N York | 93 | C1 |
| Ingleby Greenhow, N York | 93 | D1 |
| Ingleigh Green, Devon | 9 | E3 |
| Inglesbatch, Som | 24 | B3 |
| Inglesham, Wilts | 37 | B4 |
| Ingleton, Durham | 98 | C4 |
| Ingleton, N York | 92 | B4 |
| Inglewhite, Lanc | 85 | C3 |
| Ingoe, Nthumb | 103 | D3 |
| Ingoldisthorpe, Norf | 74 | C4 |
| Ingoldsby, Linc | 73 | A4 |
| Ingram, Nthumb | 109 | C3 |
| Ingrave, Essex | 41 | B4 |
| Ingst, Glouc | 35 | C4 |
| Ingthorpe, Rut | 61 | C2 |
| Ingworth, Norf | 75 | B4 |
| Inkberrow, Worc | 48 | A2 |
| Inkpen, Berks | 26 | A3 |
| Innellan, Argyll | 111 | C3 |
| Innerleithen, Bord | 108 | A2 |
| Innermessan, D & G | 100 | B4 |
| Innerwick, E Loth | 115 | C2 |
| Insch, Aber | 128 | E1 |
| Insh, High | 127 | C3 |
| Inskip, Lanc | 85 | B3 |
| Instow, Devon | 9 | D1 |
| Inver, High | 136 | D4 |
| Inver, Perth | 123 | B4 |
| Inveralligin, High | 130 | F2 |
| Inverallochy, Aber | 134 | D2 |
| Inveran, High | 136 | B3 |
| Inveraray, Argyll | 117 | C3 |
| Inverasdale, High | 135 | A4 |
| Inverbervie, Aber | 124 | D2 |
| Inver-boyndie, Aber | 134 | A2 |
| Invergarry, High | 126 | D3 |
| Invergordon, High | 132 | C2 |
| Invergowrie, Perth | 119 | C1 |
| Inverie, High | 125 | F3 |
| Inverinate, High | 126 | A2 |
| Inverkeilor, Angus | 124 | B4 |
| Inverkeithing, Fife | 114 | A2 |
| Inverkeithny, Aber | 134 | A3 |
| Inverkip, Inv | 111 | D3 |
| Inverkirkaig, High | 135 | C1 |
| Invermoriston, High | 126 | E2 |
| Inverness, High | 132 | C4 |
| Inversanda, High | 121 | C3 |
| Inveruglas, Argyll | 117 | E3 |
| Inverurie, Aber | 129 | A2 |
| Inwardleigh, Devon | 9 | E4 |
| Inworth, Essex | 42 | B2 |
| Iping, W Suss | 17 | A2 |
| Ipplepen, Devon | 5 | B3 |
| Ipsden, Oxon | 27 | A1 |
| Ipstones, Staff | 69 | C2 |
| Ipswich, Suff | 54 | A4 |
| Irby in the Marsh, Linc | 74 | A1 |
| Irby upon Humber, Linc | 84 | B2 |
| Irchester, Nhants | 50 | C2 |
| Ireby, Cumb | 96 | F2 |
| Ireby, Lanc | 92 | A4 |
| Ireland, Beds | 51 | B4 |
| Ireleth, Cumb | 91 | C3 |
| Ireshopeburn, Durham | 97 | E2 |
| Ireton Wood, Derby | 70 | C3 |
| Irlam, G Man | 79 | B3 |
| Irnham, Linc | 73 | A4 |
| Ironbridge, Shrop | 57 | A2 |
| Irons Bottom, Surr | 148 | A4 |
| Ironville, Derby | 71 | A2 |
| Irstead, Norf | 65 | B1 |
| Irthington, Cumb | 102 | D4 |
| Irthlingborough, Nhants | 50 | C1 |
| Irton, N York | 94 | D3 |
| Irvine, N Ayr | 106 | D1 |
| Isfield, E Sus | 19 | B3 |
| Isham, Nhants | 50 | C1 |
| Isington, Hamp | 27 | B4 |
| Isle Abbotts, Som | 11 | C2 |
| Isle of Dogs, G Lon | 144 | A2 |
| Isle of Whithorn, D & G | 95 | E2 |
| Isleham, Camb | 52 | C1 |
| Isleornsay, High | 125 | E2 |
| Isleworth, G Lon | 142 | A3 |
| Isley Walton, Leics | 60 | A1 |
| Islington, G Lon | 143 | B1 |
| Islip, Nhants | 51 | A1 |
| Islip, Oxon | 38 | A2 |
| Isombridge, Shrop | 57 | A2 |
| Itchen Abbas, Hamp | 15 | B1 |
| Itchen Stoke, Hamp | 15 | B1 |
| Itchingfield, W Suss | 18 | A2 |
| Itteringham, Norf | 75 | B4 |
| Itton, Devon | 10 | A4 |
| Itton, Monm | 35 | B4 |
| Ivegill, Cumb | 97 | A2 |
| Iver, Bucks | 141 | A2 |
| Iver Heath, Bucks | 141 | A1 |
| Iveston, Durham | 98 | B1 |
| Ivinghoe, Bucks | 39 | A2 |
| Ivinghoe Aston, Bucks | 39 | A2 |
| Ivington, Heref | 46 | D3 |
| Ivington Green, Heref | 46 | C3 |
| Ivybridge, Devon | 4 | D4 |
| Ivychurch, Kent | 21 | C2 |
| Iwade, Kent | 30 | B2 |
| Iwerne Minster, Dors | 12 | D3 |
| Ixworth, Suff | 53 | C1 |
| Ixworth Thorpe, Suff | 53 | C1 |
| Jack-in-the-Green, Devon | 10 | D4 |
| Jackton, S Lan | 112 | B4 |
| Jacobs Well, Surr | 146 | A2 |
| Jacobstow, Corn | 9 | B4 |
| Jacobstowe, Devon | 9 | E4 |
| Jameston, Pemb | 32 | D4 |
| Jarrow, T & W | 104 | C4 |
| Jasper's Green, Essex | 42 | A1 |
| Jaywick, Essex | 43 | C2 |
| Jealott's Hill, Berks | 140 | A3 |
| Jedburgh, Bord | 108 | D3 |
| Jeffreston, Pemb | 32 | E3 |
| Jemimaville, High | 132 | C2 |
| Jerbourg, Guer | 139 | B2 |
| Jevington, E Sus | 20 | A4 |
| Jockey End, Herts | 39 | B2 |
| John O'Groats, High | 138 | F1 |
| Johnby, Cumb | 97 | A3 |
| Johnshaven, Aber | 124 | C2 |
| Johnston, Pemb | 32 | C2 |
| Johnstone, Renf | 112 | A3 |
| Joppa, Cered | 45 | A2 |
| Jordanston, Pemb | 32 | C1 |
| Joyden's Wood, Kent | 144 | C3 |
| Jurby, I o M | 139 | C2 |
| Kaber, Cumb | 97 | D4 |
| Kames, Argyll | 111 | B3 |
| Kea, Corn | 2 | A1 |
| Keal Cotes, Linc | 73 | D1 |
| Kearsley, G Man | 79 | B2 |
| Kearsley, Nthumb | 103 | D3 |
| Kearstwick, Cumb | 92 | A3 |
| Kedington, Suff | 53 | A3 |
| Kedleston, Derby | 70 | C3 |
| Keelby, Linc | 84 | A1 |
| Keele, Staff | 69 | A3 |
| Keelham, W York | 87 | A3 |
| Keeston, Pemb | 32 | C2 |
| Keevil, Wilts | 25 | A3 |
| Kegworth, Leics | 71 | A4 |
| Kehelland, Corn | 1 | D1 |
| Keig, Aber | 128 | E2 |
| Keighley, W York | 87 | A3 |
| Keir Mill, D & G | 101 | C1 |
| Keisley, Cumb | 97 | D3 |
| Keiss, High | 138 | E2 |
| Keith, Moray | 133 | D3 |
| Keithtown, High | 132 | A3 |
| Kelbrook, Lanc | 86 | C2 |
| Kelby, Linc | 73 | A3 |
| Keld, N York | 92 | C1 |
| Kelfield, N York | 88 | C3 |
| Kelham, Notts | 72 | B2 |
| Kelhead, D & G | 102 | A3 |
| Kellamergh, Lanc | 85 | B4 |
| Kellas, Angus | 119 | D1 |
| Kellaton, Devon | 8 | B1 |
| Kelling, Norf | 75 | A3 |
| Kellington, N York | 88 | C4 |
| Kelloe, Durham | 98 | D2 |
| Kelly, Devon | 4 | B2 |
| Kelmarsh, Nhants | 50 | B1 |
| Kelmscot, Oxon | 37 | B3 |
| Kelsale, Suff | 54 | C2 |
| Kelsall, Chesh | 68 | B1 |
| Kelshall, Herts | 52 | A4 |
| Kelsick, Cumb | 96 | E1 |
| Kelso, Bord | 109 | A2 |
| Kelstedge, Derby | 70 | C1 |
| Kelstern, Linc | 84 | B3 |
| Kelston, Som | 24 | B2 |
| Kelty, Fife | 114 | A1 |
| Kelvedon, Essex | 42 | B2 |
| Kelvedon Hatch, Essex | 41 | B4 |
| Kelynack, Corn | 1 | A2 |
| Kemback, Fife | 119 | D3 |
| Kemberton, Shrop | 57 | B2 |
| Kemble, Glouc | 36 | C4 |
| Kemerton, Worc | 48 | A4 |
| Kemeys Commander, Monm | 34 | E3 |
| Kemnay, Aber | 129 | A2 |
| Kempley, Glouc | 35 | C1 |
| Kempley Green, Glouc | 35 | C1 |
| Kempsey, Worc | 47 | C3 |
| Kempsford, Glouc | 37 | B4 |
| Kempston, Beds | 51 | A3 |
| Kemsing, Kent | 29 | A3 |
| Kenardington, Kent | 21 | B1 |
| Kenchester, Heref | 46 | C4 |
| Kencot, Oxon | 37 | B3 |
| Kendal, Cumb | 91 | F2 |
| Kenfig, Brid | 22 | D1 |
| Kenilworth, Warw | 49 | A1 |
| Kenley, Shrop | 56 | D3 |
| Kenley, G Lon | 148 | C1 |
| Kenmore, Perth | 122 | E4 |
| Kenn, Devon | 5 | C1 |
| Kenn, Som | 23 | C2 |
| Kennacraig, Argyll | 110 | F3 |
| Kennerleigh, Devon | 10 | B3 |
| Kennet, Clack | 113 | B1 |
| Kennethmont, Aber | 128 | D1 |
| Kennett, Camb | 53 | A1 |
| Kennford, Devon | 5 | C1 |
| Kenninghall, Norf | 64 | A4 |
| Kennington, Oxon | 38 | A3 |
| Kennoway, Fife | 119 | D4 |
| Kenny, Som | 11 | B3 |
| Kennyhill, Suff | 63 | A4 |
| Kennythorpe, N York | 94 | B3 |
| Kensington, G Lon | 143 | A2 |
| Kensworth, Beds | 39 | B2 |
| Kentallen, High | 121 | D3 |
| Kentchurch, Heref | 35 | A1 |
| Kentford, Suff | 53 | A2 |
| Kentisbury, Devon | 22 | B4 |
| Kentish Town, G Lon | 143 | A1 |
| Kentmere, Cumb | 91 | E1 |
| Kenton, Devon | 5 | C2 |
| Kenton, Suff | 54 | A2 |
| Kent's Green, Glouc | 36 | A1 |
| Kent's Oak, Hamp | 14 | B2 |
| Kepwick, N York | 93 | C2 |
| Kerris, Corn | 1 | B2 |
| Kerry, Powys | 56 | A4 |
| Kerrycroy, Argyll | 111 | C3 |
| Kersall, Notts | 72 | A1 |
| Kersey, Suff | 53 | C4 |
| Kerswell Green, Worc | 47 | C3 |
| Kessingland, Suff | 65 | C4 |
| Kestle, Corn | 2 | C1 |
| Kestle Mill, Corn | 3 | C4 |
| Keston, G Lon | 144 | A4 |
| Keswick, Norf | 64 | B2 |
| Keswick, Cumb | 96 | F3 |
| Ketsby, Linc | 84 | C4 |
| Kettering, Nhants | 50 | C1 |
| Ketteringham, Norf | 64 | B2 |
| Kettins, Angus | 119 | C1 |
| Kettlebaston, Suff | 53 | C3 |
| Kettleburgh, Suff | 54 | B2 |
| Kettleshulme, Chesh | 80 | B4 |
| Kettlesing, N York | 87 | B1 |
| Kettlesing Bottom, N York | 87 | B1 |
| Kettlestone, Norf | 74 | E4 |
| Kettlethorpe, Linc | 83 | B4 |
| Kettlewell, N York | 92 | D4 |
| Ketton, Rut | 61 | C2 |
| Kew, G Lon | 142 | A2 |
| Kewstoke, Som | 23 | B3 |
| Kexby, Linc | 83 | C3 |
| Kexby, N York | 89 | A2 |
| Key Green, Chesh | 69 | B1 |
| Key Street, Kent | 30 | A2 |
| Keyham, Leics | 60 | C2 |
| Keyhaven, Hamp | 7 | F1 |
| Keyingham, E R of Y | 90 | B4 |
| Keynsham, Som | 24 | A2 |
| Keysoe, Beds | 51 | A2 |
| Keysoe Row, Beds | 51 | B2 |
| Keyston, Camb | 51 | A1 |
| Keyworth, Notts | 71 | B4 |
| Kibblesworth, T & W | 98 | C1 |
| Kibworth Beauchamp, Leics | 60 | C3 |
| Kibworth Harcourt, Leics | 60 | C3 |
| Kidbrooke, G Lon | 144 | A2 |
| Kidderminster, Worc | 47 | C1 |
| Kidlington, Oxon | 37 | D2 |
| Kidmore End, Oxon | 27 | A1 |
| Kidsgrove, Staff | 69 | B2 |
| Kidwelly, Carm | 33 | A3 |
| Kielder, Nthumb | 103 | A1 |
| Kiells, Argyll | 110 | C3 |
| Kilbarchan, Renf | 111 | E3 |
| Kilberry, Argyll | 110 | E3 |
| Kilbirnie, N Ayr | 111 | E4 |
| Kilburn, Derby | 70 | C3 |
| Kilburn, N York | 93 | D3 |
| Kilburn, G Lon | 142 | B1 |
| Kilby, Leics | 60 | C3 |
| Kilchattan, Argyll | 111 | C4 |
| Kilchoan, High | 120 | E3 |
| Kilchrenan, Argyll | 117 | B2 |
| Kilconquhar, Fife | 119 | E4 |
| Kilcot, Glouc | 36 | A1 |
| Kilcreggan, Argyll | 111 | D2 |
| Kildale, N York | 93 | D1 |
| Kildary, High | 132 | C1 |
| Kildrummy, Aber | 128 | D2 |
| Kildwick, N York | 86 | D2 |
| Kilfinan, Argyll | 111 | A2 |
| Kilgwrrwg Common, Monm | 35 | B4 |
| Kilham, E R of Y | 89 | D1 |
| Kilkenneth, Argyll | 120 | A4 |
| Kilkenzie, Argyll | 105 | D3 |
| Kilkhampton, Corn | 9 | B3 |
| Killamarsh, Derby | 82 | A4 |
| Killearn, Stirl | 112 | A1 |
| Killerby, Durham | 98 | C4 |
| Killerton, Devon | 10 | C4 |
| Killichonan, Perth | 122 | C3 |
| Killiecrankie, Perth | 123 | A3 |
| Killin, Stirl | 118 | B1 |
| Killinghall, N York | 88 | A1 |
| Killington, Cumb | 92 | A2 |
| Kilmacolm, Inv | 111 | E3 |
| Kilmany, Fife | 119 | D2 |
| Kilmarnock, E Ayr | 106 | E1 |
| Kilmartin, Argyll | 116 | F4 |
| Kilmaurs, E Ayr | 106 | D1 |
| Kilmelford, Argyll | 117 | A3 |
| Kilmersdon, Som | 24 | B4 |
| Kilmeston, Hamp | 15 | B2 |
| Kilmichael, Argyll | 105 | D3 |
| Kilmington, Devon | 11 | B4 |
| Kilmington, Wilts | 12 | C1 |
| Kilmington Common, Wilts | 12 | C1 |
| Kilmorack, High | 132 | A4 |
| Kilmun, Argyll | 111 | C2 |
| Kiln Pit Hill, Nthumb | 98 | A1 |
| Kilndown, Kent | 20 | B1 |
| Kilninver, Argyll | 116 | F2 |
| Kilnsea, E R of Y | 84 | C1 |
| Kilnsey, N York | 92 | D4 |
| Kilnwick, E R of Y | 89 | D2 |
| Kilpeck, Heref | 35 | A1 |
| Kilpin, E R of Y | 89 | B4 |
| Kilrenny, Fife | 119 | E4 |
| Kilsby, Nhants | 49 | C1 |
| Kilspindie, Perth | 119 | B2 |
| Kilstay, D & G | 95 | B2 |
| Kilsyth, N Lan | 112 | C2 |
| Kiltarlity, High | 132 | A4 |
| Kilton, N York | 99 | C4 |
| Kilton Thorpe, N York | 99 | C4 |
| Kilve, Som | 23 | A4 |
| Kilvington, Notts | 72 | B3 |
| Kilwinning, N Ayr | 106 | C1 |
| Kimberley, Norf | 64 | A2 |
| Kimblesworth, Durham | 98 | C1 |
| Kimbolton, Camb | 51 | B2 |
| Kimbolton, Heref | 46 | D2 |
| Kimcote, Leics | 60 | B4 |
| Kimmeridge, Dors | 7 | B2 |
| Kimpton, Hamp | 26 | A4 |
| Kimpton, Herts | 39 | C2 |
| Kinbrace, High | 138 | A4 |
| Kinbuck, Stirl | 118 | D4 |
| Kincardine, High | 136 | B4 |
| Kincardine, Fife | 113 | B1 |
| Kincardine O'Neil, Aber | 128 | E4 |
| Kincraig, High | 127 | C3 |
| Kindallachan, Perth | 123 | A4 |
| Kineton, Glouc | 37 | A1 |
| Kineton, Warw | 49 | A3 |
| Kinfauns, Perth | 119 | B2 |
| Kingarth, Argyll | 111 | C4 |
| Kingcoed, Monm | 35 | A3 |
| Kingford, Devon | 9 | B4 |
| Kingham, Oxon | 37 | B1 |
| Kinghorn, Fife | 114 | B1 |
| Kinglassie, Fife | 119 | B4 |
| Kingoldrum, Angus | 123 | D3 |
| Kings Caple, Heref | 35 | B1 |
| King's Cliffe, Nhants | 61 | C3 |
| King's Coughton, Warw | 48 | B2 |
| Kings Langley, Herts | 39 | B3 |
| King's Lynn, Norf | 62 | D1 |
| Kings Meaburn, Cumb | 97 | C4 |
| King's Mills, Guer | 139 | B2 |
| Kings Newnham, Warw | 49 | B1 |
| King's Nympton, Devon | 10 | A2 |
| King's Pyon, Heref | 46 | C3 |
| Kings Ripton, Camb | 51 | C1 |
| King's Somborne, Hamp | 14 | B1 |
| King's Stag, Dors | 12 | C3 |
| King's Stanley, Glouc | 36 | B3 |
| King's Sutton, Nhants | 49 | B4 |
| King's Walden, Herts | 39 | C1 |
| Kings Weston, Bristol | 23 | D1 |
| Kingsand, Corn | 4 | C4 |
| Kingsbarns, Fife | 119 | F3 |
| Kingsbridge, Som | 10 | C1 |
| Kingsbridge, Devon | 8 | A1 |
| Kingsbury, Warw | 59 | A3 |
| Kingsclere, Hamp | 26 | C3 |
| Kingscote, Glouc | 36 | B4 |
| Kingscott, Devon | 9 | D3 |
| Kingsdon, Som | 12 | A2 |
| Kingsdown, Kent | 31 | C4 |
| Kingsdown, Wilts | 24 | B2 |
| Kingseat, Fife | 114 | A1 |
| Kingsey, Bucks | 38 | C3 |
| Kingsfold, W Suss | 18 | A1 |
| Kingshall Street, Suff | 53 | C2 |
| Kingsheanton, Devon | 9 | E1 |
| Kingskerswell, Devon | 5 | B3 |
| Kingsland, Heref | 46 | C2 |
| Kingsley, Chesh | 78 | B4 |
| Kingsley, Hamp | 16 | B1 |
| Kingsley, Staff | 69 | C3 |
| Kingsley Green, W Suss | 17 | A1 |
| Kingsmuir, Angus | 124 | A4 |
| Kingsnorth, Kent | 21 | B1 |
| Kingsthorne, Heref | 35 | B1 |
| Kingston, Camb | 52 | A3 |
| Kingston, Corn | 4 | B2 |
| Kingston, Devon | 8 | B1 |
| Kingston, Dors | 12 | C3 |
| Kingston, Dors | 7 | C2 |
| Kingston, I of W | 8 | A2 |
| Kingston, Kent | 31 | A4 |
| Kingston Blount, Oxon | 38 | C3 |
| Kingston Lisle, Oxon | 37 | C4 |
| Kingston on Soar, Notts | 71 | A4 |
| Kingston on Spey, Moray | 133 | C2 |
| Kingston Russell, Dors | 6 | E1 |
| Kingston Seymour, Som | 23 | C2 |
| Kingston upon Thames, G Lon | 142 | A4 |
| Kingstone, Heref | 46 | C4 |
| Kingstone, Som | 11 | C3 |
| Kingstone, Staff | 70 | A4 |
| Kingswood, Surr | 148 | A4 |
| Kingswood, Bucks | 38 | B2 |
| Kingswood, Glouc | 36 | A4 |
| Kingswood, Som | 10 | D1 |
| Kingswood, Warw | 48 | C1 |
| Kingthorpe, Linc | 84 | A4 |
| Kington, Glouc | 35 | C4 |
| Kington, Worc | 48 | A3 |
| Kington, Heref | 46 | B3 |
| Kington Langley, Wilts | 25 | A1 |
| Kington Magna, Dors | 12 | C2 |
| Kington St Michael, Wilts | 25 | A1 |
| Kingussie, High | 127 | B3 |
| Kingweston, Som | 12 | A1 |
| Kinkell Bridge, Perth | 118 | E3 |
| Kinlet, Shrop | 57 | B4 |
| Kinloch, High | 137 | C4 |
| Kinloch, High | 125 | C3 |
| Kinloch, Perth | 123 | C4 |
| Kinloch Hourn, High | 126 | A3 |
| Kinloch Rannoch, Perth | 122 | D3 |
| Kinlochbervie, High | 137 | B2 |
| Kinlocheil, High | 121 | D1 |
| Kinlochewe, High | 131 | B2 |
| Kinlochlaggan, High | 126 | F4 |
| Kinlochleven, High | 121 | E3 |
| Kinlochmoidart, High | 121 | A2 |
| Kinloss, Moray | 133 | A2 |
| Kinnaird, Perth | 123 | A3 |
| Kinneff, Aber | 124 | D1 |
| Kinnerley, Shrop | 56 | B1 |
| Kinnersley, Heref | 46 | B3 |
| Kinnersley, Worc | 47 | C4 |
| Kinnerton, Powys | 46 | B2 |
| Kinnesswood, Perth | 119 | B4 |
| Kinninvie, Durham | 98 | B4 |
| Kinoulton, Notts | 72 | A4 |
| Kinross, Perth | 119 | B4 |
| Kinrossie, Perth | 119 | B1 |
| Kinsham, Heref | 46 | C2 |
| Kinsham, Worc | 48 | A4 |
| Kinsley, W York | 82 | A1 |
| Kintbury, Berks | 26 | A2 |
| Kintessack, Moray | 132 | E2 |
| Kintillo, Perth | 119 | B3 |
| Kinton, Heref | 46 | C1 |
| Kinton, Shrop | 56 | C1 |
| Kintore, Aber | 129 | A2 |
| Kintra, Argyll | 116 | B2 |
| Kintraw, Argyll | 116 | F4 |
| Kinver, Staff | 57 | C4 |
| Kippax, W York | 88 | B3 |
| Kippen, Stirl | 112 | B1 |
| Kippford or Scaur, D & G | 96 | B1 |
| Kipping's Cross, Kent | 20 | A1 |
| Kirbister, Ork | 139 | A2 |
| Kirby Bedon, Norf | 65 | A2 |
| Kirby Bellars, Leics | 60 | C1 |
| Kirby Cane, Norf | 65 | B3 |
| Kirby Grindalythe, N York | 94 | C4 |
| Kirby Hill, N York | 92 | E1 |
| Kirby Hill, N York | 93 | C4 |
| Kirby Knowle, N York | 93 | C3 |
| Kirby le Soken, Essex | 43 | C2 |
| Kirby Misperton, N York | 94 | B3 |
| Kirby Muxloe, Leics | 60 | B2 |
| Kirby Row, Norf | 65 | B3 |
| Kirby Sigston, N York | 93 | C2 |
| Kirby Underdale, E R of Y | 89 | B1 |
| Kirby Wiske, N York | 93 | B3 |
| Kirdford, W Suss | 17 | B2 |
| Kirk Bramwith, S York | 83 | A1 |
| Kirk Deighton, N York | 88 | B2 |
| Kirk Hammerton, N York | 88 | B1 |
| Kirk Ireton, Derby | 70 | B2 |
| Kirk Langley, Derby | 70 | C3 |
| Kirk Michael, I o M | 139 | C2 |
| Kirk Sandall, S York | 82 | B1 |
| Kirk Smeaton, N York | 82 | B1 |
| Kirk Yetholm, Bord | 109 | B2 |
| Kirkabister, Shet | 139 | A2 |
| Kirkandrews, D & G | 95 | F1 |
| Kirkbampton, Cumb | 96 | F1 |
| Kirkbean, D & G | 101 | D4 |
| Kirkbride, Cumb | 96 | E1 |
| Kirkburn, E R of Y | 89 | D1 |
| Kirkburton, W York | 81 | B1 |
| Kirkby, Linc | 83 | D3 |
| Kirkby, Mers | 78 | A2 |
| Kirkby, N York | 93 | D1 |
| Kirkby Fleetham, N York | 93 | B2 |
| Kirkby in Ashfield, Notts | 71 | A2 |
| Kirkby Lonsdale, Cumb | 92 | A3 |
| Kirkby Malham, N York | 86 | C1 |
| Kirkby Mallory, Leics | 60 | A3 |
| Kirkby Malzeard, N York | 93 | A4 |
| Kirkby on Bain, Linc | 73 | C1 |
| Kirkby Overblow, N York | 88 | A2 |
| Kirkby Thore, Cumb | 97 | C3 |
| Kirkby Underwood, Linc | 73 | A4 |
| Kirkby Wharf, N York | 88 | C3 |
| Kirkby-in-Furness, Cumb | 91 | C3 |
| Kirkbymoorside, N York | 94 | A3 |
| Kirkcaldy, Fife | 114 | B1 |
| Kirkcambeck, Cumb | 102 | D3 |
| Kirkcolm, D & G | 100 | A3 |
| Kirkconnel, D & G | 107 | A4 |
| Kirkcowan, D & G | 100 | D4 |
| Kirkcudbright, D & G | 96 | A1 |
| Kirkgunzeon, D & G | 101 | C4 |
| Kirkham, Lanc | 85 | B3 |
| Kirkham, N York | 94 | B4 |
| Kirkhamgate, W York | 88 | A4 |
| Kirkharle, Nthumb | 103 | D2 |
| Kirkhaugh, Nthumb | 97 | C1 |
| Kirkheaton, Nthumb | 103 | D3 |
| Kirkheaton, W York | 81 | B1 |
| Kirkhill, High | 132 | B4 |
| Kirkinner, D & G | 95 | D1 |
| Kirkintilloch, E Dunb | 112 | B2 |
| Kirkland, Cumb | 96 | D4 |
| Kirkland, D & G | 101 | C2 |
| Kirkleatham, N York | 99 | B4 |
| Kirklevington, N York | 93 | C1 |
| Kirklington, N York | 93 | B3 |
| Kirklington, Notts | 72 | A2 |
| Kirklinton, Cumb | 102 | C4 |
| Kirkliston, Edin | 114 | A2 |
| Kirkmabreck, D & G | 95 | E1 |
| Kirkmaiden, D & G | 95 | B2 |
| Kirkmichael, Perth | 123 | B3 |
| Kirkmichael, S Ayr | 106 | D4 |
| Kirkmuirhill, S Lan | 107 | B1 |
| Kirknewton, Nthumb | 109 | B2 |
| Kirknewton, W Loth | 113 | C3 |
| Kirkoswald, Cumb | 97 | B2 |
| Kirkoswald, S Ayr | 106 | C4 |
| Kirkpatrick, D & G | 101 | D2 |
| Kirkpatrick Durham, D & G | 101 | C3 |
| Kirkpatrick-Fleming, D & G | 102 | B3 |
| Kirksanton, Cumb | 91 | C3 |
| Kirkstead, Linc | 73 | B1 |
| Kirkstile, D & G | 102 | C2 |
| Kirkthorpe, W York | 88 | A4 |
| Kirkton, D & G | 101 | D2 |
| Kirkton of Glenbuchat, Aber | 128 | C2 |
| Kirkton of Logie Buchan, Aber | 129 | C1 |
| Kirkton of Menmuir, Angus | 124 | A3 |
| Kirkton of Rayne, Aber | 129 | A1 |
| Kirkton of Skene, Aber | 129 | A3 |
| Kirkton of Strathmartine, Angus | 119 | D1 |
| Kirktown of Bourtie, Aber | 129 | A1 |
| Kirkwall, Ork | 139 | A2 |
| Kirkwhelpington, Nthumb | 103 | D2 |
| Kirmington, Linc | 84 | A1 |
| Kirmond le Mire, Linc | 84 | A3 |
| Kirriemuir, Angus | 123 | E3 |
| Kirstead Green, Norf | 65 | A3 |
| Kirtlebridge, D & G | 102 | B3 |
| Kirtling, Camb | 53 | A2 |
| Kirtling Green, Camb | 53 | A3 |
| Kirtlington, Oxon | 37 | D2 |
| Kirtomy, High | 137 | F1 |
| Kirton, Aber | 128 | E2 |
| Kirton, Linc | 73 | C3 |
| Kirton, Notts | 72 | A1 |
| Kirton, Suff | 54 | B4 |
| Kirton in Lindsey, Linc | 83 | C2 |
| Kishorn, High | 130 | F4 |
| Kislingbury, Nhants | 50 | A2 |
| Kittisford, Som | 10 | D2 |
| Kivernoll, Heref | 35 | B1 |
| Knaith, Linc | 83 | B3 |
| Knaphill, Surr | 145 | B2 |
| Knaplock, Som | 10 | B1 |
| Knapp, Som | 11 | B2 |
| Knapton, N York | 88 | C2 |
| Knapton, N York | 94 | C3 |
| Knapton, Norf | 75 | C4 |
| Knapwell, Camb | 52 | A2 |
| Knaresborough, N York | 88 | A1 |
| Knarsdale, Nthumb | 97 | C1 |
| Knayton, N York | 93 | C2 |
| Knebworth, Herts | 40 | A2 |
| Kneesall, Notts | 72 | A1 |
| Kneesworth, Camb | 52 | A4 |
| Kneeton, Notts | 72 | A3 |
| Knenhall, Staff | 69 | B3 |
| Knightcote, Warw | 49 | B3 |
| Knightley, Staff | 57 | C1 |
| Knighton, Dors | 12 | B3 |
| Knighton, Powys | 46 | B1 |
| Knighton, Som | 23 | A4 |
| Knighton, Staff | 69 | A3 |
| Knighton, Staff | 69 | A4 |
| Knightwick, Worc | 47 | B3 |
| Knill, Heref | 46 | B2 |
| Knipton, Leics | 72 | B4 |
| Kniveton, Derby | 70 | B2 |
| Knock, Cumb | 97 | C3 |
| Knockally, High | 138 | D4 |
| Knockan, High | 135 | E2 |
| Knockholt, Kent | 149 | B1 |
| Knockholt Pound, Kent | 149 | B1 |
| Knockin, Shrop | 56 | B1 |
| Knocknain, D & G | 100 | A4 |
| Knodishall, Suff | 54 | C2 |
| Knole, Som | 12 | A2 |
| Knolton, Wrex | 68 | A3 |
| Knook, Wilts | 25 | B4 |
| Knossington, Leics | 61 | A2 |
| Knott End-on-Sea, Lanc | 85 | B2 |
| Knotting, Beds | 51 | A2 |
| Knotting Green, Beds | 51 | A2 |
| Knottingley, W York | 88 | B4 |
| Knowbury, Shrop | 46 | D1 |
| Knowehead, D & G | 101 | A2 |
| Knowl Hill, Berks | 27 | B1 |
| Knowle, Devon | 10 | B4 |
| Knowle, Devon | 10 | C3 |
| Knowle, Devon | 6 | A2 |
| Knowle, Som | 22 | E4 |
| Knowle, W Mids | 48 | C1 |
| Knowle Green, Lanc | 86 | A3 |
| Knowle Hill, Surr | 140 | C4 |
| Knowle St Giles, Som | 11 | B3 |
| Knowsley, Mers | 78 | A2 |
| Knowstone, Devon | 10 | B2 |
| Knox Bridge, Kent | 21 | A1 |
| Knucklas, Powys | 46 | B1 |
| Knuston, Nhants | 50 | C2 |
| Knutsford, Chesh | 79 | B4 |
| Krumlin, W York | 81 | A1 |
| Kuggar, Corn | 1 | D3 |
| Kyle of Lochalsh, High | 125 | F1 |
| Kyleakin, High | 125 | F1 |
| Kylerhea, High | 125 | F2 |
| Kynnersley, Shrop | 57 | A1 |
| Kyrewood, Worc | 47 | A2 |
| La Fontenelle, Guer | 139 | B2 |
| La Greve de Lecq, Jers | 139 | A1 |
| La Rocque, Jers | 139 | B2 |
| La Villette, Guer | 139 | B2 |
| Laceby, Linc | 84 | B2 |
| Lacey Green, Bucks | 38 | C3 |
| Lach Dennis, Chesh | 69 | A1 |
| Lackford, Suff | 53 | B1 |
| Lackford Green, Suff | 53 | B1 |
| Lacock, Wilts | 25 | A2 |
| Ladbroke, Warw | 49 | B2 |
| Laddingford, Kent | 29 | B4 |
| Ladock, Corn | 3 | C4 |
| Lady Hall, Cumb | 91 | C3 |
| Lady Village, Ork | 139 | B1 |
| Ladybank, Fife | 119 | C3 |
| Ladykirk, Bord | 109 | B1 |
| Ladywood, Worc | 47 | C2 |
| Lagavulin, Argyll | 105 | B1 |
| Laggan, High | 127 | A4 |
| Laide, High | 135 | B4 |
| Lairg, High | 136 | B2 |
| Lake, Wilts | 13 | B1 |
| Lakenheath, Suff | 63 | A4 |
| Lakesend, Norf | 62 | C3 |
| Laleham, Surr | 141 | A4 |
| Laleston, Brid | 22 | D1 |
| Lamancha, Bord | 114 | A4 |
| Lamas, Norf | 65 | A1 |
| Lamberhurst, Kent | 20 | B1 |
| Lamberhurst Down, Kent | 20 | B1 |
| Lambeth, G Lon | 143 | B2 |
| Lambley, Notts | 72 | A3 |
| Lambley, Nthumb | 103 | A4 |
| Lambourn, Berks | 26 | A1 |
| Lambourne End, Essex | 41 | A4 |
| Lambs Green, W Suss | 18 | B1 |
| Lamerton, Devon | 4 | C2 |
| Lamesley, T & W | 104 | B4 |
| Lamington, S Lan | 107 | C2 |
| Lamlash, N Ayr | 106 | A2 |
| Lamonby, Cumb | 97 | A2 |
| Lamorna, Corn | 1 | B3 |
| Lampeter, Cered | 45 | A3 |
| Lampeter Velfrey, Pemb | 32 | E2 |
| Lamphey, Pemb | 32 | D3 |
| Lamplugh, Cumb | 96 | D4 |
| Lamport, Nhants | 50 | B1 |
| Lamyatt, Som | 12 | B1 |
| Lanark, S Lan | 107 | B1 |
| Lancaster, Lanc | 85 | C1 |
| Lanchester, Durham | 98 | C1 |
| Lancing, W Suss | 18 | A4 |
| Landbeach, Camb | 52 | B2 |
| Landcross, Devon | 9 | D2 |
| Landimore, Swan | 33 | B4 |
| Landkey Town, Devon | 9 | E1 |
| Landrake, Corn | 4 | B3 |
| Land's End, Corn | 1 | A3 |
| Landscove, Devon | 5 | B3 |
| Landulph, Corn | 4 | C3 |
| Lane, Corn | 3 | B4 |
| Lane End, Bucks | 38 | C4 |
| Lane End Waberthwaite, Cumb | 91 | B2 |
| Lane Ends, Derby | 70 | B4 |
| Lane Head, Durham | 98 | B4 |
| Laneast, Corn | 4 | A1 |

| PLACE | PAGE | GRID |
|---|---|---|
| Laneham, Notts | 83 | B4 |
| Lanehead, Durham | 97 | E2 |
| Langar, Notts | 72 | A4 |
| Langbank, Renf | 111 | E2 |
| Langbar, N York | 87 | A2 |
| Langcliffe, N York | 92 | C4 |
| Langdale End, N York | 94 | C2 |
| Langdyke, Fife | 119 | C4 |
| Langenhoe, Essex | 43 | B2 |
| Langford, Beds | 51 | B4 |
| Langford, Devon | 10 | D4 |
| Langford, Essex | 42 | B3 |
| Langford, Notts | 72 | B2 |
| Langford, Oxon | 37 | B3 |
| Langford Budville, Som | 10 | D2 |
| Langford End, Beds | 51 | B3 |
| Langham, Essex | 53 | D4 |
| Langham, Norf | 75 | A3 |
| Langham, Rut | 61 | A2 |
| Langham, Suff | 53 | C1 |
| Langho, Lanc | 86 | B3 |
| Langholm, D & G | 102 | C2 |
| Langley, Hamp | 15 | A4 |
| Langley, Herts | 40 | A1 |
| Langley, Nthumb | 103 | C4 |
| Langley, Warw | 48 | C2 |
| Langley, Berks | 140 | C2 |
| Langley Burrell, Wilts | 25 | B2 |
| Langley Park, Durham | 98 | C2 |
| Langley Street, Norf | 65 | B3 |
| Langley Upper Green, Essex | 52 | B4 |
| Langold, Notts | 82 | B3 |
| Langore, Corn | 4 | A1 |
| Langport, Som | 11 | C2 |
| Langrick, Linc | 73 | C3 |
| Langridge, Som | 24 | B2 |
| Langrigg, Cumb | 96 | E1 |
| Langrish, Hamp | 16 | A2 |
| Langsett, S York | 81 | B2 |
| Langstone, Newport | 35 | A4 |
| Langthorne, N York | 93 | A2 |
| Langthorpe, N York | 93 | B4 |
| Langthwaite, N York | 92 | D1 |
| Langtoft, E R of Y | 94 | D4 |
| Langtoft, Linc | 61 | D2 |
| Langton, Durham | 98 | C4 |
| Langton, Linc | 73 | C1 |
| Langton, Linc | 73 | D1 |
| Langton, N York | 94 | B4 |
| Langton by Wragby, Linc | 84 | A4 |
| Langton Herring, Dors | 6 | F2 |
| Langton Matravers, Dors | 7 | C2 |
| Langtree, Devon | 9 | D3 |
| Langwathby, Cumb | 97 | B3 |
| Langworth, Linc | 83 | D4 |
| Lanivet, Corn | 3 | D3 |
| Lank, Corn | 3 | E2 |
| Lanlivery, Corn | 3 | E4 |
| Lanner, Corn | 1 | D1 |
| Lanreath, Corn | 3 | E4 |
| Lansallos, Corn | 3 | E4 |
| Lanteglos, Corn | 3 | E2 |
| Lanteglos Highway, Corn | 3 | E4 |
| Lanton, Bord | 108 | D3 |
| Lanton, Nthumb | 109 | C2 |
| Lapford, Devon | 10 | A3 |
| Laphroaig, Argyll | 105 | B1 |
| Lapley, Staff | 57 | C2 |
| Lapworth, Warw | 48 | C1 |
| Larbert, Falkirk | 113 | A2 |
| Largoward, Fife | 119 | E3 |
| Largs, N Ayr | 111 | D4 |
| Larkhall, S Lan | 112 | C4 |
| Larkhill, Wilts | 25 | C4 |
| Larling, Norf | 63 | C4 |
| Lartington, Durham | 98 | A4 |
| Lasham, Hamp | 27 | A4 |
| Lask Edge, Staff | 69 | B2 |
| Lastingham, N York | 94 | A2 |
| Latchingdon, Essex | 42 | B3 |
| Latchley, Corn | 4 | B2 |
| Latebrook, Staff | 69 | B2 |
| Lathbury, Bucks | 50 | C4 |
| Latheron, High | 138 | D4 |
| Latimer, Bucks | 39 | B3 |
| Latteridge, Glouc | 24 | A1 |
| Latton, Wilts | 37 | A4 |
| Lauder, Bord | 108 | C1 |
| Laugharne, Carm | 32 | F2 |
| Laughton, Leics | 60 | C4 |
| Laughton, Linc | 83 | B2 |
| Laughton, Linc | 73 | A4 |
| Laughton, E Sus | 19 | B3 |
| Laughton-en-le-Morthen, S York | 82 | B3 |
| Launcells, Corn | 9 | B4 |
| Launceston, Corn | 4 | B1 |
| Launton, Oxon | 38 | A1 |
| Laurencekirk, Aber | 124 | C2 |
| Laurieston, D & G | 101 | B4 |
| Lavendon, Bucks | 50 | C3 |
| Lavenham, Suff | 53 | C3 |
| Lavernock, Glam | 23 | A2 |
| Laversdale, Cumb | 102 | D4 |
| Laverton, Glouc | 48 | B4 |
| Laverton, N York | 93 | A4 |
| Laverton, Som | 24 | C3 |
| Lavister, Wrex | 68 | A2 |
| Law, S Lan | 113 | A4 |
| Lawers, Perth | 118 | C1 |
| Lawford, Essex | 43 | B1 |
| Lawford, Som | 11 | A1 |
| Lawhitton, Corn | 4 | B2 |
| Lawkland, N York | 92 | B4 |
| Lawrenny, Pemb | 32 | D3 |
| Lawshall, Suff | 53 | B3 |
| Laxey, I o M | 139 | D3 |
| Laxfield, Suff | 54 | B1 |
| Laxton, E R of Y | 89 | B4 |
| Laxton, Nhants | 61 | B3 |
| Laxton, Notts | 72 | A1 |
| Laycock, W York | 86 | D3 |
| Layer Breton, Essex | 43 | A2 |
| Layer Marney, Essex | 43 | A2 |
| Layham, Suff | 53 | D4 |

| PLACE | PAGE | GRID |
|---|---|---|
| Laytham, E R of Y | 89 | B3 |
| Laythes, Cumb | 96 | F1 |
| Lazonby, Cumb | 97 | B2 |
| Le Bourg, Guer | 139 | B2 |
| Le Villocq, Guer | 139 | B2 |
| Lea, Derby | 70 | C2 |
| Lea, Heref | 35 | C2 |
| Lea, Linc | 83 | B3 |
| Lea, Shrop | 56 | C4 |
| Lea, Wilts | 25 | B1 |
| Lea Marston, Warw | 59 | A3 |
| Leaden Roding, Essex | 41 | B2 |
| Leadenham, Linc | 72 | C2 |
| Leadgate, Durham | 98 | B1 |
| Leadhills, S Lan | 107 | B3 |
| Leafield, Oxon | 37 | C2 |
| Leake Common Side, Linc | 73 | D2 |
| Lealholm, N York | 94 | B1 |
| Leamington Hastings, Warw | 49 | B2 |
| Leamington Spa, Warw | 49 | A2 |
| Leasgill, Cumb | 91 | F3 |
| Leasingham, Linc | 73 | A3 |
| Leasingthorne, Durham | 98 | C3 |
| Leatherhead, Surr | 147 | B2 |
| Leathley, N York | 87 | B2 |
| Leaton, Shrop | 56 | D1 |
| Leavenheath, Suff | 53 | C4 |
| Leavening, N York | 89 | B1 |
| Leaves Green, G Lon | 149 | A1 |
| Lebberston, N York | 94 | D3 |
| Lechlade, Glouc | 37 | B3 |
| Leck, Lanc | 92 | A3 |
| Leckford, Hamp | 14 | B1 |
| Leckhampstead, Berks | 26 | B2 |
| Leckhampstead, Bucks | 50 | A4 |
| Leckhampstead Thicket, Berks | 26 | B1 |
| Leckmelm, High | 135 | D4 |
| Leconfield, E R of Y | 89 | D2 |
| Ledburn, Bucks | 39 | A2 |
| Ledbury, Heref | 47 | B4 |
| Ledgemoor, Heref | 46 | C3 |
| Ledsham, W York | 88 | B4 |
| Ledston, W York | 88 | B4 |
| Ledwell, Oxon | 37 | D1 |
| Lee, Devon | 22 | A4 |
| Lee, G Lon | 144 | A3 |
| Lee Brockhurst, Shrop | 68 | B4 |
| Lee Street, Surr | 148 | B4 |
| Leebotwood, Shrop | 56 | D3 |
| Leece, Cumb | 91 | D4 |
| Leeds, Kent | 30 | A3 |
| Leeds, W York | 88 | A3 |
| Leedstown, Corn | 1 | C2 |
| Leek, Staff | 69 | C2 |
| Leek Wootton, Warw | 49 | A1 |
| Leeming, N York | 93 | B2 |
| Leeming Bar, N York | 93 | B2 |
| Lee-on-the-Solent, Hamp | 15 | B4 |
| Lees, Derby | 70 | B4 |
| Leesthorpe, Leics | 61 | A2 |
| Leeswood, Flint | 67 | E2 |
| Leetown, Perth | 119 | B2 |
| Legbourne, Linc | 84 | C3 |
| Legerwood, Bord | 108 | D1 |
| Legsby, Linc | 84 | A3 |
| Leicester, Leics | 60 | B2 |
| Leigh, Dors | 12 | B3 |
| Leigh, Glouc | 36 | B1 |
| Leigh, G Man | 79 | A2 |
| Leigh, Kent | 29 | A4 |
| Leigh, Surr | 148 | A4 |
| Leigh, Wilts | 37 | A4 |
| Leigh, Worc | 47 | B3 |
| Leigh Delamere, Wilts | 25 | A1 |
| Leigh Green, Kent | 21 | B1 |
| Leigh Sinton, Worc | 47 | B3 |
| Leigh upon Mendip, Som | 24 | A4 |
| Leigh Woods, Som | 23 | D2 |
| Leighterton, Glouc | 36 | B4 |
| Leighton, Powys | 56 | B2 |
| Leighton, Shrop | 57 | A2 |
| Leighton Buzzard, Beds | 39 | A1 |
| Leinthall Earls, Heref | 46 | C2 |
| Leinthall Starkes, Heref | 46 | C1 |
| Leintwardine, Heref | 46 | C1 |
| Leire, Leics | 60 | B4 |
| Leiston, Suff | 54 | C2 |
| Leitfie, Perth | 123 | D4 |
| Leitholm, Bord | 109 | A1 |
| Lelant, Corn | 1 | C1 |
| Lelley, E R of Y | 90 | B3 |
| Lem Hill, Worc | 47 | B1 |
| Lenchwick, Worc | 48 | A3 |
| Lendalfoot, S Ayr | 100 | B2 |
| Lenham, Kent | 30 | B4 |
| Lenham Heath, Kent | 30 | B4 |
| Lennel, Bord | 109 | B1 |
| Lennoxtown, E Dunb | 112 | B2 |
| Lent, Bucks | 140 | B1 |
| Lenton, Linc | 73 | A4 |
| Leochel-Cushnie, Aber | 128 | D3 |
| Leominster, Heref | 46 | D2 |
| Leppington, N York | 89 | B1 |
| Lepton, W York | 81 | B1 |
| L'Eree, Guer | 139 | A2 |
| Lerryn, Corn | 3 | E4 |
| Lerwick, Shet | 139 | A2 |
| Les Quartiers, Guer | 139 | B2 |
| Les Quennevais, Jers | 139 | A2 |
| Lesbury, Nthumb | 109 | E4 |
| Leslie, Aber | 128 | E1 |
| Leslie, Fife | 119 | C4 |
| Lesmahagow, S Lan | 107 | B1 |
| Lesnewth, Corn | 3 | E1 |
| Lessingham, Norf | 75 | D4 |
| Lessonhall, Cumb | 96 | E1 |
| Leswalt, D & G | 100 | A4 |
| L'Etacq, Jers | 139 | A1 |
| Letchworth, Herts | 40 | A1 |
| Letcombe Bassett, Oxon | 26 | A1 |
| Letcombe Regis, Oxon | 26 | A1 |
| Letham, Angus | 124 | A4 |
| Letham, Fife | 119 | C3 |
| Letheringham, Suff | 54 | B2 |

| PLACE | PAGE | GRID |
|---|---|---|
| Letheringsett, Norf | 75 | A3 |
| Letterston, Pemb | 32 | C1 |
| Letton, Heref | 46 | B3 |
| Lett's Green, Kent | 149 | B1 |
| Letty Green, Herts | 40 | A2 |
| Letwell, S York | 82 | B3 |
| Leuchars, Fife | 119 | D2 |
| Levedale, Staff | 57 | C1 |
| Leven, E R of Y | 90 | A2 |
| Leven, Fife | 119 | D4 |
| Levens, Cumb | 91 | F3 |
| Levens Green, Herts | 40 | B1 |
| Leverington, Camb | 62 | C2 |
| Leverton, Linc | 73 | D3 |
| Levington, Suff | 54 | A4 |
| Levisham, N York | 94 | B2 |
| Lew, Oxon | 37 | C3 |
| Lewannick, Corn | 4 | A2 |
| Lewdown, Devon | 4 | C1 |
| Lewes, E Sus | 19 | A3 |
| Leweston, Pemb | 32 | C1 |
| Lewknor, Oxon | 38 | B4 |
| Lewson Street, Kent | 30 | B3 |
| Lewtrenchard, Devon | 4 | C1 |
| Lexworthy, Som | 11 | B1 |
| Ley Hill, Bucks | 39 | B3 |
| Leybourne, Kent | 29 | B3 |
| Leyburn, N York | 92 | E2 |
| Leygreen, Herts | 39 | C1 |
| Leyland, Lanc | 85 | C4 |
| Leys, Angus | 119 | C1 |
| Leysdown-on-Sea, Kent | 30 | C2 |
| Leysmill, Angus | 124 | B4 |
| Leysters, Heref | 46 | D2 |
| Leyton, G Lon | 144 | A1 |
| Lezant, Corn | 4 | B2 |
| Lezayre, I o M | 139 | C2 |
| Lhanbryde, Moray | 133 | C2 |
| Libanus, Powys | 34 | B1 |
| Libberton, S Lan | 107 | C1 |
| Lichfield, Staff | 58 | B2 |
| Lickey, Worc | 48 | A1 |
| Lickey End, Worc | 48 | A1 |
| Lickfold, W Suss | 17 | A2 |
| Liddesdale, High | 121 | B3 |
| Liddington, Wilts | 25 | D1 |
| Lidgate, Suff | 53 | A2 |
| Lidlington, Beds | 51 | A4 |
| Liff, Angus | 119 | C1 |
| Lifton, Devon | 4 | B1 |
| Liftondown, Devon | 4 | B1 |
| Lighthorne, Warw | 49 | A3 |
| Lilbourne, Nhants | 49 | C1 |
| Lilleshall, Shrop | 57 | B1 |
| Lilley, Herts | 39 | C1 |
| Lilliesleaf, Bord | 108 | C3 |
| Lillingstone Dayrell, Bucks | 50 | A4 |
| Lillingstone Lovell, Bucks | 50 | A4 |
| Lillington, Dors | 12 | B3 |
| Lilstock, Som | 23 | A4 |
| Lime Street, Worc | 36 | B1 |
| Limekilns, Fife | 113 | C2 |
| Limerstone, I of W | 8 | A2 |
| Limington, Som | 12 | A2 |
| Limpenhoe, Norf | 65 | B2 |
| Limpley Stoke, Wilts | 24 | B3 |
| Limpsfield, Surr | 149 | A2 |
| Limpsfield Chart, Surr | 149 | A3 |
| Linby, Notts | 71 | B2 |
| Linchmere, W Suss | 17 | A1 |
| Lincoln, Linc | 73 | A1 |
| Lincomb, Worc | 47 | C1 |
| Lindal in Furness, Cumb | 91 | D4 |
| Lindale, Cumb | 91 | E3 |
| Lindford, Hamp | 16 | B1 |
| Lindley Green, N York | 87 | B2 |
| Lindridge, Worc | 47 | A1 |
| Lindsell, Essex | 41 | B1 |
| Lindsey, Suff | 53 | C4 |
| Lindsey Tye, Suff | 53 | C3 |
| Lingdale, N York | 99 | C4 |
| Lingen, Heref | 46 | C2 |
| Lingfield, Surr | 149 | A4 |
| Lingwood, Norf | 65 | B2 |
| Linkend, Worc | 36 | B1 |
| Linkenholt, Hamp | 26 | A3 |
| Linkinhorne, Corn | 4 | B2 |
| Linley, Shrop | 56 | C3 |
| Linley Green, Heref | 47 | A3 |
| Linleygreen, Shrop | 57 | A3 |
| Linlithgow, W Loth | 113 | B2 |
| Linstead Parva, Suff | 54 | B1 |
| Linstock, Cumb | 102 | C4 |
| Linthwaite, W York | 81 | A1 |
| Lintlaw, Bord | 115 | D4 |
| Lintmill, Moray | 133 | E2 |
| Linton, Derby | 59 | B1 |
| Linton, Heref | 35 | C1 |
| Linton, Kent | 29 | B4 |
| Linton, N York | 86 | D1 |
| Linton, W York | 88 | B2 |
| Linton, Camb | 52 | C3 |
| Linton Hill, Heref | 35 | C1 |
| Linton-on-Ouse, N York | 88 | B1 |
| Linwood, Linc | 84 | A3 |
| Linwood, Renf | 112 | A3 |
| Liphook, Hamp | 16 | B1 |
| Liscombe, Som | 10 | B1 |
| Liskeard, Corn | 4 | A3 |
| Liss, Hamp | 16 | B2 |
| Lissett, E R of Y | 90 | A1 |
| Lissington, Linc | 84 | A4 |
| Litcham, Norf | 63 | B1 |
| Litchborough, Nhants | 50 | A3 |
| Litchfield, Hamp | 26 | B3 |
| Litlington, Camb | 51 | C4 |
| Litlington, E Sus | 19 | B4 |
| Little Abington, Camb | 52 | B3 |
| Little Addington, Nhants | 50 | C1 |
| Little Alne, Warw | 48 | B2 |
| Little Amwell, Herts | 40 | B2 |
| Little Asby, Cumb | 92 | B1 |
| Little Aston, Staff | 58 | B3 |
| Little Ayton, N York | 93 | D1 |
| Little Baddow, Essex | 42 | B3 |
| Little Badminton, Glouc | 24 | B1 |

| PLACE | PAGE | GRID |
|---|---|---|
| Little Bampton, Cumb | 96 | F1 |
| Little Bardfield, Essex | 41 | B1 |
| Little Barningham, Norf | 75 | B4 |
| Little Barrington, Glouc | 37 | B2 |
| Little Bavington, Nthumb | 103 | D3 |
| Little Bedwyn, Wilts | 26 | A2 |
| Little Bentley, Essex | 43 | B1 |
| Little Berkhamsted, Herts | 40 | A3 |
| Little Birch, Heref | 35 | B1 |
| Little Blencow, Cumb | 97 | A3 |
| Little Bognor, W Suss | 17 | B2 |
| Little Bolehill, Derby | 70 | C2 |
| Little Bollington, Chesh | 79 | B3 |
| Little Bourton, Oxon | 49 | B4 |
| Little Bradley, Suff | 53 | A3 |
| Little Brampton, Shrop | 56 | C4 |
| Little Brechin, Angus | 124 | B3 |
| Little Brickhill, Bucks | 39 | A1 |
| Little Brington, Nhants | 50 | A2 |
| Little Bromley, Essex | 43 | B1 |
| Little Broughton, Cumb | 96 | D3 |
| Little Budworth, Chesh | 68 | C1 |
| Little Burstead, Essex | 42 | A4 |
| Little Bytham, Linc | 61 | C1 |
| Little Casterton, Rut | 61 | C2 |
| Little Cawthorpe, Linc | 84 | C4 |
| Little Chart, Kent | 30 | B4 |
| Little Chesterford, Essex | 52 | B4 |
| Little Cheverell, Wilts | 25 | B3 |
| Little Chishill, Camb | 52 | A4 |
| Little Clacton, Essex | 43 | C2 |
| Little Clifton, Cumb | 96 | D3 |
| Little Comberton, Worc | 48 | A4 |
| Little Compton, Warw | 37 | B1 |
| Little Cornard, Suff | 53 | C4 |
| Little Cowarne, Heref | 47 | A3 |
| Little Coxwell, Oxon | 37 | C4 |
| Little Crakehall, N York | 93 | A2 |
| Little Cressingham, Norf | 63 | B3 |
| Little Crosby, Mers | 77 | D2 |
| Little Cubley, Derby | 70 | B4 |
| Little Dalby, Leics | 61 | A2 |
| Little Dewchurch, Heref | 35 | B1 |
| Little Ditton, Camb | 53 | A2 |
| Little Driffield, E R of Y | 89 | D1 |
| Little Dunham, Norf | 63 | B2 |
| Little Dunkeld, Perth | 123 | B4 |
| Little Dunmow, Essex | 41 | B2 |
| Little Durnford, Wilts | 13 | B1 |
| Little Eaton, Derby | 70 | C3 |
| Little Ellingham, Norf | 63 | C3 |
| Little Everdon, Nhants | 49 | C2 |
| Little Faringdon, Oxon | 37 | B3 |
| Little Fencote, N York | 93 | B2 |
| Little Fenton, N York | 88 | C3 |
| Little Fransham, Norf | 63 | C2 |
| Little Gaddesden, Herts | 39 | B2 |
| Little Gorsley, Heref | 35 | C1 |
| Little Gransden, Camb | 51 | C3 |
| Little Green, Som | 24 | B4 |
| Little Grimsby, Linc | 84 | C3 |
| Little Hadham, Herts | 41 | A1 |
| Little Hale, Linc | 73 | B3 |
| Little Hallingbury, Essex | 41 | A2 |
| Little Harrowden, Nhants | 50 | C1 |
| Little Haseley, Oxon | 38 | B3 |
| Little Hatfield, E R of Y | 90 | A2 |
| Little Haven, Pemb | 32 | C2 |
| Little Hay, Staff | 58 | B3 |
| Little Haywood, Staff | 58 | A1 |
| Little Hereford, Heref | 46 | D1 |
| Little Horkesley, Essex | 43 | A1 |
| Little Hormead, Herts | 40 | B1 |
| Little Horwood, Bucks | 38 | C1 |
| Little Houghton, Nhants | 50 | B2 |
| Little Houghton, S York | 82 | A2 |
| Little Hucklow, Derby | 81 | B4 |
| Little Hutton, N York | 93 | C4 |
| Little Keyford, Som | 24 | B4 |
| Little Kimble, Bucks | 38 | C3 |
| Little Kineton, Warw | 49 | A3 |
| Little Kingshill, Bucks | 39 | A3 |
| Little Langdale, Cumb | 91 | D1 |
| Little Langford, Wilts | 13 | B1 |
| Little Leigh, Chesh | 79 | A4 |
| Little Lever, G Man | 79 | B1 |
| Little Linford, Bucks | 50 | B4 |
| Little Load, Som | 12 | A2 |
| Little London, Hamp | 26 | A4 |
| Little London, Hamp | 27 | A3 |
| Little Longstone, Derby | 70 | B1 |
| Little Malvern, Worc | 47 | B4 |
| Little Maplestead, Essex | 53 | B4 |
| Little Marcle, Heref | 47 | A4 |
| Little Marlow, Bucks | 39 | A4 |
| Little Massingham, Norf | 63 | B1 |
| Little Melton, Norf | 64 | B2 |
| Little Mill, Monm | 34 | E3 |
| Little Milton, Oxon | 38 | A3 |
| Little Missenden, Bucks | 39 | A3 |
| Little Musgrave, Cumb | 97 | D4 |
| Little Ness, Shrop | 56 | C1 |
| Little Newcastle, Pemb | 32 | D1 |
| Little Newsham, Durham | 98 | B4 |
| Little Norton, Som | 12 | A3 |
| Little Oakley, Essex | 43 | C1 |
| Little Oakley, Nhants | 61 | B4 |
| Little Onn, Staff | 57 | C1 |
| Little Orton, Cumb | 97 | A1 |
| Little Packington, Warw | 59 | A4 |
| Little Paxton, Camb | 51 | B2 |
| Little Petherick, Corn | 3 | C2 |
| Little Plumstead, Norf | 65 | A2 |
| Little Ponton, Linc | 72 | C4 |
| Little Preston, Nhants | 49 | C3 |
| Little Raveley, Camb | 62 | A4 |
| Little Ribston, N York | 88 | A1 |
| Little Rissington, Glouc | 37 | B2 |
| Little Rollright, Oxon | 37 | C1 |
| Little Ryburgh, Norf | 74 | E4 |
| Little Salkeld, Cumb | 97 | B2 |
| Little Sampford, Essex | 52 | C4 |
| Little Saughall, Chesh | 68 | A1 |
| Little Saxham, Suff | 53 | B2 |
| Little Sessay, N York | 93 | C4 |
| Little Singleton, Lanc | 85 | B3 |

| PLACE | PAGE | GRID |
|---|---|---|
| Little Snoring, Norf | 74 | E4 |
| Little Sodbury, Glouc | 24 | B1 |
| Little Somerford, Wilts | 25 | B1 |
| Little Soudley, Shrop | 69 | A4 |
| Little Stainton, Durham | 98 | D4 |
| Little Stanney, Chesh | 78 | A4 |
| Little Staughton, Beds | 51 | B2 |
| Little Steeping, Linc | 74 | A1 |
| Little Stonham, Suff | 53 | D2 |
| Little Stretton, Leics | 60 | C3 |
| Little Stretton, Shrop | 56 | C3 |
| Little Strickland, Cumb | 97 | B4 |
| Little Stukeley, Camb | 51 | C1 |
| Little Swinburne, Nthumb | 103 | D3 |
| Little Tew, Oxon | 37 | C1 |
| Little Tey, Essex | 43 | A1 |
| Little Thetford, Camb | 52 | B1 |
| Little Thorpe, Durham | 99 | A2 |
| Little Thurlow Green, Suff | 53 | A3 |
| Little Torrington, Devon | 9 | D3 |
| Little Town, Lanc | 86 | A3 |
| Little Urswick, Cumb | 91 | D4 |
| Little Wakering, Essex | 43 | A4 |
| Little Walden, Essex | 52 | C4 |
| Little Waldingfield, Suff | 53 | C3 |
| Little Walsingham, Norf | 74 | E4 |
| Little Weighton, E R of Y | 89 | D3 |
| Little Wenham, Suff | 53 | D4 |
| Little Wenlock, Shrop | 57 | A2 |
| Little Whitefield, I of W | 8 | B1 |
| Little Wilbraham, Camb | 52 | B2 |
| Little Witcombe, Glouc | 36 | B2 |
| Little Witley, Worc | 47 | B2 |
| Little Wittenham, Oxon | 38 | A4 |
| Little Wolford, Warw | 48 | C4 |
| Little Woodcote, Surr | 148 | B1 |
| Little Wymington, Beds | 50 | C2 |
| Little Wymondley, Herts | 40 | A1 |
| Little Wyrley, Staff | 58 | A2 |
| Little Yeldham, Essex | 53 | B4 |
| Littleborough, G Man | 80 | B1 |
| Littleborough, Notts | 83 | B4 |
| Littlebourne, Kent | 31 | A3 |
| Littlebredy, Dors | 6 | F1 |
| Littlebury, Essex | 52 | B4 |
| Littlebury Green, Essex | 52 | B4 |
| Littledean, Glouc | 35 | C2 |
| Littleham, Devon | 9 | D2 |
| Littleham, Devon | 6 | A2 |
| Littlehampton, W Suss | 17 | B4 |
| Littlehempston, Devon | 5 | B3 |
| Littleport, Camb | 62 | D4 |
| Littlethorpe, Leics | 60 | B3 |
| Littlethorpe, N York | 93 | B4 |
| Littleton, Surr | 146 | A3 |
| Littleton, Surr | 141 | A4 |
| Littleton, Chesh | 68 | A1 |
| Littleton, Hamp | 15 | A1 |
| Littleton, Som | 12 | A1 |
| Littleton Drew, Wilts | 25 | A1 |
| Littleton-on-Severn, Glouc | 35 | C4 |
| Littletown, Durham | 98 | D2 |
| Littleworth, Oxon | 37 | C4 |
| Littleworth, Worc | 47 | C3 |
| Littleworth Common, Bucks | 140 | B1 |
| Litton, Derby | 81 | B4 |
| Litton, N York | 92 | C4 |
| Litton, Som | 24 | A3 |
| Litton Cheney, Dors | 6 | E1 |
| Liverpool, Mers | 77 | D3 |
| Liversedge, W York | 87 | B4 |
| Liverton, Devon | 5 | B2 |
| Liverton, N York | 99 | C4 |
| Livingston, W Loth | 113 | C3 |
| Livingston Village, W Loth | 113 | C3 |
| Lixton, Devon | 5 | A4 |
| Lixwm, Flint | 67 | D1 |
| Lizard, Corn | 1 | D4 |
| Llanaelhaearn, Gwyn | 66 | C3 |
| Llanafan, Cered | 45 | B1 |
| Llanallgo, Angle | 76 | C3 |
| Llanarmon Dyffryn Ceiriog, Wrex | 67 | D4 |
| Llanarmon-yn-Ial, Denb | 67 | D2 |
| Llanarth, Cered | 44 | E2 |
| Llanarth, Monm | 35 | A2 |
| Llanarthne, Carm | 33 | B2 |
| Llanasa, Flint | 77 | B4 |
| Llanbadarn Fynydd, Powys | 45 | E1 |
| Llanbadoc, Monm | 35 | A3 |
| Llanbeder, Newport | 35 | A4 |
| Llanbedr, Gwyn | 66 | E4 |
| Llanbedr, Powys | 34 | E2 |
| Llanbedr-Dyffryn-Clwyd, Denb | 67 | D2 |
| Llanbedrgoch, Angle | 76 | C4 |
| Llanbedrog, Gwyn | 66 | C4 |
| Llanbedr-y-Cennin, Ab & Col | 66 | F1 |
| Llanberis, Gwyn | 66 | E2 |
| Llanbethery, Glam | 22 | F2 |
| Llanbister, Powys | 45 | E1 |
| Llanboidy, Carm | 32 | F1 |
| Llanbradach, Caer | 34 | D4 |
| Llanbrynmair, Powys | 55 | D3 |
| Llancadle, Glam | 22 | F2 |
| Llancarfan, Glam | 22 | F2 |
| Llancloudy, Heref | 35 | B2 |
| Llandanwg, Gwyn | 66 | E4 |
| Llanddanielfab, Angle | 66 | D1 |
| Llanddarog, Carm | 33 | B2 |
| Llanddeiniol, Cered | 45 | A1 |
| Llandderfel, Gwyn | 67 | B4 |
| Llanddeusant, Angle | 76 | B3 |
| Llanddew, Powys | 34 | C1 |
| Llanddewi, Swan | 33 | B4 |
| Llanddewi Brefi, Cered | 45 | B3 |
| Llanddewi Rhydderch, Monm | 35 | A2 |
| Llanddewi Velfrey, Pemb | 32 | E2 |
| Llanddewi Ystradenni, Powys | 45 | E1 |
| Llanddoget, Ab & Col | 67 | A1 |
| Llanddona, Angle | 76 | D4 |
| Llanddowror, Carm | 32 | F2 |

| PLACE | PAGE | GRID |
|---|---|---|
| Llanddulas, Ab & Col | 77 | A4 |
| Llanddwywe, Gwyn | 55 | A1 |
| Llanddyfnan, Angle | 76 | C4 |
| Llandefaelog-Trer-Graig, Powys | 34 | D1 |
| Llandefalle, Powys | 45 | E4 |
| Llandegfan, Angle | 76 | D4 |
| Llandegla, Denb | 67 | D2 |
| Llandegley, Powys | 46 | A2 |
| Llandegveth, Monm | 34 | E4 |
| Llandeilo, Carm | 33 | C1 |
| Llandeilo Graban, Powys | 45 | E4 |
| Llandeloy, Pemb | 32 | C1 |
| Llandenny, Monm | 35 | A3 |
| Llandevaud, Newport | 35 | A4 |
| Llandevenny, Monm | 23 | C1 |
| Llandinam, Powys | 55 | E4 |
| Llandissilio, Pemb | 32 | E2 |
| Llandogo, Monm | 35 | B3 |
| Llandough, Glam | 22 | E2 |
| Llandovery, Carm | 45 | B4 |
| Llandow, Glam | 22 | E2 |
| Llandre, Carm | 45 | B4 |
| Llandre, Cered | 55 | A4 |
| Llandre Isaf, Pemb | 32 | E1 |
| Llandrillo, Denb | 67 | C4 |
| Llandrindod Wells, Powys | 45 | E2 |
| Llandrinio, Powys | 56 | B1 |
| Llandudno, Ab & Col | 76 | F4 |
| Llandudno Junction, Ab & Col | 76 | F4 |
| Llandudwen, Gwyn | 66 | B4 |
| Llandulas, Powys | 45 | C4 |
| Llandwrog, Gwyn | 66 | D2 |
| Llandybie, Carm | 33 | C2 |
| Llandyfaelog, Carm | 33 | A2 |
| Llandyfriog, Cered | 44 | E4 |
| Llandygai, Gwyn | 66 | E1 |
| Llandygwydd, Cered | 44 | D4 |
| Llandyrnog, Denb | 67 | C1 |
| Llandyssil, Powys | 56 | A3 |
| Llandysul, Cered | 44 | E4 |
| Llanedeyrn, Cardiff | 23 | A1 |
| Llanegryn, Gwyn | 55 | A2 |
| Llanegwad, Carm | 33 | B2 |
| Llaneilian, Angle | 76 | C3 |
| Llanelian-yn-Rhos, Ab & Col | 76 | F4 |
| Llanelidan, Denb | 67 | C2 |
| Llanelieu, Powys | 46 | A4 |
| Llanellen, Monm | 34 | E2 |
| Llanelli, Carm | 33 | B3 |
| Llanelltyd, Gwyn | 55 | B1 |
| Llanelwedd, Powys | 45 | E3 |
| Llanenddwyn, Gwyn | 55 | A1 |
| Llanengan, Gwyn | 66 | B4 |
| Llanerchymedd, Angle | 76 | B3 |
| Llanerfyl, Powys | 55 | E2 |
| Llanfachraeth, Angle | 76 | B4 |
| Llanfachreth, Gwyn | 55 | B1 |
| Llanfaelog, Angle | 76 | B4 |
| Llanfaelrhys, Gwyn | 66 | B4 |
| Llanfaethlu, Angle | 76 | B3 |
| Llanfair, Gwyn | 66 | E4 |
| Llanfair Caereinion, Powys | 55 | E2 |
| Llanfair Clydogau, Cered | 45 | A3 |
| Llanfair P G, Angle | 66 | D1 |
| Llanfair Talhaiarn, Ab & Col | 67 | B1 |
| Llanfair Waterdine, Shrop | 46 | B1 |
| Llanfairfechan, Ab & Col | 76 | E4 |
| Llanfair-is-gaer, Gwyn | 66 | D1 |
| Llanfair-y-Cwmwd, Angle | 66 | D1 |
| Llanfairynghornwy, Angle | 76 | B3 |
| Llanfair-yn-Neubwll, Angle | 76 | A4 |
| Llanfallteg, Carm | 32 | E2 |
| Llanfallteg West, Carm | 32 | E2 |
| Llanfarian, Cered | 45 | A1 |
| Llanfechain, Powys | 56 | A1 |
| Llanfechell, Angle | 76 | B3 |
| Llanferres, Denb | 67 | D2 |
| Llanfihangel Glyn Myfyr, Ab & Col | 67 | B2 |
| Llanfihangel Nant Bran, Powys | 45 | D4 |
| Llanfihangel Rhydithon, Powys | 46 | A2 |
| Llanfihangel yn Nhowyn, Angle | 76 | B4 |
| Llanfihangel-ar-Arth, Carm | 44 | F4 |
| Llanfihangel-y-Creuddyn, Cered | 45 | B1 |
| Llanfihangel-yng-Ngwynfa, Powys | 55 | E1 |
| Llanfihangel-y-traethau, Gwyn | 66 | E4 |
| Llanfilo, Powys | 34 | D1 |
| Llanfoist, Monm | 34 | E2 |
| Llanfor, Gwyn | 67 | B4 |
| Llanfrechfa, Torf | 34 | E4 |
| Llanfrynach, Powys | 34 | C1 |
| Llanfwrog, Denb | 67 | C2 |
| Llanfwrog, Angle | 76 | A3 |
| Llanfyllin, Powys | 56 | A1 |
| Llanfynydd, Carm | 33 | C1 |
| Llanfynydd, Flint | 67 | E2 |
| Llanfyrnach, Pemb | 32 | F1 |
| Llangadfan, Powys | 55 | E2 |
| Llangadog, Carm | 33 | D1 |
| Llangadwaladr, Angle | 66 | C1 |
| Llangaffo, Angle | 66 | D1 |
| Llangammarch Wells, Powys | 45 | D3 |
| Llangan, Glam | 22 | E1 |
| Llangarron, Heref | 35 | B2 |
| Llangathen, Carm | 33 | C2 |
| Llangattock, Powys | 34 | D2 |
| Llangattock Lingoed, Monm | 35 | A2 |
| Llangedwyn, Powys | 56 | A1 |
| Llangefni, Angle | 76 | C4 |
| Llangeinor, Brid | 34 | B4 |
| Llangeitho, Cered | 45 | A2 |
| Llangeler, Carm | 44 | E4 |
| Llangelynin, Gwyn | 55 | A2 |
| Llangendeirne, Carm | 33 | B2 |
| Llangennech, Carm | 33 | C3 |

| PLACE | PAGE | GRID |
|---|---|---|
| Llangennith, Swan | 33 | B4 |
| Llangian, Gwyn | 66 | B4 |
| Llangloffan, Pemb | 32 | C1 |
| Llanglydwen, Carm | 32 | E1 |
| Llangoed, Angle | 76 | D4 |
| Llangollen, Denb | 67 | D3 |
| Llangolman, Pemb | 32 | E1 |
| Llangors, Powys | 34 | D1 |
| Llangower, Gwyn | 67 | B4 |
| Llangranog, Cered | 44 | E3 |
| Llangristiolus, Angle | 76 | C4 |
| Llangrove, Heref | 35 | B2 |
| Llangunllo, Powys | 46 | A1 |
| Llangunnor, Carm | 33 | B2 |
| Llangurig, Powys | 55 | D4 |
| Llangwm, Ab & Col | 67 | B3 |
| Llangwm, Monm | 35 | A3 |
| Llangwm, Pemb | 32 | D3 |
| Llangwm-isaf, Monm | 35 | A3 |
| Llangwnnadl, Gwyn | 66 | B4 |
| Llangwyryfon, Cered | 45 | A1 |
| Llangybi, Cered | 45 | A3 |
| Llangybi, Gwyn | 66 | D3 |
| Llangybi, Monm | 35 | A4 |
| Llangynhafal, Denb | 67 | D1 |
| Llangynidr, Powys | 34 | D2 |
| Llangynin, Carm | 32 | F2 |
| Llangynog, Carm | 33 | A2 |
| Llangynog, Powys | 67 | C4 |
| Llangynwyd, Brid | 34 | A4 |
| Llanhamlach, Powys | 34 | C1 |
| Llanharan, Rhond | 22 | E1 |
| Llanharry, Rhond | 22 | F1 |
| Llanhennock, Monm | 35 | A4 |
| Llanhilleth, Gwent | 34 | D3 |
| Llanidloes, Powys | 55 | D4 |
| Llaniestyn, Gwyn | 66 | B4 |
| Llanigon, Powys | 46 | A4 |
| Llanilid, Rhond | 22 | E1 |
| Llanina, Cered | 44 | E2 |
| Llanishen, Monm | 35 | B3 |
| Llanllechid, Gwyn | 66 | E1 |
| Llanllowell, Monm | 35 | A4 |
| Llanllugan, Powys | 55 | E3 |
| Llanllwch, Carm | 33 | A2 |
| Llanllwni, Carm | 44 | F4 |
| Llanllyfni, Gwyn | 66 | D2 |
| Llanmadoc, Swan | 33 | B4 |
| Llanmaes, Glam | 22 | E2 |
| Llanmartin, Newport | 35 | A4 |
| Llanmiloe, Carm | 32 | F3 |
| Llannefydd, Ab & Col | 67 | B1 |
| Llannon, Carm | 33 | B3 |
| Llannor, Gwyn | 66 | C4 |
| Llanon, Cered | 44 | F2 |
| Llanover, Monm | 34 | E3 |
| Llanpumsaint, Carm | 33 | A1 |
| Llanrhaeadr-ym-Mochnant, Powys | 67 | D4 |
| Llanrhidian, Swan | 33 | B4 |
| Llanrhychwyn, Ab & Col | 67 | A1 |
| Llanrhyddlad, Angle | 76 | B3 |
| Llanrhystud, Cered | 44 | F1 |
| Llanrian, Pemb | 32 | B1 |
| Llanrothal, Heref | 35 | B2 |
| Llanrug, Gwyn | 66 | D1 |
| Llanrwst, Ab & Col | 67 | A1 |
| Llansadurnen, Carm | 32 | F3 |
| Llansadwrn, Carm | 33 | D1 |
| Llansadwrn, Angle | 76 | D4 |
| Llansaint, Carm | 33 | A3 |
| Llansanffraid Glan Conwy, Ab & Col | 76 | F4 |
| Llansannan, Ab & Col | 67 | B1 |
| Llansantffraed, Powys | 34 | D1 |
| Llansantffraed-Cwmdeuddwr, Powys | 45 | D2 |
| Llansantffraed-in-Elvel, Powys | 45 | E3 |
| Llansantffraid, Cered | 44 | F2 |
| Llansantffraid-ym-Mechain, Powys | 56 | A1 |
| Llansawel, Carm | 45 | A4 |
| Llansilin, Powys | 67 | D4 |
| Llansoy, Monm | 35 | A3 |
| Llanspyddid, Powys | 34 | C1 |
| Llanstadwell, Pemb | 32 | C3 |
| Llansteffan, Carm | 33 | A2 |
| Llanteg, Pemb | 32 | E3 |
| Llanthewy Skirrid, Monm | 34 | E2 |
| Llanthony, Monm | 34 | E1 |
| Llantilio Pertholey, Monm | 34 | E2 |
| Llantilio-Crossenny, Monm | 35 | A2 |
| Llantrisant, Monm | 35 | A4 |
| Llantrisant, Rhond | 22 | F1 |
| Llantrithyd, Glam | 22 | F2 |
| Llantwit Fardre, Rhond | 22 | F1 |
| Llantwit Major, Glam | 22 | E2 |
| Llanuwchllyn, Gwyn | 67 | A4 |
| Llanvaches, Newport | 35 | A4 |
| Llanvair Discoed, Monm | 35 | A4 |
| Llanvapley, Monm | 35 | A2 |
| Llanvetherine, Monm | 35 | A2 |
| Llanvihangel Crucorney, Monm | 34 | E2 |
| Llanwddyn, Powys | 55 | E1 |
| Llanwenog, Cered | 44 | F3 |
| Llanwern, Newport | 35 | A4 |
| Llanwinio, Carm | 32 | F1 |
| Llanwnda, Gwyn | 66 | D2 |
| Llanwnda, Pemb | 44 | A4 |
| Llanwnnen, Cered | 44 | F3 |
| Llanwnog, Powys | 55 | E3 |
| Llanwrda, Carm | 33 | D1 |
| Llanwrin, Powys | 55 | C2 |
| Llanwrthwl, Powys | 45 | D2 |
| Llanwrtyd Wells, Powys | 45 | C3 |
| Llanyblodwel, Shrop | 56 | B1 |
| Llanybri, Carm | 33 | A2 |
| Llanybydder, Carm | 44 | F4 |
| Llanycefn, Pemb | 32 | E1 |
| Llanychaer Bridge, Pemb | 44 | B4 |
| Llanymawddwy, Gwyn | 55 | D1 |
| Llanymynech, Powys | 56 | B1 |
| Llanynghenedl, Angle | 76 | B4 |
| Llanynis, Powys | 45 | D3 |

| PLACE | PAGE | GRID |
|---|---|---|
| Llanynys, Denb | 67 | C1 |
| Llanyre, Powys | 45 | E2 |
| Llanystumdwy, Gwyn | 66 | D3 |
| Llanywern, Powys | 34 | C1 |
| Llawhaden, Pemb | 32 | D2 |
| Llawryglyn, Powys | 55 | D4 |
| Llay, Wrex | 67 | E2 |
| Llechryd, Caer | 34 | C3 |
| Llechryd, Cered | 44 | D4 |
| Llechylched, Angle | 76 | B4 |
| Lledrod, Cered | 45 | A1 |
| Llithfaen, Gwyn | 66 | C3 |
| Lloc, Flint | 77 | C4 |
| Llowes, Powys | 46 | A4 |
| Llwydcoed, Rhond | 34 | B3 |
| Llwydiarth, Powys | 55 | E1 |
| Llwyncelyn, Cered | 44 | F2 |
| Llwyndafydd, Cered | 44 | E3 |
| Llwyngwril, Gwyn | 55 | A2 |
| Llwynmawr, Wrex | 67 | D4 |
| Llwynypia, Rhond | 34 | B4 |
| Llynclys, Shrop | 56 | B1 |
| Llynfaes, Angle | 76 | B4 |
| Llysfaen, Ab & Col | 77 | A4 |
| Llyswen, Powys | 46 | A4 |
| Llysworney, Glam | 22 | E2 |
| Llys-y-fran, Pemb | 32 | D1 |
| Llywel, Powys | 34 | A1 |
| Loan, Falkirk | 113 | B2 |
| Loanhead, M Loth | 114 | B3 |
| Loaningfoot, D & G | 96 | C1 |
| Loans, S Ayr | 106 | D2 |
| Lochailort, High | 121 | B1 |
| Lochaline, High | 121 | A4 |
| Lochans, D & G | 95 | A1 |
| Locharbriggs, D & G | 101 | D2 |
| Lochawe, Argyll | 117 | C2 |
| Lochboisdale, W Isles | 139 | A4 |
| Lochbuie, Argyll | 116 | D2 |
| Lochcarron, High | 131 | A4 |
| Lochdon, Argyll | 116 | E1 |
| Lochdonhead, Argyll | 116 | E1 |
| Lochearnhead, Stirl | 118 | B2 |
| Lochfoot, D & G | 101 | D3 |
| Lochgair, Argyll | 111 | A1 |
| Lochgelly, Fife | 114 | A1 |
| Lochgilphead, Argyll | 111 | A1 |
| Lochgoilhead, Argyll | 117 | D4 |
| Lochinver, High | 135 | D1 |
| Lochmaben, D & G | 101 | E2 |
| Lochmaddy, W Isles | 139 | A3 |
| Lochore, Fife | 119 | B4 |
| Lochranza, N Ayr | 111 | A4 |
| Lochwinnoch, Renf | 111 | E4 |
| Lockengate, Corn | 3 | D3 |
| Lockerbie, D & G | 102 | A2 |
| Lockeridge, Wilts | 25 | C2 |
| Locking, Som | 23 | C3 |
| Lockington, E R of Y | 89 | D2 |
| Locksbottom, G Lon | 144 | B4 |
| Lockton, N York | 94 | B2 |
| Loddington, Leics | 61 | A3 |
| Loddington, Nhants | 50 | B1 |
| Loddiswell, Devon | 8 | A1 |
| Loddon, Norf | 65 | B3 |
| Lode, Camb | 52 | B2 |
| Loders, Dors | 6 | E1 |
| Lofthouse, W York | 88 | A4 |
| Lofthouse Gate, W York | 88 | A4 |
| Loftus, N York | 99 | C4 |
| Logan, E Ayr | 106 | F3 |
| Loggerheads, Staff | 69 | A4 |
| Logie, Fife | 119 | D2 |
| Logie Coldstone, Aber | 128 | C3 |
| Logie Pert, Angus | 124 | B3 |
| Logierait, Perth | 123 | A4 |
| Logierieve, Aber | 129 | B1 |
| Login, Carm | 32 | E1 |
| Lolworth, Camb | 52 | A2 |
| Londesborough, E R of Y | 89 | C2 |
| London, G Lon | 143 | A2 |
| London Apprentice, Corn | 3 | D4 |
| London Colney, Herts | 39 | C3 |
| Londonthorpe, Linc | 72 | C3 |
| Long Ashton, Som | 23 | D2 |
| Long Bank, Worc | 47 | B1 |
| Long Bredy, Dors | 6 | E1 |
| Long Buckby, Nhants | 50 | A2 |
| Long Clawson, Leics | 72 | A4 |
| Long Compton, Staff | 57 | C1 |
| Long Compton, Warw | 37 | C1 |
| Long Crendon, Bucks | 38 | B3 |
| Long Crichel, Dors | 13 | A3 |
| Long Ditton, Surr | 142 | A4 |
| Long Duckmanton, Derby | 71 | A1 |
| Long Eaton, Derby | 71 | A4 |
| Long Green, Chesh | 68 | B1 |
| Long Green, Worc | 36 | B1 |
| Long Hanborough, Oxon | 37 | D2 |
| Long Itchington, Warw | 49 | B2 |
| Long Marston, Herts | 39 | A2 |
| Long Marston, N York | 88 | B2 |
| Long Marston, Warw | 48 | B3 |
| Long Marton, Cumb | 97 | C3 |
| Long Melford, Suff | 53 | B3 |
| Long Newnton, Glouc | 36 | B4 |
| Long Newton, E Loth | 115 | A3 |
| Long Preston, N York | 86 | C1 |
| Long Riston, E R of Y | 90 | A2 |
| Long Stratton, Norf | 64 | B3 |
| Long Street, Bucks | 50 | B3 |
| Long Sutton, Hamp | 27 | B4 |
| Long Sutton, Linc | 62 | C1 |
| Long Sutton, Som | 12 | A2 |
| Long Thurlow, Suff | 53 | D2 |
| Long Waste, Shrop | 57 | A1 |
| Long Whatton, Leics | 60 | A1 |
| Longbenton, T & W | 104 | B3 |
| Longborough, Glouc | 37 | B1 |
| Longbridge Deverill, Wilts | 12 | D1 |
| Longburton, Dors | 12 | B3 |
| Longcliffe, Derby | 70 | B2 |
| Longcombe, Devon | 5 | B4 |
| Longcot, Oxon | 37 | C4 |
| Longcross, Surr | 140 | C4 |
| Longden, Shrop | 56 | C2 |

| PLACE | PAGE | GRID |
|---|---|---|
| Longdon, Staff | 58 | B2 |
| Longdon, Worc | 47 | C4 |
| Longdon Green, Staff | 58 | B2 |
| Longdown, Devon | 5 | B1 |
| Longdowns, Corn | 2 | A2 |
| Longfield, Kent | 29 | A2 |
| Longford, Kent | 149 | C2 |
| Longford, Derby | 70 | B3 |
| Longford, Glouc | 36 | B2 |
| Longford, Shrop | 68 | C4 |
| Longford, Shrop | 57 | B1 |
| Longford, G Lon | 141 | A2 |
| Longforgan, Perth | 119 | C2 |
| Longformacus, Bord | 115 | B4 |
| Longframlington, Nthumb | 104 | A1 |
| Longham, Dors | 13 | B4 |
| Longham, Norf | 63 | C1 |
| Longhirst, Nthumb | 104 | B2 |
| Longhope, Glouc | 35 | C2 |
| Longhope, Ork | 139 | A2 |
| Longhorsley, Nthumb | 104 | A1 |
| Longhoughton, Nthumb | 109 | E3 |
| Longley, W York | 87 | A4 |
| Longleys, Perth | 123 | D4 |
| Longmorn, Moray | 133 | C2 |
| Longnewton, Durham | 98 | D4 |
| Longney, Glouc | 36 | A2 |
| Longniddry, E Loth | 114 | C2 |
| Longnor, Shrop | 56 | D3 |
| Longparish, Hamp | 26 | B4 |
| Longridge, Lanc | 86 | A3 |
| Longridge, W Loth | 113 | B3 |
| Longriggend, N Lan | 113 | A3 |
| Longrock, Corn | 1 | B2 |
| Longsdon, Staff | 69 | C2 |
| Longside, Aber | 134 | D3 |
| Longstanton, Camb | 52 | A2 |
| Longstock, Hamp | 14 | B1 |
| Longstowe, Camb | 51 | C3 |
| Longthwaite, Cumb | 97 | A3 |
| Longton, Lanc | 85 | C4 |
| Longtown, Heref | 34 | E1 |
| Longtown, Cumb | 102 | C3 |
| Longueville, Jers | 139 | B2 |
| Longwick, Bucks | 38 | C3 |
| Longwitton, Nthumb | 104 | A2 |
| Longworth, Oxon | 37 | C3 |
| Longyester, E Loth | 115 | A3 |
| Looe, Corn | 4 | A4 |
| Loosley Row, Bucks | 38 | C3 |
| Lopen, Som | 11 | C3 |
| Loppington, Shrop | 68 | B4 |
| Lornty, Perth | 123 | C4 |
| Loscoe, Derby | 71 | A3 |
| Lossiemouth, Moray | 133 | C1 |
| Lostock Gralam, Chesh | 79 | A4 |
| Lostock Green, Chesh | 79 | A4 |
| Lostwithiel, Corn | 3 | E4 |
| Lothersdale, N York | 86 | D2 |
| Loughborough, Leics | 60 | B1 |
| Loughton, Shrop | 57 | A4 |
| Lound, Linc | 61 | C1 |
| Lound, Notts | 83 | A3 |
| Lound, Suff | 65 | C3 |
| Lount, Leics | 59 | B1 |
| Louth, Linc | 84 | C3 |
| Love Clough, Lanc | 86 | B4 |
| Lover, Wilts | 14 | A2 |
| Loversall, S York | 82 | B2 |
| Loves Green, Essex | 41 | B3 |
| Loveston, Pemb | 32 | E3 |
| Lovington, Som | 12 | B1 |
| Low Ackworth, W York | 82 | A1 |
| Low Bentham, N York | 92 | A4 |
| Low Borrowbridge, Cumb | 92 | A1 |
| Low Bradfield, S York | 81 | B3 |
| Low Bradley, N York | 86 | D2 |
| Low Burnham, Linc | 83 | B2 |
| Low Crosby, Cumb | 102 | C4 |
| Low Dinsdale, Durham | 98 | D4 |
| Low Eggborough, N York | 88 | C4 |
| Low Ellington, N York | 93 | A3 |
| Low Ham, Som | 11 | C1 |
| Low Hesket, Cumb | 97 | A1 |
| Low Hill, Worc | 47 | C1 |
| Low Hutton, N York | 94 | B4 |
| Low Marnham, Notts | 72 | B1 |
| Low Mill, N York | 94 | A2 |
| Low Moorsley, T & W | 98 | D1 |
| Low Mowthorpe, N York | 94 | C4 |
| Low Newton, Cumb | 91 | E3 |
| Low Row, Cumb | 103 | A4 |
| Low Row, N York | 92 | D2 |
| Low Santon, Linc | 83 | C1 |
| Low Tharston, Norf | 64 | B3 |
| Low Worsall, N York | 93 | C1 |
| Low Wray, Cumb | 91 | E1 |
| Lowdham, Notts | 72 | A3 |
| Lower Aisholt, Som | 11 | A1 |
| Lower Ansty, Dors | 12 | C4 |
| Lower Apperley, Glouc | 36 | B1 |
| Lower Assendon, Oxon | 27 | B1 |
| Lower Beeding, W Suss | 18 | B2 |
| Lower Benefield, Nhants | 61 | C4 |
| Lower Bentley, Worc | 48 | A2 |
| Lower Boddington, Nhants | 49 | B3 |
| Lower Brailes, Warw | 49 | A4 |
| Lower Broadheath, Worc | 47 | C2 |
| Lower Caldecote, Beds | 51 | B3 |
| Lower Chapel, Powys | 45 | E4 |
| Lower Chicksgrove, Wilts | 13 | A1 |
| Lower Chute, Wilts | 26 | A3 |
| Lower Clapton, G Lon | 143 | B1 |
| Lower Cumberworth, W York | 81 | B1 |
| Lower Dean, Beds | 51 | A1 |
| Lower Diabaig, High | 130 | F2 |
| Lower Down, Shrop | 56 | B4 |
| Lower Dunsforth, N York | 93 | C4 |
| Lower End, Bucks | 50 | C4 |
| Lower Eythorne, Kent | 31 | B4 |
| Lower Failand, Som | 23 | D2 |
| Lower Feltham, G Lon | 141 | B3 |
| Lower Froyle, Hamp | 27 | B4 |
| Lower Gabwell, Devon | 5 | C3 |
| Lower Gravenhurst, Beds | 51 | B4 |

| PLACE | PAGE | GRID |
|---|---|---|
| Lower Hergest, Heref | 46 | B3 |
| Lower Kingswood, Surr | 148 | A2 |
| Lower Langford, Som | 23 | C3 |
| Lower Largo, Fife | 119 | D4 |
| Lower Lydbrook, Glouc | 35 | C2 |
| Lower Lye, Heref | 46 | C2 |
| Lower Machen, Newport | 34 | D4 |
| Lower Merridge, Som | 11 | A1 |
| Lower Moor, Worc | 48 | A3 |
| Lower Morton, Glouc | 35 | C4 |
| Lower Nazeing, Essex | 40 | B3 |
| Lower Penn, Staff | 57 | C3 |
| Lower Peover, Chesh | 79 | B4 |
| Lower Pond Street, Essex | 52 | B4 |
| Lower Quinton, Warw | 48 | C3 |
| Lower Roadwater, Som | 10 | D1 |
| Lower Seagry, Wilts | 25 | B1 |
| Lower Shelton, Beds | 51 | A4 |
| Lower Shiplake, Oxon | 27 | B1 |
| Lower Shuckburgh, Warw | 49 | B2 |
| Lower Slaughter, Glouc | 37 | B1 |
| Lower Stanton St Quintin, Wilts | 25 | A1 |
| Lower Stoke, Kent | 30 | A1 |
| Lower Stone, Glouc | 35 | C4 |
| Lower Stow Bedon, Norf | 63 | C3 |
| Lower Street, Dors | 12 | D4 |
| Lower Street, Norf | 75 | C4 |
| Lower Street, Suff | 53 | D3 |
| Lower Sundon, Beds | 39 | B1 |
| Lower Swanwick, Hamp | 15 | A3 |
| Lower Swell, Glouc | 37 | B1 |
| Lower Town, Devon | 5 | A2 |
| Lower Tysoe, Warw | 49 | A3 |
| Lower Upcott, Devon | 5 | B2 |
| Lower Upham, Hamp | 15 | B2 |
| Lower Vexford, Som | 10 | D1 |
| Lower Weare, Som | 23 | C3 |
| Lower Westmancote, Worc | 48 | A4 |
| Lower Whitley, Chesh | 79 | A4 |
| Lower Wield, Hamp | 16 | A1 |
| Lower Withington, Chesh | 69 | B1 |
| Lower Woodford, Wilts | 13 | B1 |
| Lowesby, Leics | 60 | C2 |
| Lowestoft, Suff | 65 | C3 |
| Loweswater, Cumb | 96 | E4 |
| Lowick, Nhants | 61 | C4 |
| Lowick, Nthumb | 109 | C1 |
| Lowick Green, Cumb | 91 | D3 |
| Lowsonford, Warw | 48 | C2 |
| Lowther, Cumb | 97 | B3 |
| Lowthorpe, E R of Y | 89 | D1 |
| Lowton, Som | 11 | A2 |
| Loxbeare, Devon | 10 | C3 |
| Loxhill, Surr | 17 | B1 |
| Loxhore, Devon | 9 | E1 |
| Loxhore Cott, Devon | 9 | E1 |
| Loxley, Warw | 48 | C3 |
| Loxton, Som | 23 | C3 |
| Loxwood, W Suss | 17 | B1 |
| Luccombe, Som | 22 | E4 |
| Luccombe Village, I of W | 8 | B2 |
| Lucker, Nthumb | 109 | D2 |
| Luckett, Corn | 4 | B2 |
| Luckington, Wilts | 25 | A1 |
| Luckwell Bridge, Som | 10 | C1 |
| Lucton, Heref | 46 | C2 |
| Ludborough, Linc | 84 | B2 |
| Ludbrook, Devon | 5 | A4 |
| Ludchurch, Pemb | 32 | E2 |
| Luddenden, W York | 86 | D4 |
| Luddenden Foot, W York | 86 | D4 |
| Luddesdown, Kent | 29 | B2 |
| Luddington, Linc | 83 | B1 |
| Luddington, Warw | 48 | C3 |
| Ludford, Linc | 84 | B3 |
| Ludford, Shrop | 46 | D1 |
| Ludgershall, Bucks | 38 | B2 |
| Ludgershall, Wilts | 25 | D4 |
| Ludgvan, Corn | 1 | C2 |
| Ludham, Norf | 65 | B1 |
| Ludlow, Shrop | 46 | D1 |
| Ludney, Som | 11 | C3 |
| Ludwell, Wilts | 12 | D2 |
| Ludworth, Durham | 98 | D2 |
| Luffincott, Devon | 4 | B1 |
| Lugar, E Ayr | 106 | F3 |
| Lugton, E Ayr | 111 | E4 |
| Lugwardine, Heref | 46 | D4 |
| Lulham, Heref | 46 | C4 |
| Lullington, Derby | 59 | A2 |
| Lullington, Som | 24 | B4 |
| Lulsgate Bottom, Som | 23 | D2 |
| Lulsley, Worc | 47 | B3 |
| Lumb, Lanc | 86 | C4 |
| Lumb, W York | 86 | D4 |
| Lumby, N York | 88 | B3 |
| Lumphanan, Aber | 128 | E3 |
| Lumphinnans, Fife | 114 | A1 |
| Lumsden, Aber | 128 | D2 |
| Lunan, Angus | 124 | B4 |
| Lunanhead, Angus | 124 | A4 |
| Luncarty, Perth | 119 | A2 |
| Lund, E R of Y | 89 | D2 |
| Lund, N York | 89 | A3 |
| Lundie, Angus | 119 | C1 |
| Lunsford's Cross, E Sus | 20 | B3 |
| Lunt, Mers | 77 | D2 |
| Luppitt, Devon | 11 | A3 |
| Lupridge, Devon | 5 | A4 |
| Lupton, Cumb | 91 | F3 |
| Lurgashall, W Suss | 17 | A2 |
| Lurley, Devon | 10 | C3 |
| Luscombe, Devon | 5 | B4 |
| Luss, Argyll | 111 | E1 |
| Lusta, High | 130 | A3 |
| Lustleigh, Devon | 5 | B2 |
| Luston, Heref | 46 | D2 |
| Luthermuir, Aber | 124 | B2 |
| Luthrie, Fife | 119 | C2 |
| Luton, Devon | 10 | D4 |
| Luton, Devon | 5 | C2 |
| Luton, Beds | 39 | C2 |
| Lutterworth, Leics | 60 | B4 |
| Lutton, Devon | 4 | D4 |
| Lutton, Devon | 5 | A3 |

| PLACE | PAGE | GRID |
|---|---|---|
| Lutton, Linc | 62 | C1 |
| Lutton, Nhants | 61 | D4 |
| Luxborough, Som | 10 | C1 |
| Luxulyan, Corn | 3 | D4 |
| Lybster, High | 138 | E4 |
| Lydbury North, Shrop | 56 | C4 |
| Lydd, Kent | 21 | C2 |
| Lydden, Kent | 31 | B4 |
| Lydden, Kent | 31 | B2 |
| Lyddington, Rut | 61 | B3 |
| Lyde Green, Hamp | 27 | A3 |
| Lydeard St Lawrence, Som | 11 | A1 |
| Lydford, Devon | 4 | C1 |
| Lydford on Fosse, Som | 12 | A1 |
| Lydgate, W York | 86 | C4 |
| Lydham, Shrop | 56 | B4 |
| Lydiard Millicent, Wilts | 25 | C1 |
| Lydiate Ash, Worc | 48 | A1 |
| Lydney, Glouc | 35 | C3 |
| Lydstep, Pemb | 32 | E4 |
| Lye Green, Warw | 48 | C2 |
| Lye's Green, Wilts | 25 | A4 |
| Lyford, Oxon | 37 | D4 |
| Lyme Regis, Dors | 6 | C1 |
| Lyminge, Kent | 21 | D1 |
| Lymm, Chesh | 79 | A3 |
| Lympne, Kent | 21 | C1 |
| Lympsham, Som | 23 | B3 |
| Lympstone, Devon | 5 | C1 |
| Lynch Green, Norf | 64 | B2 |
| Lyndhurst, Hamp | 14 | B3 |
| Lyndon, Rut | 61 | B2 |
| Lyne, Surr | 140 | C4 |
| Lyne of Skene, Aber | 129 | A3 |
| Lyneal, Shrop | 68 | A4 |
| Lyneham, Oxon | 37 | C2 |
| Lyneham, Wilts | 25 | B1 |
| Lyness, Ork | 139 | A2 |
| Lyng, Norf | 64 | A1 |
| Lyng, Som | 11 | B2 |
| Lynsted, Kent | 30 | B3 |
| Lynton, Devon | 22 | C4 |
| Lyon's Gate, Dors | 12 | B4 |
| Lyonshall, Heref | 46 | B3 |
| Lytchett Matravers, Dors | 13 | A4 |
| Lytchett Minster, Dors | 7 | C1 |
| Lytham St Anne's, Lanc | 85 | A4 |
| Lythe, N York | 99 | D4 |
| Mablethorpe, Linc | 84 | D3 |
| Macclesfield, Chesh | 80 | A4 |
| Macduff, Aber | 134 | B2 |
| Machen, Caer | 34 | D4 |
| Machrihanish, Argyll | 105 | D3 |
| Machynlleth, Powys | 55 | B3 |
| Mackworth, Derby | 70 | C4 |
| Macmerry, E Loth | 114 | C3 |
| Maddiston, Falkirk | 113 | B2 |
| Madeley, Staff | 69 | A3 |
| Madingley, Camb | 52 | A2 |
| Madley, Heref | 46 | C4 |
| Madresfield, Worc | 47 | B3 |
| Madron, Corn | 1 | B2 |
| Maenclochog, Pemb | 32 | E1 |
| Maendy, Glam | 22 | F1 |
| Maentwrog, Gwyn | 66 | F3 |
| Maen-y-groes, Cered | 44 | E2 |
| Maer, Staff | 69 | A3 |
| Maerdy, Rhond | 34 | B4 |
| Maesbrook, Shrop | 56 | B1 |
| Maesbury Marsh, Shrop | 56 | B1 |
| Maesllyn, Cered | 44 | E4 |
| Maesmynis, Powys | 45 | E3 |
| Maesteg, Brid | 34 | A4 |
| Maesybont, Carm | 33 | C2 |
| Maesycwmmer, Caer | 34 | D4 |
| Maggieknockater, Moray | 133 | C3 |
| Maggots End, Essex | 41 | A1 |
| Maghull, Mers | 78 | A2 |
| Maiden Bradley, Wilts | 12 | C1 |
| Maiden Head, Som | 23 | D2 |
| Maiden Newton, Dors | 12 | B4 |
| Maiden Wells, Pemb | 32 | D3 |
| Maidencombe, Devon | 5 | C3 |
| Maidenhayne, Devon | 11 | B4 |
| Maidenhead, Berks | 140 | A2 |
| Maidens, S Ayr | 106 | C4 |
| Maidenwell, Linc | 84 | C4 |
| Maidford, Nhants | 49 | C3 |
| Maidstone, Kent | 29 | B3 |
| Maidwell, Nhants | 50 | B1 |
| Mainsforth, Durham | 98 | D3 |
| Mainsriddle, D & G | 96 | C1 |
| Mainstone, Shrop | 56 | B4 |
| Maisemore, Glouc | 36 | B2 |
| Makeney, Derby | 70 | C3 |
| Malborough, Devon | 8 | A1 |
| Malden, G Lon | 142 | B4 |
| Malden Rushett, G Lon | 147 | B1 |
| Maldon, Essex | 42 | B3 |
| Malham, N York | 86 | C1 |
| Mallaig, High | 125 | E4 |
| Malltraeth, Angle | 66 | C1 |
| Mallwyd, Gwyn | 55 | C2 |
| Malmesbury, Wilts | 25 | B1 |
| Malmsmead, Devon | 22 | D4 |
| Malpas, Chesh | 68 | B3 |
| Malpas, Corn | 2 | A1 |
| Maltby, N York | 99 | A4 |
| Maltby, S York | 82 | B3 |
| Maltby le Marsh, Linc | 84 | D4 |
| Malting Green, Essex | 43 | A2 |
| Maltman's Hill, Kent | 30 | B4 |
| Malton, N York | 94 | B4 |
| Malvern Wells, Worc | 47 | B4 |
| Mamble, Worc | 47 | A1 |
| Mamhilad, Monm | 34 | E3 |
| Manaccan, Corn | 2 | A3 |
| Manafon, Powys | 55 | E3 |
| Manaton, Devon | 5 | A2 |
| Manby, Linc | 84 | C3 |
| Mancetter, Warw | 59 | B3 |
| Manchester, G Man | 80 | A2 |
| Mancot, Flint | 67 | E1 |
| Manea, Camb | 62 | C4 |
| Manfield, N York | 98 | C4 |
| Manley, Chesh | 68 | B1 |

| PLACE | PAGE | GRID |
|---|---|---|
| Manmoel, Caer | 34 | D3 |
| Manningford Bruce, Wilts | 25 | C3 |
| Manningtree, Essex | 43 | B1 |
| Manor Park, G Lon | 144 | A1 |
| Manorbier, Pemb | 32 | D4 |
| Manorbier Newton, Pemb | 32 | D3 |
| Manorowen, Pemb | 44 | A4 |
| Mansell Gamage, Heref | 46 | C4 |
| Mansell Lacy, Heref | 46 | C3 |
| Mansfield, Notts | 71 | B1 |
| Manston, Dors | 12 | D3 |
| Manswood, Dors | 13 | A3 |
| Manthorpe, Linc | 61 | C1 |
| Manton, Linc | 83 | C2 |
| Manton, Rut | 61 | B2 |
| Manuden, Essex | 41 | A1 |
| Maperton, Som | 12 | B2 |
| Maplebeck, Notts | 72 | A1 |
| Mapledurham, Oxon | 27 | A1 |
| Mapledurwell, Hamp | 27 | A4 |
| Maplehurst, W Suss | 18 | A2 |
| Maplescombe, Kent | 29 | A3 |
| Mapleton, Derby | 70 | B3 |
| Mapperley, Derby | 71 | A3 |
| Mapperton, Dors | 12 | A4 |
| Mappleton, E R of Y | 90 | B2 |
| Mapplewell, S York | 81 | C1 |
| Mappowder, Dors | 12 | C4 |
| Marazanvose, Corn | 3 | B4 |
| Marazion, Corn | 1 | C2 |
| Marbury, Chesh | 68 | B3 |
| March, Camb | 62 | B3 |
| Marcham, Oxon | 37 | D4 |
| Marchamley, Shrop | 68 | C4 |
| Marchington, Staff | 70 | A4 |
| Marchwiel, Wrex | 68 | A3 |
| Marchwood, Hamp | 14 | B3 |
| Marcross, Glam | 22 | E2 |
| Marden, Heref | 46 | D3 |
| Marden, Kent | 29 | B4 |
| Marden, Wilts | 25 | C3 |
| Marden Thorn, Kent | 29 | B4 |
| Mareham le Fen, Linc | 73 | C1 |
| Mareham on the Hill, Linc | 73 | C1 |
| Marehill, W Suss | 17 | B2 |
| Maresfield, E Sus | 19 | B2 |
| Marford, Wrex | 68 | A2 |
| Margaret Marsh, Dors | 12 | D2 |
| Margaretting, Essex | 42 | A3 |
| Margaretting Tye, Essex | 42 | A3 |
| Margate, Kent | 31 | C2 |
| Margnaheglish, N Ayr | 106 | A2 |
| Margrove Park, N York | 99 | C4 |
| Marham, Norf | 63 | A2 |
| Marhamchurch, Corn | 9 | B4 |
| Marholm, Camb | 61 | D3 |
| Mariansleigh, Devon | 10 | A2 |
| Maristow, Devon | 4 | C3 |
| Mark, D & G | 100 | B4 |
| Mark, Som | 23 | C4 |
| Mark Cross, E Sus | 19 | B3 |
| Mark Cross, E Sus | 20 | A1 |
| Markbeech, Kent | 149 | B4 |
| Markby, Linc | 84 | D4 |
| Market Bosworth, Leics | 60 | A2 |
| Market Deeping, Linc | 61 | D2 |
| Market Drayton, Shrop | 68 | C4 |
| Market Harborough, Leics | 60 | C4 |
| Market Lavington, Wilts | 25 | B3 |
| Market Overton, Rut | 61 | B1 |
| Market Rasen, Linc | 84 | A3 |
| Market Stainton, Linc | 84 | B4 |
| Market Weighton, E R of Y | 89 | C2 |
| Market Weston, Suff | 53 | C1 |
| Markfield, Leics | 60 | A2 |
| Markham, Caer | 34 | D3 |
| Markham Moor, Notts | 83 | A4 |
| Markington, N York | 93 | B4 |
| Marks Tey, Essex | 43 | A1 |
| Marksbury, Som | 24 | A3 |
| Markyate, Herts | 39 | B2 |
| Marlborough, Wilts | 25 | D2 |
| Marlcliff, Warw | 48 | B3 |
| Marldon, Devon | 5 | B3 |
| Marlesford, Suff | 54 | B2 |
| Marlingford, Norf | 64 | B2 |
| Marloes, Pemb | 32 | B3 |
| Marlow, Bucks | 27 | B1 |
| Marlpit Hill, Kent | 149 | B3 |
| Marnhull, Dors | 12 | C2 |
| Marple, G Man | 80 | B3 |
| Marr, S York | 82 | B2 |
| Marrick, N York | 92 | E2 |
| Marsden, W York | 81 | A1 |
| Marsh Baldon, Oxon | 38 | A3 |
| Marsh Chapel, Linc | 84 | C2 |
| Marsh Gibbon, Bucks | 38 | B1 |
| Marsh Green, Kent | 149 | B4 |
| Marsh Lane, Derby | 82 | A4 |
| Marsh Street, Som | 22 | E4 |
| Marsham, Norf | 64 | B1 |
| Marshbrook, Shrop | 56 | C4 |
| Marshfield, Glouc | 24 | B2 |
| Marshfield, Newport | 23 | B1 |
| Marshland St James, Norf | 62 | C2 |
| Marshwood, Dors | 11 | C4 |
| Marske, N York | 92 | E1 |
| Marske-by-the-Sea, N York | 99 | C4 |
| Marston, Heref | 46 | C2 |
| Marston, Linc | 72 | C3 |
| Marston, Staff | 69 | B4 |
| Marston, Wilts | 25 | B3 |
| Marston Magna, Som | 12 | B2 |
| Marston Meysey, Wilts | 37 | A4 |
| Marston Moretaine, Beds | 51 | A4 |
| Marston on Dove, Derby | 70 | B4 |
| Marston St Lawrence, Nhants | 49 | C4 |
| Marston Stannett, Heref | 46 | D3 |
| Marston Trussell, Nhants | 60 | C4 |
| Marstow, Heref | 35 | B2 |
| Marten, Wilts | 26 | A3 |
| Marthall, Chesh | 79 | B4 |
| Martham, Norf | 65 | B1 |
| Martin, Hamp | 13 | B2 |
| Martin, Kent | 31 | B4 |

| PLACE | PAGE | GRID |
|---|---|---|
| Martin, Linc | 73 | B2 |
| Martin, Linc | 73 | C1 |
| Martinhoe, Devon | 22 | C4 |
| Martinstown, Dors | 6 | F1 |
| Martlesham, Suff | 54 | B3 |
| Martletwy, Pemb | 32 | D2 |
| Martley, Worc | 47 | B2 |
| Martock, Som | 11 | C2 |
| Marton, Chesh | 69 | B1 |
| Marton, E R of Y | 90 | A3 |
| Marton, Linc | 83 | B4 |
| Marton, N York | 99 | B4 |
| Marton, N York | 88 | B1 |
| Marton, N York | 94 | A3 |
| Marton, Shrop | 56 | B3 |
| Marton, Warw | 49 | B1 |
| Marwood, Devon | 9 | E1 |
| Mary Tavy, Devon | 4 | C2 |
| Maryburgh, High | 132 | A3 |
| Maryculter, Aber | 129 | B4 |
| Marykirk, Aber | 124 | B2 |
| Marylebone, G Lon | 143 | A1 |
| Maryport, D & G | 95 | B2 |
| Maryport, Cumb | 96 | D2 |
| Marystow, Devon | 4 | C2 |
| Marywell, Aber | 128 | E4 |
| Marywell, Angus | 124 | B4 |
| Masham, N York | 93 | A3 |
| Mastin Moor, Derby | 82 | A4 |
| Matching Tye, Essex | 41 | A2 |
| Matfen, Nthumb | 103 | D3 |
| Mathern, Monm | 35 | B4 |
| Mathon, Heref | 47 | B3 |
| Mathry, Pemb | 32 | C1 |
| Matlask, Norf | 75 | B4 |
| Matlock, Derby | 70 | C2 |
| Mattersey, Notts | 83 | A3 |
| Mattishall, Norf | 64 | A2 |
| Mattishall Burgh, Norf | 64 | A2 |
| Mauchline, E Ayr | 106 | E2 |
| Maud, Aber | 134 | C3 |
| Maufant, Jers | 139 | B2 |
| Maugersbury, Glouc | 37 | B1 |
| Maughold, I o M | 139 | D2 |
| Maulden, Beds | 51 | A4 |
| Maulds Meaburn, Cumb | 97 | C4 |
| Maunby, N York | 93 | B3 |
| Maundown, Som | 10 | D2 |
| Mautby, Norf | 65 | C2 |
| Mavesyn Ridware, Staff | 58 | B1 |
| Mavis Enderby, Linc | 73 | D1 |
| Mawbray, Cumb | 96 | D1 |
| Mawdesley, Lanc | 78 | B1 |
| Mawdlam, Brid | 22 | D1 |
| Mawgan, Corn | 1 | D3 |
| Mawgan Porth, Corn | 3 | C3 |
| Mawla, Corn | 1 | D1 |
| Mawnan, Corn | 2 | A2 |
| Mawnan Smith, Corn | 2 | A2 |
| Maxey, Camb | 61 | D2 |
| Maxstoke, Warw | 59 | A4 |
| Maxworthy, Corn | 4 | A1 |
| Maybole, S Ayr | 106 | C4 |
| Maybury, Surr | 146 | A1 |
| Mayfield, E Sus | 20 | A2 |
| Mayfield, M Loth | 114 | C3 |
| Mayfield, Staff | 70 | A3 |
| Mayford, Surr | 146 | A2 |
| Maypole Green, Norf | 65 | B3 |
| Maypole Green, Suff | 53 | C2 |
| May's Green, Surr | 147 | A2 |
| Meadgate, Som | 24 | A3 |
| Meadle, Bucks | 38 | C3 |
| Meadwell, Devon | 4 | B2 |
| Mealrigg, Cumb | 96 | E1 |
| Meare, Som | 23 | C4 |
| Mearns, E Renf | 112 | B4 |
| Mears Ashby, Nhants | 50 | B2 |
| Measham, Leics | 59 | B2 |
| Meathop, Cumb | 91 | E3 |
| Meavy, Devon | 4 | C3 |
| Medbourne, Leics | 61 | A3 |
| Meden Vale, Notts | 71 | B1 |
| Medmenham, Bucks | 27 | B1 |
| Medomsley, Durham | 98 | B1 |
| Meerbrook, Staff | 69 | C2 |
| Meesden, Herts | 41 | A1 |
| Meeth, Devon | 9 | E3 |
| Meeting House Hill, Norf | 75 | C4 |
| Meidrim, Carm | 32 | F2 |
| Meifod, Powys | 56 | A2 |
| Meigle, Perth | 123 | D4 |
| Meikleour, Perth | 119 | B1 |
| Meinciau, Carm | 33 | B2 |
| Melbourn, Camb | 52 | A4 |
| Melbourne, Derby | 59 | B1 |
| Melbourne, E R of Y | 89 | D2 |
| Melbury Abbas, Dors | 12 | D2 |
| Melbury Bubb, Dors | 12 | B4 |
| Melbury Osmond, Dors | 12 | A3 |
| Melchbourne, Beds | 51 | A2 |
| Melcombe Bingham, Dors | 12 | C4 |
| Meldon, Devon | 4 | D1 |
| Meldon, Nthumb | 104 | A2 |
| Meldreth, Camb | 52 | A3 |
| Melin-y-wig, Denb | 67 | C3 |
| Melkinthorpe, Cumb | 97 | B3 |
| Melkridge, Nthumb | 103 | B4 |
| Melksham, Wilts | 25 | A3 |
| Melling, Lanc | 92 | A4 |
| Melling, Mers | 78 | A2 |
| Mellis, Suff | 53 | D1 |
| Mellor, G Man | 80 | B3 |
| Mellor, Lanc | 86 | A3 |
| Mellor Brook, Lanc | 86 | A3 |
| Mells, Som | 24 | B4 |
| Melmerby, Cumb | 97 | C2 |
| Melmerby, N York | 92 | E3 |
| Melmerby, N York | 93 | B3 |
| Melness, High | 137 | E1 |
| Melplash, Dors | 12 | A4 |
| Melrose, Bord | 108 | C2 |
| Melsetter, Ork | 139 | A2 |
| Melsonby, N York | 93 | A1 |
| Meltham, W York | 81 | A1 |
| Melton, E R of Y | 89 | D4 |

| PLACE | PAGE | GRID |
|---|---|---|
| Melton, Suff | 54 | B3 |
| Melton Constable, Norf | 75 | A4 |
| Melton Mowbray, Leics | 61 | A1 |
| Melton Ross, Linc | 83 | D1 |
| Melvaig, High | 135 | A4 |
| Melverley, Shrop | 56 | B1 |
| Melvich, High | 138 | A1 |
| Membury, Devon | 11 | B4 |
| Memsie, Aber | 134 | D2 |
| Memus, Angus | 123 | E3 |
| Menai Bridge, Angle | 66 | E1 |
| Mendham, Suff | 65 | A4 |
| Mendlesham, Suff | 53 | D2 |
| Mendlesham Green, Suff | 53 | D2 |
| Menheniot, Corn | 4 | A3 |
| Mennock, D & G | 107 | B4 |
| Menston, W York | 87 | B4 |
| Menstrie, Clack | 118 | D4 |
| Mentmore, Bucks | 39 | A2 |
| Meonstoke, Hamp | 15 | B2 |
| Meopham, Kent | 29 | A2 |
| Mepal, Camb | 62 | C4 |
| Meppershall, Beds | 51 | B4 |
| Mere, Chesh | 79 | B4 |
| Mere, Wilts | 12 | D1 |
| Mere Brow, Lanc | 85 | B4 |
| Mereclough, Lanc | 86 | C3 |
| Mereworth, Kent | 29 | A3 |
| Meriden, W Mids | 59 | A4 |
| Merrion, Pemb | 32 | C4 |
| Merriott, Som | 11 | C3 |
| Merrow, Surr | 146 | B3 |
| Merrymeet, Corn | 4 | A3 |
| Merstham, Surr | 148 | B2 |
| Merther, Corn | 2 | B1 |
| Merthyr Cynog, Powys | 45 | D4 |
| Merthyr Mawr, Brid | 22 | D1 |
| Merthyr Tydfil, Merth | 34 | C3 |
| Merthyr Vale, Merth | 34 | C3 |
| Merton, Devon | 9 | D3 |
| Merton, Norf | 63 | C3 |
| Merton, G Lon | 143 | A3 |
| Meshaw, Devon | 10 | A2 |
| Messing, Essex | 43 | A2 |
| Messingham, Linc | 83 | C2 |
| Metfield, Suff | 65 | A4 |
| Metherell, Corn | 4 | B3 |
| Metheringham, Linc | 73 | A1 |
| Methil, Fife | 119 | D4 |
| Methley, W York | 88 | B4 |
| Methlick, Aber | 134 | C4 |
| Methven, Perth | 119 | A2 |
| Methwold, Norf | 63 | A3 |
| Mettingham, Suff | 65 | B4 |
| Metton, Norf | 75 | B4 |
| Mevagissey, Corn | 2 | C1 |
| Mexborough, S York | 82 | A2 |
| Mey, High | 138 | E1 |
| Meyllteyrn, Gwyn | 66 | B4 |
| Meysey Hampton, Glouc | 37 | A3 |
| Miavaig, W Isles | 139 | A2 |
| Michaelchurch, Heref | 35 | B1 |
| Michaelchurch Escley, Heref | 46 | B4 |
| Michaelstone-y-Fedw, Newport | 23 | B1 |
| Michaelston-le-Pit, Glam | 23 | A2 |
| Michaelstow, Corn | 3 | E2 |
| Micheldever, Hamp | 15 | B1 |
| Micheldever Station, Hamp | 26 | C4 |
| Mickfield, Suff | 54 | A2 |
| Mickle Trafford, Chesh | 68 | A1 |
| Micklebring, S York | 82 | B3 |
| Mickleby, N York | 99 | D4 |
| Micklefield, W York | 88 | B3 |
| Mickleham, Surr | 147 | B2 |
| Mickleton, Durham | 98 | A3 |
| Mickleton, Glouc | 48 | C4 |
| Mickletown, W York | 88 | B4 |
| Mickley, N York | 93 | A3 |
| Mickley Square, Nthumb | 104 | A4 |
| Mid Calder, W Loth | 113 | C3 |
| Mid Lavant, W Suss | 17 | A3 |
| Mid Yell, Shet | 139 | A2 |
| Midbea, Ork | 139 | A1 |
| Middle Aston, Oxon | 37 | D1 |
| Middle Barton, Oxon | 37 | D1 |
| Middle Claydon, Bucks | 38 | B1 |
| Middle Duntisbourne, Glouc | 36 | C3 |
| Middle Handley, Derby | 82 | A4 |
| Middle Kames, Argyll | 111 | A1 |
| Middle Mayfield, Staff | 70 | A3 |
| Middle Rasen, Linc | 84 | A3 |
| Middle Stoke, Kent | 30 | A2 |
| Middle Town, Scilly | 139 | A2 |
| Middle Tysoe, Warw | 49 | A4 |
| Middle Wallop, Hamp | 14 | B1 |
| Middle Winterslow, Wilts | 14 | A1 |
| Middlebie, D & G | 102 | A2 |
| Middlebridge, Perth | 122 | E2 |
| Middleham, N York | 92 | E3 |
| Middlehill, Wilts | 25 | A2 |
| Middlehope, Shrop | 56 | D4 |
| Middlemarsh, Dors | 12 | B3 |
| Middlesbrough, N York | 99 | A4 |
| Middleshaw, Cumb | 91 | F2 |
| Middlesmoor, N York | 92 | E4 |
| Middlestone, Durham | 98 | C3 |
| Middlestown, W York | 81 | B1 |
| Middleton, Derby | 70 | B1 |
| Middleton, Derby | 70 | C2 |
| Middleton, Essex | 53 | B4 |
| Middleton, G Man | 80 | A2 |
| Middleton, Hamp | 26 | B4 |
| Middleton, Heref | 46 | D1 |
| Middleton, N York | 87 | A2 |
| Middleton, N York | 94 | B3 |
| Middleton, Nhants | 61 | A4 |
| Middleton, Norf | 63 | A1 |
| Middleton, Nthumb | 104 | A2 |
| Middleton, Shrop | 46 | D1 |
| Middleton, Suff | 54 | C2 |
| Middleton, Swan | 33 | A4 |
| Middleton, Warw | 59 | A3 |
| Middleton Cheney, Nhants | 49 | B4 |

| PLACE | PAGE | GRID |
|---|---|---|
| Middleton on the Hill, Heref | 46 | D2 |
| Middleton on the Wolds, E R of Y | 89 | C2 |
| Middleton Scriven, Shrop | 57 | A4 |
| Middleton St George, Durham | 98 | D4 |
| Middleton Stoney, Oxon | 38 | A1 |
| Middleton Tyas, N York | 93 | A1 |
| Middleton-in-Teesdale, Durham | 98 | A3 |
| Middleton-on-Sea, W Suss | 17 | A4 |
| Middletown, Powys | 56 | B2 |
| Middlewich, Chesh | 69 | A1 |
| Middlewood, Corn | 4 | A2 |
| Middlewood, Heref | 46 | B4 |
| Middlezoy, Som | 11 | C1 |
| Midford, Wilts | 24 | B3 |
| Midgham, Berks | 26 | C2 |
| Midgley, W York | 86 | D4 |
| Midgley, W York | 81 | B1 |
| Midhopestones, S York | 81 | B2 |
| Midhurst, W Suss | 17 | A2 |
| Midlem, Bord | 108 | C2 |
| Midsomer Norton, Som | 24 | A3 |
| Milborne Port, Som | 12 | B2 |
| Milborne St Andrew, Dors | 12 | C4 |
| Milborne Wick, Som | 12 | B2 |
| Milbourne, Nthumb | 104 | A3 |
| Milbourne, Wilts | 36 | C4 |
| Milburn, Cumb | 97 | C3 |
| Milbury Heath, Glouc | 35 | C4 |
| Milby, N York | 93 | C4 |
| Milcombe, Oxon | 49 | B4 |
| Milden, Suff | 53 | C3 |
| Mildenhall, Suff | 53 | A1 |
| Mildenhall, Wilts | 25 | D2 |
| Mileham, Norf | 63 | C1 |
| Milesmark, Fife | 113 | C1 |
| Milfield, Nthumb | 109 | C2 |
| Milford, Derby | 70 | C3 |
| Milford, Staff | 58 | A1 |
| Milford, Surr | 145 | B4 |
| Milford Haven, Pemb | 32 | C3 |
| Milford on Sea, Hamp | 7 | F1 |
| Milkwall, Glouc | 35 | C3 |
| Mill Brow, G Man | 80 | B3 |
| Mill End, Bucks | 27 | B1 |
| Mill End, Herts | 40 | B1 |
| Mill Green, Camb | 52 | C3 |
| Mill Green, Essex | 41 | B3 |
| Mill Green, Linc | 62 | A1 |
| Mill Green, Suff | 53 | C4 |
| Mill Green, Suff | 54 | A2 |
| Mill Meece, Staff | 69 | B4 |
| Mill Street, Suff | 53 | D1 |
| Milland, W Suss | 16 | B2 |
| Millbrex, Aber | 134 | C4 |
| Millbridge, Surr | 27 | B4 |
| Millbrook, Beds | 51 | A4 |
| Millbrook, Corn | 4 | C4 |
| Millbrook, Jers | 139 | B2 |
| Millcorner, E Sus | 21 | A2 |
| Milldale, Staff | 70 | A2 |
| Millerhill, M Loth | 114 | B3 |
| Miller's Dale, Derby | 81 | A4 |
| Millhalf, Heref | 46 | B3 |
| Millhouse, Argyll | 111 | A3 |
| Millhouse Green, S York | 81 | B2 |
| Millington, E R of Y | 89 | B2 |
| Millom, Cumb | 91 | C3 |
| Millport, N Ayr | 111 | C4 |
| Millthrop, Cumb | 92 | A2 |
| Milltown, D & G | 102 | B3 |
| Milltown, Devon | 9 | E1 |
| Milnathort, Perth | 119 | B4 |
| Milngavie, Dumb | 112 | B2 |
| Milnrow, G Man | 80 | A1 |
| Milnthorpe, Cumb | 91 | F3 |
| Milson, Shrop | 47 | A1 |
| Milstead, Kent | 30 | B3 |
| Milston, Wilts | 25 | D4 |
| Milton, Camb | 52 | B2 |
| Milton, Cumb | 102 | D4 |
| Milton, D & G | 95 | C1 |
| Milton, D & G | 101 | C3 |
| Milton, Derby | 70 | C4 |
| Milton, High | 132 | C1 |
| Milton, Notts | 83 | A4 |
| Milton, Oxon | 37 | D4 |
| Milton, Pemb | 32 | D3 |
| Milton, Som | 12 | A2 |
| Milton, Dumb | 112 | A2 |
| Milton Abbas, Dors | 12 | C4 |
| Milton Abbot, Devon | 4 | B2 |
| Milton Bryan, Beds | 39 | B1 |
| Milton Clevedon, Som | 12 | B1 |
| Milton Combe, Devon | 4 | C3 |
| Milton Damerel, Devon | 9 | C3 |
| Milton Ernest, Beds | 51 | A3 |
| Milton Green, Chesh | 68 | A2 |
| Milton Hill, Oxon | 37 | D4 |
| Milton Keynes, Bucks | 50 | C4 |
| Milton of Balgonie, Fife | 119 | C4 |
| Milton of Campsie, E Dunb | 112 | B2 |
| Milton on Stour, Dors | 12 | C2 |
| Milton-under-Wychwood, Oxon | 37 | B2 |
| Milverton, Som | 11 | A2 |
| Milwich, Staff | 69 | C4 |
| Minchinhampton, Glouc | 36 | B3 |
| Minehead, Som | 22 | E4 |
| Minera, Wrex | 67 | E2 |
| Minety, Wilts | 36 | C4 |
| Minffordd, Gwyn | 66 | E3 |
| Miningsby, Linc | 73 | D1 |
| Minions, Corn | 4 | A3 |
| Minllyn, Gwyn | 55 | C2 |
| Minnigaff, D & G | 100 | D4 |
| Minskip, N York | 93 | B4 |
| Minstead, Hamp | 14 | B3 |
| Minsted, W Suss | 17 | A2 |
| Minster, Kent | 30 | B2 |
| Minster, Kent | 31 | B2 |
| Minster Lovell, Oxon | 37 | C2 |
| Minsterley, Shrop | 56 | C2 |
| Minsterworth, Glouc | 36 | A2 |

| PLACE | PAGE | GRID |
|---|---|---|
| Minterne Magna, Dors | 12 | B4 |
| Minting, Linc | 84 | A4 |
| Mintlaw, Aber | 134 | D3 |
| Minto, Bord | 108 | C3 |
| Minton, Shrop | 56 | C4 |
| Mirfield, W York | 87 | B4 |
| Miserden, Glouc | 36 | C3 |
| Miskin, Rhond | 22 | F1 |
| Misson, Notts | 83 | A3 |
| Misterton, Leics | 60 | B4 |
| Misterton, Notts | 83 | B3 |
| Misterton, Som | 11 | C3 |
| Mistley, Essex | 43 | B1 |
| Mitcham, G Lon | 143 | A4 |
| Mitchel Troy, Monm | 35 | B3 |
| Mitcheldean, Glouc | 35 | C2 |
| Mitchell, Corn | 3 | C4 |
| Mitford, Nthumb | 104 | B2 |
| Mithian, Corn | 3 | B4 |
| Mixbury, Oxon | 49 | C4 |
| Mobberley, Chesh | 79 | B4 |
| Mobberley, Staff | 69 | C3 |
| Moccas, Heref | 46 | C4 |
| Mochdre, Powys | 55 | E4 |
| Mochrum, D & G | 95 | D1 |
| Mockbeggar, Kent | 29 | B4 |
| Mockerkin, Cumb | 96 | D3 |
| Modbury, Devon | 5 | A4 |
| Moddershall, Staff | 69 | B4 |
| Moelfre, Angle | 76 | C3 |
| Moelfre, Powys | 67 | D4 |
| Moffat, D & G | 107 | D4 |
| Mogerhanger, Beds | 51 | B3 |
| Moira, Leics | 59 | B1 |
| Molash, Kent | 30 | C4 |
| Mold, Flint | 67 | E1 |
| Molehill Green, Essex | 41 | B1 |
| Molland, Devon | 10 | B2 |
| Mollington, Chesh | 68 | A1 |
| Mollington, Oxon | 49 | B3 |
| Monewden, Suff | 54 | B2 |
| Moneyrow Green, Berks | 140 | A2 |
| Moniaive, D & G | 101 | C2 |
| Monikie, Angus | 119 | E1 |
| Monimail, Fife | 119 | C3 |
| Monk Fryston, N York | 88 | C4 |
| Monk Sherborne, Hamp | 26 | C3 |
| Monk Soham, Suff | 54 | A2 |
| Monkhide, Heref | 47 | A4 |
| Monkhill, Cumb | 102 | B4 |
| Monkhopton, Shrop | 57 | A3 |
| Monkland, Heref | 46 | C2 |
| Monkleigh, Devon | 9 | D2 |
| Monknash, Glam | 22 | E2 |
| Monkokehampton, Devon | 9 | E4 |
| Monks Eleigh, Suff | 53 | C3 |
| Monks Heath, Chesh | 80 | A4 |
| Monks Horton, Kent | 21 | C1 |
| Monks Kirby, Warw | 60 | A4 |
| Monksilver, Som | 10 | D1 |
| Monksthorpe, Linc | 74 | A1 |
| Monkswood, Monm | 34 | E3 |
| Monkton, Kent | 31 | B2 |
| Monkton, S Ayr | 106 | D2 |
| Monkton Deverill, Wilts | 12 | D1 |
| Monkton Farleigh, Wilts | 24 | B2 |
| Monkton Wyld, Dors | 11 | B4 |
| Monkwood, Hamp | 16 | A1 |
| Monmouth, Monm | 35 | B2 |
| Monnington on Wye, Heref | 46 | C4 |
| Monreith, D & G | 95 | D2 |
| Mont Saint, Guer | 139 | B2 |
| Montacute, Som | 12 | A3 |
| Montford, Shrop | 56 | C1 |
| Montgarrie, Aber | 128 | D2 |
| Montgarswood, E Ayr | 106 | E2 |
| Montgomery, Powys | 56 | A3 |
| Montrose, Angus | 124 | C3 |
| Monxton, Hamp | 26 | A4 |
| Monyash, Derby | 70 | A1 |
| Monymusk, Aber | 128 | E2 |
| Monzie, Perth | 118 | D2 |
| Moodiesburn, N Lan | 112 | C3 |
| Moor Monkton, N York | 88 | C1 |
| Moorby, Linc | 73 | C1 |
| Moore, Chesh | 78 | B3 |
| Moorends, S York | 83 | A1 |
| Moorgreen, Notts | 71 | A3 |
| Moorhouse, Cumb | 96 | F1 |
| Moorhouse, Notts | 72 | B1 |
| Moorlinch, Som | 11 | C1 |
| Moorsholm, N York | 99 | C4 |
| Moorside, Dors | 12 | C2 |
| Moorswater, Corn | 4 | A3 |
| Moortown, Linc | 83 | D2 |
| Morborne, Camb | 61 | D4 |
| Morchard Bishop, Devon | 10 | A3 |
| Morcombelake, Dors | 6 | D1 |
| Morcott, Rut | 61 | B3 |
| Morden, Dors | 12 | D4 |
| Morden, G Lon | 143 | A4 |
| Mordiford, Heref | 46 | D4 |
| Mordon, Durham | 98 | D3 |
| More, Shrop | 56 | B3 |
| Morebath, Devon | 10 | C2 |
| Morebattle, Bord | 109 | A3 |
| Morecambe, Lanc | 85 | B1 |
| Moreleigh, Devon | 5 | A4 |
| Moresby, Cumb | 96 | C4 |
| Morestead, Hamp | 15 | B2 |
| Moreton, Dors | 7 | A1 |
| Moreton, Essex | 41 | A3 |
| Moreton, Heref | 46 | D2 |
| Moreton, Oxon | 38 | B3 |
| Moreton Corbet, Shrop | 56 | D1 |
| Moreton Jeffries, Heref | 47 | A3 |
| Moreton Morrell, Warw | 49 | A3 |
| Moreton Pinkney, Nhants | 49 | C3 |
| Moreton Say, Shrop | 68 | C4 |
| Moreton Valence, Glouc | 36 | A3 |
| Moretonhampstead, Devon | 5 | A1 |
| Moreton-in-Marsh, Glouc | 37 | B1 |
| Morland, Cumb | 97 | C3 |
| Morley, Chesh | 80 | A4 |
| Morley, Derby | 71 | A3 |
| Morley, W York | 87 | B4 |

| PLACE | PAGE | GRID |
|---|---|---|
| Morley Green, Chesh | 80 | A4 |
| Morley St Botolph, Norf | 64 | A3 |
| Morningside, N Lan | 113 | A4 |
| Morpeth, Nthumb | 104 | B2 |
| Morrey, Staff | 58 | B1 |
| Morston, Norf | 75 | A3 |
| Mortehoe, Devon | 22 | A4 |
| Morthen, S York | 82 | A3 |
| Mortimer, Berks | 27 | A2 |
| Mortimer West End, Hamp | 27 | A3 |
| Mortlake, G Lon | 142 | B2 |
| Morton, Derby | 71 | A2 |
| Morton, Shrop | 56 | B1 |
| Morton-on-Swale, N York | 93 | B2 |
| Morvah, Corn | 1 | B2 |
| Morville, Shrop | 57 | A3 |
| Morwenstow, Corn | 9 | B3 |
| Mosborough, S York | 82 | A4 |
| Moseley, Worc | 47 | C2 |
| Moss, S York | 82 | B1 |
| Moss Edge, Lanc | 85 | B2 |
| Moss Side, Mers | 77 | D1 |
| Mossat, Aber | 128 | D2 |
| Mossblown, S Ayr | 106 | D3 |
| Mossley, G Man | 80 | B2 |
| Moss-side, High | 132 | D3 |
| Mosstodloch, Moray | 133 | C2 |
| Mossy Lea, Lanc | 78 | B1 |
| Mosterton, Dors | 11 | C4 |
| Mostyn, Flint | 77 | C4 |
| Motcombe, Dors | 12 | D2 |
| Mothecombe, Devon | 8 | B1 |
| Motherby, Cumb | 97 | A3 |
| Motherwell, N Lan | 112 | C4 |
| Motspur Park, G Lon | 142 | B4 |
| Mottingham, G Lon | 144 | A3 |
| Mottisfont, Hamp | 14 | B2 |
| Mottistone, I of W | 8 | A1 |
| Mottram in Longdendale, G Man | 80 | B2 |
| Mottram St Andrew, Chesh | 80 | A4 |
| Mouldsworth, Chesh | 68 | B1 |
| Moulin, Perth | 123 | A3 |
| Moulsford, Oxon | 26 | C1 |
| Moulsoe, Bucks | 50 | C4 |
| Moulton, Chesh | 68 | C1 |
| Moulton, Linc | 62 | A1 |
| Moulton, N York | 93 | A1 |
| Moulton, Nhants | 50 | B2 |
| Moulton, Suff | 53 | A2 |
| Moulton, Glam | 22 | F2 |
| Moulton Chapel, Linc | 62 | A1 |
| Moulton Seas End, Linc | 73 | D4 |
| Mount, Corn | 3 | E3 |
| Mount Ambrose, Corn | 1 | D1 |
| Mount Bures, Essex | 43 | A1 |
| Mount Hawke, Corn | 1 | D1 |
| Mount Lothian, M Loth | 114 | B4 |
| Mount Pleasant, Derby | 70 | C3 |
| Mount Pleasant, Suff | 53 | A3 |
| Mount Tabor, W York | 87 | A4 |
| Mountain, W York | 87 | A3 |
| Mountain Ash, Rhond | 34 | C3 |
| Mountfield, E Sus | 20 | B2 |
| Mountjoy, Corn | 3 | C4 |
| Mountnessing, Essex | 41 | B4 |
| Mounton, Monm | 35 | B4 |
| Mountsorrel, Leics | 60 | B2 |
| Mousehole, Corn | 1 | B2 |
| Mouswald, D & G | 101 | E3 |
| Mowsley, Leics | 60 | C4 |
| Moy, High | 132 | C4 |
| Moy, High | 122 | A1 |
| Moylgrove, Pemb | 44 | C4 |
| Muasdale, Argyll | 105 | D1 |
| Much Cowarne, Heref | 47 | A3 |
| Much Dewchurch, Heref | 35 | B1 |
| Much Hadham, Herts | 40 | B2 |
| Much Hoole, Lanc | 85 | C4 |
| Much Marcle, Heref | 35 | C1 |
| Much Wenlock, Shrop | 57 | A3 |
| Muchalls, Aber | 129 | B4 |
| Muchelney, Som | 11 | C2 |
| Muchelney Ham, Som | 11 | C2 |
| Muchlarnick, Corn | 4 | A4 |
| Mucklestone, Staff | 69 | A4 |
| Muckton, Linc | 84 | C4 |
| Muddiford, Devon | 9 | E1 |
| Mudford, Som | 12 | A2 |
| Mudford Sock, Som | 12 | A2 |
| Mugeary, High | 130 | C4 |
| Mugginton, Derby | 70 | C3 |
| Muir of Fowlis, Aber | 128 | D2 |
| Muir of Ord, High | 132 | A3 |
| Muirdrum, Angus | 119 | E1 |
| Muirhead, Angus | 119 | C1 |
| Muirhead, Fife | 119 | C4 |
| Muirhead, N Lan | 112 | C3 |
| Muirhouses, Falkirk | 113 | C2 |
| Muirkirk, E Ayr | 107 | A3 |
| Muirton, Perth | 118 | E3 |
| Muker, N York | 92 | C2 |
| Mulbarton, Norf | 64 | B3 |
| Mullion, Corn | 1 | D3 |
| Mullion Cove, Corn | 1 | D3 |
| Mumby, Linc | 84 | D4 |
| Munderfield Row, Heref | 47 | A3 |
| Mundesley, Norf | 75 | C4 |
| Mundford, Norf | 63 | B3 |
| Mundham, Norf | 65 | A3 |
| Mundon Hill, Essex | 42 | B3 |
| Mungrisdale, Cumb | 97 | A3 |
| Munlochy, High | 132 | B3 |
| Munsley, Heref | 47 | A4 |
| Munslow, Shrop | 56 | D4 |
| Murchington, Devon | 5 | A1 |
| Murcott, Oxon | 38 | A2 |
| Murrow, Camb | 62 | B2 |
| Mursley, Bucks | 38 | C1 |
| Murthly, Perth | 119 | A1 |
| Murton, Cumb | 97 | D4 |
| Murton, Durham | 98 | D1 |
| Murton, N York | 89 | A2 |
| Murton, Nthumb | 109 | C1 |
| Musbury, Devon | 6 | C1 |
| Musselburgh, E Loth | 114 | B2 |

| PLACE | PAGE | GRID |
|---|---|---|
| Muston, Leics | 72 | B3 |
| Muston, N York | 94 | E3 |
| Mustow Green, Worc | 47 | C1 |
| Mutehill, D & G | 96 | A1 |
| Mutford, Suff | 65 | C4 |
| Muthill, Perth | 118 | D3 |
| Mybster, High | 138 | D2 |
| Myddfai, Carm | 33 | D1 |
| Myddle, Shrop | 56 | D1 |
| Mydroilyn, Cered | 44 | F3 |
| Mylor, Corn | 2 | A2 |
| Mylor Bridge, Corn | 2 | A2 |
| Mynachlog ddu, Pemb | 32 | E1 |
| Myndtown, Shrop | 56 | C4 |
| Mynydd-bach, Monm | 35 | B4 |
| Mytchett, Surr | 145 | A2 |
| Mytholmroyd, W York | 86 | D4 |
| Myton-on-Swale, N York | 93 | C4 |
| Naburn, N York | 88 | C2 |
| Nackington, Kent | 31 | A3 |
| Nacton, Suff | 54 | A4 |
| Nafferton, E R of Y | 89 | D1 |
| Nailsbourne, Som | 11 | A2 |
| Nailsea, Som | 23 | D2 |
| Nailstone, Leics | 60 | A2 |
| Nailsworth, Glouc | 36 | B3 |
| Nairn, High | 132 | D3 |
| Nalderswood, Surr | 148 | A4 |
| Nannerch, Flint | 67 | D1 |
| Nanpantan, Leics | 60 | B1 |
| Nanpean, Corn | 3 | C4 |
| Nanstallon, Corn | 3 | D3 |
| Nant Peris, Gwyn | 66 | E2 |
| Nanternis, Cered | 44 | E2 |
| Nantgaredig, Carm | 33 | B2 |
| Nantglyn, Denb | 67 | C1 |
| Nantmel, Powys | 45 | E2 |
| Nantmor, Gwyn | 66 | E3 |
| Nantwich, Chesh | 68 | C2 |
| Nantyglo, Gwent | 34 | D3 |
| Nant-y-moel, Brid | 34 | B4 |
| Naphill, Bucks | 38 | C4 |
| Napleton, Worc | 47 | C3 |
| Napton on the Hill, Warw | 49 | B2 |
| Narberth, Pemb | 32 | E2 |
| Narborough, Leics | 60 | B3 |
| Narborough, Norf | 63 | A2 |
| Nasareth, Gwyn | 66 | D2 |
| Naseby, Nhants | 50 | A1 |
| Nash, Bucks | 50 | B4 |
| Nash, Newport | 23 | B1 |
| Nash, Shrop | 47 | A1 |
| Nash, G Lon | 149 | A1 |
| Nash's Green, Hamp | 27 | A4 |
| Nassington, Nhants | 61 | C3 |
| Nateby, Cumb | 92 | B1 |
| Nateby, Lanc | 85 | B2 |
| Natland, Cumb | 91 | F2 |
| Naughton, Suff | 53 | D3 |
| Naunton, Glouc | 37 | A1 |
| Naunton, Worc | 47 | C4 |
| Naunton Beauchamp, Worc | 48 | A3 |
| Navenby, Linc | 73 | A2 |
| Navestock, Essex | 41 | A4 |
| Navestock Side, Essex | 41 | B4 |
| Nawton, N York | 94 | A3 |
| Nayland, Suff | 53 | C4 |
| Nazeing, Essex | 40 | B3 |
| Near Cotton, Staff | 70 | A3 |
| Near Sawrey, Cumb | 91 | E2 |
| Neasden, G Lon | 142 | B1 |
| Neasham, Durham | 93 | B1 |
| Neath, Neath | 33 | D4 |
| Neatham, Hamp | 16 | B1 |
| Neatishead, Norf | 65 | A1 |
| Nebo, Cered | 45 | A2 |
| Nebo, Ab & Col | 67 | A2 |
| Nebo, Gwyn | 66 | D2 |
| Nebo, Angle | 76 | C3 |
| Necton, Norf | 63 | B2 |
| Nedd, High | 137 | A4 |
| Nedging, Suff | 53 | C3 |
| Nedging Tye, Suff | 53 | D3 |
| Needham, Norf | 64 | B4 |
| Needham Market, Suff | 53 | D3 |
| Needingworth, Camb | 52 | A1 |
| Neen Savage, Shrop | 47 | A1 |
| Neen Sollars, Shrop | 47 | A1 |
| Neenton, Shrop | 57 | A4 |
| Nefyn, Gwyn | 66 | B3 |
| Neilston, E Renf | 112 | A4 |
| Nelson, Caer | 34 | C4 |
| Nelson, Lanc | 86 | C3 |
| Nemphlar, S Lan | 107 | B1 |
| Nempnett Thrubwell, Som | 23 | D3 |
| Nenthead, Cumb | 97 | D2 |
| Nenthorn, Bord | 108 | D2 |
| Nercwys, Flint | 67 | D1 |
| Nesbit, Nthumb | 109 | C2 |
| Nesfield, N York | 87 | A2 |
| Neston, Chesh | 77 | D4 |
| Neston, Wilts | 25 | A2 |
| Netchwood, Shrop | 57 | A3 |
| Nether Alderley, Chesh | 80 | A4 |
| Nether Broughton, Leics | 60 | C1 |
| Nether Cerne, Dors | 12 | B4 |
| Nether Compton, Dors | 12 | B3 |
| Nether Dallachy, Moray | 133 | D2 |
| Nether Exe, Devon | 10 | C4 |
| Nether Haugh, S York | 82 | A2 |
| Nether Headon, Notts | 83 | B4 |
| Nether Heage, Derby | 70 | C2 |
| Nether Heyford, Nhants | 50 | A2 |
| Nether Langwith, Notts | 71 | B1 |
| Nether Moor, Derby | 70 | C1 |
| Nether Padley, Derby | 81 | B4 |
| Nether Poppleton, N York | 88 | C1 |
| Nether Silton, N York | 93 | C2 |
| Nether Stowey, Som | 11 | A1 |
| Nether Wallop, Hamp | 14 | B1 |
| Nether Wasdale, Cumb | 91 | C1 |
| Nether Whitacre, Warw | 59 | A3 |
| Nether Winchendon, Bucks | 38 | B2 |
| Netheravon, Wilts | 25 | C4 |
| Netherbury, Dors | 12 | A4 |

| PLACE | PAGE | GRID |
|---|---|---|
| Netherby, N York | 88 | A2 |
| Netherend, Glouc | 35 | C3 |
| Netherfield, E Sus | 20 | B2 |
| Netherhampton, Wilts | 13 | B1 |
| Netherhay, Dors | 11 | C4 |
| Netherseal, Derby | 59 | B2 |
| Netherthong, W York | 81 | A1 |
| Netherton, Nthumb | 109 | C4 |
| Netherton, Shrop | 57 | B4 |
| Netherton, W York | 81 | C1 |
| Nethertown, Cumb | 91 | A1 |
| Nethertown, Staff | 58 | B1 |
| Netherwitton, Nthumb | 104 | A2 |
| Nethy Bridge, High | 127 | D2 |
| Netley, Hamp | 15 | A3 |
| Netley Marsh, Hamp | 14 | B3 |
| Nettlebed, Oxon | 27 | A1 |
| Nettlecombe, Dors | 12 | A4 |
| Nettleden, Herts | 39 | B3 |
| Nettleham, Linc | 83 | D4 |
| Nettlestone, I of W | 8 | C1 |
| Nettleton, Linc | 84 | A2 |
| Nettleton, Wilts | 25 | A1 |
| Netton, Wilts | 13 | B1 |
| Nevern, Pemb | 44 | C4 |
| Nevill Holt, Leics | 61 | A3 |
| New Abbey, D & G | 101 | D4 |
| New Aberdour, Aber | 134 | C2 |
| New Addington, G Lon | 149 | A1 |
| New Alresford, Hamp | 15 | B1 |
| New Alyth, Perth | 123 | D4 |
| New Ash Green, Kent | 29 | A2 |
| New Barn, Kent | 29 | A2 |
| New Bewick, Nthumb | 109 | D3 |
| New Bolingbroke, Linc | 73 | C2 |
| New Brancepeth, Durham | 98 | C2 |
| New Buckenham, Norf | 64 | A4 |
| New Crofton, W York | 81 | C1 |
| New Cross, Som | 11 | C2 |
| New Cross, G Lon | 143 | B2 |
| New Deer, Aber | 134 | C3 |
| New Denham, Bucks | 141 | A1 |
| New Edlington, S York | 82 | B2 |
| New Ellerby, E R of Y | 90 | A3 |
| New Eltham, G Lon | 144 | B3 |
| New End, Worc | 48 | B2 |
| New Galloway, D & G | 101 | A3 |
| New Gilston, Fife | 119 | D3 |
| New Grimsby, Scilly | 139 | A1 |
| New Haw, Surr | 146 | B1 |
| New Holkham, Norf | 74 | D3 |
| New Holland, Linc | 89 | D4 |
| New Houghton, Derby | 71 | A1 |
| New Houghton, Norf | 74 | D4 |
| New Hutton, Cumb | 91 | F2 |
| New Inn, Carm | 44 | F4 |
| New Lanark, S Lan | 107 | B1 |
| New Leeds, Aber | 134 | D3 |
| New Luce, D & G | 100 | B4 |
| New Malden, G Lon | 142 | B4 |
| New Marske, N York | 99 | B4 |
| New Mill, W York | 81 | B1 |
| New Mills, Corn | 3 | C4 |
| New Mills, Derby | 80 | B3 |
| New Mills, Powys | 55 | E3 |
| New Milton, Hamp | 14 | A4 |
| New Mistley, Essex | 43 | C1 |
| New Moat, Pemb | 32 | D1 |
| New Pitsligo, Aber | 134 | C3 |
| New Quay, Cered | 44 | E2 |
| New Rackheath, Norf | 65 | A2 |
| New Radnor, Powys | 46 | A2 |
| New Romney, Kent | 21 | C2 |
| New Scone, Perth | 119 | B2 |
| New Sharlston, W York | 88 | A4 |
| New Stevenston, N Lan | 112 | C4 |
| New Town, Dors | 12 | D2 |
| New Town, Dors | 13 | A2 |
| New Town, E Loth | 114 | C3 |
| New Tredegar, Caer | 34 | D3 |
| New Trows, S Lan | 107 | B1 |
| New Waltham, Linc | 84 | B2 |
| New Wimpole, Camb | 52 | A3 |
| New Winton, E Loth | 114 | C3 |
| New York, Linc | 73 | C2 |
| Newark, Ork | 139 | B1 |
| Newark-on-Trent, Notts | 72 | B2 |
| Newarthill, N Lan | 113 | A4 |
| Newbattle, M Loth | 114 | B3 |
| Newbiggin, Cumb | 97 | B3 |
| Newbiggin, Cumb | 97 | B1 |
| Newbiggin, Cumb | 97 | C3 |
| Newbiggin, Durham | 97 | E3 |
| Newbiggin, N York | 92 | D3 |
| Newbiggin-by-the-Sea, Nthumb | 104 | C2 |
| Newbigging, Angus | 123 | D4 |
| Newbigging, Angus | 119 | E1 |
| Newbigging, S Lan | 107 | D1 |
| Newbiggin-on-Lune, Cumb | 92 | B1 |
| Newbold on Avon, Warw | 49 | B1 |
| Newbold on Stour, Warw | 48 | C3 |
| Newbold Pacey, Warw | 49 | A2 |
| Newbold Verdon, Leics | 60 | A2 |
| Newborough, Camb | 62 | A2 |
| Newborough, Angle | 66 | C1 |
| Newborough, Staff | 58 | B1 |
| Newbourne, Suff | 54 | B4 |
| Newbridge, Edin | 114 | A2 |
| Newbridge, Caer | 34 | D4 |
| Newbridge, Corn | 1 | B2 |
| Newbridge, D & G | 101 | D3 |
| Newbridge, I of W | 8 | A1 |
| Newbridge Green, Worc | 47 | C4 |
| Newbridge on Wye, Powys | 45 | E2 |
| Newbrough, Nthumb | 103 | C4 |
| Newbuildings, Devon | 10 | B4 |
| Newburgh, Aber | 129 | C1 |
| Newburgh, Fife | 119 | C3 |
| Newburgh, Lanc | 78 | B1 |
| Newburgh Priory, N York | 93 | D3 |
| Newbury, Som | 24 | B4 |
| Newbury, Berks | 26 | B2 |
| Newby, Cumb | 97 | C4 |
| Newby, Lanc | 86 | C2 |
| Newby, N York | 99 | B4 |
| Newby, N York | 92 | B4 |
| Newby Bridge, Cumb | 91 | E3 |
| Newby East, Cumb | 102 | D4 |
| Newby West, Cumb | 97 | A1 |
| Newby Wiske, N York | 93 | B2 |
| Newcastle, Monm | 35 | A2 |
| Newcastle, Shrop | 56 | B4 |
| Newcastle Emlyn, Carm | 44 | D4 |
| Newcastle upon Tyne, T & W | 104 | B4 |
| Newcastleton, Bord | 102 | D2 |
| Newcastle-under-Lyme, Staff | 69 | B3 |
| Newchapel, Pemb | 44 | D4 |
| Newchurch, Kent | 21 | C1 |
| Newchurch, Monm | 35 | A4 |
| Newchurch, Powys | 46 | A3 |
| Newchurch, Staff | 58 | B1 |
| Newcraighall, Edin | 114 | B3 |
| Newdigate, Surr | 147 | B4 |
| Newent, Glouc | 36 | A1 |
| Newfield, Durham | 98 | C3 |
| Newgale, Pemb | 32 | C1 |
| Newgate Street, Herts | 40 | A3 |
| Newhall, Chesh | 68 | C3 |
| Newhaven, E Sus | 19 | B4 |
| Newholm, N York | 94 | C1 |
| Newick, E Sus | 19 | A2 |
| Newington, Kent | 30 | A2 |
| Newington, Kent | 21 | D1 |
| Newington, Oxon | 38 | A4 |
| Newland, Glouc | 35 | B3 |
| Newland, N York | 89 | A4 |
| Newland, Som | 10 | B1 |
| Newland, Worc | 47 | B3 |
| Newlyn, Corn | 1 | B2 |
| Newlyn East, Corn | 3 | B4 |
| Newmains, N Lan | 113 | A4 |
| Newmarket, Suff | 52 | C2 |
| Newmill, Bord | 108 | B4 |
| Newmill, Moray | 133 | D3 |
| Newmillerdam, W York | 81 | C1 |
| Newmills, Monm | 35 | B3 |
| Newney Green, Essex | 41 | B3 |
| Newnham, Glouc | 35 | C2 |
| Newnham, Hamp | 27 | A3 |
| Newnham, Herts | 51 | C4 |
| Newnham, Kent | 30 | B3 |
| Newnham, Nhants | 49 | C2 |
| Newnham, Worc | 47 | A1 |
| Newport, E R of Y | 89 | C3 |
| Newport, Essex | 52 | B4 |
| Newport, Glouc | 36 | A4 |
| Newport, Pemb | 44 | B4 |
| Newport, Newport | 34 | E4 |
| Newport, I of W | 8 | A1 |
| Newport, Shrop | 57 | B1 |
| Newport Pagnell, Bucks | 50 | C4 |
| Newport-on-Tay, Fife | 119 | D2 |
| Newquay, Corn | 3 | B3 |
| Newsham, Lanc | 85 | C3 |
| Newsham, N York | 92 | E1 |
| Newsholme, E R of Y | 89 | A4 |
| Newstead, Bord | 108 | C2 |
| Newstead, Notts | 71 | B2 |
| Newstead, Nthumb | 109 | D2 |
| Newthorpe, N York | 88 | B3 |
| Newton, Beds | 51 | C4 |
| Newton, Camb | 62 | C1 |
| Newton, Camb | 52 | B3 |
| Newton, Chesh | 68 | B2 |
| Newton, Cumb | 91 | C4 |
| Newton, Derby | 71 | A2 |
| Newton, Heref | 34 | E1 |
| Newton, Heref | 46 | D3 |
| Newton, Lanc | 86 | B2 |
| Newton, Linc | 73 | A4 |
| Newton, Nhants | 61 | B4 |
| Newton, Norf | 63 | B1 |
| Newton, Notts | 72 | A3 |
| Newton, Nthumb | 103 | D4 |
| Newton, Som | 10 | D1 |
| Newton, Staff | 58 | A1 |
| Newton, Suff | 53 | C4 |
| Newton, W Loth | 113 | C2 |
| Newton, Warw | 49 | C1 |
| Newton Abbot, Devon | 5 | B3 |
| Newton Arlosh, Cumb | 96 | E1 |
| Newton Aycliffe, Durham | 98 | C3 |
| Newton Bewley, Durham | 99 | A3 |
| Newton Blossomville, Bucks | 50 | C3 |
| Newton Bromswold, Nhants | 51 | A2 |
| Newton Burgoland, Leics | 59 | B2 |
| Newton by Toft, Linc | 83 | D3 |
| Newton Ferrers, Corn | 4 | B3 |
| Newton Ferrers, Devon | 8 | B1 |
| Newton Flotman, Norf | 64 | B3 |
| Newton Harcourt, Leics | 60 | C3 |
| Newton Kyme, N York | 88 | B2 |
| Newton Longville, Bucks | 38 | C1 |
| Newton Morrell, N York | 93 | A1 |
| Newton Mountain, Pemb | 32 | D3 |
| Newton on Ouse, N York | 88 | C1 |
| Newton on Trent, Linc | 83 | B4 |
| Newton Poppleford, Devon | 6 | A1 |
| Newton Purcell, Oxon | 38 | B1 |
| Newton Reigny, Cumb | 97 | B3 |
| Newton Solney, Derby | 59 | B1 |
| Newton St Cyres, Devon | 10 | B4 |
| Newton St Faith, Norf | 64 | B1 |
| Newton St Loe, Som | 24 | B2 |
| Newton St Petrock, Devon | 9 | C3 |
| Newton Stacey, Hamp | 15 | A1 |
| Newton Stewart, D & G | 100 | D4 |
| Newton Toney, Wilts | 14 | A1 |
| Newton Tracey, Devon | 9 | D2 |
| Newton under Roseberry, N York | 99 | B4 |
| Newton upon Derwent, E R of Y | 89 | A2 |
| Newton Valence, Hamp | 16 | A1 |
| Newton Wamphray, D & G | 101 | E1 |
| Newton with Scales, Lanc | 85 | B3 |
| Newton-by-the-Sea, Nthumb | 109 | E3 |
| Newtongrange, M Loth | 114 | B3 |
| Newtonhill, Aber | 129 | B4 |
| Newton-le-Willows, Mers | 79 | A2 |
| Newton-le-Willows, N York | 93 | A2 |
| Newtonloan, M Loth | 114 | B3 |
| Newtonmore, High | 127 | B4 |
| Newton-on-Rawcliffe, N York | 94 | B2 |
| Newton-on-the-Moor, Nthumb | 109 | E4 |
| Newtown, Chesh | 68 | C3 |
| Newtown, Staff | 69 | B2 |
| Newtown, Cumb | 96 | D1 |
| Newtown, Cumb | 102 | D4 |
| Newtown, Devon | 10 | D4 |
| Newtown, Devon | 10 | A2 |
| Newtown, Glouc | 35 | C3 |
| Newtown, Hamp | 15 | B3 |
| Newtown, Heref | 35 | B1 |
| Newtown, I of W | 8 | A1 |
| Newtown, Nthumb | 109 | C3 |
| Newtown, Shrop | 56 | C1 |
| Newtown, Shrop | 68 | B4 |
| Newtown, Wilts | 12 | D2 |
| Newtown, Powys | 55 | E3 |
| Newtown Linford, Leics | 60 | B2 |
| Newtyle, Angus | 119 | C1 |
| Neyland, Pemb | 32 | D3 |
| Nicholashayne, Devon | 10 | D3 |
| Nicholaston, Swan | 33 | B4 |
| Nidd, N York | 88 | A1 |
| Nigg, High | 132 | D1 |
| Nightcott, Som | 10 | C2 |
| Ninebanks, Nthumb | 97 | D1 |
| Nineveh, Worc | 47 | A2 |
| Ninfield, E Sus | 20 | B3 |
| Ningwood, I of W | 8 | A1 |
| Nisbet, Bord | 108 | D3 |
| Nisbet Hill, Bord | 115 | C4 |
| Niton, I of W | 8 | B2 |
| No Man's Heath, Chesh | 68 | B3 |
| No Man's Heath, Warw | 59 | B2 |
| Nocton, Linc | 73 | A1 |
| Noke, Oxon | 38 | A2 |
| Nolton, Pemb | 32 | C2 |
| Nolton Haven, Pemb | 32 | C2 |
| Nomansland, Devon | 10 | B3 |
| Nomansland, Wilts | 14 | A3 |
| Noneley, Shrop | 68 | B4 |
| Nonington, Kent | 31 | B4 |
| Nook, Cumb | 91 | F3 |
| Norbiton, G Lon | 142 | B4 |
| Norbury, Chesh | 68 | B3 |
| Norbury, Derby | 70 | A3 |
| Norbury, Shrop | 56 | C3 |
| Norbury, Staff | 57 | B1 |
| Norbury, G Lon | 143 | A4 |
| Norchard, Worc | 47 | C1 |
| Nordelph, Norf | 62 | D3 |
| Nordley, Shrop | 57 | B3 |
| Norham, Nthumb | 109 | B1 |
| Norland Town, W York | 87 | A4 |
| Norley, Chesh | 78 | B4 |
| Norleywood, Hamp | 14 | B4 |
| Normanby, Linc | 83 | C1 |
| Normanby, Linc | 83 | D3 |
| Normanby, N York | 94 | A3 |
| Normanby le Wold, Linc | 84 | A3 |
| Normandy, Surr | 145 | B3 |
| Norman's Green, Devon | 10 | D4 |
| Normanton, Leics | 72 | B3 |
| Normanton, Linc | 72 | C3 |
| Normanton, Notts | 72 | A2 |
| Normanton, W York | 88 | A4 |
| Normanton le Heath, Leics | 59 | B2 |
| Normanton on Soar, Notts | 60 | B1 |
| Normanton on Trent, Notts | 72 | B1 |
| North Anston, S York | 82 | B3 |
| North Aston, Oxon | 37 | D1 |
| North Baddesley, Hamp | 15 | A2 |
| North Ballachulish, High | 121 | D3 |
| North Barrow, Som | 12 | B2 |
| North Berwick, E Loth | 115 | A1 |
| North Boarhunt, Hamp | 15 | B3 |
| North Bovey, Devon | 5 | A1 |
| North Brentor, Devon | 4 | C2 |
| North Brewham, Som | 12 | C1 |
| North Buckland, Devon | 9 | D1 |
| North Burlingham, Norf | 65 | B2 |
| North Cadbury, Som | 12 | B2 |
| North Carlton, Linc | 83 | C4 |
| North Carlton, Notts | 82 | B3 |
| North Cave, E R of Y | 89 | C3 |
| North Cerney, Glouc | 36 | C3 |
| North Charlton, Nthumb | 109 | E3 |
| North Cheam, G Lon | 142 | B4 |
| North Cheriton, Som | 12 | B2 |
| North Chideock, Dors | 6 | D1 |
| North Cliffe, E R of Y | 89 | C3 |
| North Clifton, Notts | 72 | B1 |
| North Cockerington, Linc | 84 | C3 |
| North Common, E Sus | 19 | A2 |
| North Cotes, Linc | 84 | C2 |
| North Cove, Suff | 65 | C4 |
| North Cowton, N York | 93 | B1 |
| North Crawley, Bucks | 50 | C4 |
| North Cray, G Lon | 144 | C3 |
| North Creake, Norf | 74 | D3 |
| North Curry, Som | 11 | B2 |
| North Dalton, E R of Y | 89 | C2 |
| North Deighton, N York | 88 | B2 |
| North Duffield, N York | 89 | A3 |
| North Elham, Kent | 31 | A4 |
| North Elmham, Norf | 63 | C1 |
| North Elmsall, W York | 82 | A1 |
| North End, Essex | 42 | A2 |
| North End, Hamp | 13 | B3 |
| North Erradale, High | 135 | A4 |
| North Fambridge, Essex | 42 | B4 |
| North Frodingham, E R of Y | 90 | A2 |
| North Gorley, Hamp | 14 | A3 |
| North Green, Suff | 54 | B2 |
| North Grimston, N York | 94 | B4 |
| North Hayling, Hamp | 16 | A4 |
| North Hill, Corn | 4 | A2 |
| North Hillingdon, G Lon | 141 | A1 |
| North Huish, Devon | 5 | A4 |
| North Hykeham, Linc | 72 | C1 |
| North Kelsey, Linc | 83 | D2 |
| North Kessock, High | 132 | C3 |
| North Killingholme, Linc | 84 | A1 |
| North Kilvington, N York | 93 | C3 |
| North Kilworth, Leics | 60 | B4 |
| North Kyme, Linc | 73 | B2 |
| North Landing, E R of Y | 94 | F4 |
| North Lee, Bucks | 38 | C3 |
| North Leigh, Oxon | 37 | D2 |
| North Lopham, Norf | 64 | A4 |
| North Luffenham, Rut | 61 | B2 |
| North Marden, W Suss | 16 | B3 |
| North Marston, Bucks | 38 | C1 |
| North Middleton, M Loth | 114 | C4 |
| North Molton, Devon | 10 | A1 |
| North Moreton, Oxon | 38 | A4 |
| North Muskham, Notts | 72 | B2 |
| North Newbald, E R of Y | 89 | C3 |
| North Newington, Oxon | 49 | B4 |
| North Newnton, Wilts | 25 | C3 |
| North Newton, Som | 11 | B1 |
| North Nibley, Glouc | 36 | A4 |
| North Ormsby, Linc | 84 | B3 |
| North Otterington, N York | 93 | B2 |
| North Owersby, Linc | 83 | D3 |
| North Perrott, Som | 12 | A3 |
| North Petherton, Som | 11 | B1 |
| North Petherwin, Corn | 4 | A1 |
| North Pickenham, Norf | 63 | B2 |
| North Pool, Devon | 8 | B1 |
| North Poorton, Dors | 12 | A4 |
| North Quarme, Som | 10 | C1 |
| North Queensferry, Fife | 114 | A2 |
| North Radworthy, Devon | 10 | A1 |
| North Rauceby, Linc | 73 | A3 |
| North Reston, Linc | 84 | C4 |
| North Rigton, N York | 88 | A2 |
| North Rode, Chesh | 69 | B1 |
| North Scarle, Linc | 72 | B1 |
| North Shoebury, Essex | 30 | B1 |
| North Side, Camb | 62 | A3 |
| North Somercotes, Linc | 84 | C2 |
| North Stainley, N York | 93 | B3 |
| North Stifford, Essex | 29 | A1 |
| North Stoke, Oxon | 26 | C1 |
| North Stoke, Som | 24 | B2 |
| North Stoke, W Suss | 17 | B3 |
| North Street, Berks | 27 | A2 |
| North Street, Kent | 30 | C3 |
| North Sunderland, Nthumb | 109 | E2 |
| North Tamerton, Corn | 9 | C4 |
| North Tawton, Devon | 10 | A4 |
| North Thoresby, Linc | 84 | B2 |
| North Tidworth, Wilts | 25 | D4 |
| North Town, Devon | 9 | D3 |
| North Town, Som | 23 | D4 |
| North Town, Berks | 140 | A1 |
| North Tuddenham, Norf | 64 | A2 |
| North Walsham, Norf | 75 | C4 |
| North Waltham, Hamp | 26 | C4 |
| North Weald Basset, Essex | 41 | A3 |
| North Wheatley, Notts | 83 | B3 |
| North Widcombe, Som | 23 | D3 |
| North Willingham, Linc | 84 | A3 |
| North Wingfield, Derby | 71 | A1 |
| North Witham, Linc | 61 | B1 |
| North Wootton, Dors | 12 | B3 |
| North Wootton, Norf | 62 | D1 |
| North Wootton, Som | 23 | D4 |
| North Wraxall, Wilts | 25 | A2 |
| Northall, Bucks | 39 | A2 |
| Northallerton, N York | 93 | B2 |
| Northam, Devon | 9 | D2 |
| Northampton, Worc | 47 | C2 |
| Northampton, Nhants | 50 | B2 |
| Northaw, Herts | 40 | A3 |
| Northay, Som | 11 | B3 |
| Northborough, Camb | 61 | D2 |
| Northbourne, Kent | 31 | B4 |
| Northchapel, W Suss | 17 | A2 |
| Northcott, Devon | 4 | B1 |
| Northend, Warw | 49 | B3 |
| Northill, Beds | 51 | B3 |
| Northington, Hamp | 15 | B1 |
| Northlands, Linc | 73 | D2 |
| Northleach, Glouc | 37 | A2 |
| Northleigh, Devon | 11 | A4 |
| Northlew, Devon | 9 | D4 |
| Northmoor, Oxon | 37 | D3 |
| Northmuir, Angus | 123 | E3 |
| Northolt, G Lon | 141 | B1 |
| Northop, Flint | 67 | E1 |
| Northop Hall, Flint | 67 | E1 |
| Northorpe, Linc | 83 | C2 |
| Northorpe, Linc | 73 | C4 |
| Northowram, W York | 87 | A4 |
| Northrepps, Norf | 75 | C3 |
| Northway, Som | 11 | A2 |
| Northwich, Chesh | 79 | A4 |
| Northwold, Norf | 63 | A3 |
| Northwood, Shrop | 68 | B4 |
| Northwood Green, Glouc | 36 | A2 |
| Norton, E Sus | 19 | B4 |
| Norton, Glouc | 36 | B1 |
| Norton, N York | 94 | B4 |
| Norton, Nhants | 49 | C2 |
| Norton, Powys | 46 | B2 |
| Norton, S York | 82 | B1 |
| Norton, Shrop | 57 | B3 |
| Norton, Suff | 53 | C2 |
| Norton, W Suss | 17 | A4 |
| Norton, Wilts | 25 | A1 |
| Norton, Worc | 47 | C3 |
| Norton, Worc | 48 | A3 |
| Norton Bavant, Wilts | 25 | A4 |
| Norton Bridge, Staff | 69 | B4 |
| Norton Canes, Staff | 58 | A2 |
| Norton Canon, Heref | 46 | C3 |
| Norton Disney, Linc | 72 | C2 |
| Norton Fitzwarren, Som | 11 | A2 |
| Norton Hawkfield, Som | 24 | A2 |
| Norton Heath, Essex | 41 | B3 |
| Norton in Hales, Shrop | 69 | A3 |
| Norton Lindsey, Warw | 48 | C2 |
| Norton Little Green, Suff | 53 | C2 |
| Norton Malreward, Som | 24 | A2 |
| Norton St Philip, Som | 24 | B3 |
| Norton Wood, Heref | 46 | C3 |
| Norton-Juxta-Twycross, Leics | 59 | B2 |
| Norton-le-Clay, N York | 93 | C4 |
| Norwell, Notts | 72 | B1 |
| Norwell Woodhouse, Notts | 72 | A1 |
| NORWICH, Norf | 64 | B2 |
| Norwick, Shet | 139 | B1 |
| Norwood Green, G Lon | 141 | B2 |
| Norwood Hill, Surr | 148 | A4 |
| Noseley, Leics | 61 | A3 |
| Noss Mayo, Devon | 8 | B1 |
| Nosterfield, N York | 93 | B3 |
| Notgrove, Glouc | 37 | A2 |
| Notter, Corn | 4 | B3 |
| Nottingham, Notts | 71 | B3 |
| Notton, W York | 81 | C1 |
| Notton, Wilts | 25 | A2 |
| Noutard's Green, Worc | 47 | B2 |
| Nox, Shrop | 56 | C2 |
| Nuffield, Oxon | 27 | A1 |
| Nun Monkton, N York | 88 | C1 |
| Nunburnholme, E R of Y | 89 | B2 |
| Nuneaton, Warw | 59 | B3 |
| Nunhead, G Lon | 143 | B3 |
| Nunkeeling, E R of Y | 90 | A2 |
| Nunney, Som | 24 | B4 |
| Nunnington, N York | 94 | A3 |
| Nunwick, N York | 93 | B4 |
| Nuptow, Berks | 140 | A3 |
| Nursling, Hamp | 14 | B3 |
| Nutbourne, W Suss | 16 | B4 |
| Nutbourne, W Suss | 17 | B2 |
| Nutfield, Surr | 148 | B3 |
| Nuthampstead, Herts | 52 | A4 |
| Nuthurst, W Suss | 18 | A2 |
| Nutley, E Sus | 19 | B2 |
| Nyewood, W Suss | 16 | B2 |
| Nymet Rowland, Devon | 10 | A3 |
| Nymet Tracey, Devon | 10 | A4 |
| Nympsfield, Glouc | 36 | A3 |
| Oad Street, Kent | 30 | A3 |
| Oadby, Leics | 60 | C3 |
| Oak Cross, Devon | 9 | D4 |
| Oakamoor, Staff | 70 | A3 |
| Oakdale, Caer | 34 | D4 |
| Oake, Som | 11 | A2 |
| Oaken, Staff | 57 | C3 |
| Oakenclough, Lanc | 85 | C2 |
| Oakenshaw, Durham | 98 | C2 |
| Oakenshaw, W York | 87 | B4 |
| Oaker Side, Derby | 70 | C1 |
| Oakford, Cered | 44 | F2 |
| Oakford, Devon | 10 | C2 |
| Oakham, Rut | 61 | B2 |
| Oakhill, Som | 24 | A4 |
| Oakington, Camb | 52 | A2 |
| Oakle Street, Glouc | 36 | A2 |
| Oakley, Beds | 51 | A3 |
| Oakley, Bucks | 38 | B2 |
| Oakley, Fife | 113 | C1 |
| Oakley, Hamp | 26 | C4 |
| Oakley, Suff | 54 | A1 |
| Oakley Green, Berks | 140 | B2 |
| Oakridge, Glouc | 36 | B3 |
| Oaksey, Wilts | 36 | C4 |
| Oakthorpe, Leics | 59 | B2 |
| Oakwoodhill, Surr | 18 | A1 |
| Oare, Kent | 30 | C3 |
| Oare, Som | 22 | D4 |
| Oare, Wilts | 25 | C3 |
| Oasby, Linc | 73 | A3 |
| Oath, Som | 11 | C2 |
| Oathlaw, Angus | 124 | A3 |
| Oatlands Park, Surr | 141 | B4 |
| Oban, Argyll | 117 | A2 |
| Obley, Shrop | 46 | B1 |
| Occold, Suff | 54 | A1 |
| Ochiltree, E Ayr | 106 | E3 |
| Ockbrook, Derby | 71 | A4 |
| Ockham, Surr | 146 | B2 |
| Ockle, High | 120 | F2 |
| Ockley, Surr | 18 | A1 |
| Ocle Pychard, Heref | 47 | A3 |
| Odcombe, Som | 12 | A3 |
| Oddingley, Worc | 47 | C2 |
| Oddington, Oxon | 38 | A2 |
| Odell, Beds | 50 | C2 |
| Odiham, Hamp | 27 | B4 |
| Odsey, Camb | 51 | C4 |
| Odstock, Wilts | 13 | B2 |
| Odstone, Leics | 60 | A2 |
| Offchurch, Warw | 49 | A2 |
| Offenham, Worc | 48 | B3 |
| Offham, E Sus | 19 | A3 |
| Offham, Kent | 29 | A3 |
| Offord Cluny, Camb | 51 | C2 |
| Offord Darcy, Camb | 51 | C2 |
| Offton, Suff | 53 | D3 |
| Offwell, Devon | 11 | A4 |
| Ogbourne Maizey, Wilts | 25 | D2 |
| Ogbourne St Andrew, Wilts | 25 | D2 |
| Ogbourne St George, Wilts | 25 | D2 |
| Ogle, Nthumb | 104 | A3 |
| Oglet, Mers | 78 | A4 |
| Ogmore, Glam | 22 | D1 |
| Ogmore Vale, Brid | 34 | B4 |
| Ogmore-by-Sea, Glam | 22 | D2 |
| Okeford Fitzpaine, Dors | 12 | C3 |
| Okehampton, Devon | 9 | E4 |
| Old, Nhants | 50 | B1 |
| Old Alresford, Hamp | 15 | B1 |
| Old Basing, Hamp | 27 | A3 |
| Old Bewick, Nthumb | 109 | D3 |
| Old Bolingbroke, Linc | 73 | D1 |
| Old Bracknell, Berks | 140 | A4 |
| Old Brampton, Derby | 70 | C1 |
| Old Buckenham, Norf | 64 | A3 |
| Old Burghclere, Hamp | 26 | B3 |
| Old Byland, N York | 93 | D3 |
| Old Church Stoke, Powys | 56 | B3 |
| Old Cleeve, Som | 22 | F4 |
| Old Clipstone, Notts | 71 | B1 |
| Old Dailly, S Ayr | 100 | C1 |
| Old Dalby, Leics | 60 | C1 |
| Old Deer, Aber | 134 | D3 |
| Old Edlington, S York | 82 | B2 |
| Old Ellerby, E R of Y | 90 | A3 |
| Old Forge, Heref | 35 | B2 |
| Old Grimsby, Scilly | 139 | A1 |
| Old Hunstanton, Norf | 74 | C3 |
| Old Hurst, Camb | 51 | C1 |
| Old Hutton, Cumb | 91 | F2 |
| Old Kilpatrick, Dumb | 112 | A2 |
| Old Langho, Lanc | 86 | B3 |
| Old Leake, Linc | 73 | D2 |
| Old Malton, N York | 94 | B4 |
| Old Milverton, Warw | 49 | A2 |
| Old Newton, Suff | 53 | D2 |
| Old Radnor, Powys | 46 | B2 |
| Old Rayne, Aber | 128 | E1 |
| Old Romney, Kent | 21 | C2 |
| Old Sodbury, Glouc | 24 | B1 |
| Old Somerby, Linc | 72 | C4 |
| Old Stratford, Nhants | 50 | B4 |
| Old Town, Cumb | 92 | A3 |
| Old Town, Scilly | 139 | A2 |
| Old Warden, Beds | 51 | B4 |
| Old Weston, Camb | 51 | B1 |
| Old Windsor, Berks | 140 | C3 |
| Old Wives Lees, Kent | 30 | C3 |
| Old Woking, Surr | 146 | A2 |
| Oldberrow, Warw | 48 | B2 |
| Oldbury, Shrop | 57 | B3 |
| Oldbury, Warw | 59 | B3 |
| Oldbury on the Hill, Glouc | 36 | B4 |
| Oldbury-on-Severn, Glouc | 35 | C4 |
| Oldcastle, Monm | 34 | E1 |
| Oldcotes, Notts | 82 | B3 |
| Oldfield, Worc | 47 | C2 |
| Oldford, Som | 24 | B4 |
| Oldhall Green, Suff | 53 | C3 |
| Oldham, G Man | 80 | A2 |
| Oldhamstocks, E Loth | 115 | C3 |
| Oldmeldrum, Aber | 129 | A1 |
| Oldmill, Corn | 4 | B2 |
| Oldmixon, Som | 23 | B3 |
| Oldstead, N York | 93 | D3 |
| Oldwall, Cumb | 102 | D4 |
| Oldwalls, Swan | 33 | B4 |
| Ollaberry, Shet | 139 | A2 |
| Ollerton, Chesh | 79 | B4 |
| Ollerton, Notts | 72 | A1 |
| Ollerton, Shrop | 57 | A1 |
| Olney, Bucks | 50 | C3 |
| Olveston, Glouc | 24 | A1 |
| Ombersley, Worc | 47 | C2 |
| Ompton, Notts | 72 | A1 |
| Onchan, I o M | 139 | C3 |
| Onecote, Staff | 70 | A2 |
| Onibury, Shrop | 46 | C1 |
| Onich, High | 121 | D3 |
| Onllwyn, Neath | 34 | A3 |
| Onneley, Staff | 69 | A3 |
| Onslow Village, Surr | 146 | A3 |
| Onston, Chesh | 79 | A4 |
| Opinan, High | 130 | F1 |
| Orby, Linc | 74 | A1 |
| Orchard Portman, Som | 11 | B2 |
| Orcheston, Wilts | 25 | C4 |
| Orcop, Heref | 35 | B1 |
| Orcop Hill, Heref | 35 | B1 |
| Ordhead, Aber | 128 | E3 |
| Ordie, Aber | 128 | C3 |
| Ordiequish, Moray | 133 | C3 |
| Ordley, Nthumb | 103 | D4 |
| Orford, Suff | 54 | C3 |
| Organford, Dors | 7 | C1 |
| Orleton, Heref | 46 | D2 |
| Orleton, Worc | 47 | B2 |
| Orlingbury, Nhants | 50 | C1 |
| Ormesby St Margaret, Norf | 65 | C1 |
| Ormesby St Michael, Norf | 65 | C1 |
| Ormiston, E Loth | 114 | C3 |
| Ormskirk, Lanc | 78 | A1 |
| Orpington, G Lon | 144 | B4 |
| Orrell, G Man | 78 | B2 |
| Orsett, Essex | 29 | A1 |
| Orslow, Staff | 57 | B1 |
| Orston, Notts | 72 | B3 |
| Orton, Cumb | 92 | A1 |
| Orton, Nhants | 50 | B1 |
| Orton, Staff | 57 | C3 |
| Orton-on-the-Hill, Leics | 59 | B2 |
| Orwell, Camb | 52 | A3 |
| Osbaldeston, Lanc | 86 | A3 |
| Osbaston, Leics | 60 | A2 |
| Osbaston, Shrop | 56 | B1 |
| Osbournby, Linc | 73 | A3 |
| Oscroft, Chesh | 68 | B1 |
| Osgathorpe, Leics | 60 | A1 |
| Osgodby, Linc | 83 | D3 |
| Osgodby, N York | 89 | A3 |
| Osgodby, N York | 94 | D3 |
| Osmaston, Derby | 70 | B3 |
| Osmington, Dors | 7 | A2 |
| Osmington Mills, Dors | 7 | A2 |
| Osmotherley, N York | 93 | C2 |
| Ossett, W York | 88 | A4 |
| Ossington, Notts | 72 | B1 |
| Osterley, G Lon | 142 | A2 |
| Oswaldkirk, N York | 94 | A3 |
| Oswaldtwistle, Lanc | 86 | B4 |
| Oswestry, Shrop | 67 | E4 |
| Otford, Kent | 149 | C1 |
| Othery, Som | 11 | C1 |
| Otley, Suff | 54 | A3 |
| Otley, W York | 87 | B2 |
| Otter Ferry, Argyll | 111 | A1 |
| Otterbourne, Hamp | 15 | A2 |
| Otterburn, N York | 86 | C1 |
| Otterburn, Nthumb | 103 | C1 |
| Otterham, Corn | 3 | E1 |
| Otterhampton, Som | 23 | B4 |
| Otterton, Devon | 6 | A1 |

| PLACE | PAGE | GRID |
|---|---|---|
| Ottery, Devon | 4 | C2 |
| Ottery St Mary, Devon | 10 | D4 |
| Ottringham, E R of Y | 90 | B4 |
| Oughtibridge, S York | 81 | C3 |
| Oughtrington, Chesh | 79 | B3 |
| Oulston, N York | 93 | D4 |
| Oulton, Cumb | 96 | F1 |
| Oulton, Norf | 75 | B4 |
| Oulton, Staff | 69 | B4 |
| Oulton Street, Norf | 75 | B4 |
| Oundle, Nhants | 61 | C4 |
| Ousby, Cumb | 97 | C2 |
| Ousden, Suff | 53 | A2 |
| Ousefleet, E R of Y | 89 | B4 |
| Ouston, Durham | 98 | C1 |
| Out Rawcliffe, Lanc | 85 | B2 |
| Outgate, Cumb | 91 | E1 |
| Outhgill, Cumb | 92 | B1 |
| Outhill, Warw | 48 | B2 |
| Outlane, W York | 81 | A1 |
| Outwell, Norf | 62 | C2 |
| Outwood, Surr | 148 | C4 |
| Outwoods, Staff | 57 | B1 |
| Ouzlewell Green, W York | 88 | A4 |
| Over, Camb | 52 | A1 |
| Over Compton, Dors | 12 | B3 |
| Over Haddon, Derby | 70 | B1 |
| Over Kellet, Lanc | 91 | F4 |
| Over Kiddington, Oxon | 37 | D2 |
| Over Norton, Oxon | 37 | C1 |
| Over Peover, Chesh | 79 | B4 |
| Over Silton, N York | 93 | C2 |
| Over Stowey, Som | 11 | A1 |
| Over Wallop, Hamp | 14 | B1 |
| Over Whitacre, Warw | 59 | A4 |
| Over Worton, Oxon | 37 | D1 |
| Overbury, Worc | 48 | A4 |
| Overcombe, Dors | 7 | A2 |
| Overseal, Derby | 59 | B1 |
| Oversland, Kent | 30 | C3 |
| Overstone, Nhants | 50 | B2 |
| Overstrand, Norf | 75 | C3 |
| Overthorpe, Nhants | 49 | B4 |
| Overton, Hamp | 26 | C4 |
| Overton, Lanc | 85 | B1 |
| Overton, N York | 88 | C1 |
| Overton, Shrop | 46 | D1 |
| Overton, Swan | 22 | A1 |
| Overton, W York | 81 | B1 |
| Overton, Wrex | 68 | A3 |
| Overtown, Lanc | 92 | A4 |
| Overtown, N Lan | 113 | A4 |
| Oving, Bucks | 38 | C2 |
| Oving, W Suss | 17 | A4 |
| Ovingham, Nthumb | 104 | A4 |
| Ovington, Durham | 98 | B4 |
| Ovington, Essex | 53 | A4 |
| Ovington, Hamp | 15 | B1 |
| Ovington, Norf | 63 | C3 |
| Ovington, Nthumb | 104 | A4 |
| Ower, Hamp | 14 | B3 |
| Owlswick, Bucks | 38 | C3 |
| Owmby, Linc | 83 | D2 |
| Owmby, Linc | 83 | D3 |
| Owslebury, Hamp | 15 | B2 |
| Owston, Leics | 61 | A2 |
| Owston, S York | 82 | B1 |
| Owston Ferry, Linc | 83 | B2 |
| Owstwick, E R of Y | 90 | B3 |
| Owthorne, E R of Y | 90 | C4 |
| Owthorpe, Notts | 72 | A4 |
| Oxborough, Norf | 63 | A3 |
| Oxbridge, Dors | 12 | A4 |
| Oxcombe, Linc | 84 | B4 |
| Oxen End, Essex | 42 | A1 |
| Oxen Park, Cumb | 91 | D3 |
| Oxenholme, Cumb | 91 | F2 |
| Oxenhope, W York | 86 | D3 |
| Oxenpill, Som | 23 | C4 |
| Oxenton, Glouc | 36 | C1 |
| Oxenwood, Wilts | 26 | A3 |
| Oxford, Oxon | 38 | A3 |
| Oxhill, Warw | 49 | A3 |
| Oxley Green, Essex | 43 | A2 |
| Oxley's Green, E Sus | 20 | B2 |
| Oxnam, Bord | 109 | A3 |
| Oxnead, Norf | 64 | B1 |
| Oxshott, Surr | 147 | B1 |
| Oxspring, S York | 81 | B2 |
| Oxted, Surr | 149 | A3 |
| Oxton, Bord | 115 | A4 |
| Oxton, N York | 88 | C2 |
| Oxton, Notts | 72 | A2 |
| Oxwich, Swan | 22 | A1 |
| Oxwich Green, Swan | 22 | A1 |
| Oyne, Aber | 128 | E1 |
| Packington, Leics | 59 | B1 |
| Padanaram, Angus | 123 | E4 |
| Padbury, Bucks | 38 | B1 |
| Paddington, G Lon | 143 | A2 |
| Paddlesworth, Kent | 29 | B3 |
| Paddlesworth, Kent | 21 | D1 |
| Paddock Wood, Kent | 29 | B4 |
| Padiham, Lanc | 86 | B3 |
| Padside, N York | 87 | B1 |
| Padstow, Corn | 3 | C2 |
| Padworth, Berks | 26 | C2 |
| Pagham, W Suss | 17 | A4 |
| Paglesham, Essex | 43 | A4 |
| Paignton, Devon | 5 | C3 |
| Painscastle, Powys | 46 | A3 |
| Painshawfield, Nthumb | 104 | A4 |
| Painsthorpe, E R of Y | 89 | B1 |
| Painswick, Glouc | 36 | B3 |
| Painter's Forstal, Kent | 30 | B3 |
| Paisley, Renf | 112 | A3 |
| Pakenham, Suff | 53 | C2 |
| Paley Street, Berks | 140 | A2 |
| Palgrave, Suff | 53 | D1 |
| Pallington, Dors | 7 | A1 |
| Palnackie, D & G | 101 | C4 |
| Palnure, D & G | 100 | E4 |
| Palterton, Derby | 71 | A1 |
| Pamber End, Hamp | 26 | C3 |
| Pamber Heath, Hamp | 26 | C3 |
| Pamphill, Dors | 13 | A4 |

| PLACE | PAGE | GRID |
|---|---|---|
| Pampisford, Camb | 52 | B3 |
| Panbride, Angus | 119 | E1 |
| Pancrasweek, Devon | 9 | B4 |
| Pandy, Monm | 34 | E1 |
| Pandy Tudur, Ab & Col | 67 | A1 |
| Panfield, Essex | 42 | A1 |
| Pangbourne, Berks | 27 | A1 |
| Pangdean, W Suss | 18 | B3 |
| Pannal, N York | 88 | A2 |
| Pant, Shrop | 56 | B1 |
| Pant Glas, Gwyn | 66 | D3 |
| Pantasaph, Flint | 77 | C4 |
| Pant-ffrwyth, Brid | 22 | E1 |
| Pantglas, Powys | 55 | C3 |
| Panton, Linc | 84 | A4 |
| Pant-y-dwr, Powys | 45 | D1 |
| Pant-y-mwyn, Flint | 67 | D1 |
| Panxworth, Norf | 65 | A2 |
| Papcastle, Cumb | 96 | D3 |
| Papigoe, High | 138 | F2 |
| Papplewick, Notts | 71 | B2 |
| Papworth Everard, Camb | 51 | C2 |
| Par, Corn | 3 | D4 |
| Parbold, Lanc | 78 | B1 |
| Parbrook, Som | 12 | A1 |
| Parc, Gwyn | 67 | A4 |
| Parc Seymour, Newport | 35 | A4 |
| Pardshaw, Cumb | 96 | D3 |
| Parham, Suff | 54 | B2 |
| Park, Nthumb | 103 | A4 |
| Park Corner, Oxon | 38 | B4 |
| Park Corner, Berks | 140 | A1 |
| Park Royal, G Lon | 142 | B1 |
| Park Street, Herts | 39 | C3 |
| Parkend, Glouc | 35 | C3 |
| Parkgate, Kent | 144 | C4 |
| Parkgate, D & G | 101 | E2 |
| Parkgate, Surr | 148 | A4 |
| Parkham, Devon | 9 | C2 |
| Parkmill, Swan | 33 | C4 |
| Parr Bridge, G Man | 79 | B2 |
| Parracombe, Devon | 22 | C4 |
| Parson Drove, Camb | 62 | B2 |
| Partington, G Man | 79 | B3 |
| Partney, Linc | 73 | D1 |
| Parton, Cumb | 96 | F1 |
| Parton, Cumb | 96 | C4 |
| Parton, D & G | 101 | B3 |
| Partridge Green, W Suss | 18 | A2 |
| Parwich, Derby | 70 | B2 |
| Paston, Norf | 75 | C4 |
| Patchway, Glouc | 24 | A1 |
| Pateley Bridge, N York | 92 | E4 |
| Path of Condie, Perth | 119 | A3 |
| Pathhead, M Loth | 114 | C3 |
| Patna, E Ayr | 106 | D4 |
| Patney, Wilts | 25 | C3 |
| Patrick, I o M | 139 | B3 |
| Patrick Brompton, N York | 93 | A2 |
| Patrington, E R of Y | 90 | C4 |
| Patterdale, Cumb | 97 | A4 |
| Pattingham, Staff | 57 | C3 |
| Pattishall, Nhants | 50 | A3 |
| Pattiswick Green, Essex | 42 | B1 |
| Paulerspury, Nhants | 50 | A3 |
| Paull, E R of Y | 90 | A4 |
| Paulton, Som | 24 | A3 |
| Pauperhaugh, Nthumb | 104 | A1 |
| Pavenham, Beds | 51 | A3 |
| Pawlett, Som | 23 | B4 |
| Paxford, Glouc | 48 | C4 |
| Paxton, Bord | 115 | E4 |
| Payhembury, Devon | 10 | D4 |
| Paythorne, Lanc | 86 | C2 |
| Peacehaven, E Sus | 19 | A4 |
| Peak Forest, Derby | 81 | A4 |
| Peakirk, Camb | 61 | D2 |
| Pease Pottage, W Suss | 18 | B1 |
| Peaseland Green, Norf | 64 | A1 |
| Peasemore, Berks | 26 | B1 |
| Peasenhall, Suff | 54 | C1 |
| Peaslake, Surr | 147 | A4 |
| Peasmarsh, Surr | 146 | A4 |
| Peasmarsh, E Sus | 21 | A2 |
| Peat Inn, Fife | 119 | D3 |
| Peathill, Aber | 134 | D2 |
| Peatling Parva, Leics | 60 | B4 |
| Pebmarsh, Essex | 53 | B4 |
| Pebworth, Worc | 48 | B3 |
| Pecket Well, W York | 86 | D4 |
| Peckforton, Chesh | 68 | B2 |
| Peckham, G Lon | 143 | B2 |
| Peckleton, Leics | 60 | A3 |
| Pedlinge, Kent | 21 | D1 |
| Pedwell, Som | 11 | C1 |
| Peebles, Bord | 108 | A1 |
| Peel, I o M | 139 | B3 |
| Peene, Kent | 21 | D1 |
| Pegswood, Nthumb | 104 | B2 |
| Peldon, Essex | 43 | A2 |
| Pelsall, W Mids | 58 | A2 |
| Pelton, Durham | 98 | C1 |
| Pelynt, Corn | 4 | A4 |
| Pembrey, Carm | 33 | B3 |
| Pembridge, Heref | 46 | C2 |
| Pembroke, Pemb | 32 | D3 |
| Pembroke Dock, Pemb | 32 | D3 |
| Pembury, Kent | 20 | A1 |
| Pen Rhiwfawr, Neath | 33 | D2 |
| Penallt, Monm | 35 | B2 |
| Penally, Pemb | 32 | E3 |
| Penalt, Heref | 35 | B1 |
| Penarth, Glam | 23 | A2 |
| Pen-bont Rhydybeddau, Cered | 55 | B4 |
| Penbryn, Cered | 44 | D3 |
| Pencader, Carm | 44 | F4 |
| Pencaitland, E Loth | 114 | C3 |
| Pencarnisiog, Angle | 76 | B4 |
| Pencarreg, Carm | 44 | F3 |
| Pencelli, Powys | 34 | C1 |
| Penclawdd, Swan | 33 | C4 |
| Pencoed, Brid | 22 | E1 |
| Pencombe, Heref | 47 | A3 |
| Pencraig, Heref | 35 | B2 |
| Pencraig, Powys | 67 | C4 |

| PLACE | PAGE | GRID |
|---|---|---|
| Pendeen, Corn | 1 | A2 |
| Penderyn, Rhond | 34 | B3 |
| Pendine, Carm | 32 | F3 |
| Pendlebury, G Man | 79 | B2 |
| Pendleton, Lanc | 86 | B3 |
| Pendock, Worc | 36 | A1 |
| Pendoggett, Corn | 3 | D2 |
| Pendoylan, Glam | 22 | F1 |
| Penegoes, Powys | 55 | B3 |
| Pen-ffordd, Pemb | 32 | D1 |
| Pengam, Caer | 34 | D4 |
| Penge, G Lon | 143 | B3 |
| Pengelly, Corn | 3 | D1 |
| Pengrugla, Corn | 2 | C1 |
| Penhallow, Corn | 3 | B4 |
| Penhalvean, Corn | 1 | D1 |
| Penhow, Newport | 35 | A4 |
| Penicuik, M Loth | 114 | B4 |
| Penistone, S York | 81 | B2 |
| Penkridge, Staff | 58 | A2 |
| Penlean, Corn | 9 | B4 |
| Penley, Wrex | 68 | A3 |
| Penllyn, Glam | 22 | E1 |
| Penmachno, Ab & Col | 67 | A2 |
| Penmaenmawr, Ab & Col | 76 | E4 |
| Penmaenpool, Gwyn | 55 | B1 |
| Penmark, Glam | 22 | F2 |
| Penmorfa, Gwyn | 66 | E3 |
| Penmynydd, Angle | 76 | C4 |
| Penn Street, Bucks | 39 | A4 |
| Pennal, Gwyn | 55 | B3 |
| Pennan, Aber | 134 | C2 |
| Pennant, Powys | 55 | C3 |
| Pennard, Swan | 33 | C4 |
| Pennerley, Shrop | 56 | C3 |
| Pennorth, Powys | 34 | C1 |
| Penny Bridge, Cumb | 91 | D3 |
| Penny Hill, Linc | 73 | D4 |
| Pennymoor, Devon | 10 | B3 |
| Penparc, Cered | 44 | D3 |
| Penperlleni, Monm | 34 | E3 |
| Penpoll, Corn | 3 | E4 |
| Penponds, Corn | 1 | D1 |
| Penpont, D & G | 101 | C1 |
| Pen-rhiw, Pemb | 44 | D4 |
| Penrhiwceiber, Rhond | 34 | C4 |
| Penrhiwllan, Cered | 44 | E4 |
| Penrhiw-pal, Cered | 44 | E3 |
| Penrhos, Gwyn | 66 | C4 |
| Penrhos, Monm | 35 | A2 |
| Penrhyn Bay, Ab & Col | 76 | F4 |
| Penrhyncoch, Cered | 55 | A4 |
| Penrhyndeudraeth, Gwyn | 66 | E3 |
| Penrice, Swan | 33 | B4 |
| Penrith, Cumb | 97 | B3 |
| Penrose, Corn | 3 | C3 |
| Penruddock, Cumb | 97 | A3 |
| Penryn, Corn | 2 | A2 |
| Pensarn, Ab & Col | 77 | A4 |
| Pensax, Worc | 47 | B1 |
| Penselwood, Som | 12 | C1 |
| Pensford, Som | 24 | A3 |
| Pensham, Worc | 48 | A4 |
| Penshaw, T & W | 98 | D1 |
| Penshurst, Kent | 149 | C4 |
| Penshurst Station, Kent | 149 | C4 |
| Pensilva, Corn | 4 | A3 |
| Pentewan, Corn | 2 | C1 |
| Pentir, Gwyn | 66 | E1 |
| Pentlow, Essex | 53 | B3 |
| Pentney, Norf | 63 | A2 |
| Penton Mewsey, Hamp | 26 | A4 |
| Pentonbridge, Cumb | 102 | C3 |
| Pentre, Shrop | 56 | C1 |
| Pentre Berw, Angle | 76 | C4 |
| Pentre Hodrey, Shrop | 46 | B1 |
| Pentre Llanrhaeadr, Denb | 67 | C1 |
| Pentre Meyrick, Glam | 22 | E2 |
| Pentrebach, Merth | 34 | C3 |
| Pentre-bach, Powys | 34 | B1 |
| Pentre-celyn, Denb | 67 | D2 |
| Pentre-celyn, Powys | 55 | D2 |
| Pentre-cwrt, Carm | 44 | E4 |
| Pentredwr, Denb | 67 | D3 |
| Pentrefelin, Gwyn | 66 | D3 |
| Pentrefoelas, Ab & Col | 67 | A2 |
| Pentregat, Cered | 44 | E3 |
| Pentre-Gwenlais, Carm | 33 | C2 |
| Pentre-tafarn-y-fedw, Ab & Col | 67 | A1 |
| Pentrich, Derby | 70 | C2 |
| Pentridge Hill, Dors | 13 | A3 |
| Pen-twyn, Monm | 35 | B3 |
| Pentyrch, Cardiff | 22 | F1 |
| Penwithick, Corn | 3 | D4 |
| Penybanc, Carm | 33 | C1 |
| Penybont, Powys | 45 | E2 |
| Pen-y-bont, Powys | 56 | A1 |
| Pen-y-bont-fawr, Powys | 55 | E1 |
| Pen-y-bryn, Pemb | 44 | C4 |
| Penycae, Wrex | 67 | E3 |
| Pen-y-clawdd, Monm | 35 | A3 |
| Pen-y-coedcae, Rhond | 34 | C4 |
| Pen-y-cwn, Pemb | 32 | C1 |
| Penyffordd, Flint | 67 | E1 |
| Pen-y-Garnedd, Powys | 55 | E1 |
| Penygraig, Rhond | 34 | B4 |
| Pen-y-graig, Gwyn | 66 | B4 |
| Penygroes, Carm | 33 | C2 |
| Penygroes, Gwyn | 66 | D2 |
| Pen-y-stryt, Denb | 67 | D2 |
| Penywaun, Rhond | 34 | B3 |
| Penzance, Corn | 1 | B2 |
| Peopleton, Worc | 48 | A3 |
| Peper Harow, Surr | 145 | B4 |
| Peplow, Shrop | 57 | A1 |
| Perivale, G Lon | 142 | A1 |
| Perlethorpe, Notts | 72 | A1 |
| Perranporth, Corn | 3 | B4 |
| Perranuthnoe, Corn | 1 | C2 |
| Perranwell, Corn | 2 | A1 |
| Perranzabuloe, Corn | 3 | B4 |
| Pershall, Staff | 69 | B4 |
| Pershore, Worc | 48 | A3 |
| Pertenhall, Beds | 51 | B2 |
| Perth, Perth | 119 | A2 |

| PLACE | PAGE | GRID |
|---|---|---|
| Perthy, Shrop | 68 | A4 |
| Perton, Heref | 47 | A4 |
| Perton, Staff | 57 | C3 |
| Peter Tavy, Devon | 4 | C2 |
| Peterborough, Camb | 61 | D3 |
| Peterchurch, Heref | 46 | B4 |
| Peterculter, Aber | 129 | B3 |
| Peterhead, Aber | 134 | E3 |
| Peterlee, Durham | 99 | A2 |
| Peter's Green, Herts | 39 | C2 |
| Peters Marland, Devon | 9 | D3 |
| Petersfield, Hamp | 16 | B2 |
| Petersham, G Lon | 142 | A3 |
| Peterstone Wentlooge, Newport | 23 | B1 |
| Peterstow, Heref | 35 | B1 |
| Petham, Kent | 31 | A4 |
| Petherwin Gate, Corn | 4 | A1 |
| Petrockstow, Devon | 9 | D3 |
| Pett, E Sus | 21 | A3 |
| Pettaugh, Suff | 54 | A2 |
| Pettinain, S Lan | 107 | C1 |
| Pettistree, Suff | 54 | B3 |
| Petton, Devon | 10 | D2 |
| Petts Wood, G Lon | 144 | B4 |
| Petworth, W Suss | 17 | B2 |
| Pevensey, E Sus | 20 | A4 |
| Pewsey, Wilts | 25 | D3 |
| Phepson, Worc | 48 | A2 |
| Philham, Devon | 9 | B2 |
| Phillack, Corn | 1 | C1 |
| Philleigh, Corn | 2 | B1 |
| Philpstoun, W Loth | 113 | C2 |
| Phoenix Green, Hamp | 27 | B3 |
| Pica, Cumb | 96 | D4 |
| Pickering, N York | 94 | B3 |
| Pickford, W Mids | 59 | B4 |
| Pickhill, N York | 93 | B3 |
| Picklescott, Shrop | 56 | C3 |
| Pickmere, Chesh | 79 | A4 |
| Pickney, Som | 11 | A2 |
| Pickup Bank, Lanc | 86 | B4 |
| Pickwell, Leics | 61 | A2 |
| Pickworth, Rut | 61 | C2 |
| Pickworth, Linc | 73 | A4 |
| Picton, Chesh | 68 | A1 |
| Picton, N York | 93 | C1 |
| Piddinghoe, E Sus | 19 | B4 |
| Piddington, Nhants | 50 | B3 |
| Piddington, Oxon | 38 | B2 |
| Piddlehinton, Dors | 12 | C4 |
| Piddletrenthide, Dors | 12 | C4 |
| Pidley, Camb | 52 | A1 |
| Pierowall, Ork | 139 | A1 |
| Pilham, Linc | 83 | C3 |
| Pillaton, Corn | 4 | B3 |
| Pillerton Hersey, Warw | 49 | A3 |
| Pillerton Priors, Warw | 49 | A3 |
| Pilley, Hamp | 14 | B4 |
| Pilley, S York | 81 | C2 |
| Pilling, Lanc | 85 | B2 |
| Pilning, Glouc | 23 | D1 |
| Pilsbury, Derby | 70 | A1 |
| Pilsdon, Dors | 11 | C4 |
| Pilsley, Derby | 70 | B1 |
| Pilsley, Derby | 71 | A1 |
| Pilson Green, Norf | 65 | B2 |
| Piltdown, E Sus | 19 | B2 |
| Pilton, Nhants | 61 | C4 |
| Pilton, Rut | 61 | B3 |
| Pilton, Som | 12 | B1 |
| Pimperne, Dors | 12 | D3 |
| Pinchbeck, Linc | 62 | A1 |
| Pinley Green, Warw | 48 | C2 |
| Pinn, Devon | 6 | A1 |
| Pinvin, Worc | 48 | A3 |
| Pinwherry, S Ayr | 100 | C2 |
| Pinxton, Derby | 71 | A2 |
| Pipe and Lyde, Heref | 46 | D4 |
| Pipewell, Nhants | 61 | A4 |
| Pirbright, Surr | 145 | B2 |
| Pirbright Camp, Surr | 145 | B2 |
| Pirnmill, N Ayr | 105 | F1 |
| Pirton, Herts | 39 | C1 |
| Pirton, Worc | 47 | C3 |
| Pishill, Oxon | 38 | B4 |
| Pistyll, Gwyn | 66 | C3 |
| Pitcairngreen, Perth | 119 | A2 |
| Pitcaple, Aber | 129 | A1 |
| Pitch Green, Bucks | 38 | C3 |
| Pitch Place, Surr | 17 | A1 |
| Pitchcombe, Glouc | 36 | B3 |
| Pitchcott, Bucks | 38 | C2 |
| Pitchford, Shrop | 56 | D2 |
| Pitcombe, Som | 12 | B1 |
| Pitlessie, Fife | 119 | C3 |
| Pitlochry, Perth | 123 | A3 |
| Pitmedden, Aber | 129 | B1 |
| Pitney, Som | 11 | C2 |
| Pitscottie, Fife | 119 | D3 |
| Pitsford, Nhants | 50 | B2 |
| Pitt, Devon | 10 | D3 |
| Pittenweem, Fife | 119 | E4 |
| Pittington, Durham | 98 | D2 |
| Pitton, Wilts | 14 | A1 |
| Pittulie, Aber | 134 | D2 |
| Pity Me, Durham | 98 | C1 |
| Pixham, Surr | 147 | B3 |
| Plains, N Lan | 113 | A3 |
| Plaish, Shrop | 56 | D3 |
| Plaistow, Derby | 70 | C2 |
| Plaistow, W Suss | 17 | B1 |
| Plaistow, G Lon | 144 | A1 |
| Plaitford, Hamp | 14 | B2 |
| Plas Cymyran, Angle | 76 | A4 |
| Plastow Green, Hamp | 26 | C3 |
| Platt, Kent | 29 | A3 |
| Plawsworth, Durham | 98 | C1 |
| Plaxtol, Kent | 29 | A3 |
| Play Hatch, Oxon | 27 | B1 |
| Playford, Suff | 54 | A3 |
| Playing Place, Corn | 2 | A1 |
| Playley Green, Glouc | 36 | A1 |
| Plealey, Shrop | 56 | C2 |
| Plean, Stirl | 113 | A1 |
| Pleasance, Fife | 119 | B3 |

| PLACE | PAGE | GRID |
|---|---|---|
| Pleasington, Lanc | 86 | A4 |
| Pleasley, Derby | 71 | A1 |
| Plemstall, Chesh | 68 | A1 |
| Pleshey, Essex | 42 | A2 |
| Plockton, High | 125 | F1 |
| Plowden, Shrop | 56 | C4 |
| Ploxgreen, Shrop | 56 | C2 |
| Pluckley, Kent | 30 | B4 |
| Pluckley Thorne, Kent | 30 | B4 |
| Plumbland, Cumb | 96 | E2 |
| Plumley, Chesh | 79 | B4 |
| Plumpton, Cumb | 97 | B2 |
| Plumpton, E Sus | 19 | A3 |
| Plumpton, Nhants | 49 | C3 |
| Plumpton Green, E Sus | 19 | A3 |
| Plumstead, Norf | 75 | B4 |
| Plumstead, G Lon | 144 | B2 |
| Plumtree, Notts | 71 | B4 |
| Plungar, Leics | 72 | B4 |
| Plurenden, Kent | 21 | B1 |
| Plush, Dors | 12 | C4 |
| Plwmp, Cered | 44 | E3 |
| Plymouth, Devon | 4 | C4 |
| Plympton, Devon | 4 | D4 |
| Plymtree, Devon | 10 | D4 |
| Pockley, N York | 94 | A3 |
| Pocklington, E R of Y | 89 | B2 |
| Podimore, Som | 12 | A2 |
| Podington, Beds | 50 | C2 |
| Podmore, Staff | 69 | A4 |
| Pointon, Linc | 73 | B4 |
| Polbain, High | 135 | C2 |
| Polbathic, Corn | 4 | B4 |
| Polbeth, W Loth | 113 | C3 |
| Polebrook, Nhants | 61 | C4 |
| Polesworth, Warw | 59 | A3 |
| Polglass, High | 135 | C2 |
| Polgooth, Corn | 3 | D4 |
| Poling, W Suss | 17 | B4 |
| Polkerris, Corn | 3 | E4 |
| Pollington, E R of Y | 88 | C4 |
| Polmassick, Corn | 2 | C1 |
| Polmont, Falkirk | 113 | B2 |
| Polnish, High | 121 | B1 |
| Polperro, Corn | 4 | A4 |
| Polruan, Corn | 3 | E4 |
| Polstead, Suff | 53 | C4 |
| Poltimore, Devon | 10 | C4 |
| Polton, M Loth | 114 | B3 |
| Polwarth, Bord | 115 | C4 |
| Polyphant, Corn | 4 | A2 |
| Polzeath, Corn | 3 | C2 |
| Pomathorn, M Loth | 114 | B4 |
| Pondersbridge, Camb | 62 | A3 |
| Ponsanooth, Corn | 2 | A1 |
| Ponsworthy, Devon | 5 | A2 |
| Pont Robert, Powys | 55 | E2 |
| Pontantwn, Carm | 33 | B2 |
| Pontardawe, Neath | 33 | D3 |
| Pontarddulais, Swan | 33 | C3 |
| Pontarsais, Carm | 33 | B1 |
| Pontblyddyn, Flint | 67 | E1 |
| Pontefract, W York | 88 | B4 |
| Ponteland, Nthumb | 104 | B3 |
| Ponterwyd, Cered | 55 | B4 |
| Pontesbury, Shrop | 56 | C2 |
| Pontesford, Shrop | 56 | C2 |
| Pontfadog, Wrex | 67 | E3 |
| Pontfaen, Pemb | 44 | B4 |
| Pont-faen, Powys | 45 | D4 |
| Pontgarreg, Cered | 44 | E3 |
| Ponthenry, Carm | 33 | B3 |
| Ponthir, Torf | 34 | E4 |
| Ponthirwaun, Cered | 44 | D4 |
| Pontllanfraith, Caer | 34 | D4 |
| Pontlliw, Swan | 33 | C3 |
| Pontlyfni, Gwyn | 66 | D2 |
| Pont-Nedd-Fechan, Neath | 34 | B3 |
| Pontrhydfendigaid, Cered | 45 | B2 |
| Pont-rhyd-y-fen, Neath | 34 | A4 |
| Pontrhydygroes, Cered | 45 | B1 |
| Pontrilas, Heref | 35 | A1 |
| Ponts Green, E Sus | 20 | B3 |
| Pontshaen, Cered | 44 | F3 |
| Pontshill, Heref | 35 | C2 |
| Pontsticill, Merth | 34 | C2 |
| Pontwelly, Carm | 44 | E4 |
| Pontyates, Carm | 33 | B3 |
| Pontyberem, Carm | 33 | B2 |
| Pontybodkin, Flint | 67 | E2 |
| Pontyclun, Rhond | 22 | F1 |
| Pontycymer, Brid | 34 | B4 |
| Pont-y-pant, Ab & Col | 66 | F2 |
| Pontypool, Torf | 34 | E3 |
| Pontypridd, Rhond | 34 | C4 |
| Pontywaun, Caer | 34 | D4 |
| Pool, W York | 87 | B2 |
| Pool of Muckhart, Clack | 118 | E4 |
| Pool Street, Essex | 53 | A4 |
| Poole, Dors | 7 | C1 |
| Poolewe, High | 135 | B4 |
| Pooley Bridge, Cumb | 97 | B3 |
| Poolfold, Staff | 69 | B2 |
| Poolhill, Glouc | 36 | A1 |
| Pooting's, Kent | 149 | B3 |
| Popham, Hamp | 26 | C4 |
| Poplar, G Lon | 144 | A2 |
| Porchfield, I of W | 8 | A1 |
| Porkellis, Corn | 1 | D2 |
| Porlock, Som | 22 | E4 |
| Porlock Weir, Som | 22 | D4 |
| Port Appin, Argyll | 121 | C4 |
| Port Askaig, Argyll | 110 | C3 |
| Port Bannatyne, Argyll | 111 | B3 |
| Port Carlisle, Cumb | 102 | B4 |
| Port Charlotte, Argyll | 110 | A4 |
| Port Ellen, Argyll | 105 | A1 |
| Port Erin, I o M | 139 | B4 |
| Port Glasgow, Inv | 111 | E2 |
| Port Henderson, High | 130 | F1 |
| Port Isaac, Corn | 3 | D2 |
| Port Logan, D & G | 95 | B2 |
| Port nan Long, W Isles | 139 | A3 |
| Port of Menteith, Stirl | 118 | B4 |
| Port of Ness, W Isles | 139 | B1 |
| Port Quin, Corn | 3 | D2 |

| PLACE | PAGE | GRID |
|---|---|---|
| Port Ramsay, Argyll | 121 | C4 |
| Port Soderick, I o M | 139 | C4 |
| Port St Mary, I o M | 139 | B4 |
| Port Talbot, Neath | 33 | D4 |
| Port Wemyss, Argyll | 110 | A4 |
| Port William, D & G | 95 | D2 |
| Portachoillan, Argyll | 110 | F4 |
| Portavadie, Argyll | 111 | A3 |
| Portbury, Som | 23 | D2 |
| Portchester, Hamp | 15 | B4 |
| Portencalzie, D & G | 100 | A3 |
| Portesham, Dors | 6 | F1 |
| Portfield Gate, Pemb | 32 | C2 |
| Portgate, Devon | 4 | B1 |
| Portgordon, Moray | 133 | D2 |
| Porth, Rhond | 34 | C4 |
| Porth Navas, Corn | 2 | A2 |
| Porthallow, Corn | 2 | A3 |
| Porthallow, Corn | 4 | A4 |
| Porthcawl, Brid | 22 | D1 |
| Porthcothan, Corn | 3 | C2 |
| Porthcurno, Corn | 1 | A3 |
| Porthgain, Pemb | 32 | B1 |
| Porthgwarra, Corn | 1 | A3 |
| Porthkerry, Glam | 22 | F2 |
| Porthleven, Corn | 1 | D2 |
| Porthmadog, Gwyn | 66 | E3 |
| Porthoustock, Corn | 2 | A3 |
| Porthpean, Corn | 3 | D4 |
| Porthtowan, Corn | 1 | D1 |
| Porthyrhyd, Carm | 33 | B2 |
| Portington, E R of Y | 89 | B3 |
| Portinscale, Cumb | 96 | F3 |
| Portishead, Som | 23 | D2 |
| Portknockie, Moray | 133 | E2 |
| Portlethen, Aber | 129 | B4 |
| Portloe, Corn | 2 | B1 |
| Portmahomack, High | 136 | E4 |
| Portmellon, Corn | 2 | C1 |
| Portnacroish, Argyll | 121 | C4 |
| Portnahaven, Argyll | 110 | A4 |
| Porton, Wilts | 14 | A1 |
| Portpatrick, D & G | 95 | A1 |
| Portreath, Corn | 1 | D1 |
| Portree, High | 130 | C4 |
| Portscatho, Corn | 2 | B2 |
| Portskerra, High | 138 | A1 |
| Portskewett, Monm | 35 | B4 |
| Portslade-by-Sea, E Sus | 18 | B4 |
| Portsmouth, Hamp | 16 | A4 |
| Portsoy, Aber | 134 | A2 |
| Portway, Warw | 48 | B1 |
| Portwrinkle, Corn | 4 | B4 |
| Poslingford, Suff | 53 | A3 |
| Postbridge, Devon | 4 | D2 |
| Postcombe, Oxon | 38 | B3 |
| Postling, Kent | 21 | D1 |
| Postwick, Norf | 65 | A2 |
| Potsgrove, Beds | 39 | A1 |
| Pott Shrigley, Chesh | 80 | B4 |
| Potter Brompton, N York | 94 | D3 |
| Potter Heigham, Norf | 65 | B1 |
| Potterhanworth, Linc | 73 | A1 |
| Potterhanworth Booths, Linc | 73 | A1 |
| Potterne, Wilts | 25 | B3 |
| Potterne Wick, Wilts | 25 | B3 |
| Potters Bar, Herts | 40 | A3 |
| Potters Crouch, Herts | 39 | C3 |
| Potters Marston, Leics | 60 | A3 |
| Potterspury, Nhants | 50 | B4 |
| Potterton, Aber | 129 | C2 |
| Potto, N York | 93 | C1 |
| Potton, Beds | 51 | C3 |
| Poughill, Corn | 9 | B3 |
| Poughill, Devon | 10 | B3 |
| Poulshot, Wilts | 25 | B3 |
| Poulton, Glouc | 37 | A3 |
| Poulton-le-Fylde, Lanc | 85 | A3 |
| Pound Green, E Sus | 19 | B2 |
| Poundffald, Swan | 33 | C4 |
| Poundon, Bucks | 38 | B1 |
| Poundsbridge, Kent | 149 | C4 |
| Poundsgate, Devon | 5 | A2 |
| Poundstock, Corn | 9 | B4 |
| Povey Cross, Surr | 148 | B4 |
| Powburn, Nthumb | 109 | D3 |
| Powderham, Devon | 5 | C1 |
| Powfoot, D & G | 102 | A4 |
| Powhill, Cumb | 96 | F1 |
| Powick, Worc | 47 | C3 |
| Powmill, Perth | 119 | A4 |
| Poxwell, Dors | 7 | A1 |
| Poyle, Surr | 141 | A2 |
| Poynings, W Suss | 18 | B3 |
| Poyntington, Dors | 12 | B2 |
| Poynton, Chesh | 80 | A4 |
| Poynton Green, Shrop | 56 | D1 |
| Poys Street, Suff | 54 | C1 |
| Praa Sands, Corn | 1 | C2 |
| Pratt's Bottom, Kent | 149 | B1 |
| Prees, Shrop | 68 | B4 |
| Prees Green, Shrop | 68 | B4 |
| Preesall, Lanc | 85 | B2 |
| Prendwick, Nthumb | 109 | C4 |
| Pren-gwyn, Cered | 44 | F4 |
| Prenteg, Gwyn | 66 | E3 |
| Prescot, Mers | 78 | B3 |
| Prescott, Devon | 10 | D3 |
| Prestatyn, Denb | 77 | B4 |
| Prestbury, Chesh | 80 | A4 |
| Presteigne, Powys | 46 | B2 |
| Prestleigh, Som | 12 | B1 |
| Preston, Bord | 115 | C4 |
| Preston, Dors | 7 | A2 |
| Preston, E Loth | 115 | B2 |
| Preston, E R of Y | 90 | A3 |
| Preston, Glouc | 36 | C3 |
| Preston, Herts | 39 | C1 |
| Preston, Kent | 31 | B3 |
| Preston, Nthumb | 109 | E3 |
| Preston, Rut | 61 | B3 |
| Preston, Som | 10 | D1 |
| Preston, Suff | 53 | C3 |
| Preston, Wilts | 26 | A2 |
| Preston, Lanc | 85 | C4 |

| PLACE | PAGE | GRID |
|---|---|---|
| Preston Bissett, Bucks | 38 | B1 |
| Preston Brockhurst, Shrop | 56 | D1 |
| Preston Brook, Chesh | 78 | B4 |
| Preston Candover, Hamp | 26 | C4 |
| Preston Capes, Nhants | 49 | C3 |
| Preston Gubbals, Shrop | 56 | D1 |
| Preston on Stour, Warw | 48 | C3 |
| Preston on Wye, Heref | 46 | C4 |
| Preston Patrick, Cumb | 91 | F3 |
| Preston upon the Weald Moors, Shrop | 57 | A1 |
| Preston Wynne, Heref | 46 | D3 |
| Prestonpans, E Loth | 114 | C2 |
| Preston-under-Scar, N York | 92 | E2 |
| Prestwich, G Man | 80 | A2 |
| Prestwick, S Ayr | 106 | D3 |
| Prickwillow, Camb | 62 | D4 |
| Priddy, Som | 23 | D4 |
| Priest Hutton, Lanc | 91 | F4 |
| Priestweston, Shrop | 56 | B3 |
| Primrosehill, Bord | 115 | C4 |
| Princes Risborough, Bucks | 38 | C3 |
| Princethorpe, Warw | 49 | B1 |
| Princetown, Devon | 4 | D2 |
| Priors Hardwick, Warw | 49 | B3 |
| Priors Marston, Warw | 49 | B2 |
| Priston, Som | 24 | A3 |
| Privett, Hamp | 16 | A2 |
| Prospect, Cumb | 96 | D2 |
| Prospidnick, Corn | 1 | D2 |
| Prudhoe, Nthumb | 104 | A4 |
| Publow, Som | 24 | A2 |
| Puckeridge, Herts | 40 | B1 |
| Pucklechurch, Glouc | 24 | B1 |
| Puddington, Chesh | 77 | D4 |
| Puddington, Devon | 10 | B3 |
| Puddletown, Dors | 7 | A1 |
| Pudsey, W York | 87 | B3 |
| Pulborough, W Suss | 17 | B2 |
| Pulford, Chesh | 68 | A2 |
| Pulham, Dors | 12 | C3 |
| Pulham Market, Norf | 64 | B4 |
| Pulham St Mary, Norf | 64 | B4 |
| Pulloxhill, Beds | 51 | A4 |
| Pumsaint, Carm | 45 | B4 |
| Puncheston, Pemb | 32 | D1 |
| Puncknowle, Dors | 6 | E1 |
| Purfleet, Essex | 29 | A1 |
| Puriton, Som | 23 | B4 |
| Purleigh, Essex | 42 | B3 |
| Purley, G Lon | 148 | B1 |
| Purse Caundle, Dors | 12 | B3 |
| Purtington, Som | 11 | C3 |
| Purton, Glouc | 35 | C3 |
| Purton, Glouc | 35 | C3 |
| Purton, Wilts | 37 | A4 |
| Purton Stoke, Wilts | 37 | A4 |
| Pusey, Oxon | 37 | C4 |
| Putley, Heref | 47 | A4 |
| Putloe, Glouc | 36 | A3 |
| Putney, G Lon | 142 | B3 |
| Puttenham, Surr | 145 | B3 |
| Puxley, Nhants | 50 | B4 |
| Puxton, Som | 23 | C3 |
| Pwll, Carm | 33 | B3 |
| Pwll-du, Monm | 34 | E2 |
| Pwll-glas, Denb | 67 | C2 |
| Pwllgloyw, Powys | 45 | E4 |
| Pwllheli, Gwyn | 66 | C4 |
| Pwllmeyric, Monm | 35 | B4 |
| Pwll-y-glaw, Neath | 34 | A4 |
| Pye Bridge, Derby | 71 | A2 |
| Pye Corner, Herts | 41 | A2 |
| Pyecombe, W Suss | 18 | B3 |
| Pyle, Brid | 22 | D1 |
| Pyleigh, Som | 11 | A1 |
| Pylle, Som | 12 | B1 |
| Pymore, Camb | 62 | C4 |
| Pyrford, Surr | 146 | B2 |
| Pytchley, Nhants | 50 | C1 |
| Pyworthy, Devon | 9 | C4 |
| Quabbs, Shrop | 56 | A4 |
| Quadring, Linc | 73 | C4 |
| Quainton, Bucks | 38 | C2 |
| Quarley, Hamp | 25 | D4 |
| Quarndon, Derby | 70 | C3 |
| Quarrington, Linc | 73 | A3 |
| Quarrington Hill, Durham | 98 | D2 |
| Quarter, S Lan | 112 | C4 |
| Quatford, Shrop | 57 | B4 |
| Quatt, Shrop | 57 | B4 |
| Quebec, Durham | 98 | C2 |
| Queen Adelaide, Camb | 62 | D4 |
| Queen Camel, Som | 12 | B2 |
| Queen Charlton, Som | 24 | A2 |
| Queen Oak, Dors | 12 | C1 |
| Queenhill, Worc | 47 | C4 |
| Queensbury, W York | 87 | A3 |
| Queensferry, Flint | 67 | E1 |
| Queenzieburn, N Lan | 112 | C2 |
| Quendon, Essex | 41 | A1 |
| Queniborough, Leics | 60 | C2 |
| Quenington, Glouc | 37 | A3 |
| Quethiock, Corn | 4 | B3 |
| Quidenham, Norf | 64 | A4 |
| Quidhampton, Wilts | 13 | B1 |
| Quinton, Nhants | 50 | B3 |
| Quither, Devon | 4 | C2 |
| Quoditch, Devon | 9 | C4 |
| Quorndon, Leics | 60 | B1 |
| Quoyburray, Ork | 139 | B2 |
| Quoyloo, Ork | 139 | A1 |
| Rachub, Gwyn | 66 | E1 |
| Rackenford, Devon | 10 | B2 |
| Rackham, W Suss | 17 | B3 |
| Rackheath, Norf | 65 | A1 |
| Radbourne, Derby | 70 | C4 |
| Radcliffe, G Man | 79 | B1 |
| Radcliffe, Nthumb | 104 | B1 |
| Radcliffe on Trent, Notts | 72 | A3 |
| Radclive, Bucks | 50 | A4 |
| Radford Semele, Warw | 49 | A2 |
| Radlett, Herts | 39 | C3 |
| Radley, Oxon | 38 | A4 |
| Radley Green, Essex | 41 | B3 |
| Radnage, Bucks | 38 | C4 |
| Radstock, Som | 24 | A3 |
| Radstone, Nhants | 49 | C4 |
| Radway, Warw | 49 | A3 |
| Radwell, Herts | 51 | C4 |
| Radwinter, Essex | 52 | C4 |
| Radyr, Cardiff | 23 | A1 |
| Rafford, Moray | 133 | A3 |
| Ragdale, Leics | 60 | C1 |
| Raglan, Monm | 35 | A3 |
| Ragnall, Notts | 83 | B4 |
| Rainford, Mers | 78 | B2 |
| Rainham, G Lon | 144 | C1 |
| Rainow, Chesh | 80 | B4 |
| Rainton, N York | 93 | B4 |
| Rainworth, Notts | 71 | B2 |
| Raisthorpe, N York | 89 | C1 |
| Rait, Perth | 119 | B2 |
| Raithby, Linc | 84 | B3 |
| Raithby, Linc | 73 | D1 |
| Rake, W Suss | 16 | B2 |
| Rame, Corn | 1 | D2 |
| Rame, Corn | 4 | C4 |
| Rampisham, Dors | 12 | A4 |
| Rampside, Cumb | 91 | D4 |
| Rampton, Camb | 52 | B2 |
| Rampton, Notts | 83 | B4 |
| Ramsbottom, G Man | 79 | B1 |
| Ramsbury, Wilts | 25 | D2 |
| Ramsdean, Hamp | 16 | A2 |
| Ramsdell, Hamp | 26 | C3 |
| Ramsden, Oxon | 37 | C2 |
| Ramsden Bellhouse, Essex | 42 | A4 |
| Ramsey, Camb | 62 | A4 |
| Ramsey, Essex | 43 | C1 |
| Ramsey, I o M | 139 | D2 |
| Ramsey Heights, Camb | 62 | A4 |
| Ramsey Island, Essex | 43 | A3 |
| Ramsey Mereside, Camb | 62 | A4 |
| Ramsey St Mary's, Camb | 62 | A4 |
| Ramsgate, Kent | 31 | C2 |
| Ramsgill, N York | 92 | E4 |
| Ramshope, Nthumb | 109 | A4 |
| Ramshorn, Staff | 70 | A3 |
| Ramsnest Common, Surr | 17 | A1 |
| Ranby, Linc | 84 | B4 |
| Ranby, Notts | 83 | A4 |
| Rand, Linc | 84 | A4 |
| Randwick, Glouc | 36 | B3 |
| Rangemore, Staff | 59 | A1 |
| Rangeworthy, Glouc | 24 | A1 |
| Rankinston, E Ayr | 106 | E4 |
| Rann, Lanc | 86 | B4 |
| Rannoch Station, Perth | 122 | A3 |
| Ranskill, Notts | 83 | A3 |
| Ranton, Staff | 57 | C1 |
| Ranworth, Norf | 65 | B1 |
| Rapness, Ork | 139 | B1 |
| Rapps, Som | 11 | B3 |
| Rashwood, Worc | 47 | C2 |
| Raskelf, N York | 93 | C4 |
| Ratby, Leics | 60 | B2 |
| Ratcliffe Culey, Leics | 59 | B3 |
| Ratcliffe on Soar, Notts | 71 | A4 |
| Ratcliffe on the Wreake, Leics | 60 | C1 |
| Rathen, Aber | 134 | D2 |
| Rathmell, N York | 86 | B1 |
| Ratho, Edin | 114 | A3 |
| Rathven, Moray | 133 | D2 |
| Ratley, Warw | 49 | A3 |
| Ratling, Kent | 31 | B3 |
| Ratlinghope, Shrop | 56 | C3 |
| Rattery, Devon | 5 | A3 |
| Rattlesden, Suff | 53 | C2 |
| Rattray, Perth | 123 | C4 |
| Raunds, Nhants | 51 | A1 |
| Raven Meols, Mers | 77 | D2 |
| Ravenfield, S York | 82 | A3 |
| Ravenglass, Cumb | 91 | B2 |
| Raveningham, Norf | 65 | B3 |
| Ravenscar, N York | 94 | D1 |
| Ravenscliffe, Staff | 69 | B2 |
| Ravensden, Beds | 51 | A3 |
| Ravenshead, Notts | 71 | B2 |
| Ravensthorpe, Nhants | 50 | A1 |
| Ravenstone, Bucks | 50 | B3 |
| Ravenstone, Leics | 60 | A2 |
| Ravenstonedale, Cumb | 92 | B1 |
| Ravensworth, N York | 92 | E1 |
| Rawcliffe, E R of Y | 89 | A4 |
| Rawling Street, Kent | 30 | B3 |
| Rawmarsh, S York | 82 | A2 |
| Rawreth, Essex | 42 | B4 |
| Rawridge, Devon | 11 | A4 |
| Rawtenstall, Lanc | 86 | C4 |
| Raydon, Suff | 53 | D4 |
| Rayleigh, Essex | 42 | B4 |
| Rayne, Essex | 42 | A1 |
| Raynes Park, G Lon | 142 | B4 |
| Reach, Camb | 52 | C2 |
| Read, Lanc | 86 | B3 |
| Reading, Berks | 27 | A2 |
| Reagill, Cumb | 97 | C4 |
| Rearsby, Leics | 60 | C2 |
| Reay, High | 138 | B1 |
| Reculver, Kent | 31 | A2 |
| Red Ball, Devon | 10 | D3 |
| Red Hill, Warw | 48 | B3 |
| Red Lodge, Suff | 53 | A1 |
| Red Roses, Carm | 32 | F2 |
| Red Wharf Bay, Angle | 76 | C4 |
| Redberth, Pemb | 32 | E3 |
| Redbourn, Herts | 39 | C2 |
| Redbourne, Linc | 83 | D2 |
| Redbrook, Wrex | 68 | B3 |
| Redbrook Street, Kent | 21 | B1 |
| Redcar, N York | 99 | B3 |
| Redditch, Worc | 48 | A2 |
| Rede, Suff | 53 | B3 |
| Redenhall, Norf | 65 | A4 |
| Redesmouth, Nthumb | 103 | C2 |
| Redford, Angus | 124 | A4 |
| Redford, W Suss | 17 | A2 |
| Redgrave, Suff | 53 | D1 |
| Redhill, Herts | 40 | A1 |
| Redhill, Som | 23 | D3 |
| Redhill, Surr | 148 | B3 |
| Redisham, Suff | 65 | B4 |
| Redlingfield, Suff | 54 | A1 |
| Redlingfield Green, Suff | 54 | A1 |
| Redlynch, Som | 12 | C1 |
| Redlynch, Wilts | 14 | A2 |
| Redmarley, Worc | 47 | B2 |
| Redmarshall, Durham | 98 | D4 |
| Redmile, Leics | 72 | B4 |
| Redmire, N York | 92 | E2 |
| Rednal, Shrop | 68 | A4 |
| Redruth, Corn | 1 | D1 |
| Redwick, Glouc | 23 | D1 |
| Redwick, Newport | 23 | C1 |
| Redworth, Durham | 98 | C3 |
| Reed, Herts | 52 | A4 |
| Reedham, Norf | 65 | B3 |
| Reedness, E R of Y | 89 | B4 |
| Reepham, Linc | 83 | D4 |
| Reepham, Norf | 64 | A1 |
| Reeth, N York | 92 | D2 |
| Reigate, Surr | 148 | A3 |
| Reighton, N York | 94 | E4 |
| Reiss, High | 138 | E2 |
| Relubbus, Corn | 1 | C2 |
| Remenham, Berks | 27 | B1 |
| Rempstone, Notts | 60 | B1 |
| Rendcomb, Glouc | 36 | C3 |
| Rendham, Suff | 54 | B2 |
| Renfrew, Renf | 112 | A3 |
| Renhold, Beds | 51 | B3 |
| Renishaw, Derby | 82 | A4 |
| Rennington, Nthumb | 109 | E3 |
| Renton, Dumb | 111 | E2 |
| Renwick, Cumb | 97 | C2 |
| Repps, Norf | 65 | B1 |
| Repton, Derby | 70 | C4 |
| Rescassa, Corn | 2 | C1 |
| Reskadinnick, Corn | 1 | D1 |
| Resolven, Neath | 34 | A3 |
| Reston, Bord | 115 | D3 |
| Retford, Notts | 83 | A4 |
| Rettendon, Essex | 42 | A4 |
| Revesby, Linc | 73 | C1 |
| Rew Street, I of W | 8 | A1 |
| Rewe, Devon | 10 | C4 |
| Reymerston, Norf | 64 | A2 |
| Reynoldston, Swan | 33 | B4 |
| Rhandirmwyn, Carm | 45 | C4 |
| Rhayader, Powys | 45 | D2 |
| Rhes-y-cae, Flint | 67 | D1 |
| Rhewl, Denb | 67 | C2 |
| Rhewl, Denb | 67 | D3 |
| Rhiconich, High | 137 | B2 |
| Rhigos, Rhond | 34 | B3 |
| Rhiwlas, Gwyn | 66 | E1 |
| Rhoden Green, Kent | 29 | B4 |
| Rhodiad-y-brenin, Pemb | 32 | B1 |
| Rhoose, Glam | 22 | F2 |
| Rhos, Carm | 44 | E4 |
| Rhos, Neath | 33 | D3 |
| Rhosbeirio, Angle | 76 | B3 |
| Rhoscolyn, Angle | 76 | A4 |
| Rhoscrowther, Pemb | 32 | C3 |
| Rhosesmor, Flint | 67 | D1 |
| Rhosgoch, Powys | 46 | A3 |
| Rhoshill, Pemb | 44 | C4 |
| Rhoshirwaun, Gwyn | 66 | B4 |
| Rhoslefain, Gwyn | 55 | A2 |
| Rhosllanerchrugog, Wrex | 67 | E3 |
| Rhosmeirch, Angle | 76 | C4 |
| Rhosneigr, Angle | 76 | B4 |
| Rhos-on-Sea, Ab & Col | 76 | F4 |
| Rhostryfan, Gwyn | 66 | D2 |
| Rhosybol, Angle | 76 | C3 |
| Rhos-y-gwaliau, Gwyn | 67 | B4 |
| Rhosymedre, Wrex | 67 | E3 |
| Rhu, Argyll | 111 | D1 |
| Rhuallt, Denb | 77 | B4 |
| Rhuddlan, Denb | 77 | B4 |
| Rhyd, Gwyn | 66 | E3 |
| Rhydargaeau, Carm | 33 | B1 |
| Rhydcymerau, Carm | 45 | A4 |
| Rhydlewis, Cered | 44 | E3 |
| Rhydowen, Cered | 44 | F4 |
| Rhyd-uchaf, Gwyn | 67 | B3 |
| Rhyd-y pennau, Cered | 55 | A4 |
| Rhyd-y-clafdy, Gwyn | 66 | C4 |
| Rhyd-y-foel, Ab & Col | 77 | A4 |
| Rhydyfro, Neath | 33 | D3 |
| Rhyl, Denb | 77 | B4 |
| Rhymney, Caer | 34 | C3 |
| Rhynd, Perth | 119 | B2 |
| Rhynie, Aber | 128 | D1 |
| Ribbesford, Worc | 47 | B1 |
| Ribchester, Lanc | 86 | A3 |
| Riby, Linc | 84 | A1 |
| Riccall, N York | 88 | D3 |
| Riccarton, Bord | 102 | D1 |
| Richards Castle, Heref | 46 | D1 |
| Richmond, N York | 93 | A1 |
| Rickham, Devon | 8 | A1 |
| Rickinghall, Suff | 53 | D1 |
| Rickling, Essex | 41 | A1 |
| Rickling Green, Essex | 41 | A1 |
| Rickmansworth, Herts | 39 | B4 |
| Riddlecombe, Devon | 9 | E3 |
| Ridge, Herts | 40 | A3 |
| Ridge, Wilts | 13 | A1 |
| Ridge Green, Surr | 148 | B3 |
| Ridge Lane, Warw | 59 | B3 |
| Ridgehill, Som | 23 | D3 |
| Ridgeway, Derby | 82 | A4 |
| Ridgewell, Essex | 53 | A4 |
| Ridgmont, Beds | 51 | A4 |
| Riding Mill, Nthumb | 103 | D4 |
| Ridlington, Norf | 75 | C4 |
| Ridlington, Rut | 61 | A3 |
| Ridsdale, Nthumb | 103 | C2 |
| Rievaulx, N York | 93 | D3 |
| Rigg, D & G | 102 | B4 |
| Rigsby, Linc | 84 | D4 |
| Riley Green, Lanc | 86 | A4 |
| Rilla Mill, Corn | 4 | A2 |
| Rillington, N York | 94 | C4 |
| Rimington, Lanc | 86 | B2 |
| Rimpton, Som | 12 | B2 |
| Rimswell, E R of Y | 90 | B4 |
| Rinaston, Pemb | 32 | D1 |
| Rindleford, Shrop | 57 | B3 |
| Ringford, D & G | 101 | B4 |
| Ringland, Norf | 64 | B2 |
| Ringmer, E Sus | 19 | B3 |
| Ringmore, Devon | 8 | B1 |
| Ringmore, Devon | 5 | C2 |
| Ringsfield, Suff | 65 | B4 |
| Ringshall, Herts | 39 | B2 |
| Ringshall, Suff | 53 | D3 |
| Ringshall Stocks, Suff | 53 | D3 |
| Ringstead, Nhants | 51 | A1 |
| Ringstead, Norf | 74 | C3 |
| Ringwood, Hamp | 13 | B4 |
| Ringwould, Kent | 31 | C4 |
| Ripe, E Sus | 19 | B3 |
| Ripley, Derby | 71 | A2 |
| Ripley, Hamp | 14 | A4 |
| Ripley, N York | 88 | A1 |
| Ripley, Surr | 146 | B2 |
| Riplington, Hamp | 16 | A2 |
| Ripon, N York | 93 | B4 |
| Rippingale, Linc | 73 | B4 |
| Ripple, Worc | 47 | C4 |
| Ripponden, W York | 86 | D4 |
| Risbury, Heref | 46 | D3 |
| Risby, Suff | 53 | B2 |
| Risca, Caer | 34 | E4 |
| Rise, E R of Y | 90 | A2 |
| Risegate, Linc | 73 | C4 |
| Riseley, Beds | 51 | A2 |
| Riseley, Berks | 27 | A3 |
| Rishangles, Suff | 54 | A1 |
| Rishton, Lanc | 86 | B3 |
| Rishworth, W York | 80 | B1 |
| Risley, Chesh | 79 | A3 |
| Risley, Derby | 71 | A4 |
| Risplith, N York | 93 | A4 |
| River, W Suss | 17 | A2 |
| Riverhead, Kent | 149 | C2 |
| Rivington, Lanc | 79 | A1 |
| Road Weedon, Nhants | 50 | A2 |
| Roade, Nhants | 50 | B3 |
| Roadmeetings, S Lan | 113 | A4 |
| Roadwater, Som | 10 | D1 |
| Roberton, Bord | 108 | B4 |
| Roberton, S Lan | 107 | C2 |
| Robertsbridge, E Sus | 20 | B2 |
| Roberttown, W York | 87 | B4 |
| Robeston Wathen, Pemb | 32 | E2 |
| Robin Hood's Bay, N York | 94 | C1 |
| Roborough, Devon | 9 | E3 |
| Rocester, Staff | 70 | A3 |
| Roch, Pemb | 32 | C2 |
| Rochdale, G Man | 80 | A1 |
| Roche, Corn | 3 | D4 |
| Rochester, Nthumb | 103 | C1 |
| Rochester, Kent | 29 | B2 |
| Rochford, Essex | 42 | B4 |
| Rochford, Worc | 47 | A1 |
| Rock, Corn | 3 | C2 |
| Rock, Nthumb | 109 | E3 |
| Rock, Worc | 47 | B1 |
| Rockbeare, Devon | 6 | A1 |
| Rockbourne, Hamp | 13 | B2 |
| Rockcliffe, Cumb | 102 | C4 |
| Rockcliffe, D & G | 96 | B1 |
| Rockfield, Monm | 35 | B2 |
| Rockford, Devon | 22 | C4 |
| Rockhampton, Glouc | 35 | C4 |
| Rockhill, Shrop | 46 | B1 |
| Rockland St Mary, Norf | 65 | A2 |
| Rockland St Peter, Norf | 63 | C3 |
| Rockley, Notts | 83 | A4 |
| Rockley, Wilts | 25 | C2 |
| Rockwell End, Bucks | 38 | C4 |
| Rodbourne, Wilts | 25 | B1 |
| Rodden, Dors | 6 | F1 |
| Rode, Som | 24 | B3 |
| Rode Heath, Chesh | 69 | A2 |
| Roden, Shrop | 56 | D1 |
| Rodhuish, Som | 10 | D1 |
| Rodington, Shrop | 57 | A1 |
| Rodley, Glouc | 36 | A2 |
| Rodmarton, Glouc | 36 | C4 |
| Rodmell, E Sus | 19 | A4 |
| Rodmersham, Kent | 30 | B3 |
| Rodney Stoke, Som | 23 | D4 |
| Rodsley, Derby | 70 | B3 |
| Roecliffe, N York | 93 | B4 |
| Roehampton, G Lon | 142 | B3 |
| Rogate, W Suss | 16 | B2 |
| Rogerstone, Newport | 34 | E4 |
| Rogiet, Monm | 35 | A4 |
| Roke, Oxon | 38 | B4 |
| Rollesby, Norf | 65 | B1 |
| Rolleston, Leics | 60 | C3 |
| Rolleston, Staff | 70 | B4 |
| Rolston, E R of Y | 90 | B2 |
| Rolvenden Layne, Kent | 21 | A1 |
| Romaldkirk, Durham | 98 | A3 |
| Romanno Bridge, Bord | 107 | E1 |
| Romansleigh, Devon | 10 | A2 |
| Romford, Dors | 13 | B3 |
| Romford, G Lon | 41 | A4 |
| Romiley, G Man | 80 | B3 |
| Romsey, Hamp | 14 | B2 |
| Romsley, Shrop | 57 | B4 |
| Romsley, Worc | 58 | A4 |
| Rookhope, Durham | 98 | A2 |
| Rookley, I of W | 8 | B1 |
| Rooks Bridge, Som | 23 | C4 |
| Rooks Nest, Som | 10 | D1 |
| Rookwith, N York | 93 | A3 |
| Roos, E R of Y | 90 | B3 |
| Roothams Green, Beds | 51 | B2 |
| Ropley, Hamp | 16 | A1 |
| Ropley Dean, Hamp | 16 | A1 |
| Ropsley, Linc | 73 | A4 |
| Rora, Aber | 134 | E3 |
| Rorrington, Shrop | 56 | B3 |
| Rose, Corn | 3 | B4 |
| Rose Green, Suff | 53 | C4 |
| Rose Green, Suff | 53 | C4 |
| Rosebush, Pemb | 32 | D1 |
| Rosedale Abbey, N York | 94 | A2 |
| Rosehall, High | 136 | A3 |
| Rosehearty, Aber | 134 | D2 |
| Rosemarket, Pemb | 32 | C3 |
| Rosemarkie, High | 132 | C2 |
| Rosemary Lane, Devon | 11 | A3 |
| Rosenannon, Corn | 3 | C3 |
| Rosewell, M Loth | 114 | B3 |
| Rosgill, Cumb | 97 | B4 |
| Rosley, Cumb | 96 | F2 |
| Roslin, M Loth | 114 | B3 |
| Rosliston, Derby | 59 | A1 |
| Rosneath, Argyll | 111 | D2 |
| Ross, D & G | 95 | F2 |
| Rossett, Wrex | 68 | A2 |
| Rossington, S York | 83 | A2 |
| Ross-on-Wye, Heref | 35 | C1 |
| Rostherne, Chesh | 79 | B4 |
| Rosthwaite, Cumb | 96 | F4 |
| Roston, Derby | 70 | A3 |
| Rosyth, Fife | 113 | C2 |
| Rothbury, Nthumb | 104 | A1 |
| Rotherby, Leics | 60 | C1 |
| Rotherfield, E Sus | 20 | A2 |
| Rotherfield Peppard, Oxon | 27 | A1 |
| Rotherham, S York | 82 | A3 |
| Rothersthorpe, Nhants | 50 | A2 |
| Rotherwick, Hamp | 27 | A3 |
| Rothes, Moray | 133 | C3 |
| Rothesay, Argyll | 111 | C3 |
| Rothiemay, Moray | 133 | E3 |
| Rothienorman, Aber | 134 | B4 |
| Rothley, Leics | 60 | B2 |
| Rothwell, Linc | 84 | A2 |
| Rothwell, Nhants | 61 | A4 |
| Rothwell, W York | 88 | A4 |
| Rottingdean, E Sus | 19 | A4 |
| Rottington, Cumb | 96 | C4 |
| Roucan, D & G | 101 | E3 |
| Rougham, Norf | 63 | B1 |
| Roughton, Linc | 73 | C1 |
| Roughton, Norf | 75 | B4 |
| Roughton, Shrop | 57 | B3 |
| Roundbush Green, Essex | 41 | B2 |
| Roundway, Wilts | 25 | B3 |
| Rous Lench, Worc | 48 | A3 |
| Rousdon, Devon | 6 | C1 |
| Rousham, Oxon | 37 | D1 |
| Routh, E R of Y | 90 | A2 |
| Row, Corn | 3 | E2 |
| Row, Cumb | 91 | E2 |
| Row Green, Essex | 42 | A2 |
| Row Town, Surr | 146 | B1 |
| Rowanburn, D & G | 102 | C3 |
| Rowarth, Derby | 80 | B3 |
| Rowberrow, Som | 23 | C3 |
| Rowde, Wilts | 25 | B3 |
| Rowen, Ab & Col | 66 | F1 |
| Rowfoot, Nthumb | 103 | A4 |
| Rowington, Warw | 48 | C1 |
| Rowland, Derby | 81 | B4 |
| Rowley, Durham | 98 | B1 |
| Rowley, E R of Y | 89 | D3 |
| Rowlstone, Heref | 35 | A1 |
| Rowney Green, Worc | 48 | B1 |
| Rownhams, Hamp | 14 | B3 |
| Rowrah, Cumb | 96 | D4 |
| Rowsham, Bucks | 38 | C2 |
| Rowsley, Derby | 70 | B1 |
| Rowston, Linc | 73 | B2 |
| Rowton, Chesh | 68 | A1 |
| Rowton, Shrop | 57 | A1 |
| Roxburgh, Bord | 109 | A2 |
| Roxby, Linc | 83 | C1 |
| Roxton, Beds | 51 | B3 |
| Roxwell, Essex | 41 | B3 |
| Roydon, Essex | 40 | B3 |
| Roydon, Norf | 63 | A1 |
| Roydon, Norf | 64 | A4 |
| Roydon Hamlet, Essex | 40 | B3 |
| Royston, S York | 81 | C1 |
| Royston, Herts | 52 | A4 |
| Royton, G Man | 80 | A1 |
| Rozel, Jers | 139 | B1 |
| Ruabon, Wrex | 67 | E3 |
| Ruaig, Argyll | 120 | B4 |
| Ruan Lanihorne, Corn | 2 | B1 |
| Ruan Major, Corn | 1 | D3 |
| Ruan Minor, Corn | 1 | D3 |
| Ruardean, Glouc | 35 | C2 |
| Ruardean Hill, Glouc | 35 | C2 |
| Ruardean Woodside, Glouc | 35 | C2 |
| Ruckhall, Heref | 46 | D4 |
| Ruckinge, Kent | 21 | C1 |
| Ruckley, Shrop | 56 | D3 |
| Rudby, N York | 93 | C1 |
| Rudchester, Nthumb | 104 | A4 |
| Ruddington, Notts | 71 | B4 |
| Rudgeway, Glouc | 24 | A1 |
| Rudgwick, W Suss | 18 | A1 |
| Rudley Green, Essex | 42 | B3 |
| Rudloe, Wilts | 25 | A2 |
| Rudry, Caer | 23 | A1 |
| Rudston, E R of Y | 94 | E4 |
| Rudyard, Staff | 69 | C2 |
| Rufford, Lanc | 78 | A1 |
| Rufforth, N York | 88 | C2 |
| Rugby, Warw | 49 | C1 |
| Rugeley, Staff | 58 | B1 |
| Rumbling Bridge, Perth | 119 | A4 |
| Rumburgh, Suff | 65 | A4 |
| Rumford, Falkirk | 113 | B2 |
| Runcorn, Chesh | 78 | B4 |
| Runcton, W Suss | 17 | A4 |
| Runcton Holme, Norf | 62 | D2 |
| Runfold, Surr | 145 | A3 |
| Runhall, Norf | 64 | A2 |
| Runham, Norf | 65 | B2 |
| Runnington, Som | 11 | A2 |
| Runswick, N York | 99 | D4 |
| Runwell, Essex | 42 | A4 |
| Rushall, Heref | 47 | A4 |
| Rushall, Norf | 64 | B4 |
| Rushall, Wilts | 25 | C3 |
| Rushbrooke, Suff | 53 | C2 |
| Rushbury, Shrop | 56 | D3 |
| Rushden, Herts | 40 | A1 |
| Rushden, Nhants | 50 | C2 |
| Rushett Common, Surr | 146 | A4 |
| Rushford, Norf | 63 | C4 |
| Rushlake Green, E Sus | 20 | A2 |
| Rushmere, Suff | 65 | C4 |
| Rushmoor, Surr | 17 | A1 |
| Rushock, Heref | 46 | B2 |
| Rushock, Worc | 47 | C1 |
| Rushton, Chesh | 68 | C1 |
| Rushton, Nhants | 61 | A4 |
| Rushwick, Worc | 47 | C3 |
| Rushyford, Durham | 98 | D3 |
| Ruskington, Linc | 73 | B2 |
| Rusland, Cumb | 91 | D2 |
| Rusper, W Suss | 18 | B1 |
| Ruspidge, Glouc | 35 | C2 |
| Russ Hill, Surr | 18 | B1 |
| Russell's Water, Oxon | 38 | B4 |
| Rustington, W Suss | 17 | B4 |
| Ruston, N York | 94 | C3 |
| Ruston Parva, E R of Y | 89 | D1 |
| Ruswarp, N York | 94 | C1 |
| Rutherford, Bord | 108 | D2 |
| Rutherglen, S Lan | 112 | B3 |
| Ruthernbridge, Corn | 3 | D3 |
| Ruthin, Denb | 67 | D2 |
| Ruthven, Aber | 133 | E3 |
| Ruthven, Angus | 123 | D4 |
| Ruthvoes, Corn | 3 | C3 |
| Ruthwell, D & G | 101 | E4 |
| Ruxley Corner, G Lon | 144 | B3 |
| Ruyton-XI-Towns, Shrop | 56 | C1 |
| Ryal, Nthumb | 103 | D3 |
| Ryall, Dors | 11 | C4 |
| Ryarsh, Kent | 29 | B3 |
| Rydal, Cumb | 91 | E1 |
| Ryde, I of W | 8 | B1 |
| Rye, E Sus | 21 | B2 |
| Rye Street, Worc | 47 | B4 |
| Ryhall, Rut | 61 | C2 |
| Ryhill, W York | 81 | C1 |
| Ryland, Linc | 83 | D4 |
| Ryme Intrinseca, Dors | 12 | B3 |
| Ryther, N York | 88 | C3 |
| Ryton, Shrop | 57 | B3 |
| Ryton, T & W | 104 | A4 |
| Ryton-on-Dunsmore, Warw | 49 | A1 |
| Sabden, Lanc | 86 | B3 |
| Sacombe, Herts | 40 | B2 |
| Sacriston, Durham | 98 | C1 |
| Sadberge, Durham | 98 | D4 |
| Saddell, Argyll | 105 | E2 |
| Saddington, Leics | 60 | C3 |
| Saddle Bow, Norf | 62 | D1 |
| Saddlescombe, W Suss | 18 | B3 |
| Saffron Walden, Essex | 52 | B4 |
| Sageston, Pemb | 32 | D3 |
| Saham Hills, Norf | 63 | C2 |
| Saham Toney, Norf | 63 | C3 |
| Saighton, Chesh | 68 | A1 |
| Saintbury, Glouc | 48 | B4 |
| Salcombe, Devon | 8 | A1 |
| Salcott, Essex | 43 | A2 |
| Sale, G Man | 79 | B3 |
| Sale Green, Worc | 48 | A2 |
| Saleby, Linc | 84 | D4 |
| Salehurst, E Sus | 20 | B2 |
| Salem, Cered | 55 | B4 |
| Salem, Gwyn | 66 | E2 |
| Salen, Argyll | 120 | F4 |
| Salford, Beds | 50 | C4 |
| Salford, G Man | 80 | A2 |
| Salford, Oxon | 37 | C1 |
| Salford Priors, Warw | 48 | B3 |
| Salfords, Surr | 148 | B4 |
| Salhouse, Norf | 65 | A1 |
| Saline, Fife | 113 | C1 |
| Salisbury, Wilts | 13 | B1 |
| Salkeld Dykes, Cumb | 97 | B2 |
| Salle, Norf | 64 | A1 |
| Salmonby, Linc | 84 | C4 |
| Salperton, Glouc | 37 | A2 |
| Salsburgh, N Lan | 113 | A3 |
| Salt, Staff | 69 | C4 |
| Saltash, Corn | 4 | C4 |
| Saltburn, High | 132 | C1 |
| Saltburn-by-the-Sea, N York | 99 | C4 |
| Saltby, Leics | 72 | B4 |
| Saltcoats, N Ayr | 106 | C1 |
| Salterforth, Lanc | 86 | C2 |
| Salterton, Wilts | 13 | B1 |
| Saltfleet, Linc | 84 | D3 |
| Saltfleetby All Saints, Linc | 84 | D3 |
| Saltfleetby St Clement, Linc | 84 | D3 |
| Saltfleetby St Peter, Linc | 84 | D3 |
| Saltford, Som | 24 | A2 |
| Salthouse, Norf | 75 | A3 |
| Saltmarshe, E R of Y | 89 | B4 |
| Salton, N York | 94 | A3 |
| Saltrens, Devon | 9 | D2 |
| Salwarpe, Worc | 47 | C2 |
| Salwayash, Dors | 11 | C4 |
| Sambourne, Warw | 48 | B2 |
| Sambrook, Shrop | 57 | B1 |
| Samlesbury, Lanc | 86 | A3 |
| Sampford Arundel, Som | 10 | D2 |
| Sampford Brett, Som | 10 | D1 |
| Sampford Courtenay, Devon | 9 | E4 |
| Sampford Moor, Som | 10 | D2 |
| Sampford Peverell, Devon | 10 | D3 |
| Sampford Spiney, Devon | 4 | C2 |
| Samsonlane, Ork | 139 | B1 |
| Samuelston, E Loth | 115 | A3 |
| Sanaigmore, Argyll | 110 | A3 |
| Sancreed, Corn | 1 | B2 |
| Sand Hills, W York | 88 | A3 |
| Sand Hole, E R of Y | 89 | B3 |
| Sand Hutton, N York | 89 | A1 |
| Sandal Magna, W York | 81 | C1 |

| PLACE | PAGE | GRID |
|---|---|---|
| Sandbach, Chesh | 69 | A1 |
| Sandend, Aber | 133 | E2 |
| Sanderstead, G Lon | 148 | C1 |
| Sandford, Cumb | 97 | D4 |
| Sandford, Hamp | 14 | A4 |
| Sandford, Som | 23 | C3 |
| Sandford Orcas, Dors | 12 | B2 |
| Sandford St Martin, Oxon | 37 | D1 |
| Sandhaven, Aber | 134 | D2 |
| Sandhead, D & G | 95 | B1 |
| Sandhoe, Nthumb | 103 | D4 |
| Sandhurst, Berks | 27 | B3 |
| Sandhurst, Glouc | 36 | B1 |
| Sandhurst, Kent | 21 | A2 |
| Sandhutton, N York | 93 | B3 |
| Sandilands, Linc | 84 | D4 |
| Sandleigh, Oxon | 37 | D3 |
| Sandness, Shet | 139 | A2 |
| Sandon, Essex | 42 | A3 |
| Sandon, Herts | 52 | A4 |
| Sandon, Staff | 69 | C4 |
| Sandon Bank, Staff | 69 | C4 |
| Sandown, I of W | 8 | B1 |
| Sandplace, Corn | 4 | A4 |
| Sandridge, Herts | 39 | C2 |
| Sandringham, Norf | 74 | C4 |
| Sandsend, N York | 99 | E4 |
| Sandtoft, Linc | 83 | B1 |
| Sandway, Kent | 30 | B4 |
| Sandwich, Kent | 31 | B3 |
| Sandwick, Shet | 139 | A3 |
| Sandwith, Cumb | 96 | C4 |
| Sandy, Beds | 51 | B3 |
| Sandy Lane, Wilts | 25 | B2 |
| Sandygate, I o M | 139 | C2 |
| Sandyhills, D & G | 96 | C1 |
| Sanquhar, D & G | 107 | B4 |
| Santon Bridge, Cumb | 91 | B1 |
| Santon Downham, Suff | 63 | B4 |
| Sapcote, Leics | 60 | A3 |
| Sapey Common, Heref | 47 | B2 |
| Sapiston, Suff | 53 | C1 |
| Sapperton, Glouc | 36 | C3 |
| Sapperton, Linc | 73 | A4 |
| Saracen's Head, Linc | 73 | D4 |
| Sarn, Gwyn | 66 | B4 |
| Sarn, Powys | 55 | D3 |
| Sarn, Powys | 56 | A4 |
| Sarnau, Cered | 44 | E3 |
| Sarnau, Powys | 56 | B1 |
| Sarnesfield, Heref | 46 | C3 |
| Saron, Carm | 33 | C2 |
| Sarratt, Herts | 39 | B3 |
| Sarre, Kent | 31 | B2 |
| Sarsden, Oxon | 37 | C1 |
| Satley, Durham | 98 | B2 |
| Satterleigh, Devon | 10 | A2 |
| Satterthwaite, Cumb | 91 | D2 |
| Sauchen, Aber | 129 | A2 |
| Saul, Glouc | 36 | A3 |
| Saundby, Notts | 83 | B3 |
| Saundersfoot, Pemb | 32 | E3 |
| Saunderton, Bucks | 38 | C3 |
| Sausthorpe, Linc | 73 | D1 |
| Sawbridge, Warw | 49 | C2 |
| Sawbridgeworth, Herts | 41 | A2 |
| Sawdon, N York | 94 | C3 |
| Sawley, Lanc | 86 | B2 |
| Sawley, N York | 93 | A4 |
| Sawston, Camb | 52 | B3 |
| Sawtry, Camb | 61 | D4 |
| Saxby, Leics | 61 | A1 |
| Saxby, Linc | 83 | D3 |
| Saxby All Saints, Linc | 83 | D1 |
| Saxelbye, Leics | 60 | C1 |
| Saxham Street, Suff | 53 | D2 |
| Saxilby, Linc | 83 | C4 |
| Saxlingham, Norf | 75 | A3 |
| Saxlingham Green, Norf | 65 | A3 |
| Saxlingham Thorpe, Norf | 64 | B3 |
| Saxmundham, Suff | 54 | C2 |
| Saxon Street, Camb | 53 | A2 |
| Saxondale, Notts | 72 | A3 |
| Saxtead, Suff | 54 | B2 |
| Saxtead Green, Suff | 54 | B2 |
| Saxthorpe, Norf | 75 | A4 |
| Saxton, N York | 88 | B3 |
| Sayers Common, W Suss | 18 | B2 |
| Scackleton, N York | 94 | A4 |
| Scaftworth, Notts | 83 | A3 |
| Scagglethorpe, N York | 94 | B4 |
| Scalasaig, Argyll | 110 | C1 |
| Scalby, E R of Y | 89 | B4 |
| Scalby, N York | 94 | D2 |
| Scaldwell, Nhants | 50 | B1 |
| Scaleby, Cumb | 102 | C4 |
| Scalebyhill, Cumb | 102 | C4 |
| Scales, Cumb | 96 | F3 |
| Scales, Cumb | 91 | D4 |
| Scalford, Leics | 61 | A1 |
| Scaling, N York | 99 | D4 |
| Scalloway, Shet | 139 | A2 |
| Scamblesby, Linc | 84 | B4 |
| Scampston, N York | 94 | C4 |
| Scampton, Linc | 83 | C4 |
| Scapegoat Hill, W York | 81 | A1 |
| Scarborough, N York | 94 | D2 |
| Scarcewater, Corn | 3 | C4 |
| Scarcliffe, Derby | 71 | A1 |
| Scarcroft Hill, W York | 88 | A3 |
| Scargill, Durham | 92 | E1 |
| Scarinish, Argyll | 120 | B4 |
| Scarisbrick, Lanc | 78 | A1 |
| Scarning, Norf | 63 | C2 |
| Scarrington, Notts | 72 | A3 |
| Scawby, Linc | 83 | D2 |
| Scawton, N York | 93 | D3 |
| Scayne's Hill, W Suss | 19 | A2 |
| Scethrog, Powys | 34 | C1 |
| Scholes, S York | 81 | C2 |
| Scholes, W York | 81 | B1 |
| Scissett, W York | 81 | B1 |
| Scleddau, Pemb | 44 | A4 |
| Scofton, Notts | 83 | A4 |
| Scole, Norf | 54 | A1 |
| Sconser, High | 125 | D1 |

| PLACE | PAGE | GRID |
|---|---|---|
| Scopwick, Linc | 73 | A2 |
| Scorborough, E R of Y | 89 | D2 |
| Scorrier, Corn | 1 | D1 |
| Scorton, Lanc | 85 | C2 |
| Scorton, N York | 93 | A1 |
| Scotby, Cumb | 97 | A1 |
| Scotch Corner, N York | 93 | A1 |
| Scothern, Linc | 83 | D4 |
| Scotlandwell, Perth | 119 | B4 |
| Scotter, Linc | 83 | C2 |
| Scotterthorpe, Linc | 83 | C2 |
| Scotton, Linc | 83 | C2 |
| Scotton, N York | 93 | A2 |
| Scotton, N York | 88 | A1 |
| Scoulton, Norf | 63 | C3 |
| Scourie, High | 137 | A3 |
| Scrabster, High | 138 | C1 |
| Scraesburgh, Bord | 108 | D3 |
| Scrane End, Linc | 73 | D3 |
| Scraptoft, Leics | 60 | C2 |
| Scratby, Norf | 65 | C1 |
| Scrayingham, N York | 89 | A1 |
| Scredington, Linc | 73 | B3 |
| Scremerston, Nthumb | 115 | E4 |
| Screveton, Notts | 72 | A3 |
| Scriven, N York | 88 | A1 |
| Scrooby, Notts | 83 | A3 |
| Scropton, Derby | 70 | B4 |
| Scruton, N York | 93 | B2 |
| Sculthorpe, Norf | 74 | E4 |
| Scunthorpe, Linc | 83 | C1 |
| Sea Palling, Norf | 75 | D4 |
| Seaborough, Dors | 11 | C4 |
| Seaford, E Sus | 19 | B4 |
| Seagrave, Leics | 60 | B1 |
| Seaham, Durham | 99 | A1 |
| Seahouses, Nthumb | 109 | E2 |
| Seal, Kent | 29 | A3 |
| Seale, Surr | 145 | A3 |
| Seamer, N York | 93 | C1 |
| Seamer, N York | 94 | D3 |
| Seamill, N Ayr | 106 | C1 |
| Searby, Linc | 83 | D2 |
| Seascale, Cumb | 91 | B1 |
| Seathwaite, Cumb | 91 | C2 |
| Seatoller, Cumb | 96 | F4 |
| Seaton, Corn | 4 | A4 |
| Seaton, Cumb | 96 | D3 |
| Seaton, Devon | 6 | C1 |
| Seaton, E R of Y | 90 | A2 |
| Seaton, Nthumb | 104 | C3 |
| Seaton, Rut | 61 | B3 |
| Seaton Delaval, Nthumb | 104 | C3 |
| Seaton Ross, E R of Y | 89 | B3 |
| Seatown, Dors | 6 | D1 |
| Seave Green, N York | 93 | D1 |
| Seaview, I of W | 8 | C1 |
| Seaville, Cumb | 96 | E1 |
| Seavington St Mary, Som | 11 | C3 |
| Sebergham, Cumb | 97 | A2 |
| Seckington, Warw | 59 | A2 |
| Sedbergh, Cumb | 92 | A2 |
| Sedbusk, N York | 92 | C2 |
| Sedgeberrow, Worc | 48 | A4 |
| Sedgebrook, Linc | 72 | C3 |
| Sedgefield, Durham | 98 | D3 |
| Sedgeford, Norf | 74 | C4 |
| Sedgehill, Wilts | 12 | D2 |
| Sedgwick, Cumb | 91 | F3 |
| Sedrup, Bucks | 38 | C2 |
| Seend Cleeve, Wilts | 25 | B3 |
| Seer Green, Bucks | 39 | A4 |
| Seething, Norf | 65 | A3 |
| Sefton, Mers | 78 | A2 |
| Seighford, Staff | 57 | C1 |
| Seion, Gwyn | 66 | E1 |
| Seisdon, Staff | 57 | C3 |
| Selattyn, Shrop | 67 | E4 |
| Selborne, Hamp | 16 | B1 |
| Selby, N York | 88 | C3 |
| Selham, W Suss | 17 | A2 |
| Selhurst, G Lon | 143 | B4 |
| Selkirk, Bord | 108 | C2 |
| Sellack, Heref | 35 | B1 |
| Sellindge, Kent | 21 | C1 |
| Selling, Kent | 30 | C3 |
| Sells Green, Wilts | 25 | B3 |
| Selmeston, E Sus | 19 | B3 |
| Selsdon, G Lon | 148 | C1 |
| Selsey, W Suss | 8 | E1 |
| Selside, N York | 92 | B4 |
| Selston, Notts | 71 | A2 |
| Selworthy, Som | 22 | E4 |
| Semer, Suff | 53 | C3 |
| Semington, Wilts | 25 | A3 |
| Semley, Wilts | 12 | D2 |
| Send, Surr | 146 | A2 |
| Send Marsh, Surr | 146 | B2 |
| Senghenydd, Caer | 34 | C4 |
| Sennen, Corn | 1 | A3 |
| Sennen Cove, Corn | 1 | A2 |
| Sennybridge, Powys | 34 | B1 |
| Sessay, N York | 93 | C4 |
| Setchey, Norf | 62 | D2 |
| Settle, N York | 86 | C1 |
| Settrington, N York | 94 | B4 |
| Seven Sisters, Neath | 34 | A3 |
| Seven Wells, Glouc | 48 | B4 |
| Sevenhampton, Glouc | 36 | C2 |
| Sevenhampton, Wilts | 37 | B4 |
| Sevenoaks, Kent | 149 | C2 |
| Sevenoaks Weald, Kent | 149 | C3 |
| Severn Beach, Glouc | 23 | D1 |
| Severn Stoke, Worc | 47 | C4 |
| Sewards End, Essex | 52 | C4 |
| Sewell, Beds | 39 | B1 |
| Sewerby, E R of Y | 94 | F4 |
| Seworgan, Corn | 1 | D2 |
| Sewstern, Leics | 61 | B1 |
| Shabbington, Bucks | 38 | B3 |
| Shackerstone, Leics | 59 | B2 |
| Shackleford, Surr | 145 | B4 |
| Shadforth, Durham | 98 | D2 |
| Shadingfield, Suff | 65 | B4 |
| Shadoxhurst, Kent | 21 | B1 |
| Shadwell, Norf | 63 | C4 |

| PLACE | PAGE | GRID |
|---|---|---|
| Shaftenhoe End, Herts | 52 | A4 |
| Shaftesbury, Dors | 12 | D2 |
| Shafton, S York | 82 | A1 |
| Shalbourne, Wilts | 26 | A3 |
| Shalden, Hamp | 27 | A4 |
| Shalford, Essex | 42 | A1 |
| Shalford, Surr | 146 | A3 |
| Shalford Green, Essex | 42 | A1 |
| Shalstone, Bucks | 50 | A4 |
| Shamley Green, Surr | 146 | B4 |
| Shandon, Argyll | 111 | D1 |
| Shangton, Leics | 60 | C3 |
| Shanklin, I of W | 8 | B2 |
| Shap, Cumb | 97 | B4 |
| Shapwick, Dors | 13 | A4 |
| Shapwick, Som | 11 | C1 |
| Shardlow, Derby | 71 | A4 |
| Shareshill, Staff | 58 | A2 |
| Sharlston, W York | 88 | B4 |
| Sharnbrook, Beds | 51 | A2 |
| Sharnford, Leics | 60 | A3 |
| Sharow, N York | 93 | B4 |
| Sharpenhoe, Beds | 39 | B1 |
| Sharperton, Nthumb | 109 | C4 |
| Sharpness, Glouc | 35 | C3 |
| Sharrington, Norf | 75 | A4 |
| Shatterford, Worc | 57 | B4 |
| Shaugh Prior, Devon | 4 | C3 |
| Shavington, Chesh | 69 | A2 |
| Shaw, G Man | 80 | B1 |
| Shaw, Wilts | 25 | A2 |
| Shaw Mills, N York | 87 | B1 |
| Shawbury, Shrop | 56 | D1 |
| Shawell, Leics | 60 | B4 |
| Shawhead, D & G | 101 | C3 |
| Shearsby, Leics | 60 | C4 |
| Shearston, Som | 11 | B1 |
| Shebbear, Devon | 9 | D3 |
| Shebdon, Staff | 57 | B1 |
| Sheen, Staff | 70 | A1 |
| Sheepscombe, Glouc | 36 | B3 |
| Sheepstor, Devon | 4 | D3 |
| Sheepwash, Devon | 9 | D4 |
| Sheepy Magna, Leics | 59 | B3 |
| Sheering, Essex | 41 | A2 |
| Sheerness, Kent | 30 | B2 |
| Sheerwater, Surr | 146 | B1 |
| Sheet, Hamp | 16 | B2 |
| Sheffield, S York | 81 | C3 |
| Shefford, Beds | 51 | B4 |
| Sheinton, Shrop | 57 | A2 |
| Shelderton, Shrop | 46 | C1 |
| Sheldon, Derby | 70 | B1 |
| Sheldon, Devon | 11 | A3 |
| Sheldwich, Kent | 30 | C3 |
| Shelfanger, Norf | 64 | A4 |
| Shelford, Notts | 72 | A3 |
| Shelley, Suff | 53 | D4 |
| Shelley, W York | 81 | B1 |
| Shellingford, Oxon | 37 | C4 |
| Shellow Bowells, Essex | 41 | B3 |
| Shelsley Beauchamp, Worc | 47 | B2 |
| Shelsley Walsh, Worc | 47 | B2 |
| Shelton, Beds | 51 | A1 |
| Shelton, Norf | 64 | B4 |
| Shelton, Notts | 72 | B3 |
| Shelve, Shrop | 56 | B3 |
| Shelwick, Heref | 46 | D4 |
| Shenington, Oxon | 49 | A4 |
| Shenley, Herts | 39 | C3 |
| Shenley Brook End, Bucks | 50 | B4 |
| Shenley Church End, Bucks | 50 | B4 |
| Shenmore, Heref | 46 | C4 |
| Shenstone, Staff | 58 | B2 |
| Shenstone, Worc | 47 | C1 |
| Shenton, Leics | 59 | B3 |
| Shepherd's Bush, G Lon | 142 | B2 |
| Shepherdswell, Kent | 31 | B4 |
| Shepley, W York | 81 | B1 |
| Shepperton, Surr | 141 | A4 |
| Shepperton Green, Surr | 141 | A4 |
| Shepreth, Camb | 52 | A3 |
| Shepshed, Leics | 60 | A1 |
| Shepton Mallet, Som | 24 | A4 |
| Shepton Montague, Som | 12 | B1 |
| Sheraton, Durham | 99 | A2 |
| Sherborne, Glouc | 37 | B2 |
| Sherborne, Som | 24 | A3 |
| Sherborne, Dors | 12 | B3 |
| Sherborne St John, Hamp | 27 | A3 |
| Sherbourne, Warw | 48 | C2 |
| Sherburn, Durham | 98 | D2 |
| Sherburn, N York | 94 | C3 |
| Sherburn in Elmet, N York | 88 | B3 |
| Shere, Surr | 146 | B3 |
| Shereford, Norf | 74 | D4 |
| Sherfield English, Hamp | 14 | B2 |
| Sherford, Devon | 8 | B1 |
| Sherford, Dors | 7 | B1 |
| Sheriff Hutton, N York | 94 | A4 |
| Sheriffhales, Shrop | 57 | B2 |
| Sheringham, Norf | 75 | B3 |
| Sherington, Bucks | 50 | C3 |
| Shernborne, Norf | 74 | C4 |
| Sherrington, Wilts | 13 | A1 |
| Sherston, Wilts | 25 | A1 |
| Shevington, G Man | 78 | B1 |
| Sheviock, Corn | 4 | B4 |
| Shibden Head, W York | 87 | A4 |
| Shidlaw, Nthumb | 109 | A1 |
| Shiel Bridge, High | 126 | A2 |
| Shieldaig, High | 130 | F3 |
| Shieldhill, Falkirk | 113 | B2 |
| Shifnal, Shrop | 57 | B2 |
| Shilbottle, Nthumb | 109 | E4 |
| Shildon, Durham | 98 | C3 |
| Shillingford, Devon | 10 | C2 |
| Shillingford Abbot, Devon | 5 | C1 |
| Shillingford St George, Devon | 5 | C1 |
| Shillingstone, Dors | 12 | D3 |
| Shillington, Beds | 51 | B4 |
| Shilton, Oxon | 37 | B3 |
| Shilton, Warw | 60 | A4 |
| Shimpling, Norf | 64 | B4 |

| PLACE | PAGE | GRID |
|---|---|---|
| Shimpling, Suff | 53 | B3 |
| Shimpling Street, Suff | 53 | B3 |
| Shincliffe, Durham | 98 | D2 |
| Shiney Row, T & W | 98 | D1 |
| Shipbourne, Kent | 29 | A4 |
| Shipdham, Norf | 63 | C2 |
| Shipham, Som | 23 | C3 |
| Shiplake, Oxon | 27 | B1 |
| Shipley, W Suss | 18 | A2 |
| Shipley, W York | 87 | A3 |
| Shippon, Oxon | 37 | D4 |
| Shipston on Stour, Warw | 48 | C4 |
| Shipton, Glouc | 36 | C2 |
| Shipton, N York | 88 | C1 |
| Shipton, Shrop | 56 | D3 |
| Shipton Bellinger, Hamp | 25 | D4 |
| Shipton Gorge, Dors | 6 | E1 |
| Shipton Green, W Suss | 16 | B4 |
| Shipton Moyne, Glouc | 36 | B4 |
| Shipton-on-Cherwell, Oxon | 37 | D2 |
| Shiptonthorpe, E R of Y | 89 | C2 |
| Shipton-under-Wychwood, Oxon | 37 | C2 |
| Shirburn, Oxon | 38 | B4 |
| Shirdley Hill, Lanc | 78 | A1 |
| Shirebrook, Derby | 71 | B1 |
| Shirenewton, Monm | 35 | B4 |
| Shireoaks, Notts | 82 | B4 |
| Shirland, Derby | 71 | A2 |
| Shirley, Derby | 70 | B3 |
| Shirley, G Lon | 143 | B4 |
| Shirrell Heath, Hamp | 15 | B3 |
| Shirwell, Devon | 9 | E1 |
| Shiskine, N Ayr | 105 | F2 |
| Shobdon, Heref | 46 | C2 |
| Shoby, Leics | 60 | C1 |
| Shocklach, Chesh | 68 | A2 |
| Shop, Corn | 9 | B3 |
| Shop, Corn | 3 | C2 |
| Shop Street, Suff | 54 | A1 |
| Shoreditch, G Lon | 143 | B1 |
| Shoreditch, Som | 11 | B2 |
| Shoreham-by-Sea, W Suss | 18 | B4 |
| Shorley, Hamp | 15 | B2 |
| Shorne, Kent | 29 | B2 |
| Shortgate, E Sus | 19 | B3 |
| Shortlanesend, Corn | 2 | A1 |
| Shortstown, Beds | 51 | A3 |
| Shorwell, I of W | 8 | A2 |
| Shoscombe, Som | 24 | B3 |
| Shotesham, Norf | 65 | A3 |
| Shotley, Suff | 54 | A4 |
| Shotley Bridge, Durham | 98 | B1 |
| Shotley Gate, Suff | 54 | B4 |
| Shotley Street, Suff | 54 | A4 |
| Shottenden, Kent | 30 | C3 |
| Shotteswell, Warw | 49 | B3 |
| Shottisham, Suff | 54 | B4 |
| Shottle, Derby | 70 | C2 |
| Shottlegate, Derby | 70 | C3 |
| Shotts, N Lan | 113 | A4 |
| Shotwick, Chesh | 67 | E1 |
| Shouldham, Norf | 63 | A2 |
| Shouldham Thorpe, Norf | 63 | A2 |
| Shoulton, Worc | 47 | C2 |
| Shrawardine, Shrop | 56 | C1 |
| Shrawley, Worc | 47 | B2 |
| Shreding Green, Bucks | 140 | C2 |
| Shrewley, Warw | 48 | C2 |
| Shrewsbury, Shrop | 56 | D2 |
| Shrewton, Wilts | 25 | C4 |
| Shrivenham, Oxon | 37 | B4 |
| Shropham, Norf | 63 | C3 |
| Shucknall, Heref | 47 | A4 |
| Shudy Camps, Camb | 52 | C4 |
| Shurdington, Glouc | 36 | B2 |
| Shurlock Row, Berks | 27 | B2 |
| Shurton, Som | 23 | A4 |
| Shustoke, Warw | 59 | A4 |
| Shut Heath, Staff | 57 | C1 |
| Shute, Devon | 11 | B4 |
| Shutford, Oxon | 49 | A4 |
| Shuthonger, Glouc | 47 | C4 |
| Shutlanger, Nhants | 50 | A3 |
| Shuttington, Warw | 59 | A2 |
| Shuttlewood, Derby | 82 | A4 |
| Shuttleworth, G Man | 79 | B1 |
| Sibbertoft, Nhants | 60 | C4 |
| Sibdon Carwood, Shrop | 56 | C4 |
| Sibford Ferris, Oxon | 49 | A4 |
| Sibford Gower, Oxon | 49 | A4 |
| Sible Hedingham, Essex | 53 | B4 |
| Sibley's Green, Essex | 41 | B1 |
| Sibsey, Linc | 73 | D2 |
| Sibson, Camb | 61 | D3 |
| Sibson, Leics | 59 | B3 |
| Sibthorpe, Notts | 72 | B3 |
| Sicklesmere, Suff | 53 | B2 |
| Sicklinghall, N York | 88 | A2 |
| Sidbury, Devon | 6 | B1 |
| Sidbury, Shrop | 57 | A4 |
| Sidcot, Som | 23 | C3 |
| Sidcup, G Lon | 144 | B3 |
| Siddington, Chesh | 69 | B1 |
| Siddington, Glouc | 36 | C3 |
| Sidestrand, Norf | 75 | C3 |
| Sidmouth, Devon | 6 | B1 |
| Sigglesthorne, E R of Y | 90 | A2 |
| Sigingstone, Glam | 22 | E2 |
| Silchester, Hamp | 27 | A3 |
| Sileby, Leics | 60 | B1 |
| Silecroft, Cumb | 91 | C3 |
| Silfield, Norf | 64 | A3 |
| Silk Willoughby, Linc | 73 | A3 |
| Silkstone, S York | 81 | C2 |
| Silkstone Common, S York | 81 | C2 |
| Silloth, Cumb | 96 | D1 |
| Silpho, N York | 94 | D2 |
| Silsoe, Beds | 51 | B4 |
| Silton, Dors | 12 | C2 |
| Silver End, Essex | 42 | B2 |
| Silverburn, M Loth | 114 | A4 |
| Silverdale, Lanc | 91 | E4 |
| Silverstone, Nhants | 50 | A4 |
| Silverton, Devon | 10 | C4 |
| Silvington, Shrop | 47 | A1 |

| PLACE | PAGE | GRID |
|---|---|---|
| Simonburn, Nthumb | 103 | C3 |
| Simons Burrow, Devon | 11 | A3 |
| Simonsbath, Som | 10 | B1 |
| Simonstone, Lanc | 86 | B3 |
| Simpson, Bucks | 50 | C4 |
| Sinclair's Hill, Bord | 115 | D4 |
| Sinclairston, E Ayr | 106 | E3 |
| Sinderby, N York | 93 | B3 |
| Sinderland Green, G Man | 79 | B3 |
| Sindlesham, Berks | 27 | B2 |
| Singleton, Lanc | 85 | B3 |
| Singleton, W Suss | 17 | A3 |
| Sinnington, N York | 94 | B3 |
| Sinton, Worc | 47 | C2 |
| Sissinghurst, Kent | 21 | A1 |
| Siston, Glouc | 24 | A2 |
| Sithney, Corn | 1 | D2 |
| Sittingbourne, Kent | 30 | B3 |
| Six Ashes, Shrop | 57 | B4 |
| Six Mile Bottom, Camb | 52 | C2 |
| Sixhills, Linc | 84 | A3 |
| Sixpenny Handley, Dors | 13 | A3 |
| Skares, E Ayr | 106 | E3 |
| Skateraw, Aber | 129 | B4 |
| Skeeby, N York | 93 | A1 |
| Skeffington, Leics | 61 | A3 |
| Skeffling, E R of Y | 90 | C4 |
| Skegby, Notts | 72 | B1 |
| Skegness, Linc | 74 | B1 |
| Skelbrooke, S York | 82 | B1 |
| Skeldyke, Linc | 73 | D4 |
| Skellingthorpe, Linc | 72 | C1 |
| Skellow, S York | 82 | B1 |
| Skelmanthorpe, W York | 81 | B1 |
| Skelmersdale, Lanc | 78 | A2 |
| Skelmorlie, N Ayr | 111 | C3 |
| Skelton, Cumb | 97 | A3 |
| Skelton, E R of Y | 89 | B4 |
| Skelton, N York | 99 | C4 |
| Skelton, N York | 93 | B4 |
| Skelton, N York | 88 | C1 |
| Skelwith Bridge, Cumb | 91 | D1 |
| Skendleby, Linc | 74 | A1 |
| Skenfrith, Monm | 35 | A2 |
| Skerne, E R of Y | 89 | D1 |
| Skerray, High | 137 | F1 |
| Skewsby, N York | 94 | A4 |
| Skidby, E R of Y | 89 | D3 |
| Skilgate, Som | 10 | C2 |
| Skillington, Linc | 61 | B1 |
| Skinburness, Cumb | 96 | E1 |
| Skinflats, Falkirk | 113 | B2 |
| Skipness, Argyll | 111 | A4 |
| Skipsea, E R of Y | 90 | A1 |
| Skipton, N York | 86 | D2 |
| Skipton-on-Swale, N York | 93 | B3 |
| Skipwith, N York | 89 | A3 |
| Skirlaugh, E R of Y | 90 | A3 |
| Skirling, Bord | 107 | D1 |
| Skirmett, Bucks | 38 | C4 |
| Skirpenbeck, E R of Y | 89 | B1 |
| Skirwith, Cumb | 97 | C3 |
| Skye Green, Essex | 42 | B1 |
| Slack, W York | 86 | D4 |
| Slad, Glouc | 36 | B3 |
| Slade, Devon | 10 | B2 |
| Slade Green, G Lon | 144 | C2 |
| Slade Hooton, S York | 82 | B3 |
| Slaggyford, Nthumb | 97 | C1 |
| Slaidburn, Lanc | 86 | B2 |
| Slaithwaite, W York | 81 | A1 |
| Slaley, Nthumb | 103 | D4 |
| Slamannan, Falkirk | 113 | A2 |
| Slapton, Bucks | 39 | A2 |
| Slapton, Devon | 8 | B1 |
| Slapton, Nhants | 50 | A3 |
| Slaugham, W Suss | 18 | B2 |
| Slaughterford, Wilts | 25 | A2 |
| Slawston, Leics | 61 | A3 |
| Sleaford, Hamp | 16 | B1 |
| Sleaford, Linc | 73 | A3 |
| Sleagill, Cumb | 97 | C4 |
| Sleapford, Shrop | 57 | A1 |
| Sledmere, E R of Y | 94 | C4 |
| Sleightholme, Durham | 92 | D1 |
| Sleights, N York | 94 | C1 |
| Sligachan, High | 125 | C1 |
| Slimbridge, Glouc | 36 | A3 |
| Slindon, Staff | 69 | B4 |
| Slindon, W Suss | 17 | A3 |
| Slinfold, W Suss | 18 | A1 |
| Slingsby, N York | 94 | A4 |
| Slip End, Beds | 39 | B2 |
| Slip End, Herts | 51 | C4 |
| Slipton, Nhants | 50 | C1 |
| Slitting Mill, Staff | 58 | A1 |
| Sloncombe, Devon | 5 | A1 |
| Sloothby, Linc | 74 | A1 |
| Slough, Berks | 140 | C2 |
| Slough Green, Som | 11 | B2 |
| Slyfield Green, Surr | 146 | A3 |
| Slyne, Lanc | 91 | F4 |
| Smailholm, Bord | 108 | D2 |
| Small Dole, W Suss | 18 | B3 |
| Small Hythe, Kent | 21 | B1 |
| Smallburgh, Norf | 65 | A1 |
| Smalley, Derby | 71 | A3 |
| Smallfield, Surr | 148 | C4 |
| Smallridge, Devon | 11 | B4 |
| Smallworth, Norf | 64 | A4 |
| Smannell, Hamp | 26 | A4 |
| Smarden, Kent | 30 | A4 |
| Smarden Bell, Kent | 30 | A4 |
| Smart's Hill, Kent | 149 | C4 |
| Smeatharpe, Devon | 11 | A3 |
| Smeeth, Kent | 21 | C1 |
| Smeeton Westerby, Leics | 60 | C3 |
| Smestow, Staff | 57 | C3 |
| Smisby, Derby | 59 | B1 |
| Smithfield, Cumb | 102 | C4 |
| Smith's Green, Essex | 53 | A4 |
| Smithstown, High | 130 | F1 |
| Smithton, High | 132 | C4 |
| Snailbeach, Shrop | 56 | C3 |
| Snailwell, Camb | 52 | C2 |
| Snainton, N York | 94 | C3 |

| PLACE | PAGE | GRID |
|---|---|---|
| Snaith, E R of Y | 89 | A4 |
| Snape, N York | 93 | A3 |
| Snape, Suff | 54 | C2 |
| Snape Street, Suff | 54 | C2 |
| Snarestone, Leics | 59 | B2 |
| Snarford, Linc | 83 | D4 |
| Snargate, Kent | 21 | B2 |
| Snave, Kent | 21 | C1 |
| Sneaton, N York | 94 | C1 |
| Snelland, Linc | 83 | D4 |
| Snelston, Derby | 70 | A3 |
| Snetterton, Norf | 63 | C4 |
| Snettisham, Norf | 74 | C4 |
| Snig's End, Glouc | 36 | A1 |
| Snitter, Nthumb | 109 | C4 |
| Snitterby, Linc | 83 | D3 |
| Snitterfield, Warw | 48 | C2 |
| Snitton, Shrop | 46 | D1 |
| Snodland, Kent | 29 | B3 |
| Snow End, Herts | 40 | B1 |
| Snowshill, Glouc | 48 | B4 |
| Soake, Hamp | 16 | A3 |
| Soberton, Hamp | 15 | B3 |
| Soberton Heath, Hamp | 15 | B3 |
| Sockburn, Durham | 93 | B1 |
| Soham, Camb | 52 | C1 |
| Soldridge, Hamp | 16 | A1 |
| Sole Street, Kent | 29 | A2 |
| Sole Street, Kent | 30 | C4 |
| Solihull, W Mids | 48 | C1 |
| Sollers Dilwyn, Heref | 46 | C3 |
| Sollers Hope, Heref | 35 | C1 |
| Solva, Pemb | 32 | B1 |
| Somerby, Leics | 61 | A2 |
| Somerby, Linc | 83 | D2 |
| Somercotes, Derby | 71 | A2 |
| Somerford Keynes, Glouc | 36 | C4 |
| Somerleyton, Suff | 65 | C3 |
| Somersal Herbert, Derby | 70 | A4 |
| Somersby, Linc | 84 | C4 |
| Somersham, Camb | 52 | A1 |
| Somersham, Suff | 53 | D3 |
| Somerton, Oxon | 37 | D1 |
| Somerton, Som | 12 | A2 |
| Sompting, W Suss | 18 | A4 |
| Sonning, Berks | 27 | B2 |
| Sonning Common, Oxon | 27 | A1 |
| Sopworth, Wilts | 25 | A1 |
| Sorbie, D & G | 95 | E1 |
| Sorn, E Ayr | 106 | F2 |
| Sosgill, Cumb | 96 | D3 |
| Sotby, Linc | 84 | B4 |
| Sots Hole, Linc | 73 | B1 |
| Sotterly, Suff | 65 | B4 |
| Soughton, Flint | 67 | E1 |
| Soulby, Cumb | 97 | D4 |
| Souldern, Oxon | 38 | A1 |
| Souldrop, Beds | 51 | A2 |
| Sourton, Devon | 4 | C1 |
| Soutergate, Cumb | 91 | C3 |
| South Acre, Norf | 63 | B2 |
| South Alkham, Kent | 31 | B4 |
| South Anston, S York | 82 | B4 |
| South Ascot, Berks | 140 | B4 |
| South Baddesley, Hamp | 14 | B4 |
| South Barrow, Som | 12 | B2 |
| South Beddington, G Lon | 148 | B1 |
| South Benfleet, Essex | 29 | B1 |
| South Brent, Devon | 5 | A4 |
| South Brewham, Som | 12 | C1 |
| South Broomhill, Nthumb | 104 | C1 |
| South Burlingham, Norf | 65 | B2 |
| South Carlton, Linc | 83 | C4 |
| South Cave, E R of Y | 89 | C3 |
| South Cerney, Glouc | 37 | A4 |
| South Charlton, Nthumb | 109 | E3 |
| South Cheriton, Som | 12 | B2 |
| South Cliffe, E R of Y | 89 | C3 |
| South Cockerington, Linc | 84 | C3 |
| South Cornelly, Brid | 22 | D1 |
| South Cove, Suff | 65 | C4 |
| South Creake, Norf | 74 | D4 |
| South Croxton, Leics | 60 | C2 |
| South Dalton, E R of Y | 89 | C2 |
| South Duffield, N York | 89 | A3 |
| South Elkington, Linc | 84 | B3 |
| South Elmsall, W York | 82 | A1 |
| South Fambridge, Essex | 42 | B4 |
| South Fawley, Berks | 26 | B1 |
| South Ferriby, Linc | 89 | D4 |
| South Godstone, Surr | 148 | C3 |
| South Gorley, Hamp | 14 | A3 |
| South Green, Kent | 30 | A3 |
| South Green, Norf | 64 | A2 |
| South Hanningfield, Essex | 42 | A4 |
| South Hayling, Hamp | 16 | A4 |
| South Heath, Bucks | 39 | A3 |
| South Hetton, Durham | 98 | D2 |
| South Hiendley, W York | 82 | A1 |
| South Hill, Corn | 4 | B2 |
| South Hinksey, Oxon | 38 | A3 |
| South Holmwood, Surr | 147 | B4 |
| South Hornchurch, G Lon | 144 | C1 |
| South Huish, Devon | 8 | A1 |
| South Hykeham, Linc | 72 | C1 |
| South Kelsey, Linc | 83 | D2 |
| South Killingholme, Linc | 84 | A1 |
| South Kilvington, N York | 93 | C3 |
| South Kilworth, Leics | 60 | B4 |
| South Kirkby, W York | 82 | A1 |
| South Kyme, Linc | 73 | B2 |
| South Lawn, Oxon | 37 | C2 |
| South Leigh, Oxon | 37 | D3 |
| South Leverton, Notts | 83 | B4 |
| South Lopham, Norf | 64 | A4 |
| South Luffenham, Rut | 61 | B3 |
| South Marston, Wilts | 37 | B4 |
| South Merstham, Surr | 148 | B3 |
| South Milford, N York | 88 | B3 |
| South Milton, Devon | 8 | A1 |
| South Mimms, Herts | 40 | A3 |
| South Molton, Devon | 10 | A2 |
| South Moreton, Oxon | 38 | A4 |
| South Mundham, W Suss | 17 | A4 |
| South Newbald, E R of Y | 89 | C3 |
| South Newton, Wilts | 13 | B1 |

| PLACE | PAGE | GRID |
|---|---|---|
| South Normanton, Derby | 71 | A2 |
| South Norwood, G Lon | 143 | B4 |
| South Nutfield, Surr | 148 | B3 |
| South Ockendon, Essex | 29 | A1 |
| South Ormsby, Linc | 84 | C4 |
| South Owersby, Linc | 83 | D3 |
| South Park, Surr | 148 | A3 |
| South Perrott, Dors | 12 | A3 |
| South Petherton, Som | 11 | C3 |
| South Petherwin, Corn | 4 | B2 |
| South Pickenham, Norf | 63 | B2 |
| South Pool, Devon | 8 | B1 |
| South Poorton, Dors | 12 | A4 |
| South Queensferry, Edin | 114 | A2 |
| South Radworthy, Devon | 10 | A1 |
| South Rauceby, Linc | 73 | A3 |
| South Raynham, Norf | 63 | B1 |
| South Runcton, Norf | 62 | D2 |
| South Scarle, Notts | 72 | B1 |
| South Shields, T & W | 104 | C4 |
| South Stainley, N York | 88 | A1 |
| South Stoke, Som | 24 | B3 |
| South Stoke, W Suss | 17 | B3 |
| South Street, E Sus | 19 | A2 |
| South Street, Kent | 30 | C3 |
| South Tawton, Devon | 4 | D1 |
| South Thoresby, Linc | 84 | C4 |
| South Tidworth, Wilts | 25 | D4 |
| South Weald, Essex | 41 | B4 |
| South Willingham, Linc | 84 | A4 |
| South Wingate, Durham | 99 | A2 |
| South Wingfield, Derby | 70 | C2 |
| South Witham, Linc | 61 | B1 |
| South Woodham Ferrers, Essex | 42 | B4 |
| South Wraxall, Wilts | 25 | A2 |
| South Zeal, Devon | 4 | D1 |
| Southall, G Lon | 141 | B2 |
| Southam, Glouc | 36 | C1 |
| Southam, Warw | 49 | B2 |
| Southampton, Hamp | 15 | A3 |
| Southborough, Kent | 29 | A4 |
| Southborough, G Lon | 144 | A4 |
| Southbourne, W Suss | 16 | B4 |
| Southburgh, Norf | 63 | C2 |
| Southburn, E R of Y | 89 | D1 |
| Southcott, Corn | 9 | B4 |
| Southcott, Devon | 9 | E4 |
| Southcott, Devon | 5 | A2 |
| Southease, E Sus | 19 | A4 |
| Southend, Argyll | 105 | D4 |
| Southend-on-Sea, Essex | 30 | A1 |
| Southerndown, Glam | 22 | D2 |
| Southerness, D & G | 96 | C1 |
| Southerton, Devon | 6 | A1 |
| Southery, Norf | 62 | D3 |
| Southfleet, Kent | 29 | A2 |
| Southgate, Swan | 33 | C4 |
| Southill, Beds | 51 | B4 |
| Southleigh, Devon | 6 | B1 |
| Southminster, Essex | 43 | A3 |
| Southmoor, Oxon | 37 | D4 |
| Southoe, Camb | 51 | B2 |
| Southorpe, Camb | 61 | C2 |
| Southowram, W York | 87 | A4 |
| Southport, Mers | 77 | D1 |
| Southrepps, Norf | 75 | C4 |
| Southrey, Linc | 73 | B1 |
| Southrop, Glouc | 37 | B3 |
| Southrope, Hamp | 27 | A4 |
| Southsea, Hamp | 16 | A4 |
| Southside, Durham | 98 | B3 |
| Southwaite, Cumb | 97 | A2 |
| Southwark, G Lon | 143 | B2 |
| Southwater, W Suss | 18 | A2 |
| Southwell, Notts | 72 | A2 |
| Southwick, Hamp | 16 | A3 |
| Southwick, Nhants | 61 | C3 |
| Southwick, Wilts | 25 | A3 |
| Southwold, Suff | 54 | D1 |
| Sowerby, N York | 93 | C3 |
| Sowood, W York | 87 | A4 |
| Sowton, Devon | 4 | C3 |
| Soyland Town, W York | 86 | D4 |
| Spain's End, Essex | 53 | A4 |
| Spalding, Linc | 62 | A1 |
| Spaldington, E R of Y | 89 | B3 |
| Spaldwick, Camb | 51 | B1 |
| Spalford, Notts | 72 | B1 |
| Spanby, Linc | 73 | B3 |
| Sparham, Norf | 64 | A1 |
| Spark Bridge, Cumb | 91 | D3 |
| Sparkford, Som | 12 | B2 |
| Sparkwell, Devon | 4 | D4 |
| Sparrowpit, Derby | 81 | A4 |
| Sparsholt, Oxon | 37 | C4 |
| Spaunton, N York | 94 | A2 |
| Spaxton, Som | 11 | A1 |
| Spean Bridge, High | 121 | F1 |
| Speen, Bucks | 38 | C3 |
| Speeton, N York | 94 | E4 |
| Spen Green, Chesh | 69 | B2 |
| Spennithorne, N York | 92 | E2 |
| Spennymoor, Durham | 98 | C3 |
| Spetisbury, Dors | 12 | D4 |
| Spexhall, Suff | 65 | B4 |
| Spey Bay, Moray | 133 | D2 |
| Spinkhill, Derby | 82 | A4 |
| Spinningdale, High | 136 | C4 |
| Spital, Berks | 140 | B3 |
| Spital Hill, S York | 82 | B3 |
| Spittal, High | 138 | D2 |
| Spittal, Pemb | 32 | D1 |
| Spittal of Glenshee, Perth | 123 | B2 |
| Spittalfield, Perth | 119 | A1 |
| Spixworth, Norf | 65 | A1 |
| Splatt, Devon | 9 | E4 |
| Splayne's Green, E Sus | 19 | B2 |
| Spofforth, N York | 88 | A2 |
| Spooner Row, Norf | 64 | A3 |
| Sporle, Norf | 63 | B2 |
| Spott, E Loth | 115 | B2 |
| Spratton, Nhants | 50 | A1 |
| Spreakley, Surr | 27 | B4 |
| Spreyton, Devon | 10 | A4 |
| Spriddlestone, Devon | 4 | C4 |
| Spridlington, Linc | 83 | D3 |
| Springfield, D & G | 102 | B4 |
| Springfield, Fife | 119 | C3 |
| Springholm, D & G | 101 | C3 |
| Springthorpe, Linc | 83 | C3 |
| Springwell, T & W | 104 | C4 |
| Sproatley, E R of Y | 90 | A3 |
| Sproston Green, Chesh | 69 | A1 |
| Sprotbrough, S York | 82 | B2 |
| Sproughton, Suff | 53 | D4 |
| Sprouston, Bord | 109 | A2 |
| Sproxton, Leics | 61 | B1 |
| Sproxton, N York | 93 | D3 |
| Spurstow, Chesh | 68 | B2 |
| Spyway, Dors | 6 | E1 |
| St Abbs, Bord | 115 | D3 |
| St Agnes, Corn | 3 | A4 |
| St Albans, Herts | 39 | C3 |
| St Allen, Corn | 3 | B4 |
| St Andrew, Guer | 139 | B2 |
| St Andrews, Fife | 119 | E3 |
| St Andrew's Major, Glam | 23 | A2 |
| St Ann's Chapel, Devon | 8 | A1 |
| St Anthony, Corn | 2 | A2 |
| St Arvans, Monm | 35 | B4 |
| St Asaph, Denb | 77 | B4 |
| St Athan, Glam | 22 | F2 |
| St Aubin, Jers | 139 | A2 |
| St Austell, Corn | 3 | D4 |
| St Bees, Cumb | 96 | C4 |
| St Boswells, Bord | 108 | D2 |
| St Brelade, Jers | 139 | A2 |
| St Brelade's Bay, Jers | 139 | A2 |
| St Breock, Corn | 3 | D3 |
| St Breward, Corn | 3 | E2 |
| St Briavels, Glouc | 35 | B3 |
| St Bride's Major, Glam | 22 | E2 |
| St Brides super-Ely, Glam | 22 | F1 |
| St Brides Wentlooge, Newport | 23 | B1 |
| St Buryan, Corn | 1 | B2 |
| St Catherines, Argyll | 117 | C3 |
| St Chloe, Glouc | 36 | B3 |
| St Clears, Carm | 32 | F2 |
| St Cleer, Corn | 4 | A3 |
| St Clement, Corn | 2 | B1 |
| St Clement, Jers | 139 | B2 |
| St Clether, Corn | 4 | A1 |
| St Columb Major, Corn | 3 | C3 |
| St Combs, Aber | 134 | E2 |
| St Cross South Elmham, Suff | 65 | A4 |
| St Cyrus, Aber | 124 | C3 |
| St David's, Perth | 118 | E2 |
| St David's, Pemb | 32 | B1 |
| St Day, Corn | 1 | D1 |
| St Decumans, Som | 22 | F4 |
| St Dennis, Corn | 3 | C4 |
| St Dogmaels, Cered | 44 | C3 |
| St Dominick, Corn | 4 | B3 |
| St Donats, Glam | 22 | E2 |
| St Endellion, Corn | 3 | D2 |
| St Enoder, Corn | 3 | C4 |
| St Erme, Corn | 3 | B4 |
| St Erney, Corn | 4 | B4 |
| St Erth, Corn | 1 | C2 |
| St Erth Praze, Corn | 1 | C2 |
| St Ervan, Corn | 3 | C3 |
| St Ewe, Corn | 2 | C1 |
| St Fagans, Cardiff | 23 | A1 |
| St Fergus, Aber | 134 | E3 |
| St Fillans, Perth | 118 | C2 |
| St Florence, Pemb | 32 | E3 |
| St Gennys, Corn | 9 | A4 |
| St George, Ab & Col | 77 | A4 |
| St Georges, Som | 23 | C3 |
| St George's Hill, Surr | 146 | B1 |
| St Giles in the Wood, Devon | 9 | D2 |
| St Giles-on-the-Heath, Devon | 4 | B1 |
| St Harmon, Powys | 45 | D1 |
| St Helen Auckland, Durham | 98 | C3 |
| St Helena, Norf | 64 | B1 |
| St Helens, I of W | 8 | C1 |
| St Helens, Mers | 78 | B2 |
| St Helier, G Lon | 142 | B4 |
| St Helier, Jers | 139 | B2 |
| St Hilary, Corn | 1 | C2 |
| St Hilary, Glam | 22 | F2 |
| St Ippollitts, Herts | 39 | C1 |
| St Ishmael's, Pemb | 32 | B3 |
| St Ive, Corn | 4 | B3 |
| St Ives, Camb | 51 | D1 |
| St Ives, Corn | 1 | C1 |
| St John, Corn | 4 | B4 |
| St John, Jers | 139 | B1 |
| St Johns, Kent | 149 | C2 |
| St Johns, Surr | 146 | A2 |
| St John's, I o M | 139 | B3 |
| St John's Chapel, Devon | 9 | D1 |
| St John's Fen End, Norf | 62 | C2 |
| St John's Town of Dalry, D & G | 101 | A2 |
| St John's Wood, G Lon | 143 | A1 |
| St Jude's, I o M | 139 | C2 |
| St Just, Corn | 1 | A2 |
| St Just-in-Roseland, Corn | 2 | A2 |
| St Keverne, Corn | 2 | A3 |
| St Kew Highway, Corn | 3 | D2 |
| St Keyne, Corn | 4 | A3 |
| St Lawrence, Essex | 43 | A3 |
| St Lawrence, I of W | 8 | B2 |
| St Lawrence, Jers | 139 | B2 |
| St Leonards, Bucks | 39 | A3 |
| St Leonards, Dors | 13 | B4 |
| St Lythans, Glam | 22 | F2 |
| St Mabyn, Corn | 3 | D2 |
| St Margarets, Heref | 46 | C4 |
| St Margarets, Herts | 40 | B2 |
| St Margaret's at Cliffe, Kent | 31 | C4 |
| St Margarets Hope, Ork | 139 | A2 |
| St Marks, I o M | 139 | B4 |
| St Martin, Corn | 4 | A4 |
| St Martin, Guer | 139 | B2 |
| St Martin, Jers | 139 | B2 |
| St Martins, Shrop | 67 | E4 |
| St Mary, Jers | 139 | A2 |
| St Mary Bourne, Hamp | 26 | B4 |
| St Mary Church, Glam | 22 | E2 |
| St Mary Cray, G Lon | 144 | B4 |
| St Mary in the Marsh, Kent | 21 | C2 |
| St Mary's, Ork | 139 | B2 |
| St Mary's Bay, Kent | 21 | C2 |
| St Mary's Hoo, Kent | 30 | A1 |
| St Maughans Green, Monm | 35 | B2 |
| St Mawes, Corn | 2 | A2 |
| St Mawgan, Corn | 3 | C3 |
| St Mellion, Corn | 4 | B3 |
| St Merryn, Corn | 3 | C2 |
| St Mewan, Corn | 3 | D4 |
| St Michael Caerhays, Corn | 2 | B1 |
| St Michael Church, Som | 11 | B1 |
| St Michael Penkevil, Corn | 2 | B1 |
| St Michael South Elmham, Suff | 65 | A4 |
| St Michael's on Wyre, Lanc | 85 | B3 |
| St Minver, Corn | 3 | D2 |
| St Monans, Fife | 119 | E4 |
| St Neot, Corn | 3 | E3 |
| St Neots, Camb | 51 | B2 |
| St Nicholas, Pemb | 44 | A4 |
| St Nicholas, Glam | 22 | F2 |
| St Nicholas at Wade, Kent | 31 | B2 |
| St Olaves, Norf | 65 | B3 |
| St Osyth, Essex | 43 | C2 |
| St Ouen, Jers | 139 | A2 |
| St Owens Cross, Heref | 35 | B1 |
| St Pauls Cray, G Lon | 144 | B4 |
| St Paul's Walden, Herts | 39 | C1 |
| St Peter, Jers | 139 | A2 |
| St Peter Port, Guer | 139 | B2 |
| St Peter's, Guer | 139 | B2 |
| St Sampson, Guer | 139 | B2 |
| St Saviour, Guer | 139 | B2 |
| St Saviour, Jers | 139 | B2 |
| St Stephen, Corn | 3 | C4 |
| St Stephen's Coombe, Corn | 3 | C4 |
| St Teath, Corn | 3 | D2 |
| St Tudy, Corn | 3 | D2 |
| St Twynnells, Pemb | 32 | C4 |
| St Veep, Corn | 3 | E4 |
| St Vigeans, Angus | 124 | B4 |
| St Wenn, Corn | 3 | D3 |
| St Weonards, Heref | 35 | B1 |
| Stableford, Shrop | 57 | B3 |
| Stacey Bank, S York | 81 | C3 |
| Stackhouse, N York | 92 | C4 |
| Stackpole, Pemb | 32 | D4 |
| Staddiscombe, Devon | 4 | C4 |
| Stadhampton, Oxon | 38 | A4 |
| Staffield, Cumb | 97 | B2 |
| Staffin, High | 130 | C2 |
| Stafford, Staff | 57 | C1 |
| Stagsden, Beds | 51 | A3 |
| Stainburn, Cumb | 96 | D3 |
| Stainburn, N York | 87 | B2 |
| Stainby, Linc | 61 | B1 |
| Staincross, S York | 81 | C1 |
| Staindrop, Durham | 98 | B4 |
| Staines, Surr | 141 | A3 |
| Stainforth, N York | 92 | C4 |
| Stainforth, S York | 83 | A1 |
| Staining, Lanc | 85 | A3 |
| Stainland, W York | 87 | A4 |
| Stainsacre, N York | 94 | C1 |
| Stainton, Cumb | 97 | B3 |
| Stainton, Cumb | 91 | F3 |
| Stainton, Durham | 98 | B4 |
| Stainton, S York | 82 | B3 |
| Stainton by Langworth, Linc | 83 | D4 |
| Stainton le Vale, Linc | 84 | A3 |
| Stainton with Adgarley, Cumb | 91 | D4 |
| Staintondale, N York | 94 | D2 |
| Stair, E Ayr | 106 | E3 |
| Stair Haven, D & G | 95 | C1 |
| Staithes, N York | 99 | D4 |
| Stalbridge, Dors | 12 | C3 |
| Stalbridge Weston, Dors | 12 | C3 |
| Stalham, Norf | 65 | B1 |
| Stalisfield Green, Kent | 30 | B3 |
| Stallen, Dors | 12 | B3 |
| Stallingborough, Linc | 84 | A1 |
| Stalmine, Lanc | 85 | B2 |
| Stalybridge, G Man | 80 | B2 |
| Stambourne, Essex | 53 | A4 |
| Stambourne Green, Essex | 53 | A4 |
| Stamford, Nthumb | 109 | E3 |
| Stamford, Linc | 61 | C2 |
| Stamford Bridge, Chesh | 68 | B1 |
| Stamford Bridge, E R of Y | 89 | A1 |
| Stamfordham, Nthumb | 104 | A3 |
| Stanbridge, Beds | 39 | A1 |
| Stanbury, W York | 86 | D3 |
| Standburn, Falkirk | 113 | B2 |
| Standeford, Staff | 57 | C2 |
| Standen, Kent | 21 | A1 |
| Standerwick, Som | 25 | A4 |
| Standford, Hamp | 16 | B1 |
| Standingstone, Cumb | 96 | D3 |
| Standish, G Man | 78 | B1 |
| Standon, Hamp | 15 | A2 |
| Standon, Herts | 40 | B1 |
| Standon, Staff | 69 | B4 |
| Stane, N Lan | 113 | A4 |
| Stanfield, Norf | 63 | C1 |
| Stanford, Beds | 51 | B4 |
| Stanford, Kent | 21 | D1 |
| Stanford Bishop, Heref | 47 | A3 |
| Stanford Bridge, Worc | 47 | B2 |
| Stanford Dingley, Berks | 26 | C2 |
| Stanford le Hope, Essex | 29 | B1 |
| Stanford on Avon, Nhants | 49 | C1 |
| Stanford on Soar, Notts | 60 | B1 |
| Stanfree, Derby | 82 | A4 |
| Stanghow, N York | 99 | C4 |
| Stanhoe, Norf | 74 | D4 |
| Stanhope, Durham | 98 | A2 |
| Stanion, Nhants | 61 | B4 |
| Stanley, Derby | 71 | A3 |
| Stanley, Durham | 98 | C1 |
| Stanley, Perth | 119 | A1 |
| Stanley, Staff | 69 | C2 |
| Stanley Crook, Durham | 98 | C2 |
| Stanley Pontlarge, Glouc | 36 | C1 |
| Stanmer, E Sus | 19 | A3 |
| Stannersburn, Nthumb | 103 | B2 |
| Stannington, Nthumb | 104 | B3 |
| Stannington, S York | 81 | C3 |
| Stannington Station, Nthumb | 104 | B2 |
| Stansbatch, Heref | 46 | B2 |
| Stansfield, Suff | 53 | B3 |
| Stanstead, Suff | 53 | B3 |
| Stanstead Abbots, Herts | 40 | B2 |
| Stansted, Kent | 29 | A3 |
| Stansted Mountfitchet, Essex | 41 | A1 |
| Stanton, Glouc | 48 | B4 |
| Stanton, Nthumb | 104 | A2 |
| Stanton, Staff | 70 | A3 |
| Stanton, Suff | 53 | C1 |
| Stanton by Bridge, Derby | 70 | C4 |
| Stanton by Dale, Derby | 71 | A3 |
| Stanton Drew, Som | 24 | A3 |
| Stanton Fitzwarren, Wilts | 37 | B4 |
| Stanton Harcourt, Oxon | 37 | D3 |
| Stanton in Peak, Derby | 70 | B1 |
| Stanton Lacy, Shrop | 46 | D1 |
| Stanton Lees, Derby | 70 | B1 |
| Stanton Long, Shrop | 56 | D4 |
| Stanton St John, Oxon | 38 | A3 |
| Stanton St Quintin, Wilts | 25 | A1 |
| Stanton Street, Suff | 53 | C2 |
| Stanton under Bardon, Leics | 60 | A2 |
| Stanton upon Hine Heath, Shrop | 56 | D1 |
| Stanton Wick, Som | 24 | A3 |
| Stanway, Essex | 43 | A1 |
| Stanway, Glouc | 37 | A1 |
| Stanwell, Surr | 141 | A3 |
| Stanwell Moor, Surr | 141 | A3 |
| Stanwick, Nhants | 51 | A1 |
| Stape, N York | 94 | B2 |
| Stapeley, Chesh | 68 | C2 |
| Staple, Kent | 31 | B3 |
| Staple, Som | 22 | F4 |
| Staple Cross, Devon | 10 | D2 |
| Staple Fitzpaine, Som | 11 | B2 |
| Staplefield, W Suss | 18 | B2 |
| Stapleford, Herts | 40 | A2 |
| Stapleford, Leics | 61 | A1 |
| Stapleford, Linc | 72 | C2 |
| Stapleford, Notts | 71 | A4 |
| Stapleford, Wilts | 13 | B1 |
| Stapleford Abbotts, Essex | 41 | A4 |
| Staplehay, Som | 11 | A2 |
| Staplehurst, Kent | 30 | A4 |
| Staplestreet, Kent | 30 | C3 |
| Stapleton, Heref | 46 | B2 |
| Stapleton, Leics | 60 | A3 |
| Stapleton, N York | 98 | C4 |
| Stapleton, Shrop | 56 | D2 |
| Stapleton, Som | 11 | C2 |
| Stapley, Som | 11 | A3 |
| Staploe, Beds | 51 | B2 |
| Staplow, Heref | 47 | A4 |
| Star, Fife | 119 | C4 |
| Star, Pemb | 44 | D4 |
| Starbotton, N York | 92 | D4 |
| Starcross, Devon | 5 | C2 |
| Stareton, Warw | 49 | A1 |
| Starlings Green, Essex | 41 | A1 |
| Starston, Norf | 64 | B4 |
| Startforth, Durham | 98 | B4 |
| Startley, Wilts | 25 | B1 |
| Statenborough, Kent | 31 | B3 |
| Stathe, Som | 11 | C2 |
| Stathern, Leics | 72 | B4 |
| Staughton Green, Camb | 51 | B2 |
| Staughton Highway, Camb | 51 | B2 |
| Staunton, Glouc | 35 | B2 |
| Staunton, Glouc | 36 | A1 |
| Staunton on Arrow, Heref | 46 | C2 |
| Staunton on Wye, Heref | 46 | C4 |
| Staveley, Cumb | 91 | E3 |
| Staveley, Cumb | 91 | F2 |
| Staveley, Derby | 82 | A4 |
| Staveley, N York | 88 | A1 |
| Staverton, Glouc | 36 | B1 |
| Staverton, Nhants | 49 | C2 |
| Staverton, Wilts | 25 | A3 |
| Stawell, Som | 11 | C1 |
| Stawley, Som | 10 | D2 |
| Staxigoe, High | 138 | F2 |
| Staxton, N York | 94 | D3 |
| Staynall, Lanc | 85 | B2 |
| Stean, N York | 92 | E4 |
| Steane, Nhants | 49 | C4 |
| Stearsby, N York | 93 | D4 |
| Steart, Som | 23 | B4 |
| Stebbing, Essex | 42 | A1 |
| Stebbing Green, Essex | 42 | A1 |
| Stedham, W Suss | 17 | A2 |
| Steel, Nthumb | 103 | D4 |
| Steen's Bridge, Heref | 46 | D2 |
| Steep, Hamp | 16 | B2 |
| Steep Lane, W York | 86 | D4 |
| Steeple, Dors | 7 | B2 |
| Steeple, Essex | 43 | A3 |
| Steeple Ashton, Wilts | 25 | A3 |
| Steeple Aston, Oxon | 37 | D1 |
| Steeple Bumpstead, Essex | 53 | A4 |
| Steeple Claydon, Bucks | 38 | B1 |
| Steeple Gidding, Camb | 61 | D4 |
| Steeple Langford, Wilts | 13 | A1 |
| Steeple Morden, Camb | 51 | C4 |
| Stelling Minnis, Kent | 31 | A4 |
| Stembridge, Som | 11 | C2 |
| Stenalees, Corn | 3 | D4 |
| Stenhousemuir, Falkirk | 113 | A2 |
| Stenton, E Loth | 115 | B2 |
| Stepaside, Pemb | 32 | E3 |
| Stepney, G Lon | 143 | B1 |
| Steppingley, Beds | 51 | A4 |
| Sternfield, Suff | 54 | C2 |
| Stert, Wilts | 25 | B3 |
| Stetchworth, Camb | 52 | C2 |
| Stevenage, Herts | 40 | A1 |
| Stevenston, N Ayr | 106 | C1 |
| Steventon, Hamp | 26 | C4 |
| Steventon, Oxon | 37 | D4 |
| Steventon End, Essex | 52 | C4 |
| Stevington, Beds | 51 | A3 |
| Stewartby, Beds | 51 | A4 |
| Stewarton, E Ayr | 106 | D1 |
| Stewkley, Bucks | 39 | A1 |
| Stewley, Som | 11 | B2 |
| Steyning, W Suss | 18 | A3 |
| Steynton, Pemb | 32 | C3 |
| Stibb, Corn | 9 | B3 |
| Stibb Cross, Devon | 9 | D3 |
| Stibb Green, Wilts | 25 | D3 |
| Stichill, Bord | 109 | A1 |
| Sticker, Corn | 3 | D4 |
| Stickford, Linc | 73 | D2 |
| Sticklepath, Devon | 4 | D1 |
| Stickling Green, Essex | 41 | A1 |
| Stickney, Linc | 73 | D2 |
| Stiffkey, Norf | 74 | E3 |
| Stillingfleet, N York | 88 | C3 |
| Stillington, Durham | 98 | D3 |
| Stillington, N York | 93 | D4 |
| Stilton, Camb | 61 | D4 |
| Stinchcombe, Glouc | 36 | A4 |
| Stinsford, Dors | 7 | A1 |
| Stiperstones, Shrop | 56 | C3 |
| Stirl, Stirl | 113 | A1 |
| Stirtloe, Camb | 51 | C2 |
| Stisted, Essex | 42 | B1 |
| Stithians, Corn | 1 | D2 |
| Stixwould, Linc | 73 | B1 |
| Stoak, Chesh | 78 | A4 |
| Stobo, Bord | 107 | E1 |
| Stoborough, Dors | 7 | B1 |
| Stobswood, Nthumb | 104 | B1 |
| Stock, Essex | 42 | A4 |
| Stock, Som | 23 | C3 |
| Stock Green, Worc | 48 | A2 |
| Stock Wood, Worc | 48 | A2 |
| Stockbridge, Hamp | 14 | B1 |
| Stockcross, Berks | 26 | B2 |
| Stockerston, Leics | 61 | A3 |
| Stocking, Heref | 35 | C1 |
| Stocking Pelham, Herts | 41 | A1 |
| Stockland Bristol, Som | 23 | B4 |
| Stockleigh Pomeroy, Devon | 10 | B4 |
| Stockley, Wilts | 25 | B2 |
| Stocklinch, Som | 11 | C3 |
| Stockport, G Man | 80 | A3 |
| Stocksbridge, S York | 81 | B2 |
| Stocksfield, Nthumb | 104 | A4 |
| Stockton, Heref | 46 | D2 |
| Stockton, Shrop | 57 | B1 |
| Stockton, Shrop | 57 | B3 |
| Stockton, Warw | 49 | B2 |
| Stockton on Teme, Worc | 47 | B2 |
| Stockton on the Forest, N York | 89 | A1 |
| Stockton-on-Tees, Durham | 99 | A4 |
| Stockwood, Dors | 12 | B3 |
| Stodmarsh, Kent | 31 | A3 |
| Stody, Norf | 75 | A4 |
| Stoford, Som | 12 | A3 |
| Stogumber, Som | 10 | D1 |
| Stogursey, Som | 23 | A4 |
| Stoke, Devon | 9 | B2 |
| Stoke, Hamp | 26 | B4 |
| Stoke, Hamp | 16 | A4 |
| Stoke, Kent | 30 | A2 |
| Stoke Abbott, Dors | 11 | C4 |
| Stoke Albany, Nhants | 61 | A4 |
| Stoke Ash, Suff | 53 | D1 |
| Stoke Bardolph, Notts | 72 | A3 |
| Stoke Bliss, Worc | 47 | A2 |
| Stoke Bruerne, Nhants | 50 | B3 |
| Stoke by Clare, Suff | 53 | A4 |
| Stoke Canon, Devon | 10 | C4 |
| Stoke Charity, Hamp | 15 | A1 |
| Stoke Climsland, Corn | 4 | B2 |
| Stoke Cross, Heref | 47 | A3 |
| Stoke Doyle, Nhants | 61 | C4 |
| Stoke Dry, Rut | 61 | B3 |
| Stoke Ferry, Norf | 63 | A3 |
| Stoke Fleming, Devon | 8 | B1 |
| Stoke Gabriel, Devon | 5 | B4 |
| Stoke Golding, Leics | 60 | A3 |
| Stoke Goldington, Bucks | 50 | B3 |
| Stoke Green, Bucks | 140 | C1 |
| Stoke Hammond, Bucks | 39 | A1 |
| Stoke Holy Cross, Norf | 64 | B3 |
| Stoke Lacy, Heref | 47 | A3 |
| Stoke Lyne, Oxon | 38 | A1 |
| Stoke Mandeville, Bucks | 38 | C3 |
| Stoke Newington, G Lon | 143 | B1 |
| Stoke Orchard, Glouc | 36 | B1 |
| Stoke Poges, Bucks | 140 | C1 |
| Stoke Prior, Heref | 46 | D3 |
| Stoke Prior, Worc | 48 | A2 |
| Stoke Rivers, Devon | 9 | E1 |
| Stoke Rochford, Linc | 72 | C4 |
| Stoke Row, Oxon | 27 | A1 |
| Stoke St Michael, Som | 24 | A4 |
| Stoke St Milborough, Shrop | 56 | D4 |
| Stoke sub Hamdon, Som | 12 | A3 |
| Stoke Talmage, Oxon | 38 | B3 |
| Stoke Trister, Som | 12 | C2 |
| Stoke upon Tern, Shrop | 68 | C4 |
| Stoke Wake, Dors | 12 | C4 |
| Stoke-by-Nayland, Suff | 53 | C4 |
| Stokeford, Dors | 7 | B1 |
| Stokeham, Notts | 83 | B4 |
| Stokeinteignhead, Devon | 5 | C3 |
| Stokenchurch, Bucks | 38 | C4 |
| Stokenham, Devon | 8 | B1 |
| Stoke-on-Trent, Staff | 69 | B3 |
| Stokesby, Norf | 65 | B2 |
| Stokesley, N York | 93 | D1 |
| Stolford, Som | 10 | D1 |
| Stolford, Som | 23 | A4 |
| Ston Easton, Som | 24 | A3 |
| Stondon Massey, Essex | 41 | B3 |
| Stone, Bucks | 38 | C2 |
| Stone, Glouc | 35 | C4 |
| Stone, Kent | 21 | B2 |
| Stone, S York | 82 | B3 |
| Stone, Worc | 47 | C1 |
| Stone, Staff | 69 | B4 |
| Stone Allerton, Som | 23 | C4 |
| Stone Street, Kent | 29 | A3 |
| Stone Street, Suff | 65 | B4 |
| Stonebridge, Som | 23 | C3 |
| Stonebridge, W Mids | 59 | A4 |
| Stonebroom, Derby | 71 | A2 |
| Stonecrouch, Kent | 20 | B1 |
| Stonegate, E Sus | 20 | B2 |
| Stonegrave, N York | 94 | A3 |
| Stonehall, Worc | 47 | C3 |
| Stonehaven, Aber | 124 | D1 |
| Stonehill Green, Kent | 144 | C3 |
| Stonehouse, Chesh | 68 | B1 |
| Stonehouse, Glouc | 36 | A3 |
| Stonehouse, S Lan | 107 | A1 |
| Stoneleigh, Warw | 49 | A1 |
| Stones Green, Essex | 43 | C1 |
| Stonesby, Leics | 61 | A1 |
| Stonesfield, Oxon | 37 | D2 |
| Stoney Middleton, Derby | 81 | B4 |
| Stoney Stanton, Leics | 60 | A3 |
| Stoney Stoke, Som | 12 | C1 |
| Stoney Stratton, Som | 12 | B1 |
| Stoney Stretton, Shrop | 56 | C2 |
| Stoneyburn, W Loth | 113 | B3 |
| Stoneykirk, D & G | 95 | B1 |
| Stoneywood, Aber | 129 | B2 |
| Stonham Aspal, Suff | 54 | A2 |
| Stonor, Oxon | 38 | B4 |
| Stonton Wyville, Leics | 61 | A3 |
| Stony Houghton, Derby | 71 | A1 |
| Stoodleigh, Devon | 10 | A1 |
| Stoodleigh, Devon | 10 | C2 |
| Stopham, W Suss | 17 | B2 |
| Stormy Corner, Lanc | 78 | B1 |
| Stornoway, W Isles | 139 | B2 |
| Storrington, W Suss | 18 | A3 |
| Storwood, E R of Y | 89 | A2 |
| Stotfold, Beds | 51 | C4 |
| Stottesdon, Shrop | 57 | A4 |
| Stoughton, Surr | 146 | A3 |
| Stoughton, Leics | 60 | C3 |
| Stoughton, W Suss | 16 | B3 |
| Stoulton, Worc | 47 | C3 |
| Stour Provost, Dors | 12 | C2 |
| Stour Row, Dors | 12 | D2 |
| Stourbridge, W Mids | 57 | C4 |
| Stourport-on-Severn, Worc | 47 | C1 |
| Stourton, Staff | 57 | C4 |
| Stourton, Warw | 49 | A4 |
| Stourton, Wilts | 12 | C1 |
| Stourton Caundle, Dors | 12 | C3 |
| Stow, Bord | 108 | B1 |
| Stow, Linc | 83 | C4 |
| Stow Bardolph, Norf | 62 | D2 |
| Stow Bedon, Norf | 63 | C3 |
| Stow cum Quy, Camb | 52 | B2 |
| Stow Longa, Camb | 51 | B1 |
| Stow Maries, Essex | 42 | B3 |
| Stowbridge, Norf | 62 | D2 |
| Stowe, Shrop | 46 | B1 |
| Stowe by Chartley, Staff | 69 | C4 |
| Stowell, Som | 12 | B2 |
| Stowford, Devon | 9 | D4 |
| Stowford, Devon | 22 | B4 |
| Stowford, Devon | 4 | C1 |
| Stowlangtoft, Suff | 53 | C2 |
| Stowmarket, Suff | 53 | D2 |
| Stow-on-the-Wold, Glouc | 37 | B1 |
| Stowting, Kent | 31 | A4 |
| Stowting Common, Kent | 31 | A4 |
| Stowupland, Suff | 53 | D2 |
| Strachan, Aber | 128 | E4 |
| Strachur, Argyll | 117 | C4 |
| Stradbroke, Suff | 54 | A1 |
| Stradsett, Norf | 63 | A2 |
| Stragglethorpe, Linc | 72 | C2 |
| Straiton, S Ayr | 106 | D4 |
| Straloch, Perth | 123 | B3 |
| Stramshall, Staff | 70 | A4 |
| Strang, I o M | 139 | C3 |
| Strangford, Heref | 35 | B1 |
| Stranraer, D & G | 100 | A4 |
| Stratfield Saye, Hamp | 27 | A3 |
| Stratfield Turgis, Hamp | 27 | A3 |
| Stratford, G Lon | 144 | A1 |
| Stratford St Mary, Suff | 53 | D4 |
| Stratford-upon-Avon, Warw | 48 | C3 |
| Strath, High | 130 | F1 |
| Strathaven, S Lan | 107 | A1 |
| Strathblane, Stirl | 112 | B2 |
| Strathcanaird, High | 135 | D3 |
| Strathdon, Aber | 128 | C2 |
| Strathkinness, Fife | 119 | D3 |
| Strathmiglo, Fife | 119 | B3 |
| Strathpeffer, High | 132 | A2 |
| Strathtay, Perth | 123 | A3 |
| Strathwhillan, N Ayr | 106 | A2 |
| Strathy, High | 138 | A1 |
| Strathyre, Stirl | 118 | B3 |
| Stratton, Corn | 9 | B4 |
| Stratton, Dors | 6 | F1 |
| Stratton, Glouc | 36 | C3 |
| Stratton Audley, Oxon | 38 | A1 |
| Stratton St Michael, Norf | 64 | B3 |
| Stratton Strawless, Norf | 64 | B1 |
| Stratton-on-the-Fosse, Som | 24 | A4 |
| Stream, Som | 10 | D1 |
| Streat, E Sus | 19 | A3 |
| Streatham, G Lon | 143 | A3 |
| Streatley, Beds | 39 | B1 |
| Streatley, Berks | 26 | C1 |
| Street, Som | 12 | A1 |

| PLACE | PAGE | GRID |
|---|---|---|
| Street Ashton, Warw | 60 | A4 |
| Street Dinas, Shrop | 67 | E3 |
| Street End, W Suss | 17 | A4 |
| Street Gate, T & W | 104 | B4 |
| Street on the Fosse, Som | 12 | B1 |
| Streethay, Staff | 58 | B2 |
| Streetlam, N York | 93 | B2 |
| Streetly End, Camb | 52 | C3 |
| Strelley, Notts | 71 | B3 |
| Strensall, N York | 89 | A1 |
| Strete, Devon | 8 | B1 |
| Stretford, G Man | 79 | B3 |
| Strethall, Essex | 52 | B4 |
| Stretham, Camb | 52 | B1 |
| Stretton, Chesh | 79 | A4 |
| Stretton, Derby | 71 | A1 |
| Stretton, Rut | 61 | B1 |
| Stretton, Staff | 57 | C2 |
| Stretton, Staff | 70 | B4 |
| Stretton on Fosse, Warw | 48 | C4 |
| Stretton Sugwas, Heref | 46 | D4 |
| Stretton under Fosse, Warw | 60 | A4 |
| Stretton Westwood, Shrop | 57 | A3 |
| Stretton-on-Dunsmore, Warw | 49 | B1 |
| Strichen, Aber | 134 | D3 |
| Stringston, Som | 23 | A4 |
| Strixton, Nhants | 50 | C2 |
| Stroat, Glouc | 35 | B4 |
| Stromeferry, High | 131 | A4 |
| Stromness, Ork | 139 | A2 |
| Stronachlachar, Stirl | 117 | E3 |
| Strone, Argyll | 111 | C2 |
| Stronmilchan, Argyll | 117 | C2 |
| Strontian, High | 121 | B3 |
| Strood Green, Surr | 148 | A3 |
| Stroud, Hamp | 16 | A2 |
| Stroud, Glouc | 36 | B3 |
| Stroud Green, Glouc | 36 | A3 |
| Stroude, Surr | 140 | C4 |
| Stroxton, Linc | 72 | C4 |
| Struan, High | 130 | B4 |
| Struan, Perth | 122 | E2 |
| Strumpshaw, Norf | 65 | A2 |
| Struy, High | 131 | E4 |
| Stuartfield, Aber | 134 | D3 |
| Stubbington, Hamp | 15 | B4 |
| Stubbins, Lanc | 79 | B1 |
| Stubton, Linc | 72 | C3 |
| Stud Green, Berks | 140 | A2 |
| Studham, Beds | 39 | B2 |
| Studholme, Cumb | 96 | F1 |
| Studland, Dors | 7 | C2 |
| Studley, Warw | 48 | B2 |
| Studley, Wilts | 25 | B2 |
| Studley Royal, N York | 93 | B4 |
| Stuntney, Camb | 52 | C1 |
| Sturmer, Essex | 53 | A4 |
| Sturminster Common, Dors | 12 | C3 |
| Sturminster Marshall, Dors | 13 | A4 |
| Sturminster Newton, Dors | 12 | C3 |
| Sturry, Kent | 31 | A3 |
| Sturton, Linc | 83 | D2 |
| Sturton by Stow, Linc | 83 | C4 |
| Sturton le Steeple, Notts | 83 | B4 |
| Stuston, Suff | 54 | A1 |
| Stutton, N York | 88 | B3 |
| Stutton, Suff | 54 | A4 |
| Styal, Chesh | 80 | A4 |
| Styrrup, Notts | 82 | B3 |
| Suckley, Worc | 47 | B3 |
| Sudborough, Nhants | 61 | C4 |
| Sudbourne, Suff | 54 | C3 |
| Sudbrook, Linc | 73 | A3 |
| Sudbrook, Monm | 35 | B4 |
| Sudbrooke, Linc | 83 | D4 |
| Sudbury, Derby | 70 | B4 |
| Sudbury, Suff | 53 | B4 |
| Sudbury, G Lon | 142 | A1 |
| Suddington, Worc | 47 | C2 |
| Suffield, N York | 94 | D2 |
| Suffield, Norf | 75 | B4 |
| Sugnall, Staff | 69 | A4 |
| Sugwas Pool, Heref | 46 | C4 |
| Sulby, I o M | 139 | C2 |
| Sulgrave, Nhants | 49 | C4 |
| Sulhamstead, Berks | 27 | A2 |
| Summerbridge, N York | 87 | B1 |
| Summercourt, Corn | 3 | C4 |
| Summerfield, Norf | 74 | C3 |
| Summerhouse, Durham | 98 | C4 |
| Summerseat, G Man | 79 | B1 |
| Sunbury, Surr | 141 | B4 |
| Sunderland, Cumb | 96 | E2 |
| Sunderland, Lanc | 85 | B1 |
| Sunderland, T & W | 104 | D4 |
| Sundridge, Kent | 149 | B2 |
| Sunningdale, Berks | 140 | B4 |
| Sunninghill, Berks | 140 | B4 |
| Sunningwell, Oxon | 37 | D3 |
| Sunniside, Durham | 98 | B2 |
| Surbiton, G Lon | 142 | A4 |
| Surfleet, Linc | 73 | C4 |
| Surlingham, Norf | 65 | A2 |
| Sustead, Norf | 75 | B4 |
| Susworth, Linc | 83 | B2 |
| Sutcombe, Devon | 9 | C3 |
| Sutcombemill, Devon | 9 | C3 |
| Sutterby, Linc | 84 | C4 |
| Sutterton, Linc | 73 | C4 |
| Sutton, Beds | 51 | C3 |
| Sutton, Camb | 61 | D3 |
| Sutton, Camb | 52 | B1 |
| Sutton, Devon | 8 | A1 |
| Sutton, G Lon | 148 | B1 |
| Sutton, Kent | 31 | B4 |
| Sutton, N York | 88 | B4 |
| Sutton, Norf | 65 | B1 |
| Sutton, Notts | 83 | A3 |
| Sutton, Notts | 72 | B4 |
| Sutton, Shrop | 57 | B4 |
| Sutton, Staff | 57 | B1 |
| Sutton, Suff | 54 | B3 |
| Sutton, W Suss | 17 | B3 |
| Sutton at Hone, Kent | 29 | A2 |
| Sutton Bassett, Nhants | 61 | A4 |
| Sutton Bonington, Notts | 60 | B1 |
| Sutton Bridge, Linc | 62 | C1 |
| Sutton Cheney, Leics | 60 | A3 |
| Sutton Coldfield, W Mids | 58 | B3 |
| Sutton Courtenay, Oxon | 38 | A4 |
| Sutton Grange, N York | 93 | B4 |
| Sutton Green, Surr | 146 | A2 |
| Sutton Howgrave, N York | 93 | B3 |
| Sutton Maddock, Shrop | 57 | B3 |
| Sutton Mallet, Som | 11 | C1 |
| Sutton Mandeville, Wilts | 13 | A2 |
| Sutton Montis, Som | 12 | B2 |
| Sutton on Sea, Linc | 84 | D4 |
| Sutton on the Hill, Derby | 70 | B4 |
| Sutton on Trent, Notts | 72 | B1 |
| Sutton Scotney, Hamp | 15 | A1 |
| Sutton St Edmund, Linc | 62 | B2 |
| Sutton St James, Linc | 62 | B1 |
| Sutton St Nicholas, Heref | 46 | D3 |
| Sutton upon Derwent, E R of Y | 89 | A2 |
| Sutton Valence, Kent | 30 | A4 |
| Sutton Veny, Wilts | 25 | A4 |
| Sutton Waldron, Dors | 12 | D3 |
| Sutton Weaver, Chesh | 78 | B4 |
| Sutton Wick, Oxon | 37 | D4 |
| Sutton Wick, Som | 23 | D3 |
| Sutton-in-Craven, N York | 86 | D2 |
| Sutton-on-the-Forest, N York | 93 | D4 |
| Sutton-under-Brailes, Warw | 49 | A4 |
| Sutton-under-Whitestonecliffe, N York | 93 | C3 |
| Swadlincote, Derby | 59 | B1 |
| Swaffham, Norf | 63 | B2 |
| Swaffham Bulbeck, Camb | 52 | C2 |
| Swaffham Prior, Camb | 52 | C2 |
| Swafield, Norf | 75 | C4 |
| Swainby, N York | 93 | C1 |
| Swainsthorpe, Norf | 64 | B3 |
| Swainswick, Som | 24 | B2 |
| Swalcliffe, Oxon | 49 | A4 |
| Swallow, Linc | 84 | A2 |
| Swallowcliffe, Wilts | 13 | A2 |
| Swallowfield, Berks | 27 | A2 |
| Swan, Swan | 33 | D4 |
| Swan Green, Chesh | 79 | B4 |
| Swanage, Dors | 7 | C2 |
| Swanbourne, Bucks | 38 | C1 |
| Swanland, E R of Y | 89 | D4 |
| Swanley, Kent | 144 | C4 |
| Swanmore, Hamp | 15 | B3 |
| Swannington, Leics | 60 | A1 |
| Swannington, Norf | 64 | B1 |
| Swanton Abbot, Norf | 65 | A1 |
| Swanton Morley, Norf | 64 | A1 |
| Swanton Novers, Norf | 75 | A4 |
| Swanwick, Derby | 71 | A2 |
| Swarby, Linc | 73 | A3 |
| Swardeston, Norf | 64 | B3 |
| Swarkestone, Derby | 70 | C4 |
| Swarland, Nthumb | 104 | B1 |
| Swarraton, Hamp | 15 | B1 |
| Swarthmoor, Cumb | 91 | D3 |
| Swaton, Linc | 73 | B4 |
| Swavesey, Camb | 52 | A1 |
| Swayfield, Linc | 61 | C1 |
| Sweetham, Devon | 10 | B4 |
| Sweethaws, E Sus | 19 | B2 |
| Sweets, Corn | 9 | A4 |
| Sweetshouse, Corn | 3 | E3 |
| Swefling, Suff | 54 | B2 |
| Swepstone, Leics | 59 | B2 |
| Swerford, Oxon | 37 | C1 |
| Swettenham, Chesh | 69 | A1 |
| Swiftsden, E Sus | 20 | B2 |
| Swilland, Suff | 54 | A3 |
| Swillington, W York | 88 | A3 |
| Swimbridge, Devon | 9 | E1 |
| Swinbrook, Oxon | 37 | C2 |
| Swincliffe, N York | 87 | B1 |
| Swinderby, Linc | 72 | C1 |
| Swindon, Staff | 57 | C4 |
| Swindon, Wilts | 25 | C1 |
| Swine, E R of Y | 90 | A3 |
| Swinefleet, E R of Y | 89 | B4 |
| Swineshead, Beds | 51 | A2 |
| Swineshead, Linc | 73 | C3 |
| Swinford, Leics | 49 | C1 |
| Swingfield Minnis, Kent | 31 | A4 |
| Swingfield Street, Kent | 31 | A4 |
| Swingleton Green, Suff | 53 | C3 |
| Swinhoe, Nthumb | 109 | E2 |
| Swinithwaite, N York | 92 | D2 |
| Swinside, Cumb | 96 | F4 |
| Swinstead, Linc | 61 | C1 |
| Swinton, Bord | 109 | B1 |
| Swinton, G Man | 79 | B2 |
| Swinton, N York | 93 | A3 |
| Swinton, S York | 82 | A2 |
| Swithland, Leics | 60 | B2 |
| Swynnerton, Staff | 69 | B4 |
| Swyre, Dors | 6 | E1 |
| Sychtyn, Powys | 55 | D2 |
| Syde, Glouc | 36 | C2 |
| Sydenham, Oxon | 38 | B3 |
| Sydenham, G Lon | 143 | B3 |
| Sydenham Damerel, Devon | 4 | B2 |
| Syderstone, Norf | 74 | D4 |
| Sydling St Nicholas, Dors | 12 | B4 |
| Syerston, Notts | 72 | B3 |
| Sykehouse, S York | 83 | A1 |
| Symbister, Shet | 139 | A2 |
| Symington, S Ayr | 106 | D2 |
| Symington, S Lan | 107 | C2 |
| Syreford, Glouc | 36 | C2 |
| Syresham, Nhants | 50 | A4 |
| Syston, Leics | 60 | C2 |
| Syston, Linc | 72 | C3 |
| Sywell, Nhants | 50 | B2 |
| Tackley, Oxon | 37 | D2 |
| Tacolneston, Norf | 64 | B3 |
| Tadcaster, N York | 88 | B2 |
| Taddington, Derby | 70 | A1 |
| Taddington, Glouc | 37 | A1 |
| Tadlow, Camb | 51 | C3 |
| Tadmarton, Oxon | 49 | B4 |
| Tadworth, Surr | 148 | A2 |
| Taff's Well, Cardiff | 23 | A1 |
| Taibach, Neath | 34 | A4 |
| Tain, High | 136 | D4 |
| Takeley, Essex | 41 | B2 |
| Takeley Street, Essex | 41 | B2 |
| Talaton, Devon | 10 | D4 |
| Talbenny, Pemb | 32 | B2 |
| Talerddig, Powys | 55 | D3 |
| Talgarreg, Cered | 44 | E3 |
| Talgarth, Powys | 46 | A4 |
| Taliesin, Cered | 55 | B3 |
| Talkin, Cumb | 102 | D4 |
| Talladale, High | 131 | A1 |
| Tallarn Green, Wrex | 68 | A3 |
| Tallentire, Cumb | 96 | D2 |
| Talley, Carm | 33 | C1 |
| Tallington, Linc | 61 | D2 |
| Talmine, High | 137 | E1 |
| Talog, Carm | 33 | A1 |
| Talsarn, Cered | 45 | A3 |
| Talsarnau, Gwyn | 66 | E4 |
| Talskiddy, Corn | 3 | C3 |
| Talwrn, Angle | 76 | C4 |
| Talybont, Cered | 55 | A4 |
| Tal-y-Bont, Ab & Col | 66 | F1 |
| Tal-y-Bont, Gwyn | 55 | A1 |
| Talybont-on-Usk, Powys | 34 | C1 |
| Tal-y-coed, Monm | 35 | A2 |
| Tal-y-garn, Rhond | 22 | F1 |
| Talysarn, Gwyn | 66 | D2 |
| Tamworth, Staff | 59 | A2 |
| Tan Office Green, Suff | 53 | B2 |
| Tanfield, Durham | 98 | C1 |
| Tanfield Lea, Durham | 98 | C1 |
| Tangley, Hamp | 26 | A4 |
| Tankerness, Ork | 139 | B2 |
| Tankersley, S York | 81 | C2 |
| Tannadice, Angus | 124 | A3 |
| Tannington, Suff | 54 | B2 |
| Tannochside, N Lan | 112 | C3 |
| Tansley, Derby | 70 | C2 |
| Tansor, Nhants | 61 | C4 |
| Tantobie, Durham | 98 | C1 |
| Tanton, N York | 93 | D1 |
| Tanworth in Arden, Warw | 48 | B1 |
| Tan-y-groes, Cered | 44 | D3 |
| Taplow, Bucks | 140 | B1 |
| Tarbert, Argyll | 110 | E4 |
| Tarbert, Argyll | 111 | A3 |
| Tarbert, W Isles | 139 | A3 |
| Tarbet, Argyll | 117 | E4 |
| Tarbet, High | 125 | F4 |
| Tarbolton, S Ayr | 106 | E2 |
| Tardebigge, Worc | 48 | A1 |
| Tarfside, Angus | 124 | A1 |
| Tarland, Aber | 128 | D3 |
| Tarleton, Lanc | 85 | B4 |
| Tarlton, Glouc | 36 | C3 |
| Tarnock, Som | 23 | C3 |
| Tarporley, Chesh | 68 | B1 |
| Tarr, Som | 10 | B1 |
| Tarr, Som | 10 | D1 |
| Tarrant Crawford, Dors | 12 | D4 |
| Tarrant Gunville, Dors | 12 | D3 |
| Tarrant Hinton, Dors | 13 | A3 |
| Tarrant Keyneston, Dors | 13 | A4 |
| Tarrant Launceston, Dors | 13 | A3 |
| Tarrant Monkton, Dors | 13 | A3 |
| Tarrant Rawston, Dors | 13 | A3 |
| Tarrant Rushton, Dors | 13 | A4 |
| Tarrington, Heref | 47 | A4 |
| Tarskavaig, High | 125 | D3 |
| Tarves, Aber | 129 | B1 |
| Tarvin, Chesh | 68 | B1 |
| Tasburgh, Norf | 64 | B3 |
| Tatenhill, Staff | 59 | A1 |
| Tathwell, Linc | 84 | C4 |
| Tatsfield, Surr | 149 | A2 |
| Tattenhall, Chesh | 68 | B2 |
| Tatterford, Norf | 74 | D4 |
| Tattersett, Norf | 74 | D4 |
| Tattershall, Linc | 73 | C2 |
| Tattershall Thorpe, Linc | 73 | C2 |
| Tattingstone, Suff | 54 | A4 |
| Taunton, Som | 11 | A2 |
| Taverham, Norf | 64 | B2 |
| Tavernspite, Pemb | 32 | E2 |
| Tavistock, Devon | 4 | C2 |
| Taw green, Devon | 10 | A4 |
| Tawstock, Devon | 9 | E1 |
| Taxal, Derby | 80 | B4 |
| Tayinloan, Argyll | 105 | D1 |
| Taynton, Glouc | 36 | A1 |
| Taynton, Oxon | 37 | B2 |
| Taynuilt, Argyll | 117 | B1 |
| Tayport, Fife | 119 | D2 |
| Tayvallich, Argyll | 110 | F1 |
| Tealby, Linc | 84 | A3 |
| Teangue, High | 125 | E3 |
| Tebay, Cumb | 92 | A1 |
| Tebworth, Beds | 39 | B1 |
| Tedburn St Mary, Devon | 5 | B1 |
| Teddington, Glouc | 36 | C1 |
| Teddington, G Lon | 142 | A3 |
| Tedstone Delamere, Heref | 47 | A2 |
| Tedstone Wafer, Heref | 47 | A2 |
| Teeton, Nhants | 50 | A1 |
| Teffont Evias, Wilts | 13 | A1 |
| Teffont Magna, Wilts | 13 | A1 |
| Tegryn, Pemb | 32 | F1 |
| Teigh, Rut | 61 | B1 |
| Teignmouth, Devon | 5 | C2 |
| Telford, Shrop | 57 | B2 |
| Tellisford, Som | 24 | B3 |
| Templand, D & G | 101 | E2 |
| Temple, Corn | 3 | E2 |
| Temple, M Loth | 114 | B4 |
| Temple Bar, Cered | 44 | F3 |
| Temple Cloud, Som | 24 | A3 |
| Temple Grafton, Warw | 48 | B3 |
| Temple Guiting, Glouc | 37 | A1 |
| Temple Hirst, N York | 88 | C4 |
| Temple Normanton, Derby | 71 | A1 |
| Temple Sowerby, Cumb | 97 | C3 |
| Templecombe, Som | 12 | C2 |
| Templeton, Devon | 10 | B3 |
| Templeton, Pemb | 32 | E2 |
| Tempsford, Beds | 51 | B3 |
| Ten Mile Bank, Norf | 62 | D3 |
| Tenby, Pemb | 32 | E3 |
| Tendring, Essex | 43 | C1 |
| Terling, Essex | 42 | A2 |
| Ternhill, Shrop | 68 | C4 |
| Terrington, N York | 94 | A4 |
| Terrington St Clement, Norf | 62 | D1 |
| Teston, Kent | 29 | B3 |
| Tetbury, Glouc | 36 | B4 |
| Tetchill, Shrop | 68 | A4 |
| Tetcott, Devon | 9 | C4 |
| Tetford, Linc | 84 | C4 |
| Tetney, Linc | 84 | C2 |
| Tetsworth, Oxon | 38 | B3 |
| Teversal, Notts | 71 | A1 |
| Teversham, Camb | 52 | B2 |
| Teviothead, Bord | 108 | B4 |
| Tewin, Herts | 40 | A2 |
| Tewkesbury, Glouc | 36 | B1 |
| Thakeham, W Suss | 18 | A3 |
| Thame, Oxon | 38 | B3 |
| Thames Ditton, Surr | 142 | A4 |
| Thamesmead, G Lon | 144 | B2 |
| Thankerton, S Lan | 107 | C1 |
| Tharston, Norf | 64 | B3 |
| Thatcham, Berks | 26 | C2 |
| Thaxted, Essex | 41 | B1 |
| The Braes, High | 130 | D4 |
| The Bungalow, I o M | 139 | C3 |
| The City, Bucks | 38 | C4 |
| The Den, N Ayr | 111 | E4 |
| The Forstal, Kent | 30 | B4 |
| The Forstal, Kent | 21 | C1 |
| The Green, Cumb | 91 | C3 |
| The Green, Essex | 42 | A2 |
| The Hill, Cumb | 91 | C3 |
| The Holt, Berks | 27 | B1 |
| The Lee, Bucks | 39 | A3 |
| The Lhen, I o M | 139 | C1 |
| The Mythe, Glouc | 47 | C4 |
| The Sands, Surr | 145 | A4 |
| The Strand, Wilts | 25 | A3 |
| Theakston, N York | 93 | B3 |
| Thealby, Linc | 83 | C1 |
| Theale, Berks | 27 | A2 |
| Theale, Som | 23 | C4 |
| Thearne, E R of Y | 89 | D3 |
| Theberton, Suff | 54 | C2 |
| Theddingworth, Leics | 60 | C4 |
| Theddlethorpe All Saints, Linc | 84 | D3 |
| Theddlethorpe St Helen, Linc | 84 | D3 |
| Thelnetham, Suff | 53 | D1 |
| Thelveton, Norf | 64 | B4 |
| Themelthorpe, Norf | 64 | A1 |
| Therfield, Herts | 52 | A4 |
| Thetford, Norf | 63 | B4 |
| Theydon Bois, Essex | 41 | A3 |
| Thickwood, Wilts | 25 | A2 |
| Thimbleby, Linc | 73 | C1 |
| Thimbleby, N York | 93 | C2 |
| Thirkleby, N York | 93 | C3 |
| Thirlby, N York | 93 | C3 |
| Thirlspot, Cumb | 96 | F4 |
| Thirn, N York | 93 | A3 |
| Thirsk, N York | 93 | C3 |
| Thistleton, Lanc | 85 | B3 |
| Thistleton, Rut | 61 | B1 |
| Thistley Green, Suff | 53 | A1 |
| Thixendale, N York | 89 | B1 |
| Thockrington, Nthumb | 103 | D3 |
| Tholomas Drove, Camb | 62 | B2 |
| Tholthorpe, N York | 93 | C4 |
| Thomastown, Aber | 133 | E4 |
| Thompson, Norf | 63 | C3 |
| Thong, Kent | 29 | B2 |
| Thoralby, N York | 92 | D3 |
| Thoresway, Linc | 84 | A2 |
| Thorganby, Linc | 84 | B2 |
| Thorganby, N York | 89 | A3 |
| Thorgill, N York | 94 | A2 |
| Thorington, Suff | 54 | C1 |
| Thorington Street, Suff | 53 | D4 |
| Thorlby, N York | 86 | D2 |
| Thorley, Herts | 41 | A2 |
| Thorley Street, I of W | 7 | F1 |
| Thormanby, N York | 93 | C4 |
| Thornage, Norf | 75 | A4 |
| Thornborough, Bucks | 38 | C1 |
| Thornborough, N York | 93 | B3 |
| Thornbury, Devon | 9 | C3 |
| Thornbury, Glouc | 35 | C4 |
| Thornbury, Heref | 47 | A2 |
| Thornby, Nhants | 50 | A1 |
| Thorncliff, Staff | 69 | C2 |
| Thorncombe, Dors | 11 | C4 |
| Thorncombe Street, Surr | 146 | A4 |
| Thorndon, Suff | 54 | A1 |
| Thorndon Cross, Devon | 4 | C1 |
| Thorne, S York | 83 | A1 |
| Thorne St Margaret, Som | 10 | D2 |
| Thorner, W York | 88 | A3 |
| Thornes, Staff | 58 | B2 |
| Thorney, Camb | 62 | A2 |
| Thorney, Notts | 83 | C4 |
| Thorney, Som | 11 | C2 |
| Thorney, Bucks | 141 | A2 |
| Thornfalcon, Som | 11 | B2 |
| Thornford, Dors | 12 | B3 |
| Thorngrafton, Nthumb | 103 | B4 |
| Thorngumbald, E R of Y | 90 | B4 |
| Thornham, Norf | 74 | C3 |
| Thornham Magna, Suff | 53 | D1 |
| Thornham Parva, Suff | 53 | D1 |
| Thornhaugh, Camb | 61 | C3 |
| Thornhill, D & G | 101 | C1 |
| Thornhill, Stirl | 118 | C4 |
| Thornhill, W York | 87 | B4 |
| Thornholme, E R of Y | 90 | A1 |
| Thornicombe, Dors | 12 | D4 |
| Thornington, Nthumb | 109 | B2 |
| Thornley, Durham | 98 | B2 |
| Thornley, Durham | 98 | D2 |
| Thorns, Suff | 53 | A3 |
| Thorn's Flush, Surr | 17 | B1 |
| Thornsett, Derby | 80 | B3 |
| Thornthwaite, Cumb | 96 | E3 |
| Thornthwaite, N York | 87 | B1 |
| Thornton, Angus | 123 | E4 |
| Thornton, Bucks | 50 | B4 |
| Thornton, E R of Y | 89 | B2 |
| Thornton, Fife | 119 | C4 |
| Thornton, Lanc | 85 | A2 |
| Thornton, Leics | 60 | A2 |
| Thornton, Linc | 73 | C1 |
| Thornton, N York | 99 | A4 |
| Thornton, Nthumb | 109 | C1 |
| Thornton, W York | 87 | A3 |
| Thornton Curtis, Linc | 84 | A1 |
| Thornton Dale, N York | 94 | B3 |
| Thornton Heath, G Lon | 143 | A4 |
| Thornton Hough, Mers | 77 | D4 |
| Thornton in Lonsdale, N York | 92 | A4 |
| Thornton le Moor, Linc | 83 | D2 |
| Thornton Rust, N York | 92 | D2 |
| Thornton Steward, N York | 93 | A3 |
| Thornton Watlass, N York | 93 | A3 |
| Thorntonhall, S Lan | 112 | B4 |
| Thornton-in-Craven, N York | 86 | C2 |
| Thornton-le-Beans, N York | 93 | C2 |
| Thornton-le-Clay, N York | 94 | A4 |
| Thornton-le-Moor, N York | 93 | C2 |
| Thornton-le-Moors, Chesh | 78 | A4 |
| Thornton-le-Street, N York | 93 | C3 |
| Thornythwaite, Cumb | 97 | A3 |
| Thoroton, Notts | 72 | B3 |
| Thorp Arch, W York | 88 | B2 |
| Thorpe, Derby | 70 | A2 |
| Thorpe, E R of Y | 89 | D2 |
| Thorpe, N York | 86 | D1 |
| Thorpe, Notts | 72 | B2 |
| Thorpe Abbotts, Norf | 64 | B4 |
| Thorpe Arnold, Leics | 61 | A1 |
| Thorpe Audlin, W York | 82 | A1 |
| Thorpe Bassett, N York | 94 | C4 |
| Thorpe by Water, Rut | 61 | B3 |
| Thorpe Constantine, Staff | 59 | A2 |
| Thorpe End, Norf | 65 | A2 |
| Thorpe Green, Essex | 43 | C1 |
| Thorpe Green, Suff | 53 | C3 |
| Thorpe Hesley, S York | 81 | C2 |
| Thorpe in Balne, S York | 82 | B1 |
| Thorpe in the Fallows, Linc | 83 | C4 |
| Thorpe Langton, Leics | 61 | A3 |
| Thorpe le Street, E R of Y | 89 | B2 |
| Thorpe Lea, Surr | 140 | C3 |
| Thorpe Malsor, Nhants | 50 | B1 |
| Thorpe Mandeville, Nhants | 49 | C4 |
| Thorpe Market, Norf | 75 | C4 |
| Thorpe Morieux, Suff | 53 | C3 |
| Thorpe on the Hill, Linc | 72 | C1 |
| Thorpe Salvin, S York | 82 | B4 |
| Thorpe Satchville, Leics | 60 | C2 |
| Thorpe St Peter, Linc | 74 | A1 |
| Thorpe Thewles, Durham | 99 | A3 |
| Thorpe Tilney, Linc | 73 | B2 |
| Thorpe Underwood, N York | 88 | B1 |
| Thorpe Willoughby, N York | 88 | C3 |
| Thorpe-le-Soken, Essex | 43 | C1 |
| Thorpeness, Suff | 54 | D2 |
| Thorrington, Essex | 43 | B2 |
| Thorverton, Devon | 10 | C4 |
| Thrandeston, Suff | 53 | D1 |
| Thrapston, Nhants | 51 | A1 |
| Threapwood, Chesh | 68 | A3 |
| Threapwood, Staff | 69 | C3 |
| Three Cocks, Powys | 46 | A4 |
| Three Cups Corner, E Sus | 20 | A2 |
| Three Leg Cross, E Sus | 20 | B1 |
| Three Legged Cross, Dors | 13 | B4 |
| Three Mile Cross, Berks | 27 | A2 |
| Threekingham, Linc | 73 | B4 |
| Threlkeld, Cumb | 96 | F3 |
| Thrigby, Norf | 65 | B2 |
| Thrintoft, N York | 93 | B2 |
| Thriplow, Camb | 52 | B3 |
| Throcking, Herts | 40 | B1 |
| Throckmorton, Worc | 48 | A3 |
| Throop, Dors | 7 | B1 |
| Thropton, Nthumb | 103 | D1 |
| Throwleigh, Devon | 5 | A1 |
| Throwley Forstal, Kent | 30 | B3 |
| Thrumpton, Notts | 71 | B4 |
| Thrumster, High | 138 | E3 |
| Thrupp, Glouc | 36 | B3 |
| Thrushesbush, Essex | 41 | A3 |
| Thrussington, Leics | 60 | C1 |
| Thruxton, Hamp | 26 | A4 |
| Thruxton, Heref | 46 | C4 |
| Thulston, Derby | 71 | A4 |
| Thurcaston, Leics | 60 | B2 |
| Thurcroft, S York | 82 | A3 |
| Thurgarton, Norf | 75 | B4 |
| Thurgoland, S York | 81 | C2 |
| Thurlaston, Leics | 60 | A3 |
| Thurlaston, Warw | 49 | B1 |
| Thurlbear, Som | 11 | B2 |
| Thurlby, Linc | 72 | C1 |
| Thurlby, Linc | 61 | D1 |
| Thurlby, Linc | 84 | D4 |
| Thurleigh, Beds | 51 | A2 |
| Thurlestone, Devon | 8 | A1 |
| Thurlow, Suff | 53 | A3 |
| Thurlstone, S York | 81 | B2 |
| Thurlton, Norf | 65 | B3 |
| Thurnby, Leics | 60 | C2 |
| Thurne, Norf | 65 | B1 |
| Thurning, Nhants | 61 | D4 |
| Thurning, Norf | 75 | A4 |
| Thurnscoe, S York | 82 | A2 |
| Thursby, Cumb | 96 | F1 |
| Thursford, Norf | 74 | E4 |
| Thursley, Surr | 17 | A1 |
| Thurso, High | 138 | C1 |
| Thurstaston, Mers | 77 | D3 |
| Thurston, Suff | 53 | C2 |
| Thurstonland, W York | 81 | B1 |
| Thurton, Norf | 65 | A3 |
| Thurvaston, Derby | 70 | B3 |
| Thwaite, N York | 92 | C2 |
| Thwaite, Suff | 53 | D2 |
| Thwaite Head, Cumb | 91 | D2 |
| Thwaite St Mary, Norf | 65 | A3 |
| Thwing, E R of Y | 94 | D4 |
| Tibbermore, Perth | 119 | A2 |
| Tibberton, Glouc | 36 | A2 |
| Tibberton, Shrop | 57 | A1 |
| Tibberton, Worc | 47 | C2 |
| Tibenham, Norf | 64 | B4 |
| Tibshelf, Derby | 71 | A1 |
| Tibthorpe, E R of Y | 89 | C1 |
| Tichborne, Hamp | 15 | B1 |
| Tickencote, Rut | 61 | C2 |
| Tickenham, Som | 23 | C2 |
| Tickhill, S York | 82 | B3 |
| Ticklerton, Shrop | 56 | D4 |
| Ticknall, Derby | 59 | B1 |
| Tickton, E R of Y | 89 | D2 |
| Tidcombe, Wilts | 26 | A3 |
| Tiddington, Oxon | 38 | B3 |
| Tiddington, Warw | 48 | C3 |
| Tidebrook, E Sus | 20 | A1 |
| Tideford, Corn | 4 | B4 |
| Tidenham, Glouc | 35 | B4 |
| Tideswell, Derby | 81 | A4 |
| Tidmington, Warw | 48 | C4 |
| Tiers Cross, Pemb | 32 | C2 |
| Tiffield, Nhants | 50 | A3 |
| Tigh a Ghearraidh, W Isles | 139 | A3 |
| Tighnabruaich, Argyll | 111 | B2 |
| Tigley, Devon | 5 | A3 |
| Tilbrook, Camb | 51 | A1 |
| Tilbury, Essex | 29 | A1 |
| Tilford, Surr | 145 | A4 |
| Tilham Street, Som | 12 | A1 |
| Tillicoultry, Clack | 118 | E4 |
| Tillingham, Essex | 43 | A3 |
| Tillington, Heref | 46 | D4 |
| Tillington, W Suss | 17 | A2 |
| Tillington Common, Heref | 46 | C3 |
| Tillyfourie, Aber | 128 | E2 |
| Tilmanstone, Kent | 31 | B4 |
| Tilney All Saints, Norf | 62 | D1 |
| Tilney High End, Norf | 62 | D1 |
| Tilney St Lawrence, Norf | 62 | D2 |
| Tilshead, Wilts | 25 | B4 |
| Tilstock, Shrop | 68 | B3 |
| Tilston, Chesh | 68 | B2 |
| Tilsworth, Beds | 39 | B1 |
| Tiltups End, Glouc | 36 | B4 |
| Timberland, Linc | 73 | B2 |
| Timbersbrook, Chesh | 69 | B1 |
| Timberscombe, Som | 22 | E4 |
| Timble, N York | 87 | B1 |
| Timsbury, Hamp | 14 | B2 |
| Timsbury, Som | 24 | A3 |
| Timworth, Suff | 53 | B1 |
| Tincleton, Dors | 7 | A1 |
| Tindale, Cumb | 103 | A4 |
| Tindale Crescent, Durham | 98 | C3 |
| Tingewick, Bucks | 38 | B1 |
| Tingley, W York | 88 | A4 |
| Tingrith, Beds | 39 | B1 |
| Tinhay, Devon | 4 | B1 |
| Tinsley Green, W Suss | 18 | B1 |
| Tintagel, Corn | 3 | D1 |
| Tintern Parva, Monm | 35 | B3 |
| Tintwistle, Derby | 80 | B2 |
| Tinwell, Rut | 61 | C2 |
| Tippacott, Devon | 22 | C4 |
| Tipp's End, Norf | 62 | C3 |
| Tipton St John, Devon | 6 | A1 |
| Tiptree, Essex | 43 | A2 |
| Tiptree Heath, Essex | 42 | B2 |
| Tirabad, Powys | 45 | C4 |
| Tirley, Glouc | 36 | B1 |
| Tirril, Cumb | 97 | B3 |
| Tisbury, Wilts | 13 | A2 |
| Tissington, Derby | 70 | B2 |
| Titchfield, Hamp | 15 | B4 |
| Titchmarsh, Nhants | 51 | A1 |
| Titchwell, Norf | 74 | C3 |
| Tithby, Notts | 72 | A4 |
| Titley, Heref | 46 | B2 |
| Titsey, Surr | 149 | A2 |
| Tittensor, Staff | 69 | B3 |
| Tittleshall, Norf | 63 | C1 |
| Titton, Worc | 47 | C1 |
| Tiverton, Chesh | 68 | B2 |
| Tiverton, Devon | 10 | C3 |
| Tivetshall St Margaret, Norf | 64 | B4 |
| Tivington, Som | 22 | E4 |
| Tixall, Staff | 58 | A1 |
| Tixover, Rut | 61 | C3 |
| Tobermory, Argyll | 120 | F3 |
| Toberonochy, Argyll | 116 | F3 |
| Tockenham, Wilts | 25 | B1 |
| Tockholes, Lanc | 86 | A4 |
| Tockington, Glouc | 24 | A1 |
| Tockwith, N York | 88 | B2 |
| Todber, Dors | 12 | C2 |
| Todburn, Nthumb | 104 | A1 |
| Toddington, Beds | 39 | B1 |
| Toddington, Glouc | 36 | C1 |
| Todenham, Glouc | 48 | C4 |
| Todhills, Angus | 119 | D1 |
| Todhills, Cumb | 102 | C4 |
| Todmorden, W York | 86 | D4 |
| Todwick, S York | 82 | A3 |
| Toft, Camb | 52 | A3 |
| Toft, Linc | 61 | C1 |
| Toft, Shet | 139 | A2 |
| Toft Hill, Durham | 98 | B3 |
| Toft Monks, Norf | 65 | B3 |
| Toft next Newton, Linc | 83 | D3 |
| Toftrees, Norf | 74 | E4 |

| PLACE | PAGE | GRID |
|---|---|---|
| Togston, Nthumb | 104 | B1 |
| Tokers Green, Oxon | 27 | A1 |
| Toll Bar, S York | 82 | B1 |
| Tollard Royal, Wilts | 13 | A3 |
| Toller Fratrum, Dors | 12 | A4 |
| Toller Porcorum, Dors | 12 | A4 |
| Toller Whelme, Dors | 12 | A4 |
| Tollerton, N York | 88 | C1 |
| Tollerton, Notts | 71 | B4 |
| Tollesbury, Essex | 43 | A2 |
| Tolleshunt D'Arcy, Essex | 43 | A2 |
| Tolleshunt Major, Essex | 43 | A2 |
| Tolpuddle, Dors | 7 | A1 |
| Tolsta, W Isles | 139 | B2 |
| Tolworth, G Lon | 142 | A4 |
| Tomatin, High | 127 | C1 |
| Tomintoul, Moray | 128 | A2 |
| Tomnavoulin, Moray | 128 | A1 |
| Tonbridge, Kent | 29 | A4 |
| Tondu, Brid | 22 | E1 |
| Tong, Kent | 30 | B3 |
| Tong, Shrop | 57 | B2 |
| Tong, W York | 87 | B3 |
| Tong Norton, Shrop | 57 | B2 |
| Tonge, Leics | 60 | A1 |
| Tongham, Surr | 145 | A3 |
| Tongland, D & G | 96 | A1 |
| Tongue, High | 137 | E2 |
| Tongwynlais, Cardiff | 23 | A1 |
| Tonna, Neath | 34 | A4 |
| Tonwell, Herts | 40 | B2 |
| Tonypandy, Rhond | 34 | B4 |
| Tonyrefail, Rhond | 34 | C4 |
| Toot Hill, Essex | 41 | A3 |
| Tooting, G Lon | 143 | A3 |
| Tooting Bec, G Lon | 143 | A3 |
| Topcliffe, N York | 93 | C4 |
| Topcroft, Norf | 65 | A3 |
| Topcroft Street, Norf | 65 | A3 |
| Toppesfield, Essex | 53 | A4 |
| Toprow, Norf | 64 | B3 |
| Topsham, Devon | 5 | C1 |
| Torbeg, N Ayr | 105 | F2 |
| Torbryan, Devon | 5 | B3 |
| Torcross, Devon | 8 | B1 |
| Tore, High | 132 | B3 |
| Torksey, Linc | 83 | B4 |
| Tormarton, Glouc | 24 | B1 |
| Toronto, Durham | 98 | C3 |
| Torpenhow, Cumb | 96 | E2 |
| Torphichen, W Loth | 113 | B3 |
| Torphins, Aber | 128 | E3 |
| Torpoint, Corn | 4 | C4 |
| Torquay, Devon | 5 | C3 |
| Torrance, E Dunb | 112 | B2 |
| Torridon, High | 131 | A3 |
| Torrin, High | 125 | D2 |
| Torryburn, Fife | 113 | C1 |
| Tortan, Worc | 47 | C1 |
| Torteval, Guer | 139 | A2 |
| Torthorwald, D & G | 101 | E3 |
| Tortworth, Glouc | 36 | A4 |
| Torver, Cumb | 91 | D2 |
| Torworth, Notts | 83 | A3 |
| Toseland, Camb | 51 | C2 |
| Tosside, N York | 86 | B1 |
| Tostock, Suff | 53 | C2 |
| Totaig, High | 130 | A3 |
| Tote, High | 130 | C3 |
| Totnes, Devon | 5 | B3 |
| Tottenhill, Norf | 62 | D2 |
| Totternhoe, Beds | 39 | B2 |
| Tottington, G Man | 79 | B1 |
| Totton, Hamp | 14 | B3 |
| Toulton, Som | 11 | A1 |
| Tow Law, Durham | 98 | B2 |
| Towcester, Nhants | 50 | A3 |
| Towednack, Corn | 1 | B1 |
| Towersey, Oxon | 38 | B3 |
| Towie, Aber | 128 | C2 |
| Town End, Cumb | 91 | D2 |
| Townhead, S York | 81 | B2 |
| Towns End, Hamp | 26 | C3 |
| Townshend, Corn | 1 | C2 |
| Towthorpe, N York | 89 | A1 |
| Towton, N York | 88 | B3 |
| Towyn, Ab & Col | 77 | A4 |
| Toy's Hill, Kent | 149 | B3 |
| Traethsaith, Cered | 44 | D3 |
| Trallong, Powys | 34 | B1 |
| Tranent, E Loth | 114 | C2 |
| Trapp, Carm | 33 | C2 |
| Traquair, Bord | 108 | A2 |
| Traveller's Rest, Devon | 9 | E2 |
| Trawden, Lanc | 86 | C3 |
| Trawsfynydd, Gwyn | 66 | F4 |
| Trealaw, Rhond | 34 | C4 |
| Treales, Lanc | 85 | B3 |
| Trearddur Bay, Angle | 76 | A4 |
| Trebarwith, Corn | 3 | D1 |
| Trebetherick, Corn | 3 | C2 |
| Treborough, Som | 10 | D1 |
| Trebullett, Corn | 4 | B2 |
| Treburley, Corn | 4 | B2 |
| Trecastle, Powys | 34 | A1 |
| Trecwn, Pemb | 32 | D1 |
| Tredegar, Gwent | 34 | D3 |
| Tredington, Glouc | 36 | B1 |
| Tredington, Warw | 48 | C4 |
| Tredunhock, Monm | 35 | A4 |
| Treen, Corn | 1 | B3 |
| Treeton, S York | 82 | A3 |
| Trefasser, Pemb | 44 | A4 |
| Trefecca, Powys | 34 | D1 |
| Trefeglwys, Powys | 55 | D4 |
| Treffgarne, Pemb | 32 | C1 |
| Treffgarne Owen, Pemb | 32 | C1 |
| Trefilan, Cered | 45 | A2 |
| Trefnant, Denb | 67 | C1 |
| Trefonen, Shrop | 67 | E4 |
| Trefor, Gwyn | 66 | C3 |
| Trefrew, Corn | 3 | E1 |
| Trefriw, Ab & Col | 67 | A1 |
| Tregadillett, Corn | 4 | A1 |
| Tregare, Monm | 35 | A3 |
| Tregaron, Cered | 45 | B2 |

| PLACE | PAGE | GRID |
|---|---|---|
| Tregarth, Gwyn | 66 | E1 |
| Tregeare, Corn | 4 | A1 |
| Tregeiriog, Wrex | 67 | D4 |
| Tregele, Angle | 76 | B3 |
| Tregidden, Corn | 2 | A3 |
| Treglemais, Pemb | 32 | B1 |
| Tregonce, Corn | 3 | C2 |
| Tregonetha, Corn | 3 | C3 |
| Tregony, Corn | 2 | B1 |
| Tregoyd, Powys | 46 | A4 |
| Tre-groes, Cered | 44 | E4 |
| Tregynon, Powys | 55 | E3 |
| Trehafod, Rhond | 34 | C4 |
| Trehan, Corn | 4 | B4 |
| Treharris, Merth | 34 | C4 |
| Treherbert, Rhond | 34 | B4 |
| Trekenner, Corn | 4 | B2 |
| Treknow, Corn | 3 | D1 |
| Trelawnyd, Flint | 77 | B4 |
| Trelech, Carm | 32 | F1 |
| Treleddyd-fawr, Pemb | 32 | B1 |
| Trelights, Corn | 3 | D2 |
| Trelill, Corn | 3 | D2 |
| Trelleck, Monm | 35 | B3 |
| Trelogan, Flint | 77 | B4 |
| Trelow, Corn | 3 | C3 |
| Tremadog, Gwyn | 66 | E3 |
| Tremail, Corn | 3 | E1 |
| Tremain, Cered | 44 | D3 |
| Tremaine, Corn | 4 | A1 |
| Tremar, Corn | 4 | A3 |
| Trematon, Corn | 4 | B4 |
| Tremeirchion, Denb | 77 | B4 |
| Trenance, Corn | 3 | C3 |
| Trenance, Corn | 3 | C3 |
| Trencreek, Corn | 9 | A4 |
| Trenear, Corn | 1 | D2 |
| Treneglos, Corn | 4 | A1 |
| Trent, Dors | 12 | B2 |
| Trentishoe, Devon | 22 | B4 |
| Treoes, Glam | 22 | E1 |
| Treorchy, Rhond | 34 | B4 |
| Trequite, Corn | 3 | D2 |
| Trerhyngyll, Glam | 22 | F1 |
| Trerulefoot, Corn | 4 | B4 |
| Trescowe, Corn | 1 | C2 |
| Tresean, Corn | 3 | B4 |
| Tresham, Glouc | 36 | A4 |
| Tresillian, Corn | 2 | B1 |
| Treskinnick Cross, Corn | 9 | B4 |
| Tresmeer, Corn | 4 | A1 |
| Tresparrett, Corn | 3 | E1 |
| Treswell, Notts | 83 | B4 |
| Trethevey, Corn | 3 | D1 |
| Trethewey, Corn | 1 | A3 |
| Trethurgy, Corn | 3 | D4 |
| Tretire, Heref | 35 | B1 |
| Tretower, Powys | 34 | D2 |
| Treuddyn, Flint | 67 | E2 |
| Trevague, Corn | 4 | A2 |
| Trevalga, Corn | 3 | E1 |
| Trevalyn, Wrex | 68 | A2 |
| Trevarrian, Corn | 3 | C3 |
| Treveal, Corn | 3 | B4 |
| Treveighan, Corn | 3 | D2 |
| Trevellas Downs, Corn | 3 | B4 |
| Trevelmond, Corn | 4 | A3 |
| Treverva, Corn | 2 | A2 |
| Trevine, Pemb | 32 | B1 |
| Treviscoe, Corn | 3 | C4 |
| Trevone, Corn | 3 | C2 |
| Trevor, Denb | 67 | E3 |
| Trewalder, Corn | 3 | D2 |
| Trewarlett, Corn | 4 | B2 |
| Trewarmett, Corn | 3 | D1 |
| Treween, Corn | 4 | A2 |
| Trewen, Corn | 3 | D2 |
| Trewint, Corn | 4 | A2 |
| Trewithian, Corn | 2 | B1 |
| Trewoon, Corn | 3 | D4 |
| Treyford, W Suss | 16 | B2 |
| Triangle, W York | 87 | A4 |
| Trimdon, Durham | 98 | D2 |
| Trimdon Colliery, Durham | 98 | D2 |
| Trimdon Grange, Durham | 98 | D2 |
| Trimingham, Norf | 75 | C3 |
| Trimley, Suff | 54 | B4 |
| Trimley Heath, Suff | 54 | B4 |
| Trimsaran, Carm | 33 | B3 |
| Trimstone, Devon | 22 | A4 |
| Tring, Herts | 39 | A2 |
| Trinity, Angus | 124 | B3 |
| Trinity, Jers | 139 | B2 |
| Triscombe, Som | 10 | C1 |
| Triscombe, Som | 11 | A1 |
| Trispen, Corn | 3 | B4 |
| Tritlington, Nthumb | 104 | B1 |
| Trochry, Perth | 118 | E1 |
| Troedrhiwfuwch, Caer | 34 | D3 |
| Troedyraur, Cered | 44 | E3 |
| Troedyrhiw, Merth | 34 | C3 |
| Troon, Corn | 1 | D1 |
| Troon, S Ayr | 106 | D2 |
| Troston, Suff | 53 | C1 |
| Trotshill, Worc | 47 | C3 |
| Trottiscliffe, Kent | 29 | A3 |
| Troughend, Nthumb | 103 | C1 |
| Troutbeck, Cumb | 91 | E1 |
| Troutbeck Bridge, Cumb | 91 | E1 |
| Troway, Derby | 81 | C4 |
| Trowbridge, Wilts | 25 | A3 |
| Trowell, Notts | 71 | A3 |
| Trowse Newton, Norf | 65 | A2 |
| Trudoxhill, Som | 24 | B4 |
| Trull, Som | 11 | A2 |
| Trumpet, Heref | 47 | A4 |
| Trumpsgreen, Surr | 140 | C4 |
| Trunch, Norf | 75 | C4 |
| Truro, Corn | 2 | A1 |
| Trusham, Devon | 5 | B2 |
| Trusley, Derby | 70 | B4 |
| Trusthorpe, Linc | 84 | D4 |
| Trysull, Staff | 57 | C3 |
| Tubney, Oxon | 37 | D3 |
| Tuckenhay, Devon | 5 | B4 |
| Tuckhill, Shrop | 57 | B4 |

| PLACE | PAGE | GRID |
|---|---|---|
| Tuddenham, Suff | 53 | A1 |
| Tuddenham, Suff | 54 | A3 |
| Tudeley, Kent | 29 | A4 |
| Tudhoe, Durham | 98 | C2 |
| Tudweiloig, Gwyn | 66 | B4 |
| Tuesley, Surr | 145 | B4 |
| Tufton, Hamp | 26 | B4 |
| Tufton, Pemb | 32 | D1 |
| Tugby, Leics | 61 | A3 |
| Tugford, Shrop | 56 | D4 |
| Tughall, Nthumb | 109 | E2 |
| Tullibody, Clack | 113 | A1 |
| Tullynessle, Aber | 128 | D2 |
| Tulse Hill, G Lon | 143 | B3 |
| Tumble, Carm | 33 | C2 |
| Tumby, Linc | 73 | C2 |
| Tumby Woodside, Linc | 73 | C2 |
| Tummel Bridge, Perth | 122 | D3 |
| Tunbridge Wells, Kent | 20 | A1 |
| Tunstall, E R of Y | 90 | B3 |
| Tunstall, Kent | 30 | B3 |
| Tunstall, Lanc | 92 | A4 |
| Tunstall, N York | 93 | A2 |
| Tunstall, Norf | 65 | B2 |
| Tunstall, Staff | 69 | A4 |
| Tunstall, Suff | 54 | C3 |
| Tunstead, Derby | 81 | A4 |
| Tunstead, Norf | 65 | A1 |
| Tunworth, Hamp | 27 | A4 |
| Tur Langton, Leics | 60 | C3 |
| Turkdean, Glouc | 37 | A2 |
| Turleigh, Wilts | 24 | B3 |
| Turnastone, Heref | 46 | C4 |
| Turnberry, S Ayr | 106 | C4 |
| Turner's Hill, W Suss | 19 | A1 |
| Turners Puddle, Dors | 7 | B1 |
| Turnworth, Dors | 12 | D3 |
| Turriff, Aber | 134 | B3 |
| Turton Bottoms, Lanc | 79 | B1 |
| Turves, Camb | 62 | B3 |
| Turvey, Beds | 50 | C3 |
| Turville, Bucks | 38 | C4 |
| Turweston, Bucks | 49 | C4 |
| Tushingham cum Grindley, Chesh | 68 | B3 |
| Tutbury, Staff | 70 | B4 |
| Tutshill, Glouc | 35 | B4 |
| Tuttington, Norf | 75 | B4 |
| Tuxford, Notts | 72 | B1 |
| Twechar, E Dunb | 112 | C2 |
| Twelve Oaks, E Sus | 20 | B2 |
| Twelveheads, Corn | 2 | A1 |
| Twemlow Green, Chesh | 69 | A1 |
| Twenty, Linc | 61 | D1 |
| Twickenham, G Lon | 142 | A3 |
| Twigworth, Glouc | 36 | B1 |
| Twineham, W Suss | 18 | B2 |
| Twinstead, Essex | 53 | B4 |
| Twitchen, Devon | 10 | B1 |
| Two Dales, Derby | 70 | C1 |
| Twycross, Leics | 59 | B2 |
| Twyford, Berks | 27 | B1 |
| Twyford, Bucks | 38 | B1 |
| Twyford, Leics | 60 | C2 |
| Twyford, Norf | 64 | A1 |
| Twynholm, D & G | 96 | A1 |
| Twyning, Glouc | 47 | C4 |
| Twyning Green, Glouc | 47 | C4 |
| Twynllanan, Carm | 33 | D1 |
| Twywell, Nhants | 50 | C1 |
| Tyberton, Heref | 46 | C4 |
| Tycroes, Carm | 33 | C2 |
| Tycrwyn, Powys | 55 | E1 |
| Tydd Gote, Linc | 62 | C1 |
| Tydd St Giles, Camb | 62 | B1 |
| Tydd St Mary, Linc | 62 | C1 |
| Tye Green, Essex | 52 | C4 |
| Tyldesley, G Man | 79 | A2 |
| Tyler Hill, Kent | 31 | A3 |
| Tylers Green, Surr | 148 | C3 |
| Tylorstown, Rhond | 34 | C4 |
| Ty-nant, Ab & Col | 67 | B3 |
| Tyndrum, Stirl | 117 | E1 |
| Ty'n-dwr, Denb | 67 | D3 |
| Tynemouth, T & W | 104 | C3 |
| Tyninghame, E Loth | 115 | B2 |
| Tynron, D & G | 101 | C1 |
| Tynygraig, Cered | 45 | B1 |
| Ty'n-y-Groes, Ab & Col | 67 | A1 |
| Tyringham, Bucks | 50 | C3 |
| Tythegston, Brid | 22 | D1 |
| Tytherington, Glouc | 35 | C4 |
| Tytherington, Wilts | 12 | D1 |
| Tytherleigh, Devon | 11 | B4 |
| Tytherton Lucas, Wilts | 25 | B2 |
| Tywardreath, Corn | 3 | E4 |
| Tywyn, Gwyn | 55 | A3 |
| Ubbeston Green, Suff | 54 | B1 |
| Ubley, Som | 23 | D3 |
| Uckerby, N York | 93 | A1 |
| Uckfield, E Sus | 19 | B2 |
| Uckington, Glouc | 36 | B1 |
| Uckington, Shrop | 56 | D2 |
| Udimore, E Sus | 21 | A2 |
| Udny Green, Aber | 129 | B1 |
| Udny Station, Aber | 129 | B1 |
| Uffculme, Devon | 10 | D3 |
| Uffington, Oxon | 37 | C4 |
| Uffington, Shrop | 56 | D2 |
| Ufford, Camb | 61 | D2 |
| Ufford, Suff | 54 | B3 |
| Ufton, Warw | 49 | A2 |
| Ufton Nervet, Berks | 27 | A2 |
| Ugborough, Devon | 5 | A4 |
| Uggeshall, Suff | 65 | B4 |
| Ughill, S York | 81 | B3 |
| Ugley, Essex | 41 | A1 |
| Ugley Green, Essex | 41 | A1 |
| Ugthorpe, N York | 99 | D4 |
| Uig, High | 130 | C2 |
| Ulbster, High | 138 | E3 |
| Ulcat Row, Cumb | 97 | A3 |
| Ulceby, Linc | 84 | A1 |
| Ulceby, Linc | 84 | C4 |
| Ulceby Skitter, Linc | 84 | A1 |
| Ulcombe, Kent | 30 | A4 |

| PLACE | PAGE | GRID |
|---|---|---|
| Uldale, Cumb | 96 | F2 |
| Uley, Glouc | 36 | A4 |
| Ulgham, Nthumb | 104 | B1 |
| Ullapool, High | 135 | D3 |
| Ullenhall, Warw | 48 | B2 |
| Ulleskelf, N York | 88 | C3 |
| Ullesthorpe, Leics | 60 | B4 |
| Ulley, S York | 82 | A3 |
| Ullingswick, Heref | 47 | A3 |
| Ullock, Cumb | 96 | D3 |
| Ulpha, Cumb | 91 | C2 |
| Ulrome, E R of Y | 90 | A1 |
| Ulsta, Shet | 139 | A2 |
| Ulverston, Cumb | 91 | D3 |
| Ulwell, Dors | 7 | C2 |
| Umberleigh, Devon | 9 | E2 |
| Unapool, High | 137 | B4 |
| Under River, Kent | 29 | A4 |
| Underbarrow, Cumb | 91 | F2 |
| Underwood, Notts | 71 | A2 |
| Undy, Monm | 23 | C1 |
| Union Mills, I o M | 139 | C3 |
| Unstone, Derby | 81 | C4 |
| Up Cerne, Dors | 12 | B4 |
| Up Exe, Devon | 10 | C4 |
| Up Holland, Lanc | 78 | B2 |
| Up Marden, W Suss | 16 | B3 |
| Up Nately, Hamp | 27 | A4 |
| Up Somborne, Hamp | 15 | A1 |
| Up Sydling, Dors | 12 | B4 |
| Upavon, Wilts | 25 | C3 |
| Upchurch, Kent | 30 | A2 |
| Upcott, Devon | 10 | A2 |
| Upcott, Som | 10 | C2 |
| Updown Hill, Surr | 145 | B1 |
| Upgate, Norf | 64 | B1 |
| Uphall, Dors | 12 | A4 |
| Upham, Devon | 10 | B3 |
| Upham, Hamp | 15 | B2 |
| Uphampton, Heref | 46 | C2 |
| Uphill, Som | 23 | B3 |
| Uplawmoor, E Renf | 112 | A4 |
| Upleadon, Glouc | 36 | A1 |
| Upleatham, N York | 99 | C4 |
| Uploders, Dors | 6 | E1 |
| Uplowman, Devon | 10 | D3 |
| Uplyme, Devon | 6 | C1 |
| Upottery, Devon | 11 | A3 |
| Upper Affcot, Shrop | 56 | C4 |
| Upper Arley, Worc | 57 | B4 |
| Upper Basildon, Berks | 26 | C1 |
| Upper Beeding, W Suss | 18 | A3 |
| Upper Benefield, Nhants | 61 | C4 |
| Upper Bentley, Worc | 48 | A2 |
| Upper Bighouse, High | 138 | B2 |
| Upper Boddington, Nhants | 49 | B3 |
| Upper Brailes, Warw | 49 | A4 |
| Upper Broadheath, Worc | 47 | B3 |
| Upper Broughton, Notts | 72 | A4 |
| Upper Bucklebury, Berks | 26 | C2 |
| Upper Burgate, Hamp | 13 | B3 |
| Upper Caldecote, Beds | 51 | B3 |
| Upper Catesby, Nhants | 49 | C2 |
| Upper Chapel, Powys | 45 | E4 |
| Upper Chute, Wilts | 26 | A3 |
| Upper Clapton, G Lon | 143 | B1 |
| Upper Coberley, Glouc | 36 | C2 |
| Upper Cound, Shrop | 56 | D2 |
| Upper Cumberworth, W York | 81 | B1 |
| Upper Dallachy, Moray | 133 | D2 |
| Upper Dean, Beds | 51 | A2 |
| Upper Denby, W York | 81 | B1 |
| Upper Dicker, E Sus | 20 | A3 |
| Upper Dunsforth, N York | 88 | B1 |
| Upper Egleton, Heref | 47 | A4 |
| Upper Elkstone, Staff | 70 | A2 |
| Upper Ellastone, Staff | 70 | A3 |
| Upper Framilode, Glouc | 36 | A3 |
| Upper Froyle, Hamp | 27 | B4 |
| Upper Green, Berks | 26 | A3 |
| Upper Grove Common, Heref | 35 | B1 |
| Upper Hambleton, Rut | 61 | B2 |
| Upper Harbledown, Kent | 30 | C3 |
| Upper Hartfield, E Sus | 19 | B1 |
| Upper Heaton, W York | 87 | B4 |
| Upper Helmsley, N York | 89 | A1 |
| Upper Hergest, Heref | 46 | B3 |
| Upper Heyford, Nhants | 50 | A2 |
| Upper Heyford, Oxon | 37 | D1 |
| Upper Hill, Heref | 46 | D3 |
| Upper Hockenden, Kent | 144 | C4 |
| Upper Hopton, W York | 87 | B4 |
| Upper Hulme, Staff | 69 | C1 |
| Upper Inglesham, Wilts | 37 | B4 |
| Upper Killay, Swan | 33 | C4 |
| Upper Lambourn, Berks | 26 | A1 |
| Upper Landywood, Staff | 58 | A2 |
| Upper Langford, Som | 23 | C3 |
| Upper Langwith, Derby | 71 | B1 |
| Upper Largo, Fife | 119 | D4 |
| Upper Leigh, Staff | 69 | C4 |
| Upper Lybster, High | 138 | E4 |
| Upper Lydbrook, Glouc | 35 | C2 |
| Upper Lye, Heref | 46 | C2 |
| Upper Minety, Wilts | 36 | C4 |
| Upper Norwood, W Suss | 17 | A3 |
| Upper Pond Street, Essex | 52 | B4 |
| Upper Poppleton, N York | 88 | C1 |
| Upper Quinton, Warw | 48 | C3 |
| Upper Ratley, Hamp | 14 | B2 |
| Upper Sapey, Heref | 47 | A2 |
| Upper Shelton, Beds | 51 | A4 |
| Upper Sheringham, Norf | 75 | B3 |
| Upper Slaughter, Glouc | 37 | A1 |
| Upper Soudley, Glouc | 35 | C3 |
| Upper Standen, Kent | 21 | D1 |
| Upper Stoke, Norf | 65 | A3 |
| Upper Stondon, Beds | 51 | B4 |
| Upper Stowe, Nhants | 50 | A3 |
| Upper Street, Hamp | 13 | B2 |
| Upper Street, Norf | 65 | A1 |
| Upper Street, Norf | 65 | B1 |
| Upper Sundon, Beds | 39 | B1 |
| Upper Swell, Glouc | 37 | B1 |
| Upper Tasburgh, Norf | 64 | B3 |

| PLACE | PAGE | GRID |
|---|---|---|
| Upper Tean, Staff | 69 | C3 |
| Upper Town, Derby | 70 | B1 |
| Upper Town, Heref | 47 | A3 |
| Upper Town, Suff | 53 | C2 |
| Upper Tysoe, Warw | 49 | A4 |
| Upper Wardington, Oxon | 49 | B3 |
| Upper Weedon, Nhants | 50 | A2 |
| Upper Wellingham, E Sus | 19 | B3 |
| Upper Weybread, Suff | 54 | A1 |
| Upper Wield, Hamp | 16 | A1 |
| Upper Winchendon, Bucks | 38 | C2 |
| Upper Woodford, Wilts | 13 | B1 |
| Upper Wraxall, Wilts | 24 | B2 |
| Uppermill, G Man | 80 | B2 |
| Upperthong, W York | 81 | A1 |
| Upperton, W Suss | 17 | A2 |
| Uppingham, Rut | 61 | B3 |
| Uppington, Shrop | 57 | A2 |
| Upsall, N York | 93 | C3 |
| Upsettlington, Bord | 109 | B1 |
| Upshire, Essex | 40 | B3 |
| Upstreet, Kent | 31 | A3 |
| Upton, Berks | 140 | C2 |
| Upton, Bucks | 38 | C2 |
| Upton, Camb | 61 | D3 |
| Upton, Camb | 51 | B1 |
| Upton, Corn | 4 | A2 |
| Upton, Devon | 10 | D4 |
| Upton, Devon | 8 | A1 |
| Upton, Dors | 7 | A2 |
| Upton, Hamp | 26 | A3 |
| Upton, Hamp | 14 | B3 |
| Upton, Leics | 59 | B3 |
| Upton, Linc | 83 | C3 |
| Upton, Norf | 65 | B2 |
| Upton, Notts | 72 | B2 |
| Upton, Notts | 83 | B4 |
| Upton, Oxon | 26 | C1 |
| Upton, Som | 10 | C2 |
| Upton, Som | 11 | C2 |
| Upton, W York | 82 | A1 |
| Upton, Wilts | 12 | D1 |
| Upton Cheyney, Glouc | 24 | A2 |
| Upton Cressett, Shrop | 57 | A3 |
| Upton Cross, Corn | 4 | A2 |
| Upton Grey, Hamp | 27 | A4 |
| Upton Hellions, Devon | 10 | B4 |
| Upton Magna, Shrop | 56 | D2 |
| Upton Noble, Som | 12 | C1 |
| Upton Scudamore, Wilts | 25 | A4 |
| Upton upon Severn, Worc | 47 | C4 |
| Upton Warren, Worc | 48 | A2 |
| Upwaltham, W Suss | 17 | A3 |
| Upwell, Norf | 62 | C3 |
| Upwick Green, Herts | 41 | A1 |
| Upwood, Camb | 62 | A4 |
| Urchfont, Wilts | 25 | B3 |
| Urmston, G Man | 79 | B3 |
| Urquhart, Moray | 133 | C2 |
| Urra, N York | 93 | D1 |
| Urray, High | 132 | A3 |
| Usan, Angus | 124 | C3 |
| Ushaw Moor, Durham | 98 | C2 |
| Usk, Monm | 35 | A3 |
| Usselby, Linc | 84 | A3 |
| Utkinton, Chesh | 68 | B1 |
| Uton, Devon | 10 | B4 |
| Utterby, Linc | 84 | B3 |
| Uttoxeter, Staff | 70 | A4 |
| Uxbridge, G Lon | 141 | A1 |
| Uyeasound, Shet | 139 | A1 |
| Uzmaston, Pemb | 32 | D2 |
| Vale, Guer | 139 | B2 |
| Valley End, Surr | 140 | B4 |
| Valtos, High | 130 | D2 |
| Vaynor, Merth | 34 | C3 |
| Velindre, Powys | 46 | A4 |
| Venn Ottery, Devon | 6 | A1 |
| Venngreen, Devon | 9 | C3 |
| Ventnor, I of W | 8 | B2 |
| Venton, Devon | 4 | D4 |
| Vernham Dean, Hamp | 26 | A3 |
| Vernham Street, Hamp | 26 | A3 |
| Verwood, Dors | 13 | B3 |
| Veryan, Corn | 2 | B1 |
| Victoria, Corn | 3 | D3 |
| Vidlin, Shet | 139 | A2 |
| Vigo, Kent | 29 | A3 |
| Vines Cross, E Sus | 20 | A3 |
| Virginstow, Devon | 4 | B1 |
| Vobster, Som | 24 | B4 |
| Voe, Shet | 139 | A2 |
| Vowchurch, Heref | 46 | C4 |
| Wackerfield, Durham | 98 | B3 |
| Wacton, Norf | 64 | B3 |
| Wadborough, Worc | 47 | C3 |
| Waddesdon, Bucks | 38 | C2 |
| Waddingham, Linc | 83 | D2 |
| Waddington, Lanc | 86 | B2 |
| Waddington, Linc | 73 | A1 |
| Waddon, Dors | 6 | F1 |
| Wadebridge, Corn | 3 | D2 |
| Wadeford, Som | 11 | B3 |
| Wadenhoe, Nhants | 61 | C4 |
| Wadesmill, Herts | 40 | B2 |
| Wadhurst, E Sus | 20 | A1 |
| Wadshelf, Derby | 70 | C1 |
| Wadworth, S York | 82 | B2 |
| Wainfleet All Saints, Linc | 74 | A2 |
| Wainstalls, W York | 87 | A4 |
| Waitby, Cumb | 92 | B1 |
| Waithe, Linc | 84 | B2 |
| Wakefield, W York | 88 | A4 |
| Wakerley, Nhants | 61 | B3 |
| Wakes Colne, Essex | 42 | C1 |
| Walberswick, Suff | 54 | D1 |
| Walcombe, Som | 23 | D4 |
| Walcot, Linc | 73 | A4 |
| Walcot, Linc | 73 | B2 |
| Walcot, Shrop | 57 | A2 |
| Walcot Green, Norf | 64 | B4 |
| Walcote, Leics | 60 | B4 |
| Walcott, Norf | 75 | D4 |
| Walden Stubbs, N York | 82 | B1 |
| Walderton, W Suss | 16 | B3 |
| Walditch, Dors | 6 | E1 |

| PLACE | PAGE | GRID |
|---|---|---|
| Waldridge, Durham | 98 | C1 |
| Waldringfield, Suff | 54 | B4 |
| Waldron, E Sus | 20 | A2 |
| Wales, S York | 82 | A4 |
| Walesby, Linc | 84 | A3 |
| Walesby, Notts | 72 | A1 |
| Walford, Heref | 46 | C1 |
| Walford, Heref | 35 | C2 |
| Walford Heath, Shrop | 56 | C1 |
| Walgherton, Chesh | 69 | A3 |
| Walgrave, Nhants | 50 | B1 |
| Walk Mill, Lanc | 86 | C4 |
| Walkden, G Man | 79 | B2 |
| Walkerburn, Bord | 108 | B2 |
| Walkeringham, Notts | 83 | B3 |
| Walkerith, Linc | 83 | B3 |
| Walkern, Herts | 40 | A1 |
| Walker's Green, Heref | 46 | D3 |
| Walkhampton, Devon | 4 | C3 |
| Walkington, E R of Y | 89 | D3 |
| Wall, Nthumb | 103 | C3 |
| Wall, Staff | 58 | B2 |
| Wallasey, Mers | 77 | D3 |
| Wallingford, Oxon | 38 | A4 |
| Wallington, G Lon | 143 | A4 |
| Wallington, Herts | 51 | C4 |
| Walls, Shet | 139 | A2 |
| Wallsend, T & W | 104 | C4 |
| Wallyford, E Loth | 114 | C3 |
| Walmer Bridge, Lanc | 85 | C4 |
| Walpole, Suff | 54 | C1 |
| Walpole Cross Keys, Norf | 62 | C1 |
| Walpole Highway, Norf | 62 | C2 |
| Walpole St Andrew, Norf | 62 | C1 |
| Walpole St Peter, Norf | 62 | C1 |
| Walsall, W Mids | 58 | A3 |
| Walsden, W York | 86 | D4 |
| Walsham le Willows, Suff | 53 | C1 |
| Walshaw, W York | 86 | D3 |
| Walshford, N York | 88 | B1 |
| Walston, S Lan | 107 | D1 |
| Waltham, Kent | 30 | C4 |
| Waltham, Linc | 84 | B2 |
| Waltham Abbey, Essex | 40 | B3 |
| Waltham on the Wolds, Leics | 61 | A1 |
| Waltham St Lawrence, Berks | 27 | B1 |
| Walton, Bucks | 50 | C4 |
| Walton, Cumb | 102 | D4 |
| Walton, Derby | 70 | C1 |
| Walton, Leics | 60 | B4 |
| Walton, Powys | 46 | B2 |
| Walton, Shrop | 57 | A1 |
| Walton, Som | 11 | C1 |
| Walton, W Suss | 16 | B4 |
| Walton, W York | 81 | C1 |
| Walton, W York | 88 | B2 |
| Walton Cardiff, Glouc | 36 | B1 |
| Walton East, Pemb | 32 | D1 |
| Walton Elm, Dors | 12 | C3 |
| Walton on the Hill, Surr | 148 | A2 |
| Walton on the Naze, Essex | 43 | D1 |
| Walton on the Wolds, Leics | 60 | B1 |
| Walton-in-Gordano, Som | 23 | C2 |
| Walton-on-Thames, Surr | 141 | B4 |
| Walton-on-the-Hill, Staff | 58 | A1 |
| Walton-on-Trent, Derby | 59 | A1 |
| Walworth, Durham | 98 | C4 |
| Walworth, G Lon | 143 | B2 |
| Walwyn's Castle, Pemb | 32 | C2 |
| Wambrook, Som | 11 | B3 |
| Wanborough, Surr | 145 | B3 |
| Wanborough, Wilts | 25 | D1 |
| Wandsworth, G Lon | 142 | B3 |
| Wangford, Suff | 54 | C1 |
| Wanlip, Leics | 60 | B2 |
| Wanlockhead, D & G | 107 | B4 |
| Wansford, Camb | 61 | C3 |
| Wansford, E R of Y | 89 | D1 |
| Wanshurst Green, Kent | 29 | B4 |
| Wanstrow, Som | 24 | B4 |
| Wanswell, Glouc | 35 | C3 |
| Wantage, Oxon | 37 | D4 |
| Wapley, Glouc | 24 | B1 |
| Wappenham, Nhants | 50 | A3 |
| Warbleton, E Sus | 20 | A2 |
| Warborough, Oxon | 38 | A4 |
| Warboys, Camb | 62 | A4 |
| Warbstow, Corn | 4 | A1 |
| Warburton, G Man | 79 | B3 |
| Warcop, Cumb | 97 | D4 |
| Warden, Nthumb | 103 | C4 |
| Wardington, Oxon | 49 | B3 |
| Wardle, Chesh | 68 | C2 |
| Wardle, G Man | 80 | A1 |
| Wardley, Rut | 61 | A3 |
| Wardlow, Derby | 81 | B4 |
| Wardy Hill, Camb | 62 | C4 |
| Ware, Herts | 40 | B2 |
| Wareham, Dors | 7 | B1 |
| Warenford, Nthumb | 109 | D2 |
| Wareside, Herts | 40 | B2 |
| Waresley, Camb | 51 | C3 |
| Warfield, Berks | 140 | A3 |
| Warfleet, Devon | 5 | B4 |
| Wargrave, Berks | 27 | B1 |
| Warham St Mary, Norf | 74 | E3 |
| Wark, Nthumb | 109 | B1 |
| Wark, Nthumb | 103 | C3 |
| Warkton, Nhants | 61 | B4 |
| Warkworth, Nhants | 49 | B4 |
| Warkworth, Nthumb | 109 | E4 |
| Warlaby, N York | 93 | B2 |
| Warleggan, Corn | 3 | E3 |
| Warlingham, Surr | 148 | C2 |
| Warmingham, Chesh | 69 | A1 |
| Warmington, Nhants | 61 | C4 |
| Warmington, Warw | 49 | B3 |
| Warminster, Wilts | 25 | A4 |
| Warmwell, Dors | 7 | A1 |
| Warnford, Hamp | 16 | A2 |
| Warnham, W Suss | 18 | A1 |
| Warningcamp, W Suss | 17 | B3 |
| Warninglid, W Suss | 18 | B2 |
| Warren, Chesh | 69 | B1 |

| PLACE | PAGE | GRID |
|---|---|---|
| Willoughby, Linc | 74 | A1 |
| Willoughby, Warw | 49 | C2 |
| Willoughby Waterleys, Leics | 60 | B3 |
| Willoughton, Linc | 83 | C3 |
| Willows Green, Essex | 42 | A2 |
| Willtown, Som | 11 | C2 |
| Wilmcote, Warw | 48 | C2 |
| Wilmington, Kent | 144 | C3 |
| Wilmington, E Sus | 20 | A4 |
| Wilmslow, Chesh | 80 | A4 |
| Wilpshire, Lanc | 86 | A3 |
| Wilsden, W York | 87 | A3 |
| Wilsford, Linc | 73 | A3 |
| Wilsford, Wilts | 25 | C3 |
| Wilsford, Wilts | 13 | B1 |
| Wilshaw, W York | 81 | A1 |
| Wilson, Leics | 60 | A1 |
| Wilsontown, S Lan | 113 | B4 |
| Wilstead, Beds | 51 | A4 |
| Wilsthorpe, Linc | 61 | D2 |
| Wilstone, Herts | 39 | A2 |
| Wilton, Heref | 35 | C1 |
| Wilton, N York | 99 | B4 |
| Wilton, N York | 94 | C3 |
| Wilton, Wilts | 25 | D3 |
| Wilton, Wilts | 13 | B1 |
| Wimbish, Essex | 52 | C4 |
| Wimbledon, G Lon | 142 | B3 |
| Wimblington, Camb | 62 | B3 |
| Wimboldsley, Chesh | 68 | D1 |
| Wimborne Minster, Dors | 13 | A4 |
| Wimborne St Giles, Dors | 13 | A3 |
| Wimbotsham, Norf | 62 | D2 |
| Wincanton, Som | 12 | C2 |
| Winchburgh, W Loth | 113 | C2 |
| Winchcombe, Glouc | 36 | C1 |
| Winchelsea, E Sus | 21 | B3 |
| Winchester, Hamp | 15 | A2 |
| Winchet Hill, Kent | 20 | B1 |
| Winchfield, Hamp | 27 | B3 |
| Wincle, Chesh | 69 | C1 |
| Windermere, Cumb | 91 | E2 |
| Winderton, Warw | 49 | A4 |
| Windlesham, Surr | 145 | B1 |
| Windmill, Corn | 3 | C2 |
| Windmill Hill, Som | 11 | B3 |
| Windrush, Glouc | 37 | B2 |
| Windsor, Berks | 140 | B2 |
| Windygates, Fife | 119 | C4 |
| Wineham, W Suss | 18 | B2 |
| Winestead, E R of Y | 90 | B4 |
| Winfarthing, Norf | 64 | A4 |
| Winford, Som | 23 | D2 |
| Winforton, Heref | 46 | B3 |
| Winfrith Newburgh, Dors | 7 | A1 |
| Wing, Bucks | 39 | A1 |
| Wing, Rut | 61 | B2 |
| Wingate, Durham | 99 | A2 |
| Wingerworth, Derby | 70 | C1 |
| Wingfield, Beds | 39 | B1 |
| Wingfield, Suff | 54 | A1 |
| Wingfield, Wilts | 25 | A3 |
| Wingham, Kent | 31 | B3 |
| Wingmore, Kent | 31 | A4 |
| Wingrave, Bucks | 39 | A2 |
| Winkburn, Notts | 72 | A2 |
| Winkfield, Berks | 140 | A3 |
| Winkfield Row, Berks | 140 | A3 |
| Winkfield Street, Berks | 140 | A3 |
| Winkhill, Staff | 70 | A2 |
| Winkhurst Green, Kent | 149 | C3 |
| Winkleigh, Devon | 9 | E3 |
| Winksley, N York | 93 | A4 |
| Winlaton, T & W | 104 | B4 |
| Winmarleigh, Lanc | 85 | C2 |
| Winsford, Chesh | 68 | C1 |
| Winsford, Som | 10 | C1 |
| Winsham, Devon | 9 | D1 |
| Winsham, Som | 11 | C4 |
| Winskill, Cumb | 97 | B2 |
| Winslade, Hamp | 27 | A4 |
| Winsley, Wilts | 24 | B3 |
| Winslow, Bucks | 38 | C1 |
| Winson, Glouc | 37 | A3 |
| Winsor, Hamp | 14 | B3 |
| Winster, Cumb | 91 | E2 |
| Winster, Derby | 70 | B2 |
| Winston, Durham | 98 | B4 |
| Winston, Suff | 54 | A2 |
| Winstone, Glouc | 36 | C3 |
| Winswell, Devon | 9 | D3 |
| Winterborne Clenston, Dors | 12 | D4 |
| Winterborne Herrington, Dors | 6 | F1 |
| Winterborne Kingston, Dors | 12 | D4 |
| Winterborne Monkton, Dors | 6 | F1 |
| Winterborne Stickland, Dors | 12 | D4 |
| Winterborne Whitechurch, Dors | 12 | D4 |
| Winterborne Zelston, Dors | 12 | D4 |
| Winterbourne, Berks | 26 | B2 |
| Winterbourne Abbas, Dors | 6 | F1 |
| Winterbourne Bassett, Wilts | 25 | C2 |
| Winterbourne Dauntsey, Wilts | 14 | A1 |
| Winterbourne Earls, Wilts | 14 | A1 |
| Winterbourne Monkton, Wilts | 25 | C2 |
| Winterbourne Steepleton, Dors | 6 | F1 |
| Winterbourne Stoke, Wilts | 13 | B1 |
| Winterburn, N York | 86 | D1 |
| Winteringham, Linc | 89 | C4 |
| Winterley, Chesh | 69 | A2 |
| Winterslow, Wilts | 14 | A1 |
| Winterton, Linc | 89 | C4 |
| Winterton-on-Sea, Norf | 65 | C1 |
| Winthorpe, Notts | 72 | B2 |
| Winton, Cumb | 92 | B1 |
| Wintringham, N York | 94 | C4 |
| Winwick, Camb | 61 | D4 |

| PLACE | PAGE | GRID |
|---|---|---|
| Winwick, Chesh | 79 | A3 |
| Winwick, Nhants | 50 | A1 |
| Wirksworth, Derby | 70 | C2 |
| Wirswall, Chesh | 68 | B3 |
| Wisbech, Camb | 62 | C2 |
| Wisbech St Mary, Camb | 62 | B2 |
| Wisborough Green, W Suss | 17 | B2 |
| Wiseman's Bridge, Pemb | 32 | E3 |
| Wiseton, Notts | 83 | A3 |
| Wishaw, N Lan | 113 | A4 |
| Wishaw, Warw | 59 | A3 |
| Wisley, Surr | 146 | B1 |
| Wispington, Linc | 73 | C1 |
| Wissett, Suff | 54 | C1 |
| Wissington, Suff | 43 | A1 |
| Wistanstow, Shrop | 56 | C4 |
| Wistanswick, Shrop | 68 | C4 |
| Wistaston, Chesh | 68 | C2 |
| Wiston, Pemb | 32 | D2 |
| Wiston, S Lan | 107 | C2 |
| Wiston, W Suss | 18 | A3 |
| Wistow, Camb | 62 | A4 |
| Wistow, N York | 88 | C3 |
| Wiswell, Lanc | 86 | B3 |
| Witcham, Camb | 62 | C4 |
| Witchampton, Dors | 13 | A4 |
| Witchford, Camb | 52 | B1 |
| Witham, Essex | 42 | B2 |
| Witham Friary, Som | 24 | B4 |
| Witham on the Hill, Linc | 61 | C1 |
| Withcall, Linc | 84 | B3 |
| Witherenden Hill, E Sus | 20 | A2 |
| Witheridge, Devon | 10 | B3 |
| Witherley, Leics | 59 | B3 |
| Withern, Linc | 84 | D4 |
| Withernsea, E R of Y | 90 | C4 |
| Withernwick, E R of Y | 90 | A3 |
| Withersdale Street, Suff | 65 | A4 |
| Withersfield, Suff | 52 | C3 |
| Witherslack, Cumb | 91 | E3 |
| Witherslack Hall, Cumb | 91 | E3 |
| Withiel, Corn | 3 | D3 |
| Withiel Florey, Som | 10 | C1 |
| Withington, Glouc | 36 | C2 |
| Withington, Heref | 46 | D4 |
| Withington, Shrop | 56 | D2 |
| Withington, Staff | 69 | C4 |
| Withleigh, Devon | 10 | C3 |
| Withybed Green, Worc | 48 | A1 |
| Withybrook, Warw | 60 | A4 |
| Withypool, Som | 10 | B1 |
| Witley, Surr | 17 | A1 |
| Witnesham, Suff | 54 | A3 |
| Witney, Oxon | 37 | C3 |
| Wittering, Camb | 61 | C3 |
| Wittersham, Kent | 21 | B2 |
| Witton, Norf | 65 | A2 |
| Witton Gilbert, Durham | 98 | C1 |
| Witton le Wear, Durham | 98 | B3 |
| Witton Park, Durham | 98 | C3 |
| Wiveliscombe, Som | 10 | D2 |
| Wivelrod, Hamp | 16 | A1 |
| Wivelsfield, E Sus | 19 | A2 |
| Wivelsfield Green, E Sus | 19 | A2 |
| Wivenhoe, Essex | 43 | B2 |
| Wiveton, Norf | 75 | A3 |
| Wix, Essex | 43 | C1 |
| Wixford, Warw | 48 | B3 |
| Wixoe, Suff | 53 | A4 |
| Woburn, Beds | 39 | A1 |
| Woking, Surr | 146 | A1 |
| Wokingham, Berks | 27 | B2 |
| Wold Newton, E R of Y | 94 | D4 |
| Wold Newton, Linc | 84 | B2 |
| Woldingham, Surr | 149 | A2 |
| Wolferton, Norf | 74 | B4 |
| Wolfhill, Perth | 119 | B1 |
| Wolf's Castle, Pemb | 32 | C1 |
| Wolfsdale, Pemb | 32 | C2 |
| Wollaston, Nhants | 50 | C2 |
| Wollaston, Shrop | 56 | B2 |
| Wollerton, Shrop | 68 | C4 |
| Wolseley Bridge, Staff | 58 | A1 |
| Wolsingham, Durham | 98 | B2 |
| Wolston, Warw | 49 | B1 |
| Wolverhampton, W Mids | 57 | C3 |
| Wolverley, Worc | 47 | C1 |
| Wolverton, Hamp | 26 | C3 |
| Wolverton, Warw | 48 | C2 |
| Wolvesnewton, Monm | 35 | A3 |
| Wolvey, Warw | 60 | A4 |
| Wolviston, Durham | 99 | A3 |
| Wombleton, N York | 94 | A3 |
| Wombourne, Staff | 57 | C3 |
| Wombwell, S York | 82 | A2 |
| Womenswold, Kent | 31 | A4 |
| Womersley, N York | 88 | C4 |
| Wonersh, Surr | 146 | A4 |
| Wood Bevington, Warw | 48 | B3 |
| Wood Dalling, Norf | 75 | A4 |
| Wood End, Herts | 40 | B1 |
| Wood End, Warw | 48 | B1 |
| Wood End, G Lon | 141 | B2 |
| Wood Enderby, Linc | 73 | C1 |
| Wood Norton, Norf | 75 | A4 |
| Wood Street, Norf | 65 | B1 |
| Wood Street, Surr | 145 | B3 |
| Wood Walton, Camb | 62 | A4 |
| Woodall, S York | 82 | A4 |
| Woodbastwick, Norf | 65 | A1 |
| Woodborough, Notts | 72 | A3 |
| Woodborough, Wilts | 25 | C3 |
| Woodbridge, Devon | 11 | A4 |
| Woodbridge, Suff | 54 | B3 |
| Woodbury, Devon | 6 | A1 |
| Woodbury Salterton, Devon | 6 | A1 |
| Woodchester, Glouc | 36 | B3 |
| Woodchurch, Kent | 21 | B1 |
| Woodcombe, Som | 22 | E4 |
| Woodcote, Oxon | 27 | A1 |
| Woodcote, Shrop | 57 | B1 |
| Woodcote, G Lon | 148 | B1 |
| Woodeaton, Oxon | 38 | A2 |
| Woodend, Nhants | 49 | C3 |

| PLACE | PAGE | GRID |
|---|---|---|
| Woodend, W Suss | 16 | B3 |
| Woodfalls, Wilts | 14 | A2 |
| Woodford, Glouc | 35 | C4 |
| Woodford, G Man | 80 | A4 |
| Woodford, Nhants | 51 | A1 |
| Woodford Halse, Nhants | 49 | C3 |
| Woodgate, W Suss | 17 | A4 |
| Woodgate, Worc | 48 | A2 |
| Woodgreen, Hamp | 14 | A3 |
| Woodhall, N York | 92 | D2 |
| Woodhall Spa, Linc | 73 | B1 |
| Woodham, Surr | 146 | B1 |
| Woodham, Bucks | 38 | B2 |
| Woodham Ferrers, Essex | 42 | B3 |
| Woodham Mortimer, Essex | 42 | B3 |
| Woodham Walter, Essex | 42 | B3 |
| Woodhead, Aber | 134 | B4 |
| Woodhill, Som | 11 | C2 |
| Woodhorn, Nthumb | 104 | C2 |
| Woodhouse, Leics | 60 | B1 |
| Woodhouse Eaves, Leics | 60 | B2 |
| Woodhurst, Camb | 52 | A1 |
| Woodkirk, W York | 87 | B4 |
| Woodland, Devon | 5 | B3 |
| Woodland, Durham | 98 | B3 |
| Woodland, Kent | 31 | A4 |
| Woodlands, Hamp | 14 | B3 |
| Woodlands Park, Berks | 140 | A2 |
| Woodlands St Mary, Berks | 26 | A2 |
| Woodleigh, Devon | 5 | A4 |
| Woodmancote, Glouc | 36 | C1 |
| Woodmancote, Glouc | 36 | C3 |
| Woodmancote, W Suss | 18 | B3 |
| Woodmancott, Hamp | 26 | C4 |
| Woodmansey, E R of Y | 89 | D3 |
| Woodmansgreen, W Suss | 17 | A2 |
| Woodmansterne, Surr | 148 | B1 |
| Woodnewton, Nhants | 61 | C3 |
| Woodplumpton, Lanc | 85 | C3 |
| Woodrising, Norf | 63 | C2 |
| Woodrow, Worc | 47 | C1 |
| Wood's Green, E Sus | 20 | A1 |
| Woodseaves, Staff | 57 | B1 |
| Woodsetts, S York | 82 | B4 |
| Woodside, Berks | 140 | B3 |
| Woodside, Fife | 119 | D3 |
| Woodside, Perth | 119 | B1 |
| Woodside, G Lon | 143 | B4 |
| Woodstock, Oxon | 37 | D2 |
| Woodton, Norf | 65 | A3 |
| Woodtown, Devon | 9 | C2 |
| Woofferton, Shrop | 46 | D1 |
| Wookey, Som | 23 | D4 |
| Wookey Hole, Som | 23 | D4 |
| Wool, Dors | 7 | B1 |
| Woolacombe, Devon | 22 | A4 |
| Woolage Green, Kent | 31 | B4 |
| Woolaston, Glouc | 35 | C3 |
| Woolaston Common, Glouc | 35 | C3 |
| Woolavington, Som | 23 | B4 |
| Woolbeding, W Suss | 17 | A2 |
| Wooler, Nthumb | 109 | C2 |
| Woolfardisworthy, Devon | 9 | C2 |
| Woolfardisworthy, Devon | 10 | B3 |
| Woolhampton, Berks | 26 | C2 |
| Woolhope, Heref | 47 | A4 |
| Woolland, Dors | 12 | C3 |
| Woolley, Camb | 51 | B1 |
| Woolley, Som | 24 | B2 |
| Woolley, W York | 81 | C1 |
| Woolmer Green, Herts | 40 | A2 |
| Woolmere Green, Worc | 48 | A2 |
| Woolminstone, Som | 11 | C3 |
| Woolpit, Suff | 53 | C2 |
| Woolstaston, Shrop | 56 | C3 |
| Woolsthorpe, Linc | 72 | B4 |
| Woolston, Chesh | 79 | A3 |
| Woolston, Shrop | 56 | B1 |
| Woolston, Shrop | 56 | C4 |
| Woolston, Som | 10 | D1 |
| Woolston, Som | 12 | B2 |
| Woolstone, Bucks | 50 | C4 |
| Woolstone, Glouc | 36 | C1 |
| Woolstone, Oxon | 26 | A1 |
| Woolton Hill, Hamp | 26 | B3 |
| Woolverstone, Suff | 54 | A4 |
| Woolverton, Som | 24 | B3 |
| Woolwich, G Lon | 144 | B2 |
| Woore, Shrop | 69 | A3 |
| Wootten Green, Suff | 54 | A1 |
| Wootton, Beds | 51 | A4 |
| Wootton, Heref | 46 | B3 |
| Wootton, Kent | 31 | A4 |
| Wootton, Linc | 84 | A1 |
| Wootton, Nhants | 50 | B3 |
| Wootton, Oxon | 37 | D2 |
| Wootton, Staff | 70 | A3 |
| Wootton Bassett, Wilts | 25 | C1 |
| Wootton Bridge, I of W | 8 | B1 |
| Wootton Courtenay, Som | 22 | E4 |
| Wootton Rivers, Wilts | 25 | D3 |
| Wootton St Lawrence, Hamp | 26 | C3 |
| Wootton Wawen, Warw | 48 | B2 |
| Worcester, Worc | 47 | C3 |
| Worcester Park, G Lon | 142 | B4 |
| Worfield, Shrop | 57 | B3 |
| Workington, Cumb | 96 | C3 |
| Worksop, Notts | 82 | B4 |
| Worlaby, Linc | 83 | D1 |
| Worlds End, Hamp | 16 | A3 |
| World's End, Berks | 26 | B1 |
| Worleston, Chesh | 68 | C2 |
| Worlingham, Suff | 65 | B4 |
| Worlington, Devon | 10 | A3 |
| Worlington, Suff | 53 | A1 |
| Worlingworth, Suff | 54 | A1 |
| Wormald Green, N York | 93 | B4 |
| Wormbridge, Heref | 35 | A1 |
| Wormegay, Norf | 63 | A2 |
| Wormelow Tump, Heref | 35 | B1 |
| Wormhill, Derby | 81 | A4 |
| Wormingford, Essex | 43 | A1 |
| Worminghall, Bucks | 38 | B3 |

| PLACE | PAGE | GRID |
|---|---|---|
| Wormington, Glouc | 48 | A4 |
| Wormit, Fife | 119 | D2 |
| Wormleighton, Warw | 49 | B3 |
| Wormley, Surr | 17 | A1 |
| Wormsley, Heref | 46 | C3 |
| Worplesdon, Surr | 146 | A2 |
| Worrall, S York | 81 | C3 |
| Worsbrough, S York | 81 | C2 |
| Worsley, G Man | 79 | B2 |
| Worstead, Norf | 65 | A1 |
| Worston, Devon | 4 | D4 |
| Worston, Lanc | 86 | B2 |
| Worth, Kent | 31 | B3 |
| Worth, W Suss | 18 | B1 |
| Worth Abbey, W Suss | 19 | A1 |
| Worth Matravers, Dors | 7 | C2 |
| Wortham, Suff | 53 | D1 |
| Worthen, Shrop | 56 | B2 |
| Worthenbury, Wrex | 68 | A3 |
| Worthing, Norf | 63 | C1 |
| Worthing, W Suss | 18 | A4 |
| Worthington, Leics | 60 | A1 |
| Wortley, S York | 81 | C2 |
| Worton, Wilts | 25 | B3 |
| Wortwell, Norf | 65 | A4 |
| Wotton, Surr | 147 | A3 |
| Wotton Underwood, Bucks | 38 | B2 |
| Wotton-under-Edge, Glouc | 36 | A4 |
| Woundale, Shrop | 57 | B3 |
| Wrabness, Essex | 43 | C1 |
| Wrafton, Devon | 9 | D1 |
| Wragby, Linc | 84 | A4 |
| Wragby, W York | 82 | A1 |
| Wrangaton, Devon | 5 | A4 |
| Wrangle, Linc | 73 | D2 |
| Wrawby, Linc | 83 | D1 |
| Wraxall, Som | 23 | D2 |
| Wraxall, Som | 12 | B1 |
| Wray, Lanc | 92 | A4 |
| Wraysbury, Berks | 140 | C1 |
| Wrayton, Lanc | 92 | A4 |
| Wrea Green, Lanc | 85 | B3 |
| Wreay, Cumb | 97 | A1 |
| Wrelton, N York | 94 | B3 |
| Wrenbury, Chesh | 68 | C3 |
| Wreningham, Norf | 64 | B3 |
| Wrentnall, Shrop | 56 | C2 |
| Wressle, E R of Y | 89 | A3 |
| Wressle, Linc | 83 | D1 |
| Wrestlingworth, Beds | 51 | C3 |
| Wrexham, Wrex | 67 | E2 |
| Wrinehill, Staff | 69 | A3 |
| Wrington, Som | 23 | D3 |
| Wrockwardine, Shrop | 57 | A2 |
| Wroot, Linc | 83 | A2 |
| Wroughton, Wilts | 25 | C1 |
| Wroxall, I of W | 8 | B2 |
| Wroxall, Warw | 48 | C1 |
| Wroxeter, Shrop | 56 | D2 |
| Wroxham, Norf | 65 | A1 |
| Wroxton, Oxon | 49 | B4 |
| Wyaston, Derby | 70 | B3 |
| Wyberton East, Linc | 73 | D3 |
| Wyboston, Beds | 51 | B2 |
| Wybunbury, Chesh | 69 | A2 |
| Wychbold, Worc | 47 | C2 |
| Wychnor, Staff | 59 | A1 |
| Wyck, Hamp | 16 | B1 |
| Wyck Rissington, Glouc | 37 | B2 |
| Wycliffe, Durham | 98 | B4 |
| Wycoller, Lanc | 86 | D3 |
| Wycomb, Leics | 61 | A1 |
| Wyddial, Herts | 40 | B1 |
| Wye, Kent | 30 | C4 |
| Wyke, Surr | 145 | B3 |
| Wyke, Dors | 12 | C2 |
| Wyke Champflower, Som | 12 | B1 |
| Wykeham, N York | 94 | C3 |
| Wyken, Shrop | 57 | B3 |
| Wykey, Shrop | 56 | C1 |
| Wylam, Nthumb | 104 | A4 |
| Wylye, Wilts | 13 | A1 |
| Wymeswold, Leics | 60 | B1 |
| Wymington, Beds | 50 | C2 |
| Wymondham, Leics | 61 | A1 |
| Wymondham, Norf | 64 | A3 |
| Wynford Eagle, Dors | 12 | B4 |
| Wyre Piddle, Worc | 48 | A3 |
| Wysall, Notts | 71 | B4 |
| Wythall, Worc | 48 | B1 |
| Wytham, Oxon | 37 | D3 |
| Wyton, E R of Y | 90 | A3 |
| Wyverstone, Suff | 53 | D2 |
| Y Ferwig, Cered | 44 | C3 |
| Y Ffor, Gwyn | 66 | C3 |
| Y Gyffylliog, Denb | 67 | C2 |
| Y Maerdy, Ab & Col | 67 | C3 |
| Y Rhiw, Gwyn | 66 | B4 |
| Yafforth, N York | 93 | B2 |
| Yalberton, Devon | 5 | B4 |
| Yalding, Kent | 29 | B4 |
| Yanwath, Cumb | 97 | B3 |
| Yanworth, Glouc | 37 | A2 |
| Yapham, E R of Y | 89 | B2 |
| Yapton, W Suss | 17 | B4 |
| Yarborough, Som | 23 | C3 |
| Yarburgh, Linc | 84 | C3 |
| Yarcombe, Devon | 11 | B3 |
| Yard, Devon | 10 | B2 |
| Yardley Gobion, Nhants | 50 | B4 |
| Yardley Hastings, Nhants | 50 | C2 |
| Yarkhill, Heref | 47 | A4 |
| Yarley, Som | 23 | D4 |
| Yarlington, Som | 12 | B2 |
| Yarm, N York | 99 | A4 |
| Yarmouth, I of W | 7 | F1 |
| Yarnbrook, Wilts | 25 | A3 |
| Yarnscombe, Devon | 9 | E2 |
| Yarnton, Oxon | 37 | D2 |
| Yarpole, Heref | 46 | D2 |
| Yarrowford, Bord | 108 | B2 |
| Yarwell, Nhants | 61 | C3 |
| Yate, Glouc | 24 | B1 |
| Yateley, Hamp | 27 | B3 |

| PLACE | PAGE | GRID |
|---|---|---|
| Yatesbury, Wilts | 25 | C2 |
| Yattendon, Berks | 26 | C2 |
| Yatton, Heref | 46 | C2 |
| Yatton, Heref | 35 | C1 |
| Yatton, Som | 23 | C2 |
| Yatton Keynell, Wilts | 25 | A1 |
| Yaverland, I of W | 8 | B1 |
| Yaxham, Norf | 63 | C2 |
| Yaxley, Camb | 61 | D3 |
| Yaxley, Suff | 54 | A1 |
| Yazor, Heref | 46 | C3 |
| Yeading, G Lon | 141 | B1 |
| Yeadon, W York | 87 | B3 |
| Yealand Conyers, Lanc | 91 | F4 |
| Yealand Redmayne, Lanc | 91 | F4 |
| Yealmpton, Devon | 4 | D4 |
| Yearsley, N York | 93 | D4 |
| Yeaton, Shrop | 56 | C1 |
| Yeaveley, Derby | 70 | B3 |
| Yeavering, Nthumb | 109 | C2 |
| Yedingham, N York | 94 | C3 |
| Yelford, Oxon | 37 | C3 |
| Yelling, Camb | 51 | C2 |
| Yelvertoft, Nhants | 49 | C1 |
| Yelverton, Devon | 4 | C3 |
| Yelverton, Norf | 65 | A3 |
| Yenston, Som | 12 | C2 |
| Yeoford, Devon | 10 | B4 |
| Yeolmbridge, Corn | 4 | B1 |
| Yeovil, Som | 12 | A3 |
| Yeovilton, Som | 12 | A2 |
| Yesnaby, Ork | 139 | A2 |
| Yettington, Devon | 6 | A1 |
| Yetts o'Muckhart, Clack | 118 | E4 |
| Yielden, Beds | 51 | A2 |
| Yiewsley, G Lon | 141 | A2 |
| Ynysboeth, Rhond | 34 | C4 |
| Ynysddu, Caer | 34 | D4 |
| Ynysybwl, Rhond | 34 | C4 |
| Yockleton, Shrop | 56 | C2 |
| Yokefleet, E R of Y | 89 | B4 |
| York, N York | 88 | C2 |
| York Town, Surr | 145 | A1 |
| Yorkletts, Kent | 30 | C3 |
| Yorkley, Glouc | 35 | C3 |
| Youlgreave, Derby | 70 | B1 |
| Youlthorpe, E R of Y | 89 | B1 |
| Youlton, N York | 88 | B1 |
| Yoxall, Staff | 58 | B1 |
| Yoxford, Suff | 54 | C1 |
| Ysbyty Ifan, Ab & Col | 67 | A3 |
| Ysbyty Ystwyth, Cered | 45 | B1 |
| Ysceifiog, Flint | 67 | D1 |
| Ystalyfera, Neath | 33 | D3 |
| Ystrad, Rhond | 34 | B4 |
| Ystrad Aeron, Cered | 44 | F3 |
| Ystrad Meurig, Cered | 45 | B2 |
| Ystrad Mynach, Caer | 34 | D4 |
| Ystradfellte, Powys | 34 | B2 |
| Ystradgynlais, Powys | 34 | A3 |
| Ystradowen, Glam | 22 | F1 |
| Ythanwells, Aber | 134 | A4 |
| Zeals, Wilts | 12 | C1 |
| Zelah, Corn | 3 | B4 |
| Zennor, Corn | 1 | B1 |
| Zouch, Notts | 60 | A1 |

| PLACE | PAGE | GRID |
|---|---|---|

# DISTANCES CHART

**1 MILE = 1.6 KILOMETRES**

| | London | Aberdeen | Aberystwyth | Ayr | Berwick-upon-Tweed | Birmingham | Blackpool | Bournemouth | Braemar | Brighton | Bristol | Cambridge | Cardiff | Carlisle | Doncaster | Dover | Dundee | Edinburgh | Exeter | Fishguard | Fort William | Glasgow | Gloucester | Great Yarmouth | Harwich | Holyhead | Inverness | John o'Groats | Kingston upon Hull | Kyle of Lochalsh | Land's End | Leeds | Leicester | Lincoln | Liverpool | Manchester | Newcastle upon Tyne | Norwich | Nottingham | Oban | Oxford | Plymouth | Portsmouth | Sheffield | Shrewsbury | Southampton | Stranraer | Swansea | York |
|---|---|---|---|---|---|---|---|---|---|---|---|---|---|---|---|---|---|---|---|---|---|---|---|---|---|---|---|---|---|---|---|---|---|---|---|---|---|---|---|---|---|---|---|---|---|---|---|---|---|
| London | | 517 | 211 | 394 | 352 | 117 | 234 | 107 | 482 | 52 | 122 | 54 | 157 | 301 | 171 | 71 | 448 | 390 | 181 | 260 | 510 | 397 | 109 | 128 | 76 | 269 | 550 | 663 | 184 | 586 | 297 | 189 | 97 | 131 | 202 | 185 | 286 | 114 | 122 | 499 | 57 | 218 | 70 | 159 | 160 | 77 | 402 | 194 | 207 |
| Aberdeen | 517 | | 445 | 183 | 182 | 420 | 308 | 564 | 59 | 573 | 493 | 471 | 505 | 221 | 344 | 588 | 67 | 125 | 569 | 504 | 149 | 145 | 468 | 517 | 535 | 439 | 105 | 232 | 364 | 189 | 692 | 327 | 414 | 383 | 341 | 340 | 235 | 496 | 393 | 178 | 483 | 615 | 560 | 360 | 399 | 547 | 228 | 507 | 319 |
| Aberystwyth | 211 | 445 | | 317 | 311 | 114 | 153 | 207 | 405 | 253 | 125 | 214 | 105 | 224 | 176 | 292 | 376 | 320 | 201 | 56 | 430 | 320 | 102 | 294 | 281 | 111 | 486 | 601 | 223 | 499 | 313 | 169 | 153 | 199 | 104 | 129 | 257 | 276 | 164 | 412 | 154 | 237 | 222 | 159 | 77 | 201 | 325 | 73 | 195 |
| Ayr | 394 | 183 | 317 | | 134 | 289 | 180 | 436 | 143 | 446 | 370 | 357 | 382 | 93 | 235 | 478 | 117 | 73 | 446 | 373 | 133 | 33 | 330 | 402 | 425 | 305 | 199 | 328 | 251 | 212 | 570 | 212 | 299 | 274 | 213 | 212 | 149 | 382 | 274 | 94 | 353 | 492 | 430 | 245 | 269 | 417 | 51 | 379 | 214 |
| Berwick-upon-Tweed | 352 | 182 | 311 | 134 | | 274 | 181 | 412 | 148 | 409 | 362 | 306 | 368 | 87 | 184 | 424 | 113 | 57 | 428 | 371 | 190 | 101 | 318 | 345 | 372 | 311 | 215 | 342 | 185 | 263 | 552 | 156 | 252 | 224 | 219 | 196 | 64 | 328 | 221 | 180 | 324 | 474 | 401 | 190 | 265 | 388 | 170 | 383 | 148 |
| Birmingham | 117 | 420 | 114 | 289 | 274 | | 123 | 147 | 385 | 163 | 81 | 100 | 103 | 196 | 94 | 194 | 349 | 292 | 157 | 170 | 392 | 292 | 56 | 180 | 167 | 148 | 458 | 574 | 134 | 471 | 281 | 113 | 39 | 90 | 93 | 80 | 207 | 166 | 50 | 384 | 64 | 203 | 141 | 76 | 45 | 128 | 297 | 119 | 130 |
| Blackpool | 234 | 308 | 153 | 180 | 181 | 123 | | 270 | 281 | 286 | 204 | 208 | 209 | 87 | 94 | 312 | 239 | 183 | 282 | 209 | 296 | 183 | 174 | 252 | 275 | 148 | 348 | 478 | 128 | 461 | 405 | 48 | 158 | 123 | 49 | 48 | 129 | 232 | 111 | 285 | 187 | 328 | 264 | 86 | 98 | 251 | 188 | 216 | 96 |
| Bournemouth | 107 | 564 | 207 | 436 | 412 | 147 | 270 | | 524 | 82 | 83 | 154 | 117 | 343 | 235 | 174 | 495 | 439 | 82 | 225 | 539 | 439 | 99 | 240 | 187 | 288 | 597 | 724 | 264 | 618 | 205 | 255 | 158 | 209 | 234 | 227 | 347 | 214 | 183 | 530 | 90 | 128 | 52 | 216 | 185 | 31 | 444 | 167 | 269 |
| Braemar | 482 | 59 | 405 | 143 | 148 | 385 | 281 | 524 | | 534 | 477 | 438 | 483 | 196 | 310 | 553 | 52 | 91 | 550 | 493 | 125 | 110 | 443 | 477 | 504 | 426 | 75 | 202 | 327 | 159 | 665 | 293 | 389 | 357 | 318 | 318 | 201 | 457 | 353 | 141 | 465 | 587 | 547 | 320 | 371 | 532 | 194 | 505 | 285 |
| Brighton | 52 | 573 | 253 | 446 | 409 | 163 | 286 | 82 | 534 | | 147 | 116 | 182 | 370 | 236 | 82 | 517 | 456 | 184 | 291 | 575 | 468 | 159 | 180 | 128 | 334 | 617 | 741 | 245 | 651 | 308 | 260 | 166 | 197 | 272 | 257 | 352 | 175 | 193 | 565 | 108 | 224 | 48 | 226 | 226 | 61 | 475 | 222 | 275 |
| Bristol | 122 | 493 | 125 | 370 | 362 | 81 | 204 | 83 | 477 | 147 | | 169 | 45 | 277 | 175 | 202 | 430 | 373 | 76 | 154 | 486 | 373 | 35 | 275 | 217 | 206 | 539 | 668 | 233 | 552 | 200 | 194 | 120 | 183 | 161 | 161 | 299 | 252 | 145 | 465 | 74 | 122 | 97 | 161 | 103 | 76 | 378 | 85 | 222 |
| Cambridge | 54 | 471 | 214 | 357 | 306 | 100 | 208 | 154 | 438 | 116 | 169 | | 190 | 264 | 116 | 125 | 406 | 345 | 249 | 270 | 479 | 372 | 123 | 82 | 67 | 270 | 505 | 630 | 139 | 555 | 374 | 145 | 68 | 85 | 194 | 165 | 241 | 62 | 83 | 468 | 83 | 293 | 144 | 120 | 159 | 148 | 379 | 227 | 165 |
| Cardiff | 157 | 505 | 105 | 382 | 368 | 103 | 209 | 117 | 483 | 182 | 45 | 190 | | 289 | 209 | 238 | 441 | 385 | 121 | 112 | 485 | 385 | 56 | 284 | 246 | 216 | 549 | 680 | 244 | 564 | 245 | 232 | 154 | 208 | 165 | 183 | 325 | 262 | 172 | 477 | 108 | 167 | 142 | 194 | 111 | 121 | 390 | 41 | 244 |
| Carlisle | 301 | 221 | 224 | 93 | 87 | 196 | 87 | 343 | 196 | 370 | 277 | 264 | 289 | | 142 | 389 | 152 | 96 | 353 | 297 | 206 | 96 | 247 | 320 | 336 | 231 | 262 | 391 | 158 | 275 | 477 | 119 | 206 | 191 | 120 | 119 | 57 | 289 | 194 | 188 | 260 | 399 | 348 | 152 | 176 | 324 | 101 | 309 | 121 |
| Doncaster | 171 | 344 | 176 | 235 | 184 | 94 | 94 | 235 | 310 | 236 | 175 | 116 | 209 | 142 | | 242 | 275 | 219 | 251 | 247 | 357 | 249 | 150 | 167 | 194 | 181 | 383 | 507 | 47 | 432 | 374 | 29 | 74 | 39 | 86 | 61 | 114 | 147 | 43 | 346 | 145 | 297 | 234 | 18 | 109 | 209 | 257 | 232 | 34 |
| Dover | 71 | 588 | 292 | 478 | 424 | 194 | 312 | 174 | 553 | 82 | 202 | 125 | 238 | 389 | 242 | | 523 | 462 | 248 | 331 | 596 | 488 | 191 | 185 | 125 | 360 | 622 | 747 | 256 | 671 | 381 | 260 | 185 | 202 | 299 | 276 | 358 | 174 | 205 | 585 | 141 | 300 | 130 | 245 | 251 | 143 | 496 | 274 | 282 |
| Dundee | 448 | 67 | 376 | 117 | 113 | 349 | 239 | 495 | 52 | 517 | 430 | 406 | 441 | 152 | 275 | 523 | | 56 | 518 | 460 | 127 | 83 | 410 | 484 | 469 | 394 | 132 | 259 | 295 | 186 | 642 | 258 | 349 | 314 | 286 | 285 | 166 | 422 | 328 | 117 | 433 | 552 | 514 | 291 | 330 | 500 | 167 | 473 | 250 |
| Edinburgh | 390 | 125 | 320 | 73 | 57 | 292 | 183 | 439 | 91 | 456 | 373 | 345 | 385 | 96 | 219 | 462 | 56 | | 450 | 399 | 144 | 44 | 349 | 386 | 413 | 333 | 158 | 285 | 234 | 216 | 574 | 202 | 295 | 258 | 216 | 215 | 110 | 366 | 262 | 123 | 372 | 496 | 453 | 235 | 274 | 438 | 124 | 412 | 194 |
| Exeter | 181 | 569 | 201 | 446 | 428 | 157 | 282 | 82 | 550 | 184 | 76 | 249 | 121 | 353 | 251 | 248 | 518 | 450 | | 230 | 560 | 449 | 111 | 335 | 279 | 282 | 618 | 744 | 309 | 628 | 123 | 270 | 196 | 247 | 237 | 236 | 364 | 308 | 221 | 549 | 156 | 46 | 135 | 237 | 179 | 105 | 454 | 161 | 287 |
| Fishguard | 260 | 504 | 56 | 373 | 371 | 170 | 209 | 225 | 493 | 291 | 154 | 270 | 112 | 297 | 247 | 331 | 460 | 399 | 230 | | 486 | 376 | 153 | 366 | 337 | 167 | 542 | 671 | 280 | 567 | 353 | 237 | 209 | 272 | 160 | 197 | 329 | 343 | 220 | 481 | 205 | 264 | 251 | 215 | 145 | 233 | 392 | 67 | 261 |
| Fort William | 510 | 149 | 430 | 133 | 190 | 392 | 296 | 539 | 125 | 575 | 486 | 479 | 485 | 206 | 357 | 596 | 127 | 144 | 560 | 486 | | 101 | 454 | 527 | 543 | 438 | 66 | 195 | 369 | 79 | 686 | 329 | 422 | 399 | 329 | 329 | 253 | 504 | 401 | 49 | 472 | 595 | 555 | 348 | 382 | 541 | 195 | 496 | 330 |
| Glasgow | 397 | 145 | 320 | 33 | 101 | 292 | 183 | 439 | 110 | 468 | 373 | 372 | 385 | 96 | 249 | 488 | 83 | 44 | 449 | 376 | 101 | | 346 | 419 | 432 | 330 | 166 | 295 | 254 | 179 | 573 | 215 | 314 | 291 | 216 | 215 | 148 | 385 | 293 | 92 | 356 | 495 | 448 | 248 | 272 | 433 | 84 | 409 | 217 |
| Gloucester | 109 | 468 | 102 | 330 | 318 | 56 | 174 | 99 | 443 | 159 | 35 | 123 | 56 | 247 | 150 | 191 | 410 | 349 | 111 | 153 | 454 | 346 | | 225 | 196 | 191 | 504 | 628 | 198 | 528 | 235 | 174 | 85 | 159 | 140 | 126 | 266 | 204 | 110 | 441 | 52 | 157 | 119 | 126 | 77 | 105 | 343 | 89 | 189 |
| Great Yarmouth | 128 | 517 | 294 | 402 | 345 | 180 | 252 | 240 | 477 | 180 | 275 | 82 | 284 | 320 | 167 | 185 | 484 | 386 | 335 | 366 | 527 | 419 | 225 | | 82 | 334 | 553 | 677 | 169 | 602 | 446 | 196 | 140 | 128 | 240 | 212 | 281 | 20 | 153 | 515 | 200 | 365 | 221 | 166 | 225 | 220 | 426 | 329 | 201 |
| Harwich | 76 | 535 | 281 | 425 | 372 | 167 | 275 | 187 | 504 | 128 | 217 | 67 | 246 | 336 | 194 | 125 | 469 | 413 | 279 | 337 | 543 | 432 | 196 | 82 | | 349 | 569 | 693 | 196 | 611 | 390 | 223 | 147 | 155 | 265 | 228 | 308 | 73 | 150 | 524 | 145 | 309 | 166 | 187 | 240 | 164 | 435 | 267 | 228 |
| Holyhead | 269 | 439 | 111 | 305 | 311 | 148 | 148 | 288 | 426 | 334 | 206 | 270 | 216 | 231 | 181 | 360 | 394 | 333 | 282 | 167 | 438 | 330 | 191 | 334 | 349 | | 474 | 603 | 231 | 514 | 405 | 176 | 190 | 216 | 102 | 124 | 272 | 311 | 185 | 427 | 238 | 328 | 311 | 168 | 113 | 293 | 338 | 184 | 204 |
| Inverness | 550 | 105 | 486 | 199 | 215 | 458 | 348 | 597 | 75 | 617 | 539 | 505 | 549 | 262 | 383 | 622 | 132 | 158 | 542 | 66 | 166 | 504 | 553 | 569 | 474 | | 129 | 394 | 84 | 741 | 360 | 461 | 427 | 382 | 373 | 268 | 529 | 430 | 117 | 532 | 664 | 613 | 393 | 438 | 598 | 262 | 572 | 352 |
| John o'Groats | 663 | 232 | 601 | 328 | 342 | 574 | 478 | 724 | 202 | 741 | 668 | 630 | 680 | 391 | 507 | 747 | 259 | 285 | 744 | 671 | 195 | 295 | 628 | 677 | 693 | 603 | 129 | | 518 | 189 | 868 | 487 | 588 | 554 | 511 | 500 | 395 | 654 | 557 | 244 | 656 | 790 | 737 | 520 | 567 | 723 | 379 | 696 | 479 |
| Kingston upon Hull | 184 | 364 | 223 | 251 | 185 | 134 | 128 | 264 | 327 | 245 | 233 | 139 | 244 | 158 | 47 | 256 | 295 | 234 | 309 | 280 | 369 | 254 | 198 | 169 | 196 | 231 | 394 | 518 | | 445 | 421 | 55 | 102 | 44 | 130 | 95 | 132 | 149 | 90 | 346 | 192 | 355 | 269 | 65 | 169 | 256 | 259 | 264 | 37 |
| Kyle of Lochalsh | 586 | 189 | 499 | 212 | 263 | 471 | 372 | 618 | 159 | 651 | 552 | 555 | 564 | 275 | 432 | 671 | 186 | 216 | 628 | 567 | 79 | 179 | 528 | 602 | 611 | 514 | 84 | 189 | 445 | | 763 | 394 | 500 | 476 | 407 | 406 | 318 | 582 | 479 | 128 | 550 | 674 | 633 | 427 | 451 | 618 | 263 | 594 | 407 |
| Land's End | 297 | 692 | 313 | 570 | 552 | 281 | 405 | 205 | 665 | 308 | 200 | 374 | 245 | 477 | 374 | 381 | 642 | 574 | 123 | 353 | 686 | 573 | 235 | 446 | 390 | 405 | 741 | 868 | 421 | 763 | | 405 | 320 | 371 | 361 | 361 | 498 | 421 | 345 | 665 | 274 | 89 | 259 | 361 | 303 | 228 | 585 | 285 | 411 |
| Leeds | 189 | 327 | 169 | 212 | 156 | 113 | 72 | 255 | 293 | 260 | 194 | 145 | 232 | 119 | 29 | 260 | 258 | 202 | 270 | 237 | 329 | 215 | 174 | 196 | 223 | 176 | 360 | 487 | 55 | 394 | 405 | | 95 | 68 | 75 | 40 | 92 | 176 | 70 | 307 | 168 | 316 | 257 | 33 | 109 | 232 | 220 | 248 | 24 |
| Leicester | 97 | 414 | 153 | 299 | 252 | 39 | 140 | 158 | 389 | 166 | 120 | 68 | 154 | 206 | 74 | 185 | 349 | 295 | 196 | 209 | 422 | 314 | 85 | 140 | 147 | 190 | 461 | 588 | 102 | 500 | 320 | 95 | | 51 | 130 | 92 | 187 | 119 | 25 | 419 | 73 | 242 | 162 | 62 | 84 | 137 | 330 | 177 | 108 |
| Lincoln | 131 | 383 | 199 | 274 | 224 | 90 | 128 | 209 | 357 | 197 | 183 | 85 | 208 | 191 | 39 | 202 | 314 | 258 | 247 | 272 | 399 | 291 | 159 | 128 | 155 | 216 | 427 | 554 | 44 | 476 | 371 | 68 | 51 | | 129 | 84 | 159 | 105 | 35 | 387 | 137 | 293 | 201 | 46 | 133 | 204 | 298 | 233 | 75 |
| Liverpool | 202 | 341 | 104 | 213 | 219 | 93 | 49 | 234 | 318 | 272 | 161 | 194 | 165 | 120 | 86 | 299 | 286 | 216 | 237 | 160 | 329 | 216 | 140 | 240 | 265 | 102 | 382 | 511 | 130 | 407 | 361 | 75 | 130 | 129 | | 35 | 168 | 220 | 98 | 308 | 172 | 283 | 254 | 72 | 58 | 239 | 221 | 195 | 99 |
| Manchester | 185 | 340 | 129 | 212 | 196 | 80 | 48 | 227 | 318 | 257 | 161 | 165 | 183 | 119 | 61 | 276 | 285 | 215 | 236 | 197 | 329 | 215 | 126 | 212 | 228 | 124 | 373 | 500 | 95 | 406 | 361 | 40 | 92 | 84 | 35 | | 132 | 185 | 73 | 307 | 144 | 283 | 236 | 38 | 69 | 221 | 220 | 187 | 64 |
| Newcastle upon Tyne | 286 | 235 | 257 | 149 | 64 | 207 | 129 | 347 | 201 | 352 | 299 | 241 | 325 | 57 | 114 | 358 | 166 | 110 | 364 | 329 | 253 | 148 | 266 | 281 | 308 | 272 | 268 | 395 | 132 | 318 | 498 | 92 | 187 | 159 | 168 | 132 | | 264 | 157 | 233 | 260 | 410 | 337 | 125 | 201 | 324 | 158 | 347 | 84 |
| Norwich | 114 | 496 | 276 | 382 | 328 | 166 | 232 | 214 | 457 | 175 | 252 | 62 | 262 | 289 | 147 | 174 | 422 | 366 | 308 | 343 | 504 | 385 | 204 | 20 | 73 | 311 | 529 | 654 | 149 | 582 | 421 | 176 | 119 | 105 | 220 | 185 | 264 | | 130 | 492 | 145 | 343 | 207 | 146 | 205 | 206 | 403 | 301 | 181 |
| Nottingham | 122 | 393 | 164 | 274 | 221 | 50 | 111 | 183 | 353 | 193 | 145 | 83 | 172 | 194 | 43 | 205 | 328 | 262 | 221 | 220 | 401 | 293 | 110 | 153 | 150 | 185 | 430 | 557 | 90 | 479 | 345 | 70 | 25 | 35 | 98 | 73 | 157 | 130 | | 390 | 109 | 267 | 191 | 37 | 93 | 176 | 290 | 192 | 77 |
| Oban | 499 | 178 | 412 | 94 | 180 | 384 | 285 | 530 | 141 | 565 | 465 | 468 | 477 | 188 | 346 | 585 | 117 | 123 | 549 | 481 | 49 | 92 | 441 | 515 | 524 | 427 | 117 | 244 | 346 | 128 | 665 | 307 | 419 | 387 | 308 | 307 | 233 | 492 | 390 | | 462 | 587 | 545 | 339 | 364 | 530 | 148 | 506 | 309 |
| Oxford | 57 | 483 | 154 | 353 | 324 | 64 | 187 | 90 | 465 | 108 | 74 | 83 | 108 | 260 | 145 | 141 | 433 | 372 | 156 | 205 | 472 | 356 | 52 | 200 | 145 | 238 | 532 | 656 | 192 | 550 | 274 | 168 | 73 | 137 | 172 | 144 | 260 | 145 | 109 | 462 | | 199 | 77 | 135 | 106 | 64 | 379 | 141 | 181 |
| Plymouth | 218 | 615 | 237 | 492 | 474 | 203 | 328 | 128 | 587 | 224 | 122 | 293 | 167 | 399 | 297 | 300 | 552 | 496 | 46 | 264 | 595 | 495 | 157 | 365 | 309 | 328 | 664 | 790 | 355 | 674 | 89 | 316 | 242 | 293 | 283 | 283 | 410 | 343 | 267 | 587 | 199 | | 176 | 283 | 225 | 151 | 500 | 206 | 333 |
| Portsmouth | 70 | 560 | 222 | 430 | 401 | 141 | 264 | 52 | 547 | 48 | 97 | 144 | 142 | 348 | 234 | 130 | 514 | 453 | 135 | 251 | 555 | 448 | 119 | 221 | 166 | 311 | 613 | 737 | 269 | 633 | 259 | 257 | 162 | 201 | 254 | 236 | 337 | 207 | 191 | 545 | 77 | 176 | | 230 | 207 | 21 | 461 | 182 | 278 |
| Sheffield | 159 | 360 | 159 | 245 | 190 | 76 | 86 | 216 | 320 | 226 | 161 | 120 | 194 | 152 | 18 | 245 | 291 | 235 | 237 | 215 | 348 | 248 | 126 | 166 | 187 | 168 | 393 | 520 | 65 | 427 | 361 | 33 | 62 | 46 | 72 | 38 | 125 | 146 | 37 | 339 | 135 | 283 | 230 | | 82 | 199 | 263 | 217 | 52 |
| Shrewsbury | 160 | 399 | 77 | 269 | 265 | 45 | 98 | 185 | 371 | 226 | 103 | 159 | 111 | 176 | 109 | 251 | 330 | 274 | 179 | 145 | 382 | 272 | 77 | 225 | 240 | 113 | 438 | 567 | 169 | 451 | 303 | 109 | 84 | 133 | 58 | 69 | 201 | 205 | 93 | 364 | 106 | 225 | 207 | 82 | | 185 | 277 | 118 | 133 |
| Southampton | 77 | 547 | 201 | 417 | 388 | 128 | 251 | 31 | 532 | 61 | 76 | 148 | 121 | 324 | 209 | 143 | 500 | 438 | 105 | 233 | 541 | 433 | 105 | 220 | 164 | 293 | 598 | 723 | 256 | 618 | 228 | 232 | 137 | 204 | 239 | 221 | 324 | 206 | 176 | 530 | 64 | 151 | 21 | 199 | 185 | | 445 | 161 | 258 |
| Stranraer | 402 | 228 | 325 | 51 | 170 | 297 | 188 | 444 | 194 | 475 | 378 | 379 | 390 | 101 | 257 | 496 | 167 | 124 | 454 | 392 | 195 | 84 | 343 | 426 | 435 | 338 | 262 | 379 | 259 | 263 | 585 | 220 | 330 | 298 | 221 | 220 | 158 | 403 | 290 | 148 | 379 | 500 | 461 | 263 | 277 | 445 | | 417 | 222 |
| Swansea | 194 | 507 | 73 | 379 | 383 | 119 | 216 | 167 | 505 | 222 | 85 | 227 | 41 | 309 | 232 | 274 | 473 | 412 | 161 | 67 | 496 | 409 | 89 | 329 | 267 | 184 | 572 | 696 | 264 | 594 | 285 | 248 | 177 | 233 | 195 | 187 | 347 | 301 | 192 | 506 | 141 | 206 | 182 | 217 | 118 | 161 | 417 | | 272 |
| York | 207 | 319 | 195 | 214 | 148 | 130 | 96 | 269 | 285 | 275 | 222 | 165 | 244 | 121 | 34 | 282 | 250 | 194 | 287 | 261 | 330 | 217 | 189 | 201 | 228 | 204 | 352 | 479 | 37 | 407 | 411 | 24 | 108 | 75 | 99 | 64 | 84 | 181 | 77 | 309 | 181 | 333 | 278 | 52 | 133 | 258 | 222 | 272 | |